REDUCTION WITH COMPLEX METAL HYDRIDES

REDUCTION WITH COMPLEX METAL HYDRIDES

NORMAN G. GAYLORD

Interchemical Corporation, New York, New York

1956

INTERSCIENCE PUBLISHERS, INC., NEW YORK

INTERSCIENCE PUBLISHERS LTD., LONDON

TO MARILYN

and

LORAINE, RICHARD, KATHY and CORINNE

whose patience and understanding

made this possible

Library of Congress Catalog Card Number 55-8227

© 1956 by

INTERSCIENCE PUBLISHERS, INC.

INTERSCIENCE PUBLISHERS, INC.
250 Fifth Ave., New York 1, N. Y.

For Great Britain and Northern Ireland:
INTERSCIENCE PUBLISHERS LTD.
88/90 Chancery Lane, London W.C. 2, England

PRINTED IN THE UNITED STATES OF AMERICA

PREFACE

This book began in 1951 as a review article on reductions with lithium aluminum hydride. Although the initial announcement of the preparation and behavior of this reagent was made at an American Chemical Society Symposium in 1946, the first fully detailed articles appeared in 1947 in the *Journal of the American Chemical Society*. The idea of a review article was quickly abandoned and replaced by the plan for a monograph when an examination of *Chemical Abstracts* revealed that while a total of 187 pertinent references had appeared from 1947 through 1950, 226 references were included in 1951 alone. Further, 149 references were found in the *Journal of the American Chemical Society* in 1951. The majority of these were not included in *Chemical Abstracts* on account of the unavoidable 6 to 12 months time lag between the publication of the original articles and the publication of their abstracts. Since a great number of the newer references were concerned with new applications of the reagent rather than additional examples of previously reported applications, it was realized that a more or less stable position had not yet been reached and that any review article would be out-of-date before it appeared in print. Consequently, it was decided to cover the literature through 1952 with the resultant decision to prepare a monograph rather than a review article.

In the process of deciding to prepare a monograph the decision was made to expand the coverage to include the preparation and all reported reactions, inorganic as well as organic, of the complex metal hydrides. Thus, in addition to lithium aluminum hydride, the monograph includes material relating to aluminum hydride, magnesium aluminum hydride, zinc aluminum hydride, lithium gallium hydride, sodium borohydride, potassium borohydride, lithium borohydride, and sodium trimethoxyborohydride, as well as those aluminohydrides and borohydrides whose preparation has been reported but whose reactions have not as yet been investigated.

Owing to the analogy between the reactions of the complex metal hydrides, in particular lithium aluminum hydride, with the Grignard reaction, comparisons of the former with the latter as well as Meerwein-Ponnderf-Verley and catalytic reductions are made where deemed advantageous.

This monograph covers the literature up to January 1953. This includes *Chemical Abstracts* and the following journals which have been examined page by page from 1947 to 1953:

The Analyst
Analytica Chimica Acta

Analytical Chemistry
Annalen der Chemie, Justus Liebig
Bulletin de la société chimique de France
Canadian Journal of Chemistry
Chemische Berichte
Chemistry and Industry
Collection of Czech Chemical Communications
Comptes rendus
Experientia
Helvetica Chimica Acta
Industrial and Engineering Chemistry
Journal of the American Chemical Society
The Journal of the American Oil Chemists' Society
Journal of the American Pharmaceutical Association, Scientific Edition
Journal of Applied Chemistry (London)
The Journal of Biological Chemistry
Journal of Chemical Education
The Journal of Chemical Physics
Journal of the Chemical Society
The Journal of Organic Chemistry
The Journal of Physical Chemistry
Journal of Research of the National Bureau of Standards
Monatshefte für Chemie
Nature
Proceedings of the Royal Society (London)
Recueil des travaux chimiques des Pays-Bas
Research (London)
Science

It was found that page-by-page examination of the indicated journals
produced additional references to those obtained from *Chemical Abstracts*
since in some cases where the complex metal hydride was used in the
preparation of a material which was the subject of an investigation
rather than where the hydride reaction itself was the subject, the abstract contained no reference to the use of the hydride. All references
obtained from *Chemical Abstracts* relating to journals other than those
listed were examined in the original form. After the completion of the
manuscript, examination of the references in *Chemical Abstracts* up to
January 1954 has shown that all but 55 out of some 400 pertinent references were covered in the survey of the original literature. Consequently
the monograph covers the abstract literature completely through 1952 and
approximately 85% of the abstract literature for 1953.

In addition to the published literature, including a comprehensive survey of the patent literature, a considerable amount of material, unpub-

lished through 1954, is included. This was obtained by contacting individuals who had presented papers at meetings of the American Chemical Society and other organizations. A request for more detailed information on a particular reaction in many cases resulted in the acquisition of relevant unreported work. In some cases this work, although included in the monograph, is appearing in the appropriate journals in 1955.

The arrangement of material in the monograph, in particular the reactions of the complex metal hydrides, is based on the reactions of functional groups. Although a considerable number of cross references are included, no attempt to avoid duplication has been made and in fact, in many cases duplication has been intentionally fostered. Thus, where a compound containing several functional groups has been subjected to treatment with a complex metal hydride, this compound is tabulated in each of the appropriate tables so that cross-referencing and undesirable page-turning is unnecessary.

It has been reported that under the proper experimental conditions normally unreactive groups have been attacked by the complex metal hydrides. It has therefore been deemed desirable to tabulate those compounds and experimental conditions which have resulted in non-reduction as well as the examples of successful reactions.

The chapter on the "Handling of the Complex Metal Hydrides on a Commercial Scale" was prepared by M. Douglas Banus and Robert D. Gray, of the staff of Metal Hydrides, Incorporated, Beverly, Massachusetts, whose cooperation is gratefully acknowledged. The photographs were provided by Bradford H. Arthur of Metal Hydrides, Incorporated.

This monograph was conceived and written while the author was associated with E. I. du Pont de Nemours & Co., Inc. A vote of thanks is hereby tendered to the members of the Publications Committee of the Yerkes Research Laboratory of the Film Department of the du Pont Co. for their cooperation during the preparation of the manuscript. The patience of Dr. Emmette Izard was a particular inspiration. The assistance of Miss Jean Ouiderkirk of the Library Staff in obtaining copies of patents and many foreign references made possible the comprehensive coverage of this book. The extreme cooperation of the Stenographic Staff under Mrs. Carol Nicholson, in particular Mrs. Miriam Norris and Miss Marjorie Bartow, resulted in the evolution of a manuscript which can be held up as a model for the stenographic arts.

NORMAN G. GAYLORD

Interchemical Corporation
The Research Laboratories
New York, N. Y.

CONTENTS

CHAPTER 1

INTRODUCTION

The complex metal hydrides are among the recent discoveries of inorganic chemistry which have found wide application in the organic field. Among the hydrides which have been readily accepted by the organic as well as the inorganic chemist are the commercially available lithium aluminum hydride and lithium, sodium and potassium borohydrides. The easily prepared magnesium aluminum hydride, lithium gallium hydride, and the aluminum hydride-aluminum chloride addition compound are of potential future interest but to date have not been extensively investigated.

Although aluminum and beryllium borohydrides were first reported in 1940, their spontaneous inflammability in air did not make them particularly inviting reagents. On the other hand, the more ionic borohydrides, such as the sodium and potassium compounds, are unusually stable substances. Although the reducing action of these materials is limited in most cases to aldehydes, ketones, acid chlorides and a few other functional groups, this seeming limitation may in many instances be highly desirable for selective reductions. Sodium borohydride is an effective reducing agent in water, methanol, or dioxane solution but is not very soluble in organic solvents such as diethyl ether. Lithium borohydride is soluble in ether, although usually used in tetrahydrofuran and is a stronger reducing agent than the sodium compound. However, the number of reducible groups is still small and selective reductions are possible.

Magnesium aluminum hydride and lithium gallium hydride in ether solution are stronger reducing agents than the borohydrides. However, the limited investigations that have thus far been carried out do not permit far-reaching generalizations as to the scope and limitations of these reagents.

Lithium aluminum hydride, hereinafter referred to as LAH, is an extremely powerful reducing agent. Since the initial report of the application of LAH to the reduction of organic compounds before the Symposium on Hydrides and Related Compounds at the Chicago meeting of the American Chemical Society on September 10, 1946, the uses of this reagent have become legend. Although its violent reaction with water and the liberation of hydrogen and decomposition of the reagent with substances containing active hydrogen do not permit its use for the reduction of water soluble compounds, it reacts readily and, in many cases, quantitatively with substances soluble in ether-type solvents such as diethyl ether and tetrahydrofuran. Functional groups which have resisted other

1

methods of reduction have successfully been reduced with LAH under conditions similar to those used with the Grignard reagent. The action of LAH is often highly specific, yielding products of a high degree of purity due to the avoidance of side reactions, condensations and cleavage often encountered with other reducing agents.

The chemical properties of aluminum hydride are similar to those of LAH. However, the ether solution of the former is unstable and polymeric aluminum hydride is precipitated. The addition of aluminum chloride to the ether solution, prior to the precipitation, results in the formation of a stable, ether-soluble aluminum hydride-aluminum chloride addition compound. The material, in ether solution, is an excellent reducing agent which is somewhat milder than LAH. The properties of this addition compound have not been extensively covered.

The complex metal hydrides which have been discovered and investigated to date present a cross-section of reduction efficiency. Although several different agents may serve for the reduction of a particular functional group, in the presence of other groups which it is desired to retain in the reduced product, selective and directed reduction is necessary. The difference in reducing ability among the complex hydrides makes possible the selection of the appropriate agent for the specific task.

A number of excellent reviews and summaries have been published relating to the use of the complex metal hydrides in the reduction of organic compounds as well as in the preparation of hydrides and complex hydrides (1-20). The rapid growth of the area of application of these reagents has in many cases made a given review out-of-date prior to its date of publication.

REFERENCES

1. Bell, R. P., and H. J. Emeléus, "The Boron Hydrides and Related Compounds," in *Quart. Rev.*, 2, 132 (1948).
2. Bohlman, F., *Pharmazie*, 5, 306 (1950).
3. Brown, H. C., *Chem. Eng. News*, 29, 5231 (1951).
4. Brown, W. G., "Reductions by Lithium Aluminum Hydride," in R. Adams, ed., *Organic Reactions*, Vol. VI, Chapter 10, Wiley, New York, 1951, pp. 469-509.
5. Ferles, M., and J. Rudinger, *Chem. Listy*, 47, 91 (1953).
6. Garber, H. J., *Ind. Eng. Chem.*, 42, 1760 (1950).
7. Gibb, T. R. P., Jr., *J. Chem. Ed.*, 25, 577 (1948).
8. Johnson, A. W., in *Annual Reports on the Progress of Chemistry for 1949*, Vol. XLVI, 1950, The Chemical Society, London, pp. 140-146.
9. Johnson, A. W., *Sci. Progress*, 37, 512 (1949).
10. Krajkeman, A. J., *Mfg. Chemist*, 22, 147 (1951).
11. Kvasnicka, E., *Österr. Chem. Ztg.*, 52, 26 (1951).
12. Rudinger, J., M. Ferles, and M. Protiva, *Chem. Listy*, 45, 309 (1951).
13. Rudinger, J., M. Ferles, and M. Protiva, *Chem. Listy*, 45, 339 (1951).

14. Rydon, H. N., in *Annual Reports on the Progress of Chemistry for 1950*, Vol. XLVII, 1951, The Chemical Society, London, pp. 154-155.
15. Saunders, B. C., in *Annual Reports on the Progress of Chemistry for 1948*, Vol. XLV, 1949, The Chemical Society, London, pp. 122-123.
16. Solms, U., *Chimia*, 5, 25 (1951).
17. Walker, J., in *Annual Reports on the Progress of Chemistry for 1951*, Vol. XLVIII, 1952, The Chemical Society, London, p. 143.
18. Wiberg, E., *Angew. Chem.*, 63, 485 (1951).
19. Wiberg, E., *Angew. Chem.*, 64, 354 (1952).
20. Wiberg, E., *Angew. Chem.*, 65, 16 (1953).

CHAPTER 2

PREPARATION AND PROPERTIES OF
COMPLEX METAL HYDRIDES

The work of H. I. Schlesinger and E. Wiberg and their co-workers has resulted in the preparation of numerous compounds containing complex hydride anions. Only a limited number have been investigated in any detail as regards their reactions with inorganic reactants and their utility as reducing agents for organic functional groups. The preparation and properties of those complex metal hydrides which have been so investigated and applied are considered in this section. A considerable portion of the patent literature refers to the use of LAH and aluminum hydride interchangeably in the reduction of organic compounds. The latter though not a complex hydride is therefore included in this discussion.

2.1 LITHIUM ALUMINUM HYDRIDE (LAH) AND ALUMINUM HYDRIDE

2.1.1 Preparation

2.1.1.a *Lithium aluminum hydride.* LAH is prepared in good yield by the reaction of lithium hydride and aluminum chloride in ether solution (1-9), according to the equation:

$$4 \text{ LiH} + \text{AlCl}_3 \rightarrow \text{LiAlH}_4 + 3 \text{ LiCl} \tag{2-1}$$

A solution of aluminum chloride in ether is added to a slurry of finely pulverized lithium hydride in ether containing a small amount of previously formed LAH. The rate of addition is controlled so as to maintain continuous refluxing. Stirring is continued for a short time after the addition is complete. The precipitated lithium chloride and excess lithium hydride are separated from the ether solution by filtration under nitrogen pressure (1). The yield of LAH is 85-90% and the purity is 93-98% although it may become as high as 99% without recrystallization if the reaction mixture is permitted to stand before filtration (1-3).

The addition of previously prepared LAH controls the reaction velocity. In its absence, an induction period is observed, after which the reaction sets in with such vigor as to make control difficult (1). A small portion of iodine aids in the formation of the initial LAH which catalyzes the reaction (4). Mirza (10) has shown that the induction period is due to residual traces of water in the ether used in the preparation. Distillation of the ether over LAH or careful drying over sodium eliminates the induction period and results in a smooth reaction. The induction period is apparently the time required to remove the protective film of lithium hy-

4

Figure 1. Plant equipment for preparation of lithium aluminum hydride.
(Courtesy of Metal Hydrides Inc.)

droxide from the surface of the powdered lithium hydride. Once the unreactive coating is removed a vigorous reaction occurs due to the presence
of a large amount of aluminum chloride.

Aluminum hydride is probably an intermediate in the formation of LAH
(11,12):

$$3 \text{ LiAlH}_4 \text{ (seed)} + \text{AlCl}_3 \longrightarrow 4 \text{ AlH}_3 + 3 \text{ LiCl} \qquad (2\text{-}2)$$

$$4 \text{ AlH}_3 + 4 \text{ LiH} \longrightarrow 4 \text{ LiAlH}_4 \qquad (2\text{-}3)$$

The reaction of aluminum hydride with lithium hydride in ether is reported
to produce LAH (13), although the former is difficultly accessible in
monomeric form.

The lithium hydride may be prepared from lithium and hydrogen (7,14)
or by heating lithium oxide with magnesium metal (powder or flakes) in
the presence of hydrogen at a temperature of $500\text{--}900°$. The resultant,
mechanically, inseparable mixture of lithium hydride and magnesium oxide
is treated with an ethereal solution of aluminum chloride (15,16):

$$4 \text{ (MgO + LiH)} + \text{AlCl}_3 \longrightarrow \text{LiAlH}_4 + 3 \text{ LiCl} + 4 \text{ MgO} \qquad (2\text{-}4)$$

The lithium chloride residues from LAH preparations can be purified by

heating with excess ammonium chloride at $580°$ in order to obtain anhydrous lithium chloride (17).

The substitution of aluminum bromide for aluminum chloride results in
a simplified procedure overcoming the disadvantages inherent with the
use of the latter. Thus, the lithium hydride does not have to be finely
pulverized as pea size pieces dissolve smoothly in the ethereal aluminum bromide solution. The use of LAH as a "primer" is unnecessary
since the heat of reaction and the heat of formation of lithium bromide are
less than in the analogous reaction with aluminum chloride. An excess of
lithium hydride is not necessary since the reaction quantitatively consumes the hydride permitting the use of stoichiometric quantities. When
aluminum chloride is used, the ether-insoluble lithium chloride partially
covers the insoluble hydride and so hinders further reaction. Although
the ether solution of LAH obtained from the bromide in 97% yield is saturated with lithium bromide, it is reported to behave normally in hydrogenation reactions (18).

By heating lithium hydride with hydrogen gas containing tritium at $350°$
lithium hydride-t has been prepared. The use of lithium hydride-t has
made possible the preparation of lithium aluminum hydride-t ($LiAlT_4$). The
direct exchange of LAH with a hydrogen-tritium mixture at $100°$ could not
be carried out (19). The commercially available lithium aluminum deuteride is probably prepared from lithium deuteride.

Schmitz-Dumont and Habernickel (20) have studied the preparation of
various addition compounds of aluminum ethylate. The addition of a small
amount of LAH to an ethereal solution of lithium hydride and aluminum
ethylate results in the formation of an addition compound:

$$LiH + Al(OC_2H_5)_3 \longrightarrow Li[HAl(OC_2H_5)_3] \qquad (2\text{-}5)$$

However, a substitution of the ethoxy group with hydrogen occurs
simultaneously.

$$Li[HAl(OC_2H_5)_3] + LiH \longrightarrow Li[H_2Al(OC_2H_5)_2] + LiOC_2H_5 \qquad (2\text{-}6)$$

This substitution reaction proceeds until lithium aluminum hydride is
formed.

The ethereal solution of LAH prepared according to equation (2-1) can
be analyzed as discussed in Section 2.1.2 and used without isolation of
the solid hydride, or the latter can be isolated by evaporation of the ether
at atmospheric pressure and removal of the residual solvent in vacuo at
$70°$ (1). The purification of LAH can be carried out by its repeated solution in ether and precipitation with benzene (21). Explosions have been
reported in the evaporation of ethereal LAH solutions due to the presence
of carbon dioxide (22) or excessive peroxides (23).

2.1.1.b *Aluminum hydride.* Aluminum hydride was first prepared by
passing a mixture of trimethylaluminum and an excess of hydrogen through

a glow discharge. Volatile methylaluminum hydrides, in dimeric form, were isolated from the complex mixture of products, indicating a stepwise replacement of methyl groups by hydrogen.

$$Al(CH_3)_3 + n\ H_2 \longrightarrow Al(CH_3)_{3-n}H_n + n\ RH \tag{2-7}$$

Treatment of the non-volatile products with trimethylamine gave the addition compound $AlH_3 \cdot 2N(CH_3)_3$ which, when heated in a vacuum, liberated trimethylamine and formed aluminum hydride-rich products $(AlH_3)_n \cdot N(CH_3)_3$. Above $100°$, a non-volatile, high polymeric aluminum hydride $(AlH_3)_x$ was obtained (24-27).

The work of Schlesinger and his co-workers has led to a convenient synthesis of monomeric aluminum hydride. In ether solution, in the presence of excess aluminum chloride, lithium hydride yields aluminum hydride, according to the equation:

$$3\ LiH + AlCl_3 \longrightarrow AlH_3 + 3\ LiCl \tag{2-8}$$

A mixture of magnesium oxide and lithium hydride, prepared as described in Section 2.1.1.a, can be used in place of the pure hydride. Treatment of an ethereal solution of LAH with aluminum chloride in a 3 : 1 ratio at room temperature yields a solution of aluminum hydride (1-3,27,28):

$$3\ LiAlH_4 + AlCl_3 \longrightarrow 4\ AlH_3 + 3\ LiCl \tag{2-9}$$

The ethereal solution of aluminum hydride is unstable since the latter spontaneously polymerizes to a high molecular weight, ether-insoluble, polymerization product. This is postulated as arising as follows (28):

$$3\ LiAlH_4 + AlCl_3 \longrightarrow Al(AlH_4)_3 + 3\ LiCl \tag{2-10}$$

$$x\ Al(AlH_4)_3 \longrightarrow 4\ (AlH_3)_x \tag{2-11}$$

The $Al(AlH_4)_3$ is considered the ether soluble form of aluminum hydride.

It is impossible to remove all the ether by evaporation without decomposing the aluminum hydride. Solid products containing varying amounts of bound ether are obtained by different drying procedures. The composition may reach proportions corresponding to six moles of aluminum hydride per mole of diethyl ether (1-3,29). The etherate containing three moles of aluminum hydride per mole of ether has been reported to show an unusual and characteristic x-ray diffraction pattern rather than to exist in the amorphous form (30). Irrespective of its composition, the solid is not appreciably soluble in ether, but either the original solution of aluminum hydride or the ether-insoluble solids may be used in place of LAH in subsequent reactions (1-3,11).

Whereas the etherate of aluminum hydride is unstable in diethyl ether solution, precipitating as the insoluble polymeric form, the etherate with tetrahydrofuran is more stable (31). The monomeric hydride can be stabilized with trimethylamine (29) as well as by treatment with an ethereal solution of an aluminum halide (28). The reaction of aluminum hydride with aluminum chloride, in varying proportions, yields AlH_2Cl or $AlHCl_2$ or the addition compound $AlH_2Cl \cdot AlHCl_2$ (32). The reaction of aluminum hydride with aluminum bromide (33) or aluminum iodide (34) yields either the mono- or dihalo derivatives AlH_2X or $AlHX_2$. The reaction of the mono- and dichloro compounds with LAH in ether yields an ethereal solution of aluminum hydride from which the polymeric form precipitates.

$$AlH_2X + LiAlH_4 \longrightarrow 2 AlH_3 + LiX \qquad (2\text{-}12)$$

$$AlHX_2 + 2 LiAlH_4 \longrightarrow 3 AlH_3 + 2 LiX \qquad (2\text{-}13)$$

$$AlX_3 + LiAlH_4 \longrightarrow 4 AlH_3 + LiX \qquad (2\text{-}14)$$

However, the reaction of the mono- and dibromo compounds with LAH in ether yields a stable ethereal solution. Similarly, the preparation of aluminum hydride by the reaction of aluminum bromide and LAH according to equation (2-14) yields a stable ethereal solution. Wiberg *et al.* have proposed that the solutions probably contain lithium bromoaluminum hydride $LiAlH_3Br$ (35).

2.1.2 Analysis

Analysis of solid LAH to determine its purity as well as analysis of ethereal solutions to determine the LAH concentration can be carried out in several ways. The vigorous reaction of LAH with water liberates hydrogen according to the equation:

$$LiAlH_4 + 4 H_2O \longrightarrow 4 H_2 + LiOH + Al(OH)_3 \qquad (2\text{-}15)$$

Measurement of the hydrogen gas evolved permits determination of LAH concentration (1-3,7,9,36). Gas volumes are determined in an apparatus such as is used in the Zerewitinoff determination of active hydrogen (37). If the gas volume is kept constant, the evolved hydrogen can be measured by the change in pressure (21,38).

In addition to measurement of the evolved hydrogen, the solution resulting from hydrolysis of LAH can be analyzed for aluminum (1,21) or lithium (1).

The measurement of the hydrogen evolved on decomposition of excess LAH after completion of a reduction, permits determination of the extent of reduction as well as the stoichiometric relationship involved. In addition to the usual equipment, several gas burets have been proposed for this purpose (37,39).

Hydrogen evolved on pyrolysis of LAH at $150\text{-}220°$, according to equation (2-16), can also be determined gasometrically (1).

$$LiAlH_4 \longrightarrow LiH + Al + 1.5 H_2 \qquad (2\text{-}16)$$

Additional hydrogen is obtained by treatment of the residue with water (1).

$$LiH + Al + 4 H_2O \longrightarrow LiOH + Al(OH)_3 + 2.5 H_2 \qquad (2\text{-}17)$$

A faster and more accurate method for LAH analysis, developed in France, involves the addition of excess standard iodine in benzene to an ethereal LAH solution and back-titrating with sodium thiosulfate (36,40). Direct titration of the LAH solution with a benzene solution of iodine may be 20% in error while the same error is involved when the excess of iodine is insufficient, i.e., less than three moles per mole of LAH. The reaction of one mole of LAH with four moles of iodine consumes exactly two moles of iodine according to the equation:

$$LiAlH_4 + 2 I_2 \rightarrow 2 H_2 + LiI + AlI_3 \qquad (2\text{-}18)$$

This reaction is analogous to the reaction of the Grignard reagent with insufficient iodine (41).

$$2 RMgX + I_2 \rightarrow RR + 2 MgXI \qquad (2\text{-}19)$$

The normal reaction of Grignard reagents with excess iodine is:

$$RMgX + I_2 \rightarrow RI + MgXI \qquad (2\text{-}20)$$

but the analogous reaction of LAH

$$LiAlH_4 + 4 I_2 \rightarrow 4 HI + LiI + AlI_3 \qquad (2\text{-}21)$$

is not observed. The iodometric method is accurate for 0.1 to 1.0 M LAH solutions while the gasometric method based on hydrolysis is accurate for 0.5 to 1.0 M solutions (36).

Analysis of aluminum hydride is carried out essentially as for LAH, by hydrolysis according to the equation:

$$AlH_3 + 3 H_2O \rightarrow Al(OH)_3 + 3 H_2 \qquad (2\text{-}22)$$

2.1.3. Properties

2.1.3.a   *Lithium aluminum hydride.*   LAH is a microcrystalline solid which is stable in dry air at room temperature. Brown (11) has pointed out that there is no conclusive evidence that the intensively dried solid is not a mixture of lithium hydride and aluminum hydride from which LAH slowly reforms when the material is suspended in ether. However, Finholt and Jacobson (42) have reported that LAH gradually deteriorates after several months exposure to light and occasional exposure to air. Dissolving the deteriorated LAH in ether, followed by filtration and evaporation of the ethereal solution to dryness in vacuo at 70–80° gives a dark colored solid. The low decomposition temperature is considered indicative of the formation of unstable aluminum hydride by the action of light or air on lithium hydride present as an impurity in the LAH.

LAH has been postulated as a complex salt

$$Li^{\oplus}[AlH_4]^{\ominus}$$

Infrared and Raman spectra have indicated a tetrahedral structure for the aluminohydride ($AlH_4{}^-$) ion in ether solution (43). Paddock (44) has shown the presence of ions in ethereal solutions of LAH by determination of the specific conductivity. The value for a molar solution of LAH was 4.43×10^{-5} ohm^{-1} cm^{-1} at $15°$ which may be compared with the value of 6.14×10^{-5} ohm^{-1} cm^{-1} for a molar solution of ethylmagnesium bromide at $20°$.

LAH appears to be somewhat less polar than lithium borohydride which has been shown by x-ray diffraction measurements to consist of lithium ions and tetrahedral borohydride ions (45). Wiberg (46) considered LAH as a double hydride LiH·AlH_3 and has advanced a homopolar structure (I) while a covalent structure (II) has also been proposed (47).

$$\text{I} \qquad\qquad\qquad\qquad \text{II}$$

Ebullioscopic measurements have shown that the value obtained for the molecular weight of LAH in ether is a function of the concentration of LAH. In an 0.08 molar solution a dimeric molecule $(LiAlH_4)_2$ is indicated, while a tenfold increase to a 0.8 molar solution indicates a trimeric molecule $(LiAlH_4)_3$. This is explained by an increase in the number of hydrogen bridges with increased LAH concentration (35).

$$(2\text{-}23)$$

LAH may be heated without appreciable decomposition to temperatures below $100°$ in vacuo. At $150°$ decomposition results in the evolution of hydrogen and the formation of lithium hydride and aluminum (1-4,48).

$$LiAlH_4 \rightarrow LiH + Al + 1.5\ H_2 \qquad\qquad (2\text{-}24)$$

Garner and Haycock (49) have intensively studied the thermal decomposition of LAH and conclude that there are three stages: (*a*) an initial surface reaction during the induction period, followed by (*b*) an interface reaction giving an S-shaped pressure against time curve, corresponding to the reaction

$$LiAlH_4 \rightarrow LiAlH_2 + H_2 \qquad\qquad (2\text{-}25)$$

and (*c*) a slow process during which a third hydrogen atom is liberated.

$$LiAlH_2 \rightarrow LiH + Al + \tfrac{1}{2}\ H_2 \qquad\qquad (2\text{-}26)$$

The initial reaction, which is rapid at first and then slows down to a constant rate, occurs to the extent of about 0.7% of the total decomposition and penetrates the surface to a depth of several molecular layers. In the surface reaction the loss of hydrogen results in the formation of surface defects which aggregate and collapse to give nuclei at which a normal interface reaction proceeds.

The decomposition indicated in equation (2-24) occurs in ether solution at room temperature in the presence of finely divided titanium, silicon, iron, copper, aluminum, boron (4), mercury (50), or silver (51). This decomposition can be prevented by the addition of excess lithium hydride to produce a stabilized LAH solution which is unchanged after several months (4).

The density of LAH at $25°$, determined by displacement of toluene, is 0.917 g./cc. The specific heat is 0.48 ± 0.01 cal./g./deg. The standard heat of formation is reported to be -24.08 kcal./mole at $25°$ (21).

Examination of the nuclear magnetic resonance in LAH has shown that at room temperature the width of the resonance absorption line is 8.7 gauss (52).

LAH is soluble in compounds of the ether class. The reported solubilities, in grams per 100 g. of solvent at $25°$, are as follows (1):

Diethyl ether	25-30; 0.83 molar (53)
Tetrahydrofuran	13
Dibutyl ether	2
Dioxane	0.1
Ethylene glycol dimethyl ether	1.1 molar (53)

Other ethers have been used in carrying out LAH reactions. These are considered in Section 17. Ethereal solutions are miscible with some hydrocarbons, permitting reactions to be carried out in which reactants are ether-insoluble but hydrocarbon-soluble.

2.1.3.b *Aluminum hydride.* As discussed in Section 2.1.1.b, monomeric aluminum hydride exists in ether solution but spontaneously precipitates as a solid polymeric $(AlH_3)_x$. Ebullioscopic molecular weight determinations on freshly prepared ether solutions indicate the presence of monomeric aluminum hydride, probably in the form of an etherate $AlH_3 \cdot 2(C_2H_5)_2O$. The monomeric etherate cannot be isolated from the solution since evaporation of the solvent ether releases part of the ether bound in the etherate and results in the precipitation of the polymeric hydride (29).

The monomeric aluminum hydride can be stabilized with excess trimethylamine in the form of a solid diaminate (III),

$$\begin{array}{c}
H \\
H \rightarrow Al \\
H
\end{array}
\begin{array}{c}
N(CH_3)_3 \\
\\
N(CH_3)_3
\end{array}$$

III

whereas with a 1:1 ratio of aluminum hydride and trimethylamine a solid aminate is formed which, in benzene solution, appears to be an aminate of dimeric aluminum hydride (IV).

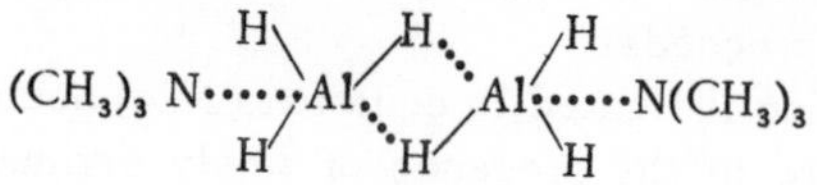

$$(CH_3)_3 \; N \cdots \overset{H}{\underset{H}{\diagdown}} Al \overset{H}{\underset{H}{<}} Al \overset{H}{\underset{H}{\diagup}} \cdots N(CH_3)_3$$

IV

In ether solution the hydrogen bridge is apparently broken to form the adduct

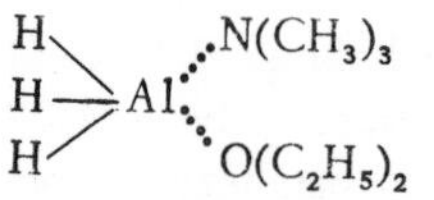

$$\overset{H}{\underset{H}{\overset{H}{\diagdown}}} Al \overset{N(CH_3)_3}{\underset{O(C_2H_5)_2}{<}}$$

V

Evaporation of the ethereal solution of the aminate-etherate (V) yields the dimeric aminate (IV) in contrast to the conversion of the amine-free etherate to polymeric $(AlH_3)_x$.

Gibb (54) has postulated the product of reaction of LAH with aluminum chloride as a very highly ionized addition or coordination compound of aluminum hydride with LAH, possibly containing ether of constitution. Further, aluminum hydride is postulated as existing in an unstable ionized form, presumably as aluminohydride ion, which rapidly is transformed to the stable polymeric form (28,54).

The polymeric $(AlH_3)_x$ has been postulated as the product of the polymerization of the monomeric material by the continued formation of hydrogen bridges, with each aluminum atom coordinated with six hydrogen atoms (31).

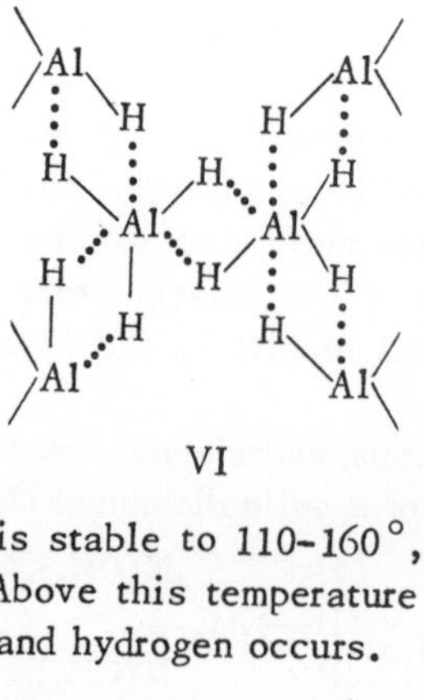

VI

The polymeric hydride is stable to 110–160°, dependent upon the degree of polymerization. Above this temperature quantitative decomposition to metallic aluminum and hydrogen occurs.

$$(AlH_3)_x \; \longrightarrow \; x \; Al + 1\tfrac{1}{2} x \; H_2 \qquad (2\text{-}27)$$

2.2 SODIUM BOROHYDRIDE

2.2.1 Preparation

In contrast to the limited number of methods available for the preparation of LAH, sodium borohydride may be prepared by a variety of methods which have, for the most part, been the result of the work of H. I. Schlesinger and H. C. Brown, and their co-workers.

Sodium trimethoxyborohydride is the starting material for several syntheses of sodium borohydride. The trimethoxyborohydride may be prepared by the reaction of sodium hydride with refluxing methyl borate (55-58) or by treatment of metallic sodium with a mixture of hydrogen and methyl borate at 250° under pressure (59).

$$NaH + B(OCH_3)_3 \longrightarrow NaBH(OCH_3)_3 \qquad (2\text{-}28)$$

$$2\ Na + H_2 + 2\ B(OCH_3)_3 \longrightarrow 2\ NaBH(OCH_3)_3 \qquad (2\text{-}29)$$

Sodium trimethoxyborohydride reacts rapidly and almost quantitatively with diborane to form sodium borohydride (55-58,60).

$$2\ NaBH(OCH_3)_3 + B_2H_6 \longrightarrow 2\ NaBH_4 + 2\ B(OCH_3)_3 \qquad (2\text{-}30)$$

The reaction proceeds so rapidly that it may be used to absorb diborane almost completely from a stream of gas containing a relatively low concentration of diborane. Dimethoxyborine, which may be present in the gas stream, reacts in a similar manner with the trimethoxy derivative (60).

$$NaBH(OCH_3)_3 + 3\ (CH_3O)_2BH \longrightarrow NaBH_4 + 3\ B(OCH_3)_3 \qquad (2\text{-}31)$$

The diborane utilized in equation (2-30) may be prepared by the arc process from hydrogen and boron tribromide vapor (61) or by the reaction of sodium, potassium, lithium, or magnesium borohydrides (62) or sodium, lithium, or potassium trimethoxyborohydrides (62,63) or lithium (63,64) or sodium (63) hydrides, or lithium aluminum hydride (1,65) and boron trifluoride etherate.

The reaction of sodium hydride with sodium trimethoxyborohydride at 250-270° yields 78% sodium borohydride, which is extracted with isopropylamine (59,66).

$$NaBH(OCH_3)_3 + 3\ NaH \longrightarrow NaBH_4 + 3\ NaOCH_3 \qquad (2\text{-}32)$$

By disproportionation of sodium trimethoxyborohydride at 230° an equilibrium mixture of products, including sodium borohydride, is obtained.

$$4\ NaBH(OCH_3)_3 \longrightarrow NaBH_4 + 3\ NaB(OCH_3)_4 \qquad (2\text{-}33)$$

To drive reaction (2-33) to completion the sodium tetramethoxyborohydride must be decomposed according to equation (2-34)

$$NaB(OCH_3)_4 \rightleftharpoons NaOCH_3 + B(OCH_3)_3 \qquad (2\text{-}34)$$

and the methyl borate must be continuously removed in vacuum. Even under these conditions the reaction is not clean-cut, since some dimethoxyborine is evolved according to the equation:

$$NaBH(OCH_3)_3 \rightarrow NaOCH_3 + (CH_3O)_2BH \tag{2-35}$$

and pure sodium borohydride is not obtained (56,58,59).

The reaction of sodium tetramethoxyborohydride, prepared from the trimethoxyborohydride and methanol, with diborane yields 85% sodium borohydride (60,67).

$$3\,NaB(OCH_3)_4 + 2\,B_2H_6 \rightarrow 3\,NaBH_4 + 4\,B(OCH_3)_3 \tag{2-36}$$

The methyl borate is accompanied by a by-product, dimethoxyborine, which may result from the secondary reaction of diborane and methyl borate (60).

$$B_2H_6 + 4\,B(OCH_3)_3 \rightarrow 6\,BH(OCH_3)_2 \tag{2-37}$$

The reaction of sodium tetramethoxyborohydride with sodium hydride at 250° yields 66% sodium borohydride of 91% purity (59).

$$NaB(OCH_3)_4 + 4\,NaH \rightarrow NaBH_4 + 4\,NaOCH_3 \tag{2-38}$$

Sodium methoxide, prepared by the decomposition of sodium tetramethoxyborohydride at 210-240°, rapidly absorbs diborane to form sodium borohydride with considerable evolution of heat (58,60,68).

$$NaB(OCH_3)_4 \rightarrow NaOCH_3 + B(OCH_3)_3 \tag{2-39}$$
$$3\,NaOCH_3 + 2\,B_2H_6 \rightarrow 3\,NaBH_4 + B(OCH_3)_3 \tag{2-40}$$

Dimethoxyborine, probably formed according to equation (2-37), is isolated as a by-product. The reaction of the methoxide is interpreted (55) as consisting of the primary formation of an acid-base complex in which the methoxide ion is the basic substance.

$$NaOCH_3 + \tfrac{1}{2}B_2H_6 \rightarrow NaBH_3(OCH_3) \tag{2-41}$$

followed by the reactions:

$$NaBH_3(OCH_3) + \tfrac{1}{2}B_2H_6 \rightarrow NaBH_4 + BH_2(OCH_3) \tag{2-42}$$
$$3\,BH_2(OCH_3) \rightarrow B_2H_6 + B(OCH_3)_3 \tag{2-43}$$

Sodium hydride and methyl borate in the correct proportions undergo a rapid reaction at 225-275° to produce sodium borohydride of high purity and in a yield of 94%, according to the equation (58,59,66):

$$4\,NaH + B(OCH_3)_3 \rightarrow NaBH_4 + 3\,NaOCH_3 \tag{2-44}$$

The sodium borohydride may be extracted from the reaction mixture by liquid ammonia or isopropylamine in which the borohydride is very soluble, but in which the methoxide is almost insoluble. The methyl borate in equation (2-44) may be replaced by higher esters such as ethyl and *n*-butyl borate. The sodium borohydride prepared from the alkyl borates may be brought to a high state of purity by recrystallization from water as the dihydrate or by recrystallization from isopropylamine (59). A major portion of the impurities may be removed by treatment of the impure borohydride with diborane to produce low boiling alkyl borates which are removed by distillation (69). The isopropylamine solution of the borohydride may be treated to effect purification before isolation of the solid borohydride. The addition of water equivalent to 50% by weight of the impurities results in the precipitation of a compound insoluble in the organic solvent. The alkyl alcohol formed by the reaction of water with the dissolved impurities or the excess water or both are removed by the addition of calcium hydride, barium oxide, calcium sulfate hemihydrate, activated alumina or silica gel, which are insoluble in the solvent but which react rapidly with the water or alkyl alcohol forming an insoluble product. Color is removed from the solution of sodium borohydride with active carbon or charcoal, following which the solvent is evaporated to yield the borohydride in fairly high purity (70).

Several methods which give sodium borohydride in somewhat lower yield than those discussed heretofore have been examined. The reaction of metallic sodium with a mixture of hydrogen and methyl borate at 240–250° in the approximate proportions required by the reaction

$$4\ Na + 2\ H_2 + B(OCH_3)_3 \longrightarrow NaBH_4 + 3\ NaOCH_3 \qquad (2\text{-}45)$$

gives sodium borohydride contaminated with sodium trimethoxyborohydride, produced according to equation (2-29) (59,66). By grinding sodium hydride and boric oxide together in a ball mill at 330–350° for 20 to 48 hours, an approximately 60% yield of sodium borohydride has been obtained (59,66).

$$4\ NaH + 2\ B_2O_3 \longrightarrow 3\ NaBO_2 + NaBH_4 \qquad (2\text{-}46)$$

All attempts to prepare sodium borohydride by a reaction between sodium hydride and diborane have been unsuccessful (60).

Stock and Laudenklos (71) reported that the reaction of diborane and a sodium amalgam gave a compound which they called disodium diborane. Kasper, McCarty, and Newkirk (72) repeated the preparation and found that the product is sodium borohydride.

In an investigation of the disproportionation reactions of the dimethylaminoboron hydrides, Burg and Randolph (73) reported that the reaction of N,N-dimethylaminoborine with sodium hydride at 110° gave bis-dimethylaminoborine and sodium borohydride.

$$2\ (CH_3)_2NBH_2 + NaH \longrightarrow NaBH_4 + [(CH_3)_2N]_2BH \qquad (2\text{-}47)$$

The purity of the borohydride obtained in this manner was not further investigated.

The reaction of sodium hydride and boron trifluoride etherate at temperatures up to $100°$, according to the equation

$$6 \text{ NaH} + 8 \text{ BF}_3 : O(C_2H_5)_2 \rightarrow 6 \text{ NaBF}_4 + B_2H_6 + 8 (C_2H_5)_2O \quad (2\text{-}48)$$

serves for the preparation of diborane (63). Goubeau and Bergmann (74) reported that the compound, $NaBHF_3$, formed at $200°$ from sodium hydride and boron trifluoride, can react further with sodium hydride at $200°$ to form NaH_2BF_2, and that sodium borohydride can probably be prepared by the following sequence, although these authors did not actually prepare the borohydride.

$$\text{NaH} + \text{BF}_3 \rightarrow \text{NaBHF}_3 \quad (2\text{-}49)$$

$$\text{NaBHF}_3 + \text{NaH} \rightarrow \text{NaBH}_2F_2 + \text{NaF} \quad (2\text{-}50)$$

$$\text{NaBH}_2F_2 + \text{NaH} \rightarrow \text{NaBH}_3F + \text{NaF} \quad (2\text{-}51)$$

$$\text{NaBH}_3F + \text{NaH} \rightarrow \text{NaBH}_4 + \text{NaF} \quad (2\text{-}52)$$

Wittig and Hornberger (75) prepared sodium borohydride in 85-90% yield by the reaction of 0.33 mole of sodium hydride and 0.05 mole of boron trifluoride etherate in ether in a bomb tube at $125°$.

$$4 \text{ NaH} + \text{BF}_3 \rightarrow \text{NaBH}_4 + 3 \text{ NaF} \quad (2\text{-}53)$$

The direct exchange of solid sodium borohydride with a hydrogen-tritium mixture at $350°$ yields the isotopic compound, $NaBH_4$-t, with an approximately statistical isotopic distribution (76).

The purification of sodium borohydride prepared by any of the preceding reactions can be carried out by recrystallization from water as the dihydrate, $NaBH_4 \cdot 2H_2O$. The water may be removed from the dihydrate *in vacuo* to give sodium borohydride of high purity (60). Although the borohydride is soluble in several amines, recrystallization from isopropylamine is particularly satisfactory for the preparation of pure material (21,60).

2.2.2 Analysis

Measurement of the amount of hydrogen evolved upon acidification of an aqueous solution of sodium borohydride serves as a fairly accurate method for the analysis of the borohydride (21,60,77).

$$\text{NaBH}_4 + 2 \text{ H}_2O \rightarrow 4 \text{ H}_2 + \text{NaBO}_2 \quad (2\text{-}54)$$

The boron and sodium in the resulting solution can be determined by the usual procedures (60).

The same reaction can be made the basis of a volumetric procedure involving titration with a standard solution of hydrochloric acid using methyl red as an indicator. The end point is reported to be sharp and the precision better than 0.1% (21). The boric acid in the solution, resulting from the titration with hydrochloric acid, can be titrated with a standard solution of sodium hydroxide in the usual manner using phenolphthalein indicator and mannitol. The precision of this method of analysis, however, is less than that of the titration with hydrochloric acid (21).

Matthews (78) utilized an analytical procedure based upon the titration of sodium borohydride with a solution of iodine in a buffered solution at pH 7.0. Although no details are given in the publication, it has been pointed out (79) that the method appears to be limited to pH 7.0, a pH at which sodium borohydride is less stable than in alkaline medium.

The reduction of iodate with borohydride is the basis of a volumetric assay of sodium borohydride based on the equation (79)

$$3\ BH_4^- + 4\ IO_3^- \longrightarrow 4\ I^- + 3\ H_2BO_3^- + 3\ H_2O \qquad (2\text{-}55)$$

The sample of borohydride, either solid or in alkaline solution, is added to an excess of a standard potassium iodate solution. If solid sodium borohydride is used, alkali must be added to the iodate. Potassium iodide is then added, followed by acid, and the liberated iodine is titrated with standard thiosulfate. A large excess of iodate is required for a quantitative determination.

A somewhat analogous reaction has been proposed (80) involving the direct titration of a sodium borohydride solution with a standard sodium hypochlorite solution, using Bordeaux red as an indicator.

$$H^+ + BH_4^- + 4\ OCl^- \longrightarrow 4\ Cl^- + H_3BO_3 + H_2O \qquad (2\text{-}56)$$

The pH of the solution during the titration, maintained with a carbonate buffer, is critical, having an optimum value in the range 9.6 to 10.3.

2.2.3 Properties

Sodium borohydride is a white crystalline, salt-like solid of remarkable stability. X-ray diffraction data as well as infrared absorption data indicate that the substance exists in an ionic lattice of tetrahedral borohydride ions and sodium ions, $Na^+ BH_4^-$ (81–83). The crystal structure is face-centered cubic, $a = 6.14$ A, the unit cell containing four sodium and four boron atoms (81). Measurement of the nuclear magnetic resonance yields a value of 6.0 gauss for the width of the resonance absorption line (52).

The solid borohydride is stable in dry air to $300°$. No apparent change occurs in vacuum at temperatures approaching $400°$. Above $400°$ a relatively slow evolution of hydrogen occurs (60). The decomposition becomes rapid above $550°$ giving principally hydrogen and traces of diborane (84). The solid borohydride ignites from a free flame in air and burns quietly.

The density of sodium borohydride has been reported to be 1.074 (81) and 1.08 (21) g./cc. The specific heat is 0.55 ± 0.01 cal./g./deg. and the standard heat of formation is -43.83 ± 0.07 kcal./mole (21). The reduction potential is reported to be -0.43 volt in acid solution and -1.37 volts in basic solution (84).

Sodium borohydride dissolves in cold water without extensive evolution of hydrogen and may be crystallized as a dihydrate in the cold. At room temperature and higher, the hydrolysis proceeds more rapidly although the material is fairly stable in basic solution. No appreciable reaction with water at room temperature occurs above pH 11.5. The reaction of sodium borohydride with water is discussed in Section 3.1.

In contrast to the slow reaction with water at room temperature, the borohydride reacts at an appreciable rate at $-40°$ with methanol (60).

$$NaBH_4 + 4\ CH_3OH \longrightarrow NaB(OCH_3)_4 + 4\ H_2 \qquad (2\text{-}57)$$

The borohydride is not appreciably soluble in diethyl ether, dioxane, diethyl cellosolve, ethyl acetate and methyl borate. It is very soluble in liquid ammonia and in the lower aliphatic amines. The reported solubilities, in grams per 100 g. of solvent at the indicated temperatures, are as follows (60):

Solvent	Temp., °C.	Solubility
Water	20	55
Ethyl alcohol	20	4 (reacts slowly)
Isopropyl alcohol	20	0.25 (reacts slowly)
Liquid ammonia	25	104
Methylamine	−20	27.6
Ethylamine	17	20.9
n-Propylamine	28	9.7
Isopropylamine	28	6.0
n-Butylamine	28	4.9
Ethylene diamine	75	22
Cyclohexylamine	28	1.8
Aniline	75	0.6
Pyridine	25, 75	3.1, 3.4
Morpholine	25, 75	1.4, 2.5
Acetonitrile	28	0.9

2.3 POTASSIUM BOROHYDRIDE

2.3.1 Preparation

Potassium borohydride is prepared by the action of diborane on potassium tetramethoxyborohydride. The latter is obtained by the reaction of potassium methoxide with methyl borate (60,67).

$$KOCH_3 + B(OCH_3)_3 \longrightarrow KB(OCH_3)_4 \qquad (2\text{-}58)$$

$$3\ KB(OCH_3)_4 + 2\ B_2H_6 \longrightarrow 3\ KBH_4 + 4\ B(OCH_3)_3 \qquad (2\text{-}59)$$

The borohydride is accompanied by dimethoxyborine resulting from the reaction of diborane and methyl borate (equation 2-37).

In contrast to the behavior of sodium methoxide prepared by decomposition of sodium tetramethoxyborohydride, potassium methoxide, prepared by the action of metallic potassium on methanol, does not react with diborane (60). Schlesinger and Brown and their collaborators (55) have pointed out that the physical state of the material is an important factor in these reactions. Consequently, the reactions of diborane with sodium methoxide prepared by the reaction of sodium with methanol, as well as its reaction with potassium methoxide prepared by decomposition of potassium tetramethoxyborohydride, should be studied.

Attempts to prepare potassium borohydride by the action of diborane on potassium hydride within the temperature range 185-200° have been reported to be unsuccessful (85).

By allowing aluminum borohydride to remain in contact with potassium chloride for 40 hours, the borohydride was absorbed to an extent which indicated that the reaction

$$Al(BH_4)_3 + 3\ KCl \longrightarrow 3\ KBH_4 + AlCl_3 \qquad (2\text{-}60)$$

had proceeded about 59% to completion although the potassium compound was not actually isolated (86).

2.3.2 Analysis

An aqueous solution of potassium borohydride, heated to 100°, liberates hydrogen which can be quantitatively measured (60). The residual solution can be analyzed for potassium and for boron in the usual manner.

Since the behavior of potassium borohydride is similar to that of the sodium salt, the methods suitable for the analysis of the latter should be applicable to the assay of the potassium salt. The direct volumetric assay with standard sodium hypochlorite (equation 2-56) has been applied to potassium borohydride (80).

2.3.3 Properties

Potassium borohydride is a white crystalline material which is non-hygroscopic and stable in moist and dry air. Decomposition without melting occurs at about 500° in vacuum with evolution of hydrogen. Above 500° potassium distills off. Ignition from a free flame in air results in quiet burning. The solid borohydride will not ignite at 300° except by a free flame.

Water solutions of the borohydride are stabilized up to the reflux temperature by the addition of base. The material has a negative heat of solution and is soluble in water, alcohol and liquid ammonia and generally insoluble in ethers and hydrocarbons (87).

2.4 LITHIUM BOROHYDRIDE

2.4.1 Preparation

Lithium borohydride may be prepared, on a small scale, by the action of gaseous diborane or aluminum borohydride on ethyllithium (88):

$$3 \text{ LiC}_2\text{H}_5 + 2 \text{ B}_2\text{H}_6 \rightarrow 3 \text{ LiBH}_4 + (\text{C}_2\text{H}_5)_3\text{B} \qquad (2\text{-}61)$$

$$3 \text{ LiC}_2\text{H}_5 + \text{Al(BH}_4)_3 \rightarrow 3 \text{ LiBH}_4 + (\text{C}_2\text{H}_5)_3\text{Al} \qquad (2\text{-}62)$$

In the absence of solvents, no reaction between diborane and lithium hydride occurs, even at elevated temperatures and pressures. In the presence of diethyl ether, diborane is quantitatively absorbed by the hydride with the formation of the monoetherate of lithium borohydride in a state of high purity (60,64,89).

$$2 \text{ LiH} + \text{B}_2\text{H}_6 + 2 \text{ (C}_2\text{H}_5)_2\text{O} \rightarrow 2 \text{ LiBH}_4 \cdot (\text{C}_2\text{H}_5)_2\text{O} \qquad (2\text{-}63)$$

The ether may be removed by heating the etherate to from 70 to 100° *in vacuo*.

The reaction of lithium methoxide, prepared by the action of the metal on methanol, with diborane proceeds slowly. Lithium ethoxide, on the other hand, reacts rapidly and completely with the evolution of considerable heat (55,60).

$$3 \text{ LiOC}_2\text{H}_5 + 2 \text{ B}_2\text{H}_6 \rightarrow 3 \text{ LiBH}_4 + \text{B(OC}_2\text{H}_5)_3 \qquad (2\text{-}64)$$

Lithium tetramethoxyborohydride, obtained by treating the methoxide with excess methyl borate and then removing the excess *in vacuo*, reacts slowly with diborane to yield impure lithium borohydride which can be purified by recrystallization from ether (60,67).

$$\text{LiOCH}_3 + \text{B(OCH}_3)_3 \rightarrow \text{LiB(OCH}_3)_4 \qquad (2\text{-}65)$$

$$3 \text{ LiB(OCH}_3)_4 + 2 \text{ B}_2\text{H}_6 \rightarrow 3 \text{ LiBH}_4 + 4 \text{ B(OCH}_3)_3 \qquad (2\text{-}66)$$

The reaction of lithium hydride with methyl borate at 100° yields lithium trimethoxyborohydride, according to the equation

$$\text{LiH} + \text{B(OCH}_3)_3 \rightarrow \text{LiBH(OCH}_3)_3 \qquad (2\text{-}67)$$

Treatment of the trimethoxyborohydride with diborane and distillation of the methyl borate yields 85% lithium borohydride (57).

$$2 \text{ LiBH(OCH}_3)_3 + \text{B}_2\text{H}_6 \rightarrow 2 \text{ LiBH}_4 + 2 \text{ B(OCH}_3)_3 \qquad (2\text{-}68)$$

The reaction in equation (2-67) does not proceed smoothly, the product is not homogeneous and appears to undergo relatively rapid disproportionation and other types of decomposition at the temperatures required for its formation.

$$2 \text{ LiBH(OCH}_3)_3 \rightarrow \text{LiB(OCH}_3)_4 + \text{LiBH}_2(\text{OCH}_3)_2 \qquad (2\text{-}69)$$

At 200° the trimethoxyborohydride produces methyl borate and dimethoxyborine (56).

The reaction between lithium hydride and methyl borate at 225-275° yields 70% lithium borohydride as contrasted with 90-94% in the case of sodium borohydride (59).

$$4 \text{ LiH} + \text{B(OCH}_3)_3 \longrightarrow \text{LiBH}_4 + 3 \text{ LiOCH}_3 \qquad (2\text{-}70)$$

Difficulties are encountered in attempting to extract the borohydride from the crude reaction mixture. The borohydride has also been prepared by the reaction of tributyl borate with lithium hydride (75).

Lithium borohydride may be prepared from the sodium salt by metathesis in solution. Addition of a small excess of lithium chloride to a solution of sodium borohydride in methyl-, ethyl-, or isopropylamines results in the precipitation of sodium chloride. Evaporation of the solution followed by an extraction with ethyl ether yields 90-95% lithium borohydride of 97-98% purity (86).

$$\text{NaBH}_4 + \text{LiCl} \longrightarrow \text{LiBH}_4 + \text{NaCl} \qquad (2\text{-}71)$$

Boron trifluoride etherate reacts with lithium hydride at temperatures up to 100° to form diborane in accordance with the overall equation (62-64,90,91)

$$6 \text{ LiH} + 8 \text{ BF}_3 \xrightarrow{\text{ether}} 6 \text{ LiBF}_4 + \text{B}_2\text{H}_6 \qquad (2\text{-}72)$$

When the reaction is carried out at lower temperatures, considerable amounts of lithium borohydride are formed (63,91). Lithium borohydride has been shown to be an intermediate in the production of diborane from boron trifluoride etherate and lithium aluminum hydride (65) as well as lithium hydride (64). By suppressing the formation of diborane or by preventing the escape of the gas by the use of pressure to force the reaction between lithium hydride and diborane, the hydride is converted completely to lithium borohydride and lithium fluoride (64,75,92,93).

$$4 \text{ LiH} + \text{BF}_3 \longrightarrow \text{LiBH}_4 + 3 \text{ LiF} \qquad (2\text{-}73)$$

Direct exchange of solid lithium borohydride with a hydrogen-tritium mixture occurs at 200° to yield the isotopic compound, LiBH$_4$-t, containing an approximately statistic isotopic distribution (76).

Lithium borohydride may be purified by recrystallization from isopropylamine or diethyl ether. Solution of the borohydride in the ether and evaporation of the filtered solution yields a crystalline monoetherate. By heating the etherate to 100° *in vacuo* the ether is readily removed and the residual lithium borohydride is analytically pure (21,60).

2.4.2 Analysis

Treatment of lithium borohydride with methanol proceeds smoothly to yield hydrogen, as the only volatile product, accompanied by lithium boromethoxide.

$$LiBH_4 + 4\ CH_3OH \longrightarrow LiB(OCH_3)_4 + 4\ H_2 \qquad (2\text{-}74)$$

Upon heating the non-volatile residue methyl borate is liberated.

$$LiB(OCH_3)_4 \longrightarrow B(OCH_3)_3 + LiOCH_3 \qquad (2\text{-}75)$$

This substance is treated with water and the boron estimated as boric acid by titration with barium hydroxide solution. The non-volatile lithium salt is determined as lithium hydroxide by titration with dilute hydrochloric acid (88).

Hydrolysis of lithium borohydride quantitatively yields hydrogen according to the equation (21,60,64)

$$LiBH_4 + 4\ H_2O \longrightarrow 4\ H_2 + LiOH + H_3BO_3 \qquad (2\text{-}76)$$

The aqueous solution is analyzed for lithium by titration with acid (21, 64) and boric acid is determined, after mannitol addition, by a potentiometric titration (64) or by titration with a standard solution of sodium hydroxide using phenolphthalein indicator (21).

A cobaltous chloride-catalyzed hydrolysis results in a more rapid evolution of hydrogen, as depicted in equation (2-76) (64,94).

2.4.3 Properties

Lithium borohydride is a white crystalline salt-like solid. X-ray diffraction data and infrared absorption spectra indicate the presence of an ionic lattice containing tetrahedral borohydride ions, $Li^+\ BH_4^-$ (45,82, 83,88,95). The crystal structure is orthorhombic with the cell dimensions $a = 6.81$ A, $b = 4.43$ A, and $c = 7.17$ A (45). The width of the resonance absorption line at room temperature is reported to be 6.0 gauss (52).

Lithium borohydride is quite hygroscopic and may occasionally ignite on contact with water. A coating of white oxide will form on all surfaces within 2–3 minutes after initial exposure (96). Contact with cellulosic material, e.g., paper and cloth, is reported to result in spontaneous combustion within two minutes, consuming both cellulosic material and any hydride attached thereto or in immediate vicinity of the fire (96).

The compound melts at 284° with decomposition and exerts no appreciable vapor pressure at temperatures up to this point (88). Prolonged heating *in vacuo* above 200°, however, results in decomposition (96). Thermal decomposition becomes appreciable at from 250 to 275°, and seems to involve an intermediate reversible step in which a compound $LiBH_2$ is formed (1).

The density of lithium borohydride has been reported to be 0.66 (45) and 0.681 (21) g./cc. The specific heat is 0.84 ± 0.01 cal./g./deg., and the standard heat of formation is −44.15 ± 0.30 kcal./mole (21).

The borohydride is soluble (with reaction) in the lower alcohols (equation (2-74)). The solubility per 100 g. of solvent is approximately 2.5 g. at 19° (60), 3 g. at 25° (97) in diethyl ether (forms monoetherate), 3–4 g. at 25° in isopropylamine (60) and 28 g. at 25° in tetrahydrofuran (97). The latter is the preferred solvent for organic reductions.

2.5   SODIUM TRIMETHOXYBOROHYDRIDE

2.5.1   Preparation

The exothermic reaction between sodium hydride and refluxing methyl borate proceeds with moderate rapidity and with a great increase in the bulk of the solid to quantitatively yield sodium trimethoxyborohydride (56,58,98).

$$NaH + B(OCH_3)_3 \longrightarrow NaBH(OCH_3)_3 \qquad (2\text{-}77)$$

Treatment of metallic sodium with a mixture of hydrogen and methyl borate at 250° under pressure gives good yields of the trimethoxy derivative (59).

$$2\,Na + H_2 + 2\,B(OCH_3)_3 \longrightarrow 2\,NaBH(OCH_3)_3 \qquad (2\text{-}78)$$

The salt may be purified by recrystallization from liquid ammonia or from isopropylamine.

2.5.2   Analysis

Hydrolysis of the salt in warm water or in acidified cold water yields one mole of hydrogen per mole of salt. The compound is analyzed for base and for boron by titration of an aqueous solution, first by acid to the methyl red end point and after addition of mannitol, to the phenolphthalein end point by carbonate-free base (56).

2.5.3   Properties

Sodium trimethoxyborohydride is a microcrystalline white solid which is stable in dry air and only slowly attacked by air of average humidity. After exposure to humid air, traces of hydrogen gas are evolved. After the initial vigorous reaction which results on dissolving the compound in cold water, additional hydrogen is generated only slowly. Water can therefore be used as a solvent for the reaction between aqueous solutions of various metal ions and sodium trimethoxyborohydride.

The decomposition of the trimethoxyborohydride at its melting point 230° yields sodium borohydride and the evolution of methyl borate (equations 2-33, 2-34 and 2-35) (56,59).

The trimethoxyborohydride reacts with methanol rapidly and completely in the cold to liberate hydrogen (56).

$$NaBH(OCH_3)_3 + CH_3OH \longrightarrow NaB(OCH_3)_4 + H_2 \qquad (2\text{-}79)$$

Although the rate of hydrogen evolution in the hydrolysis of borohydrides decreases with the increasing basicity of the solution, in the reaction with methanol the neutral product does not appreciably alter the acidity of the mixture resulting in a uniform rate of hydrogen evolution.

The approximate solubilities of sodium trimethoxyborohydride in grams per 100 g. of solvent are as follows (56):

Solvent	Temp., $^\circ$C.	Solubility
Pyridine	24, 75	0.4, 3.0
Morpholine	24, 75	0.3, 2.3
Dioxane	25, 75	1.6, 4.5
Isopropylamine	25	9.0
Ethylene diamine	25, 75	0.2, 0.2 (99)
Liquid ammonia	−33	5.6

2.6   OTHER COMPLEX METAL HYDRIDES

Numerous other complex metal hydrides containing aluminohydride and borohydride ions have been prepared by metathetical reactions utilizing inorganic halides and LAH and alkali metal borohydrides, respectively. The majority of these hydrides, discussed in Section 3.14, have been prepared so recently that very little has been reported regarding their reactions and possible utility as reducing agents. A number of these compounds are stable only at extremely low temperatures so that their potentialities are obviously limited. In addition to those hydrides discussed heretofore a number of others have been utilized, although only to a limited extent, in the reduction of inorganic and organic compounds. The preparation and some properties of these hydrides are briefly discussed in this section.

2.6.1   Magnesium aluminum hydride

This is prepared by treatment of the etherate of magnesium bromide with an ethereal solution of LAH (31,46):

$$MgBr_2 + 2 LiAlH_4 \longrightarrow Mg(AlH_4)_2 + 2 LiBr \qquad (2\text{-}80)$$

or by the reaction of an ethereal solution of excess magnesium hydride with an ethereal solution of aluminum chloride (31,46,100,101).

$$4 MgH_2 + 2 AlCl_3 \longrightarrow Mg(AlH_4)_2 + 3 MgCl_2 \qquad (2\text{-}81)$$

With an excess of aluminum chloride the product is aluminum hydride (101). The magnesium hydride is prepared by the thermal decomposition of diethylmagnesium (101-103) or ethylmagnesium halide (100,102,103) *in vacuo* at 175°,

$$Mg(C_2H_5)_2 \longrightarrow MgH_2 + 2\ C_2H_4 \qquad (2\text{-}82)$$

$$2\ C_2H_5MgX \longrightarrow MgH_2 + MgX_2 + 2\ C_2H_4 \qquad (2\text{-}83)$$

by the reaction of diethylmagnesium with diborane (102) or LAH (104) in ether,

$$3\ Mg(C_2H_5)_2 + B_2H_6 \longrightarrow 3\ MgH_2 + 2\ B(C_2H_5)_3 \qquad (2\text{-}84)$$

$$2\ Mg(C_2H_5)_2 + LiAlH_4 \longrightarrow 2\ MgH_2 + LiAl(C_2H_5)_4 \qquad (2\text{-}85)$$

by the reaction of an ethereal solution of magnesium chloride with lithium hydride (105)

$$MgCl_2 + 2\ LiH \longrightarrow MgH_2 + 2\ LiCl \qquad (2\text{-}86)$$

or from the elements at 570° and 200 atm. pressure in the presence of magnesium iodide (106)

$$Mg + H_2 \xrightarrow{\ MgI_2\ } MgH_2 \qquad (2\text{-}87)$$

Magnesium aluminum hydride is a white solid which is stable up to 140°. Above this temperature, and especially at 200°, the complex hydride decomposes into magnesium hydride, aluminum and hydrogen (100).

$$Mg(AlH_4)_2 \longrightarrow MgH_2 + 2\ Al + 3\ H_2 \qquad (2\text{-}88)$$

The hydride is postulated as possessing a resonance bridge structure similar to that proposed for LAH (46,103):

VII

and in ether solution is analogous to LAH in its reducing properties.

2.6.2   Aluminum borohydride

This is an unstable non-polar liquid in which covalent structures make a bigger contribution than ionic structures (82,83,95,107-109). It can be prepared by the reaction of diborane with trimethylaluminum (86,109,110), aluminum hydride (25,26) or lithium aluminum hydride (1).

$$(CH_3)_3Al + 2\ B_2H_6 \longrightarrow (CH_3)_3B + Al(BH_4)_3 \qquad (2\text{-}89)$$

$$2\ AlH_3 + 3\ B_2H_6 \longrightarrow 2\ Al(BH_4)_3 \qquad (2\text{-}90)$$

$$LiAlH_4 + 2\ B_2H_6 \longrightarrow LiBH_4 + Al(BH_4)_3 \qquad (2\text{-}91)$$

In addition aluminum borohydride may be prepared by the reaction of aluminum hydride and boron trichloride (1) as well as by the action of aluminum chloride or bromide on sodium, lithium, or potassium borohydrides (86,111).

$$4 \text{ AlH}_3 + 3 \text{ BCl}_3 \rightarrow \text{Al(BH}_4)_3 + 3 \text{ AlCl}_3 \qquad (2\text{-}92)$$

$$3 \text{ MBH}_4 + \text{AlX}_3 \rightarrow \text{Al(BH}_4)_3 + 3 \text{ MX} \qquad (2\text{-}93)$$

The liquid aluminum borohydride, whose density at $0°$ is 0.569 g./cc. (112), melts at $-64.5°$ and has an extrapolated boiling point of $44.5°$ (110). The standard heat of formation, based on its vigorous reaction with water, is -72.1 kcal./mole (113).

The borohydride reacts with diethyl ether and trimethylamine to yield an etherate and a trimethylamminate, respectively, which decompose to yield mixtures of products other than the parent substances (110).

Aluminum borohydride is an extremely hazardous material. The vapor of the compound ignites spontaneously on exposure to air containing only traces of moisture (86,110,114). In dry air the material is not spontaneously inflammable at room temperature although higher temperatures induce vigorous decomposition (114). The induced combustion of olefins with aluminum borohydride occurs in dry oxygen, 1-butene exploding after an induction period while 1,3-butadiene explodes immediately (115). Actually, ethylene, propylene and 1-butene react with the borohydride in the absence of oxygen (116,117), and this is considered as the starting mechanism of the explosive oxidation.

A second hazard in the handling of aluminum borohydride results from the decomposition which evolves hydrogen at room temperature. Even though the hydrogen evolution is slow, high pressures may develop in closed containers in the course of time (86).

Although aluminum borohydride is required for the preparation of the borohydrides of heavy metals, such as uranium, thorium, hafnium, zirconium, and titanium, its hazardous nature is a deterrent to its widespread usage.

2.6.3 Lithium gallium hydride

This is prepared by the reaction of excess, powdered lithium hydride with gallium chloride in ether solution (1,118).

$$4 \text{ LiH} + \text{GaCl}_3 \rightarrow \text{LiGaH}_4 + 3 \text{ LiCl} \qquad (2\text{-}94)$$

The compound forms a dietherate which is converted to a monoetherate on removal of the ether *in vacuo*.

Lithium gallium hydride decomposes in a comparatively short time at room temperature, more rapidly at $150°$, to yield metallic gallium (1,118).

$$2 \text{ LiGaH}_4 \rightarrow 2 \text{ LiH} + 2 \text{ Ga} + 3 \text{ H}_2 \qquad (2\text{-}95)$$

The finely divided metallic gallium makes the reaction autocatalytic.

In ether solution the complex gallium ionic hydride is a milder reducing agent than LAH.

REFERENCES

1. Finholt, A. E., A. C. Bond, Jr., and H. I. Schlesinger, *J. Am. Chem. Soc.*, 69, 1199 (1947).
2. Schlesinger, H. I., and A. E. Finholt, U.S. Pat. 2,567,972 (September 18, 1951).
3. Schlesinger, H. I., and A. E. Finholt, U.S. Pat. 2,576,311 (November 27, 1951).
4. Wiberg, E., R. Bauer, M. Schmidt, and R. Usón, *Z. Naturforsch.*, 6b, 393 (1951).
5. Schwarzkopf, O., and H. J. Cahnmann, Brit. Pat. 660,368 (November 7, 1951).
6. Schwarzkopf, O., and H. J. Cahnmann, Ger. Pat. 828,543 (January 17, 1952).
7. Mahé, J., J. Rollet, and A. Willemart, *Bull. soc. chim. France*, [5] 16, 481 (1949).
8. Reynaud, P., and J. Matti, *Bull. soc. chim. France*, [5] 18, 612 (1951).
9. Rosenmund, K. W., and F. Zymalkowski, *Chem. Ber.*, 85, 152 (1952).
10. Mirza, R., *Nature*, 170, 669 (1952).
11. Brown, W. G., in R. Adams, ed., *Organic Reactions*, Vol. VI, Wiley, New York, 1951, Chapter 10, p. 483.
12. Gibb, T. R. P., Jr., M. D. Banus, R. W. Bragdon, and A. A. Hinckley, *Abstracts of Papers*, 119th Meeting American Chemical Society, Cleveland, Ohio, April 1951, p. 39P.
13. Schlesinger, H. I., unpublished report to the Naval Research Laboratory; through J. E. Johnson, R. H. Blizzard, and H. W. Carhart, *J. Am. Chem. Soc.*, 70, 3664 (1948).
14. Abert, P., and J. Mahé, *Bull. soc. chim. France*, [5] 17 1165 (1950).
15. Gibb, T. R. P., Jr., U.S. Pat. 2,468,260 (April 26, 1949).
16. Gibb, T. R. P., Jr., Can. Pat. 474,826 (June 26, 1951).
17. Gibb, T. R. P., Jr., U.S. Pat. 2,519,644 (August 22, 1950).
18. Wiberg, E., and M. Schmidt, *Z. Naturforsch.*, 7b, 59 (1952).
19. Wilzbach, K. E. and L. Kaplan, *J. Am. Chem. Soc.*, 72, 5795 (1950).
20. Schmitz-Dumont, O., and V. Habernickel, *Naturwissenschaften*, 39, 20 (1952).
21. Davis, W. D., L. S. Mason, and G. Stegeman, *J. Am. Chem. Soc.*, 71, 2775 (1949).
22. Barbaras, G., G. D. Barbaras, A. E. Finholt, and H. I. Schlesinger, *J. Am. Chem. Soc.*, 70, 877 (1948).
23. *Chem. Eng. News*, 31, 2334 (1953).
24. Wiberg, E., and O. Stecher, *Angew. Chem.*, 52, 372 (1939).
25. Stecher, O., and E. Wiberg, *Ber.*, 75, 2003 (1942).
26. Wiberg, E., *Ber.*, 77A, 75 (1944).
27. Wiberg, E., *Angew. Chem.*, 63, 485 (1951).
28. Wiberg, E., and M. Schmidt, *Z. Naturforsch.*, 6b, 333 (1951).
29. Wiberg, E., H. Graf, M. Schmidt, and R. Usón, *Z. Naturforsch.*, 7b, 578 (1952).
30. Gibb, T. R. P., Jr., M. D. Banus, R. W. Bragdon, and A. A. Hinckley, *Abstracts of Papers*, 119th Meeting American Chemical Society, Cleveland, Ohio, April 1951, p. 38P.
31. Wiberg, E., *Angew. Chem.*, 65, 16 (1953).
32. Wiberg, E., and M. Schmidt, *Z. Naturforsch.*, 6b, 460 (1951).
33. Wiberg, E., and M. Schmidt, *Z. Naturforsch.*, 6b, 459 (1951).
34. Wiberg, E., and M. Schmidt, *Z. Naturforsch.*, 6b, 458 (1951).

35. Wiberg, E., H. Graf, M. Schmidt, and R. Usón, Z. *Naturforsch.*, in press; through ref. 31.
36. Felkin, H., *Bull. soc. chim. France*, [5] *18*, 347 (1951).
37. Orchin, M., and I. Wender, *Anal. Chem.*, *21*, 875 (1949).
38. Krynitsky, J. A., J. E. Johnson, and H. W. Carhart, *Anal. Chem.*, *20*, 311 (1948).
39. Nelson, L. S., D. E. Laskowski, and H. A. Porte, *J. Chem. Ed.*, *28*, 648 (1951).
40. *Chem. Week*, *70*, 34 (1952).
41. Job, A., and R. Reich, *Bull. soc. chim. France*, [4] *33*, 1414 (1923).
42. Finholt, A. E., and E. C. Jacobson, *J. Am. Chem. Soc.*, *74*, 3943 (1952).
43. Lippincott, E. R., *J. Chem. Phys.*, *17*, 1351 (1949).
44. Paddock, N. L., *Nature*, *167*, 1070 (1951).
45. Harris, P. M., and E. P. Meibohm, *J. Am. Chem. Soc.*, *69*, 1231 (1947).
46. Wiberg, E., and R. Bauer, Z. *Naturforsch.*, *5b*, 397 (1950).
47. Solms, U., *Chimia*, *5*, 26 (1951).
48. Gibb, T. R. P., Jr., *J. Chem. Ed.*, *25*, 577 (1948).
49. Garner, W. E., and E. W. Haycock, *Proc. Roy. Soc. (London)*, *211*, 335 (1951).
50. Wiberg, E., and W. Henle, Z. *Naturforsch.*, *6b*, 461 (1951).
51. Wiberg, E., and W. Henle, Z. *Naturforsch.*, *7b*, 250 (1952).
52. Garstens, M. A., *Phys. Rev.*, *79*, 397 (1950).
53. Gilman, H., and T. N. Goreau, *J. Am. Chem. Soc.*, *73*, 2939 (1951).
54. Gibb, T. R. P., Jr., private communication.
55. Schlesinger, H. I., and H. C. Brown with B. Abraham, A. C. Bond, N. Davidson, A. E. Finholt, J. R. Gilbreath, H. Hoekstra, L. Horvitz, E. K. Hyde, J. J. Katz, J. Knight, R. A. Lad, D. L. Mayfield, L. Rapp, D. M. Ritter, A. M. Schwartz, I. Sheft, L. D. Tuck, and A. O. Walker, *J. Am. Chem. Soc.*, *75*, 186 (1953).
56. Brown, H. C., H. I. Schlesinger, I. Sheft, and D. M. Ritter, *J. Am. Chem. Soc.*, *75*, 192 (1953).
57. Schlesinger, H. I., and H. C. Brown, U.S. Pat. 2,461,661 (February 15, 1949).
58. Schlesinger, H. I., H. R. Hoekstra, and H. C. Brown, *Abstracts of Papers*, 115th Meeting American Chemical Society, San Francisco, Calif., March 1949, p. 9 O.
59. Schlesinger, H. I., H. C. Brown, and A. E. Finholt, *J. Am. Chem. Soc.*, *75*, 205 (1953).
60. Schlesinger, H. I., H. C. Brown, H. R. Hoekstra, and L. R. Rapp, *J. Am. Chem. Soc.*, *75*, 199 (1953).
61. Schlesinger, H. I., H. C. Brown, B. Abraham, N. Davidson, A. E. Finholt, R. A. Lad, J. Knight, and A. M. Schwartz, *J. Am. Chem. Soc.*, *75*, 191 (1953).
62. Schlesinger, H. I., and H. C. Brown, U.S. Pat. 2,543,511 (February 27, 1951).
63. Schlesinger, H. I., H. C. Brown, J. R. Gilbreath, and J. J. Katz, *J. Am. Chem. Soc.*, *75*, 195 (1953).
64. Elliott, J. R., E. M. Boldebuck, and G. F. Roedel, *J. Am. Chem. Soc.*, *74*, 5047 (1952).
65. Shapiro, I., H. G. Weiss, M. Schmich, S. Skolnik, and G. B. L. Smith, *J. Am. Chem. Soc.*, *74*, 901 (1952).
66. Schlesinger, H. I., and H. C. Brown, U.S. Pat. 2,534,533 (December 19, 1950).

67. Schlesinger, H. I., and H. C. Brown, U.S. Pat. 2,461,663 (1949).
68. Schlesinger, H. I., and H. C. Brown, U.S. Pat. 2,461,662 (1949).
69. Gibb, T. R. P., Jr., U.S. Pat. 2,615,788 (October 28, 1952).
70. Banus, M. D., and T. R. P. Gibb, Jr., U.S. Pat. 2,542,746 (February 20, 1951).
71. Stock, A., and H. Laudenklos, Z. anorg. allgem. Chem., 228, 178 (1936).
72. Kasper, J. S., L. V. McCarty, and A. E. Newkirk, J. Am. Chem. Soc., 71, 2583 (1949).
73. Burg, A. B., and C. L. Randolph, Jr., J. Am. Chem. Soc., 73, 953 (1951).
74. Goubeau, J., and R. Bergmann, Z. anorg. chem., 263, 69 (1950).
75. Wittig, G., and P. Hornberger, Ann., 577, 11 (1952).
76. Brown, W. G., L. Kaplan, and K. E. Wilzbach, J. Am. Chem. Soc., 74, 1343 (1952).
77. Chaikin, S. W., and W. G. Brown, J. Am. Chem. Soc., 71, 122 (1949).
78. Mathews, M. D., J. Biol. Chem., 176, 229 (1948).
79. Lyttle, D. A., E. H. Jensen, and W. A. Struck, Anal. Chem., 24, 1843 (1952).
80. Chaikin, S. W., Anal. Chem., 25, 831 (1953).
81. Soldate, A. M., J. Am. Chem. Soc., 69, 987 (1947).
82. Price, W. C., H. C. Longuet-Higgins, B. Rice, and T. F. Young, J. Chem. Phys., 17, 217 (1949).
83. Price, W. C., J. Chem. Phys., 17, 1044 (1949).
84. Metal Hydrides, Inc., Technical Bulletin 502-D, "Sodium Borohydride."
85. Goubeau, J., U. Jacobshagen and M. Rahtz, Z. anorg. chem., 263, 63 (1950).
86. Schlesinger, H. I., H. C. Brown, and E. K. Hyde, J. Am. Chem. Soc., 75, 209 (1953).
87. Metal Hydrides, Inc., Technical Bulletin, "Potassium Borohydride."
88. Schlesinger, H. I., and H. C. Brown, J. Am. Chem. Soc., 62, 3429 (1940).
89. Schlesinger, H. I., and H. C. Brown, U.S. Pat. 2,545,633 (March 20, 1951).
90. Schlesinger, H. I., H. C. Brown, et al., Final Report on Contracts OEM sr-117 and OEM sr-368 (1943); through ref. 64.
91. Burgess, D. S., et al., Naval Research Laboratory Report No. P-2571, July 16, 1945; through ref. 64.
92. Winternitz, P. F., U.S. Pat. 2,523,217 (November 28, 1950).
93. Wittig, G., and P. Hornberger, Z. Naturforsch., 6b, 225 (1951).
94. Schlesinger, H. I., Report on Contract W3434, sc-174 (1944); through ref. 64.
95. Longuet-Higgins, H. C., J. Chem. Soc., 1946, 139.
96. Metal Hydrides Inc., Technical Bulletin 402-B "Lithium Borohydride."
97. Elliott, J. R., W. L. Roth, G. F. Roedel, and E. M. Boldebuck, J. Am. Chem. Soc., 74, 5211 (1952).
98. Schlesinger, H. I., and H. C. Brown, U.S. Pat. 2,494,968 (January 17, 1950).
99. Metal Hydrides Inc., Technical Bulletin 504-B, "Sodium Trimethoxyborohydride."
100. Wiberg, E., and R. Bauer, Z. Naturforsch., 7b, 131 (1952).
101. Wiberg, E., R. Bauer, and P. Buchheit, Angew. Chem., 62, 448 (1950).
102. Wiberg, E., and R. Bauer, Z. Naturforsch., 5b, 396 (1950).
103. Wiberg, E., and R. Bauer, Chem. Ber., 85, 593 (1952).
104. Barbaras, G. D., C. Dillard, A. E. Finholt, T. Wartik, K. E. Wilzbach, and H. I. Schlesinger, J. Am. Chem. Soc., 73, 4585 (1951).
105. Wiberg, E., and R. Bauer, Z. Naturforsch., 6b, 171 (1951).
106. Wiberg, E., H. Goeltzer, and R. Bauer, Z. Naturforsch., 6b, 394 (1951).
107. Beach, J. Y., and S. H. Bauer, J. Am. Chem. Soc., 62, 3440 (1940).

108. Bauer, S. H., *J. Am. Chem. Soc.*, 72, 622, 1864 (1950).
109. Schlesinger, H. I., R. T. Sanderson, and A. B. Burg, *J. Am. Chem. Soc.*, 61, 536 (1939).
110. Schlesinger, H. I., R. T. Sanderson, and A. B. Burg, *J. Am. Chem. Soc.*, 62, 3421 (1940).
111. Schlesinger, H. I., and H. C. Brown, U.S. Pat. 2,599,203 (June 3, 1952).
112. Smith, S. H., Jr., and R. R. Miller, *J. Am. Chem. Soc.*, 72, 1452 (1950).
113. Rulon, R. M., and L. S. Mason, *J. Am. Chem. Soc.*, 73, 5491 (1951).
114. Badin, E. J., P. C. Hunter, and R. N. Pease, *J. Am. Chem. Soc.*, 71, 2950 (1949).
115. Brokaw, R. S., E. J. Badin, and R. N. Pease, *J. Am. Chem. Soc.*, 72, 1793 (1950).
116. Brokaw, R. S., *Princeton Univ. Tech. Paper* No. 42 (1948) (NP-242); *Nuclear Sci. Abstracts*, 3, 233 (1949).
117. Brokaw, R. S., and R. N. Pease, *J. Am. Chem. Soc.*, 72, 3237 (1950).
118. Wiberg, E., and M. Schmidt, *Z. Naturforsch.*, 6b, 171 (1951).

CHAPTER 3

REACTIONS WITH INORGANIC REACTANTS

3.1 WATER

In the presence of excess water, *lithium aluminum hydride* reacts vigorously with the evolution of hydrogen (1,2):

$$LiAlH_4 + 4 H_2O \rightarrow LiOH + Al(OH)_2 + 4 H_2 \qquad (3\text{-}1)$$

This reaction is used as a basis for the analysis of LAH, as discussed in Section 2.1.2. The product of the reaction has also been represented as lithium aluminate (2,3).

$$LiAlH_4 + 2 H_2O \rightarrow LiAlO_2 + 4 H_2 \qquad (3\text{-}2)$$

The formation of a protective coating of aluminum hydroxide (1) or lithium aluminate (3) over the solid hydride is regarded as the cause of the relatively slow decomposition in moist air.

According to the above equations, with water in excess, the mole ratio of $H_2/H_2O = 1.00$. In the presence of small amounts of water, however, where LAH is in excess, the mole ratio of $H_2/H_2O = 1.50$ to 1.60. This is explained by secondary reactions.

$$6 LiAlH_4 + 15 H_2O \rightarrow 6 LiOH + 3 Al_2O_3 + 24 H_2 \qquad (3\text{-}3)$$

$$2 LiAlH_4 + 5 H_2O \rightarrow LiOH + LiH(AlO_2)_2 + 8 H_2 \qquad (3\text{-}4)$$

By treatment of an organic liquid such as a hydrocarbon with a solution of LAH in diethylene glycol diethyl ether and measurement of the evolved hydrogen, the water content can be determined with a precision of $\pm0.005\%$ in a concentration of 0.1% (4).

The reaction of LAH in di-*n*-butyl ether with heavy water at $0°$ has been used for the preparation of high purity (97–99%) hydrogen deuteride (5–8). Among the by-products isolated have been hydrogen and deuterium (5).

$$LiAlH_4 + 4 D_2O \rightarrow LiOD + Al(OD)_3 + 4 HD \qquad (3\text{-}5)$$

The use of sodium hydride in place of LAH in the reaction with heavy water reduces the yield of deuteride (5).

The reaction of LAH with water containing tritium has been used for the assay of tritium activity (9). This method has been utilized for the determination of tritium in cholesterol-H^3 and in samples doubly labeled with C^{14} as well as H^3. The dry sample is burned in a quartz combustion vessel in a stream of oxygen. The tritium oxide-water mixture is collected in a trap and treated with LAH in carbitol to yield a hydrogen-tritium mixture. The H^3 activity is measured with a vibrating reed electrometer (10).

The treatment of LAH with a dilute aqueous solution of hydrochloric acid has been utilized in the determination of the heat of formation of LAH (11). The equation involved in the calorimetric determination is represented as:

$$LiAlH_4 + 10 (HCl \cdot 50 H_2O) \rightarrow (LiCl + AlCl_3 + 6 HCl) \cdot 500 H_2O + 4 H_2$$
$$(3-6)$$

Sodium borohydride dissolves in cold water without extensive evolution of hydrogen and may be recrystallized as the dihydrate, $NaBH_4 \cdot 2 H_2O$, from aqueous solution. The water may be removed from the dihydrate *in vacuo* to give pure sodium borohydride.

At higher temperatures sodium borohydride is hydrolyzed rapidly with the evolution of hydrogen (12,13).

$$NaBH_4 + 2 H_2O \rightarrow NaBO_2 + 4 H_2 \qquad (3-7)$$

A total of 2.37 liters of hydrogen (gas at S.T.P.) are liberated per gram of sodium borohydride (14). Addition of acid to the stable cold water solution of the borohydride, rapidly liberates the theoretical quantity of hydrogen. This may be used as the basis for the analysis of sodium borohydride by hydrolysis with dilute hydrochloric acid.

$$NaBH_4 + 3 H_2O + HCl \rightarrow H_3BO_3 + NaCl + 4 H_2 \qquad (3-8)$$

Sodium borohydride containing tritium, $NaBH_4$-t, has been analyzed by this method by determining the tritium content of the generated hydrogen (15). The heat of formation of the borohydride has been determined (11), by utilizing the following equation:

$$NaBH_4 + 1.25 (HCl \cdot 200 H_2O) \rightarrow$$
$$(NaCl + H_3BO_3 + 0.25 HCl) \cdot 247 H_2O + 4 H_2 \quad (3-9)$$

In the absence of acid, the initial rate of hydrogen evolution decreases after a short time due to the increasing pH of the solution caused by the formation of the strongly basic metaborate ion. Thus, solution of the borohydride in a slightly basic solution largely prevents the initial generation of hydrogen and permits the use of the reagent as a reducing agent in aqueous solution.

The generation of hydrogen in the laboratory and in the field requires a rapid reaction and a convenient method of handling the reactants. The use of pellets, containing sodium borohydride and various accelerators, permits the convenient and controlled generation of hydrogen (14,16). The incorporation of various solid acidic materials in the pellets results in accelerated hydrolysis. The stronger the acid the greater the acceleration. The rate of hydrolysis is dependent on the pH and generally independent of the specific acids and salts used. Pellets containing equal weights of sodium borohydride and boric oxide are very effective, possibly due to the reaction with the sodium metaborate to give the tetraborate.

$$NaBH_4 + 2 H_2O \longrightarrow NaBO_2 + 4 H_2 \qquad (3\text{-}10)$$

$$2 NaBO_2 + B_2O_3 \longrightarrow Na_2B_4O_7 \qquad (3\text{-}11)$$

Oxalic acid, succinic acid, phosphorus pentoxide, and aluminum chloride are also effective accelerators, although disadvantages such as difficulty in pellet preparation or decreased stability are present in the use of these materials.

Various metal salts are effective catalytic accelerators in the hydrolysis of sodium borohydride. Pellets containing 5% of anhydrous cobaltous chloride are approximately as effective as pellets containing 50% by weight of boric oxide. The reaction of cobaltous chloride with a borohydride solution results in the rapid evolution of hydrogen and the formation of a black precipitate. This black material, whose analysis corresponds to a cobalt boride, Co_2B, appears to be the effective catalyst, rather than cobaltous chloride itself (14).

The solubility of sodium borohydride in cold water has been utilized in an attempt to carry out an isotopic exchange between the borohydride and deuterium oxide (17). Analysis of the gaseous products evolved in acid catalyzed hydrolysis of the solid reaction product failed to reveal significant amounts of hydrogen deuteride indicating that the hydrogen of sodium borohydride does not exchange with water.

Potassium borohydride is somewhat similar to sodium borohydride. It reacts insignificantly with cold water in which it is very soluble. Aqueous solutions are stabilized up to the reflux temperature by the addition of a small amount of base (18). Heating the aqueous solution to 100° results in the liberation of hydrogen and permits the analysis of the residual solution. By analogy with the behavior of the sodium compound the hydrolysis may be represented:

$$KBH_4 + 2 H_2O \longrightarrow KBO_2 + 4 H_2 \qquad (3\text{-}12)$$

Lithium borohydride is an extremely hygroscopic material and although the powder may ignite when moistened, it can be dissolved in ice water with slow decomposition. The hydrolysis reaction, which is catalyzed by cobaltous ion, is formulated as

$$LiBH_4 + 2 H_2O \longrightarrow LiBO_2 + 4 H_2 \qquad (3\text{-}13)$$

One gram of borohydride liberates more than 4 liters of hydrogen (gas at S.T.P.) by this reaction (19). Actually, when lithium borohydride is dissolved in water only a portion of the available hydrogen is liberated and the solution becomes strongly basic (20). In acid solution, the reaction is qualitatively much faster and analysis of the borohydride can be carried out by measurement of the hydrogen evolved in this manner. The heat of formation of the borohydride has been determined (11) utilizing the equation:

$$LiBH_4 + 1.25(HCl \cdot 200\ H_2O) \rightarrow$$

$$(LiCl + H_3BO_3 + 0.25\ HCl) \cdot 247\ H_2O + 4\ H_2 \quad (3\text{-}14)$$

Kilpatrick and McKinney (21) have studied the kinetics of the reaction of lithium borohydride in aqueous acid solution and have found that the reaction occurs in two steps. The first reaction produces diborane,

$$LiBH_4 + HCl \rightarrow \frac{1}{2}\ B_2H_6 + H_2 \quad (3\text{-}15)$$

and the second involves the slower hydrolysis of the diborane

$$\frac{1}{2}\ B_2H_6 + 3\ H_2O \rightarrow H_3BO_3 + 3\ H_2 \quad (3\text{-}16)$$

with the over-all reaction

$$LiBH_4 + HCl + 3\ H_2O \rightarrow LiCl + H_3BO_3 + 4\ H_2 \quad (3\text{-}17)$$

Kinetic studies using sulfuric acid instead of hydrochloric acid showed that the reaction represented in equation (3-15) is first order with respect to lithium borohydride and hydrogen ion.

Frequent exposure of dry lithium borohydride to air results in fairly rapid deterioration. A thin layer of powder is completely decomposed at 25° in a few hours in air at 80% relative humidity (19).

Sodium trimethoxyborohydride dissolves in cold water with a short initial burst of hydrogen followed by a slow evolution of additional hydrogen. In hot water, or upon acidification of the aqueous solution, complete hydrolysis occurs rapidly to yield one mole of hydrogen per mole of salt (22).

Other aluminohydrides, such as *magnesium aluminum hydride*, react with water in a manner analogous to the behavior of LAH (23).

$$Mg(AlH_4)_2 + 8\ H_2O \rightarrow Mg(OH)_2 + 2\ Al(OH)_3 + 8\ H_2 \quad (3\text{-}18)$$

Other borohydrides, such as *beryllium borohydride* (23) and *aluminum borohydride* (24), hydrolyze in a manner analogous to the monovalent metal borohydrides.

$$Be(BH_4)_2 + 8\ H_2O \rightarrow Be[B(OH)_4]_2 + 8\ H_2$$
$$\downarrow$$
$$Be(OH)_2 + 2\ H_3BO_3 \quad (3\text{-}19)$$

$$Al(BH_4)_3 + 12\ H_2O \rightarrow Al[B(OH)_4]_3 + 12\ H_2$$
$$\downarrow$$
$$Al(OH)_3 + 3\ H_3BO_3 \quad (3\text{-}20)$$

Direct hydrolysis of liquid aluminum borohydride with liquid water in a bomb calorimeter is reported to produce dark colored residues, strong odors and variation in the extent of reaction (25). The presence of water is considered to be a prerequisite to the spontaneous ignition of aluminum borohydride vapor in air or oxygen at room temperature. In the absence of water vapor, the explosive decomposition occurs at higher temperatures (26).

Lithium gallium hydride is hydrolyzed as in the case of LAH (27):

$$LiGaH_4 + 4 H_2O \rightarrow LiGa(OH)_4 + 4 H_2 \qquad (3\text{-}21)$$

3.2 AMMONIA

By measurement of evolved hydrogen, the following stoichiometric equation has been postulated for the reaction of LAH with ammonia (1):

$$2 LiAlH_4 + 5 NH_3 \rightarrow [LiAlH(NH_2)_2]_2NH + 6 H_2 \qquad (3\text{-}22)$$

The reaction with ammonia has been carried out in tetrahydrofuran for the purpose of preparing a derivative suitable for the titration of very weak acids (28), as discussed in Section 5.1.1. However, the insolubility of the reaction product in tetrahydrofuran or other ethers made it unsuitable for this purpose.

Sodium borohydride is soluble in liquid ammonia at 25° to the extent of 104 g. per 100 g. of solvent. Evaporation of a liquid ammonia solution of the borohydride results in the separation of a crystalline solvate which preliminary data indicate to be a diammoniate (13).

Potassium borohydride (18) and sodium trimethoxyborohydride (22) are also soluble in liquid ammonia, although no information relative to compound formation has been reported.

Lithium borohydride is inert toward liquid ammonia (1).

3.3 HYDROGEN CHLORIDE

The lithium and sodium borohydrides react readily with hydrogen chloride at temperatures as low as −80° to immediately liberate hydrogen and diborane (13,20,22).

$$2 LiBH_4 + 2 HCl \rightarrow 2 LiCl + 2 H_2 + B_2H_6 \qquad (3\text{-}23)$$

The divalent borohydrides, such as beryllium borohydride (29), the trivalent borohydrides, such as aluminum borohydride (24), and the tetravalent borohydrides, such as uranium borohydride (30), react with hydrogen chloride in an analogous manner.

Magnesium borohydride reacts very slowly with hydrogen chloride in the absence of ether. With hydrogen chloride in ether solution, the borohydride reacts at −40° to yield hydrogen and diborane.

$$Mg(BH_4)_2 + 2 HCl \rightarrow MgCl_2 + 2 H_2 + B_2H_6 \qquad (3\text{-}24)$$

An unstable intermediate complex salt is postulated (31):

$$Mg(BH_4)_2 + 2\ HCl \rightarrow MgCl_2 + 2\ HBH_4$$
$$\downarrow$$
$$2\ H_2 + B_2H_6 \qquad (3\text{-}25)$$

In contrast to the behavior of the borohydrides, when hydrogen chloride is passed through sodium trimethoxyborohydride and the volatile products are immediately trapped at $-80°$, very little hydrogen is generated. The trapped material, however, when warmed to room temperature, does liberate hydrogen. No diborane is generated (22).

$$NaBH(OCH_3)_3 + HCl \rightarrow NaCl + CH_3OH + (CH_3O)_2BH \qquad (3\text{-}26)$$

3.4 BORON HYDRIDES

The reaction of LAH with diborane yields a mixture of lithium and aluminum borohydrides (1).

$$LiAlH_4 + 2\ B_2H_6 \rightarrow LiBH_4 + Al(BH_4)_3 \qquad (3\text{-}27)$$

Aluminum hydride reacts with diborane to yield aluminum borohydride (32).

Sodium trimethoxyborohydride reacts rapidly and quantitatively with diborane to yield sodium borohydride (12,13,22,33).

$$2\ NaBH(OCH_3)_3 + B_2H_6 \rightarrow 2\ NaBH_4 + 2\ B(OCH_3)_3 \qquad (3\text{-}28)$$

Lithium trimethoxyborohydride similarly reacts with diborane to yield lithium borohydride (33). The reactions of sodium, potassium, and lithium tetramethoxyborohydrides with diborane yield the corresponding borohydrides (13,34).

$$3\ NaB(OCH_3)_4 + 2\ B_2H_6 \rightarrow 3\ NaBH_4 + 4\ B(OCH_3)_3 \qquad (3\text{-}29)$$

Borazole, $(HBNH)_3$, prepared by the reaction of lithium borohydride with ammonium chloride, does not react appreciably with lithium borohydride (35).

3.5 HYDRAZOIC ACID

The reaction of hydrazoic acid with LAH in anhydrous ether yields the azide analogue

$$LiAlH_4 + 4\ HN_3 \rightarrow LiAl(N_3)_4 + 4\ H_2 \qquad (3\text{-}30)$$

A wide range of simple and mixed metal hydrides can undergo this reaction. Aluminum hydride yields the solid $Al(N_3)_3$ whereas aluminum borohydride yields the azide analogue $Al[B(N_3)_4]_3$, which is about 90% by weight nitrogen. These compounds are stable at room temperature in the absence of air or moisture but are very explosive on shock (36).

3.6   HYDROGEN CYANIDE

The reaction of LAH with hydrogen cyanide yields the theoretical amount of hydrogen and lithium aluminum tetracyanide (37).

$$LiAlH_4 + 4 HCN \rightarrow LiAl(CN)_4 + 4 H_2 \qquad (3\text{-}31)$$

The complex salt precipitates from ether solution as a colorless, amorphous powder which is unstable even in the absence of oxygen and moisture. In water it decomposes to regenerate hydrogen cyanide.

$$LiAl(CN)_4 + 3 H_2O \rightarrow 3 HCN + Al(OH)_3 + LiCN \qquad (3\text{-}32)$$

Treatment of monomeric aluminum hydride with hydrogen cyanide in ether solution yields aluminum tricyanide which crystallizes with one mole of ether (37).

$$AlH_3 + 3 HCN \rightarrow Al(CN)_3 + 3 H_2 \qquad (3\text{-}33)$$

The tricyanide is stable in the absence of oxygen and moisture but decomposes in water.

Ethereal hydrogen cyanide and lithium borohydride yield lithium boron tetracyanide (38)

$$LiBH_4 + 4 HCN \rightarrow LiB(CN)_4 + 4 H_2 \qquad (3\text{-}34)$$

Reaction with excess hydrogen cyanide at $100°$ yields lithium cyanoborohydride which crystallizes with two moles of dioxane from a dioxane-ether solution (38,39)

$$LiBH_4 + HCN \rightarrow LiBH_3CN + H_2 \qquad (3\text{-}35)$$

In contrast to lithium borohydride, the monocyano compound is fairly stable to acids. It does not react further with excess hydrogen cyanide in ether solution or even at $100°$.

3.7   CARBON DIOXIDE

The reaction of carbon dioxide with LAH can follow three courses, each of which represents a definite degree of reduction.

$$4 CO_2 + 3 LiAlH_4 \rightarrow LiAl(OCH_3)_4 + 2 LiAlO_2 \qquad (3\text{-}36)$$

$$2 CO_2 + LiAlH_4 \rightarrow LiAl(OCH_2)_2 \qquad (3\text{-}37)$$

$$4 CO_2 + LiAlH_4 \rightarrow LiAl(OCH_3)_4 \qquad (3\text{-}38)$$

Hydrolysis or alcoholysis of the salts would give methanol, formaldehyde or formic acid, respectively.

Ethereal solutions of LAH rapidly absorb carbon dioxide, and formaldehyde has been isolated from such mixtures (1,2,40,41). Two moles of carbon dioxide are absorbed per mole of hydride, consistent with reduction to the formaldehyde stage as depicted in equation (3-37) (42). It was originally erroneously reported (1) that one mole of carbon dioxide was required per mole of LAH. Attempts to control the ratio of reagents according to equation (3-37) have resulted in yields of formaldehyde of not over 25% based on the carbon dioxide which reacted (41,43).

With LAH in excess, 0.75 mole of LAH is consumed per mole of carbon dioxide, and reduction proceeds to the formation of a methanol complex according to equation (3-36) (41). The complex is decomposed to yield methanol. However, isolation of methanol from ether-water mixtures is troublesome and yields are reduced. By the use of diethyl carbitol as a non-volatile solvent replacing diethyl ether and n-butyl carbitol to decompose the excess LAH and liberate the methanol by alcoholysis, higher yields have been obtained (41). The first stage of this process is represented by equation (3-36) above. The second stage is represented in equation (3-39):

$$LiAl(OCH_3)_4 + 4\ ROH \rightarrow LiAl(OR)_4 + 4\ CH_3OH \qquad (3\text{-}39)$$
$$R = n\text{-}C_4H_9OCH_2CH_2OCH_2CH_2\text{---}$$

This method has been applied to the preparation of labeled methanol containing C^{13} (44) and C^{14} (45-47), as well as formaldehyde-C^{14} (48), by the use of carbon dioxide labeled with carbon isotopes.

Since labeled methanol prepared with the use of the carbitols may contain impurities such as ethanol and butanol arising from cleavage of the ether linkages (45,58), the use of solvents which cannot afford such volatile by-products has been proposed. Thus tetrahydrofurfuryloxytetrahydropyran, prepared by the reaction of Δ^2-dihydropyran with tetrahydrofurfuryl alcohol, has been used as the solvent for LAH, and tetrahydrofurfuryl alcohol has been used for the alcoholysis in the preparation of methanol-C^{13} and C^{14} of high purity (45,49). While the methanol prepared by utilizing the diethyl and monobutyl ethers of diethylene glycol contains water and formaldehyde as well as ethanol and butanol (45,49), and even traces of diethyl ether (46), the only impurities detected in very small amounts when the tetrahydrofurfuryl alcohol derivatives are used are water and formaldehyde. Benzyl alcohol and the monophenyl ether of ethylene glycol have also been used for the alcoholysis step (45).

Although 0.75 mole of LAH is consumed per mole of carbon dioxide in the reduction to methanol, it has been shown that even when the LAH is in 100% excess some carbon dioxide is not reduced further than to formate, and formaldehyde is always present in the methanol liberated by alcoholysis of the complex (45). It has therefore been postulated that the reduction proceeds through formate and formaldehyde, the latter as metallic derivatives of methanediol which undergo a nucleophilic displacement reaction with AlH_4^- ions, giving a methoxide.

The use of lithium aluminum deuteride permits the preparation of CD_3OH (50).

Formic acid has been prepared in good yield according to equation (3-38). A high ratio of carbon dioxide to hydride as well as the use of highly purified LAH in dilute ether solution are essential conditions for good yields. The importance of concentration is evident in the reduction in the yield from 81% to 43% on increasing the LAH concentration from 0.44% to 3.53%. Similar results are obtained with diethylene glycol diethyl ether as solvent. Unless the LAH is carefully purified the yields of formic acid are erratic. Formaldehyde is identified as a by-product in all the reductions while methanol is also isolated in experiments using the more highly concentrated solutions. The overall yield of formic acid is raised to 88% by oxidation of the formaldehyde with barium peroxide prior to the final isolation of the acid (43).

The reaction of carbon dioxide with aluminum hydride has also been utilized in the preparation of formic acid, although the highest yield that could be obtained was 52% (43).

The presence of carbon dioxide as an impurity has been suggested as the cause of explosions occurring in the evaporation of dimethyl ether solutions of LAH (51). A similar explosion has been reported in the distillation of diethylene glycol dimethyl ether which had been dried over LAH. Analysis of these ethers has indicated double the concentration of peroxides present in normal ethers (52). Diethyl ether solutions of LAH, which can ordinarily be safely evaporated, may explode if first treated with carbon dioxide (51).

The use of lithium borohydride in ether solution at $0°$ reduces carbon dioxide to formic acid in 69–88% yield (53–55). Treatment of carbon dioxide-C^{14} has given 71% formic acid-C^{14} and 13% methanol-C^{14} (53). Diborane is liberated but formaldehyde has not been detected among the products. The reduction to formate with the simultaneous production of diborane is represented:

$$2 \text{ LiBH}_4 + 2 \text{ CO}_2 \rightarrow 2 \text{ LiOOCH} + \text{B}_2\text{H}_6 \qquad (3\text{-}40)$$

Since lithium formate is not reduced by the borohydride, the preparation of methanol is considered analogous to the LAH reaction:

$$3 \text{ LiBH}_4 + 4 \text{ CO}_2 \rightarrow \text{LiB(OCH}_3)_4 + 2 \text{ LiBO}_2 \qquad (3\text{-}41)$$

The isolation of a solid containing not only formate but also boron and active hydrogen has been considered indicative of complex secondary processes. The reaction, equation (3-40), does not occur at $-80°$, and elevation of the reaction temperature from $0°$ to $30°$ does not increase the yield but reduces carbon dioxide absorption. Diethyl carbitol as solvent increases gas absorption but lowers the yield of formic acid. No reaction occurs in tripropylamine solution.

Passage of gaseous carbon dioxide through solid sodium trimethoxyborohydride results in the generation of heat and the formation of sodium formate and methyl borate (22).

$$NaBH(OCH_3)_3 + CO_2 \rightarrow HCOONa + B(OCH_3)_3 \qquad (3-42)$$

3.8 CARBON MONOXIDE

Although it was originally reported that carbon monoxide did not react with LAH (56), it has since been shown that on reduction, not only methanol but also substantial yields of methane (up to 37%) are liberated on alcoholysis. This suggests that intermediates in the reduction probably contain $AlOCH_2Al$ groupings, susceptible to further attack by aluminohydride ions with the formation of methylaluminum (45).

3.9 OXYGEN

Although no products have been reported from the reaction of LAH and oxygen, it has been observed that in the determination of active hydrogen, if the reactions are carried out in air a slow reaction occurs between the hydride and oxygen leading to the liberation of hydrogen and resulting in erratic values for active hydrogen (57). Similarly, it has been found that there is a decrease in the effective LAH concentration when dry oxygen is bubbled through an LAH solution (58).

The existence of a reaction between sodium or potassium borohydrides and oxygen has not been reported. Sodium borohydride is stable in dry air although it decomposes slowly in moist air and is handled as an inflammable hygroscopic powder. Potassium borohydride is non-hygroscopic and is stable in moist and dry air. Lithium borohydride may be handled in the air only with great caution. Transfer in dry nitrogen or argon is the recommended procedure, although lumps may be handled in dry air with due allowance for the inflammable nature of the compound (19). A coating of white oxide will form on all surfaces within 2-3 minutes after initial exposure to air.

Aluminum borohydride vapor detonates spontaneously and violently in ordinary air giving a blue-white flash of unusual brilliance (24). With dry oxygen no explosions occur at 20° over the range 1-300 mm. pressure with 14 mole % aluminum borohydride. At 110° explosions occur above 25-30 mm. pressure with 5-50 mole % borohydride. With moist oxygen, saturated at 20° and containing 2.3 mole % of water, explosions occur from 5-90 mole % aluminum borohydride above 25-75 mm. pressure. Rapid hydrolysis appears to be a prerequisite to explosion at room temperature (26).

The heat of combustion of the borohydride, −989.1 kcal./mole, has been determined in a combustion bomb (25), utilizing the equation:

$$2 \text{ Al(BH}_4)_3 + 12 \text{ O}_2 \rightarrow \text{Al}_2\text{O}_3 + 3 \text{ B}_2\text{O}_3 + 12 \text{ H}_2\text{O} \qquad (3\text{-}43)$$

The induced combustion of various hydrocarbons with aluminum borohydride in dry oxygen has been found to involve an initial reaction between the hydrocarbon and the borohydride. While *n*-butane does not explode, 1-butene explodes after an induction period and 1,3-butadiene explodes immediately (59).

Beryllium borohydride ignites violently in air (29). While uranium (IV) borohydride does not react rapidly with air at room temperature (30,60), uranium (III) borohydride, obtained by decomposition of the uranium (IV) compound at 100°, is pyrophoric and likely to detonate on contact with air (30).

3.10   NITRIC OXIDE

By bubbling gaseous nitric oxide through an ethereal solution of LAH, hyponitrous acid is formed and isolated as silver hyponitrite (61,62). The course of the reaction is represented:

$$2 \text{ NO} \rightarrow \text{ON}-\text{NO} \qquad (3\text{-}44)$$

$$\text{ON}-\text{NO} + \text{LiAlH}_4 \rightarrow \text{ON}-\text{N}\Big\langle {{\text{OMe}} \atop {\text{H}}} \qquad (3\text{-}45)$$

$$\text{ON}-\text{N}\Big\langle {{\text{OMe}} \atop {\text{H}}} + \text{H}_2\text{O} \rightarrow \text{ON}-\text{N}\Big\langle {{\text{OH}} \atop {\text{H}}} \rightleftharpoons \text{HON}=\text{NOH} \qquad (3\text{-}46)$$

Me = Li or Al

The analogous reaction of nitric oxide with phenylmagnesium bromide yields nitrosophenylhydroxylamine (63).

$$\text{ON}-\text{NO} + \text{C}_6\text{H}_5\text{MgBr} \rightarrow \text{ON}-\text{N}\Big\langle {{\text{OMgX}} \atop {\text{C}_6\text{H}_5}} \xrightarrow{\text{H}_2\text{O}} \text{ON}-\text{N}\Big\langle {{\text{OH}} \atop {\text{C}_6\text{H}_5}} \qquad (3\text{-}47)$$

3.11   PHOSGENE

Reduction of phosgene with LAH yields methanol (2,56). Aluminum borohydride reacts violently with phosgene to liberate carbon monoxide, diborane, and hydrogen (64).

3.12   METAL OXIDES

Addition of finely pulverized molybdenum trioxide, MoO_3, to an ethereal LAH solution in an anhydrous nitrogen atmosphere causes a color change from blue to red. An x-ray diagram of the isolated reaction product is identical with that of the red hydroxide $Mo_5O_7(OH)_8$ obtained from MoO_3

and nascent or atomic hydrogen. The blue intermediate stage corresponds to the blue hydroxides $Mo_4O_{10}(OH)_2$ and $Mo_2O_4(OH)_2$.

Tungsten trioxide, WO_3, rapidly becomes deep blue when added to an ethereal LAH solution. The product, whose composition corresponds to the formula $H_{0.1}WO_3$, is identical with that obtained with nascent and atomic hydrogen. Tungstic acid, H_2WO_4, in the presence of LAH, yields a hydroxide of the formula $WO_{2.82} \cdot x\, H_2O$.

Color changes are also observed on treatment of germanium dioxide, GeO_2, titanium dioxide, TiO_2, vanadium pentoxide, V_2O_5, niobium pentoxide, Nb_2O_5, uranium oxide, U_3O_8, and manganese dioxide, MnO_2, with ethereal LAH solutions (65).

Diethyl aluminum hydride, $(C_2H_5)_2AlH$, prepared as described in Section 16.3.1, in ether solution results in color changes with the molybdenum, tungsten, and vanadium oxides. The reaction, however, does not proceed to the extent observed with LAH. In the absence of ether no reaction is obtained on treatment of these oxides with liquid diethyl aluminum hydride (65).

3.13 HALOGENS

The reaction between iodine and LAH is utilized in an iodometric method devised for the accurate analysis of ethereal LAH solutions (66,67), as discussed in Section 2.1.2. The postulated reaction, equation (3-48), is analogous to the reaction of the Grignard reagent (68).

$$LiAlH_4 + 2\,I_2 \longrightarrow 2\,H_2 + LiI + AlI_3 \qquad (3\text{-}48)$$

$$2\,RMgX + I_2 \longrightarrow RR + 2\,MgXI \qquad (3\text{-}49)$$

Bromine in carbon tetrachloride is immediately decolorized by an aqueous solution of sodium trimethoxyborohydride (22).

3.14 INORGANIC HALIDES AND SALTS

The reaction of inorganic halides with LAH in ether solution yields complex hydrides of the type $MeH_n \cdot nAlH_3 = Me(AlH_4)_n$.

$$MeCl_n + n\,LiAlH_4 \longrightarrow Me(AlH_4)_n + n\,LiCl \qquad (3\text{-}50)$$

The complex hydrides formed by the above equation are in many cases unstable at ordinary temperatures and decompose to form the simple hydrides. When the reaction is carried out at ordinary temperatures, the complex hydride is not detected and the reaction with LAH or aluminum hydride proceeds to form the corresponding simple hydride (1,2,23,40,69,70).

$$4\,MeCl_n + n\,LiAlH_4 \longrightarrow 4\,MeH_n + n\,LiCl + n\,AlCl_3 \qquad (3\text{-}51)$$

$$3\,MeCl_n + n\,AlH_3 \longrightarrow 3\,MeH_n + n\,AlCl_3 \qquad (3\text{-}52)$$

The reaction of inorganic halides with lithium borohydride yields the corresponding borohydrides $MeH_n \cdot nBH_3 = Me(BH_4)_n$.

$$MeCl_n + n\,LiBH_4 \longrightarrow Me(BH_4)_n + n\,LiCl \qquad (3\text{-}53)$$

Borohydrides may also be prepared by the action of sodium, potassium, or aluminum borohydrides. As in the case of the complex aluminum hydrides, the borohydrides are in many cases unstable at ordinary temperatures and are therefore prepared at low temperatures (23).

The action of lithium gallium hydride yields the complex gallium hydrides $MeH_n \cdot nGaH_3 = Me(GaH_4)_n$ (23).

$$MeCl_n + n\,LiGaH_4 \longrightarrow Me(GaH_4)_n + n\,LiCl \qquad (3\text{-}54)$$

The reactions of specific halides and salts will be considered in the order of the groups in the periodic table as recently utilized by Wiberg (23).

3.14.1 Group I

3.14.1.a *Lithium compounds.*   While lithium carbonate is inert to LAH, by the addition of boron trifluoride etherate it is converted to lithium borofluoride which reacts with LAH to yield diborane (71). Diborane is also generated by the reaction of lithium borofluoride and lithium borohydride in ether or tetrahydrofuran. Under the same conditions, lithium hydride does not react with the borofluoride. However, the addition of a small amount of either lithium borohydride or methyl borate initiates a reaction to generate diborane (72).

$$LiBF_4 \xrightarrow{\ LAH\ } B_2H_6 \qquad (3\text{-}55)$$

$$LiBF_4 + 3\,LiBH_4 \longrightarrow 2\,B_2H_6 + 4\,LiF \qquad (3\text{-}56)$$

$$2\,LiBF_4 + 6\,LiH \xrightarrow{\text{promoter}} B_2H_6 + 8\,LiF \qquad (3\text{-}57)$$

Lithium formate is not reduced by lithium borohydride alone or in the presence of methanol (53).

3.14.2 Group I-B

3.14.2.a *Copper compounds.*   Cupric chloride undergoes a vigorous reaction with LAH in ether to yield a black product containing metallic copper and lithium chloride (73).

Warf and Feitknecht (73) reported that the reaction of cuprous iodide with LAH in ether gives a hydrogen-rich product containing a ratio of $H/Cu = 0.50$. The exact nature of this product has not been determined. Wiberg and Henle (74) found that the reaction of a solution of cuprous iodide in pyridine at room temperature with a solution of LAH in ether-pyridine (prepared by treatment of a concentrated ether solution of LAH with absolute pyridine) gives a blood red solution of cuprous hydride in pyridine.

$$4 \text{ CuI} + \text{LiAlH}_4 \longrightarrow 4 \text{ CuH} + \text{LiI} + \text{AlI}_3 \qquad (3\text{-}58)$$

The pyridine-insoluble aluminum iodide is removed by centrifugation, and addition of ether to the filtrate precipitates the cuprous hydride as a red-brown powder. If the solution of cuprous iodide in pyridine-tetrahydrofuran-ether and ethereal LAH are mixed, the cuprous hydride precipitates directly while the aluminum and lithium iodides remain in solution. The hydride obtained in this manner, which is stable to 60°, is identical with the product obtained by the reduction of copper sulfate with hypophosphite or hyposulfite except that the product obtained from the non-aqueous system is water-free. Consequently it reduces benzoyl chloride to benzaldehyde while the hydride obtained from the aqueous solution and air drying contains water and converts benzoyl chloride to benzoic acid.

Treatment of a suspension of cuprous chloride in tetrahydrofuran with an ethereal solution of lithium borohydride at −20° quantitatively yields cuprous borohydride.

$$\text{CuCl} + \text{LiBH}_4 \longrightarrow \text{CuBH}_4 + \text{LiCl} \qquad (3\text{-}59)$$

The compound is soluble in the 1:1 ether-tetrahydrofuran mixture and in solution at 0° decomposes to form copper hydride and diborane as well as boron and hydrogen.

$$2 \text{ CuBH}_4 \nearrow \begin{array}{l} 2 \text{ CuH} + \text{B}_2\text{H}_6 \qquad (3\text{-}60) \\ \searrow \; 2 \text{ CuH} + 2 \text{ B} + 3 \text{ H}_2 \qquad (3\text{-}61) \end{array}$$

The solution of the borohydride is stabilized by the presence of pyridine which forms a light green complex. After standing several days at room temperature, the cuprous borohydride-pyridine complex crystallizes from solution (75).

The reaction of an ethereal cupric chloride solution at −45° with lithium borohydride yields cuprous borohydride instead of the expected cupric borohydride (23).

$$2 \text{ CuCl}_2 + 4 \text{ LiBH}_4 \longrightarrow 2 \text{ CuBH}_4 + \text{B}_2\text{H}_6 + \text{H}_2 + 4 \text{ LiCl} \qquad (3\text{-}62)$$

The cupric borohydride apparently decomposes to cuprous borohydride, diborane, and hydrogen.

Cuprous borohydride reacts with methanol to form cuprous hydride, methyl borate, and hydrogen (75).

$$\text{CuBH}_4 + 3 \text{ CH}_3\text{OH} \longrightarrow \text{CuH} + \text{B(OCH}_3)_3 + 3 \text{ H}_2 \qquad (3\text{-}63)$$

3.14.2.b *Silver compounds.* The reaction of silver perchlorate and LAH in ether at −80° yields a yellow, ether-insoluble solid considered to be silver aluminum hydride.

$$AgClO_4 + LiAlH_4 \rightarrow AgAlH_4 + LiClO_4 \qquad (3\text{-}64)$$

The lithium perchlorate, which does not react with LAH even at room temperature, stays in solution. In the presence of a two- to threefold excess of LAH, the precipitate is coarse and can be separated by decantation of the ether solution. The pure silver aluminum hydride in ether suspension decomposes above $-50°$ into the elements.

$$AgAlH_4 \rightarrow Ag + Al + 2\,H_2 \qquad (3\text{-}65)$$

The decomposition probably proceeds in two steps in which first the silver hydride component of the complex hydride decomposes and then the finely powdered silver catalyzes the decomposition of the metastable aluminum hydride. However, the two steps cannot be separated. The method of formation of the complex silver aluminum hydride indicates a stage between homopolar and metallic bonds (76).

The reaction of silver perchlorate and lithium borohydride in ether at $-80°$ quantitatively yields a white ether-insoluble silver borohydride.

$$AgClO_4 + LiBH_4 \rightarrow AgBH_4 + LiClO_4 \qquad (3\text{-}66)$$

In ether suspension the borohydride decomposes at $-30°$ with the liberation of hydrogen and diborane and the precipitation of silver and boron. The primary reaction

$$2\,AgBH_4 \rightarrow 2\,Ag + H_2 + 2\,BH_3 \qquad (3\text{-}67)$$

yields finely divided silver which catalytically acts on the monomeric borane.

$$2\,BH_3 \rightarrow 2\,B + 3\,H_2 \qquad (3\text{-}68)$$

Diborane is formed by dimerization of the borane. Silver borohydride is soluble in cold pyridine at $-40°$ but is insoluble in ether, tetrahydrofuran, or trimethylamine. The borohydride reacts with methanol at $-30°$ to yield silver, hydrogen, and trimethyl borate (77).

$$2\,AgBH_4 + 6\,CH_3OH \rightarrow 2\,Ag + 2\,B(OCH_3)_3 + 7\,H_2 \qquad (3\text{-}69)$$

Silver gallium hydride, prepared by the reaction of ethereal solutions of silver perchlorate and lithium gallium hydride at $-100°$, is an orange, ether-insoluble compound which decomposes in ether suspension at $-75°$.

$$AgClO_4 + LiGaH_4 \rightarrow AgGaH_4 + LiClO_4 \qquad (3\text{-}70)$$

$$2\,AgGaH_4 \rightarrow 2\,Ag + H_2 + 2\,GaH_3 \qquad (3\text{-}71)$$

The finely divided silver catalytically reduces the gallium hydride to the elements so that after 24 hours at room temperature an overall decomposition to the elements has occurred (78).

$$AgGaH_4 \rightarrow Ag + Ga + 2\,H_2 \qquad (3\text{-}72)$$

3.14.2.c *Gold Compounds*. Wiberg has compared the decomposition temperatures of the hydrides of Group IIb with those of Group Ib and has postulated that the decomposition temperature of gold hydride, AuH, determined by extrapolation, should be $-150°$ to $-160°$. Attempts to prepare the hydride by the action of LAH on gold salts has yielded little result, since at these low temperatures reaction is not noticeable and suitable solvents for the starting materials are lacking (23,76).

3.14.3 Group II

3.14.3.a *Beryllium compounds*. Treatment of beryllium chloride in ether solution, at room temperature, with ethereal LAH yields beryllium aluminum hydride (27).

$$BeCl_2 + 2\,LiAlH_4 \rightarrow Be(AlH_4)_2 + 2\,LiCl \qquad (3\text{-}73)$$

The ether solubility indicates a hydrogen bonded structure (I).

I

Beryllium chloride in ether solution reacts with excess lithium hydride to yield a white precipitate which is either beryllium hydride, BeH_2, or lithium beryllium hydride, $BeH_2 \cdot n\text{LiH}$ (27). Beryllium hydride can also be prepared by the reaction of dimethylberyllium with LAH or dimethylaluminum hydride (79).

The reaction of beryllium bromide and sodium (12) or lithium (80) borohydride yields the volatile beryllium borohydride which is also prepared by the reaction of dimethylberyllium and diborane (29).

$$BeBr_2 + MeBH_4 \rightarrow Be(BH_4)_2 + 2\,MeBr \qquad (3\text{-}74)$$

$$Me = Na \text{ or } Li$$

3.14.3.b *Magnesium compounds*. The reaction of magnesium bromide etherate with an ethereal solution of LAH yields magnesium aluminum hydride (81).

$$MgBr_2 + 2\,LiAlH_4 \rightarrow Mg(AlH_4)_2 + 2\,LiBr \qquad (3\text{-}75)$$

The same product is obtained by the reaction of an ethereal solution of excess magnesium hydride with an ethereal solution of aluminum chloride (81,82). The complex hydride is stable to $140°$ in high vacuum and above this temperature decomposes to magnesium hydride, aluminum, and hydrogen (82).

$$Mg(AlH_4)_2 \rightarrow MgH_2 + 2\,Al + 3\,H_2 \qquad (3\text{-}76)$$

The properties of magnesium aluminum hydride are discussed in Section 2.6.1.

3.14.4   Group II-B

3.14.4.a   *Zinc compounds.* Schlesinger and Finholt (2) reported the preparation of zinc hydride by the reaction of zinc chloride and LAH in ether. Wiberg and his co-workers (83,84) found that LAH reacts with zinc iodide in ether solution at $-40°$ to give the stable, ether-insoluble hydride.

$$ZnI_2 + 2 LiAlH_4 \rightarrow ZnH_2 + 2 AlH_3 + 2 LiI \qquad (3\text{-}77)$$

It was postulated that the initial product, zinc aluminum hydride, $Zn(AlH_4)_2$, is so unstable that it was not detected. The aluminum hydride polymerizes to the polymeric form. The zinc hydride, which decomposes into its elements at $90°$, is also obtained by the reaction of zinc chloride with the aluminum hydride-aluminum chloride complex (Section 3.14.5.b) at $-80°$ (83).

When the reaction represented in equation (3-77) is carried out with a great excess of zinc iodide a mixed compound, zinc hydrogen iodide, is obtained (84). The reaction of sublimed zinc iodide with excess, pulverized lithium hydride in ether yields a white, stable iodine-containing zinc hydride whose composition falls between ZnHI and ZnH_2, depending on experimental conditions.

$$ZnI_2 + (1 + a) LiH \rightarrow ZnH_{1+a}I_{1-a} + (1 + a) LiI \qquad (3\text{-}78)$$

Zinc hydrogen iodide decomposes at $110°$ in high *vacuo* to zinc, hydrogen and zinc iodide. By refluxing in ether with excess lithium hydride, the iodine content does not decrease, whereas with LAH zinc hydride is obtained.

$$ZnHI + LiAlH_4 \rightarrow ZnH_2 + LiI + AlH_3 \qquad (3\text{-}79)$$

At $-40°$, the temperature of the reaction between zinc iodide and LAH (equation 3-77), the zinc hydrogen iodide does not react with LAH (84).

The reaction of zinc chloride and lithium borohydride, in ether solution at room temperature results in the precipitation of lithium chloride while the ether-soluble zinc borohydride remains in solution.

$$ZnCl_2 + 2 LiBH_4 \rightarrow Zn(BH_4)_2 + 2 LiCl \qquad (3\text{-}80)$$

A chlorozinc borohydride, $ZnClBH_4$, is formed as an intermediate in reaction (3-80). It can be obtained in a pure state by utilizing the reagents in a 1:1 ratio.

$$ZnCl_2 + LiBH_4 \rightarrow ZnClBH_4 + LiCl \qquad (3\text{-}81)$$

While the ether-soluble zinc borohydride decomposes at $85°$ into the elements

$$Zn(BH_4)_2 \rightarrow Zn + 2 B + 4 H_2 \qquad (3\text{-}82)$$

the similarly ether-soluble chlorozinc borohydride is more stable, decomposing at 120° (85).

$$2 \text{ ZnClBH}_4 \rightarrow \text{ZnCl}_2 + \text{Zn} + 2 \text{ B} + 4 \text{ H}_2 \qquad (3\text{-}83)$$

3.14.4.b *Cadmium compounds.* The reaction of ethereal LAH at −70° to −40° with a solution of cadmium iodide in tetrahydrofuran yields a voluminous white precipitate of cadmium hydride.

$$\text{CdI}_2 + 2 \text{ LiAlH}_4 \rightarrow \text{CdH}_2 + 2 \text{ AlH}_3 + 2 \text{ LiI} \qquad (3\text{-}84)$$

The intermediate cadmium aluminum hydride, $\text{Cd(AlH}_4)_2$, is so unstable that no trace of it is detected and only its decomposition products are obtained. The polymerization of monomeric aluminum hydride to the ether-insoluble polymeric form is retarded at low temperatures so that centrifugation permits separation of the cadmium hydride precipitate from the other soluble reaction products. Inversion of reagents in the preparation results in the production of aluminum iodide owing to the localized excess of cadmium iodide.

$$2 \text{ CdI}_2 + \text{LiAlH}_4 \rightarrow 2 \text{ CdH}_2 + \text{AlI}_3 + \text{LiI} \qquad (3\text{-}85)$$

The insolubility of the aluminum compound prevents the isolation of pure cadmium hydride. The latter decomposes into the elements slowly at −20° and spontaneously at room temperature (86).

At 0° cadmium chloride reacts with an ethereal solution of lithium borohydride to yield ether-soluble cadmium borohydride.

$$\text{CdCl}_2 + 2 \text{ LiBH}_4 \rightarrow \text{Cd(BH}_4)_2 + 2 \text{ LiCl} \qquad (3\text{-}86)$$

The borohydride is stable to 25° and decomposes into the elements. While hydrolysis of the borohydride with dilute acid yields the cadmium ion,

$$\text{Cd(BH}_4)_2 + 4 \text{ H}^+ + 6 \text{ H}_2\text{O} \rightarrow \text{Cd}^{++} + 2 \text{ B(OH)}_3 + 8 \text{ H}_2 \qquad (3\text{-}87)$$

hydrolysis with water precipitates metallic cadmium.

A chlorocadmium borohydride, CdClBH_4, is formed as an intermediate in reaction (3-86). This compound, which decomposes at 85°,

$$2 \text{ CdClBH}_4 \rightarrow \text{CdCl}_2 + \text{Cd} + 2 \text{ B} + 4 \text{ H}_2 \qquad (3\text{-}88)$$

forms a double compound with lithium borohydride (87).

$$\text{CdCl}_2 + 2 \text{ LiBH}_4 \rightarrow \text{CdClBH}_4 \cdot \text{LiBH}_4 + \text{LiCl} \qquad (3\text{-}89)$$

3.14.4.c *Mercury compounds.* A solution of mercuric iodide in an ether-tetrahydrofuran-petroleum ether mixture reacts with LAH in the same solvents at −135° to yield a white voluminous precipitate of mercury hydride.

$$\text{HgI} + 2 \text{ LiAlH}_4 \rightarrow \text{HgH}_2 + 2 \text{ AlH}_3 + 2 \text{ LiI} \qquad (3\text{-}90)$$

The hydride precipitate is only stable to $-125°$ and decomposes above this temperature to the elements. If the two starting solutions are mixed above the decomposition temperature of mercury hydride, i.e., at $-100°$, and warmed to room temperature, the finely divided mercury, formed by the decomposition, catalyzes the decomposition of aluminum hydride to metallic aluminum. The slow decomposition of mercury hydride at lower temperatures yields a granular form of mercury which does not decompose the aluminum hydride (88).

3.14.5 Group III

3.14.5.a *Boron compounds.* The reaction of LAH and boron trichloride in ether solution gives a high yield of diborane (2,89–95).

$$3 \text{ LiAlH}_4 + 4 \text{ BCl}_3 \rightarrow 2 \text{ B}_2\text{H}_6 + 3 \text{ LiCl} + 3 \text{ AlCl}_3 \qquad (3\text{-}91)$$

Boron tribromide (73) and trifluoride (93,96) have also been utilized in this synthesis. Completely deuterated diborane, B_2D_6, has been prepared from boron trifluoride and lithium aluminum deuteride in ether (96), while isotopically labeled diboranes, $\text{B}_2{}^{10}\text{H}_6$ and $\text{B}_2{}^{10}\text{D}_6$, have been prepared by the reaction of B^{10}F_3 (from labeled calcium fluoborate) etherate and LAH and lithium aluminum deuteride, respectively (93).

If boron trichloride and LAH are refluxed at $75°$ for one hour in the absence of ether, no volatile boron-containing material is detected. Upon the addition of ether at low temperatures, a violent reaction occurs at the melting point of ether and diborane is obtained (97).

Kinetic studies of the reaction of LAH and boron trichloride (98) and trifluoride (71) etherates have indicated that two separate reactions occur in the process, the sum of the two stages being represented in equation (3-91). The individual steps are probably:

$$3 \text{ LiAlH}_4 + 3 \text{ BX}_3 \rightarrow 3 \text{ LiBH}_4 + 3 \text{ AlX}_3 \qquad (3\text{-}92)$$
$$3 \text{ LiBH}_4 + \text{ BX}_3 \rightarrow 2 \text{ B}_2\text{H}_6 + 3 \text{ LiX} \qquad (3\text{-}93)$$

By adding the boron halide to LAH, the reactions occur successively so that no diborane is evolved until the mole ratio of BX_3 to LAH is 1.00. The buildup of lithium borohydride can lead to a large surge of gas upon formation of diborane according to equation (3-93). The addition of LAH to the halide results in the concurrent occurrence of both reactions and a steady flow of diborane is obtained. In the study involving boron trifluoride, a small proportion of lithium borofluoride and sometimes a fluoroaluminate complex salt have been found (71).

Aluminum hydride, like LAH, reacts with boron trichloride in ether to form diborane (1). Since diborane reacts with aluminum hydride to give aluminum borohydride, reaction in accordance with the equation

$$4 \text{ AlH}_3 + 3 \text{ BCl}_3 \rightarrow \text{ Al(BH}_4)_3 + 3 \text{ AlCl}_3 \qquad (3\text{-}94)$$

has yielded the borohydride in 88% yield.

As in the case of LAH, at temperatures up to 180° boron halides react only superficially with lithium hydride. On the other hand, boron trifluoride etherate reacts with either sodium or lithium hydride to form diborane (72,99). The reaction proceeds by two different courses dependent on the reaction conditions (72). If ether-soluble, active hydrogen-containing promoters, such as lithium borohydride and lithium trimethoxyborohydride, are present, or if pressure is used to force the reaction between lithium hydride and diborane, the hydride is converted completely to lithium borohydride and lithium fluoride before diborane is evolved.

$$6 \text{ LiH} + 1.5 \text{ BF}_3 \rightarrow 1.5 \text{ LiBH}_4 + 4.5 \text{ LiF} \qquad (3\text{-}95)$$

$$\underline{1.5 \text{ LiBH}_4 + 0.5 \text{ BF}_3 \rightarrow \text{B}_2\text{H}_6 + 1.5 \text{ LiF}} \qquad (3\text{-}96)$$

$$6 \text{ LiH} + 2 \text{ BF}_3 \rightarrow \text{B}_2\text{H}_6 + 6 \text{ LiF} \qquad (3\text{-}97)$$

In the absence of soluble promoters, diborane is continuously evolved, lithium borofluoride is formed, and lithium borohydride does not accumulate.

$$6 \text{ LiH} + 8 \text{ BF}_3 \rightarrow \text{B}_2\text{H}_6 + 6 \text{ LiBF}_4 \qquad (3\text{-}98)$$

In tetrahydrofuran as a solvent, the two-stage process, equation (3-97), occurs with or without added promoter. The reaction of lithium hydride and boron trichloride in ethyl ether proceeds according to equation (3-97), even in the absence of promoter. In promoted reactions, unless the minimum amount of promoter is 3.5-5 mole % of the initial lithium hydride, diborane is evolved according to equation (3-98).

Diborane may also be prepared by the direct reaction of lithium borohydride and boron trifluoride etherate (13,72,99,100).

$$3 \text{ LiBH}_4 + \text{BF}_3 \rightarrow 3 \text{ LiF} + 2 \text{ B}_2\text{H}_6 \qquad (3\text{-}99)$$

If an excess of etherate is used, lithium borofluoride rather than the fluoride is obtained (13).

$$3 \text{ LiBH}_4 + 4 \text{ BF}_3 \rightarrow 3 \text{ LiBF}_4 + 2 \text{ B}_2\text{H}_6 \qquad (3\text{-}100)$$

In the absence of ether, gaseous boron fluoride does not react significantly with lithium borohydride (13). However, the reaction occurs readily with the tetrahydrofuran complex as well as with the etherate (72).

Sodium borohydride reacts quantitatively with boron trifluoride etherate to liberate diborane (12,13,99,100).

$$3 \text{ NaBH}_4 + 4 \text{ BF}_3 \rightarrow 3 \text{ NaBF}_4 + 2 \text{ B}_2\text{H}_6 \qquad (3\text{-}101)$$

Potassium and magnesium borohydrides as well as sodium trimethoxyborohydride are also suitable for the preparation of diborane by reaction with boron trifluoride in ether (100).

Boron trifluoride is rapidly absorbed by sodium trimethoxyborohydride at room temperature to liberate methyl borate (22,99).

$$NaBH(OCH_3)_3 + BF_3 \rightarrow NaBHF_3 + B(OCH_3)_3 \qquad (3\text{-}102)$$

The use of the etherate of boron trifluoride results in the rapid evolution of diborane (12,22,99,100).

$$6\ NaBH(OCH_3)_3 + 8\ BF_3 \rightarrow B_2H_6 + 6\ NaBF_4 + 6\ B(OCH_3)_3 \qquad (3\text{-}103)$$

By using twice the theoretical quantity of the etherate, quantitative yields of diborane are obtained (99). The use of lithium or potassium trimethoxyborohydrides and the use of the addition compounds of boron trifluoride with dimethyl ether, di-*n*-butyl ether or dioxane have also been investigated in the synthesis of diborane (99,100).

The reactions of substituted boron halides and LAH present an interesting contrast. While bis-dimethylaminoboron chloride is reduced by LAH to bis-dimethylaminoborine (101),

$$[(CH_3)_2N]_2BCl \xrightarrow{\text{LAH}} [(CH_3)_2N]_2BH \qquad (3\text{-}104)$$

bis-silylaminoboron dichloride, $(SiH_3)_2NBCl_2$, prepared by the reaction of tris-silylamine and boron trichloride, is not reduced by LAH in ether (89).

3.14.5.b　*Aluminum compounds.* The reaction of an ether solution of LAH with aluminum chloride in a 3:1 ratio yields a solution of aluminum hydride (1,2,40,102-104) as described in Section 2.1.1.b. It has been postulated (102,105) that aluminum hydride is capable of existence in ionized form, presumably aluminohydride.

$$3\ LiAlH_4 + AlCl_3 \rightarrow Al(AlH_4)_3 + 3\ LiCl \qquad (3\text{-}105)$$

The aluminum hydride solution is unstable and spontaneously polymerizes to a high molecular weight, ether-insoluble, polymerization product.

$$x\ Al(AlH_4)_3 \rightarrow 4\ (AlH_3)_x \qquad (3\text{-}106)$$

The preparation of aluminum hydride by the reaction of LAH and aluminum bromide yields a stable ethereal solution. Wiberg *et al.* (106) have postulated that the monomeric aluminum hydride fails to polymerize due to complex formation. The solution probably contains lithium bromoaluminum hydride, $LiBr \cdot AlH_3 = LiAlH_3Br$.

Treatment of the soluble aluminum hydride obtained in reaction (3-105), or even of the polymeric material, in a 1:1 ratio with aluminum chloride in ether solution, yields an ether-soluble addition compound $AlH_3 \cdot AlCl_3 = AlH_2Cl \cdot AlHCl_2$ (II), which is isolated as a colorless liquid distillable

$$(3\text{-}107)$$

II

at 95° in high vacuum (102,107). The ethereal solution behaves chemically like a mixture of aluminum chloride and monomeric aluminum hydride and permits the carrying out of more selective reductions than with LAH (102). If the addition compound is heated over a free flame a stable aluminum mirror is formed (107).

$$2 \text{ AlH}_3 \cdot \text{AlCl}_3 \rightarrow 2 \text{ Al} + 3 \text{ H}_2 + 2 \text{ AlCl}_3 \qquad (3\text{-}108)$$

If the reaction of aluminum hydride and aluminum chloride is carried out in a 2:1 ratio, the addition compound is formed and the excess aluminum hydride precipitates as the ether-insoluble polymeric material. If the reaction is carried out in a 1:2 ratio in ether solution the product is monomeric dichloroaluminum hydride (107).

$$\text{AlH}_3 + 2 \text{ AlCl}_3 \rightarrow 3 \text{ AlHCl}_2 \qquad (3\text{-}109)$$

Reaction of the ethereal solution of aluminum hydride with an ether solution of aluminum iodide in a 1:1 ratio yields an equimolar mixture of mono- and diiodo compounds

$$\text{AlH}_3 + \text{AlI}_3 \rightarrow \text{AlH}_2\text{I} + \text{AlHI}_2 \qquad (3\text{-}110)$$

and not an addition compound as in the reaction with the chloride (108, 109). Reaction in a 1:2 ratio at room temperature yields a clear ethereal solution of diiodoaluminum hydride etherate.

$$\text{AlH}_3 + 2 \text{ AlI}_3 \rightarrow 3 \text{ AlHI}_2 \cdot \text{etherate} \qquad (3\text{-}111)$$

On evaporation *in vacuo*, the diiodo compound is isolated in crystalline form, m.p. 80°. The compound can be distilled in high vacuum at 110–120° with some disproportionation according to equation (3-112):

$$2 \text{ AlHI}_2 \rightarrow \text{AlH}_2\text{I} + \text{AlI}_3 \qquad (3\text{-}112)$$

Reaction in a 2:1 ratio yields an ethereal solution of monoiodoaluminum hydride, m.p. 35°.

$$2 \text{ AlH}_3 + \text{AlI}_3 \rightarrow 3 \text{ AlH}_2\text{I} \cdot \text{etherate} \qquad (3\text{-}113)$$

On distillation in high vacuum disproportionation occurs:

$$2 \text{ AlH}_2\text{I} \rightarrow \text{AlH}_3 + \text{AlHI}_2 \qquad (3\text{-}114)$$

Ether solutions of the iodo compounds are stable indefinitely in the absence of moisture which decomposes the compounds according to equations (3-115) and (3-116).

$$\text{AlHI}_2 + 3 \text{ H}_2\text{O} \rightarrow \text{H}_2 + 2 \text{ HI} + \text{Al(OH)}_3 \qquad (3\text{-}115)$$

$$\text{AlH}_2\text{I} + 3 \text{ H}_2\text{O} \rightarrow 2 \text{ H}_2 + \text{HI} + \text{Al(OH)}_3 \qquad (3\text{-}116)$$

Reaction of the ethereal solution of aluminum hydride with an ethereal solution of aluminum bromide in a 1:1 ratio at room temperature yields an equimolar mixture of mono- and dibromo compounds analogous to the reaction with the iodide (109,110).

$$AlH_3 + AlBr_3 \rightarrow AlH_2Br + AlHBr_2 \qquad (3\text{-}117)$$

Reaction in a $1:2$ ratio yields an ethereal solution of the etherate of dibromoaluminum hydride.

$$AlH_3 + 2\ AlBr_3 \rightarrow 3\ AlHBr_2 \qquad (3\text{-}118)$$

Distillation in high vacuum yields the pure dibromo compound, m.p. $-15°$. Disproportionation occurs during distillation

$$2\ AlHBr_2 \rightarrow AlH_2Br + AlBr_3 \qquad (3\text{-}119)$$

and above $150°$ decomposition to aluminum and hydrogen occurs. Reaction in a $2:1$ ratio yields the monobromo compound which rapidly decomposes and precipitates polymeric aluminum hydride.

$$2\ AlH_3 + AlBr_3 \rightarrow 2\ AlH_2Br \cdot etherate \qquad (3\text{-}120)$$

$$2\ AlH_2Br \rightarrow (AlH_3)_x + AlHBr_2 \qquad (3\text{-}121)$$

Distillation above $35°$ increases the disproportionation with precipitation of the polymeric hydride, while above $95°$ the dibromo compound distills as a clear liquid. Above $160°$ aluminum hydride decomposes to aluminum and hydrogen. Ether solutions of the mono- and dibromo compounds are stable at room temperature, but in the presence of moisture, hydrolysis occurs analogous to that observed with the iodo compounds, equations (3-115) and (3-116).

Treatment of mono- and dibromoaluminum hydride with LAH in ether solution yields a stable ethereal aluminum hydride solution.

$$AlH_2Br + LiAlH_4 \rightarrow 2\ AlH_3 + LiBr \qquad (3\text{-}122)$$

$$AlHBr_2 + LiAlH_4 \rightarrow 3\ AlH_3 + 2\ LiBr \qquad (3\text{-}123)$$

The latter solution is similar to that obtained from aluminum bromide in that the aluminum hydride does not precipitate in the polymeric form but is stabilized as lithium bromoaluminum hydride, $LiBr \cdot AlH_3 = LiAlH_3Br$. In contrast, the ethereal solution of aluminum hydride obtained from the reaction of mono- and dichloroaluminum hydride as well as aluminum chloride with LAH precipitates the polymeric $(AlH_3)_x$ (106).

The reaction of lithium, sodium or potassium borohydride and aluminum chloride or bromide yields the volatile aluminum borohydride (12,80,111) (Section 2.6.2).

$$3\ MeBH_4 + AlX_3 \rightarrow Al(BH_4)_3 + 3\ MeCl \qquad (3\text{-}124)$$

$$Me = Li,\ Na\ and\ K$$

Sodium aluminum hydride is prepared by the reaction of sodium hydride and aluminum bromide in dimethyl ether. The properties of this aluminohydride are like those of LAH except that it is somewhat more stable toward thermal decomposition and is only very slightly soluble in diethyl ether (2).

3.14.6 Group III-B

3.14.6.a *Gallium compounds*. Gallium chloride does not react with LAH in ether at $-80°$. At $-30°$ precipitation of lithium chloride begins and at $0°$ ether-soluble gallium aluminum hydride is formed (112).

$$GaCl_3 + LiAlH_4 \rightarrow Ga(AlH_4)_3 + 3\ LiCl \qquad (3\text{-}125)$$

The colorless ether solution is unstable and at $0°$ yields polymeric aluminum hydride and gallium hydride (112,113).

$$Ga(AlH_4)_3 \rightarrow GaH_3 + 3\ AlH_3 \qquad (3\text{-}126)$$

The gallium hydride forms an etherate $GaH_3 \cdot O(C_2H_5)_2$ which is isolated in crystalline form after evaporation of the ether *in vacuo* at $20°$. The etherate, as well as the ethereal gallium aluminum hydride solution, decomposes above $35°$ to yield gallium and hydrogen (112,114).

$$Ga(AlH_4)_3 \rightarrow Ga + 1.5\ H_2 + 3\ AlH_3 \qquad (3\text{-}127)$$

Owing to its ether solubility a homopolar structure with hydrogen bridges has been proposed for the complex hydride (III) (112).

III

The reaction of gallium chloride in ether solution at room temperature with lithium hydride yields lithium gallium hydride (1,27), as discussed in Section 2.6.3.

$$4\ LiH + GaCl_3 \rightarrow LiGaH_4 + 3\ LiCl \qquad (3\text{-}128)$$

Treatment of an ether solution of lithium gallium hydride at $0°$ with an ether solution of gallium chloride results in the precipitation of lithium chloride while gallium hydride remains in solution (114).

$$GaCl_3 + 3\ LiGaH_4 \rightarrow 4\ GaH_3 + 3\ LiCl \qquad (3\text{-}129)$$

At $35°$ hydrogen is evolved and metallic gallium is precipitated. At room temperature white, high polymeric gallium hydride, $(GaH_3)_x$, is precipitated after several days. The polymeric hydride undergoes practically no reaction with water while hydrogen is evolved with dilute acid (23,114).

$$GaH_3 + 3\ H^+ \rightarrow Ga^{+++} + 3\ H_2 \qquad (3\text{-}130)$$

The hydride is exceedingly stable. At $140°$ *in vacuo* hydrogen evolution is observed but the hydride appearance is unchanged. Hydrogen evolution is increased at higher temperatures until at $380\text{-}400°$ metallic gallium is formed. The evolution of hydrogen at $140°$ probably accompanies a transformation of the gallium (III) hydride to the more stable gallium (I) hydride.

3.14.6.b *Indium compounds.* The reaction of an ethereal LAH solution with an ether solution of indium chloride at $-70°$ yields indium aluminum hydride which precipitates from the ether

$$InCl_3 + 3 LiAlH_4 \rightarrow In(AlH_4)_3 + 3 LiCl \qquad (3\text{-}131)$$

and above $-40°$ decomposes according to the equation

$$2 In(AlH_4)_3 \rightarrow 2 In + 3 H_2 + 6 AlH_3 \qquad (3\text{-}132)$$

Indium hydride, InH_3, is probably formed as an intermediate in the decomposition. At $160°$ the aluminum hydride is also decomposed to the elements (115).

The reaction of indium chloride with LAH in ether solution at room temperature yields a white precipitate of dichloroindium aluminum hydride, $InCl_2(AlH_4)$, so long as not more than one-third of the required amount of LAH is added:

$$InCl_3 + LiAlH_4 \rightarrow InCl_2(AlH_4) + LiCl \qquad (3\text{-}133)$$

Upon further addition of LAH the initially formed dichloro compound is converted to indium aluminum hydride which spontaneously decomposes as in equation (3-132). The dichloro compound is more stable than indium hydride and decomposes above $100°$ to precipitate indium and evolve hydrogen and hydrogen chloride. The ether insolubility of both indium aluminum hydride and the dichloroindium aluminum hydride is considered indicative of the absence of hydrogen bridges (115).

Treatment of indium trichloride in ether solution at room temperature with lithium hydride yields a white solid which was originally considered to be either indium hydride or lithium indium hydride (115). The compound is contaminated with excess lithium hydride making analytical differentiation difficult. The material has since been shown to be the polymeric form of indium hydride (23)

$$InCl_3 + LiH \rightarrow InH_3 + 3 LiCl \qquad (3\text{-}134)$$

which above $80°$ decomposes to the elements.

$$(InH_3)_x \rightarrow x In + 1.5x H_2 \qquad (3\text{-}135)$$

3.14.6.c *Thallium compounds.* The reaction of thallic chloride and LAH at $-115°$ yields thallium aluminum hydride which spontaneously decomposes at $-115°$ to metallic thallium (116).

$$TlCl_3 + 3 LiAlH_4 \rightarrow Tl(AlH_4)_3 + 3 LiCl \qquad (3\text{-}136)$$

$$Tl(AlH_4)_3 \rightarrow Tl + 1.5 H_2 + 3 AlH_3 \qquad (3\text{-}137)$$

In contrast, treatment of thallic chloride with an ethereal solution of the aluminum hydride-aluminum chloride addition product at $-115°$ yields chlorothallium aluminum hydride which is stable to $-95°$ and decomposes to thallous chloride, hydrogen and aluminum hydride (116).

$$3 \text{ TlCl}_3 + 8 \text{ AlH}_3 \rightarrow 3 \text{ TlCl(AlH}_4)_2 + 2 \text{ AlCl}_3 \qquad (3\text{-}138)$$

$$\text{TlCl(AlH}_4)_2 \rightarrow \text{TlCl} + \text{H}_2 + 2 \text{ AlH}_3 \qquad (3\text{-}139)$$

The fact that the reaction at $-115°$ only replaces two chlorine atoms with aluminohydride is analogous to the alkylation of thallic chloride with dialkyl zinc or Grignard compounds, wherein only two of the three atoms of chlorine are replaced

$$\text{TlCl}_3 + 2 \text{ RMgCl} \rightarrow \text{R}_2\text{TlCl} + 2 \text{ MgCl}_2 \qquad (3\text{-}140)$$

The reaction with lithium gallium hydride at $-115°$ replaces all three chlorine atoms to yield the ether-insoluble complex hydride (117).

$$\text{TlCl}_3 + 3 \text{ LiGaH}_4 \rightarrow \text{Tl(GaH}_4)_3 + 3 \text{ LiCl} \qquad (3\text{-}141)$$

At $-90°$ the thallium gallium hydride decomposes to metallic thallium and gallium hydride.

$$2 \text{ Tl(GaH}_4)_3 \rightarrow 2 \text{ Tl} + 3 \text{ H}_2 + 6 \text{ GaH}_3 \qquad (3\text{-}142)$$

Treatment of thallic chloride with lithium hydride at $-115°$ yields the elements of thallium hydride rather than the hydride itself (23).

$$2 \text{ TlCl}_3 + 6 \text{ LiH} \rightarrow 2 \text{ Tl} + 3 \text{ H}_2 + 6 \text{ LiCl} \qquad (3\text{-}143)$$

3.14.7 Group IV

3.14.7.a *Carbon compounds*. The reduction of the compounds of carbon, including the halides, is discussed in the various sections on the reduction of organic compounds.

3.14.7.b *Silicon compounds*. The reaction of silicon tetrachloride with LAH in ether solution yields silane in almost quantitative yield (1,2,40,70,89,118).

$$\text{SiCl}_4 + \text{LiAlH}_4 \rightarrow \text{SiH}_4 + \text{LiCl} + \text{AlCl}_3 \qquad (3\text{-}144)$$

When the reaction is carried out at reflux temperature, in the absence of ether, the yield of silane is negligible. If ether is added at $-196°$ and the temperature permitted to rise, silane is obtained in 96% yield at the melting point of ether (97). When dioxane is used as solvent, the generation of silane is smoother but the yield is reduced (119,120).

Reduction of hexachlorodisilane with LAH in ether similarly results in complete replacement of halogen atoms to give disilane in 87% yield (70).

Condensation of dimethylaminotrichlorosilane on powdered LAH in a vacuum apparatus and warming to room temperature, results in a very slow reaction which is complete after forty hours to yield 95% silane and a small quantity of hydrogen (121).

$$(CH_3)_2NSiCl_3 \xrightarrow{LAH} SiH_4 + H_2 \qquad (3\text{-}145)$$

When the reaction is carried out in ether, the same products are obtained after only two hours. In a similar manner, the reaction of bis-dimethyl-aminodichlorosilane with powdered LAH in the absence of ether is complete only after three days to yield 90% silane and a trace of hydrogen. The same products are obtained in the presence of ether (121).

$$[(CH_3)_2N]_2SiCl_2 \xrightarrow{LAH} SiH_4 + H_2 \qquad (3\text{-}146)$$

This work indicates that LAH reduces not only chlorine but also cleaves the Si—N bond.

3.14.8 Group IV-A

3.14.8.a *Titanium compounds.* At −110° titanium tetrachloride and LAH yield titanium aluminum hydride which decomposes above −85° to metallic titanium and aluminum. The decomposition of the intermediate aluminum hydride is apparently catalyzed by the presence of metallic titanium (122).

$$TiCl_4 + 4\ LiAlH_4 \rightarrow Ti(AlH_4)_4 + 4\ LiCl \qquad (3\text{-}147)$$
$$Ti(AlH_4)_4 \rightarrow Ti + 4\ Al + 8\ H_2 \qquad (3\text{-}148)$$

Aluminum, beryllium, and lithium borohydrides will reduce titanium (IV) to the (III) state, whereas sodium borohydride does not reduce titanium (IV) at room temperature. Titanium (III) borohydride has been prepared by the action of lithium borohydride on titanium tetrachloride (123).

$$2\ TiCl_4 + 8\ LiBH_4 \rightarrow 2\ Ti(BH_4)_3 + 8\ LiCl + B_2H_6 + H_2 \quad (3\text{-}149)$$

The reaction between titanium tetrachloride and aluminum borohydride is violent unless carried out at a low temperature (−30 to −40°), and yields the mono- and dichloroborohydrides of aluminum as well as titanium (III) monochloroborohydride. The monochloroborohydride of aluminum disproportionates rapidly to the dichloro compound and aluminum borohydride. The overall reaction is represented

$$2\ TiCl_4 + 3\ Al(BH_4)_3 \rightarrow 2\ TiCl(BH_4)_2 + 3\ AlCl_2BH_4 + B_2H_6 + H_2 \qquad (3\text{-}150)$$

The reaction of titanium monochloroborohydride with lithium borohydride yields titanium (III) borohydride (123).

$$TiCl(BH_4)_2 + LiBH_4 \rightarrow Ti(BH_4)_3 + LiCl \qquad (3\text{-}151)$$

No reaction occurs between aluminum borohydride and either titanium trifluoride, titanium tetrafluoride, or the double salt sodium titanium tetrafluoride. Titanium (III) borohydride is the most volatile known compound of trivalent titanium. It decomposes completely within several days at room temperature to hydrogen and a non-volatile solid which deposits as a metallic mirror.

3.14.8.b   *Zirconium compounds.* No reaction occurs between aluminum borohydride and zirconium tetrafluoride. Reaction with zirconium tetrachloride yields zirconium borohydride as well as a complex mixture of aluminum chloroborohydrides which are difficult to separate (123). The borohydride has been prepared satisfactorily by the reaction of aluminum borohydride and the double salt sodium zirconium pentafluoride, prepared from sodium fluoride and zirconium tetrafluoride (123,124).

$$NaZrF_5 + 2\ Al(BH_4)_3 \longrightarrow Zr(BH_4)_4 + 2\ AlF_2BH_4 + NaF \quad (3\text{-}152)$$

Zirconium borohydride is the most volatile known compound of this element, m.p. 28.7°, extrapolated b.p. 123°, and ignites in air.

3.14.8.c   *Hafnium compounds.* No reaction occurs between aluminum borohydride and hafnium tetrafluoride at room temperature after several days or when heated in a sealed tube at 65° for six days (123). However, reaction of the borohydride and sodium hafnium pentafluoride yields hafnium borohydride, analogous to the reaction of the zirconium compound (123,124). Beryllium borohydride can be used in place of aluminum borohydride (124).

$$NaHfF_5 + 2\ Al(BH_4)_3 \longrightarrow Hf(BH_4)_4 + 2\ AlF_2BH_4 + NaF \quad (3\text{-}153)$$

Hafnium borohydride is a volatile solid, m.p. 29.0°, extrapolated b.p. 118°, resembling aluminum borohydride in character, and is considered to be the most volatile known hafnium compound. Like the borohydrides of aluminum, beryllium, and zirconium it inflames violently when exposed to air.

3.14.8.d   *Thorium compounds.* Thorium tetrafluoride and aluminum borohydride react at room temperature to yield thorium borohydride.

$$ThF_4 + 2\ Al(BH_4)_3 \longrightarrow Th(BH_4)_4 + 2\ AlF_2BH_4 \quad (3\text{-}154)$$

The reaction mixture is heated to 150° to disproportionate aluminum difluoroborohydride to aluminum borohydride and aluminum fluoride, while the thorium borohydride sublimes and condenses above the heated zone. Thorium borohydride, m.p. 204° (with decomposition), is a salt-like, stable material resembling the lithium and sodium compounds in its properties (123).

3.14.9   Group IV-B

3.14.9.a   *Germanium compounds.* Germanium tetrachloride and LAH in ether yield 30% germane (2,40,70). Although no details are specifically given, this reaction is apparently carried out at room temperature or slightly below.

$$GeCl_4 + LiAlH_4 \rightarrow GeH_4 + LiCl + AlCl_3 \qquad (3\text{-}155)$$

3.14.9.b *Tin compounds*. Schlesinger and his co-workers (2,40,70) prepared stannane, SnH_4, in 20% yield by the reaction of stannic chloride and LAH in ether at $-30°$. Finely divided tin is also obtained and the stannane decomposes to form a tin mirror after twelve hours at room temperature. Less than 1% of the theoretical quantity of stannane is obtained when lithium hydride is used in place of LAH (70).

Wiberg and Bauer (125) found that the reaction of stannic chloride with LAH in ether at $-60°$ gives a tin aluminum hydride which is stable to $-40°$.

$$SnCl_4 + 4 LiAlH_4 \rightarrow Sn(AlH_4)_4 + 4 LiCl \qquad (3\text{-}156)$$

Above $-40°$ this decomposes to stannane or tin and hydrogen and aluminum hydride.

$$Sn(AlH_4)_4 \begin{cases} \rightarrow SnH_4 + 4 AlH_3 & (3\text{-}157) \\ \rightarrow H_2 + 2 AlH_3 + Sn(AlH_4)_2 & (3\text{-}158) \\ \qquad\qquad\quad \downarrow \\ \qquad Sn + H_2 + 2 AlH_3 & (3\text{-}159) \end{cases}$$

3.14.10 Group V

3.14.10.a *Nitrogen compounds*. The reaction of lithium borohydride with ammonium chloride at $230°$ yields 30–35% borazole, $(HBNH)_3$, which does not react appreciably with lithium borohydride (35).

$$3 NH_4Cl + 3 LiBH_4 \rightarrow B_3N_3H_6 + 3 LiCl + 9 H_2 \qquad (3\text{-}160)$$

The reaction of methylammonium chloride with the borohydride in ether gives N-trimethylborazole in 98% yield (126).

$$3 CH_3NH_3Cl + 3 LiBH_4 \rightarrow (CH_3)_3N_3B_3H_3 + 3 LiCl + 9 H_2 \qquad (3\text{-}161)$$

Reaction of dimethylammonium chloride with the borohydride yields N,N-dimethylaminoborine while trimethylammonium chloride yields N-trimethylamine-borine (126).

$$(CH_3)_2NH_2Cl + LiBH_4 \rightarrow (CH_3)_2NBH_2 + LiCl + 2 H_2 \qquad (3\text{-}162)$$

$$(CH_3)_3NHCl + LiBH_4 \rightarrow (CH_3)_3N:BH_3 + LiCl + H_2 \qquad (3\text{-}163)$$

3.14.10.b *Phosphorus compounds*. The rapid reaction of phosphorus trichloride with LAH in ether at less than $0°$ produces phosphine in good yield. When the reactants are refluxed at $75°$ for one hour in the absence of ether, the yield of phosphine is 0.25% (97).

$$4 PCl_3 + 3 LiAlH_4 \rightarrow 4 PH_3 + 3 LiCl + 3 AlCl_3 \qquad (3\text{-}164)$$

3.14.11   Group V-B

3.14.11.a   *Arsenic compounds.*   Arsenic halides and LAH yield the corresponding hydride (2,40).

$$4\ AsCl_3 + 3\ LiAlH_4 \rightarrow 4\ AsH_3 + 3\ LiCl + 3\ AlCl_3 \qquad (3\text{-}165)$$

3.14.11.b   *Antimony compounds.*   Antimony halides and LAH yield stibene (2,40).

$$4\ SbCl_3 + 3\ LiAlH_4 \rightarrow 4\ SbH_3 + 3\ LiCl + 3\ AlCl_3 \qquad (3\text{-}166)$$

3.14.12   Group VI-A

3.14.12.a   *Uranium compounds.*   Uranium (IV) borohydride is prepared by the reaction of uranium (IV) fluoride with excess aluminum borohydride at room temperature (30,60).

$$UF_4 + 2\ Al(BH_4)_3 \rightarrow U(BH_4)_4 + 2\ Al(BH_4)F_2 \qquad (3\text{-}167)$$

Uranium (IV) chloride can also be used as can lithium borohydride in the presence of ether. The green crystals of the borohydride are volatile at room temperature without melting. At temperatures below 70° it is fairly stable. At 100° it decomposes to give uranium (III) borohydride.

$$2\ U(BH_4)_4 \rightarrow 2\ U(BH_4)_3 + 2\ Al(BH_4)F_2 \qquad (3\text{-}168)$$

At 150–200° uranium (IV) borohydride undergoes decomposition to give a metallic mirror.

$$U(BH_4)_4 \rightarrow UB_4 \ (or\ U + 4B) + 8\ H_2 \qquad (3\text{-}169)$$

Uranium (IV) borohydride is fairly stable to dry air while uranium (III) borohydride is pyrophoric.

3.15   REACTIONS IN AQUEOUS SOLUTION

The stability of aqueous solutions of sodium borohydride and tri-methoxyborohydride permits the use of such solutions in the reduction of various inorganic cations and anions.

3.15.1   Sodium Borohydride

In aqueous solution sodium borohydride reduces silver, bismuth, arsenic, and antimony salts to the free metal (33). Ions of cerium (IV), chromium (VI), thallium (III) and (I), mercury (II) and (I), and iron (III) are reduced to the next lower stable valence state (127). Iron may be determined analytically by reduction to the ferrous state with an excess of sodium borohydride in a slightly alkaline solution (14,127).

The reduction of nickel (II) sulfate and cobalt (II) chloride in aqueous solution yields black precipitates whose analyses correspond to nickel boride, Ni_2B (33), and cobalt boride, Co_2B (14), respectively. Manganese (II), iron (II), nickel (II), and copper (II) chlorides similarly yield dark suspensions or precipitates which are probably borides. These precipitates are effective catalysts for the generation of hydrogen from an aqueous solution of sodium borohydride. The catalytic action is highest in the case of the cobalt product, somewhat less for nickel and least for iron, manganese, and copper (14).

The boride precipitates have been prepared and isolated for use as hydrogenation catalysts (128). The black precipitate prepared from nickel (II) chloride or sulfate and sodium borohydride in aqueous or methanol solution contains 7.7% boron (theoretical for Ni_2B = 8.5%) and is slightly less active than Raney nickel, but if nickel (II) acetate is used the catalyst is as active as Raney nickel. A similar precipitate prepared from a cobalt (II) salt contains 7.9% boron (theoretical for Co_2B = 8.5%) but is less active than the nickel catalyst while a copper catalyst is still less active. The addition of sodium borohydride to a solution of nickel (II) chloride and chromium (VI) sulfate yields a complex catalyst containing 5.3% boron and 2% chromium. Similar catalysts containing 2% molybdenum or 2% tungsten have also been prepared. These complex catalysts are much more active than Raney nickel. Cobalt-chromium and cobalt-tungsten complexes containing 2% chromium or tungsten are more active than the simple cobalt boride catalyst.

The reduction of iodine (129), potassium iodate (130), and sodium hypochlorite (131) to the corresponding halides has been utilized in the volumetric assay of aqueous sodium borohydride solutions.

3.15.2 Sodium Trimethoxyborohydride

Aqueous sodium trimethoxyborohydride solutions reduce silver nitrate, arsenious oxide, bismuth nitrate, and antimony trichloride to the free metal. Mercuric (II) chloride is reduced to a mixture of mercurous (I) chloride and free mercury. Lead nitrate and zinc nitrate are converted to the insoluble white hydroxides. Nickel, cobalt, and ferrous salts yield black precipitates which are probably the borides. Copper sulfate solutions give dark brown precipitates which do not contain boron and, in contrast to the copper hydride prepared by reducing copper solutions with potassium hypoborate, do not evolve hydrogen. Bromine in carbon tetrachloride is immediately decolorized while ferricyanide ion is reduced to ferrocyanide ion (22). Potassium permanganate, ceric sulfate, and hydrogen peroxide solutions are also reduced by the trimethoxyborohydride (132).

REFERENCES

1. Finholt, A. E., A. C. Bond, Jr., and H. I. Schlesinger, *J. Am. Chem. Soc.*, 69, 1199 (1947).
2. Schlesinger, H. I., and A. E. Finholt, U. S. Pat. 2,576,311 (November 27, 1951).

3. Metal Hydrides Inc., Beverly, Mass., Bulletin 401B, "Lithium Aluminum Hydride."
4. Baker, B. B., Jr., and W. M. MacNevin, *Anal. Chem.*, 22, 364 (1950).
5. Wender, I., R. A. Friedel, and M. Orchin, *J. Am. Chem. Soc.*, 71, 1140 (1949).
6. Fookson, A., P. Pomerantz, and E. H. Rich, *Science*, 112, 748 (1950).
7. Fookson, A., P. Pomerantz, and E. H. Rich, *J. Research Natl. Bur. Standards*, 47, 31 (1951).
8. Davison, S., and M. Burton, *J. Am. Chem. Soc.*, 74, 2307 (1952).
9. Siri, W., unpublished work; through ref. 10.
10. Biggs, M. W., D. Kritchevsky, and M. R. Kirk, *Anal. Chem.*, 24, 223 (1952).
11. Davis, W. D., L. S. Mason, and G. Stegeman, *J. Am. Chem. Soc.*, 71, 2775 (1949).
12. Schlesinger, H. I., H. R. Hoekstra, and H. C. Brown, *Abstracts of Papers*, 115th Meeting American Chemical Society, San Francisco, Calif., March 1949, p. 9 O.
13. Schlesinger, H. I., H. C. Brown, H. R. Hoekstra, and L. R. Rapp, *J. Am. Chem. Soc.*, 75, 199 (1953).
14. Schlesinger, H. I., H. C. Brown, A. E. Finholt, J. R. Gilbreath, H. R. Hoekstra, and E. K. Hyde, *J. Am. Chem. Soc.*, 75, 215 (1953).
15. Brown, W. G., L. Kaplan, and K. E. Wilzbach, *J. Am. Chem. Soc.*, 74, 1343 (1952).
16. Ethyl Corporation, PB-6330.
17. Girardot, P. R., and R. W. Parry, *J. Am. Chem. Soc.*, 73, 2368 (1951).
18. Metal Hydrides Inc., Technical Bulletin, "Potassium Borohydride."
19. Metal Hydrides Inc., Technical Bulletin 402-B, "Lithium Borohydride."
20. Schlesinger, H. I., and H. C. Brown, *J. Am. Chem. Soc.*, 62, 3429 (1940).
21. Kilpatrick, M., and C. D. McKinney, Jr., *J. Am. Chem. Soc.*, 72, 5474 (1950).
22. Brown, H. C., H. I. Schlesinger, I. Sheft, and D. M. Ritter, *J. Am. Chem. Soc.*, 75, 192 (1953).
23. Wiberg, E., *Angew. Chem.*, 65, 16 (1953).
24. Schlesinger, H. I., R. T. Sanderson, and A. B. Burg, *J. Am. Chem. Soc.*, 62, 3421 (1940).
25. Rulon, R. M. and L. S. Mason, *J. Am. Chem. Soc.*, 73, 5491 (1951).
26. Badin, E. J., P. C. Hunter, and R. N. Pease, *J. Am. Chem. Soc.*, 71, 2950 (1949).
27. Wiberg, E., and M. Schmidt, *Z. Naturforsch.*, 6b, 171 (1951).
28. Higuchi, T., J. Concha, and R. Kuramoto, *Anal. Chem.*, 24, 685 (1952).
29. Burg, A. B., and H. I. Schlesinger, *J. Am. Chem. Soc.*, 62, 3425 (1940).
30. Schlesinger, H. I., and H. C. Brown, *J. Am. Chem. Soc.*, 75, 219 (1953).
31. Wiberg, E., and R. Bauer, *Z. Naturforsch.*, 7b, 58 (1952).
32. Stecher, O., and E. Wiberg, *Ber.*, 75, 2003 (1942).
33. Schlesinger, H. I., and H. C. Brown, U. S. Pat. 2,461,661 (February 15, 1949).
34. Schlesinger, H. I., and H. C. Brown, U. S. Pat. 2,461,663 (1949).
35. Schaeffer, G. W., R. Schaeffer, and H. I. Schlesinger, *J. Am. Chem. Soc.*, 73, 1612 (1951).
36. Wiberg, E., through *European Scientific Notes*, No. 7–15, 174 (August 1, 1953).
37. Wittig, G., and H. Bille, *Z. Naturforsch.*, 6b, 226 (1951).
38. Wittig, G., and P. Raff, *Z. Naturforsch.*, 6b, 225 (1951).
39. Wittig, G., and P. Raff, *Ann.*, 573, 195 (1951).
40. Schlesinger, H. I., and A. E. Finholt, U. S. Pat. 2,567,972 (September 18, 1951).

41. Nystrom, R. F., W. H. Yanko, and W. G. Brown, *J. Am. Chem. Soc.*, 70, 441 (1948).
42. Schlesinger, H. I., and A. E. Finholt, unpublished work; through ref. 41 and 43.
43. Finholt, A. E., and E. C. Jacobson, *J. Am. Chem. Soc.*, 74, 3943 (1952).
44. Baddiley, J., G. Ehrensvärd, R. Johansson, L. Reio, E. Saluste, and R. Stjernholm, *J. Biol. Chem.*, 183, 771 (1950).
45. Cox, J. D., H. S. Turner, and R. J. Warne, *J. Chem. Soc.*, 1950, 3167.
46. Nystrom, R. F., W. J. Skraba, and R. J. Mansfield, ORNL-395 U.S.A.E.C.; through ref. 43 and 45.
47. Ostwald, R., P. T. Adams, and B. M. Tolbert, *J. Am. Chem. Soc.*, 74, 2425 (1952).
48. Berg, P., *J. Biol. Chem.*, 190, 31 (1951).
49. Cox, J. D., and R. J. Warne, *Nature*, 165, 563 (1950).
50. Metal Hydrides Inc., Technical Bulletin 410-A, "Deuterides."
51. Barbaras, G., G. D. Barbaras, A. E. Finholt, and H. I. Schlesinger, *J. Am. Chem. Soc.*, 70, 877 (1948).
52. *Chem. Eng. News*, 31, 2334 (1953).
53. Burr, J. G., Jr., W. G. Brown, and H. E. Heller, *J. Am. Chem. Soc.*, 72, 2560 (1950).
54. Brown, W. G., and J. G. Burr, Jr., AECD 2482, nd, Declass. February 18, 1949; *Nuclear Science Abst.*, 2, 299 (1949).
55. Burr, J. G., H. E. Heller, and W. Brown, ORNL-396, December 13, 1949; *Nucleonics*, 7, 54 (1950).
56. Brown, W. G., A. E. Finholt, R. F. Nystrom, and H. I. Schlesinger, *Abstracts of Papers*, 110th Meeting American Chemical Society, Chicago, Ill., September 1946, P. 27P.
57. Hochstein, F. A., *J. Am. Chem. Soc.*, 71, 305 (1949).
58. Higuchi, T., *Anal. Chem.*, 22, 955 (1950).
59. Brokaw, R. S., E. J. Badin, and R. N. Pease, *J. Am. Chem. Soc.*, 72, 1793 (1950).
60. Schlesinger, H. I., and H. C. Brown, U. S. Pat. 2,600,370 (June 10, 1952).
61. Karrer, P., and R. Schwyzer, *Rec. trav. chim.*, 69, 474 (1950).
62. Karrer, P., *Bull. soc. chim. France*, [5] 17, 907 (1950).
63. Sand, J., and F. Singer, *Ann.*, 329, 190 (1903).
64. Gerstein, M., R. A. Lad, and H. I. Schlesinger, *Abstracts of Papers*, 110th Meeting American Chemical Society, Chicago, Ill., September 1946, p. 26P.
65. Glemser, O., U. Hauschild, and O. Bimmermann, *Angew. Chem.*, 64, 457 (1952).
66. Felkin, H., *Bull. soc. chim. France*, [5] 18, 347 (1951).
67. *Chem. Week*, 70, 34 (1952).
68. Job, A., and R. Reich, *Bull. soc. chim. France*, [4] 33, 1414 (1923).
69. Wiberg, E., *Angew. Chem.*, 63, 485 (1951); 64, 354 (1952).
70. Finholt, A. E., A. C. Bond, Jr., K. E. Wilzbach, and H. I. Schlesinger, *J. Am. Chem. Soc.*, 69, 2692 (1947).
71. Shapiro, I., H. G. Weiss, M. Schmich, S. Skolnik, and G. B. L. Smith, *J. Am. Chem. Soc.*, 74, 901 (1952).
72. Elliott, J. R., E. M. Boldebuck, and G. F. Roedel, *J. Am. Chem. Soc.*, 74, 5047 (1952).
73. Warf, J. C., and W. Feitknecht, *Helv. Chim. Acta*, 33, 613 (1950).
74. Wiberg, E., and W. Henle, *Z. Naturforsch.*, 7b, 250 (1952).
75. Wiberg, E., and W. Henle, *Z. Naturforsch.*, 7b, 582 (1952).

76. Wiberg, E., and W. Henle, *Z. Naturforsch.*, *7b*, 250 (1952).
77. Wiberg, E., and W. Henle, *Z. Naturforsch.*, *7b*, 575 (1952).
78. Wiberg, E., and W. Henle, *Z. Naturforsch.*, *7b*, 576 (1952).
79. Barbaras, G. D., C. Dillard, A. E. Finholt, T. Wartik, K. E. Wilzbach, and H. I. Schlesinger, *J. Am. Chem. Soc.*, 73, 4585 (1951).
80. Schlesinger, H. I., H. C. Brown, and E. K. Hyde, *J. Am. Chem. Soc.*, 75, 209 (1953).
81. Wiberg, E., and R. Bauer, *Z. Naturforsch.*, *5b*, 397 (1950).
82. Wiberg, E., and R. Bauer, *Z. Naturforsch.*, *7b*, 131 (1952).
83. Wiberg, E., W. Henle, and R. Bauer, *Z. Naturforsch.*, *6b*, 393 (1951).
84. Wiberg, E., and W. Henle, *Z. Naturforsch.*, *7b*, 249 (1952).
85. Wiberg, E., and W. Henle, *Z. Naturforsch.*, *7b*, 579 (1952).
86. Wiberg, E., and W. Henle, *Z. Naturforsch.*, *6b*, 461 (1951).
87. Wiberg, E., and W. Henle, *Z. Naturforsch.*, *7b*, 582 (1952).
88. Wiberg, E., and W. Henle, *Z. Naturforsch.*, *6b*, 461 (1951).
89. Burg, A. B., and E. S. Kuljian, *J. Am. Chem. Soc.*, 72, 3103 (1950).
90. Stone, F. G. A., and H. J. Emeléus, *J. Chem. Soc.*, *1950*, 2755.
91. Rollier, M. A., *Gazz. chim. ital.*, *81*, 272 (1951).
92. Emeléus, H. J., and F. G. A. Stone, *J. Chem. Soc.*, *1951*, 840.
93. Lord, R. C., and E. Nielsen, *J. Chem. Phys.*, *19*, 1 (1951).
94. Burg, A. B., *J. Am. Chem. Soc.*, 74, 1340 (1952).
95. Lacher, J. R., R. E. Scruby, and J. D. Park, *J. Am. Chem. Soc.*, 74, 5292 (1952).
96. Maybury, P. C., and W. S. Koski, *J. Chem. Phys.*, *21*, 742 (1953).
97. Paddock, N. L., *Nature*, *167*, 1070 (1951).
98. Burrows, W. L., through *European Scientific Notes*, 6, 140 (1952).
99. Schlesinger, H. I., H. C. Brown, J. R. Gilbreath, and J. J. Katz, *J. Am. Chem. Soc.*, 75, 195 (1953).
100. Schlesinger, H. I., and H. C. Brown, U. S. Pat. 2,543,511, (February 27, 1951).
101. Coates, G. E., *J. Chem. Soc.*, *1950*, 3481.
102. Wiberg, E., and M. Schmidt, *Z. Naturforsch.*, *6b*, 333 (1951).
103. Gibb, T. R. P., Jr., M. D. Banus, R. W. Bragdon, and A. A. Hinckley, *Abstracts of Papers*, 119th Meeting American Chemical Society, Cleveland, Ohio, April 1951, p. 38P.
104. Gibb, T. R. P., Jr., M. D. Banus, R. W. Bragdon, and A. A. Hinckley, *Abstracts of Papers*, 119th Meeting American Chemical Society, Cleveland, Ohio, April 1951, p. 39P.
105. Gibb, T. R. P., Jr., private communication.
106. Wiberg, E., H. Graf, M. Schmidt, and R. Usón, *Z. Naturforsch.*, in press; through ref. 23.
107. Wiberg, E., and M. Schmidt, *Z. Naturforsch.*, *6b*, 460 (1951).
108. Wiberg, E., and M. Schmidt, *Z. Naturforsch.*, *6b*, 458 (1951).
109. *Chem. Week*, *71*, 36 (1952).
110. Wiberg, E., and M. Schmidt, *Z. Naturforsch.*, *6b*, 459 (1951).
111. Schlesinger, H. I., and H. C. Brown, U. S. Pat. 2,599,203 (June 3, 1952).
112. Wiberg, E., and M. Schmidt, *Z. Naturforsch.*, *6b*, 172 (1951).
113. Finholt, A. E., H. I. Schlesinger, and K. E. Wilzbach, *Abstracts of Papers*, 110th Meeting American Chemical Society, Chicago, Ill., September 1946, p. 27P.
114. Wiberg, E., and M. Schmidt, *Z. Naturforsch.*, *7b*, 577 (1952).
115. Wiberg, E., and M. Schmidt, *Z. Naturforsch.*, *6b*, 172 (1951).
116. Wiberg, E., and M. Schmidt, *Z. Naturforsch.*, *6b*, 334 (1951).

117. Wiberg, E., and M. Schmidt, *Z. Naturforsch.*, *6b*, 335 (1951).
118. Van Artsdalen, E. R., and J. Gavis, *J. Am. Chem. Soc.*, *74*, 3196 (1952).
119. Peake, J. S., W. H. Nebergall, and Yun Ti Chen, *J. Am. Chem. Soc.*, *74*, 1526 (1952).
120. Emeléus, H. J., through *European Scientific Notes*, No. 6–23, 294 (December 1, 1952).
121. Cass, R., and G. E. Coates, *J. Chem. Soc.*, *1952*, 2347.
122. Wiberg, E., and R. Usón, *Z. Naturforsch.*, *6b*, 392 (1951).
123. Hoekstra, H. R., and J. J. Katz, *J. Am. Chem. Soc.*, *71*, 2488 (1949).
124. Hoekstra, H. R., and J. J. Katz, U. S. Pat. 2,575,760 (November 20, 1951).
125. Wiberg, E., and R. Bauer, *Z. Naturforsch.*, *6b*, 392 (1951).
126. Schaeffer, G. W., and E. R. Anderson, *J. Am. Chem. Soc.*, *71*, 2143 (1949).
127. Schaeffer, G. W., and J. W. Frank, unpublished work; through Metal Hydrides Inc., Technical Bulletin 502-D, "Sodium Borohydride."
128. Paul, R., P. Buisson and N. Joseph, *Compt. rend.*, *232*, 627 (1951).
129. Mathews, M. B., *J. Biol. Chem.*, *176*, 229 (1948).
130. Lyttle, D. A., E. H. Jensen, and W. A. Struck, *Anal. Chem.*, *24*, 1843 (1952).
131. Chaikin, S. W., *Anal. Chem.*, *25*, 831 (1953).
132. Metal Hydrides Inc., Technical Bulletin 504-B, "Sodium Trimethoxyborohydride."

CHAPTER 4

REACTIONS WITH
ORGANIC DERIVATIVES OF INORGANIC REACTANTS

4.1 COMPOUNDS CONTAINING HALOGEN

As in the reduction of inorganic halides with LAH, alkyl or aryl derivatives of such halides are reduced to the corresponding hydrides. The reaction can be represented (1-3) by the generalized equation:

$$(4 - x) \text{LiAlH}_4 + \text{ER}_x\text{Cl}_{4-x} \longrightarrow (4 - x) \text{LiCl} + (4 - x) \text{AlCl}_3 + 4 \text{ER}_x\text{H}_{4-x}$$

$$(4\text{-}1)$$

$$x = 0 \text{ to } 3 \qquad \text{R} = \text{alkyl or aryl}$$

4.1.1 Organohalosilanes

The reduction of mono-, di-, and tri-substituted chlorosilanes in ether solution has been carried out in the synthesis of the corresponding silanes in high yield. The fluorine atom in triethylfluorosilane has been replaced to yield 85% triethylsilane (4). Diethylchlorodisilane has been reduced to diethyldisilane (1) while various bis-trichlorosilylalkanes have been reduced to the corresponding disilylalkanes (5). Among the latter it has been observed that when excess LAH solution is added to bis-trichlorosilylmethane no product is obtained. However, when the chlorosilane is added to the ethereal LAH solution an 80% yield of disilylmethane is obtained (5).

$$\text{Cl}_3\text{SiCH}_2\text{SiCl}_3 \xrightarrow{\text{LAH}} \text{H}_3\text{SiCH}_2\text{SiH}_3 \qquad (4\text{-}2)$$

Tritium-labeled triphenylsilane has been prepared by the reduction of the trichloro compound with $\text{LiAlH}_4\text{-t}$ (6).

Reductions of organohalosilanes with LAH in ether solution are summarized in Table I.

While LAH reduction of diethyldichlorosilane proceeds in ether in good yield, the use of lithium hydride requires higher temperatures necessitating the use of dioxane as solvent. When sodium hydride is used in dioxane, no reaction occurs until aluminum chloride is added to give a 23% yield of diethylsilane (1,3). The influence of aluminum chloride suggests that sodium aluminum hydride is the effective reducing agent.

The reaction of dimethylaminotrichlorosilane or bis-dimethylamino-dichlorosilane with powdered LAH, or with LAH in ether solution, affords an excellent yield of silane and a trace of hydrogen (7).

$$(\text{CH}_3)_2\text{NSiCl}_3 \xrightarrow{\text{LAH}} \text{SiH}_4 + \text{H}_2 \qquad (4\text{-}3)$$

TABLE I

LAH Reduction of Organohalosilanes

Halosilane	Product	% Yield	Ref.
Methyltrichlorosilane	Methylsilane	...	1,2
Ethyltrichlorosilane	Ethylsilane	...	1–3
n-Propyltrichlorosilane	n-Propylsilane	...	1–3
n-Butyltrichlorosilane	n-Butylsilane	...	3
Phenyltrichlorosilane	Phenylsilane	...	1–3
		86	4
		69	5
Diethyldichlorosilane	Diethylsilane	...	1–3
Di-n-propyldichlorosilane	Di-n-propylsilane	80	2,3
Di-n-butyldichlorosilane	Di-n-butylsilane	...	1,2
Diphenyldichlorosilane	Diphenylsilane	76	5
Triphenylchlorosilane	Triphenylsilane-t	...	6
Diphenyl-p-chlorophenylchlorosilane	Diphenyl-p-chlorophenylsilane	56	7
Diphenyl-m-dimethylaminophenylchlorosilane	Diphenyl-m-dimethylaminophenylsilane	83	7
Diphenyl-p-methoxyphenylchlorosilane	Diphenyl-p-methoxyphenylsilane	76	7
Diphenyl-m-tolylchlorosilane	Diphenyl-m-tolylsilane	62	7
Diphenyl-p-tolylchlorosilane	Diphenyl-p-tolylsilane	79	7
Tricyclohexylchlorosilane	Tricyclohexylsilane	90	8
Tri-(p-dimethylaminophenyl)chlorosilane	Tri-(p-dimethylaminophenyl)silane	98	9
Tri-1-naphthylchlorosilane	Tri-1-naphthylsilane	95	10
Triethylfluorosilane	Triethylsilane	85	11
Diethylchlorodisilane	Diethyldisilane	...	3
Dichlorosilyltrichlorosilylmethane	Disilylmethane	52[12]	13
Bis-trichlorosilylmethane	Disilylmethane	0[12]	13
		80	13
1,1-Bis-trichlorosilylethane	1,1-Disilylethane	8	13
1,2-Bis-trichlorosilylethane	1,2-Disilylethane	5	13
1,2-Bis-trichlorosilylpropane	1,2-Disilylpropane	...[14]	13

References—Table I

[1]H. I. Schlesinger and A. E. Finholt, U.S. Pat. 2,567,972 (September 18, 1951).

[2]H. I. Schlesinger and A. E. Finholt, U.S. Pat. 2,576,311 (November 27, 1951).

[3]A. E. Finholt, A. C. Bond, Jr., K. E. Wilzbach, and H. I. Schlesinger, *J. Am. Chem. Soc.*, 69, 2692 (1947).

[4]W. H. Nebergall, *ibid.*, 72, 4702 (1950).

[5]R. A. Benkeser, H. Landesman, and D. J. Foster, *ibid.*, 74, 648 (1952).

[6]L. Kaplan and K. E. Wilzbach, *ibid.*, 74, 6152 (1952).

[7]H. Gilman and G. E. Dunn, *ibid.*, 73, 3404 (1951).

[8]W. H. Nebergall and O. H. Johnson, *ibid.*, 71, 4022 (1949).

[9]H. Gilman, M. A. Plunkett, and G. E. Dunn, *ibid.*, 73, 1686 (1951).

[10]H. Gilman and C. G. Brannen, *ibid.*, 73, 4640 (1951).

[11]C. Eaborn, *J. Chem. Soc.*, 1950, 3077.

[12]Inverse addition.

[13]W. D. English, A. Taurins, and R. V. V. Nicholls, *Can. J. Chem.*, 30, 646 (1952).

[14]Product not completely pure.

$$[(CH_3)_2N]_2SiCl_2 \xrightarrow{LAH} SiH_4 + H_2 \qquad (4\text{-}4)$$

LAH is thus able to reduce the chlorine and in addition cleaves the silicon-nitrogen bond. The ease of cleavage of the silicon-nitrogen bond has been shown by the reaction of tri-silylamine and boron trichloride at $-78°$ to yield N,N-bis-silylaminodichloroborine (8).

$$(SiH_3)_3N + BCl_3 \rightarrow (SiH_3)_2NBCl_2 + ClSiH_3 \qquad (4\text{-}5)$$

4.1.2 Organohalogermanes

The reduction of organohalogermanes, according to equation (4-1), has been applied to the preparation of substituted germanes (1-3). Triphenylbromogermane is readily reduced by LAH in ether to the corresponding hydride (9,10). This reaction has been utilized in a unique separation technique. Bromination of tetraphenylgermane or hexaphenyldigermane yields a mixture of triphenylbromogermane and diphenyldibromogermane whose fractionation is difficult due to the similarity of physical properties. Subjection of the mixture to reduction with LAH yields a mixture of triphenylgermane and diphenylgermane which is readily fractionated. The diphenylgermane is readily brominated to yield dibromophenylgermane (11).

A similar technique has been applied to the LAH reduction, in isopropyl ether, of the mixture of propylchlorogermanes produced by the reaction of germanium tetrachloride and *n*-propyllithium.

$$GeCl_4 + C_3H_7Li \rightarrow C_3H_7GeCl_3 + (C_3H_7)_2GeCl_2 + (C_3H_7)_3GeCl$$
$$\downarrow LAH$$
$$C_3H_7GeH_3 + (C_3H_7)_3GeH \qquad (4\text{-}6)$$

Although dipropyldichlorogermane is present in the mixture obtained from the reaction with n-propyllithium, no dipropylgermane has been detected among the LAH reduction products (12).

The reaction of n-propyltrichlorogermane with LAH in isopropyl ether produces n-propylgermane in 85% yield. When the reaction is carried out in dioxane at 100°, the germanium-carbon bond is attacked as well as the germanium-chlorine bond resulting in the deposition of germanium metal and the formation of germane (12).

$$C_3H_7GeCl_3 \underset{\substack{\longrightarrow \\ 100°}}{\overset{\substack{68° \\ \longrightarrow \\ LAH}}{}} \begin{array}{l} C_3H_7GeH_3 \qquad (4\text{-}7) \\ \\ GeH_4 + Ge \quad (4\text{-}8) \end{array}$$

The reactions of tricyclohexylchlorogermane (10) and tri-1-naphthylbromogermane (13) with LAH yield 87% tricyclohexylgermane and 82% tri-1-naphthylgermane, respectively.

4.1.3 Organohalostibenes, Halostannanes, and Haloarsines

The reduction of organohaloantimony (2,3), tin (1-3), and arsenic (2,3) derivatives yields the corresponding stibenes, stannanes and arsines. LAH reduction of methyltrichlorostannane (1), dimethyldichlorostannane (1,14), trimethylchlorostannane (1), and triphenylbromostannane (15) yields methylstannane, dimethylstannane, trimethylstannane, and triphenylstannane, respectively. A mixture of mono-, di-, and trialkylchlorostannanes has been reduced with LAH because the hydrogen compounds are easier to separate from each other than are the chloro derivatives (1). Substitution of lithium hydride for LAH in the reduction of tin compounds results in slower reactions, and the yields are satisfactory only when a large excess of the hydride is employed.

Treatment of tris-trifluoromethylarsine with iodine yields trifluoromethyldiiodoarsine and di-trifluoromethyliodoarsine. Reaction of the mono- and diiodo compounds with LAH yields the corresponding arsines (16).

$$(CF_3)_3As + I_2 \longrightarrow CF_3AsI_2 + (CF_3)_2AsI$$
$$\downarrow {\scriptstyle LAH} \qquad\qquad \downarrow {\scriptstyle LAH} \qquad (4\text{-}9)$$
$$CF_3AsH_2 \quad (CF_3)_2AsH$$

4.1.4 Organohalophosphines

The reduction of phenyldichlorophosphine with LAH (17-19) or lithium hydride (18) in ether yields phenylphosphine.

$$C_6H_5PCl_2 \longrightarrow C_6H_5PH_2 \qquad (4\text{-}10)$$

When the reduction is carried out with lithium borohydride in tetrahydro-

furan the phenylphosphine is accompanied by an unidentified white solid
(19).

4.1.5 Organohaloborines

While it has been reported (8) that N,N-bis-silylaminodichloroborine,
$(SiH_3)_2NBCl_2$, prepared as in equation (4-5), could not be reduced with
LAH in ether, the reaction of bis-dimethylaminochloroborine with powdered LAH readily yields the corresponding hydride (20).

$$[(CH_3)_2N]_2BCl \xrightarrow{\text{LAH}} [(CH_3)_2N]_2BH \qquad (4\text{-}11)$$

4.1.6 Organolead halides

Application of LAH reduction to organolead halides has been reported
to result in partial reduction to metallic lead and to the formation of unstable, volatile lead compounds which were not identified (1).

4.1.7 Organomagnesium Halides

Treatment of a Grignard compound with LAH yields a substituted magnesium aluminum hydride (21).

$$RMgX + LiAlH_4 \rightarrow RMgAlH_4 + LiX \qquad (4\text{-}12)$$

4.2 COMPOUNDS CONTAINING OXYGEN

Tricyclohexylgermanol, a germanium analog of a tertiary alcohol, is reduced by LAH to tricyclohexylgermane in "practically quantitative"
yield (10).

$$4\,(C_6H_{11})_3GeOH + LiAlH_4 \rightarrow 4\,(C_6H_{11})_3GeH + LiOH + Al(OH)_3$$
$$(4\text{-}13)$$

The cleavage of the germanium-oxygen bond is also observed in the reduction of di-triphenylgermyl oxide to triphenylgermane (10).

$$(C_6H_5)_3Ge\!-\!O\!-\!Ge(C_6H_5)_3 \xrightarrow{\text{LAH}} (C_6H_5)_3GeH \qquad (4\text{-}14)$$

The silicon-oxygen bond is cleaved in the reduction of tri-1-naphthyl-
ethoxysilane with LAH in ether to give tri-1-naphthylsilane in 90% yield
(22).

$$R_3SiOC_2H_5 \xrightarrow{\text{LAH}} R_3SiH \qquad (4\text{-}15)$$
$$R = 1\text{-naphthyl}$$

Treatment of copper aluminum ethoxide, $Cu\,[Al(OC_2H_5)_4]_2$, with LAH
results in no visible reaction (23).

Sodium hydride reacts smoothly with aluminum ethylate in ether solution, in the presence of a small amount of LAH, to form a crystalline
ether-soluble addition compound.

$$Al(OC_2H_5)_3 + NaH \xrightarrow{\text{LAH}} Na\,[(C_2H_5O)_3AlH] \qquad (4\text{-}16)$$

An analogous reaction occurs with lithium hydride. However, an alkoxy group is simultaneously replaced by hydrogen, leading ultimately to the formation of LAH (24).

$$Al(OC_2H_5)_3 + LiH \xrightarrow{\text{LAH}} Li[(C_2H_5O)_3AlH] \qquad (4\text{-}17)$$

$$Li[(C_2H_5O)_3AlH] + LiH \longrightarrow Li[(C_2H_5O)_2AlH_2] + LiOC_2H_5 \qquad (4\text{-}18)$$

$$Li[(C_2H_5O)_2AlH_2] + 2\,LiH \longrightarrow LiAlH_4 + 2\,LiOC_2H_5 \qquad (4\text{-}19)$$

The reductive cleavage of the organic esters of nitric and nitrous acids with LAH is discussed fully under the reduction of esters (Section 9.1.1.a). Briefly, the reaction of nitrates and nitrites with LAH proceeds in two steps: the reaction step yields nitrous oxide and hydrogen while the hydrolysis step yields ammonia, hydrogen and the parent carbinol. Nitrites produce relatively more nitrous oxide and less ammonia than nitrates (25).

$$RONO_2 \xrightarrow[\text{2. H}_2\text{O}]{\text{1. LAH}} ROH + N_2O + NH_3 + H_2 \qquad (4\text{-}20)$$

$$RONO \xrightarrow[\text{2. H}_2\text{O}]{\text{1. LAH}} ROH + N_2O + NH_3 + H_2 \qquad (4\text{-}21)$$

This reaction has been applied to sugar nitrates (26,27) as well as simpler organic esters (25).

The reductive cleavage of phosphates with LAH is also discussed in Section 9.1.1.a. Among the reduction products are phosphoric acid, phosphine and the parent carbinol (28).

$$R\overset{\displaystyle OH}{\underset{\displaystyle OH}{O\!P}}\!=\!O \xrightarrow[\text{2. H}_2\text{O}]{\text{1. LAH}} ROH + H_3PO_4 + PH_3 \qquad (4\text{-}22)$$

4.3 METAL ALKYLS

The reaction between LAH and metal alkyls has been utilized in the preparation of hitherto unknown or difficultly accessible hydrides.

4.3.1 Beryllium Alkyls

Schlesinger and his co-workers have reported the preparation of beryllium hydride by the treatment of dimethylberyllium with LAH in ether solution (2,3,29,30).

$$(CH_3)_2Be + LiAlH_4 \longrightarrow BeH_2 + LiAlH_3(CH_3) \qquad (4\text{-}23)$$

The hydride cannot be obtained ether-free by this procedure. An attempt to prepare an ether-free product by the reaction of dimethylberyllium with liquid dimethyl aluminum hydride, in the absence of solvents and in iso-pentane solution, according to the equation, failed to produce a product free from methyl groups.

$$(CH_3)_2Be + 2 (CH_3)_2AlH \rightarrow 2 Al(CH_3)_3 + BeH_2 \qquad (4-24)$$

The isolation of solid methyl beryllium hydride (29,31) in an experiment in which an excess of dimethylberyllium was used, indicates the possi-ble existence of an intermediate, reversible reaction represented by the equation

$$(CH_3)_2Be + (CH_3)_2AlH \rightleftharpoons CH_3BeH + Al(CH_3)_3 \qquad (4-25)$$

4.3.2 Magnesium Alkyls

Wiberg and Bauer (21) reported that although the reaction of a Grignard reagent with LAH yields a substituted magnesium aluminum hydride, a dialkylmagnesium does not react with LAH. Schlesinger *et al.* (29,31,32) found that a reaction occurs to yield magnesium hydride but that the purity and possibly the nature of the product depend on the proportions of the reactants, the order of their addition and the concentration of the so-lutions. Addition of an ether solution of diethylmagnesium to a large ex-cess of an ethereal solution of LAH, followed by addition to benzene, results in the deposition of a solid containing ether, whose composition is indicative of either a compound of the formula $HMgAlH_4$ or a mixture of magnesium and aluminum hydrides. If an ether solution of LAH is added to an excess of an ethereal solution of diethylmagnesium, a product is obtained which is contaminated with ether and whose analysis corre-sponds to magnesium hydride of 75% purity (29).

4.3.3 Zinc Alkyls

The addition of dimethylzinc to an ether solution of LAH results in the precipitation of zinc hydride in excellent yield (2,3,14,29,31,33).

$$(CH_3)_2Zn + 2 LiAlH_4 \rightarrow ZnH_2 + 2 LiAlH_3(CH_3) \qquad (4-26)$$

The hydride is also obtained by the reaction of dimethylzinc with di-methyl aluminum hydride (29). Volatile products such as dimethyl alu-minum hydride and methyl zinc hydride are apparently intermediates in the LAH reaction (29,31).

4.3.4 Cadmium Alkyls

While beryllium and zinc hydrides are stable at room temperature, cad-mium hydride undergoes rapid decomposition at about $0°$, necessitating the carrying out of the reaction between dimethylcadmium and LAH in ether solution at $-78.5°$. If the temperature is allowed to rise to $2°$, the hydride decomposes into metallic cadmium and hydrogen (29-31).

$$(CH_3)_2Cd + 2 LiAlH_4 \rightarrow CdH_2 + 2 LiAlH_3(CH_3) \qquad (4-27)$$

4.3.5 Mercury Alkyls

Attempts to prepare a hydride of mercury by the reaction of an alkyl mercury compound and LAH have led, even at $-80°$, to the rapid production of mercury and hydrogen (29,31). The reaction of diphenylmercury in ether with excess LAH results in the immediate separation of mercury and the isolation of benzene (34).

4.3.6 Aluminum Alkyls

The reaction of trimethylaluminum with LAH in a sealed tube at $70°$ yields dimethyl aluminum hydride (2,29,31).

$$(CH_3)_3Al + LiAlH_4 \longrightarrow (CH_3)_2AlH + LiAlH_3(CH_3) \qquad (4-28)$$

Diethyl chloroaluminum, resulting from the interaction of aluminum triethyl and aluminum chloride, reacts with lithium or sodium hydride to form diethyl aluminum hydride (35).

$$2 (C_2H_5)_3Al + AlCl_3 \longrightarrow 3 (C_2H_5)_2AlCl \qquad (4-29)$$

$$(C_2H_5)_2AlCl + LiH \longrightarrow (C_2H_5)_2AlH + LiCl \qquad (4-30)$$

The stepwise addition of ethylene to aluminum hydride also yields the diethyl aluminum hydride (35).

4.3.7 Gallium Alkyls

Dimethyl aluminum hydride is obtained by the reaction of LAH with trimethylgallium (31).

$$(CH_3)_3Ga + LiAlH_4 \longrightarrow (CH_3)_2AlH + LiGaH_3(CH_3) \qquad (4-31)$$

4.3.8 Boron Alkyls

The reaction of trimethylboron with LAH also yields dimethyl aluminum hydride (29,31).

$$(CH_3)_3B + LiAlH_4 \longrightarrow (CH_3)_2AlH + LiBH_3(CH_3) \qquad (4-32)$$

Treatment of dimethylammonium chloride with lithium borohydride yields N,N-dimethylaminoborine (36). The borine derivative reacts with aluminum borohydride to yield a complex mixture of products, including a dimethylaminoboron hydride and some aminoborohydrides of aluminum (A).

$$(CH_3)_2NH_2Cl + LiBH_4 \longrightarrow (CH_3)_2NBH_2 + LiCl + 2 H_2 \quad (4-33)$$

$$(CH_3)_2NBH_2 + Al(BH_4)_3 \longrightarrow (CH_3)_2NB_2H_5 + A \qquad (4-34)$$

The oily liquid aluminum aminoborohydrides (A) are spontaneously inflammable and react with diborane to form the dimethylaminoboron hydride and aluminum borohydride (37).

4.3.9 Lithium Alkyls

The interaction of methyllithium with excess LAH in ether solution yields lithium hydride (29,31).

$$CH_3Li + LiAlH_4 \rightarrow LiH + LiAlH_3(CH_3) \qquad (4\text{-}35)$$

The analogous reaction between ethyllithium and aluminum borohydride yields lithium borohydride (38,39).

$$3 C_2H_5Li + Al(BH_4)_3 \rightarrow 3 LiBH_4 + (C_2H_5)_3Al \qquad (4\text{-}36)$$

The reactions shown in equations (4-23), (4-26), (4-27), (4-28), and (4-35) indicate the formation of a methyl derivative of LAH. Although no evidence for the existence of such a derivative has as yet been published, it has been indicated that such evidence is forthcoming (29). Ziegler (35) has reported that LAH and ethylene readily undergo an addition reaction at a little above $100°$ to give, stepwise, ethylated lithium aluminum hydrides and, finally, as the end product, lithium aluminum tetraethyl.

$$LiAlH_4 + C_2H_4 \rightarrow LiAlH_3(C_2H_5) \rightarrow \ldots \rightarrow LiAl(C_2H_5)_4 \qquad (4\text{-}37)$$

All monosubstituted ethylenes behave in the same manner to yield lithium aluminum tetraalkyls.

REFERENCES

1. Finholt, A. E., A. C. Bond, Jr., K. E. Wilzbach, and H. I. Schlesinger, *J. Am. Chem. Soc.*, 69, 2692 (1947).
2. Schlesinger, H. I., and A. E. Finholt, U.S. Pat. 2,567,972 (September 18, 1951).
3. Schlesinger, H. I., and A. E. Finholt, U.S. Pat. 2,576,311 (November 27, 1951).
4. Eaborn, C., *J. Chem. Soc., 1950,* 3077.
5. English, W. D., A. Taurins, and R. V. V. Nicholls, *Can. J. Chem.,* 30, 646 (1952).
6. Kaplan, L., and K. E. Wilzbach, *J. Am. Chem. Soc.,* 74, 6152 (1952).
7. Cass, R., and G. E. Coates, *J. Chem. Soc., 1952,* 2347.
8. Burg, A. B., and E. S. Kuljian, *J. Am. Chem. Soc.,* 72, 3103 (1950).
9. Johnson, O. H., and D. M. Harris, *J. Am. Chem. Soc.,* 72, 5566 (1950).
10. Johnson, O. H., and W. H. Nebergall, *J. Am. Chem. Soc.,* 71, 1720 (1949).
11. Johnson, O. H., and D. M. Harris, *J. Am. Chem. Soc.,* 72, 5564 (1950).
12. Johnson, O. H., and L. V. Jones, *J. Org. Chem.,* 17, 1172 (1952).
13. West, R., *J. Am. Chem. Soc.,* 74, 4363 (1952).
14. Finholt, A. E., A. C. Bond, Jr., and H. I. Schlesinger, *J. Am. Chem. Soc.,* 69, 1199 (1947).
15. Wittig, G., F. J. Meyer, and G. Lange, *Ann.,* 571, 195 (1951).
16. Walaschewski, E. G., through *European Scientific Notes,* 6, 142 (1952).
17. Horvat, R. J., and A. Furst, *J. Am. Chem. Soc.,* 74, 562 (1952).
18. Weil, T., B. Prijs and H. Erlenmeyer, *Helv. Chim. Acta,* 35, 616 (1952).

19. Freedman, L. D., and G. O. Doak, *J. Am. Chem. Soc.*, 74, 3414 (1952).
20. Coates, G. E., *J. Chem. Soc.*, *1950*, 3481.
21. Wiberg, E., and R. Bauer, *Z. Naturforsch.*, 5b, 397 (1950).
22. Gilman, H., and C. G. Brannen, *J. Am. Chem. Soc.*, 73, 4640 (1951).
23. Warf, J. C., and W. Feitknecht, *Helv. Chim. Acta*, 33, 613 (1950).
24. Schmitz-Dumont, O., and V. Habernickel, *Naturwissenschaften*, 39, 20 (1952).
25. Soffer, L. M., E. W. Parrotta, and J. Di Domenico, *J. Am. Chem. Soc.*, 74, 5301 (1952).
26. Ansell, E. G., J. Honeyman and G. H. Williams, *Chemistry and Industry*, *1952*, 149.
27. Ansell, E. G., and J. Honeyman, *J. Chem. Soc.*, *1952*, 2778.
28. Karrer, P., and E. Jucker, *Helv. Chim. Acta*, 35, 1586 (1952).
29. Barbaras, G. D., C. Dillard, A. E. Finholt, T. Wartik, K. E. Wilzbach, and H. I. Schlesinger, *J. Am. Chem. Soc.*, 73, 4585 (1951).
30. Final Reports to the Navy 1947-1948 on Contract N6 ori-20, Task Order X; through ref. 29.
31. Schlesinger, H. I., and T. Wartik, *Abstracts of Papers*, 115th Meeting American Chemical Society, San Francisco, Calif., March 1949, p. 11 O.
32. Final Reports to the Navy 1946-1947 on Contract NRL No. 3147, p. 8; through ref. 29.
33. Final Reports to the Navy 1945-1946 on Contract No. 173s-10421, p. 8; through ref. 29.
34. Barton, D. H. R., and W. J. Rosenfelder, *J. Chem. Soc.*, *1951*, 2381.
35. Ziegler, K., *Angew. Chem.*, 64, 323 (1952).
36. Schaeffer, G. W., and E. R. Anderson, *J. Am. Chem. Soc.*, 71, 2143 (1949).
37. Burg, A. B., and C. L. Randolph, Jr., *J. Am. Chem. Soc.*, 73, 953 (1951).
38. Schlesinger, H. I., R. T. Sanderson, and A. B. Burg, *J. Am. Chem. Soc.*, 62, 3421 (1940).
39. Schlesinger, H. I., and H. C. Brown, *J. Am. Chem. Soc.*, 62, 3429 (1940).

CHAPTER 5

COMPLEX METAL HYDRIDES AS
ANALYTICAL REAGENTS

The rapidity and quantitative nature of the reactions of LAH with organic compounds, as well as the great variety of functional groups which are reduced by the reagent has prompted expanding application of LAH as an analytical reagent. The absence of the usual side reactions, polymerizations, condensations, or cleavages, as well as the fact that reactions can in most cases be carried out with standard techniques, similar to those used in Grignard reactions, make LAH a valuable addition to the tools of analytical research. The measurement of the hydrogen liberated by the reaction of LAH with compounds containing active hydrogen affords a method of quantitatively carrying out such determinations. Measurement of the amount of reagent consumed permits the determination of reactive functional groups. The keto-enol content of tautomeric substances can be determined in an analogous manner. The appearance of the azo color on the reduction of nitro, nitroso and azoxy compounds with LAH permits the reagent to be used as a qualitative test reagent. The commercial availability of LAH coupled with the continual broadening of application of the reagent, guarantees its place as an analytical tool.

The water solubility of sodium borohydride has permitted its application in the quantitative determination of reactive functional groups of water-soluble, ether-insoluble compounds.

5.1 DETERMINATION OF ACTIVE HYDROGEN
AND FUNCTIONAL GROUPS

5.1.1 Analytical Techniques

The quantitative nature of the reaction of LAH with various types of organic compounds and the similarity of its behavior to that of the Grignard reagent have led to the development of analytical methods similar to the Zerewitinoff procedure. These methods utilize LAH in the quantitative determination of active hydrogen and reducible groups in organic compounds.

The reaction of LAH with compounds containing active hydrogen results in the consumption of one-quarter mole of LAH and the liberation of one mole of hydrogen gas for each atom of active hydrogen present. Analyses are carried out in modifications of the apparatus used for the

Zerewitinoff determination with methylmagnesium iodide. A known amount of material is added to an ether solution of LAH and the liberated gas is measured (1-7). Measurement of the hydrogen evolved on a macro scale is suitable for following the course of an LAH reduction (8). The determination of the concentration of LAH in organic solution, e.g., ether, is carried out in an analogous manner by measuring the hydrogen evolved by the hydrolysis of a known volume of solution (1,4,9-15). By reversing the procedure, the same overall reaction can be used for the determination of water in organic compounds. Treatment of the sample, such as a hydrocarbon, with a 1% solution of LAH in diethylene glycol diethyl ether and measurement of the evolved hydrogen, permits the analysis in concentrations of 0.1% to be performed with a precision of $\pm 0.005\%$ (16). The hydrolysis of an LAH solution can be utilized to determine the extent of reduction by LAH in a reaction mixture (4,14). Determination of the amount of reagent consumed permits the determination of reactive functional groups (2,4,14).

The gasometric method for the microanalytical determination of active hydrogen, and functional groups has been modified so that the end reaction is volumetric. Thus, the hydrogen liberated on treatment of a sample with an n-propyl ether solution of LAH is carried with a stream of nitrogen into a combustion tube, wherein it is heated to $1100°$ over copper oxide. The hydrogen is oxidized to water which reacts with hot carbon to form carbon monoxide. The latter reacts with iodine pentoxide with liberation of iodine, which is oxidized to iodate by bromine in glacial acetic acid, and the iodate is determined by iodometric titration with sodium thiosulfate (7,17,18). A further modification of this procedure calls for trapping the sublimed iodine in a potash tube from which it is washed out and determined volumetrically with thiosulfate (19).

A totally volumetric method involving an electrometric titration has been developed by Higuchi, based on the sharp change in the reduction potential of the system when the last trace of LAH is removed by reaction. A solution of LAH in tetrahydrofuran is added to the sample in the same solvent, and the excess LAH is back titrated potentiometrically with a standard solution of ethanol or propanol in benzene (20,21). Since molecular oxygen reacts rapidly with LAH in solution, all analyses and storage of reagents are carried out under nitrogen (22).

A further advance in volumetric methods has been the application of various N-substituted p-aminoazobenzene derivatives as color indicators in place of the potentiometric end point (23). The indicator with the sharpest end point is N-phenyl-p-aminoazobenzene. The color reaction with the p-aminoazobenzene derivatives has been postulated as proceeding according to the following equations:

yellow

$$(5\text{-}1)$$

red

Although LAH is satisfactory for the titration of very weak acids by the above method, it suffers from the drawback that its strong reducing action results in the reduction of other functional groups. Lithium aluminum amides, prepared by the reaction of LAH in tetrahydrofuran on *n*-butylamine, di-*n*-butylamine, pyrrolidine and piperidine, have been reported to be suitable basic reagents for the titration of alcohols and phenols (24). The mole ratio of LAH and amine is adjusted so that only one hydrogen is displaced from each amine molecule. Replacement of the second hydrogen results in the precipitation of the reaction product, attributed to the formation of polymer structures. The amide formed from LAH and ammonia is unsuitable for use in the titration procedure because of its insolubility in tetrahydrofuran or other ethers, whereas the product derived from aniline darkens on standing. The indicator developed for LAH titrations is satisfactory for the titrations using the lithium aluminum amides. Compounds like acetophenone and benzophenone behave like monobasic acids with excess basic reagent, whereas benzoic acid takes up three equivalents of base per mole.

Analyses of functional groups in aqueous solution by sodium borohydride are carried out by the addition of a standard solution of the borohydride in 0.1 N sodium hydroxide. The pH is reduced to a value of 9–10 during the reduction by the addition of boric acid. After reduction, the solution is acidified to pH 1, the excess borohydride decomposes and the evolved hydrogen is measured (25). The volumetric procedures reported for the analysis of solutions of sodium borohydride are applicable to the analysis of functional groups, by utilizing such procedures for the determination of excess unreacted borohydride.

5.1.2 Scope and Applications

Comparison of the action of LAH with that of the Grignard reagent for the determination of active hydrogen has shown that in most cases the former reagent is superior, proceeding more vigorously and rapidly at a lower temperature, and further toward completion with fewer side reactions and steric influences (1-3). Reactions are carried out at temperatures ranging from 0° to 100° in diethyl ether, di-*n*-propyl ether, di-*n*-butyl ether, or N-ethyl-morpholine. An important factor, in the determinations, is the solubility in the reaction medium of both the starting material and the intermediate products. Hydroquinone, succinic acid, and terephthalic acid are reported to react very slowly and inconclusively with LAH in active hydrogen determinations in ether at 0° due to the formation of insoluble material which inhibits the reaction (1).

Alcohols (1,3,26,27), glycols (1,3), phenols (1,3,5,6,17), acids (1-3,5, 6,17,26), amides (1,3), amines (1,3,6,28,29), and various miscellaneous compounds react with LAH to give results in good agreement with calculated values. Primary amines and unsubstituted amides liberate two hydrogen atoms at 0° (1) or at ordinary temperatures (3) with LAH while the Grignard reagent liberates one hydrogen atom at ordinary temperatures and the second on heating (30). With LAH at 100°, 1-phenyl-2-naphthylamine shows 1.94 active hydrogen atoms per mole of compound while with methylmagnesium iodide only one active hydrogen atom is detected under the same conditions (28). Aniline with LAH at 98° reveals 2.01 active hydrogen atoms while the Grignard reagent indicates 1.52 atoms (2).

An interesting contrast in the behavior of LAH and the Grignard reagent in the determination of active hydrogen in a compound containing a secondary amino group has been reported and indicates the effects of side reactions (31). When the reaction mixture obtained by adding phenylmagnesium bromide to styryl cyanide is hydrolyzed with an ice cold aqueous ammonium chloride solution, a 40% yield of dimeric compound having the proposed structure (I) is obtained. Active hydrogen determina-

$$
\begin{array}{ccc}
\text{H} & \text{H} & \\
C_6H_5C\!-\!\!-\!\!-C\!-\!\!-\!\!-CC_6H_5 \\
| & | & \| \\
 & HCC_6H_5 & \\
 & | & \\
 & CH_2 & \\
 & | & \\
HN\!-\!\!-\!\!-C\!-\!\!-\!\!-N \\
 & | & \\
 & C_6H_5 & \\
\end{array}
$$

I

tions using a 0.5 mole excess of methylmagnesium iodide indicate one active hydrogen per molecule. With a large excess of Grignard reagent, a total of 1.7 active hydrogens per molecule is indicated and at the same time a clear orange solution is formed instead of the white precipitate as in the previous case. This behavior is attributed to the formation of a polymolecular complex in the presence of a large concentration of Grignard reagent. Determinations using LAH show the presence of 1.0 active hydrogens even when a large excess is used.

LAH indicates the presence of two active hydrogen atoms (1,3) in nitrobenzene while the Grignard reagent indicates between 1.0 and 1.9 atoms (32). Nitromethane shows more than two active hydrogens with LAH (1) and less than one with Grignard reagent (33,34). Benzoic acid with LAH at 98° shows 1.02 active hydrogen atoms while methylmagnesium iodide shows 1.17 atoms (2). However, the superiority of the hydride is seen in the measurement of reagent consumed in this case since a quantitative reaction occurs with LAH but not with the Grignard reagent. In a similar manner, treatment of *trans*-2,5-diphenyl-4-carbethoxyoxazoline (II) with LAH indicates that one of the hydrogens of

$$C_6H_5CH\text{---}CHCOOC_2H_5$$

II

the oxazoline nucleus is mobile while reaction with the Grignard reagent in the Zerewitinoff apparatus is negative (35).

The presence of steric hindrance or enolizable groups points up the superiority of LAH in many cases. With methylmagnesium iodide α,α-diphenyl-β-propiolactone (III) (2,36) and methyl α,α-diphenylpropionate (2) are practically inert even on heating, but with LAH at room temperature the theoretical quantity of reducing agent for one ester group is consumed.

$$(C_6H_5)_2C\text{------}C\text{==}O \qquad (C_6H_5)_2CCN \qquad (C_6H_5)_2CCN$$

III   IV   V

Zaugg and Horrom (2) have compared the behavior of a series of nitriles of varying complexity. With diphenylacetonitrile, LAH offers no advantage over the Grignard reagent. Similarly, increasing complexity of substitution of the α-carbon, as in (IV) and (V), does not affect reactivity since both reagents act quantitatively on heating. Substitution of a cyclohexyl for a phenyl group results in hindrance to addition to the nitrile group. Cyclohexylphenylacetonitrile (VI) reacts with both reagents with more difficulty than the diphenyl compound. However, while a 92%

$$C_6H_5CHCN$$
$$|$$
$$C_6H_{11}$$

VI

$$C_6H_5C \overset{CN}{\underset{C_6H_{11}}{\diagdown}} CH_2CH_2N(C_2H_5)_2$$

VII

reaction is obtained with LAH, under the same conditions methylmagnesium iodide gives only a 75% reaction. Further, LAH indicates only half of the amount of active hydrogen, due to enolization, shown by the Grignard reagent. In the case of the more hindered nitrile (VII), practically no reaction of the Grignard reagent is observed even on long heating while heating with LAH produces a satisfactory result. An unexplained significant amount of active hydrogen is indicated with both reagents.

Both reagents behave similarly with diphenylacetamide. The reaction with the amide function is not quantitative and high results are obtained for active hydrogen. The hindered amide derived from VII gives a normal value for active hydrogen with LAH while the Grignard reagent gives a lower value. Although reaction of the amide group with LAH is not quantitative, practically no reaction takes place with methylmagnesium iodide.

The reaction of phenylhydrazine with LAH gives erratic results which average more than three apparent active hydrogen atoms. Partial cleavage of the N-N bond is suggested as responsible for this effect. The determination of moles of LAH consumed in the reduction of an unsaturated compound containing functional groups gives unsatisfactory results in many cases due to the reduction of the unsaturated linkage at the temperatures utilized in the determinations (1).

It has been proposed that in the reduction of the ethyl ester of *erythro*-β-*p*-nitrophenylserine (VIII) LAH reacts first with the oxygenated functions, the hydroxyl and ester groups, and subsequently with nitrogen containing functional groups, the amino and nitro groups (37). This is sur-

$$O_2N \diagup \!\!\!\!\!\bigcirc\!\!\!\!\! \diagup \overset{\textstyle CH-CH-COOC_2H_5}{\underset{\textstyle OH \quad NH_2}{|\qquad |}}$$

VIII

prising in view of the expected greater rapidity of reaction of the groups containing active hydrogen.

The electrometric method described in Section 5.1.1 has been applied by Higuchi to the analysis of essential oils and essential oil isolates, giving experimental values in fair agreement with theory (38). The LAH equivalence has been suggested as an index for purity and identity of volatile oils (38). This method has also been applied to a series of pharmaceutical compounds, including alkaloids, with an average error of less than 2% (39).

The analytical procedure described in Section 5.1.1 has been applied to the estimation of aldoses and ketoses by the reduction of the sugars in aqueous solution with sodium borohydride (25).

In what is not a strictly analytical application, LAH has been utilized in the conversion of various complex molecules to more readily characterized and identified units. Thus, the reaction of a protein with LAH in a suspension of N-ethylmorpholine results in the reduction of the terminal carboxyl groups of primary alcohols. After hydrolysis of the protein and extraction of the amino alcohols, they are identified by paper chromatography. This method permits the characterization of the amino acids situated at the ends of peptide chains and has been utilized to identify glycine and alanine residues in insulin (40-44) and phenylalanine in ovomucoid (42,44). Reduction with lithium borohydride in tetrahydrofuran has also been utilized in the determination of the structural units comprising the insulin molecule (45,46).

Sodium borohydride in aqueous solution has been utilized in an analogous manner in the reduction of "polyaldehydes" resulting from the periodate oxidation of polysaccharides. The "polyalcohols" formed in such reductions are hydrolyzed and the cleavage products separated by partition chromatography and determined quantitatively. The results obtained in this manner provide information concerning the nature and amount of glycosidic linkages in a polysaccharide (47).

5.2 KETO-ENOL TAUTOMERISM

Compounds exhibiting keto-enol tautomerism react with LAH as though they are partially enolized. The rapidity of the reaction with the keto form prevents complete enolization (1,18). This is in marked contrast to the Grignard reagent which indicates the existence of such compounds mostly in the enol form. Thus, ethyl acetoacetate is 50-70% enolized according to its reaction with LAH (1,3,18) and 90-100% according to the Grignard reaction (30,48). Diethyl malonate reacts with the hydride as though it were 50-60% enolized (1,3,18) and with the Grignard reagent as though it existed 100% in the enol form (48).

Höfling, Lieb, and Schöniger (18) have pointed out that the enol content obtained with the use of LAH is in many cases tenfold that obtained by bromination, physicochemical methods, etc. The discrepancy may be partially explained by the enolizing influence of ethereal solvents. Meyer (49-51) has shown that in ether solutions, results indicate a higher enol content than with the pure substance in the absence of solvent, e.g., acetoacetic ester contains 7.4% enol content in the pure state and 50-100% in ethereal solution, as indicated above. A further explanation for the high results with LAH is the possible displacement of the equilibrium by the alcoholate formed by the reaction of LAH with the tautomeric substance (18). It has been shown that solvents play little part in the tautomerism of monosubstituted malonic esters since neither as pure liquids nor in solvents can detectable amounts of enol be determined. However, in the presence of LAH in ethereal solution, the enol content is found to range from 18 to 28% (1,3,18). This is considered as evidence for the enolizing influence of the hydride (18).

Höfling and his co-workers have reported that while the same LAH solution can be used for a series of analyses in the determination of active hydrogen with non-enolizing substances, this is not possible for the examination of tautomeric compounds since in these cases high results are obtained. Reproducible results are obtained only when a fresh LAH solution is used for each analysis (18).

Application of LAH analysis to 3,5-dicarbethoxy-4-methylcyclopentan-1,2-dione (IX) indicates reaction in the dienol form (52). However, the

$$
\begin{array}{c}
O\!=\!C \!-\!\!-\! C\!=\!O \\
\quad| \qquad\quad | \\
C_2H_5OCOCH \quad CHCOOC_2H_5 \\
\diagdown \;\; \diagup \\
CH \\
| \\
CH_3 \\
IX
\end{array}
$$

enolizing influence of the reagent must be taken into consideration in interpreting such results.

Due to the difference in reactivity of LAH and the Grignard reagent, both reagents can be profitably used in the analysis of compounds of unknown structure. The influence of steric factors plays an important part in these determinations. Thus, acetomesitylene is approximately 80% enolized according to the Zerewitnoff procedure (53) but only 1 to 3% enol content is shown with LAH (3). Ethyl diphenylacetate (X) and 3,3-diphenylbutan-2-one (XI) both react completely on heating with the Grignard reagent but with 22% and 28% enolization, respectively. The hy-

$$(C_6H_5)_2CHCOOC_2H_5 \qquad\qquad (C_6H_5)_2CCOCH_3$$
$$\qquad\qquad\qquad\qquad\qquad\qquad\qquad | $$
$$\qquad\qquad\qquad\qquad\qquad\qquad\qquad CH_3$$

$$\qquad\quad X \qquad\qquad\qquad\qquad\qquad\qquad\quad XI$$

dride produces complete reduction at room temperature without hydrogen evolution (2).

The alcoholate formed by the reaction of LAH with an enol, regenerates the original enol upon hydrolysis. In the reduction of α-angelica lactone the intermediate enolate on hydrolysis reverts to the ketonic form to yield pentan-4-on-1-ol (3).

5.3   LAH AS A QUALITATIVE TEST REAGENT

In one of their first papers on the reduction of organic compounds by LAH, Nystrom and Brown (54) stated that "the immediate appearance of the azo color upon adding an aromatic nitro compound to LAH at room temperature constitutes a simple and sensitive test for the nitro group." This suggestive statement has been developed into a color test applicable to the detection of aromatic nitro, nitroso, azoxy and hydrazo compounds.   The test is carried out in diethyl ether (55–57) or ethylene glycol diethyl ether (56) and is based on a change in the color of the solution or the formation of a colored precipitate.   Aliphatic nitro compounds, nitrates and nitriles do not interfere.   Phenylacetonitrile (55) is reported to give a false positive test while 2-chloro-5-nitrobenzenesulfonic acid in ether (55) as well as potassium 2,4-dinitrobenzenesulfonate in ethylene glycol diethyl ether (56) fail to give positive tests.   The failure of the latter is probably due to its insolubility, since 2,4-dinitrobenzenesulfonic acid and the lithium salt give positive tests.   The potassium salt gives a positive test if the reaction time is extended to two hours (56).

REFERENCES

1. Krynitsky, J. A., J. E. Johnson, and H. W. Carhart, *J. Am. Chem. Soc.*, 70, 486 (1948).
2. Zaugg, H. E., and B. W. Horrom, *Anal. Chem.*, 20, 1026 (1948).
3. Hochstein, F. A., *J. Am. Chem. Soc.*, 71, 305 (1949).
4. Orchin, M., and I. Wender, *Anal. Chem.*, 21, 875 (1949).
5. Lieb, H., and W. Schöniger, *Mikrochemie ver. Mikrochim. Acta*, 35, 400 (1950).
6. Lieb, H., and W. Schöniger, *Österr. Chem. Ztg.*, 51, 107 (1950).
7. Lévy, R., *Bull. soc. chim. France*, [5] 19, 685 (1952).
8. Nelson, L. S., D. E. Laskowski and H. A. Porte, *J. Chem. Education*, 28, 648 (1951).
9. Finholt, A. E., A. C. Bond, Jr., and H. I. Schlesinger, *J. Am. Chem. Soc.*, 69, 1199 (1947).
10. Schlesinger, H. I., and A. E. Finholt, U.S. Pat. 2,567,972 (September 18, 1951).
11. Schlesinger, H. I., and A. E. Finholt, U.S. Pat. 2,576,311 (November 27, 1951).
12. Mahé, J., J. Rollet, and A. Willemart, *Bull. soc. chim. France*, [5] 16, 481 (1949).
13. Rosenmund, K. W., and F. Zymalkowski, *Chem. Ber.*, 85, 152 (1952).
14. Felkin, H., *Bull. soc. chim. France*, [5] 18, 347 (1951).
15. Davis, W. D., L. S. Mason, and G. Stegeman, *J. Am. Chem. Soc.*, 71, 2775 (1949).
16. Baker, B. B., Jr., and W. M. MacNevin, *Anal. Chem.*, 22, 364 (1950).
17. Schöniger, W., *Z. anal. Chem.*, 133, 4 (1951).
18. Höfling, E., H. Lieb, and W. Schöniger, *Monatsh.*, 83, 60 (1952).
19. Lieb, H., and W. Schöniger, *Abstracts of Papers*, XIIth International Congress of Pure and Applied Chemistry, September, 1951, New York, N.Y., p. 41.

20. Higuchi, T., C. J. Lintner, and R. H. Schleif, *Science*, *111*, 63 (1950).
21. Lintner, C. J., R. H. Schleif, and T. Higuchi, *Anal. Chem.*, *22*, 534 (1950).
22. Higuchi, T., *Anal. Chem.*, *22*, 955 (1950).
23. Higuchi, T., and D. A. Zuck, *J. Am. Chem. Soc.*, *73*, 2676 (1951).
24. Higuchi, T., J. Concha, and R. Kuramoto, *Anal. Chem.*, *24*, 685 (1952).
25. Lindberg, B., and A. Misiorny, *Svensk Paperstidn.*, *55*, 13 (1952); *Chem. Abstracts*, *46*, 7942 (1952).
26. Nunn, J. R., *J. Chem. Soc.*, *1952*, 313.
27. Moulin, F., *Helv. Chim. Acta*, *35*, 167 (1952).
28. Zaugg, H. E., M. Freifelder, and B. W. Horrom, *J. Org. Chem.*, *15*, 1197 (1950).
29. Snyder, H. R., E. L. Eliel, and R. E. Carnahan, *J. Am. Chem. Soc.*, *73*, 970 (1951).
30. Zerewitinoff, T., *Ber.*, *41*, 2233 (1908).
31. Piper, D. E., and G. F. Wright, *J. Am. Chem. Soc.*, *72*, 1669 (1950).
32. Gilman, H., and R. E. Fothergill, *J. Am. Chem. Soc.*, *49*, 2815 (1927).
33. Cuisa, R., *Gazz. chim. ital.*, *50*, II, 53 (1920).
34. Zerewitinoff, T., *Ber.*, *43*, 3590 (1910).
35. Elphimoff-Felkin, I., H. Felkin, B. Tchoubar, and Z. Welvart, *Bull. soc. chim. France*, [5] *19*, 252 (1952).
36. Zaugg, H. E., *J. Am. Chem. Soc.*, *72*, 2998 (1950).
37. Carrara, G., E. Pace, and G. Cristiani, *J. Am. Chem. Soc.*, *74*, 4949 (1952).
38. Lintner, C. J., J. V. Swintosky, D. A. Zuck, and T. Higuchi, *J. Am. Pharm. Assoc., Sci. Ed.*, *39*, 415 (1950).
39. Lintner, C. J., D. A. Zuck, and T. Higuchi, *J. Am. Pharm. Assoc., Sci. Ed.*, *39*, 418 (1950).
40. Fromageot, C., M. Jutisz, D. Meyer, and L. Pénasse, *Biochim. et Biophys. Acta*, *6*, 283 (1950).
41. Fromageot, C., M. Jutisz, D. Meyer, and L. Pénasse, *Compt. rend.*, *230*, 1905 (1950).
42. Jutisz, M., *Bull. soc. chim. France*, [5] *19*, 821 (1952).
43. Jolles, P., and C. Fromageot, *Biochim. et Biophys. Acta*, *9*, 416 (1952).
44. Pénasse, L., M. Jutisz, C. Fromageot, and H. Fraenkel-Conrat, *Biochim. et Biophys. Acta*, *9*, 551 (1952).
45. Chibnall, A. C., and M. W. Rees, *Biochim. J.*, *48*, xlvii (1951).
46. Chibnall, A. C., and M. W. Rees, *Biochim. J.*, *52*, iii (1952).
47. Abdel-Akher, M., J. K. Hamilton, R. Montgomery, and F. Smith, *J. Am. Chem. Soc.*, *74*, 4970 (1952).
48. Fuchs, W., N. H. Ishler, and A. G. Sandhoff, *Ind. Eng. Chem., Anal. Ed.*, *12*, 507 (1940).
49. Meyer, K. H., *Ann.*, *380*, 212 (1911).
50. Meyer, K. H., *Ber.*, *45*, 2843 (1912).
51. Meyer, K. H., *Ber.*, *47*, 826 (1914).
52. Höfling, E., and W. Schöniger, through F. Petuely and V. Künssberg, *Monatsh.*, *83*, 86 (1952).
53. Kohler, E. P., J. F. Stone, Jr., and R. C. Fuson, *J. Am. Chem. Soc.*, *49*, 3181 (1927).
54. Nystrom, R. F., and W. G. Brown, *J. Am. Chem. Soc.*, *70*, 3738 (1948).
55. Nelson, L. S., and D. E. Laskowski, *Anal. Chem.*, *23*, 1495,1776 (1951).
56. Gilman, H., and T. N. Goreau, *J. Am. Chem. Soc.*, *73*, 2939 (1951).
57. McElvain, S. M., *The Characterization of Organic Compounds*, MacMillan Co., New York, 1953, p. 144.

CHAPTER 6

REDUCTION OF
ORGANIC COMPOUNDS WITH COMPLEX METAL HYDRIDES
GENERAL

The greatest interest in the complex metal hydrides in general, and in LAH in particular, has been in the reduction of organic compounds. The general behavior of the hydrides in such reductions, including the types of functional groups generally attacked as well as some of the proposed reaction mechanisms, are surveyed in this section. A detailed discussion of the reduction of the various types of functional groups as well as the experimental conditions utilized in such reductions are given in succeeding sections. Lithium aluminum hydride has been utilized in the reduction of organic compounds to a greater extent than any other complex metal hydride. Sodium, potassium and lithium borohydrides have also found considerable application, especially when selective reduction is desired. The other complex metal hydrides discussed in this and succeeding sections have had only limited investigation.

6.1 REDUCTIONS WITH LITHIUM ALUMINUM HYDRIDE

LAH has been applied with considerable success to the reduction of various functional groups which have resisted other methods of reduction. By its use, the side reactions such as polymerization, condensation and cleavage often encountered with other reducing agents are avoided. The reactions are rapid and almost quantitative in many cases and yield products of a high degree of purity.

6.1.1 General Mechanisms and Stereochemistry

Gibb (1) has indicated that LAH is a highly ionized addition or coordination compound of aluminum hydride with LAH. Wiberg (2) has suggested that the ether-soluble LAH can be represented by a resonance bridge structure and that the complex hydride can be considered as $LiH \cdot AlH_3$

$$Li \overset{H}{\underset{H}{\cdots}} Al \overset{H}{\underset{H}{\diagup}}$$

Brown (3) has stated that there is no conclusive evidence that intensively dried LAH is not a mixture of lithium hydride and aluminum hydride from which LAH slowly reforms when the material is suspended in ether. Reductions with LAH are generally carried out in diethyl ether solution although other ether-type solvents such as tetrahydrofuran, di-*n*-butyl ether, and dioxane have been employed. It has been postulated that an ethereal solution of LAH consists of lithium ions and aluminohydride anions (AlH_4^-). Infrared and Raman spectra of an ethereal LAH solution have indicated a tetrahedral model for the aluminohydride ion in solution (4). Paddock (5) has proved the presence of ions in the ethereal solution by measurements of the specific conductivity. A value of 4.43×10^{-5} ohm^{-1} cm^{-1} at $15°$ for a molar solution of LAH compares with a value of 6.14×10^{-5} ohm^{-1} cm^{-1} at $20°$ for the specific conductivity of a molar solution of ethylmagnesium bromide.

Trevoy and Brown (6) have observed that most LAH reductions involve the displacement of a strongly electronegative atom, such as oxygen, nitrogen, or halogen, by hydrogen, the reaction probably involving initially an attack of the aluminohydride ion on carbon. A bimolecular nucleophilic displacement proceeding by an S_N^2 mechanism in which hydrogen is transferred as hydride to the center of low electron density, i.e., the carbon atom, has been postulated. The exact nature of the attacking anion is a matter of speculation. Trevoy and Brown have postulated that the reactant is actually a series of complex aluminohydride ions $AlH_{4-n}R_n^-$ which act as carriers for the hydride ion where n progresses from 0 to 4 during the course of a reaction. This mechanism is illustrated with reference to the reduction of an epoxide:

$$AlH_4^{\ominus} + \begin{array}{c} \diagup\,C\diagdown \\ \big| \quad O \\ \diagup\,C\diagdown \end{array} \rightarrow AlH_3 + \begin{array}{c} \diagup\,C\!-\!O^{\ominus} \\ \big| \\ HC \diagup\diagdown \end{array} \qquad (6\text{-}1)$$

The neutral aluminum hydride immediately coordinates with the alkoxide anion forming AlH_3OR^- which is successively converted through the series $AlH_2(OR)_2^-$, $AlH(OR)_3^-$, and $Al(OR)_4^-$.

In support of this mechanism, it has been found that inversion of configuration occurs on the carbon atom attacked in the LAH reduction of epoxides. Thus, 1,2-dimethyl-1,2-epoxycyclopentane and 1,2-dimethyl-1,2-epoxycyclohexane which possess the *cis* configuration are reduced to the *trans* cyclanols. Mousseron and his co-workers (7) have similarly reported inversions in the reduction of substituted epoxycyclohexanes.

As further evidence for the mechanism, Trevoy and Brown (6) have observed that styrene oxide and 3,4-epoxy-1-butene are attacked by LAH preferentially at the terminal carbon atom to yield the corresponding secondary alcohols, although some primary alcohol is also formed in the latter case. The reactions of malonic and acetoacetic esters with epoxides have been shown to proceed by a bimolecular displacement reaction. Since the direction of ring opening in styrene oxide and 3,4-epoxy-1-

butene with these reagents is the same as with LAH, the postulation of an analogous mechanism with the latter appears valid. Adams and Vander Werf (8) have pointed out further that the attack on the primary carbon indicates that the participating ions in an LAH reduction are comparable in size to the acetoacetic ester anion. This has been pointed out clearly in an investigation of concentration effects in the LAH reduction of 3,4-epoxy-1-butene (9). Although, electronically, the complex alkoxide ions postulated in the mechanism of Trevoy and Brown are quite similar, steric requirements increase markedly with the number of coordinated alkoxide ions. Fuchs and Vander Werf (9) have observed that an increase in the LAH/epoxide ratio with its resultant increase in the AlH_4^- concentration results in an increase in the secondary attack to yield the primary alcohol. Further, on partial hydrolysis of the LAH with methyl isobutyl carbinol prior to the epoxide reduction, the presence of AlH_3OR^- as the predominant ionic species decreases the percentage of secondary attack. These results are considered consistent with the postulated mechanism.

Bothner-By (10) has applied the principle of partial reaction to the preparation of optically active alcohols. The partial reaction of LAH with d-camphor yields a species of forms $AlH_{4-n}(OR)_n$, where $-OR$ represents the alkoxy group derived from the ketone, which is capable of the asymmetric reduction of ketones. Thus, the addition of methyl ethyl ketone or pinacolone to the complex formed by the partial reaction of LAH and d-camphor yields, after hydrolysis, the optically active 2-butanol and pinacolyl alcohol, respectively, accompanied by d-isoborneol.

Noyce and Denney (11) have investigated the steric requirements of the LAH reduction of various ketones. Although the bimolecular inversion mechanism would indicate that the addition of hydrogen to a carbonyl group should occur from the side opposite a hindering group to give a product with the hydroxyl group in the cis position, it has been found in a series of methylcyclohexanones that the proportion of cis epimer is not as great as in the reduction with aluminum isopropoxide, probably due to the smaller steric requirements of the reducing step of the reaction. Even in the case of l-menthone, the steric effects are not sufficient to produce a large amount of cis product, whereas both catalytic hydrogenation and reduction with aluminum isopropoxide afford a marked preponderance of cis isomer. When steric hindrance is sufficiently great, as in the reduction of d-camphor, clear predominance of the addition of hydrogen from the unhindered side occurs to yield 90% of the cis form, isoborneol, and 10% of borneol. Trevoy and Brown (6) have carried out the LAH reduction of d-camphor and a number of 1,2-diketones and in all cases have obtained mixtures of the various possible stereoisomers.

Additional evidence for the bimolecular nature of LAH reductions has been obtained in the reduction of various halides (6,12). Primary aliphatic halides react more readily than secondary halides which are more reactive than tertiary halides. Bromides are more reactive than chlorides. Eliel (13) has found that the reduction of optically active α-chloroethyl-benzene proceeds with Walden inversion to yield optically active ethyl-benzene. Eliel and Freeman (14) have postulated an internal displace-ment reaction with inversion in the LAH reduction of optically active 2-chloro-2-phenylpropionic acid and its methyl ester. Mousseron *et al.* (7) have reported the occurrence of inversion in the reduction of chloro-epoxycyclohexanes. However, an asymmetric center adjacent to a re-ducible group is unaffected by reduction (11).

The reduction of the tosylates of various stereoisomeric phenylbutanols to yield phenylbutanes of almost the same rotation, is considered indica-tive that the reaction is that of simple nucleophilic displacement of the *p*-tosylate group by AlH_4^- ion (15).

Paddock (5) has argued that the mechanism of Trevoy and Brown ig-nores the solvent, and has proposed that there is an equilibrium in solution:

$$AlH_4^{\ominus} \rightleftharpoons H^{\ominus} + AlH_3 \qquad (6\text{-}2)$$

The function of the ether is to coordinate with the aluminum hydride and drive the equilibrium to the right. This implies that the active entity is the H^- ion rather than the aluminohydride ion (5,16). Paddock has stated that this has been substantiated by conductometric titrations with hydro-gen chloride and methyl chloride and by the study of precipitation reac-tions with tertiary amines (16). This mechanism has been utilized to ex-plain various hydrogenolysis reactions occurring under the influence of LAH (17). Lavie and Bergmann (18) have proposed that in the reduction of various polar carbon-carbon double bonds the reducing agent is, in ef-fect, lithium hydride Li^+H^-.

Nystrom and Brown (19) have advanced the following general equation for the LAH reduction of esters:

$$2\,RCOOR' + LiAlH_4 \rightarrow LiAl(OR')_2(OCH_2R)_2 \xrightarrow{H_2O} R'OH + RCH_2OH$$
$$(6\text{-}3)$$

Mousseron *et al.* (7) have postulated that in the LAH reduction of amides to amines and of esters to primary alcohols, the active entity is the AlH_2^+ ion. In the latter case:

$$2\,R-\underset{\underset{O}{\|}}{C}-OR' \xrightarrow{AlH_2^{\oplus}LiH_2^{\ominus}} \begin{bmatrix} RCH-OR' \\ | \quad\quad | \\ O-Al-O \\ | \quad\quad | \\ R'O-CHR \end{bmatrix}^{\oplus} LiH_2^{\ominus} \xrightarrow{H_2O}$$

$$2\,RCH_2OH \quad (6\text{-}4)$$

$$I$$

Conover and Tarbell (2) have invoked the AlH_2^+ ion to account for the hydrogenolysis of o- and p-amino substituted aromatic acids and carbonyl compounds.

Although the mechanism of Trevoy and Brown indicates, especially in the case of epoxides, that the AlH_3 formed by the initial bimolecular displacement reaction coordinates with available anions and continues the sequence of displacement reactions, Johnson, Blizzard and Carhart (21) have reported that in the reduction of various alkyl halides not all of the four hydrogen atoms in LAH show the same reactivity. The reaction is postulated as proceeding in at least two steps where the first is presumed to be much more rapid than the second.

$$LiAlH_4 + RX \rightarrow RH + LiX + AlH_3 \tag{6-5}$$

$$AlH_3 + 3\,RX \rightarrow AlX_3 + 3\,RH \tag{6-6}$$

Although lithium hydride does not reduce alkyl halides, in the presence of a small amount of LAH hydrogenolysis proceeds rapidly and to completion, the LAH apparently acting as a hydrogen carrier.

Bordwell and McKellin (22) have proposed that the reduction of organic sulfur compounds can be formulated as being initiated by the nucleophilic attack of the aluminohydride ion on sulfur. Thus, the reduction of disulfides, sulfenyl chlorides, sulfenyl thiocyanates, sulfinic acids, sulfoxides, sulfonyl chlorides, aryl sulfonates, thiosulfonates, and sulfones may be represented as the displacement of chlorine, oxygen, or sulfur by the attack of the aluminohydride ions on sulfur. An alternative representation involves attack on chlorine or oxygen.

Carbon-carbon double bonds are normally not attacked by LAH. However, the reduction of such bonds in cinnamyl alcohol has been formulated as proceeding through an intermediate cyclic organometallic complex (II) in which the aluminum is bound, with a coordination number of four, to two carbon atoms and two oxygen atoms (23).

II   III

A similar intermediate (III) has been proposed in the reduction of the triple bond to the double bond (24). In either case, on hydrolysis, the aluminum atom is replaced by hydrogen supplied by the hydrolyzing agent.

The fact that the complex (II) does not react with carbon dioxide has led to the postulation of the carbon-aluminum bond rather than a carbon-lithium bond.   However, in the reduction of the polar double bond in the dibenzofulvenes, Lavie and Bergmann (18) have proposed that the primary attack involves the attachment of H^- on the positive pole of the double bond while the lithium cation adds to the C_9 atom of the fluorenic system which represents the negative pole of the double bond.   The color observed in the course of the reduction as well as the addition of benzyl chloride to the complex is considered indicative of a carbon-lithium bond rather than a carbon-aluminum bond.

Ziegler (25) has shown that the double bond in ethylene and α-olefins can be reduced with LAH, the addition reaction proceeding stepwise with the formation of carbon-aluminum bonds.

$$\text{Li}\left[\begin{matrix}H\\H\end{matrix}\!\!>\!\!\text{Al}\!\!<\!\!\begin{matrix}H\\H\end{matrix}\right] + 4\ CH_2\!=\!\!=\!\!CH_2 \rightarrow \text{Li}\left[\begin{matrix}CH_3CH_2\\CH_3CH_2\end{matrix}\!\!>\!\!\text{Al}\!\!<\!\!\begin{matrix}CH_2CH_3\\CH_2CH_3\end{matrix}\right] \qquad (6\text{-}7)$$

$$\text{IV}$$

6.1.2   Analogy with the Grignard Reagent

The reactions of LAH with various functional groups are in many ways analogous to the reactions of the Grignard reagent.   Differences in the nature and extent of the reactions are due to the greater reactivity of the hydride and the influence of steric factors.   The hydride and the Grignard reagent both respond to the Gilman-Schulze color test.   This test, involving reaction with Michler's ketone, is characteristic for compounds having carbon-metal bonds (26).   The test has been used in determining the stoichiometry of reactions with LAH.

Paddock (5) has indicated that the analogy with the Grignard reagent extends to the necessity for a donor solvent.   No reduction occurs on treatment of phosphorous, boron and silicon halides with LAH in the absence of ether.   The addition of ether results in successful reduction. On the other hand, acetone and benzonitrile, both possessing donor properties, are reduced without the addition of ether.

The sometimes direct analogy between LAH and organomagnesium reactions is clearly illustrated in the case of ether cleavage.   Generally, ethers are stable at ordinary temperatures in the presence of the Grignard reagent.   However, in the presence of cobalt chloride various ethers are cleaved by the Grignard reagent (27).   Similarly, phenyl benzyl ether and phenyl allyl ether which are not cleaved by LAH even at their boiling points, are cleaved to phenol in the presence of cobalt chloride (28).

Additional analogies are found in the fact that both organomagnesium reagents and LAH react with the quaternary salts of cyclic bases to give N-alkyl o-dihydro derivatives (29).   Further, p-toluenesulfonic esters react with Grignard reagents to give principally hydrocarbons (30).   The reaction between alkyl tosylates and LAH yields the corresponding hydrocarbon (31). Karrer (32) pointed out the similarity between many reactions of LAH and those of organomagnesium compounds while commemorating the fiftieth anniversary of the work of Victor Grignard.

6.1.3   1,2-Addition versus 1,4- and 1,6-Addition

Although LAH reductions generally proceed with a 1,2-addition of the reagent, the reduction of α,β-unsaturated ketones such as the dibenzoylethylenes proceeds with 1,4-addition to the conjugated unsaturated system (33,34). While the Grignard reaction similarly involves 1,4-addition, reduction by aluminum isopropoxide proceeds with 1,2-addition (35). The LAH reduction of 1,4-naphthaquinone yields, among other products, 1,2,3,4-tetrahydro-4-hydroxy-1-ketonaphthalene, apparently involving 1,4-addition (36).

The reduction of tropolone with LAH to cyclohept-4-ene-1,2-dione has been postulated as proceeding by 1,4- or 1,6-addition of LAH to the dienone system (37). An initial 1,6-addition has been proposed in the LAH reduction of benzhydrylidene-anthrone to sym-tetraphenyl-bis-(9,10-dihydro-9-anthryl)ethane (38). The Grignard reaction with methylene anthrone also proceeds with 1,6-addition (39).

6.1.4   LAH as a Base

The reactions of LAH have in some cases been related to its behavior as a strong base, whereas in others involving Wagner-Meerwein rearrangements its behavior has been characteristic of a Lewis acid. The action of LAH on thiobenzamide yields benzonitrile as the major product at low temperatures (40). This behavior is analogous to that exhibited with sodium alkoxide. The LAH reduction of N-α-naphthoyl-N-methylfluorenylamine (V) in ether yields the tertiary amine (VI). When the reduction is carried out in tetrahydrofuran or when VI is treated with LAH in tetrahydrofuran the secondary amine (VII) is formed.

(6-8)

LAH-Et₂O

CH₃NCH₂-Nap

VI

LAH-THF

CH₃NCO-Nap

V

LAH-THF

(6-9)

CH₃NH   CH₂-Nap

Nap = α-naphthyl

VII

The formation of VII directly from V apparently proceeds through the initial formation of the tertiary amine which then undergoes rearrangement. A similar rearrangement occurs in the reduction of the β-naphthoyl analog (41). The LAH appears to act here as a strong base, analogous to phenyllithium or sodium alcoholate since the latter reagents cause rearrangements in the quaternary base (VIII) and the ether (IX).

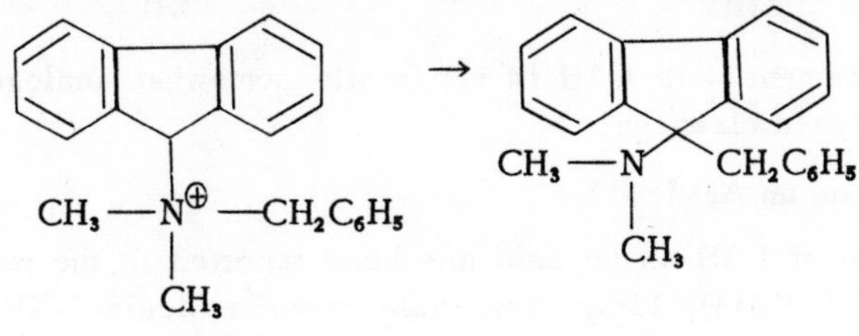

$$CH_3 - \overset{\oplus}{N} - CH_2C_6H_5 \qquad (6\text{-}10)$$

VIII

$$OCH_2C_6H_5 \qquad (6\text{-}11)$$

IX

Treatment of the piperidide (X) with LAH in ether solution has been reported to yield the expected piperidine (XI) accompanied by 1,1-diphenyl-3-dimethylamino-1-propanol (XII) and piperidine (42).

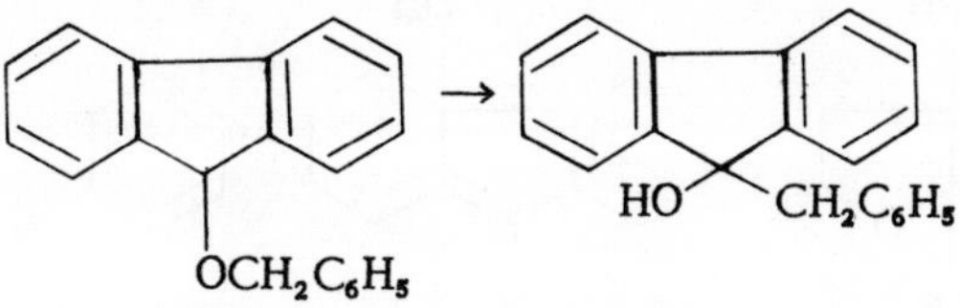

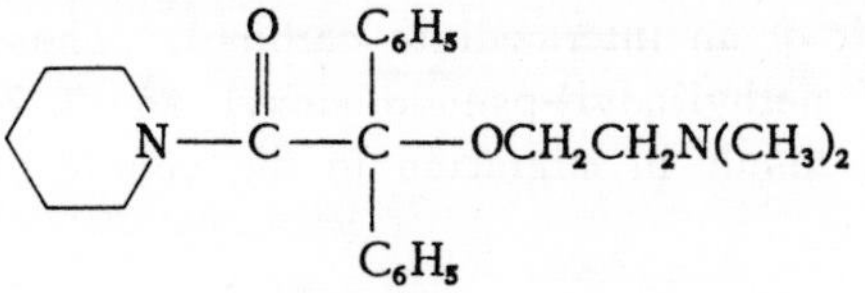

X

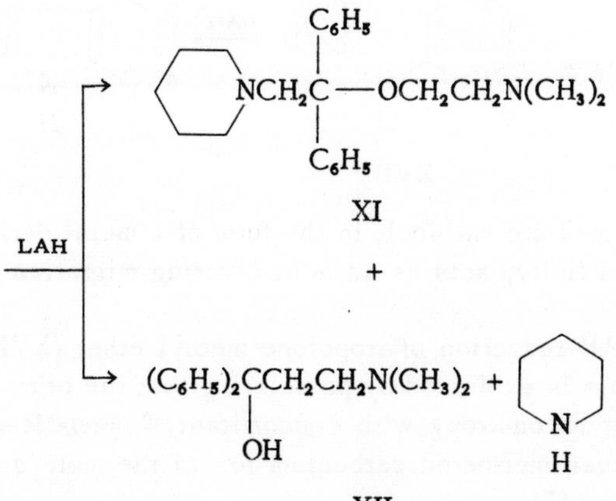

XI

+

$$(6\text{-}12)$$

$$(C_6H_5)_2CCH_2CH_2N(CH_3)_2 \;+\; $$
$$\qquad\quad OH$$

XII

Heating (2-dimethylaminoethoxy)diphenylmethane (XIII) in benzene with powdered sodium also yields XII.

$$(C_6H_5)_2CH—O—CH_2CH_2N(CH_3)_2 \xrightarrow{Na} (C_6H_5)_2\underset{\underset{OH}{|}}{C}CH_2CH_2N(CH_3)_2 \qquad (6\text{-}13)$$

XIII   XII

The rearrangement with LAH is apparently somewhat analogous to the sodium catalyzed cleavage.

6.1.5 LAH as an Acid

The action of LAH as an acid has been reported in the reduction of quinamine (XIV) (43), 11-hydroxytetrahydrocarbazolenine (XV) (44) and 2-phenyl-3-methyl-3-hydroperoxyindolenine (XVI) (45).

XIV   XV   XVI

In each case, after the initial reaction, the resultant intermediate tertiary alcohol splits out the elements of water to form the oxygen free heterocyclic nucleus. In a more striking case, LAH acts as the rearranging agent in the Wagner-Meerwein shift of an intermediate carbinol. Thus, the reactions of 2-methyl-2,3′-(2′-methylindyl)-pseudoindoxyl and 2,2-bis-(3′-indyl)-pseudoindoxyl (XVII) result in migration in the course of the reduction (46).

XVII

The intermediate carbinol, in the form of a metal derivative, owing to its electron affinity, acts as an acid favoring migration as well as the loss of water.

The LAH reduction of tropolone methyl ether (XVIII) yields benzaldehyde. This is explained by postulating that the primary reduction product undergoes anionotropy with concomitant Wagner-Meerwein rearrangement of the seven membered carbonium ion to the more stable benzenoid carbonium ion (37).

(6-15)

The LAH reduction of phenylpropargyl aldehyde yields cinnamyl alco-hol. The same product has been isolated in the reduction of the cyclic trimer (47). Here possibly the hydride acts as an acid in the depolymeri-zation of the acid-sensitive cyclic acetal.

6.1.6 Functional Groups Reduced

Successful reductions under the influence of LAH have been reported with many types of organic compounds and functional groups. Although in most cases the reactions proceed without complication, in a limited number of compounds the nature of the reduction product is a function of the quantity of LAH utilized and the reaction conditions. In other com-pounds, groups which are reduced either slowly or not at all under normal conditions are attacked under more drastic conditions, while in some cases the reduction of a functional group, such as a double or triple bond, is dependent upon the presence of an additional particular group in the same compound, such as in the reduction of cinnamaldehyde.

The types of functional groups which are reduced under normal condi-tions, i.e., utilizing a slight excess of LAH in refluxing ether, are out-lined in Table II. Reduction products obtained with calculated quantities of LAH and variations in the reaction temperature are also indicated. Hydrogenolysis reactions occurring under drastic conditions as well as reactions which are not normal for the isolated functional group are not included in this tabulation but are considered in the detailed tabulations and discussions of succeeding sections.

In all tables in succeeding sections relating to the reduction of organic compounds with LAH, diethyl ether is the reaction medium unless indica-tions to the contrary are made in the footnotes to the individual tables.

6.2   REDUCTIONS WITH ALUMINUM HYDRIDE

Although aluminum hydride in ether solution is an extremely strong re-ducing agent, it is not convenient to use for such purposes due to its in-stability. Treatment of aluminum chloride in ether solution with LAH

TABLE II
Functional Groups Reduced by Lithium Aluminum Hydride

Functional Group		Product	
Oxygen-Containing Groups			
Aldehyde	$RCHO$	Primary alcohol	RCH_2OH
Ketone	$R_2C{=}O$	Secondary alcohol	R_2CHOH
Quinone	$O{=}\bigcirc{=}O$	Hydroquinone	$HO-\bigcirc-OH$
Carboxylic acid	$RCOOH$	Primary alcohol	RCH_2OH
Acid anhydride	$(RCO)_2O$	Primary alcohol	RCH_2OH
Acyl halide	$RCOX$	Primary alcohol	RCH_2OH
Ester	$RCOOR'$	Primary alcohols	$RCH_2OH + R'OH$
Lactone	$\overline{\lceil-COO\rceil}$ / $\lfloor-R\rfloor$	Diol	$HOCH_2ROH$
Epoxide	$R_2C{-}CR_2$ / $\backslash O /$	Alcohol	R_2CHCR_2 / $\vert$ / OH
Orthoester	$R(OR')_3$	Acetal	$R(OR')_2$
Hydroperoxide	$ROOH$	Alcohol	ROH
Peroxide	$ROOR$	Alcohol	ROH
Ozonide	$R_2C{-}O{-}CR_2$ / $O{-}O$	Alcohol	R_2CHOH
Sulfur-Containing Groups			
Dithiol	$R_2C(SH)_2$	Mercaptan	R_2CHSH
Disulfide	$RSSR$	Mercaptan	RSH
Trisulfide	$RSSSR$ $\overset{S}{\uparrow}$	Mercaptan	RSH
Tetrasulfide	$RSSSR$	Mercaptan	RSH
Episulfide	$R_2C{-}CR_2$ / $\backslash S /$	Mercaptan	R_2CCHR_2 / $\vert$ / SH
Sulfoxide	$\overset{O}{\underset{\uparrow}{RSR}}$	Sulfide	RSR
Sulfone	RSO_2R	Sulfide	RSR
Sulfonic anhydride	$(RSO_2)_2O$	Sulfinic acid / Mercaptan	RSO_2H / RSH
Sulfonyl halide	RSO_2X	Mercaptan	RSH
Sulfonic ester			
alkyl	$ROSO_2R$	Hydrocarbon	RH
aryl	$ArOSO_2R$	Phenol	$ArOH$
Sulfinic acid	RSO_2H	Disulfide + Mercaptan	$RSSR + RSH$

TABLE II (*Continued*) 97

Functional Group		Product	
Sulfur-Containing Groups (Continued)			
Sulfenyl halide	RSX	Disulfide	RSSR
Thioester	RCOSR	Alcohol	RCH_2OH
Thioamide	$RCSNH_2$	Amine + Nitrile	RCH_2NH_2 + RCN
Thiocyanate	RSCN	Mercaptan	RSH
Isothiocyanate	RNCS	Amine	$RNHCH_3$
Nitrogen-Containing Groups			
Amide			
unsubstituted	$RCONH_2$	Primary amine	RCH_2NH_2
monosubstituted	RCONHR′	Secondary amine	RCH_2NHR'
disubstituted	$RCONR'_2$	Tertiary amine	$RCH_2NR'_2$
		Aldehyde	RCHO
Lactam	⌐CONH⌐ / ⌐R⌐	Amine	⌐CH_2NH⌐ / ⌐R⌐
Imide	⌐CONHCO⌐ / ⌐R⌐	Amine	⌐CH_2NHCH_2⌐ / ⌐R⌐
Carbamate	RNHCOOR′	Amine + Alcohol	$RNHCH_3$ + R′OH
Nitrile	RCN	Primary amine	RCH_2NH_2
		Aldehyde	RCHO
Isocyanide	RNC	Secondary amine	$RNHCH_3$
Oxime	$R_2C=NOH$	Amine	R_2CHNH_2
Isocyanate	RNCO	Secondary amine	$RNHCH_3$
Nitrogen oxide	$N \rightarrow O$	Amine	N
C-Nitroso compound	R_3CNO	Amine	R_3CNH_2
Nitrosamine	R_2NNO	Hydrazine	R_2NNH_2
Nitro, alkyl	RNO_2	Primary amine	RNH_2
Nitro, aryl	$ArNO_2$	Azo compound	$ArN=NAr$
Hydroxylamine	RNHOH	Amine	RNH_2
Azoxy compound	$ArN=NAr$ ↓ O	Azo compound	$ArN=NAr$
Azide	RN_3	Amine	RNH_2
Diazo compound	RN_2	Amine	RNH_2
Quaternary salts			
cyclic	(pyridinium N⁺R X⁻)	o-Dihydroamine	(N—R)
acyclic	RCH=NR / R′ X	Amine	RCH_2NHR
Halogen-Containing Groups			
Alkyl halide	R_2CHX	Alkane	R_2CH_2

yields an ethereal solution of monomeric aluminum hydride which on standing deposits a solid polymeric $(AlH_3)_x$.

The ethereal solution of the monomeric hydride has been utilized in the reduction of carbonyl, ester, amide and nitrile groups. Various patents involving the reduction of carbonyl and ester groups by LAH have indicated the equivalence of aluminum hydride for these reductions. Wiberg and Jahn (48) have examined the reduction of acetaldehyde and ethyl acetate to ethanol. In each case, the reaction of calculated amounts of the reagent and the reducible compound gives aluminum ethylate as the isolable intermediate. Therefore, it has been postulated that the primary reaction involves the addition of the electropositive aluminum to the electronegative oxygen of the carbonyl group and the corresponding addition of the hydrogen to the electropositive carbon.

$$Al\begin{matrix} H \\ -H \\ H \end{matrix} + \begin{matrix} O=CHCH_3 \\ O=CHCH_3 \\ O=CHCH_3 \end{matrix} \rightarrow Al\begin{matrix} OCH_2CH_3 \\ -OCH_2CH_3 \\ OCH_2CH_3 \end{matrix} \xrightarrow{H_2O} 3\ CH_3CH_2OH \quad (6\text{-}16)$$

In the case of ethyl acetate the addition of the hydride to the carbonyl double bond occurs twice:

$$CH_3C\begin{matrix} O \\ \\ OC_2H_5 \end{matrix} \xrightarrow{+ \ alH} CH_3CH\begin{matrix} Oal \\ \\ OC_2H_5 \end{matrix} \xrightarrow{-\ alOC_2H_5,}$$

$$CH_3CH=O \xrightarrow{+\ alH} CH_3CH_2Oal \quad (6\text{-}17)$$

$$al = 1 \text{ equivalent Aluminum} = \frac{AlH_3}{3}$$

The stable addition compound $AlH_2Cl \cdot AlHCl_2$, formed by treatment of an ethereal aluminum hydride solution with an ethereal solution of aluminum chloride, can be utilized for more selective reductions than are possible with LAH (49,50). Ether solutions of $AlHBr_2$ and $AlHI_2$, from aluminum hydride and the bromide and iodide, respectively, are also suitable for organic reductions.

$$\begin{matrix} H \\ H \end{matrix} Al \begin{matrix} H \\ Cl \end{matrix} Al \begin{matrix} Cl \\ Cl \end{matrix} \longleftrightarrow \begin{matrix} H \\ H \end{matrix} Al \begin{matrix} H \\ Cl \end{matrix} Al \begin{matrix} Cl \\ Cl \end{matrix} \quad (6\text{-}18)$$

$(AlH_3 \cdot AlCl_3)$ $(AlH_2Cl \cdot AlHCl_2)$

XIX

The chlorine-containing addition compound, which has been postulated (51) as possessing the structure (XIX) has been utilized in the reduction of the various types of functional groups summarized in Table III.

TABLE III

Reductions with the Aluminum Hydride-Aluminum Chloride Addition Compound

Functional Group	Product
A. Functional Groups Reduced	
Aldehyde	Primary alcohol
Ketone, aliphatic	Secondary alcohol
Quinone	Hydroquinone
Acid	Primary alcohol
Acid chloride	Primary alcohol
Ester	Primary alcohol
Amide	Amine
Nitrile	Primary amine
Nitro, aliphatic	Primary amine
Nitro, aromatic	Primary amine
Halide, benzyl	Hydrocarbon
B. Functional Groups not Reduced	
Ketone, aromatic	
Halide, aliphatic	

Reductions with the addition compound have been formulated in a manner similar to that shown in equation (6-17).

$$-C\underset{\text{OH}}{\overset{\text{O}}{\diagdown}} \xrightarrow{+ \text{ alH}} -C\underset{\text{OH}}{\overset{\text{Oal}}{\diagdown}}H \xrightarrow{- \text{ alOH}} -CH=O \xrightarrow{+ \text{ alH}}$$

$$-CH_2-Oal \xrightarrow{+ H_2O} -CH_2OH \qquad (6\text{-}19)$$

While LAH converts aliphatic nitro groups to amines and aromatic nitro groups to azo derivatives, with amines as by-products, reduction with the halogenated aluminum hydride, $AlH_{3-n}X_n$, yields amines in both cases, with azo compounds as by-products from the aromatic nitro derivatives.

The apparent selectivity of these reductions is indicated in the non-reduction of the aromatic ketone. The non-reduction of the alkyl halide is not surprising in view of the resistance of such groups to LAH under normal conditions.

6.3   REDUCTIONS WITH MAGNESIUM ALUMINUM HYDRIDE

The behavior of magnesium aluminum hydride in ether solution is analogous to that of other aluminum hydrides in reducing polar double and triple bonds, i.e., carbonyl and nitrile groups, while nonpolar groups are not attacked (52-54). The structure of the ether-soluble complex hydride has been postulated as a resonance bridge structure, analogous to that proposed for LAH (52,55).

XX

The functional groups which have been subjected to treatment with an ethereal magnesium aluminum hydride solution are summarized in Table IV.

TABLE IV

Reductions with Magnesium Aluminum Hydride

Functional Group	Product
A. Functional Groups Reduced	
Aldehyde	Primary alcohol
Ketone	Secondary alcohol
Quinone	Hydroquinone
Acid	Primary alcohol
Ester	Primary alcohol
Amide	Amine
Nitrile	Primary amine
B. Functional Groups not Reduced	
Double bond	
Triple bond	

The few examples available indicate that magnesium aluminum hydride is similar to LAH in its reduction characteristics, although the non-reduction of the double bond in cinnamic acid and the triple bond in propargyl aldehyde represent points of difference.

6.4 REDUCTIONS WITH SODIUM ALUMINUM HYDRIDE

Schlesinger and Finholt (56) have indicated that the properties of sodium aluminum hydride are like those of LAH. Whereas diethyl ether can not be used as a solvent, reductions are carried out in tetrahydrofuran. Reductions are similar for the two hydrides with aldehydes, ketones, carboxylic acids, esters, acid chlorides, alkyl halides, nitriles and alkyl and aryl nitro compounds. The double bond in cinnamaldehyde is reduced by the direct addition technique while inverse addition yields the unsaturated alcohol. Direct addition converts benzonitrile to benzylamine while inverse addition yields benzaldehyde (70).

6.5 REDUCTIONS WITH SODIUM BOROHYDRIDE

Sodium borohydride is a crystalline, salt-like compound whose structure probably consists of tetrahedral borohydride ions (BH_4^-) and sodium ions. X-ray powder diffraction data (57) as well as infrared spectra (58) indicate the highly ionic character of the hydride, which has been represented (59) as:

$$Na^{\oplus} \left[\begin{array}{c} H \\ H \end{array} \!\! B \!\! \begin{array}{c} H \\ H \end{array} \right]^{\ominus}$$

The salt-like character of sodium borohydride results in ether insolubility and water solubility. The reduction of organic compounds with the borohydride may be carried out in water, methanol or dioxane solution. Aqueous systems can be utilized since the borohydride is very soluble in cold water with very little decomposition. Therefore, ether-insoluble compounds such as the sugars can be reduced in aqueous solution where LAH is unsuitable. In the case where hydrolytic side reactions may occur, as in the reduction of acid chlorides, dioxane or other non-hydrolytic solvents are used. In some cases, as in the reduction of sugars, the formation of boron containing complexes makes the work-up and isolation of reduction products difficult. This may be overcome by acetylation of reduction products and/or passage through ion-exchange columns.

The reduction behavior of sodium borohydride under normal reaction conditions, as reported by Chaikin and Brown (60) and others, is summarized in Table V.

TABLE V

Reductions with Sodium Borohydride

Functional Group	Product
A. Functional Groups Reduced	
Aldehyde	Primary alcohol
Ketone	Secondary alcohol
Acid chloride	Primary alcohol
Lactone	Dialcohol
Hydroperoxide	Alcohol
Quaternary ammonium salt	o-Dihydro derivative
Sulfoxide	Mercaptan
B. Functional Group Normally not Reduced	
Acid	
Anhydride	
Ester	
Amide	
Imide	
Acetal	
Nitrile	
Nitro, aromatic	
Halide	
Double bond	

The lower reactivity of sodium borohydride as compared with LAH is advantageous in permitting the selective reduction of acid chloride or carbonyl groups in the presence of functional groups which would be reduced with LAH but which are not attacked by the borohydride. Although esters are normally not reduced by sodium borohydride, the reagent has been utilized in the reduction of various uronates (61) and steroid esters (62).

6.6 REDUCTIONS WITH POTASSIUM BOROHYDRIDE

The properties of potassium borohydride are similar to those of sodium borohydride. Reductions of organic compounds can be carried out in aqueous or alcoholic solution. Although aldehydes, ketones, and acid chlorides are reduced to alcohols and cyclic quaternary ammonium salts are reduced to o-dihydro or tetrahydro derivatives, in general, acids, esters, amides, imides, acetals, aromatic nitro compounds, and halides are not attacked by potassium borohydride. Esters are reduced by an equimolar mixture of the borohydride and lithium chloride in tetrahydrofuran.

6.7 REDUCTIONS WITH LITHIUM BOROHYDRIDE

Lithium borohydride is a crystalline, salt-like compound containing tetrahedral borohydride ions (63). It is a more powerful reducing agent than sodium borohydride but is milder than LAH. The reagent is soluble in ether although most of the reported reductions have been carried out in tetrahydrofuran. The differentiation between reducible and non-reducible

TABLE VI

Reductions with Lithium Borohydride

Functional Group	Product
A. Functional Groups Reduced	
Aldehyde	Primary alcohol
Ketone	Secondary alcohol
Ester	Primary alcohol
Acid chloride	Primary alcohol
B. Functional Groups of Intermediate Reducibility	
Acid, aliphatic	Primary alcohol
Nitro, aromatic	Amine and azo derivatives
C. Functional Groups Normally not Reduced	
Acid, aromatic	
Amide	
Acetal	
Nitrile	
Halide	

groups is not always clearly defined and is usually a function of compound structure and/or reaction conditions. Aldehydes and ketones are generally reduced rapidly at room temperature while esters react slowly and require several hours refluxing. Thus, the selective reduction of a ketone group in a ketoester can be accomplished at low temperatures. On the other hand, carboxylic acid and aromatic nitro groups which are generally resistant to attack by lithium borohydride are partially reduced under prolonged refluxing (64).

The reduction behavior of lithium borohydride under normal reaction conditions is summarized in Table VI.

A mixture of lithium hydride and lithium borohydride has been used in the hydrogenolysis of halides without reducing nitro, amide, nitrile, imine and acetal groups (65).

An equimolar mixture of lithium chloride and potassium borohydride in tetrahydrofuran has been substituted for lithium borohydride in the reduction of esters to primary alcohols (66).

6.8   REDUCTIONS WITH ALUMINUM BOROHYDRIDE

Aluminum borohydride is an unstable covalent liquid which has been represented by a resonance bridge structure (59,67).

$$Al \left[\begin{array}{c} H \quad\quad H \\ \diagdown \quad B \diagdown \\ H \quad\quad H \end{array} \right]_3$$

The extreme reactivity of the compound, including spontaneous ignition on exposure to moist air and the explosive reaction with water, preclude any widespread utilization of the reagent in organic reductions. However, it has been reported that both orthoesters and acetals are reduced to ethers. The removal of halogen from polyhalomethanes is apparently related to the intermediate formation of carbon borohydrides which immediately lose borine or hydrogen or both to yield halogen-containing or halogen-free hydrocarbons (68).

6.9   REDUCTIONS WITH LITHIUM GALLIUM HYDRIDE

Lithium gallium hydride in ether solution is a milder reducing agent than LAH. Its structure is considered to be analogous to that of the latter, consisting of a resonance bridged complex.

$$Li \begin{array}{c} H \quad\quad H \\ \diagdown \quad Ga \diagdown \\ H \quad\quad H \end{array}$$

The reduction behavior of the hydride has only briefly been investigated (69) and is summarized in Table VII.

TABLE VII

Reductions with Lithium Gallium Hydride

Functional Group	Product
A. Functional Groups Reduced	
Aldehyde, aliphatic	Primary alcohol
Ketone, aliphatic	Secondary alcohol
Quinone	Hydroquinone
Acid, aliphatic	Primary alcohol
Amide	Amine
Nitrile, aliphatic	Primary amine
B. Functional Groups Normally not Reduced	
Aldehyde, aromatic	
Ketone, aromatic	
Ester	
Nitrile, aromatic	

6.10 REDUCTIONS WITH OTHER COMPLEX METAL HYDRIDES

Although various other complex metal hydrides are known, as discussed in Section 3.14, the action of these compounds on organic molecules other than alcohol and amines has not yet been examined.

REFERENCES

1. Gibb, T. R. P., Jr., private communication.
2. Wiberg, E., *Angew. Chem.*, 65, 16 (1953).
3. Brown, W. G., in R. Adams, ed., *Organic Reactions*, Vol. VI, Chapter 10, Wiley, New York, 1951, p. 484.
4. Lippincott, E. R., *J. Chem. Phys.*, 17, 1351 (1949).
5. Paddock, N. L., *Nature*, 167, 1070 (1951).
6. Trevoy, L. W., and W. G. Brown, *J. Am. Chem. Soc.*, 71, 1675 (1949).
7. Mousseron, M., R. Jacquier, M. Mousseron-Canet and R. Zagdoun, *Bull. soc. chim. France*, [5] 19, 1042 (1952).
8. Adams, R. M., and C. A. Vander Werf, *J. Am. Chem. Soc.*, 72, 4368 (1950).
9. Fuchs, R., and C. A. Vander Werf, *J. Am. Chem. Soc.*, 74, 5917 (1952).
10. Bothner-By, A. A., *J. Am. Chem. Soc.*, 73, 846 (1951).
11. Noyce, D. S., and D. B. Denney, *J. Am. Chem. Soc.*, 72, 5743 (1950).
12. Johnson, J. E., R. H. Blizzard, and H. W. Carhart, *J. Am. Chem. Soc.*, 70, 3664 (1948).
13. Eliel, E. L., *J. Am. Chem. Soc.*, 71, 3970 (1949).
14. Eliel, E. L., and J. P. Freeman, *J. Am. Chem. Soc.*, 74, 923 (1952).
15. Cram, D. J., *J. Am. Chem. Soc.*, 74, 2149 (1952).
16. Paddock, N. L., *Chemistry and Industry*, 1953, 63.
17. Gaylord, N. G., *Experientia*, 10, 166 (1954).
18. Lavie, D., and E. D. Bergmann, *Bull. soc. chim. France*, [5] 18, 250 (1951).
19. Nystrom, R. F., and W. G. Brown, *J. Am. Chem. Soc.*, 69, 1197 (1947).

20. Conover, L. H., and D. S. Tarbell, *J. Am. Chem. Soc.*, 72, 3586 (1950).
21. Johnson, J. E., R. H. Blizzard, and H. W. Carhart, *J. Am. Chem. Soc.*, 70, 3664 (1948).
22. Bordwell, F. G., and W. H. McKellin, *J. Am. Chem. Soc.*, 73, 2251 (1951).
23. Hochstein, F. A., and W. H. McKellin, *J. Am. Chem. Soc.*, 70, 3484 (1948).
24. Attenburrow, J., A. F. B. Cameron, J. H. Chapman, R. M. Evans, B. A. Hems, A. B. A. Jansen, and T. Walker, *J. Chem. Soc.*, 1952, 1094.
25. Ziegler, K., *Angew. Chem.*, 64, 323 (1952).
26. Nystrom, R. F., and W. G. Brown, *J. Am. Chem. Soc.*, 70, 3738 (1948).
27. Kharasch, M. S., and W. H. Urry, *J. Org. Chem.*, 13, 101 (1948).
28. Karrer, P., and O. Rüttner, *Helv. Chim. Acta*, 33, 812 (1950).
29. Schmid, H., and P. Karrer, *Helv. Chim. Acta*, 32, 960 (1949).
30. Gilman, H., *J. Am. Chem. Soc.*, 45, 839 (1923); 47, 518 (1925); 50, 2223 (1928).
31. Schmid, H., and P. Karrer, *Helv. Chim. Acta*, 32, 1371 (1949).
32. Karrer, P., *Bull. soc. chim. France*, [5] 17, 907 (1950).
33. Lutz, R. E. and J. S. Gillespie, Jr., *J. Am. Chem. Soc.*, 72, 2002 (1950).
34. Lutz, R. E. and D. F. Hinkley, *J. Am. Chem. Soc.*, 72, 4091 (1950).
35. Lutz, R. E. and J. S. Gillespie, Jr., *J. Am. Chem. Soc.*, 72, 344 (1950).
36. Boyland, E., and D. Manson, *J. Chem. Soc.*, 1951, 1837.
37. Cook, J. W., R. A. Raphael, and A. I. Scott, *J. Chem. Soc.*, 1952, 4416.
38. Bergmann, E. D., Y. Hirshberg, and D. Lavie, *Bull. soc. chim. France*, [5] 19, 268 (1952).
39. Julian, P. L., and W. Cole, *J. Am. Chem. Soc.*, 57, 1607 (1935).
40. Cronyn, M. W., and J. E. Goodrich, *J. Am. Chem. Soc.*, 74, 3936 (1952).
41. Dahn, H., and U. Solms, *Helv. Chim. Acta*, 34, 907 (1951).
42. Morrison, A. L., R. F. Long, and M. Königstein, *J. Chem. Soc.*, 1951, 952.
43. Culvenor, C. C. J., L. J. Goldsworthy, K. S. Kirby, and R. Robinson, *J. Chem. Soc.*, 1950, 1485.
44. Witkop, B., and J. B. Patrick, *Experientia*, 6, 183 (1950); *J. Am. Chem. Soc.*, 73, 2188 (1951).
45. Witkop, B., and J. B. Patrick, *J. Am. Chem. Soc.*, 74, 3855 (1952).
46. Witkop, B., and J. B. Patrick, *J. Am. Chem. Soc.*, 73, 713 (1951).
47. Wille, F., and F. Knörr, *Chem. Ber.*, 85, 841 (1952).
48. Wiberg, E., and A. Jahn, *Z. Naturforsch.*, 7b, 581 (1952).
49. Wiberg, E., and M. Schmidt, *Z. Naturforsch.*, 6b, 333 (1951).
50. Wiberg, E., and A. Jahn, *Z. Naturforsch.*, 7b, 580 (1952).
51. Wiberg, E., and M. Schmidt, *Z. Naturforsch.*, 6b, 460 (1951).
52. Wiberg, E., and R. Bauer, *Z. Naturforsch.*, 5b, 397 (1950).
53. Wiberg, E., R. Bauer, and P. Buchheit, *Angew. Chem.*, 62, 448 (1950).
54. Wiberg, E., and R. Bauer, *Z. Naturforsch.*, 7b, 131 (1952).
55. Wiberg, E., and R. Bauer, *Chem. Ber.*, 85, 593 (1952).
56. Schlesinger, H. I., and A. E. Finholt, U. S. Pat. 2,576,311 (November 27, 1951).
57. Soldate, A. M., *J. Am. Chem. Soc.*, 69, 987 (1947).
58. Price, W. C., H. C. Longuet-Higgins, B. Rice, and T. F. Young, *J. Chem. Phys.*, 17, 217 (1949).
59. Wiberg, E., and R. Bauer, *Z. Naturforsch.*, 7b, 58 (1952).
60. Chaikin, S. W., and W. G. Brown, *J. Am. Chem. Soc.*, 71, 122 (1949).
61. Wolfrom, M. L., and K. Anno, *J. Am. Chem. Soc.*, 74, 5583 (1952).
62. Heymann, H., and L. F. Fieser, *J. Am. Chem. Soc.*, 73, 5252 (1951).
63. Harris, P. M. and E. P. Meibohm, *J. Am. Chem. Soc.*, 69, 1231 (1947).

64. Nystrom, R. F., S. W. Chaikin, and W. G. Brown, *J. Am. Chem. Soc.*, *71*, 3245 (1949).
65. Friedman, L., *Abstracts of Papers*, 122nd Meeting American Chemical Society, Atlantic City, N. J., September 1952, p. 46M.
66. Paul, R., and N. Joseph, *Bull. soc. chim. France*, [5] *19*, 550 (1952).
67. Longuet-Higgins, H. C., *J. Chem. Soc.*, *1946*, 139.
68. Gerstein, M., R. A. Lad, and H. I. Schlesinger, *Abstracts of Papers*, 110th Meeting American Chemical Society, Chicago, Ill., September 1946, p. 26P.
69. Wiberg, E., and M. Schmidt, *Z. Naturforsch.*, *6b*, 171 (1951).
70. Finholt, A. E., E. C. Jacobson, A. E. Ogard, and P. Thompson, *J. Am. Chem. Soc.*, 77, 4163 (1955).

CHAPTER 7

Reduction of

OXYGEN-CONTAINING ORGANIC COMPOUNDS

I. Carbonyl Derivatives

7.1 ALDEHYDES

7.1.1 Reductions with Lithium Aluminum Hydride

The reduction of the polar carbonyl group in aldehydes with LAH proceeds with considerable ease to yield primary alcohols (1-3). The reaction requires one-quarter mole of LAH per mole of aldehyde according to
the equation:

$$4 \text{ RCHO} + \text{LiAlH}_4 \longrightarrow (\text{RCH}_2\text{O})_4\text{LiAl} \xrightarrow{\text{H}_2\text{O}} 4 \text{ RCH}_2\text{OH} \qquad (7\text{-}1)$$

The reduction can be carried out equally well with aliphatic and aromatic aldehydes without interference from other functional groups. Reductions of saturated and unsaturated aliphatic and alicyclic as well as
aromatic and heterocyclic aldehydes are summarized in Table VIII.

7.1.1.a *Aliphatic and alicyclic aldehydes.* Hayes and Drake (4) have
carried out the LAH reduction of several amino aldehydes and compared
the yields with those of the Meerwein-Ponndorf-Verley reaction. While
both LAH in ether and aluminum isopropoxide in isopropanol give the
amino alcohol in approximately 85% yield in the reduction of the tertiary amino aldehyde (I), the beta-amino aldehyde bearing an alpha-hydrogen
(II) gives 86% yield of alcohol with LAH and a 66% yield with the aluminum alkoxide.

$$(\text{C}_2\text{H}_5)_2\text{NCH}_2\text{C}(\text{CH}_3)_2\text{CHO} \qquad (\text{CH}_3)_2\text{NCH}_2\text{CHCHO} \qquad \text{CH}_3\text{NHCH}_2\text{C}(\text{CH}_3)_2\text{CHO}$$

$$\overset{|}{\text{CH}(\text{CH}_3)_2}$$

I   II   III

The secondary amino aldehyde (III), when reduced with aluminum isopropoxide, gives an 8-27% yield of the corresponding alcohol, and, when
a large excess of LAH (5 equivalents) is employed, the yield is 72%.

The reduction of aldehydes containing isolated or conjugated double
bonds usually proceeds without difficulty to yield the corresponding unsaturated alcohols. Aldehydes in which the carbonyl group is conjugated
with a series of double bonds, e.g., crotonaldehyde, are reduced with
LAH to the corresponding alcohols in satisfactory yield. The same re-

TABLE VIII

Reduction of Aldehydes with LAH

	Aldehyde	Product	% Yield	Ref.
	A. Saturated Aliphatic and Alicyclic			
CH_2O	Formaldehyde	Methanol	100	1
$C_2H_3Cl_3O_2$	Chloral hydrate	2,2,2-Trichloroethanol	50	1
			...	2
$C_4H_5F_3O$	4,4,4-Trifluorobutyraldehyde	4,4,4-Trifluoro-1-butanol	86	3
$C_5H_8Br_2O$	3-Bromomethyl-4-bromobutyraldehyde	3-Methyl-1-butanol	44[4]	5
$C_6H_{13}NO$	2,2-Dimethyl-3-methylaminopropionaldehyde	2,2-Dimethyl-3-methylamino-1-propanol	72	6
$C_7H_{14}O$	n-Heptaldehyde	n-Heptanol	86	2,7
$C_8H_{17}NO$	2-Isopropyl-3-dimethylaminopropionaldehyde	2-Isopropyl-3-dimethylamino-1-propanol	86	6
$C_9H_{10}O$	2-Phenylpropionaldehyde	2-Phenyl-1-propanol	98	8
$C_9H_{19}NO$	2,2-Dimethyl-3-diethylaminopropionaldehyde	2,2-Dimethyl-3-diethylamino-1-propanol	86	6
$C_{10}H_{12}O_2$	2-(p-Methoxyphenyl)propionaldehyde	2-(p-Methoxyphenyl)-1-propanol	...	8,9
$C_{10}H_{12}O_3$	2,5-Furandipropionaldehyde	2,5-Di-(3-hydroxypropyl)furan	...	10
$C_{10}H_{20}O$	3-Methylnonanal[11]	3-Methyl-1-nonanol	...	12
$C_{11}H_{17}NO_6$	N,N,-Di-(1-formyl-1-carbethoxymethyl)-methylamine	N,N-Di-[1,1-di(hydroxymethyl)methyl]-methylamine	...	13
$C_{11}H_{20}O$	1,1,3,3-Tetramethylcyclohexane-4-carboxaldehyde[14]	1,1,3,3-Tetramethyl-4-hydroxycyclohexane	51	15
$C_{12}H_{20}O_6$	Diacetonemannose	Diacetone-mannitol crystalline compound, m.p. 138.5°	...	16
$C_{15}H_{12}N_2O_2$	Benzoylglyoxal phenylhydrazone		...	17
$C_{17}H_{30}O_2$	Hydroxyaldehyde, m.p. 200° (I)	Glycol, m.p. 133°, $[\alpha]_D$ -26.6°	85[18]	19
$C_{20}H_{16}O_2$	Phenyl-(2-biphenylyl)glyoxal	1-Phenyl-1-(2-biphenylyl)ethylene glycol	93	20
	B. Unsaturated Aliphatic, Alicyclic, and Aromatic			
C_4H_6O	Crotonaldehyde	Crotyl alcohol	70	2,7
	trans-Crotonaldehyde	trans-Crotyl alcohol	65	21,22
			77	23
			...	24,25

B. Unsaturated Aliphatic, Alicyclic, and Aromatic (Continued)

Formula	Aldehyde	Alcohol		
C_5H_6O	trans-Penta-2,4-dienal	trans-Penta-2,4-dien-1-ol	77[26]	27
$C_7H_6O_2$	3-α-Furylacrolein	3-(α-Furyl)allyl alcohol	40	28
$C_7H_{10}O_2$	1-Cyclohexenecarboxaldehyde	1-Hydroxymethyl-1-cyclohexene	65	29,30
$C_8H_{12}O$	3-Methyl-1-cyclohexene-1-carboxaldehyde	3-Methyl-1-(hydroxymethyl)-1-cyclohexene	83	31
C_9H_6O	Phenylpropargyl aldehyde	Cinnamyl alcohol	57	32
C_9H_8O	Cinnamaldehyde	Hydrocinnamyl alcohol	87	33
		Cinnamyl alcohol	90[34]	35
$C_9H_{14}O$	3,3-Dimethyl-1-cyclohexene-1-carboxaldehyde	3,3-Dimethyl-1-(hydroxymethyl)-1-cyclohexene	69	31
$C_{10}H_{10}O$	p-Methylcinnamaldehyde	3-(p-Tolyl)-1-propanol	80	36
$C_{11}H_{10}N_2O_4$	α-Acetamido-p-nitrocinnamaldehyde	p-Nitrophenylacetol[37]	...[34,38]	39
$C_{11}H_{18}O$	2,5,6-Tetramethyl-1-cyclohexene-1-carboxaldehyde	2,5,6-Tetramethyl-1-(hydroxymethyl)-1-cyclohexene	68	40
	4,4,6-Tetramethyl-1-cyclohexene-1-carboxaldehyde[14]	4,4,6-Tetramethyl-1-(hydroxymethyl)-1-cyclohexene	19	15
$C_{14}H_{22}O$	2-Methyl-4-(2',6',6'-trimethyl-1'-cyclohexen-1'-yl)-2-buten-1-al ("β-C14 aldehyde")	2-Methyl-4-(2',6',6'-trimethyl-1'-cyclohexen-1'-yl)-2-buten-1-ol	88	41
$C_{15}H_{14}O$	9-Phenyl-2,4,6,8-nonatetraen-1-al	9-Phenyl-2,4,6,8-nonatetraen-1-ol	50[42]	43
$C_{15}H_{22}O$	β-Ionylideneacetaldehyde	β-Ionylideneethanol	94	44
$C_{15}H_{24}O$	3,7,11-Trimethyldodeca-2,6,10-trien-1-al ("Farnésal")	3,7,11-Trimethyldodeca-2,6,10-trien-1-ol ("Farnésol")	...	45
$C_{20}H_{28}O$	"β-Bicyclofarnésal" (II)	"β-Bicyclofarnésol"	97	46
	Vitamin A aldehyde (retinene)	Vitamin A	...	47,48
$C_{20}H_{28}O_2$	Retinene₁-5,6-epoxide (III)	Vitamin A₁-5,6-epoxide	70–75	49
			...	50

C. Aromatic

Formula	Aldehyde	Alcohol		
$C_7H_5NO_3$	m-Nitrobenzaldehyde	m,m'-Azobenzyl alcohol	28.5	51

(Continued)

TABLE VIII (*Continued*)

	Aldehyde	Product	% Yield	Ref.
		C. Aromatic (Continued)		
C_7H_6O	Benzaldehyde	Benzyl alcohol	85	7
$C_7H_6O_2$	p-Hydroxybenzaldehyde	p-Hydroxybenzyl alcohol	…	2,52
$C_7H_6O_3$	2,4-Dihydroxybenzaldehyde	reaction mixture solidified	…	53
$C_8H_6O_3$	Piperonal	Piperonyl alcohol	…[54]	55
$C_8H_8O_3$	Vanillin	glassy, high boiling product	95	56
$C_9H_{10}O_2$	2,4-Dimethyl-6-hydroxybenzaldehyde	2-Hydroxymethyl-3,5-dimethylphenol	…	56
$C_9H_{10}O_3$	Veratraldehyde	glassy, high boiling product	29	57,58
	2-(β-Hydroxyethyl)-4-hydroxybenzaldehyde	6-Hydroxyisochroman	…	56
$C_9H_{11}NO$	p-Dimethylaminobenzaldehyde	p-Dimethylaminobenzyl alcohol	66	59
		N,N-Dimethyl-p-toluidine	95	33
$C_{10}H_{12}O_2$	2,3,6-Trimethyl-4-hydroxybenzaldehyde	2,3,5-Trimethyl-4-hydroxymethylphenol	75	60
$C_{13}H_{15}NO$	9-Julolidinecarboxaldehyde (V)	9-Julolidinemethanol	78[54,61]	62
$C_{17}H_{12}O_3$	Methyl 5-formyl-4-phenanthrenecarboxylate	4,5-Di-(hydroxymethyl)phenanthrene	100	63
$C_{18}H_{14}O_3$	9-Formyl-9,10-dihydro-9,10-ethanoanthracene-12-carboxylic acid (VI)	9,10-Dihydro-9,12-di-(hydroxymethyl)-9,10-ethanoanthracene	55	64
$C_{18}H_{16}O_2$	9-Formyl-9,10-dihydro-12-hydroxymethyl-9,10-ethanoanthracene	9,10-Dihydro-9,12-di-(hydroxymethyl)-9,10-ethanoanthracene	90	65
		D. Heterocyclic		
C_5H_4OS	2-Thiophenecarboxaldehyde	2-Thenyl alcohol	75	66
$C_{10}H_{13}NO_3$	2,4-Dimethyl-5-carbethoxypyrrole-3-carboxaldehyde	See text	…[38]	67
$C_{13}H_{13}NO_3$	3-(2-Acetoxyethyl)-2-indolecarboxaldehyde	2-(Hydroxymethyl)-3-(2-hydroxyethyl)indole	…	68

CHART TO TABLE VIII

References—Table VIII

[1]R. F. Nystrom, unpublished work; through W. G. Brown, in R. Adams, ed., *Organic Reactions*, Vol. VI, Wiley, New York, 1951, Chapter 10, p. 469.

[2]H. I. Schlesinger and A. E. Finholt, U.S. Pat. 2,576,311 (November 27, 1951).

[3]E. T. McBee, A. E. Kelley, and E. Rapkin, *J. Am. Chem. Soc.*, 72, 5071 (1950).

[4]LAH-lithium hydride mixture.

[5]M. S. Kharasch and G. Büchi, *J. Org. Chem.*, 14, 84 (1949).

[6]K. Hayes and G. Drake, *ibid.*, 15, 873 (1950).

[7]R. F. Nystrom and W. G. Brown, *J. Am. Chem. Soc.*, 69, 1197 (1947).

[8]S. Winstein and K. C. Schreiber, *ibid.*, 74, 2171 (1952).

[9]I. Wender, H. Greenfield, and M. Orchin, *ibid.*, 73, 2656 (1951).

[10]I. D. Webb and G. T. Borcherdt, *ibid.*, 73, 752 (1951).

[11]Mixture of aldehyde and acid obtained on ozonolysis of (+)-4-methyl-1-decene.

[12]R. T. Letsinger and J. G. Traynham, *J. Am. Chem. Soc.*, 72, 849 (1950).

[13]M. Viscontini, J. Bally, and J. Meier, *Helv. Chim. Acta*, 35, 451 (1952).

[14]Mixture of saturated and unsaturated aldehydes obtained on LAH reduction of 1,1,5,5-tetramethyl-4-isobutyloxymethylenecyclohexan-3-one and acid hydrolysis of reduction product.

[15]R. Vonderwahl and H. Schinz, *Helv. Chim. Acta*, 35, 2368 (1952).

[16]M. Abdel-Akher and F. Smith, *Nature*, 166, 1037 (1950).

[17]I. Elphimoff-Felkin, H. Felkin, B. Tchoubar, and Z. Welvart, *Bull. soc. chim. France*, [5] 19, 252 (1952).

[18]Reduction carried out in N-ethylmorpholine.

[19]C. Collin-Asselineau, E. Lederer, D. Mercier, and J. Polonsky, *Bull. soc. chim. France*, [5] 17, 720 (1950).

[20]F. L. Weisenborn and D. Taub, *J. Am. Chem. Soc.*, 74, 1329 (1952).

[21]L. F. Hatch and S. S. Nesbitt, *ibid.*, 72, 727 (1950).

[22]L. F. Hatch and S. S. Nesbitt, *ibid.*, 73, 358 (1951).

[23]L. Crombie, A. J. B. Edgar, S. H. Harper, M. W. Lowe, and D. Thompson, *J. Chem. Soc.*, 1950, 3552.

[24]D. Y. Curtin and S. M. Gerber, *J. Am. Chem. Soc.*, 74, 4052 (1952).

[25]C. G. Moore and E. S. Waight, *J. Chem. Soc.*, 1952, 4237.

[26]Normal or inverse addition.

[27]L. Crombie, S. H. Harper, and D. Thompson, *J. Chem. Soc.*, 1951, 2906.

[28]R. Lukeš and J. Jarý, unpublished work; through M. Ferles and J. Rudinger, *Chem. Listy*, 47, 112 (1953).

[29]R. Jacquier and R. Zagdoun, *Bull. soc. chim. France*, [5] 19, 698 (1952).

[30]M. Mousseron, R. Jacquier, M. Mousseron-Canet, and R. Zagdoun, *ibid.*, [5] 19, 1042 (1952).

[31]P. Seifert and H. Schinz, *Helv. Chim. Acta*, 34, 728 (1951).

[32]F. Wille and F. Knörr, *Chem. Ber.*, 85, 841 (1952).

[33]R. F. Nystrom and W. G. Brown, *J. Am. Chem. Soc.*, 70, 3738 (1948).

[34]Inverse addition, calculated amount LAH.

[35]F. A. Hochstein and W. G. Brown, *J. Am. Chem. Soc.*, 70, 3484 (1948).

[36]P. P. T. Sah, *Z. Vitamin-, Hormon- u Fermentforsch.*, 3, 324 (1949–1950); through M. Ferles and J. Rudinger, *Chem. Listy*, 47, 112 (1953).

[37]See text.

[38]Reduction carried out in tetrahydrofuran.

[39]K. Eiter and E. Sackl, *Monatsh.*, 83, 123 (1952).

[40]H. Favre and H. Schinz, *Helv. Chim. Acta*, 35, 1627 (1952).

[41]H. H. Inhoffen, F. Bohlmann, and M. Bohlmann, *Ann.*, 565, 35 (1949).

[42]Reduction carried out in benzene-ether mixture.

[43]F. Bohlmann, *Chem. Ber.*, 85, 114 (1952).

[44]H. O. Huisman, A. Smit, S. Vromen, and L. G. M. Fisscher, *Rec. trav. chim.*, 71, 899 (1952).

[45]M. Stoll and A. Commarmont, *Helv. Chim. Acta*, 32, 2440 (1949).

[46]M. Stoll and A. Commarmont, *ibid.*, 32, 1836 (1949).

[47]J. F. Arens and D. A. van Dorp, *Rec. trav. chim.*, 68, 604 (1949).

[48]P. Meunier, J. Jouanneteau, and G. Zwingelstein, *Compt. rend.*, 231, 1170 (1950).

[49]N. L. Wendler, C. Rosenblum, and M. Tishler, *J. Am. Chem. Soc.*, 72, 234 (1950).

[50]R. Mallein, *Compt. rend.*, 234, 143 (1952).

[51]N. G. Gaylord and J. A. Snyder, *Rec. trav. chim.*, 72, 1007 (1953).

[52]H. Felkin, *Bull. soc. chim. France*, [5] 18, 347 (1951).

[53]E. Wiberg and M. Schmidt, *Z. Naturforsch.*, 6b, 171 (1951).

[54]Reduction carried out in diethyl ether-di-*n*-butyl ether mixture.

[55]L. H. Conover and D. S. Tarbell, *J. Am. Chem. Soc.*, 72, 3586 (1950).

[56]E. Larsson, *Trans. Chalmers Univ. Technol.*, Gothenburg, 94, 15 (1950); *Chem. Abstracts*, 45, 1494 (1951).

[57]S. R. Finn and J. W. G. Musty, *Chemistry and Industry*, 1950, 677.

[58]S. R. Finn and J. W. G. Musty, *J. Appl. Chem. (London)*, 1, 182 (1951).

[59]L. Schieler and R. D. Sprenger, *J. Am. Chem. Soc.*, 73, 4045 (1952).

[60]H. B. Hass and M. L. Bender, *ibid.*, 71, 1767 (1949).

[61]Reaction carried out for 7 days at 80° with large excess LAH.

[62]F. Wessely, K. Benedikt, H. Benger, G. Friedrich, and F. Prillinger, *Monatsh.*, 81, 1071 (1950).

[63]P. A. S. Smith and Tung-Yin Yu, *J. Org. Chem.*, 17, 1281 (1952).

[64]G. M. Badger, J. E. Campbell, J. W. Cook, R. A. Raphael, and A. I. Scott, *J. Chem. Soc.*, 1950, 2326.

[65]J. S. Meek, B. T. Poon, and S. J. Cristol, *J. Am. Chem. Soc.*, 74, 761 (1952).

[66]T. L. Cairns and B. C. McKusick, *J. Org. Chem.*, 15, 790 (1950).

[67]A. Treibs and H. Scherer, *Ann.*, 577, 139 (1952).

[68]R. Goutarel, M. M. Janot, V. Prelog, and W. I. Taylor, *Helv. Chim. Acta*, 33, 150 (1950).

sult is obtained when the side chain double bonds are conjugated with a cyclohexene ring, as in the reduction of vitamin A aldehyde (IV) (5–7).

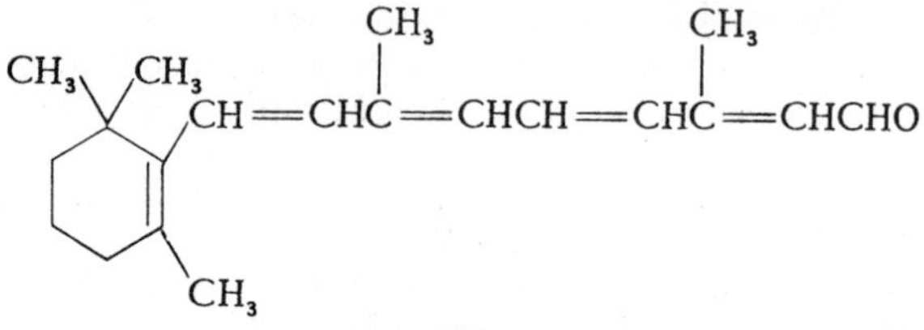

IV

While the reduction of IV with LAH gives vitamin A in good yield, the corresponding reduction with aluminum isopropoxide usually proceeds in lower yield (5,8,9). The LAH reduction of 1-cyclohexenecarboxaldehyde similarly yields the unsaturated carbinol (10,11). However, cinnamaldehyde, in which the double bond conjugated with the carbonyl group is also conjugated with the adjacent phenyl group, is reduced under the usual conditions, i.e., addition of an ether solution of the aldehyde to an ethereal LAH solution at room temperature, to hydrocinnamyl alcohol (12). The unsaturated alcohol, cinnamyl alcohol, is obtained by the inverse addition of the calculated amount of LAH at $-10°$ (13). This will be discussed in more detail in Section 15.1.1.b.1 on the reduction of carbon-carbon double bonds. The reduction of 9-phenylnona-2,4,6,8-tetraen-1-al, in which the carbonyl group is separated from the phenyl group by four conjugated double bonds, yields the corresponding unsaturated carbinol (14).

The reduction of α-acetamido-p-nitrocinnamaldehyde (V) with a calculated amount of LAH in tetrahydrofuran, as well as with aluminum isopropoxide in isopropanol, yields the corresponding unsaturated alcohol which is tautomeric with an N-substituted ketoimine whose hydrolysis yields the acetol (VI) (15).

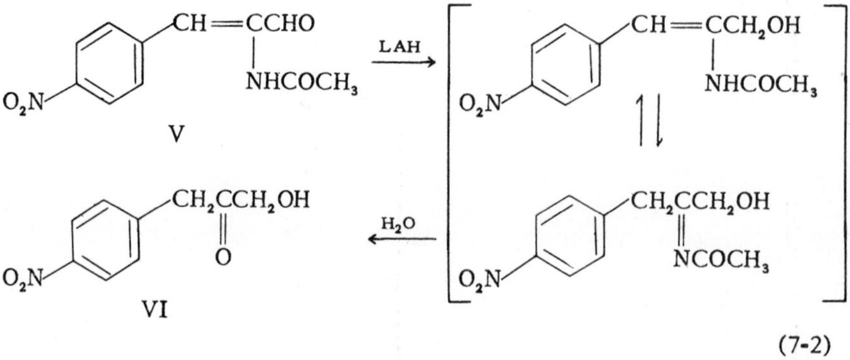

(7-2)

No reduction takes place when glucoreductone (VII) is treated with

$$
\begin{array}{ccc}
HC\!=\!\!O & \quad\quad & HC\!=\!\!O \\
| & & | \\
COH & & COH \\
\| & & \| \\
HCOH & & HOCH \\
\end{array}
$$

VII

LAH. This is attributed to the presence of a mesomeric system in which the π-electrons are relatively equally distributed and therefore are polarized with difficulty (16).

The LAH reduction of phenylpropargyl aldehyde is reported to yield cinnamyl alcohol (17). The trimer of the aldehyde yields a small quantity of cinnamyl alcohol on treatment with LAH in refluxing ether.

$$C_6H_5C \equiv CCHO \xrightarrow[57\%]{LAH} C_6H_5CH\!=\!CHCH_2OH \qquad (7\text{-}3)$$

The reduction of the phenylhydrazone of benzoylglyoxal with LAH in ether has been reported to give a crystalline, red compound, m.p. 138.5 °C. which contains approximately 16.7% nitrogen (18). This compound, however, has not been studied further.

LAH reduction of aldehydes has been utilized in the study of carbohydrates for the reduction of diacetone mannose (19) and various uronic acids (20). LAH, however, has the disadvantage, as far as carbohydrates are concerned, of requiring non-hydroxylic solvents and must be rigorously protected from moisture.

The non-reduction of acetals with LAH (21,22) permits the reduction of other functional groups without at the same time reducing the aldehyde group. Thus, the reduction of acetal esters with LAH results in the formation of acetal alcohols which on hydrolysis yield aldehydo alcohols (23,24).

$$
\begin{array}{ccccc}
CH_3CHCOOC_2H_5 & \xrightarrow{LAH} & CH_3CHCH_2OH & \xrightarrow{H^+} & CH_3CHCH_2OH \qquad (7\text{-}4) \\
| & & | & & | \\
CH(OC_2H_5)_2 & & CH(OC_2H_5)_2 & & CHO \\
\end{array}
$$

7.1.1.b *Aromatic aldehydes.* The reduction of aromatic aldehydes generally proceeds satisfactorily. The reduction of phenolic aldehydes presents an interesting picture. It has been reported that attempts to reduce 2,4-dimethyl-6-hydroxybenzaldehyde (VIII) by various agents generally result in recovery of the unchanged aldehyde, while hydrogenation in the presence of a palladium catalyst results in reduction to 2,3,5-trimethylphenol (25). However, reduction with LAH gives the corresponding benzyl alcohol in 29% yield (25,26).

VIII   IX   X

Other phenolic aldehydes have also been reduced with LAH (27,28). Reduction of the p-hydroxybenzaldehyde (IX) gives a 66% yield of 6-hydroxy-isochroman (X) (28).

Attempts to reduce vanillin and veratraldehyde to the corresponding alcohols with LAH have been reported to give glassy high boiling or not distillable products which were not examined further (29).

Reduction of p-dimethylaminobenzaldehyde with sodium amalgam in ethanol yields 20% of p-dimethylaminobenzyl alcohol accompanied by a stereoisomeric mixture of 1,2-di-(p-dimethylaminophenyl)ethylene glycols. Electrolytic reduction also yields only 20% of the substituted benzyl alcohol as well as 15% of N,N-dimethyl-p-toluidine and various other by-products (30). Reduction with LAH in ether gives the benzyl alcohol in 75–95% yield (12,31). When the reduction is carried out with excess LAH for 7 days at 80° in a mixture of diethyl and di-n-butyl ethers, the aldehyde is converted to N,N-dimethyl-p-toluidine in 78% yield (32). This hydrogenolysis is discussed further in Section 16.1.

Reduction of the cyanohydrin from 3,4-dibenzyloxybenzaldehyde with LAH in ether has been reported to yield, in addition to the expected amino alcohol, 3,4-dibenzyloxybenzyl alcohol by reduction of the aldehyde from the dissociated cyanohydrin (33).

Treatment of 5-formyl-4-phenanthrenecarboxylic acid (XI), which has been assigned a lactol structure since it forms no carbonyl derivatives, with diazomethane yields the methyl ester (XII) which forms carbonyl derivatives. With methanol in the presence of hydrogen chloride the pseudo methyl ester (XIII), which does not yield carbonyl derivatives, is formed. Reduction of either of the methyl esters with LAH gives the diol (XIV) in excellent yields (34). The pseudo ethyl ester (XV), formed by treatment of the aldehydo acid with ethanol and a trace of sulfuric acid, similarly yields the diol (XIV) (35).

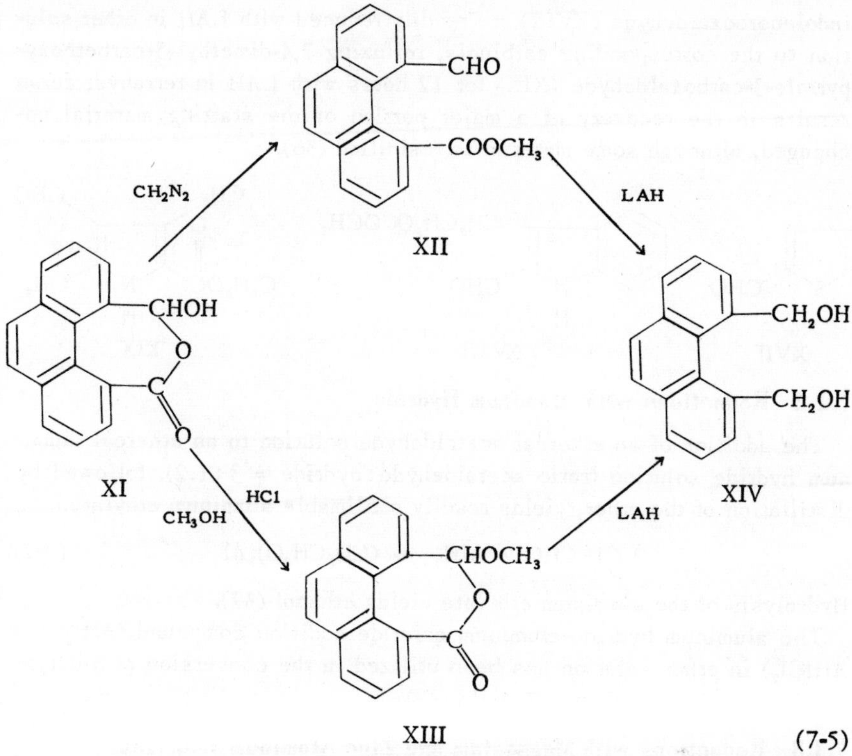

(7-5)

Hydrogenation of the pseudo ethyl ester over copper chromite in absolute alcohol at 130°C. and 2000 p.s.i. pressure gives unchanged starting material. However, distillation of a mixture of the ester, aluminum isopropoxide and toluene gives the lactone of 5-(hydroxymethyl)-4-phenanthrenecarboxylic acid (XVI) in 56% yield (35).

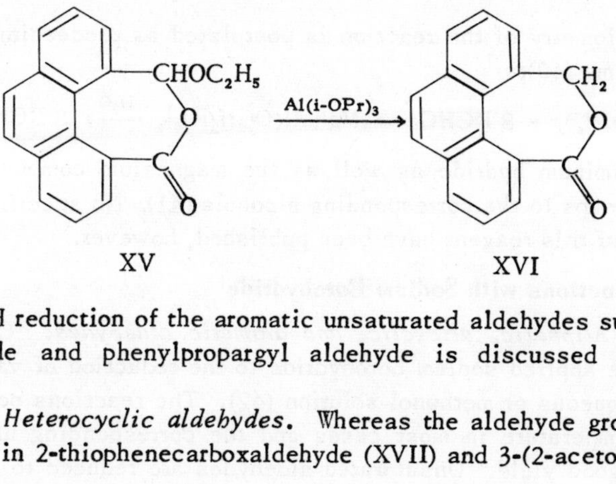

(7-6)

The LAH reduction of the aromatic unsaturated aldehydes such as cinnamaldehyde and phenylpropargyl aldehyde is discussed in Section 7.1.1.a.

7.1.1.c *Heterocyclic aldehydes.* Whereas the aldehyde groups in the α-position in 2-thiophenecarboxaldehyde (XVII) and 3-(2-acetoxyethyl)-2-

indolecarboxaldehyde (XVIII) are readily reduced with LAH in ether solution to the corresponding carbinols, refluxing 2,4-dimethyl-5-carbethoxy-pyrrole-3-carboxaldehyde (XIX) for 12 hours with LAH in tetrahydrofuran results in the recovery of a major portion of the starting material unchanged, although some material is resinified (36).

XVII   XVIII   XIX

7.1.2 Reductions with Aluminum Hydride

The addition of an ethereal acetaldehyde solution to an ethereal aluminum hydride solution (ratio acetaldehyde : hydride = 3 : 1.2), followed by distillation of the ether, yields readily sublimable aluminum ethylate.

$$3 \ CH_3CHO + AlH_3 \rightarrow (CH_3CH_2O)_3Al \qquad (7\text{-}7)$$

Hydrolysis of the aluminum ethylate yields ethanol (37).

The aluminum hydride-aluminum chloride addition compound (AlH_2Cl + $AlHCl_2$) in ether solution has been utilized in the conversion of n-butyraldehyde to 1-butanol in 71% yield (38).

7.1.3 Reductions with Magnesium and Zinc Aluminum Hydrides

Magnesium aluminum hydride reduces polar groups without attacking non-polar groups. Treatment of an ethereal propargyl aldehyde solution with an ethereal solution of the aluminum hydride yields propargyl alcohol (39,40).

$$HC \equiv CCHO \xrightarrow{Mg(AlH_4)_2} HC \equiv CCH_2OH \qquad (7\text{-}8)$$

The stoichiometry of the reaction is postulated as proceeding according to the scheme (40):

$$Mg(AlH_4)_2 + 8 \ RCHO \rightarrow Mg[Al(OCH_2R)_4]_2 \xrightarrow{H_2O} 8 \ RCH_2OH \quad (7\text{-}9)$$

Zinc aluminum hydride as well as the magnesium compound reduces carbonyl groups to the corresponding alcohols (41). No specific examples of the use of this reagent have been published, however.

7.1.4 Reductions with Sodium Borohydride

7.1.4.a *Aliphatic, alicyclic, and aromatic aldehydes.* Chaikin and Brown have applied sodium borohydride to the reduction of various aldehydes in aqueous or methanol solution (42). The reactions occur rapidly at room temperature in most cases and the corresponding alcohols are formed in good yield. Unsaturated aldehydes are reduced to the unsaturated alcohols. Thus, while cinnamaldehyde is reduced with LAH to the saturated alcohol, in the reduction with sodium borohydride in methanol solution, the final product is cinnamyl alcohol. The lower reactivity of the borohydride permits the selective reduction of the aldehyde group in the presence of other functional groups, e.g., *m*-nitrobenzaldehyde and 4-nitro-1-butanal are reduced to *m*-nitrobenzyl alcohol and 4-nitro-1-butanol, respectively. The stoichiometry of the reaction may be represented.

$$NaBH_4 + 4\ RCHO \rightarrow NaB(OCH_2R)_4 \xrightarrow{H_2O} 4\ RCH_2OH \qquad (7\text{-}10)$$

The reduction of various aldehydes with sodium borohydride is summarized in Table IX.

The value of selective reduction is illustrated in the following sequence of reactions (43):

$$(7\text{-}11)$$

Hunger and Reichstein have reduced the aldehyde groups in a number of cardiac active glycosides and aglycones with sodium borohydride in

TABLE IX

Reduction of Aldehydes with Sodium Borohydride

Aldehyde	Product	Reaction Medium[1]	% Yield	Ref.
	A. Aliphatic			
n-Butyraldehyde	1-Butanol	W	85	2
Chloral hydrate	2,2,2-Trichloroethanol	W	61	2
Crotonaldehyde	Crotyl alcohol	W	85	2
4,4-Dinitro-1-pentanal	4,4-Dinitro-1-pentanol	W-M	67.6	3
4-Methyl-4-nitro-1-pentanal	4-Methyl-4-nitro-1-pentanol	W-M	54.8	3
4-Nitro-1-butanal	4-Nitro-1-butanol	W-M	33.4	3
4-Nitro-1-pentanal	4-Nitro-1-pentanol	W-M	56.3	3
2-Phthalimido-1-p-nitrophenylpropan-1-ol-3-al	2-Phthalimido-1-p-nitrophenyl-1,3-propanediol	M	....	4
	B. Aromatic			
Anisaldehyde	Anisyl alcohol	M	96	2
Cinnamaldehyde	Cinnamyl alcohol	M	97	2
p-Dimethylaminobenzaldehyde	p-Dimethylaminobenzyl alcohol	M	96	2
m-Hydroxybenzaldehyde	m-Hydroxybenzyl alcohol	M	93	2
m-Nitrobenzaldehyde	m-Nitrobenzyl alcohol	M	82	2

[1]Reaction medium: W = water, M = methanol.
[2]S. W. Chaikin and W. G. Brown, J. Am. Chem. Soc., 71, 122 (1949).
[3]H. Schechter, D. E. Ley, and L. Zeldin, ibid, 74, 3664 (1952).
[4]Société des Usines Chimiques Rhone Poulenc, Australian Pat. Appln. 955/51 (February 21, 1951).

dioxane solution (44,45): strophanthidin (XX), convallatoxin, desgluco-hellebrin, corotoxigenin, gofruside.

Lycoctonine, $C_{25}H_{39-41}NO_7$, an alkaloid of unknown structure, is oxidized with chromic acid to an aldehyde, lycoctonal, $C_{25}H_{37-39}NO_7$. Reduction of the aldehyde with sodium borohydride in aqueous methanol yields 90% lycoctonine (46).

7.1.4.b *Carbohydrate aldehydes*. Although sodium borohydride is less reactive than LAH, it can be utilized in aqueous or methanolic solution and is therefore a satisfactory reagent for converting reducing sugars to the corresponding alcohols.

Chaikin and Brown have reported that the reduction of glucose with sodium borohydride results in the formation of boron-containing compounds which interfere with the isolation of the sugar alcohol (42). Abdel-Akher, Hamilton, and Smith (47) have overcome this difficulty by converting the reduction product into the fully acetylated derivative which crystallizes with ease. The use of ion exchange resins (47,48) or treatment of the crude alcohol with methanolic hydrogen chloride also overcomes the difficulty arising from borate complex formation. Various mono- and oligosaccharides containing aldehyde groups, reduced by these methods, are indicated in Table X.

Various acid degraded cellulose samples, i.e., wet hydrocellulose, have been reduced with sodium borohydride in aqueous solution at pH 8 to transform terminal aldehyde groups to alcoholic groups. The resultant alkaline reduced hydrocellulose has a decreased "hot alkali stability" value (49).

TABLE X

Reduction of Aldehydo Sugars with Sodium Borohydride in Aqueous Solution

Compound	Product	Method of Isolation[1]	% Yield	Ref.
	Monosaccharides			
L-Arabinose	L-Arabitol pentaacetate	a	87.5	2
D-Galactose	Dulcitol hexaacetate	a	87	2
	Dulcitol	b	40	2
D-Glucose	Sorbitol hexaacetate	a	78	2
D-Mannose	D-Mannitol hexaacetate	a	92	2
	D-Mannitol	c	90	2
D-Xylose	Xylitol pentaacetate	a	80	2
Sodium calcium D-galacturonate hexahydrate	L-Galactono-γ-lactone	b	24	3
Sodium D-glucuronate monohydrate	L-Gulono-γ-lactone	b	30	3
	Oligosaccharides			
Cellobiose	Cellobiitol	d,e		2
Lactose	Lactitol	d,f		2
Maltose	Maltitol nonaacetate	a	70	2
Amylose	Amylitol	g,h		2
Laminarin	Laminaritol	i		2

[1]Method of isolation: (a) Crude reduction product acetylated with acetic anhydride. (b) Crude reduction product passed through ion exchange resins. (c) Crude reduction product boiled with methanolic hydrogen chloride. (d) Failed to crystallize in free state or as acetate. (e) Hydrolysis gave glucose and sorbitol. (f) Hydrolysis gave galactose and sorbitol. (g) Reduction with sodium borohydride in water or in dilute sodium hydroxide solution gave the non-reducing polysaccharide. In the presence of acetic acid, the original amylose isolated. (h) Reduction product isolated by precipitation with methanol. (i) Reduction product isolated by precipitation with ethanol.

2M. Abdel-Akher, J. K. Hamilton, and F. Smith, J. Am. Chem. Soc., 73, 4691 (1951).

3M. L. Wolfrom and K. Anno, ibid., 74, 5583 (1952).

Dextran, average molecular weight 66,000, containing terminal aldehyde groups, has been quantitatively reduced with the borohydride in
aqueous solution to non-reducing hydrodextran, average molecular weight
66,000 (50).

The use of sodium borohydride as a quantitative reagent for the estimation of aldoses has been discussed in Section 5.1. The method has been
applied to the analysis of the following aldoses (51): glucose, galactose,
mannose, arabinose, xylose, rhamnose, lactose, maltose.

Periodate oxidation of various polysaccharides yields "polyaldehydes"
which on reduction with sodium borohydride in aqueous solution are converted to "polyalcohols." Hydrolysis of the latter and determination of
the cleavage products provides information concerning the nature and
amount of glycosidic linkages in the polysaccharide. This method has
been applied to amylopectin, glycogen, amylose, cellulose, and a dextran (52).

7.1.5 Reductions with Potassium Borohydride

The only application of potassium borohydride to the reduction of an
aldehyde reported to date, involves the reduction of 2-phthalimido-1-p-
nitrophenylpropan-1-ol-3-al in aqueous or methanol solution to the corresponding 1,3-propanediol (43,53), according to the sequence in equation (7-11).

7.1.6 Reductions with Lithium Borohydride

Nystrom, Chaikin, and Brown (54) have applied lithium borohydride in
tetrahydrofuran solution to the reduction of a number of carbonyl compounds including the following aldehydes:

Compound	Product	% Yield
n-Heptaldehyde	n-Heptanol	83
Benzaldehyde	Benzyl alcohol	91
Crotonaldehyde	Crotyl alcohol	70

The reductions proceed rapidly at room temperature and the mild reducing
action of lithium borohydride permits its use in the selective reduction of
aldehydes in the presence of nitro, carboxyl as well as ester groups.

Treatment of lithium borohydride with hydrogen gas containing tritium
yields borohydride containing tritium. The reaction of benzaldehyde in
tetrahydrofuran with the borohydride prepared in this manner has been
used for the synthesis, in 91% yield, of benzyl alcohol containing tritium
(55).

7.1.7 Reductions with Lithium Gallium Hydride

Lithium gallium hydride in ether solution is a milder reducing agent
than LAH. While propionaldehyde is reduced to 1-propanol by this re-

agent, the aromatic p-hydroxybenzaldehyde does not undergo reduction (56).

7.2 KETONES

7.2.1 Reductions with Lithium Aluminum Hydride

The reduction of ketones with LAH proceeds very readily to yield the corresponding alcohols, with a consumption of one-quarter mole of LAH per mole of ketone (1-3).

$$4 \, R_2CO + LiAlH_4 \rightarrow (R_2CHO)_4LiAl \xrightarrow{H_2O} R_2CHOH \qquad (7\text{-}13)$$

The characteristics of aldehyde reductions, as regards yields, side reactions, etc., are applicable to ketone reductions.

The various reported modifications in the reduction of acetone are illustrative of the many variations possible with higher molecular weight ketones. Thus, acetone is reduced with LAH to 2-propanol.

$$CH_3COCH_3 \xrightarrow{LAH} CH_3\underset{\underset{\displaystyle OH}{|}}{C}HCH_3 \qquad (7\text{-}14)$$

Reduction with lithium aluminum deuteride yields 2-deutro-2-propanol (57,58).

$$CH_3COCH_3 \xrightarrow{LiAlD_4} CH_3\underset{\underset{\displaystyle OH}{|}}{C}DCH_3 \qquad (7\text{-}15)$$

Reduction of acetone-C^{14} with LAH yields 2-propanol-2-C^{14} (59).

$$CH_3\underset{\underset{\displaystyle O}{\|}}{C}{}^{14}CH_3 \xrightarrow{LAH} CH_3\underset{\underset{\displaystyle OH}{|}}{C}{}^{14}HCH_3 \qquad (7\text{-}16)$$

Treatment of acetone with deuterium oxide yields acetone-d_6 (XXI). Reduction of XXI with LAH yields propane-1,1,1,3,3,3-d_6-2-ol (58,60).

$$CD_3COCD_3 \xrightarrow{LAH} CD_3\underset{\underset{\displaystyle OH}{|}}{C}HCD_3 \qquad (7\text{-}17)$$

XXI

Reduction of XXI with lithium aluminum deuteride yields propane-1,1,1,-2,3,3,3,-d_7-2-ol (60).

$$CD_3COCD_3 \xrightarrow{LiAlD_4} CD_3\underset{\underset{\displaystyle OH}{|}}{C}DCD_3 \qquad (7\text{-}18)$$

XXI

The reduction of ketones, as well as many other functional groups, is postulated as a polar nucleophilic displacement reaction on carbon. The reactive species is presumed to be a series of complex aluminohydride ions which act as carriers for the hydride ion (61). Paddock postulated that ether plays an essential part in LAH reductions, an equilibrium

$$AlH_4^{\ominus} \rightleftharpoons AlH_3 + H^{\ominus} \qquad (7\text{-}19)$$

existing in solution, the function of the ether being to coordinate with the aluminum hydride (62,63). However, the donor properties of ketones cause the latter to coordinate with AlH_3 even more readily than ether (62,64). With this hypothesis in mind, acetone has been successfully reduced with LAH in the absence of ether (62).

If the coordination of the carbonyl group with aluminum hydride is followed by a rate-determining step consisting of the transfer of hydrogen from coordinated hydride, the carbon-oxygen bond is converted in the transition state to a single bond with two directions open to it, corresponding to isomeric carbinols (63). Unsymmetrical ketones, including alicyclic compounds such as keto steroids, yield a new asymmetric carbon atom on reduction introducing the possibility of stereochemical specificity.

7.2.1.a *Dialkyl ketones.* The reduction of saturated and unconjugated unsaturated dialkyl ketones proceeds as in the case of acetone discussed in the preceding section.

The reduction of highly chlorinated ketones has been carried out with LAH where reduction with aluminum isopropoxide gave little or no yield of the secondary alcohol. Thus, hexachloracetone (XXII) is reduced to hexachloro-2-propanol in 97% yield with LAH while only traces are obtained with the aluminum alkoxide (65).

$$Cl_3CCOCCl_3 \xrightarrow{\text{LAH}} Cl_3CCHCCl_3 \qquad (7\text{-}20)$$
$$\underset{OH}{|}$$

XXII

Reduction of 1,3-dichloroacetone (XXIII) proceeds in 77% yield with LAH and 20–25% yield with aluminum isopropoxide (66).

$$ClCH_2COCH_2Cl \rightarrow ClCH_2CHCH_2Cl \qquad (7\text{-}21)$$
$$\underset{OH}{|}$$

XXIII

In contrast to the ease of reduction of XXII and XXIII, as well as octachloro-2-butanone, decachloro-3-pentanone is very stable to LAH. Under vigorous conditions, a product of undetermined structure, involving chiefly chlorine cleavage, is formed (65). The LAH reduction of trifluoroacetone proceeds readily and in good yield to give 3,3,3-trifluoro-2-propanol (67,68).

Sterically hindered alkyl ketones are readily reduced by LAH while surface active catalysts are relatively ineffective. Thus, 1,1-diphenylacetones are reduced with LAH to the corresponding carbinols in good yield (69,70). The reduction of 3,4-dimorpholino-4-phenyl-2-butanone (XXIV) with LAH in an ether-benzene mixture yields 99% of the substituted 2-butanol, consisting of two racemic mixtures.

$$C_6H_5CH\text{——}CHCOCH_3 \qquad \xrightarrow{LAH} \qquad C_6H_5CH\text{——}CH\text{—}CHCH_3 \qquad (7\text{-}22)$$

XXIV

Catalytic hydrogenation over platinum oxide, palladium-on-charcoal, palladium-on-barium sulfate or Raney nickel, as well as treatment with aluminum isopropoxide, are reported to be unsuccessful in the attempted reduction of XXIV. The LAH reduction of 3,4-bis-(dimethylamino)-, 3,4-dipiperidino-, 3,4-di-(p-methoxy-N-methylbenzylamino)- and 3-morpholino-4-tetrahydroquinolino-4-phenyl-2-butanone in ethereal solution has been readily carried out in good yield (71).

Methadone (6-dimethylamino-4,4-diphenyl-3-heptanone) (XXV) contains a relatively unreactive carbonyl group. It does not give a semicarbazone under the usual conditions and resists reduction with aluminum isopropoxide or sodium amalgam (72). It is unaffected when subjected to catalytic hydrogenation with Raney nickel (72) or palladium (73). However, catalytic hydrogenation of dl-methadone (XXV) with platinum oxide yields α-dl-methadol (72-74).

$$\underset{C_6H_5}{\overset{\overset{O}{\parallel}\;\;\;\;C_6H_5\;\;\;\;CH_3}{C_2H_5C\text{—}C\text{—}CH_2\underset{*}{C}HN(CH_3)_2}} \rightarrow \underset{C_6H_5}{\overset{OH\;\;\;\;C_6H_5\;\;\;\;CH_3}{C_2H_5\underset{*}{C}H\text{—}C\text{—}CH_2\underset{*}{C}HN(CH_3)_2}} \qquad (7\text{-}23)$$

XXV

Only one of the two possible diastereoisomers is obtained. Reduction of dl-methadone with LAH occurs very readily to give the same isomeric racemic alcohol mixture, α-dl-methadol, in over 90% yield (73,75). Reduction of the optical isomers of methadone with LAH or by catalytic hydrogenation over platinum oxide similarly gives only one of the two possible isomeric alcohols, designated as α-methadols, with reversal of the sign of rotation. If the reduction of the ketone group is effected with sodium and propanol, the second diastereoisomeric form, β-methadol, is the predominant product, along with appreciable amounts of the α-isomer (76–78).

In contrast to methadone, isomethadone (6-dimethylamino-4,4-diphenyl-5-methyl-3-hexanone) (XXVI) is not reduced by catalytic hydrogenation over platinum oxide (75) as well as under other conditions (73). Reduction of XXVI with LAH yields the α-isomer to the exclusion of the β-isomethadol (73,75). Reduction of the optical isomers of isomethadone with LAH similarly yields the α-alcohols but, in contrast to the methadone series, the LAH reduction is not accompanied by a change in the sign of rotation.

$$\underset{\text{XXVI}}{\overset{\displaystyle O}{\underset{\displaystyle C_6H_5}{C_2H_5C\!-\!\overset{C_6H_5}{\underset{|}{C}}\!-\!CHCH_2N(CH_3)_2}}} \rightarrow \underset{}{\overset{\displaystyle OH}{\underset{\displaystyle C_6H_5}{C_2H_5CH\!-\!\overset{C_6H_5\ CH_3}{\underset{|}{C}}\!-\!CHCH_2N(CH_3)_2}}} \quad (7\text{-}24)$$

Reduction of dl-isomethadone and its enantiomorphs with sodium and propanol affords 30–40% yields of the β-isomethadols and 10–20% of the α-forms. The sign of rotation of the optical isomers of the isomethadols is opposite to that of the parent ketone (77).

Analogs of methadone and isomethadone behave in a manner similar to the parent compounds. Thus, the mono-p-chloro derivative of methadone (79) and the morpholinyl analog of methadone (73) are readily reduced with LAH. The latter is also reduced by catalytic hydrogenation over platinum oxide. On the other hand, the morpholinyl analog of isomethadone is readily reduced with LAH but is not affected by catalytic hydrogenation (73).

Bothner-By has utilized the complex aluminohydride ions, $Al(OR)_nH_{4-n}$, -OR representing the alkoxyl group derived from a ketone, in the preparation of optically active alcohols. Partial reaction of LAH with d-camphor gives a species capable of asymmetric reduction of ketones. Reductions of methyl ethyl ketone and pinacolone with LAH-d-camphor give optically active 2-butanol and pinacolyl alcohol, respectively (80).

$$\text{camphor} + LiAlH_4 \rightarrow Al(OC)_nH_{4-n} \quad (7\text{-}25)$$

$$CH_3COC_2H_5 + Al(OC)_nH_{4-n} \rightarrow \underset{OH}{CH_3CHC_2H_5} \quad (7\text{-}26)$$

Cram and Abd Elhafez have carried out a stereochemical study in which asymmetric induction has resulted from the synthesis of mixtures of diastereomeric secondary alcohols by the reaction of ketones with LAH (64).

$$H-\overset{\displaystyle R}{\underset{\displaystyle C_6H_5}{\overset{|}{\underset{|}{C}}}}-C\overset{\displaystyle O}{\underset{\displaystyle R_1}{\diagup}} \quad\xrightarrow{\text{LAH}}\quad H-\overset{\displaystyle R}{\underset{\displaystyle C_6H_5}{\overset{|}{\underset{|}{C}}}}-\overset{\displaystyle OH}{\underset{\displaystyle R_1}{\overset{|}{\underset{*}{C}}}}-H \qquad (7\text{-}27)$$

R	R_1	erythro : threo ratio
CH_3	CH_3	1 : 2.5
C_2H_5	CH_3	1 : 3
CH_3	C_2H_5	1 : 2
CH_3	C_6H_5	> 4 : 1

The tabulated results prompted the formulation of the rule that "that diastereomer will predominate which would be formed by the approach of the entering group from the least hindered side of the double bond when the rotational conformation of the carbon-carbon bond is such that the double bond is flanked by the two least bulky groups attached to the adjacent asymmetric center."

The LAH reduction of p-tolyl acetonyl sulfone (XXVII) in ether solution is reported to yield the hydrogenolysis product, p-tolyl-n-propyl sulfone (81).

$$CH_3\text{-}C_6H_4\text{-}\overset{O}{\underset{O}{\overset{\uparrow}{\underset{\downarrow}{S}}}}\text{-}CH_2\overset{O}{\overset{\|}{C}}CH_3 \quad\xrightarrow[75\%]{\text{LAH}}\quad CH_3\text{-}C_6H_4\text{-}\overset{O}{\underset{O}{\overset{\uparrow}{\underset{\downarrow}{S}}}}\text{-}CH_2CH_2CH_3 \qquad (7\text{-}28)$$

XXVII

The LAH reduction of various saturated and unconjugated unsaturated dialkyl ketones is summarized in Table XI.

7.2.1.b *Alkyl alicyclic ketones.* The LAH reduction of several saturated alkyl alicyclic ketones has been successfully carried out to yield the corresponding alkyl alicyclic carbinols.

	Ketone	% Carbinol	Ref.
C_5H_8O	Methyl cyclopropyl ketone	76	82
		80	83
$C_{19}H_{28}O_2$	1-Methyl-2-(5'-keto-1',2',3',4',5',6',7',8'-octahydronaphthylacetyl)cyclohexane	....	84
$C_{25}H_{48}O$	n-Octadecyl cyclohexyl ketone	97	85

The reduction of methyl cyclopropyl ketone (XXVIII) represents an interesting comparison of the effectiveness of various procedures. Reduc-

TABLE XI

LAH Reduction of Saturated and Unconjugated Unsaturated Dialkyl Ketones

	Ketone	Product	% Yield	Ref.
C_3Cl_6O	Hexachloroacetone	1,1,1,3,3,3-Hexachloro-2-propanol	97	1
C_3HCl_5O	Pentachloroacetone	1,1,1,3,3-Pentachloro-2-propanol	…	2
$C_3H_2BrF_3O$	3-Bromo-1,1,1-trifluoro-2-propanone	3-Bromo-1,1,1-trifluoro-2-propanol	74.8 }	3
		1,1,1-Trifluoro-2-propanol	…	
$C_3H_3F_3O$	1,1,1-Trifluoro-2-propanone	1,1,1-Trifluoro-2-propanol	82	4
			85	5
$C_3H_4Cl_2O$	1,3-Dichloro-2-propanone	1,3-Dichloro-2-propanol	77	6
			…	7
$C_3H_5N_3O$	Triazoacetone	1-Amino-2-propanol	48.1	8
C_3H_6O	Acetone	2-Propanol	…	9,10
			…	11
		2-Deutero-2-propanol[12]	53	13
			…	14
	2-Propanone-2-C^{14}	2-Propanol-2-C^{14}	…	15
C_3D_6O	Acetone-d_6	Propane-1,1,1,3,3,3-$d_6$2-ol	73	14
			100	16
		Propane-1,1,1,2,3,3-d_7-2-ol[12]	100	16
C_4Cl_8O	1,1,1,3,3,4,4,4-Octachloro-2-butanone	1,1,1,3,3,4,4-Octachloro-2-butanol	65	1
C_4H_8O	2-Butanone	2-Butanol	…	10
			80	17
		Optically active 2-butanol[18]	…	19
		[20]		
$C_5Cl_{10}O$	1,1,1,2,2,4,4,5,5,5-Decachloro-3-pentanone	2,5-Hexanediol	…	1
$C_6H_{10}O_2$	2,5-Hexanedione	2,5-Hexanediol	60–65	21
$C_6H_{10}O_3$	Ethyl acetoacetate	1,3-Butanediol	30	22
$C_6H_{12}O$	4-Methyl-2-pentanone	4-Methyl-2-pentanol	87	23
	Pinacolone	Optically active 3,3-dimethyl-2-butanol[18]	…	19

(Continued)

TABLE XI (Continued)

	Ketone	Product	% Yield	Ref.
$C_7H_{12}O_3$	Methyl hexan-4-on-1-oate	1,4-Hexanediol	...	24
$C_7H_{14}O$	Ethyl 2-methylacetoacetate	2-Methyl-1,3-butanediol	60	22
	4,4-Dimethyl-2-pentanone	4,4-Dimethyl-2-pentanol	63	25
$C_8H_{12}O$	4-Octen-2,7-dione	4-Octen-2,7-diol	74	26
$C_8H_{14}O$	6-Methylhept-5-en-2-one	6-Methylhept-5-en-2-ol	...	27
$C_8H_{14}O_3$	Methyl heptan-4-on-1-oate	1,4-Heptanediol	...	24
$C_8H_{15}NO$	4-(1'-Pyrrolidyl)-2-butanone	4-(1'-Pyrrolidyl)-2-butanol	...	28,29
	3-(1'-Pyrrolidyl)-2-butanone	3-(1'-Pyrrolidyl)-2-butanol	92.6	28
$C_8H_{16}O_2$	3-Hydroxymethyl-4-heptanone	2-Ethyl-1,3-hexanediol	...	30
$C_8H_{17}NO$	N-Butyl-4-amino-2-butanone	N-Butyl-4-amino-2-butanol	79	31
$C_9H_{10}O$	Phenylacetone	1-Phenyl-2-propanol	44	32
$C_9H_{14}O_5$	Diethyl acetonedicarboxylate	1,3,5-Pentanetriol	...	33
$C_9H_{17}NO$	1-(1'-Methyl-2'-piperidyl)-2-propanone (N-methyl-isopelletierine)	1-(1'-Methyl-2'-piperidyl)-2-propanol[34]	40	35
$C_9H_{18}O$	Hexamethylacetone	1,1,3,3,3-Hexamethyl-2-propanol	...	36
	2-Methyl-4-octanone	2-Methyl-4-octanol	...	37
$C_{10}H_{12}O$	3-Phenyl-2-butanone	3-Phenyl-2-butanol[38]	34	39
$C_{10}H_{12}O_2$	p-Anisylacetone	1-p-Anisyl-2-propanol	...	32
	1-Phenylbutan-2-on-1-ol	1-Phenyl-1,2-butanediol	75	40
$C_{10}H_{12}O_3S$	p-Tolylacetonyl sulfone	p-Tolyl-n-propyl sulfone	70	41
$C_{10}H_{13}NO$	1-(2'-Pyridyl)-4-pentanone	5-(2'-Pyridyl)-2-pentanol	75	42
$C_{10}H_{17}NO_2$	N-Acetylisopelletierine	1-(1'-Ethyl-2'-piperidyl)-2-propanol	71	43
$C_{10}H_{20}O$	5-Decanone	5-Decanol	99	37
$C_{11}H_{13}ClO_2$	4-Chloro-3,5-dimethylphenoxyacetone	1-(4'-Chloro-3',5'-dimethylphenoxy)-2-propanol	64	44
$C_{11}H_{14}O$	3-Phenyl-2-pentanone	3-Phenyl-2-pentanol[45]	80	39
	2-Phenyl-3-pentanone	2-Phenyl-3-pentanol[46]	...	39

Formula	Ketone	Product		
$C_{11}H_{17}O_5$	1,3-Diacetoxy-2-heptanone	1,2,3-Heptanetriol	85	47
$C_{11}H_{22}O$	5-Undecanone	5-Undecanol	84	37
$C_{11}H_{22}O_3$	1,1-Dibutoxy-2-propanone	1,1-Dibutoxy-2-propanol	74	48
$C_{11}H_{12}OS$	3-Methyl-2-thianaphthenylacetone	1-(3'-Methyl-2'-thianaphthenyl)-2-propanol	78	49
$C_{12}H_{14}O_2$	Dodeca-4,6,8,10-tetraen-2,3-dione	Dodeca-4,6,8,10-tetraen-2,3-diol	77[50]	51
$C_{12}H_{18}O_4$	Methyl 8-methylnon-7-en-2,4-dione-1-oate	8-Methylnona-4,7-dien-1,2-diol	68	52
$C_{12}H_{18}N_4O_2$	1,12-Bisdiazododecan-2,11-dione	2,11-Dodecanedione	24 ⎱	53
		Resin	...... ⎰	
$C_{12}H_{24}O$	6-Dodecanone	6-Dodecanol	84	37
$C_{13}H_{16}O_3$	Ethyl 2-benzylacetoacetate	2-Benzyl-1,3-butanediol	70	22
$C_{14}H_{22}N_2O$	3,4-Bis-(dimethylamino)-4-phenyl-2-butanone	3,4-Bis-(dimethylamino)-4-phenyl-2-butanol	87	54
$C_{15}H_{12}Cl_2O$	1,1-Di-p-chlorophenyl-2-propanone	1,1-Di-p-chlorophenyl-2-propanol	95	55
$C_{15}H_{14}O$	1,1-Diphenyl-2-propanone	1,1-Diphenyl-2-propanol	84,5[56]	58
			95[57]	58
$C_{15}H_{14}O_2$	9-Phenylnona-4,6,8-trien-2,3-dione	9-Phenylnona-4,6,8-trien-2,3-diol	75	59
$C_{15}H_{25}O_5$	1,3-Diacetoxy-2-undecanone	1,2,3-Undecanetriol	76	47
$C_{16}H_{16}O$	3,3-Diphenyl-2-butanone	3,3-Diphenyl-2-butanol	86	58
$C_{18}H_{26}N_2O_3$	3,4-Dimorpholino-4-phenyl-2-butanone	3,4-Dimorpholino-4-phenyl-2-butanol[34]	99[50]	54
$C_{19}H_{35}NO_4$	Methyl 2-oximinooctadecan-2-on-1-oate	Mixture of long-chain amines[20]	......	60
		2-Amino-1,3-octadecanediol (dihydrosphingosine)	......[61]	62
$C_{19}H_{36}N_2O$	1-Diazo-2-nonadecanone	1-Amino-2-nonadecanol	99	53
$C_{20}H_{34}O_3$	3,4-Bis-(p-anisyl)-2-hexanone	3,4-Bis-(p-anisyl)-2-hexanol[34]	95	63
$C_{20}H_{30}N_2O$	3,4-Dipiperidino-4-phenyl-2-butanone	3,4-Didiperidino-4-phenyl-2-butanol	84	54
$C_{21}H_{26}ClNO$	6-Dimethylamino-4-p-chlorophenyl-4-phenyl-3-heptanone	6-Dimethylamino-4-p-chlorophenyl-4-phenyl-3-heptanol	98	64

(Continued)

TABLE XI (Continued)

	Ketone	Product	% Yield	Ref.
C₂₁H₂₇NO	dl-6-Dimethylamino-4,4-diphenyl-3-heptanone (dl-Methadone)	α-dl-Dimethylamino-4,4-diphenyl-3-heptanol (α-dl-Methadol)	90	65
			98	66
	dl-6-Dimethylamino-4,4-diphenyl-5-methyl-3-hexanone (dl-Isomethadone)	α-dl-6-Dimethylamino-4,4-diphenyl-5-methyl-3-hexanol (α-dl-Isomethadol)	....	67
			75	65
			100	66
	l-Isomethadone	α-l-Isomethadol	84	68
	d-Isomethadone	α-d-Isomethadol	84	68
C₂₃H₂₈N₂O₂	3-Morpholino-4-tetrahydroquinolino-4-phenyl-2-butanone	3-Morpholino-4-tetrahydroquinolino-4-phenyl-2-butanol	81	54
C₂₃H₂₉NO₂	4,4-Diphenyl-6-morpholinyl-3-heptanone	4,4-Diphenyl-6-morpholinyl-3-heptanol	"good"	66
	4,4-Diphenyl-5-methyl-6-morpholinyl-3-hexanone	4,4-Diphenyl-5-methyl-6-morpholinyl-3-hexanol	"good"	66
C₂₈H₃₄N₂O₃	3,4-Di-(p-methoxy-N-methylbenzylamino)-4-phenyl-2-butanone	3,4-Di-(p-methoxy-N-methylbenzylamino)-4-phenyl-2-butanol	....	54

References—Table XI

[1] M. Geiger, E. Usteri, and C. Gränacher, *Helv. Chim. Acta,* 34, 1335 (1951).
[2] Ciba Ltd., Australian Pat. Appln. 9261/52.
[3] E. T. McBee and T. M. Burton, *J. Am. Chem. Soc.,* 74, 3022 (1952).
[4] A. L. Henne, M. A. Smook, and R. L. Pelley, *ibid.,* 72, 4756 (1950).
[5] A. L. Henne and R. L. Pelley, *ibid.,* 74, 1426 (1952).
[6] H. Schlenk and B. Lamp, *ibid.,* 73, 5493 (1951).
[7] H. Schlenk and B. W. De Haas, *Nuclear Sci. Abstracts,* 5, 543 (1951); A.E.C.U. 1261.
[8] J. H. Boyer, *J. Am. Chem. Soc.,* 73, 5865 (1951).
[9] H. Felkin, *Bull. soc. chim. France,* [5] 18, 347 (1951).
[10] H. I. Schlesinger and A. E. Finholt, U. S. Pat. 2,576,311 (November 11, 1951).
[11] N. L. Paddock, *Nature,* 167, 1070 (1951); reduction carried out in absence of ether.
[12] Reduction with lithium aluminum deuteride.
[13] A. Leo and F. H. Westheimer, *J. Am. Chem. Soc.,* 74, 4383 (1952).
[14] V. J. Shiner, Jr., *ibid.,* 74, 5285 (1952).
[15] A. V. Logan and J. Murray, *ibid.,* 74, 2436 (1952).
[16] F. E. Condon, *ibid.,* 73, 4675 (1951).
[17] R. F. Nystrom and W. G. Brown, *ibid.,* 69, 1197 (1947).
[18] Treatment of ketone with complex from *d*-camphor and LAH.
[19] A. A. Bothner-By, *J. Am. Chem. Soc.,* 73, 846 (1951).
[20] Product of undetermined structure.
[21] M. M. Sprung and F. O. Guenther, *J. Am. Chem. Soc.,* 73, 1884 (1951).
[22] E. Buchta and H. Bayer, *Ann.,* 573, 227 (1951).
[23] E. Larsson, *Trans. Chalmers Univ. Technol., Gothenburg,* 94, 15 (1950).
[24] C. J. Morel and W. G. Stoll, *Helv. Chim. Acta,* 35, 2561 (1952).
[25] N. G. Gaylord and L. Caul, unpublished work.
[26] P. Karrer and C. H. Eugster, *Helv. Chim. Acta,* 32, 1934 (1949).
[27] L. Bateman, J. I. Cunneen, and J. A. Lyons, *J. Chem. Soc.,* 1951, 2290.
[28] R. B. Moffett, *J. Org. Chem.,* 14, 862 (1949).
[29] W. B. Reid, Jr., U. S. Pat. 2,605,266 (July 29, 1952).
[30] R. L. Wear, *J. Am. Chem. Soc.,* 73, 2390 (1951).
[31] N. J. Leonard, S. Swann, Jr., and H. L. Dryden, Jr., *ibid.,* 74, 2871 (1952).
[32] S. Winstein, M. Brown, K. C. Schreiber, and A. H. Schlesinger, *ibid.,* 74, 1140 (1952).
[33] M. Viscontini and C. Ebnöther, *Helv. Chim. Acta,* 34, 116 (1951).
[34] Mixture of isomers.
[35] L. Marion and M. Chaput, *Can. J. Research,* 27B, 215 (1949).
[36] N. C. Cook and W. C. Percival, *J. Am. Chem. Soc.,* 71, 4141 (1949).
[37] M. Protiva, O. Exner *et al., Chem. Listy,* 46, 37 (1952); through M. Ferles and J. Rudinger, *Chem. Listy,* 47, 113 (1953).
[38] Ratio erythro:threo = 1:2.5.
[39] D. J. Cram and F. A. Abd Elhafez, *J. Am. Chem. Soc.,* 74, 5828 (1952).
[40] J. W. Lynn and J. English, Jr., *ibid.,* 73, 4284 (1951).
[41] H. J. Backer, J. Strating, and J. Drenth, *Rec. trav. chim.,* 70, 365 (1951).
[42] V. Boekelheide and J. H. Mason, *J. Am. Chem. Soc.,* 73, 2356 (1951).
[43] F. Galinovsky and O. Vogl, *Monatsh.,* 83, 1055 (1952).
[44] B. J. Ludwig, W. A. West, and W. E. Currie, *J. Am. Chem. Soc.,* 74, 1935 (1952).
[45] Ratio erythro:threo = 1:3.
[46] Ratio erythro:threo = 1:2.

[47]M. Proštenik and J. Biščan, *Arhiv Kemi*, 22, 177 (1951); through *Chem. Abstracts*, 46, 3951 (1952).

[48]L. Hough and J. K. N. Jones, *J. Chem. Soc.*, 1952, 4052.

[49]R. Gaertner, *J. Am. Chem. Soc.*, 74, 2991 (1952).

[50]Reduction carried out in benzene-ether mixture.

[51]F. Bohlmann, *Chem. Ber.*, 85, 386 (1952).

[52]R. Helg and H. Schinz, *Helv. Chim. Acta*, 35, 2406 (1952).

[53]W. Gruber and H. Renner, *Monatsh.*, 81, 751 (1950).

[54]N. H. Cromwell and Kwan-Chung Tsou, *J. Org. Chem.*, 15, 1219 (1950).

[55]E. J. Skerrett and D. Woodcock, *J. Chem. Soc.*, 1952, 3308.

[56]From solid isomer of 1,1-diphenylacetone.

[57]From liquid isomer of 1,1-diphenylacetone.

[58]S. Winstein, B. K. Morse, E. Grunwald, K. C. Schreiber, and J. Corse, *J. Am. Chem. Soc.*, 74, 1113 (1952).

[59]F. Bohlman, *Chem. Ber.*, 85, 1144 (1952).

[60]G. I. Gregory and T. Malkin, *J. Chem. Soc.*, 1951, 2453.

[61]Isolated as tribenzoyl derivative.

[62]N. Fisher, *Chemistry and Industry*, 1952, 130.

[63]J. H. Burckhalter and J. Sam, *J. Am. Chem. Soc.*, 74, 187 (1952).

[64]M. E. Speeter, L. C. Cheney, and S. B. Binkley, *ibid.*, 72, 1659 (1950).

[65]E. L. May and E. Mosettig, *J. Org. Chem.*, 13, 663 (1948).

[66]M. E. Speeter, W. M. Byrd, L. C. Cheney, and S. B. Binkley, *J. Am. Chem. Soc.*, 71, 57 (1949).

[67]N. B. Eddy, E. L. May, and E. Mosettig, *J. Org. Chem.*, 17, 321 (1952).

[68]E. L. May and N. B. Eddy, *ibid.*, 17, 1210 (1952).

tion of XXVIII with LAH in ether gives methyl cyclopropyl carbinol (XXIX) in 76–80% yield (82,83).

$$ \text{(7-29)} $$

Meerwein-Ponndorf reduction of XXVIII with aluminum isopropoxide yields 23% XXIX accompanied by higher-boiling condensation products (83). Reduction of XXVIII with sodium in ethanol yields 42% XXIX (82) while reduction with sodium in liquid ammonia yields exclusively the ring opening products, 2-pentanone and 2-pentanol (83). Catalytic hydrogenation over Raney nickel in ethanol at 90–125 °C. under 1200 psi pressure yields 34% XXIX and 30% 2-pentanol (82). The same products in a 3 : 2 ratio are obtained over nickel-on-kieselguhr at 50–60° under 600–1100 psi pressure (83). Hydrogenation over barium-promoted copper chromite under 1750 psi pressure, at 100° yields 90% XXIX, at 120° yields 87% XXIX and at 150° yields 76% XXIX contaminated with 2-pentanol (82). Operating with Raney nickel, at ordinary temperature and pressure in the presence of sodium hydroxide, is reported to satisfactorily yield the corresponding carbinol without opening the cyclopropyl ring in the reduction of ethyl and butyl cyclopropyl ketones (86).

The α- and β-mycolic acids have been isolated from a virulent strain of Mycobacterium tuberculosis. By careful chromic acid oxidation, the acids are converted to methoxy-α- and β-normycolanone, $C_{87}H_{174}O_2$, m.p. 64–67° and 85–88°, respectively. Reduction of the carbonyl compounds, which have been given the partial structure $(CH_3OC_{60}H_{120})$—CO—CH_2-$C_{24}H_{49}$, with LAH yields the corresponding carbinol derivatives, m.p. 70–74° and 88–92°, respectively (87).

7.2.1.c   *Alkyl and alicyclic aryl ketones.* Alkyl and alicyclic phenyl, naphthryl, phenanthryl, anthracyl, and indanyl ketones have been successfully reduced to the corresponding carbinols. Steric factors here, as with the alkyl ketones, seem to present little hindrance to successful reduction. Acetomesitylene (XXX) is reduced to the carbinol in quantitative yield (1-3).

$$ \text{(7-30)} $$

The treatment of 1,4-di-(2'-hydroxy-3',4',6'-trimethylphenyl)-1,4-butane-
dione (XXXI) with LAH is reported to result in "poor reduction" (88).
The absence of experimental details prevents attributing the apparent
poor results to steric factors or the precipitation of the complex formed
by the reaction of LAH and the active hydrogen.

XXXI   XXXII

The reduction of 1,3-diphenyl-2-acetoxy-3-piperidino-1-propanone
(XXXII) with LAH yields 63% of 1,3-diphenyl-3-piperidino-1,2-propane-
diol. No reaction occurs upon the attempted catalytic hydrogenation of
XXXII with 45 psi hydrogen pressure over Raney nickel, platinum oxide
or palladium-on-charcoal (89).

LAH reduction of 1-phenyl-4-(2'-pyridyl)-1-butanone (XXXIII) yields
the corresponding carbinol while catalytic hydrogenation over platinum
oxide in ethanol results in cyclization and yields 4-phenylquinolizidine
(XXXIV) (90).

XXXIII   XXXIV

LAH reduction of 9-acetylanthracene (XXXV) and 9-(1'-keto-3'-morpho-
linopropyl)anthracene (XXXVI) yields the corresponding carbinol (91).

XXXV   (7-31)

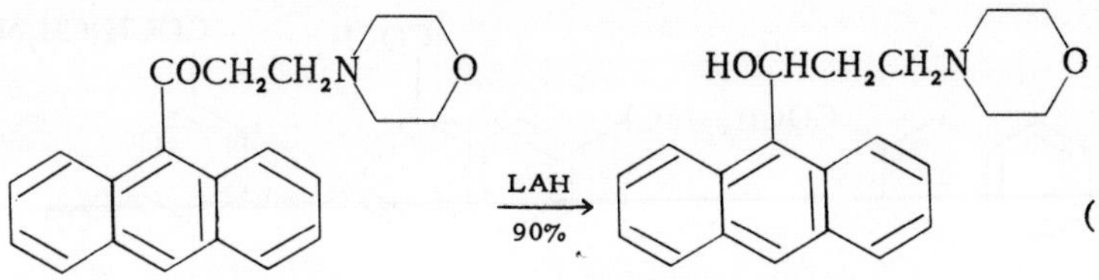

(7-32)

XXXVI

Reduction of XXXV and XXXVI with two moles of hydrogen over platinum oxide in alcohol results in reduction of the terminal ring but leaves the carbonyl group intact (92).

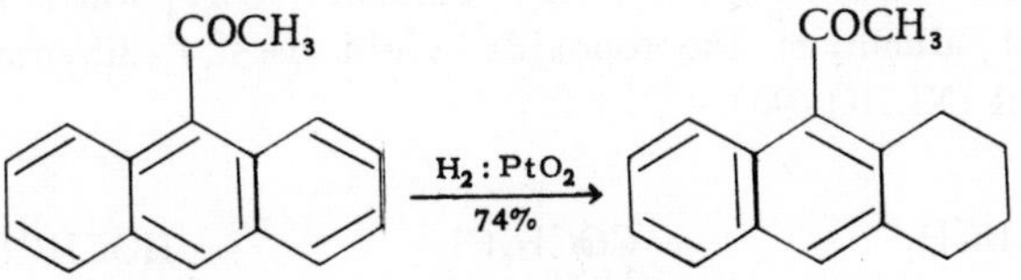

(7-33)

XXXV

Reduction of α,β-dimorpholinoisobutyrophenone (XXXVII) with LAH yields 1-phenyl-2-methyl-2,3-dimorpholino-1-propanol. Attempts to reduce XXXVII by catalytic hydrogenation at 80° in acetic acid results in its cleavage to morpholine and α-morpholinoisobutyrophenone (93).

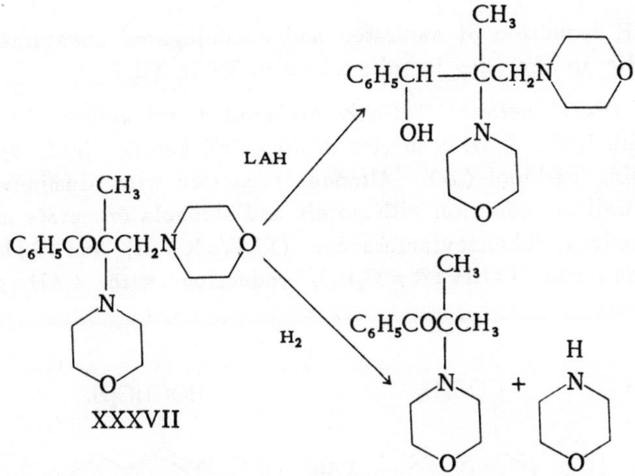

(7-34)

XXXVII

Reduction of 6-chloro-2-acetonaphthone (XXXVIII) (94), 7-chloro-1-acetonaphthone (XXXIX) (95), and adrenalone (XL) (96) with LAH and with aluminum isopropoxide results in equivalent yields of the corresponding carbinols.

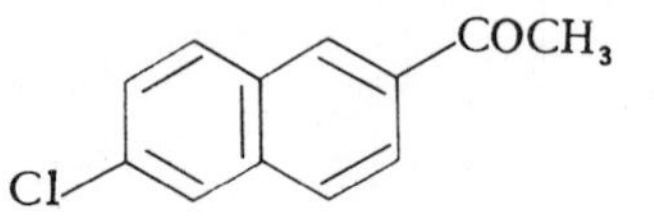

XXXVIII 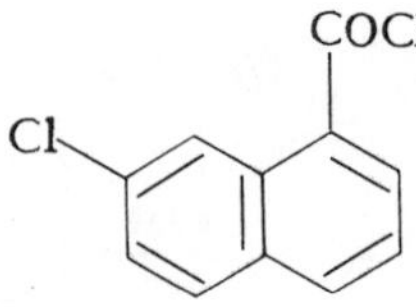   XXXIX 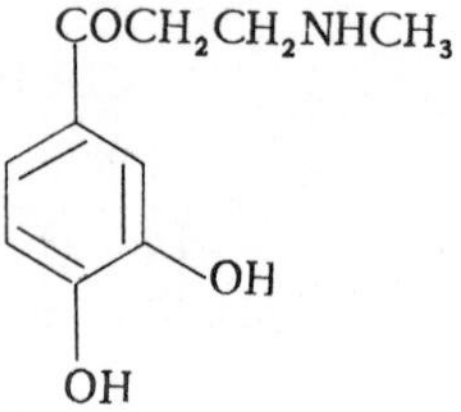   XL

Reduction of XL with sodium borohydride yields 98% of the carbinol, adrenaline. Reduction of α-chloro-3,4-dihydroxyacetophenone (XLI) with LAH yields 1-(3′,4′-dihydroxyphenyl)ethanol (XLII) while sodium borohydride and aluminum isopropoxide yield 1-(3′,4′-dihydroxyphenyl)-2-chloroethanol (XLIII) (96).

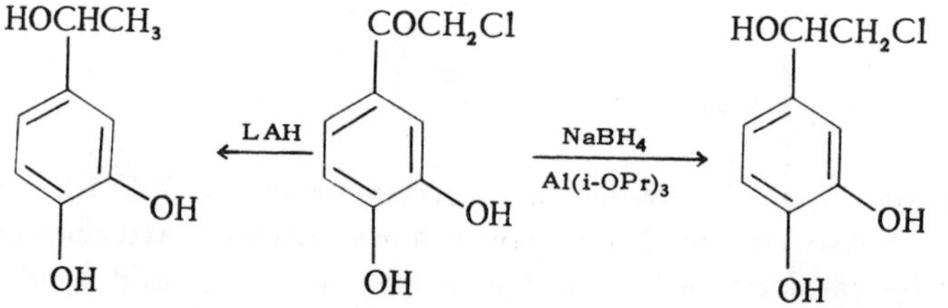

XLII   XLI   XLIII   (7-35)

The LAH reduction of saturated and unconjugated unsaturated alkyl and alicyclic aryl ketones is summarized in Table XII.

7.2.1.d *Diaryl ketones.* Highly hindered diaryl ketones are readily reduced with LAH. LAH reduction of dimesityl ketone yields 93% of the corresponding carbinol (97). Although reduction with aluminum isopropoxide as well as reduction with metals and alcohols or metals and acids fails to reduce 9-benzoylanthracene (XLIV : R = H) and 9-phenyl-10-benzoylanthracene (XLIV : R = C$_6$H$_5$), reduction with LAH proceeds smoothly (98).

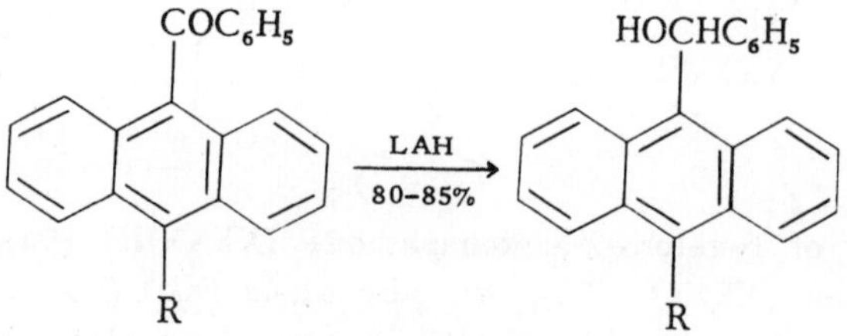

R = H and C$_6$H$_5$

XLIV   (7-36)

TABLE XII

LAH Reduction of Saturated and Unconjugated Unsaturated Alkyl and Alicyclic Aryl Ketones

	Ketone	Product	% Yield	Ref.
$C_8H_6Br_2O$	p-Bromophenacyl bromide	1-(p-Bromophenyl)ethanol	85	1
		1-(p-Bromophenyl)-2-bromoethanol	90	2
C_8H_6BrClO	p-Chlorophenacyl bromide	1-(p-Chlorophenyl)-2-bromoethanol	69	2
$C_8H_6N_2O$	Diazoacetophenone	1-Phenyl-2-aminoethanol	77	2
		Acetophenone	93 } 3	3
C_8H_7BrO	ω-Bromoacetophenone	1-Phenylethanol	…	4
	p-Bromoacetophenone	1-(p-Bromophenyl)ethanol	83	5
C_8H_7ClO	p-Chloroacetophenone	1-(p-Chlorophenyl)ethanol	…	5
	ω-Chloro-3,4-dihydroxyacetophenone	1-(3,4-Dihydroxyphenyl)ethanol	34	6
$C_8H_7NO_2$	ω-Oximinoacetophenone	1-Phenyl-2-oximinoethanol	49.5	7
$C_8H_7N_3O$	Phenacyl azide	1-Phenyl-2-aminoethanol	84	8
C_8H_8O	Acetophenone	1-Phenylethanol	95	9
				10
$C_9H_{11}NO_3$	ω-Methylamino-3,4-dihydroxyacetophenone (Adrenalone)	1-(3,4-Dihydroxyphenyl)-2-methylaminoethanol (Adrenaline)	81.9	6
$C_{10}H_{10}N_2O_3$	ω-Diazo-3,4-dimethoxyacetophenone	no definite product	…	3
$C_{10}H_{13}NO$	ω-Dimethylaminoacetophenone	1-Phenyl-2-dimethylaminoethanol	83	11
$C_{11}H_{11}NO_4$	Ethyl 2-benzoyl-2-oximinoacetate	poorly defined products (see text)	…	12,13
		allo-dl-3-Phenylserinol	…	14
$C_{11}H_{12}O_4$	Methyl 6-methoxy-2-acetylbenzoate	1-(3-Methoxy-2-hydroxymethylphenyl) ethanol	97	15
$C_{11}H_{14}O$	Acetomesitylene	1-Mesitylethanol	100	16,17
$C_{11}H_{14}O_3$	1-(3,5-Dihydroxyphenyl)-1-pentanone	1-(3,5-Dihydroxyphenyl)-1-pentanol	90	18
$C_{11}H_{15}NO$	p-Dimethylaminopropiophenone	1-(p-Dimethylaminophenyl)-1-propanol	55	19
$C_{12}H_9ClO$	7-Chloro-1-acetonaphthone	1-(7-Chloro-1-naphthyl)ethanol	85	20
	6-Chloro-2-acetonaphthone	1-(6-Chloro-2-naphthyl)ethanol	75–80	21
$C_{12}H_{16}O$	Caprophenone	1-Phenyl-1-hexanol	84	22

(Continued)

TABLE XII (Continued)

	Ketone	Product	% Yield	Ref.
C$_{12}$H$_{17}$NO	p-Dimethylaminobutyrophenone	1-(p-Dimethylaminophenyl)-1-butanol	61	19
C$_{13}$H$_{15}$ClO	1-Chloro-1-benzoylcyclohexane	1-(1'-Chlorocyclohexyl)-1-phenylmethanol	50	23
C$_{13}$H$_{15}$NO$_4$	Ethyl 2-acetamidobenzoylacetate	dl-erythro-1-Phenyl 2-acetamido-1,3-propanediol	...[24]	25
C$_{13}$H$_{18}$O$_3$	1-(3,5-Dimethoxyphenyl)-1-pentanone	1-(3,5-Dimethoxyphenyl)-1-pentanol	89	18
C$_{14}$H$_{10}$O$_2$	Benzil	Hydrobenzoin	93	9
		Hydrobenzoin (meso)	81[26]	1
		Isohydrobenzoin	5	1
		Hydrobenzoin (meso)	90[27]	1
		Isohydrobenzoin	...	
C$_{14}$H$_{11}$BrO	Desyl bromide	erythro-1,2-Diphenyl-2-bromoethanol	10	2
C$_{14}$H$_{11}$ClO	Desyl chloride	erythro-1,2-Diphenyl-2-chloroethanol	30–76	2
		erythro- and threo- 1,2-Diphenyl-2-chloroethanol (1:1)	95	23
C$_{14}$H$_{19}$NO$_2$	α-Morpholinoisobutyrophenone	1-Phenyl-2-morpholino-2-methyl-1-propanol	50[28]	29
C$_{15}$H$_{12}$O$_2$	Benzalacetophenone oxide	1,3-Diphenyl-1,2-propanediol	77	30
C$_{15}$H$_{12}$N$_2$O$_2$	Benzoylglyoxal phenylhydrazone	crystalline compound, m.p. 138.5°	...	12
C$_{15}$H$_{13}$NO$_2$	o-Acetylbenzanilide	1-(2-Benzylaminophenyl) ethanol	...	31
C$_{15}$H$_{14}$O	1,2-Diphenyl-1-propanone	1,2-Diphenyl-1-propanol[32]	95	33
	D(+)-1,2-Diphenyl-1-propanone	(−)-erythro-1,2-Diphenyl-1-propanol	67	35
		(−)-threo-1,2-Diphenyl-1-propanol	[34]	
C$_{15}$H$_{15}$NO	1-Phenyl-4-(2'-pyridyl)-1-butanone	1-Phenyl-4-(2'-pyridyl)-1-butanol	54	36
	ω-Benzylaminoacetophenone	1-Phenyl-2-benzylaminoethanol	88	37
C$_{16}$H$_{12}$O	9-Acetylanthracene	9-(1-Hydroxyethyl)anthracene	80	38
	2-Acetylphenanthrene	1-(2-Phenanthryl)ethanol	95	39
	3-Acetylphenanthrene	1-(3-Phenanthryl)ethanol	96.5	39
C$_{16}$H$_{14}$O$_2$	1,4-Diphenyl-1,4-butanedione	1,4-Diphenyl-1,4-butanediol	100[40]	41
C$_{16}$H$_{16}$O$_2$	1,4-Diphenylbutan-1-ol-4-one	1,4-Diphenyl-1,4-butanediol	...[40]	41
C$_{17}$H$_{16}$N$_2$O$_3$	Ethyl 2-phenylhydrazinobenzoylacetate	Benzaldehyde phenylhydrazone	45	14

Formula	Ketone	Product	Yield	Ref.
C17H17NO3	1-p-Biphenylyl-2-acetamidopropan-3-ol-1-one	1-p-Biphenylyl-2-acetamido-1,3-propanediol	....	42
C18H25NO	Spiro(cyclohexane-1,1'-x'-acetyl-3'-dimethylaminoindane)	Spiro[cyclohexane-1,1',3'-dimethylamino-x'-(1-hydroxyethyl)indane]	99	43
C18H26N2O3	1-Phenyl-2,3-dimorpholino-1-butanone	1-Phenyl-2,3-dimorpholino-1-butanol	80	44
	1-Phenyl-2-methyl-2,3-dimorpholino-1-propanone	1-Phenyl-2-methyl-2,3-dimorpholino-1-propanol	87–90	29
C19H16O	1-Naphthylmethyl o-tolyl ketone	1-(o-Tolyl)-2-(1-naphthyl)ethanol	....	45
C19H18N2OS	9ω-(2'-Thiazolylaminoacetyl)-1,2,3,4-tetrahydrophenanthrene	1-(1,2,3,4-Tetrahydrophenanthryl)-2-(2'-thiazolylamino)ethanol	"good"	46
C19H19NO	9-(1-Keto-3-dimethylaminopropyl)anthracene	9-(1-Hydroxy-3-dimethylaminopropyl)anthracene	45	38
C19H21NO3	1,3-Diphenyl-3-morpholinopropan-2-ol-1-one	1,3-Diphenyl-3-morpholino-1,2-propanediol	50	47
C20H23NO2	1,3-Diphenyl-3-piperidinopropan-2-ol-1-one	1,3-Diphenyl-3-piperidino-1,2-propanediol	72	47
C20H24O	Desoxymesitoin	1,2-Dimesitylethanol	100	48
C20H26O3	1-[3-(α-p-Methoxyphenylpropyl)-4-methoxy]-phenyl-1-propanone	1-[3-(α-p-Methoxyphenylpropyl)-4-methoxy]-phenyl-1-propanol	....	49
C20H29NO	Spiro(cyclohexane-1,1'-x'-n-butyryl-3'-dimethylaminoindane)	Spiro[cyclohexane-1,1',3'-dimethylamino-x'-(1-hydroxybutyl)indane]	99	43
C20H30N2O2	1-Phenyl-2,3-dipiperidino-1-butanone	1-Phenyl-2,3-dipiperidino-1-butanol	85	44
C21H21NO2	9-(1-Keto-3-morpholinopropyl)anthracene	9-(1-Hydroxy-3-morpholinopropyl)anthracene	90[29]	38
C21H24N2O	2-Benzoyl-2-phenyl-4-diethylaminobutyronitrile	Benzaldehyde	....	51
		2-Phenyl-4-diethylaminobutyronitrile	....	51
C21H26O	1,2-Dimesityl-1-propanone	1,2-Dimesityl-1-propanol	80	48
C21H26O2	2-Phenacylbenzophenone	2-(2-Hydroxy-2-phenylethyl) benzhydrol	43	50
C21H26N2O2	1-Phenyl-2-morpholino-3-N-methylbenzylamino-1-propanone	1-Phenyl-2-morpholino-3-N-methylbenzylamino-1-propanol	38	29
	1-Phenyl-2-methyl-2-benzylamino-3-morpholino-1-propanone	1-Phenyl-2-methyl-2-benzylamino-3-morpholino-1-propanol	10	29
C22H25NO3	1,3-Diphenyl-2-acetoxy-3-piperidino-1-propanone	1,3-Diphenyl-3-piperidino-1,2-propanediol	63	52
C22H26O2	1,2-Dimesitoylethane	1,4-Dimesityl-1,4-butanediol	....	41
C22H26O4	1,4-Di:(2-hydroxy-3,4,6-trimethylphenyl)-1,4-butanedione	"poor reduction"	....	53

(Continued)

TABLE XII (Continued)

Ketone	Product	% Yield	Ref.
C$_{22}$H$_{28}$O$_2$ 1,4-Dimesitylbutan-1-ol-4-one	1,4-Dimesityl-1,4-butanediol	....	41
C$_{23}$H$_{20}$N$_2$OS 9-(ω-2-Benzothiazolylaminoacetyl)-1,2,3,4-tetrahydrophenanthrene	1-(1,2,3,4-Tetrahydrophenanthryl)-2-(2'-benzothiazolylamino)ethanol	"good"	46
C$_{23}$H$_{28}$N$_2$O$_3$ 1,3-Diphenyl-2,3-dimorpholino-1-propanone	1,3-Diphenyl-2,3-dimorpholino-1-propanol	75	54
C$_{24}$H$_{23}$NO$_2$ 1,3-Diphenyl-3-tetrahydroisoquinolinopropan-2-ol-1-one	1,3-Diphenyl-3-tetrahydroisoquinolino-1,2-propanediol	85	55
C$_{24}$H$_{25}$NO 9-(ω-2-Phenylethylaminoacetyl)-1,2,3,4-tetrahydrophenanthrene	1-(1,2,3,4-Tetrahydrophenanthryl)-2-(2-phenylethylamino)ethanol	"good"	46
C$_{25}$H$_{25}$NO$_3$ 1,3-Diphenyl-2-acetoxy-3-N-methylbenzylamino-1-propanone	1,3-Diphenyl-3-N-methylbenzylamino-1,2-propanediol	45	52
C$_{26}$H$_{30}$N$_2$O 9-(ω-p-N,N-Diethylaminoanilinoacetyl)-1,2,3,4-tetrahydrophenanthrene	1-(1,2,3,4-Tetrahydrophenanthryl)-2-(p-N,N-diethylaminoanilino)ethanol	"good"	46
C$_{27}$H$_{27}$NO$_3$ 1,3-Diphenyl-2-acetoxy-3-piperidino-1-propanone	1,3-Diphenyl-3-piperidino-1,2-propanediol	63	52
C$_{27}$H$_{30}$N$_2$O$_2$ 1-Phenyl-2-dibenzylamino-3-morpholino-1-propanone	1-Phenyl-2-dibenzylamino-3-morpholino-1-propanol	71	29
C$_{27}$H$_{35}$NO 9-(1-Keto-3-diamylaminopropyl)anthracene	9-(1-Hydroxy-3-diamylaminopropyl)anthracene	....	38
C$_{28}$H$_{30}$N$_2$O$_2$ 1,3-Diphenyl-2-morpholino-3-tetrahydroquinolino-1-propanone	1,3-Diphenyl-2-morpholino-3-tetrahydroquinolino-1-propanol	80	54
C$_{28}$H$_{32}$N$_2$O$_2$ 1-Phenyl-2-methyl-2-dibenzylamino-3-morpholino-1-propanone	1-Phenyl-2-methyl-2-dibenzylamino-3-morpholino-1-propanol	73	29
C$_{30}$H$_{22}$O$_2$ 9,10-Bis-(phenylacetyl)anthracene	9,10-Bis-(1-hydroxyphenylethyl)anthracene	....	56
9,10-Diphenacylanthracene	9,10-Bis-(2-hydroxyphenylethyl)anthracene	....	56

References—Table XII

[1]L. W. Trevoy and W. G. Brown, *J. Am. Chem. Soc.*, 71, 1675 (1949).

[2]R. E. Lutz, R. L. Wayland, Jr., and H. G. France, *ibid.*, 72, 5511 (1950).

[3]W. Gruber and H. Renner, *Monatsh.*, 81, 751 (1950).

[4]L. W. Trevoy, unpublished work; through S. W. Chaikin and W. G. Brown, *J. Am. Chem. Soc.*, 71, 122 (1949).

[5]K. B. Everard, L. Kumar, and L. E. Sutton, *J. Chem. Soc.*, 1951, 2807.

[6]A. L. P. Coll, *Afinidad*, 27, 549 (1950); *Chem. Abstracts*, 45, 7981 (1951).

[7]H. Felkin, *Compt. rend.*, 230, 304 (1950).

[8]J. H. Boyer, *J. Am. Chem. Soc.*, 73, 5865 (1951).

[9]E. Larsson, *Trans. Chalmers Univ. Technol.*, Gothenburg, 94, 15 (1950).

[10]M. S. Kharasch, A. Fono, and W. Nudenberg, *J. Org. Chem.*, 15, 753 (1950).

[11]M. Protiva and J. O. Jílek, *Chem. Listy*, in press; through M. Ferles and J. Rudinger, *Chem. Listy*, 47, 113 (1953).

[12]I. Elphimoff-Felkin, H. Felkin, B. Tchoubar, and Z. Welvart, *Bull. soc. chim. France*, [5] 19, 252 (1952).

[13]M. Viscontini and K. Adank, *Helv. Chim. Acta*, 35, 1342 (1952).

[14]M. Viscontini, *ibid.*, 35, 1803 (1952).

[15]R. Kuhn and K. Dury, *Chem. Ber.*, 84, 848 (1951).

[16]R. F. Nystrom and W. G. Brown, *J. Am. Chem. Soc.*, 69, 1197 (1947).

[17]H. I. Schlesinger and A. E. Finholt, U. S. Pat. 2,576,311 (November 27, 1951).

[18]R. Adams, M. Harfenist and S. Loewe, *J. Am. Chem. Soc.*, 71, 1642 (1949).

[19]A. W. Nineham, *J. Chem. Soc.*, 1952, 635.

[20]C. C. Price and Sing-Tuh Voong, *J. Org. Chem.*, 14, 111 (1949).

[21]C. C. Price and G. H. Schilling, *J. Am. Chem. Soc.*, 70, 4265 (1948).

[22]M. Protiva, unpublished work; through J. Rudinger, M. Ferles and M. Protiva, *Chem. Listy*, 45, 342 (1951).

[23]H. Felkin, *Compt. rend.*, 231, 1316 (1950).

[24]Isolated as triacetyl derivative after acetylation.

[25]G. Carrara, V. D'Ameto, and M. Bellenghi, *Gazz. chim. ital.*, 80, 822 (1950).

[26]Reaction carried out at $35°$.

[27]Reaction carried out at $-80°$.

[28]Isolated as hydrochloride.

[29]A. L. Williams and A. R. Day, *J. Am. Chem. Soc.*, 74, 3875 (1952).

[30]W. Herz, *ibid.*, 74, 2928 (1952).

[31]B. Witkop and J. B. Patrick, *ibid.*, 74, 3855 (1952).

[32]Ratio erythro : threo => 4 : 1

[33]D. J. Cram and F. A. Abd Elhafez, *J. Am. Chem. Soc.*, 74, 5828 (1952).

[34]Isolated as *p*-nitrobenzoate.

[35]F. A. Abd Elhafez and D. J. Cram, *ibid.*, 74, 5846 (1952).

[36]V. Boekelheide and E. J. Agnello, *J. Am. Chem. Soc.*, 72, 5005 (1950).

[37]C. L. Browne and R. E. Lutz, *J. Org. Chem.*, 17, 1187 (1952).

[38]E. L. May and E. Mosettig, *J. Am. Chem. Soc.*, 73, 1301 (1951).

[39]C. C. Price and B. D. Halpern, *ibid.*, 73, 818 (1951).

[40]Equal amounts of two isomers, m.p. $113°$ and m.p. $90°$.

[41]R. E. Lutz and J. S. Gillespie, Jr., *J. Am. Chem. Soc.*, 72, 2002 (1950).

[42]M. Colonna and C. Runti, *Ann. chim. (Rome)*, 41, 740 (1951); through M. Ferles and J. Rudinger, *Chem. Listy*, 47, 115 (1953).

[43]L. H. Schwartzman and G. F. Woods, *J. Org. Chem.*, 17, 492 (1952).

[44]J. D. Sculley and N. H. Cromwell, *ibid.*, 16, 94 (1951).

[45]W. S. Johnson, J. Szmuszkovicz, and M. Miller, *J. Am. Chem. Soc.*, 72, 3726 (1950).

[46]H. Wishingsky and M. Rubin, *Abstracts of Papers*, XIIth International Congress of Pure and Applied Chemistry, New York, N. Y., September 1951, p. 307.

[47]N. H. Cromwell and N. G. Barker, *J. Am. Chem. Soc.*, 72, 4110 (1950).

[48]R. E. Lutz and D. F. Hinkley, *ibid.*, 72, 4091 (1950).

[49]J. M. Van der Zanden and G. de Vries, *Rec. trav. chim.*, 71, 879 (1952).

[50]S. Siegel, S. K. Coburn, and D. R. Levering, *J. Am. Chem. Soc.*, 73, 3163 (1951).

[51]P. Reynaud and J. Matti, *Bull. soc. chim. France*, [5] 18, 612 (1951).

[52]N. H. Cromwell and F. W. Starks, *J. Am. Chem. Soc.*, 72, 4108 (1950).

[53]L. I. Smith and R. R. Holmes, *ibid.*, 73, 3851 (1951).

[54]N. H. Cromwell and Kwan-Chung Tsou, *J. Org. Chem.*, 15, 1219 (1950).

[55]N. G. Barker and N. H. Cromwell, *J. Am. Chem. Soc.*, 73, 1051 (1951).

[56]G. Rio, *Compt. rend.*, 235, 964 (1952).

Conover and Tarbell (32) have reported that the reduction of various aromatic ketones, in which an amino group is ortho or para to the oxygenated function, with excess LAH results in hydrogenolysis to the methylene group. Thus, treatment of *p*-aminobenzophenone (XLV) with 4.5 equivalents (1.125 moles) of LAH (2.5 equivalents excess over the amount required for reaction with the active amino hydrogen) after three hours at 80° in a diethyl ether-di-*n*-butyl ether mixture yields 97% of *p*-aminobenzhydrol and 2% of *p*-aminodiphenylmethane. Reaction with 9 equivalents (2.25 moles) of LAH after one hour at 80° gives 15% *p*-aminobenzhydrol and 57% *p*-aminodiphenylmethane.

$$(7\text{-}37)$$

Treatment of *p,p'*-diaminobenzophenone (XLVI) with 13 equivalents (3.25 moles) of LAH (9 equivalents excess over the amount required for reaction with active hydrogen) for 3 days at 60° gives 32% of *p,p'*-diaminodiphenylmethane, based on the starting material consumed. Treatment of *p,p'*-dimethoxybenzophenone (XLVII) with over 20 equivalents (5 moles) of LAH after 11 days at 90° gives 46% *p,p'*-dimethoxydiphenylmethane.

It is postulated that the reduction proceeds with rapid formation of the benzyl alcohol which undergoes hydrogenolysis to yield the methylene compound. This is discussed more fully in Section 16.1.

The LAH reduction of various diaryl ketones is summarized in Table XIII.

7.2.1.e *Alkyl heterocyclic ketones.* A limited number of ketones containing heterocyclic rings alpha to the carbonyl group have been reduced with LAH. Reduction of 2-acetylthiophene (XLVIII) with LAH yields 1-(2-thienyl)ethanol while catalytic hydrogenation yields 1-(2-tetrahydrothienyl)ethanol (99).

TABLE XIII

LAH Reduction of Diaryl Ketones

	Ketone	Product	% Yield	Ref.
$C_{13}H_8Cl_2O$	p,p'-Dichlorobenzophenone	Di-p-chlorophenylcarbinol	81	1
			....	2
$C_{13}H_{10}O$	Benzophenone	Diphenylcarbinol	86	3
$C_{13}H_{11}NO$	p-Aminobenzophenone	p-Aminobenzhydrol	97	5
		p-Aminodiphenylmethane	2[4]	5
		p-Aminobenzhydrol	15	5
		p-Aminodiphenylmethane	57	5
$C_{13}H_{12}N_2O$	p,p'-Diaminobenzophenone	p,p'-Diaminodiphenylmethane	32[4]	5
$C_{15}H_{14}O_3$	p,p'-Dimethoxybenzophenone	p,p'-Dimethoxydiphenylmethane	46[4]	5
$C_{19}H_{14}O_3$	2-(o-Toluoyl)-1-naphthoic acid	Lactone of 2-(α-hydroxy-o-methylbenzyl)-1-naphthoic acid	57	6
		(1-Hydroxymethyl-2-naphthyl)-o-tolylcarbinol	16	6
$C_{19}H_{12}O$	Dimesityl ketone	Dimesityl carbinol	93	1
$C_{21}H_{14}O$	9-Benzoylanthracene	Phenyl 9-anthracylcarbinol	80	7
$C_{21}H_{16}O_2$	2-Phenacylbenzophenone	2-(2-Hydroxy-2-phenylethyl)benzhydrol	43	8
$C_{27}H_{18}O$	9-Phenyl-10-benzoylanthracene	Phenyl 9-phenyl-10-anthracyl carbinol	85	7

[1] M. S. Newman and N. C. Deno, *J. Am. Chem. Soc.*, *73*, 3644 (1951).

[2] E. Wiberg and M. Schmidt, *Z. Naturforsch.*, *6b*, 171 (1951).

[3] E. Larsson, *Trans. Chalmers Univ. Technol.*, *Gothenburg*, *94*, 15 (1950).

[4] Reduction carried out with a large excess of LAH in a diethyl ether–di-*n*-butyl ether mixture at an elevated temperature (see text).

[5] L. H. Conover and D. S. Tarbell, *J. Am. Chem. Soc.*, *72*, 3586 (1950).

[6] M. S. Newman and R. Gaertner, *ibid.*, *72*, 264 (1950).

[7] P. L. Julian, W. Cole, G. Diemer, and J. G. Schafer, *ibid.*, *71*, 2058 (1949).

[8] S. Siegel, S. K. Coburn, and D. R. Levering, *ibid.*, *73*, 3163 (1951).

$$\underset{\text{XLVIII}}{\underset{\substack{\text{S} \quad\quad \text{CCH}_3\\ \parallel\\ \text{O}}}{}} \xrightarrow[75\%]{\text{LAH}} \quad \underset{\substack{\text{S} \quad \text{CHCH}_3\\ |\\ \text{OH}}}{} \qquad \xrightarrow{\text{H}_2:\text{RuO}_2} \quad \underset{\substack{\text{S} \quad \text{CHCH}_3\\ |\\ \text{OH}}}{} \qquad (7\text{-}38)$$

Reduction of ethyl α-oximinofuroylacetate (XLIX:R = C$_2$H$_5$) with LAH yields the 1-(2-furyl)-2-amino-1,3-propanediol, isolated in 2% yield as the oxalate. Reduction of the methyl ester (XLIX:R = CH$_3$) with LAH gives a "poor" yield of the same product. Catalytic hydrogenation of XLIX (R = CH$_3$) over palladium in an acetic acid-acetic anhydride mixture gives 79% methyl α-acetaminofuroylacetate (100).

$$\begin{array}{c}
\underset{\substack{\text{O} \quad\quad \text{C}-\text{CCOOR}\\ \parallel \quad \parallel\\ \text{O} \quad \text{NOH}}}{}\\
\text{XLIX}
\end{array}$$

$$\underset{\substack{\text{O} \quad \text{CH}-\text{CHCH}_2\text{OH}\\ | \qquad |\\ \text{OH} \quad\; \text{NH}_2}}{} \xleftarrow{\text{LAH}} \qquad \xrightarrow[\substack{(\text{CH}_3\text{CO})_2\text{O}}]{\text{H}_2:\text{Pd}} \quad \underset{\substack{\text{O} \quad\quad \text{C}-\text{CHCOOR}\\ \parallel \qquad |\\ \text{O} \quad\; \text{NHCOCH}_3}}{} \qquad (7\text{-}39)$$

The reduction of 4-acetyl-(L:R = CH$_3$) and 4-propionyl-(L:R = C$_2$H$_5$) 4-phenyl-1-methylpiperidine with LAH yields 80 and 84%, respectively, of the corresponding carbinols (101).

$$\underset{\substack{\text{N}\\ |\\ \text{CH}_3\\ \text{L}}}{\overset{\text{C}_6\text{H}_5 \quad \text{COR}}{}} \xrightarrow{\text{LAH}} \underset{\substack{\text{N}\\ |\\ \text{CH}_3}}{\overset{\substack{\text{OH}\\ |\\ \text{C}_6\text{H}_5 \quad \text{CHR}}}{}} \qquad (7\text{-}40)$$

Treibs and Scherer (36) reported that the reduction of 2,4-dimethyl-3-acetylpyrrole (LI) with excess LAH in refluxing ether gives not the expected methyl pyrryl carbinol but kryptopyrrole (LII), identified through analysis of various derivatives. A higher molecular weight fraction was assigned the structure of an α,β-dipyrrylmethane (LIII) while the distillation residue apparently contains a polymethane (LIV).

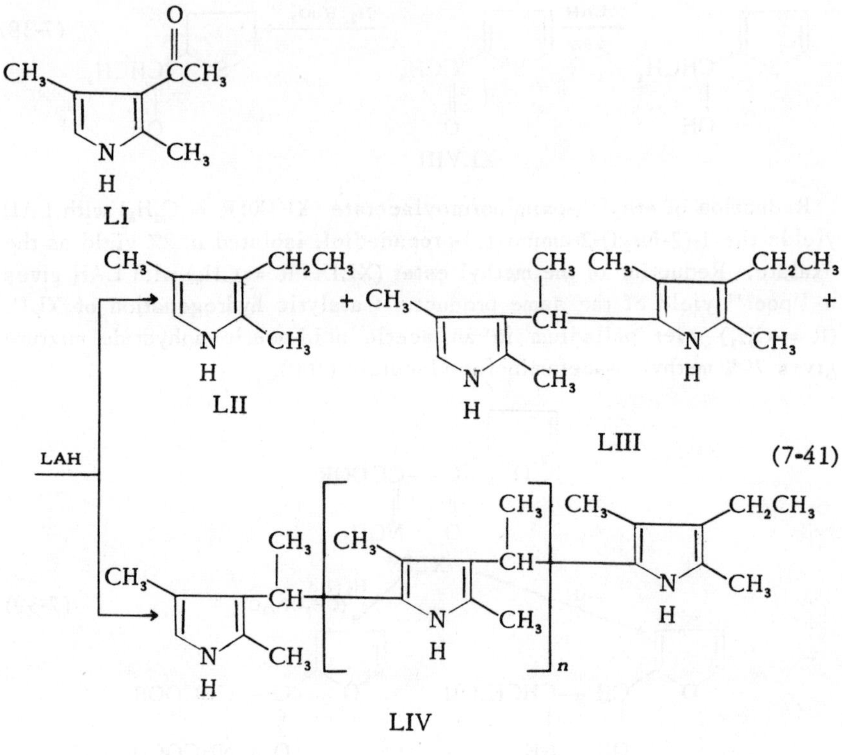

LI

LII + LIII

LAH

LIV

(7-41)

The high molecular weight products are explained on the grounds that the expected 1-hydroxyethyl compound reacts with LII to form dipyrrylmethane (LIII) and the polymethane, with aluminum compounds acting as condensation agents. In an experiment in which the LAH solution contained undissolved material, "aluminum sludge" according to the authors, only the high molecular product was obtained, which decomposed upon distillation at 250 °C. The formation of 2,4-dimethylpyrrole as a cleavage product indicates the decomposition of a polymethane. The formation of LII is indicative of a hydrogenolysis reaction as discussed in Section 16.1.

7.2.1.f *Alicyclic ketones.* The LAH reduction of alicyclic ketones generally proceeds without difficulty as with the corresponding straight chain compounds.

The ketone 2-(2,3-dimethoxyphenyl)-2-ethylcyclohexanone (LV), does not form an oxime, semicarbazone or 2,4-dinitrophenylhydrazone and does not condense with allylmagnesium bromide or zinc and ethyl bromoacetate. Treatment with methylmagnesium iodide in butyl ether and xylene at room temperature does not yield any active hydrogen. However, on reduction with LAH the carbonyl absorption band in the infrared spectrum disappears (102).

LV   LVI

The reaction of octahydro-1,4-diketopentalene (LVI) with the methyl
Grignard reagent yields the expected 1,4-dimethyl-1,4-dihydroxy derivative. The diketone readily absorbs two moles of hydrogen over Raney
nickel to yield octahydro-1,4-dihydroxypentalene as a non-crystalline
glass, presumably a mixture of stereoisomerides. A similar product is
obtained from reduction with LAH (103).

The reduction of 2-phenyl-2-β-diethylaminoethylcyclohexanone (LVII)
with LAH gives a mixture of *cis*- and *trans*-cyclohexanol derivatives. Reduction of LVII with aluminum isopropoxide yields a single isomer (104).

LVII   (7-42)

Noyce and Denney have shown that the LAH reduction of *l*-menthone
(LVIII) yields a mixture of menthols (71% *l*-menthol, 29% neomenthol (*cis*)
which is reoxidized to *l*-menthone with insignificant change of rotation.
This demonstrates that an asymmetric center next to a carbonyl group is
unaffected by LAH reduction (105).

LVIII   (7-43)

Both catalytic hydrogenation and reduction with aluminum isopropoxide
afford a marked preponderance of the *cis* isomer. Since the LAH reduction of a carbonyl group should result in the approach of the reducing
species from the side opposite a hindering group to give a product with
the hydroxyl group in the *cis* position, the steric requirements of the reducing step of the LAH reaction are probably smaller than in the case of

the other reduction methods. "Random reduction" which might be expected to occur in the case of little or no hindrance does not necessarily lead to formation of equal amounts of the two isomers, the more stable isomer, here the *trans* isomer, predominating.

Noyce and Denney (105) reported that the *trans*-carbinols predominate, from the LAH reduction of the 2-, 3-, and 4-methylcyclohexanones. Goering and Serres (106) demonstrated that the previously accepted assignments of configuration for *cis*- and *trans*-3-methylcyclohexanol are in error and therefore the *cis*-epimer (formerly called *trans*) predominates from the LAH reduction of 3-methylcyclohexanone. However, it has been found that the *trans* isomer is the more stable one in the case of the 1,2- and 1,4-disubstituted cyclohexanes while the more stable isomer of 3-methylcyclohexanol is the *cis* isomer. Therefore, the work of Noyce and Denney is evidence that the LAH reduction of an unhindered ketone results in the predominant formation of the more stable isomer. When steric hindrance is sufficiently great, the predominant addition of hydrogen occurs from the unhindered side of the molecule, as in the reduction of *d*-camphor (LIX) to a mixture of isoborneol and borneol containing 90% of the *cis* isomer, isoborneol.

$$\text{(7-44)}$$

LIX

The reduction of 5-methyl-6-ethoxy-1,2,3,4,4aα,5,8,8aα-octahydronaphthalene-1,4-dione (LX) with LAH in tetrahydrofuran yields 80% of the 1β, 4β-diol (107).

$$\text{(7-45)}$$

LX

The highly stereospecific reduction, as indicated by the isolation of a single isomer, demonstrates that the face of the *cis*-decalin molecule is unhindered and that the opposite face is decidedly hindered for both carbonyl groups (108).

The LAH reduction of 6-acetoxy-6-cyanobicyclo[3.2.0]-2-heptene (LXI) yields a mixture of the 6-aminomethyl-6-hydroxy compound and bicyclo-[3.2.0]-2-hepten-6-ol (LXII). The latter probably results from reduction of the ketone formed by reversal of the cyanohydrin formation (109).

LXI   LXII

(7-46)

The LAH reduction of cyclohexane-1,2-dione at 35° is reported to yield 41% of cyclohexan-2-ol-1-one and one mole of hydrogen gas (61). As discussed later in this section, apparently the dione reacts in the form of the enol ketone, with reduction of the keto group to the carbinol and the retention of the enol form. On hydrolysis of the reduction mixture the keto carbinol is recovered.

The LAH reduction of various saturated and unconjugated unsaturated alicyclic ketones is summarized in Table XIV.

The following saturated cyclic amines containing a ketone group have been reduced with LAH to the corresponding carbinol.

	Ketone		% Carbinol	Ref.
$C_7H_{11}NO$	3-quinuclidone	LXIII	100	110
$C_8H_{13}NO$	8-ketoöctahydropyrrocoline	LXIV	58	111
	tropinone	LXV	100	112
$C_8H_{15}NO$	1-butyl-3-pyrrolidone		80	113
$C_{10}H_{19}NO$	1-methyl-3,5-diethyl-4-piperidone		95	114

LXIII   LXIV   LXV

Mirza (112) reported that reduction of the ketone group in tropinone (LXV) to a secondary alcohol yields two internally compensated stereo-isomerides, tropine and *pseudo*tropine, the nature of the reduction product depending upon the reducing agent used. When the reduction is carried out electrolytically or with zinc and hydriodic acid the main product is tropine, contaminated with small amounts of *pseudo*tropine. Reduction with sodium amalgam yields *pseudo*tropine as the only product. LAH re-

TABLE XIV

LAH Reduction of Saturated and Unconjugated Unsaturated Alicyclic Ketones

	Ketone	Product	% Yield	Ref.
C_4H_6O	Cyclobutanone	Cyclobutanol	90	1
C_5H_8O	Cyclopentanone	Cyclopentanol	...	2,3
			62	4
			85	1
			100	5
	Cyclopentanone-1-C^{14}	Cyclopentanol-1-C^{14}	84	6
$C_6H_8O_2$	1,2-Cyclohexanedione	Cyclohexan-1-ol-2-one	41	7
C_6H_9ClO	2-Chlorocyclohexanone	2-Chlorocyclohexanol (equal parts cis and trans)	65	8
$C_6H_{10}O$	Cyclohexanone	Cyclohexanol	...	2
C_7H_9NO	2-Cyanocyclohexanone	trans-2-Aminomethylcyclohexanol	...	9
			70–75	10
$C_7H_{10}O$	4-Methylcyclohex-3-en-1-one	4-Methylcyclohex-3-en-1-ol	54	11
$C_7H_{10}O_3$	2-Carbomethoxycyclopentanone	2-Methylenecyclopentanol	42	13
		2-Hydroxymethylcyclopentanol	25 }12	
		1-Hydroxymethyl-1-cyclopentene	8	
$C_7H_{12}O$	2,2-Dimethylcyclopentanone	2,2-Dimethylcyclopentanol	...	14
	2-Ethylcyclopentanone	2-Ethylcyclopentanol (primarily cis)	...	15
	2-Methylcyclohexanone	cis-2-Methylcyclohexanol 36 } trans-2-Methylcyclohexanol 64 }		16
	3-Methylcyclohexanone	trans-3-Methylcyclohexanol 8 } cis-3-Methylcyclohexanol 92 }	88^{17}	16
	4-Methylcyclohexanone	cis-4-Methylcyclohexanol 19 } trans-4-Methylcyclohexanol 81 }		16
	Suberone	Cycloheptanol	50	18

Formula	Ketone	Product	Yield	Ref
$C_7H_{12}O_2$	Cycloheptan-2-one-1-ol	1,2-Cycloheptanediol	69	19
$C_8H_{10}O$	2-Hydroxymethylcyclohexanone	2-Hydroxymethylcyclohexanol [21]	64	13
	Bicyclo[3.3.0]-2-octen-6-one (I) } [20]		84	22
	Bicyclo[3.3.0]-2-octen-7-one (II) }			
$C_8H_{10}O_2$	Octahydro-1,4-diketopentalene (III)	Octahydro-1,4-dihydroxypentalene	...	23
$C_8H_{12}O_3$	2-Carbethoxycyclopentanone	2-Hydroxymethylcyclopentanol	22	24
$C_8H_{14}O$	2-Isopropylcyclopentanone	2-Isopropylcyclopentanol (primarily cis)	...	15
$C_8H_{14}O_4S$	2-Methyl-2-hydroxymethylcyclopentanone mesylate	2,2-Dimethylcyclopentanol	89	14
$C_8H_{15}NO$	2-Dimethylaminocyclohexanone	trans-2-Dimethylaminocyclohexanol	...	25
$C_9H_{14}O_3$	2-Methyl-2-carbethoxycyclopentanone	2-Methyl-2-hydroxymethylcyclopentanol	80	10
	2-Carbethoxycyclohexanone	2-Hydroxymethylcyclohexanol	66	24
		2-Methylenecyclohexanol	17	24
		1-Hydroxymethyl-1-cyclohexene	52 }	
		2-Hydroxymethylcyclohexanol	21 } [12]	13
			11	
$C_9H_{16}O$	Cyclononanone	Cyclononanol	94	26
$C_{10}H_{14}O_2$	d-2,3-Camphorquinone	d-2,3-Camphanediol	97, 98 [27]	7
$C_{10}H_{16}O$	d-Camphor	Isoborneol 90 } Borneol 10 }	94	16
	Camphor	d-(−)-Isoborneol } d-(+)-Borneol }	97, 97 [27]	7
		d-Isoborneol	...	28
		Borneol	92	29
	Fenchone	Fenchyl alcohol	95	30
	Bicyclo[5.3.0]-2-decanone (IV)	Bicyclo[5.3.0]-2-decanol	...	31
$C_{10}H_{16}O_3$	2-Methyl-2-carbethoxycyclohexanone	2-Methyl-2-hydroxymethylcyclohexanol (mixture cis and trans)	87	24

(Continued)

TABLE XIV (*Continued*)

	Ketone	Product	% Yield	Ref.
$C_{10}H_{18}O$	Cyclodecanone	Cyclodecanol	93.6 91	32 33
	l-Menthone	*l*-Menthol 71 } *cis*-Neomenthol 29 }	90	16
$C_{10}H_{18}O_2$	Cyclodecan-1-one-2-ol (sebacoin)	1,2-Cyclodecanediol	52	32
$C_{11}H_{18}O_3$	1,1-Dimethyl-2-carbethoxy-3-cyclohexanone	1,1-Dimethyl-2-hydroxymethyl-3-cyclohexanol	76	34
$C_{12}H_{12}O$	1,2,3,8,9,10-Hexahydro-2-ketocyclopent[a]-indene (V)	1,2,3,8,9,10-Hexahydro-2-hydroxycyclopent[a]-indene	88	35
$C_{12}H_{16}O_2$	1,2,3,4,8,9-Hexahydro-1-keto-6-methoxy-9-methylnaphthalene	1,2,3,4,6,7,8,9-Octahydro-1-hydroxy-6-keto-9-methylnaphthalene[36]	...	37
$C_{13}H_{18}O_3$	5-Methyl-6-ethoxy-1,2,3,4,4aα,5,8,8aα-octahydronaphthalene-1,4-dione	5-Methyl-6-ethoxy-1,2,3,4,4aα,5,8,8aα-octahydronaphthalene-1β,4β-diol	80	38
$C_{14}H_{22}O_2$	Oxido ketone, m.p. 62–63°, from caryophyllene (VI)	Oxido alcohol, $C_{14}H_{24}O_2$, m.p. 140–141°	...	39
$C_{15}H_{18}O$	1-Keto-12-methyl-1,2,3,4,9,10,11,12-octa-hydrophenanthrene	1-Hydroxy-12-methyl-1,2,3,4,9,10,11,12-octa-hydrophenanthrene	...	40
$C_{15}H_{21}NO_2$	2-Phenoxy-6-dimethylaminomethyl-1-cyclohexanone	2-Phenoxy-6-dimethylaminomethyl-1-cyclohexanol	...	41
$C_{16}H_{22}O_2$	2,13-Dimethyl-1,7-diketo-Δ^{9,14}-dodecahydrophenanthrene	2,13-Dimethyl-Δ^{9,14}-dodecahydrophenanthrene-1,7-diol 43	...	42
$C_{16}H_{22}O_3$	2-(2,3-Dimethoxyphenyl)-2-ethylcyclohexanone	2,3-Dimethyl-2,3-diphenylcyclopropanol	...	44
$C_{17}H_{16}O$	2,3-Dimethyl-2,3-diphenylcyclopropanone	2-Phenoxy-6-morpholinomethyl-1-cyclohexanol	...	45
$C_{17}H_{23}NO_3$	2-Phenoxy-6-morpholinomethyl-1-cyclohexanone	8-Hydroxydihydrocodeine	...	41
$C_{18}H_{21}NO_4$	8-Hydroxydihydrocodeinone (VII)	2-Phenoxy-6-piperidinomethyl-1-cyclohexanol	80	46
$C_{18}H_{25}NO_2$	2-Phenoxy-6-piperidinomethyl-1-cyclohexanone	2-[2'-(1''-Cyclohexenyl)-1'-cyclohexenyl]-cyclohexanol	...	41
$C_{18}H_{26}O$	2-[2'-(1''-Cyclohexenyl)-1'-cyclohexenyl]-cyclohexanone	2-Phenyl-2-β-diethylaminoethylcyclohexanol (mixture of *cis* and *trans*)	79	47
$C_{18}H_{27}NO$	2-Phenyl-2-p-diethylaminoethylcyclohexanone		...	48

Formula				Ref.
$C_{18}H_{31}NO$	2-(1'-Cyclohexenyl)-6-β-diethylaminoethyl-cyclohexanone	2-(1'-Cyclohexenyl)-6-β-diethylaminoethyl-1-cyclohexanol[49]	83	48
$C_{18}H_{34}O_2$	Cyclooctadecan-1-ol-2-one	1,2-Cyclooctadecanediol	74	50
$C_{19}H_{20}O$	2,2-Diphenylcycloheptanone	2,2-Diphenylcycloheptanol	82.5	51
$C_{19}H_{24}O_2$	1-Keto-8-methoxy-1,2,3,4,4a,4b,5,6,10b,11,12,12a-dodecahydrochrysene	1-Hydroxy-8-methoxy-1,2,3,4,4a,4b,5,6,10b,11,12,12a-dodecahydrochrysene		
	α-isomer, m.p. 169–170°	α-isomer, m.p. 114.5–115.5°	22	52
	β-isomer, m.p. 153.4–154.8°	β-isomer, m.p. 140.3–141°	100	52
	δ-isomer, m.p. 111–112.5° (VIII)	carbinol derived from VIII	...	52
$C_{20}H_{27}NO_3S$	Ethylthiodihydrothebainone (IX)	5-Ethylthiodihydrothebainol	97	53
$C_{20}H_{28}O_4S$	d-Camphor-10-sulfonate of L(+)-2-s-butylphenol	L(+)-2-s-Butylphenol[54]	44	55
$C_{20}H_{29}NO$	Base, m.p. 185°, obtained by pyrolysis of veatchine with selenium at 290° (X)	Tetrahydro base $C_{20}H_{33}NO$[56]	...	57,58
	Base, m.p. 140–142°, obtained by pyrolysis of atisine with selenium (XI)	Tetrahydro base $C_{20}H_{33}NO$[59]	...	58
$C_{35}H_{38}O_2$	2,13-Dimethyl-7-triphenylmethoxy-1-keto-Δ9,14-dodecahydrophenanthrene	2,13-Dimethyl-7-triphenylmethoxy-1-hydroxy-Δ9,14-dodecahydrophenanthrene	...	42

CHART TO TABLE XIV

References—Table XIV

[1] J. D. Roberts and C. W. Sauer, *J. Am. Chem. Soc.*, 71, 3925 (1949).

[2] H. I. Schlesinger and A. E. Finholt, U. S. Pat. 2,576,311 (November 27, 1951).

[3] S. Winstein, B. K. Morse, E. Grunwald, H. W. Jones, J. Corse, D. Trifan, and H. Marshall, *J. Am. Chem. Soc.*, 74, 1127 (1952).

[4] R. F. Nystrom and W. G. Brown, *ibid.*, 69, 1197 (1947).

[5] Reduction carried out in boiling tetrahydrofuran; R. F. Nystrom, unpublished work, through W. G. Brown, in *Organic Reactions*, Vol. VI, Chapter 10, p. 475.

[6] R. B. Loftfield, *J. Am. Chem. Soc.*, 73, 4707 (1951).

[7] L. W. Trevoy and W. G. Brown, *ibid.*, 71, 1675 (1949).

[8] H. Felkin, *Compt. rend.*, 231, 1316 (1950).

[9] M. Mousseron and M. Canet, *Bull. soc. chim. France*, [5] 19, 247 (1952).

[10] M. Mousseron, R. Jacquier, M. Mousseron-Canet and R. Zagdoun, *ibid.*, [5] 19, 1042 (1952); *Compt. rend.*, 235, 177 (1952).

[11] M. I. Bowman, C. C. Ketterer, and G. Dinga, *J. Org. Chem.*, 17, 563 (1952).

[12] See text.

[13] A. S. Dreiding and J. A. Hartman, *J. Am. Chem. Soc.*, 75, 939 (1953).

[14] A. Eschenmoser and A. Frey, *Helv. Chim. Acta*, 35, 1660 (1952).

[15] V. M. Mičović, *Bull. soc. chim. Belgrade*, 14, 181 (1949); through *Chem. Abstracts*, 46, 11121 (1952).

[16] D. S. Noyce and D. B. Denney, *J. Am. Chem. Soc.*, 72, 5743 (1950).

[17] Configurations actually reversed by authors (see text).

[18] P. A. S. Smith and D. R. Baer, *J. Am. Chem. Soc.*, 74, 6135 (1952).

[19] J. D. Knight and D. J. Cram, *ibid.*, 73, 4136 (1951).

[20] Mixture containing 85% 6-keto and 15% 7-keto compounds.

[21] Complex mixture of alcohols containing both stereo and position isomers.

[22] J. D. Roberts and W. F. Gorham, *J. Am. Chem. Soc.*, 74, 2278 (1952).

[23] C. T. Blood and R. P. Linstead, *J. Chem. Soc.*, 1952, 2255.

[24] E. Buchta and H. Bayer, *Ann.*, 573, 227 (1951).

[25] M. Mousseron and M. Canet, *Bull. soc. chim. France*, [5] 18, 792 (1951).

[26] A. T. Blomquist, Liang Huang Liu, and J. C. Bohrer, *J. Am. Chem. Soc.*, 74, 3643 (1952).

[27] At 35° and −80°, respectively.

[28] A. A. Bothner-By, *J. Am. Chem. Soc.*, 73, 846 (1951).

[29] E. Larsson, *Trans. Chalmers Univ. Technol., Gothenburg*, 94, 15 (1950).

[30] W. B. Wheatley, W. E. Fitzgibbon, L. C. Cheney, and S. B. Binkley, *J. Am. Chem. Soc.*, 73, 229 (1951).

[31] H. Pommer, *Naturwissenschaften*, 39, 44 (1952); through M. Ferles and J. Rudinger, *Chem. Listy*, 47, 113 (1953).

[32] A. T. Blomquist, R. E. Burge, Jr., and A. C. Sucsy, *J. Am. Chem. Soc.*, 74, 3636 (1952).

[33] V. Prelog, K. Schenker and H. H. Günthard, *Helv. Chim. Acta*, 35, 1598 (1952).

[34] R. Helg and H. Schinz, *ibid.*, 35, 2406 (1952).

[35] L. H. Groves and G. A. Swan, *J. Chem. Soc.*, 1951, 867.

[36] Isolated after acid hydrolysis of reduction product.

[37] A. J. Birch, J. A. K. Quartey, and H. Smith, *J. Chem. Soc.*, 1952, 1768.

[38] L. H. Sarett, R. M. Lukes, G. I. Poos, J. M. Robinson, R. E. Beyler, J. M. Vandegrift, and G. E. Arth, *J. Am. Chem. Soc.*, 74, 1393 (1952).

[39] D. H. R. Barton and A. S. Lindsey, *J. Chem. Soc.*, 1951, 2988.

[40] G. Stork and A. Burgstahler, *J. Am. Chem. Soc.*, 73, 3544 (1951).

[41]F. Winternitz and N. J. Antia, *Bull. soc. chim. France*, [5] *19*, 248 (1952).

[42]H. M. E. Cardwell, J. W. Cornforth, S. R. Duff, H. Holtermann, and R. Robinson, *Chemistry and Industry*, *1951*, 389.

[43]Reduction effected but product not isolated.

[44]M. S. Newman and W. L. Mosby, *J. Am. Chem. Soc.*, *73*, 3738 (1951).

[45]J. F. Cogdell and O. R. Quayle, *Abstracts of Papers*, 118th Meeting American Chemical Society, Chicago, Ill., September, 1950, p. 6N.

[46]S. P. Findlay and L. F. Small, *J. Am. Chem. Soc.*, *73*, 4001 (1951).

[47]J. Mleziva, *Chem. Listy*, in press; through M. Ferles and J. Rudinger, *loc. cit.*

[48]F. Winternitz and R. M. Thakkar, *Bull. soc. chim. France*, [5] *18*, 792 (1951); *19*, 471 (1952).

[49]Mixture of stereoisomers.

[50]R. B. Ingraham, D. M. MacDonald, and K. Wiesner, *Can. J. Research*, *28B*, 453 (1950).

[51]R. E. Lyle and G. G. Lyle, *J. Am. Chem. Soc.*, *74*, 4059 (1952).

[52]W. S. Johnson, D. K. Banerjee, W. P. Schneider, C. D. Gutsche, W. E. Shelberg, and L. J. Chinn, *ibid.*, *74*, 2832 (1952).

[53]T. D. Perrine and L. F. Small, *J. Org. Chem.*, *17*, 1540 (1952).

[54]Product derived from camphor portion of starting material not isolated.

[55]F. Hawthorne and D. J. Cram, *J. Am. Chem. Soc.*, *74*, 5859 (1952).

[56]Isolated as O,N-diacetate[58] and as N-hydroxyethyl derivative, m.p. 172°[59].

[57]M. F. Bartlett, W. I. Taylor, and K. Wiesner, *Chemistry and Industry*, *1953*, 173.

[58]M. F. Bartlett, J. Edwards, W. I. Taylor, and K. Wiesner, *Chemistry and Industry*, *1953*, 323.

[59]Isolated as N-hydroxyethyl derivative, m.p. 145°.

duction in ether gives *pseudo*tropine in quantitative yield, under a variety of experimental conditions.

Paddock (63) postulated that in the reduction of alicyclic ketones that configuration is favored in which, for a 3-keto group, the carbon-oxygen bond is most nearly *trans* to C_1C_2 and C_4C_5. This hypothesis allows the conclusion that in *pseudo*tropine the hydroxyl group and the methylamino bridge have the *trans* configuration since here the carbon-oxygen bond is parallel to the C_1C_2 and C_4C_5 bonds (LXVI).

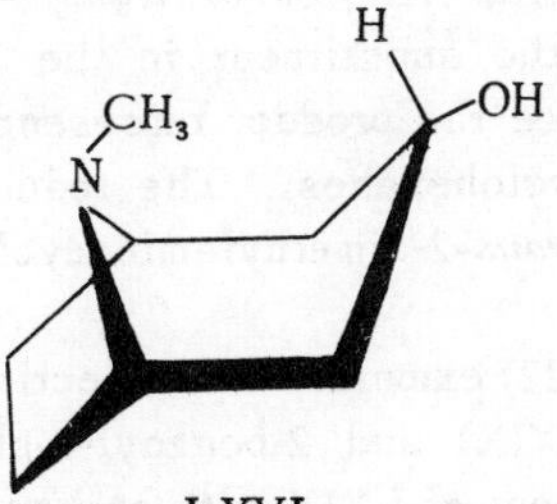

LXVI

Clemo and Jack (115) showed that based on dipole moments and infrared spectra the configuration of *pseudo*tropine is *cis*. Sparke (116) reconciled these conflicting views by showing that if the chair form is assumed for the piperidine ring (LXVII) then the preferential formation of *pseudo*tropine from tropinone on reduction with LAH is explicable since the hydroxyl group is in the equatorial conformation.

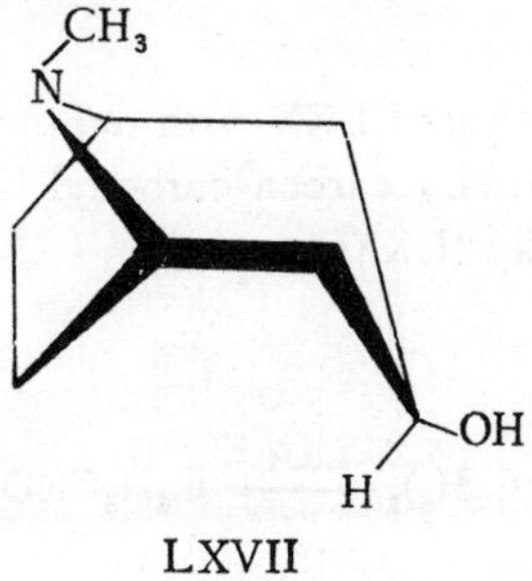

LXVII

7.2.1.g   *Ketones with reducible* α- *or* β-*substituents.*

1. α-*Ketonitriles.* The LAH reduction of aroyl cyanides yields the corresponding 2-substituted ethanolamine.

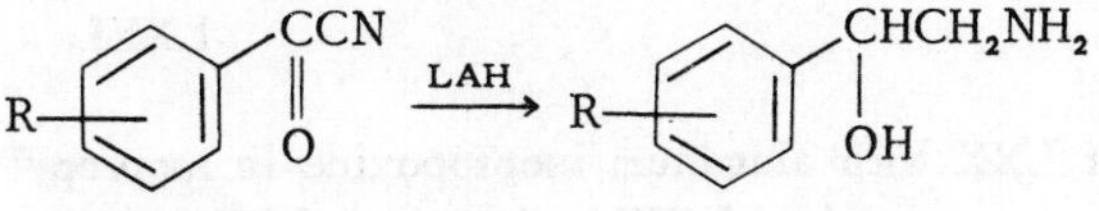

(7-47)

LXVIII

	Aroyl cyanide	% Carbinol	Ref.
C$_8$H$_4$ClNO	p-chlorobenzoyl cyanide	89	117
C$_8$H$_5$NO	benzoyl cyanide	....	118
		86	117
C$_{11}$H$_{11}$NO$_4$	3,4,5-trimethoxybenzoyl cyanide	61	119
C$_{15}$H$_{11}$NO$_2$	m-benzyloxybenzoyl cyanide	....	118

2. *β-Ketonitriles*. The course of the reduction of β-ketonitriles is determined by the substituents in the alpha position. The LAH reduction of 2-cyanocyclohexane yields 70–75% of *trans*-2-aminomethylcyclohexanol (11,120). Apparently the substituent in the 2-position presents little hindrance to attack since the product represents the more stable isomer for 1,2-disubstituted cyclohexanes. The reduction of 2-dimethylamino-cyclohexanone to 80% *trans*-2-dimethylaminocyclohexanol conforms to the same picture (11,121).

Reynaud and Matti (122) examined the selective reduction of 2-benzoyl-2-phenylacetonitrile (LXIX) and 2-benzoyl-2-phenyl-4-diethylaminobuty-ronitrile (LXX). Treatment of LXIX with one-quarter mole of LAH results in the evolution of hydrogen and the formation of an ether-insoluble complex which, upon hydrolysis, gives a quantitative recovery of the starting material. In contrast, reduction of LXIX with aluminum isopropoxide in isopropyl alcohol gives the expected 1,2-diphenyl-2-cyanoethanol.

$$C_6H_5C\underset{\underset{O}{\|}}{\overset{}{-}}\underset{\underset{CN}{|}}{CHC_6H_5} \xrightarrow[25-30\%]{Al(i\text{-}PrO)_3} C_6H_5CH\underset{\underset{OH}{|}}{\overset{}{-}}\underset{\underset{CN}{|}}{CHC_6H_5} \qquad (7\text{-}48)$$

$$\text{LXIX}$$

Reduction of the disubstituted LXX with one-quarter mole of LAH results in cleavage of the quaternary carbon-carbonyl bond to yield benzaldehyde and the aminobutyronitrile (LXXI).

$$C_6H_5C\underset{\underset{O}{\|}}{\overset{}{-}}\underset{\underset{CN}{|}}{\overset{\overset{C_6H_5}{|}}{C}}-CH_2CH_2N(C_2H_5)_2 \xrightarrow{LAH} C_6H_5CHO +$$

$$\text{LXX}$$

$$C_6H_5CHCH_2CH_2N(C_2H_5)_2 \qquad (7\text{-}49)$$
$$\underset{CN}{|}$$
$$\text{LXXI}$$

Reduction of LXX with aluminum isopropoxide in isopropyl alcohol also results in cleavage to yield LXXI and isopropyl benzoate.

3. *α-Ketoamides.* The LAH reduction of ketoamides yields the substituted ethanolamine. Thus, phenylglyoxylamide (LXXII:R = H) is reduced to 2-phenylethanolamine, while N,N-diethylphenylglyoxylamide

$$C_6H_5COCONR_2 \xrightarrow[34\%]{LAH} \underset{\underset{OH}{|}}{C_6H_5CHCH_2NR_2} \qquad (7\text{-}50)$$

LXXII

(LXXII:R = C_2H_5) yields 33% of 2-phenyl-N,N-diethylethanolamine (118).

4. *α-Ketoacids.* The LAH reduction of phenylglyoxylic acid (LXXIII) yields 1-phenylethylene glycol (2,123).

$$C_6H_5COCOOH \xrightarrow[80\%]{LAH} \underset{\underset{OH}{|}}{C_6H_5CHCH_2OH} \qquad (7\text{-}51)$$

LXXIII

5. *Diazoketones.* The product of the reduction of diazoketones is affected by the reduction method. LAH reduction of 1-diazo-2-nonadecanone (LXXIV) gives 1-amino-2-nonadecanol while catalytic hydrogenation gives 2-nonadecanone but no aminoalcohol (124).

$$\underset{\underset{OH}{|}}{CH_3(CH_2)_{16}CHCH_2NH_2} \xleftarrow[99\%]{LAH} \underset{\underset{O}{\parallel}}{CH_3(CH_2)_{16}CCHN_2} \xrightarrow{H_2:PtO_2} \underset{\underset{O}{\parallel}}{CH_3(CH_2)_{16}CCH_3}$$

LXXIV   (7-52)

Both LAH reduction and catalytic hydrogenation over platinum oxide converts the diazoketone from sebacic acid (LXXV) to 2,11-dodecanedione.

$$\underset{\underset{COCHN_2}{|}}{\overset{\overset{COCHN_2}{|}}{(CH_2)_8}} \longrightarrow \underset{\underset{COCH_3}{|}}{\overset{\overset{COCH_3}{|}}{(CH_2)_8}} \qquad (7\text{-}53)$$

LXXV

LAH reduction of diazoacetophenone (LXXVI) gives 93% of 2-phenylethanolamine and 3% of acetophenone while catalytic hydrogenation over platinum gives 21-50% of acetophenone with no aminoalcohol or other products. Reduction of LXXVI over platinum oxide gives 15% of acetophenone, 3% of aminoalcohol and 47% of 2,5-diphenylpyrazine resulting from dehydration and dehydrogenation of the aminoketone.

$$C_6H_5COCHN_2 \begin{cases} \xrightarrow{\text{LAH}} C_6H_5CHCH_2NH_2 + C_6H_5COCH_3 \\ \qquad\qquad\quad | \\ \qquad\qquad\ \ OH \\ \\ \xrightarrow{H_2 : Pt} C_6H_5COCH_3 \\ \\ \xrightarrow{H_2 : PtO_2} C_6H_5COCH_3 + C_6H_5CHCH_2NH_2 + \\ \qquad\qquad\qquad\qquad\qquad\quad\ | \\ \qquad\qquad\qquad\qquad\qquad\ \ OH \end{cases}$$

LXXVI   (7-54)

LAH reduction of 3,4-dimethoxy-ω-diazoacetophenone is reported to give no definite product (124).

6. *Ketoazides.* The reduction of ketoazides with LAH yields the 2-substituted ethanolamine. Thus, phenacyl azide (LXXVII : R = C_6H_5) yields 49.5% 2-phenylethanolamine while triazoacetone (LXXVII : R = CH_3) yields 48% 1-amino-2-propanol (125).

$$RCOCH_2N_3 \xrightarrow{\text{LAH}} RCHCH_2NH_2$$
$$\qquad\qquad\qquad\quad |$$
$$\qquad\qquad\qquad\ \ OH$$
$$\text{LXXVII}$$

(7-55)

7. *α-Ketooximes.* The LAH reduction of α-oximinoketones presents a picture of unusually poor and ill-defined reductions. The inverse addition of the theoretical amount of LAH to an ethereal solution of isonitrosoacetophenone (LXXVIII) permits the selective reduction of the carbonyl function to yield 1-phenyl-2-oximinoethanol (126).

$$\begin{array}{ccc} \quad\ H & & \quad\ H \\ C_6H_5CC=NOH & \xrightarrow[34\%]{\text{LAH}} & C_6H_5CHC=NOH \\ \ \ \| & & \qquad | \\ \ \ O & & \qquad OH \\ \text{LXXVIII} & & \end{array}$$

(7-56)

Gregory and Malkin (127) reported that attempts to reduce methyl 2-oximino-3-ketooctadecanoate (LXXIX) with LAH gave a mixture of long-chain amines from which no pure substance could be isolated. Fisher (128) obtained 2-amino-1,3-octadecanediol, isolated as the tribenzoyl derivative, from this reduction.

$$CH_3(CH_2)_{14}C\!\!-\!\!CCOOCH_3 \xrightarrow{\text{LAH}} CH_3(CH_2)_{14}CH\!\!-\!\!CHCH_2OH \quad (7\text{-}57)$$
$$\underset{O}{\|}\quad \underset{NOH}{\|} \qquad\qquad \underset{OH}{|}\quad \underset{NH_2}{|}$$

LXXIX

As mentioned earlier in Section 7.2.1.e (equation (7-38)), LAH reduction of ethyl and methyl α-oximinofuroylacetate yields the aminodiol in very poor yield (100).

Attempts to reduce ethyl α-oximinobenzoylacetate (LXXX) with LAH are reported to yield poor results (18). Reduction in the cold gives a mixture of products from which only one product has been isolated. The structure of this product has been postulated as the Schiff's base or the oxazolidine derivative (129). Reduction in a refluxing ethereal solution with excess LAH gives *allo-dl*-3-phenylserinol (130).

$$C_6H_5C\!\!-\!\!CCOOC_2H_5$$
$$\underset{O}{\|}\quad \underset{NOH}{\|}$$

LXXX

$$\xrightarrow[\text{cold}]{\text{LAH}} \quad C_6H_5CH\!\!-\!\!CH\!\!-\!\!N\!\!=\!\!CHC_6H_5 \qquad \text{or} \qquad C_6H_5CH\!\!-\!\!CHCOOH$$
$$\underset{OH}{|}\quad \underset{COOH}{|} \qquad\qquad\qquad O\quad NH$$
$$\underset{CH}{\diagdown\diagup}$$
$$\underset{C_6H_5}{|} \qquad (7\text{-}58)$$

$$\xrightarrow[\text{warm}]{\text{LAH}} \quad C_6H_5CH\!\!-\!\!CHCH_2OH$$
$$\underset{OH}{|}\quad \underset{NH_2}{|}$$

8. *α-Ketophenylhydrazones.* The LAH reduction of the phenylhydrazone of benzoylglyoxal (LXXXI) is reported to yield a crystalline compound, m.p. 138.5°, which has not been further examined (18). The reduction of ethyl 2-phenylhydrazinobenzoylacetate (LXXXII) gives a 45% yield of the phenylhydrazone of benzaldehyde (130).

$$C_6H_5C\!\!-\!\!C\!\!=\!\!NNHC_6H_5 \qquad\qquad\qquad C_6H_5C\!\!-\!\!C\!\!=\!\!NNHC_6H_5$$
$$\underset{O}{\|}\quad \underset{CHO}{|} \qquad\qquad\qquad\qquad \underset{O}{\|}\quad \underset{COOC_2H_5}{|}$$

LXXXI   LXXXII

9. *β-Ketoesters.* The reduction of β-ketoesters is influenced by the tendency toward enolization. The following β-keotesters have been reduced with LAH to the corresponding 1,3-diols:

		% Yield	Ref.
$C_6H_{10}O_3$	ethyl acetoacetate	30	131
$C_7H_{12}O_3$	ethyl 2-methylacetoacetate	60	131
$C_8H_7NO_4$	methyl α-oximinofuroylacetate	"poor"	100
$C_8H_{12}O_3$	2-carbethoxy-1-cyclopentanone	22	131
$C_9H_9NO_4$	ethyl α-oximinofuroylacetate	2	100
$C_9H_{14}O_3$	2-carbethoxy-2-methyl-1-cyclopentanone	66	131
	2-carbethoxy-1-cyclohexanone	17	131
$C_9H_{14}O_5$	1,3-dicarbethoxyacetone	40	132
$C_{10}H_{16}O_3$	2-carbethoxy-2-methyl-1-cyclohexanone	87	131
$C_{11}H_{11}NO_4$	ethyl 2-oximinobenzoylacetate	....	18,129,130
$C_{11}H_{18}O_3$	2-carbethoxy-3,3-dimethyl-1-cyclohexanone	76	133
$C_{13}H_{15}NO_4$	ethyl 2-acetamidobenzoylacetate	....	134
$C_{13}H_{16}O_3$	ethyl 2-benzylacetoacetate	70	131
$C_{19}H_{35}NO_4$	methyl 2-oximinooctadecan-3-one-1-oate	....	127,128

The reduction of ethyl acetoacetate proceeds in relatively low yield (131), but the *O*-ethyl derivative is resistant to reduction (135). Among the 2-substituted acetocetic esters the yield increases with an increase in the size of the substituent due to an apparent hindrance to enolization. The reduction of 2-carbethoxy-1-cyclopentanone (LXXXIII) yields 22% of the diol while the 2-methyl-2-carbethoxy-1-cyclopentanone (LXXXIV) yields 66% of the diol (131). 3,5-Dicarbethoxy-4-methyl-1,2-cyclopentanedione (LXXXV) is reported to react with LAH in the dienol form (136).

LXXXIII   LXXXIV   LXXXV

Dreiding and Hartman (137) have investigated the LAH reduction of various enolizable β-ketoesters. Buchta and Bayer (131) reported that reduction of 2-carbethoxy-1-cyclopentanone (LXXXIII) gives 22% of 2-hydroxymethylcyclopentanol, but Dreiding and Hartman found that the LAH reduction of 2-carbomethoxy-1-cyclopentanone (LXXXVI) gives a mixture of 42% of 2-methylenecyclopentanol (LXXXVII), 25% of 2-hydroxymethylcyclopentanol (LXXXVIII) and 8% of 1-hydroxymethyl-1-cyclopentene (LXXXIX). The reduction of 2-hydroxymethylene-1-cyclopentanone (XC) gives 57% of LXXXVII, 5% of LXXXVIII and 12% of LXXXIX.

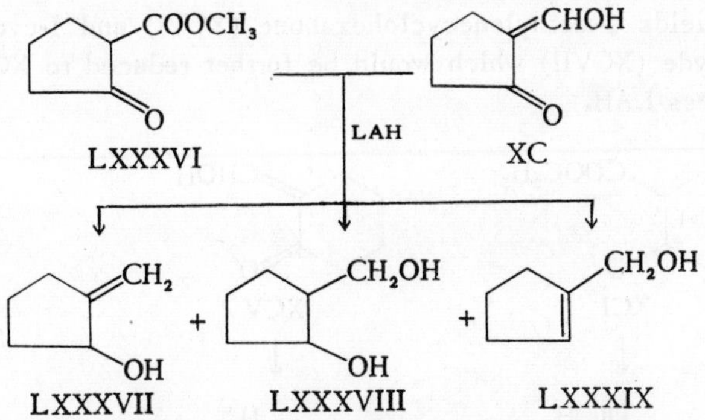

$$\text{(7-59)}$$

Similarly, while 2-carbethoxy-1-cyclohexanone (XCI) has been reported (131) to yield 17% 2-hydroxymethylcyclohexanol, Dreiding and Hartman found that the products include 52% of 2-methylenecyclohexanol (XCII), 21% of 1-hydroxymethyl-1-cyclohexene (XCIII) and 11% of 2-hydroxymethyl-cyclohexanol (XCIV). The reduction of 2-hydroxymethylene-1-cyclo-hexanone (XCV) gives 50% of XCII, 18% of XCIII and 11% of XCIV.

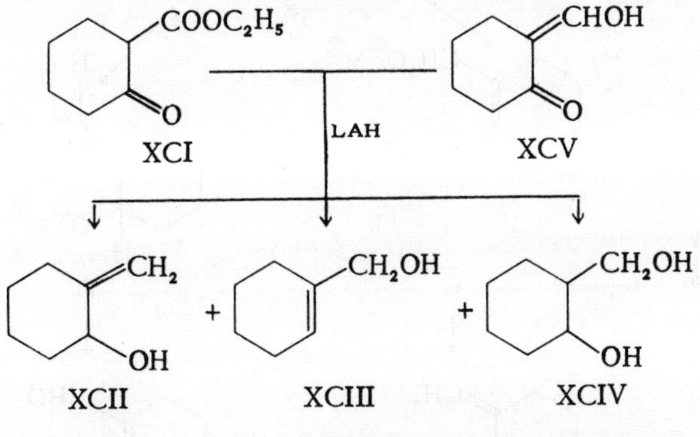

$$\text{(7-60)}$$

Since the reduction of 2-hydroxymethylcyclohexanone with LAH gives XCIV in good yield, the following course of the reaction has been postulated to account for the formation of unsaturated alcohols in the indicated reductions:

The non-enolic portions of XCI and XCV are reduced with LAH to the diols while the enolic portions react to form the enolate salts A and B along with hydrogen. This interpretation is supported by the quantity of hydrogen evolved and by the increased yield of diols from the reduction of compounds containing a methyl group in place of the active hydrogen (131,137,138). Replacement of the ethoxy group in A by hydrogen yields B, which would then be intermediate in the reduction of both XCI and XCV. A hydride attack on the enolate salt B at either position a or b yields the intermediates C and D, respectively. Loss of oxygen from C

and D yields 2-methylenecyclohexanone (XCVI) and 1-cyclohexanecar-
boxaldehyde (XCVII) which would be further reduced to XCII and XCIII
with excess LAH.

$$M = \text{Li or Al} \qquad (7\text{-}61)$$

The formation of 20% of 1-cyclohexenecarboxaldehyde (XCVII) by the
partial reduction of XCV, the reduction of XCVI to XCII and the reduction of the sodium enolate of 2-carbomethoxycyclopentanone to yield 2-
methylenecyclopentanol and 1-hydroxymethyl-1-cyclopentene are con-

sistent with the postulated mechanism. In contrast to the formation of the unsaturated alcohols by the LAH reduction of the sodium enolate of the cyclopentanone ester, the sodium enolate of 2-methylcyclohexanone is resistant to attack by LAH (137).

Although 1,2-diketones generally react without difficulty to yield the corresponding 1,2-diols, the LAH reduction of 1,2-cyclohexanedione (XCVIII) apparently proceeds through the enol ketone form since the product formed in 41% yield, cyclohexan-2-ol-1-one, is accompanied by the evolution of one mole of hydrogen (61).

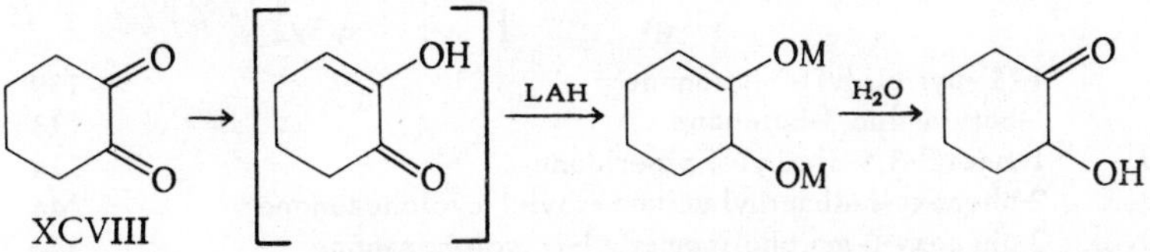

$$(7\text{-}62)$$

XCVIII

Reductic acid (XCIX), analogous to glucoreductone, is not reduced with LAH due to the presence of a mesomeric system (16).

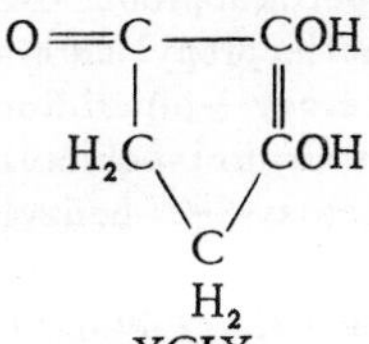

XCIX

7.2.1.h   α- and β-Amino and hydroxy ketones. The presence of α- and β-substituents such as amino and hydroxy groups in many cases results in side reactions or non-reduction in the catalytic hydrogenation or Meerwein-Ponndorf reduction of ketones to the corresponding carbinols. It is therefore of interest to tabulate those substituted carbonyl derivatives which have been successfully reduced with LAH to the corresponding carbinols.

α-Aminoketones		Ref.
$C_8H_{13}NO$	8-ketooctahydropyrrocoline	111
$C_8H_{15}NO$	2-dimethylaminocyclohexanone	11,121
	1-butyl-3-pyrrolidone	113
	3-(1'-pyrrolidyl)-2-butanone	139
$C_{10}H_{13}NO$	ω-dimethylaminoacetophenone	140
$C_{13}H_{15}NO_4$	ethyl 2-acetamidobenzoylacetate	134
$C_{14}H_{19}NO_2$	α-morpholinoisobutyrophenone	93
$C_{15}H_{15}NO$	phenacyl benzylamine	141
$C_{17}H_{17}NO_3$	1-p-biphenylyl-2-acetamidopropan-3-ol-1-one	142

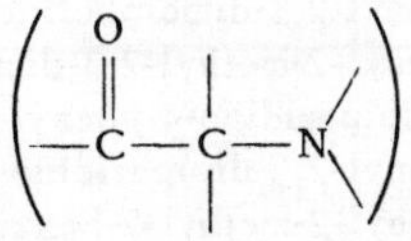

$C_{19}H_{18}N_2OS$	9-ω-thiazolylaminoacetyl-1,2,3,4-tetrahydrophenanthrene	143
$C_{23}H_{20}N_2OS$	9-ω-benzothiazolylaminoacetyl-1,2,3,4-tetrahydro-phenanthrene	143
$C_{24}H_{25}NO$	9-ω-(β-phenylethyl)aminoacetyl-1,2,3,4-tetrahydro-phenanthrene	143
$C_{26}H_{30}N_2O$	9-ω-(p-diethylaminoanilino)acetyl-1,2,3,4-tetrahydro-phenanthrene	143

β-Aminoketones

$C_8H_{15}NO$	4-(1'-pyrrolidyl)-2-butanone	139
$C_8H_{17}NO$	1-butylamino-3-butanone	113
$C_{10}H_{19}NO$	1-methyl-3,5-diethyl-4-piperidone	114
$C_{15}H_{21}NO_2$	2-phenoxy-6-dimethylaminomethyl-1-cyclohexanone	144
$C_{17}H_{23}NO_3$	2-phenoxy-6-morpholinomethyl-1-cyclohexanone	144
$C_{18}H_{25}NO_2$	2-phenoxy-6-piperidinomethyl-1-cyclohexanone	144
$C_{19}H_{19}NO$	9-(1-keto-3-dimethylaminopropyl)anthracene	91
$C_{19}H_{21}NO_3$	1,3-diphenyl-3-morpholinopropan-2-ol-1-one	145
$C_{20}H_{23}NO_2$	1,3-diphenyl-3-piperidinopropan-2-ol-1-one	145
$C_{21}H_{21}NO_2$	9-(1-keto-3-morpholinopropyl)anthracene	91
$C_{22}H_{25}NO_3$	1,3-diphenyl-2-acetoxy-3-piperidino-1-propanone	89
$C_{24}H_{23}NO_2$	1,3-diphenyl-3-tetrahydroisoquinolinopropan-2-ol-1-one	146
$C_{25}H_{25}NO_3$	1,3-diphenyl-2-acetoxy-3-(N-benzyl-N-methylamino)-1-propanone	89
$C_{27}H_{27}NO_3$	1,3-diphenyl-2-benzoxy-3-piperidino-1-propanone	89
$C_{27}H_{35}NO$	9-(1-keto-3-diamylaminopropyl)anthrгcene	91

α,β-Diaminoketones

$C_{14}H_{22}N_2O$	3,4-bis-(dimethylamino)-4-phenyl-2-butanone	71
$C_{18}H_{26}N_2O_3$	3,4-dimorpholino-4-phenyl-2-butanone	71
	1-phenyl-2,3-dimorpholino-1-butanone	147
	1-phenyl-2-methyl-2,3-dimorpholino-1-propanone	93
$C_{20}H_{30}N_2O$	3,4-dipiperidino-4-phenyl-2-butanone	71
	1-phenyl-2,3-dipiperidino-1-butanone	147
$C_{21}H_{26}N_2O_2$	1-phenyl-2-methyl-2-benzylamino-3-morpholino-1-propanone	93
	1-phenyl-2-morpholino-3-N-methylbenzylamino-1-propanone	93
$C_{23}H_{28}N_2O_2$	3-morpholino-4-tetrahydroquinolino-4-phenyl-2-butanone	71
$C_{23}H_{28}N_2O_3$	1,3-diphenyl-2,3-dimorpholino-1-propanone	71
$C_{27}H_{30}N_2O_2$	1-phenyl-2-dibenzylamino-3-morpholino-1-propanone	93
$C_{28}H_{30}N_2O_2$	1,3-diphenyl-2-morpholino-3-tetrahydroquinolino-1-propanone	71

$C_{28}H_{32}N_2O_2$	1-phenyl-2-methyl-2-dibenzylamino-3-morpholino-1-propanone	93
$C_{28}H_{34}N_2O_3$	3,4-bis-(N-methyl-p-methoxybenzylamino)-4-phenyl-2-butanone	71

$$\alpha\text{-}Hydroxyketones \left(\begin{array}{c} O \\ \parallel \ \mid \\ -C-C-OH \\ \mid \end{array} \right)$$

$C_7H_{12}O_2$	cycloheptan-2-ol-1-one	148
$C_{10}H_{12}O_2$	1-phenylpropan-1-ol-2-one	149
$C_{10}H_{18}O_2$	cyclodecan-2-ol-1-one	150
$C_{18}H_{34}O_2$	cyclooctadecan-2-ol-1-one	151
$C_{19}H_{21}NO_3$	1,3-diphenyl-3-morpholinopropan-2-ol-1-one	145
$C_{20}H_{23}NO_2$	1,3-diphenyl-3-piperidinopropan-2-ol-1-one	145
$C_{24}H_{23}NO_2$	1,3-diphenyl-3-tetrahydroisoquinolinopropan-2-ol-1-one	146

$$\beta\text{-}Hydroxyketones \left(\begin{array}{c} O \\ \parallel \ \mid \ \mid \\ -C-C-C-OH \\ \mid \ \mid \end{array} \right)$$

$C_7H_{12}O_2$	2-hydroxymethylcyclohexanone	137
$C_8H_{16}O_2$	3-hydroxymethyl-4-heptanone	152
$C_{17}H_{17}NO_3$	1-p-biphenylyl-2-acetamidopropan-3-ol-1-one	142
$C_{18}H_{21}NO_4$	8-hydroxydihydrocodeinone	153

$$\alpha\text{-}Acyloxyketones \left(\begin{array}{c} O \\ \parallel \ \mid \\ -C-C-OCOR \\ \mid \end{array} \right)$$

$C_{11}H_{17}O_5$	1,3-diacetoxy-2-heptanone	154
$C_{15}H_{25}O_5$	1,3-diacetoxy-2-undecanone	154
$C_{22}H_{25}NO_3$	1,3-diphenyl-2-acetoxy-3-piperidino-1-propanone	89
$C_{25}H_{25}NO_3$	1,3-diphenyl-2-acetoxy-3-(N-methylbenzylamino)-1-propanone	89
$C_{27}H_{27}NO_3$	1,3-diphenyl-2-benzoxy-3-piperidino-1-propanone	89

Wear (152) reported that the ketoalcohol (C), formed by the LAH reduction of ethylketene dimer, is readily reduced with LAH to the 1,3-diol.

$$C_2H_5CH = C - CHC_2H_5 \xrightarrow{LAH} C_2H_5CH_2C - CHC_2H_5 \xrightarrow{LAH}$$

with lower structures:

$$\begin{array}{cc} \mid & \mid \\ O-C=O & O \ CH_2OH \\ & C \end{array}$$

$$C_2H_5CH_2CH - CHC_2H_5 \qquad (7\text{-}63)$$
$$\mid \qquad \mid$$
$$OH \qquad CH_2OH$$

On the other hand, Spriggs, Hill and Senter reported that the ketoalcohols CII formed by the LAH reduction of cyclohexylketene dimer (CI: $n = 0$) and (ω-cyclohexylalkyl)ketene dimers (CI: $n = 1,2,4$) could not be further reduced with LAH (155).

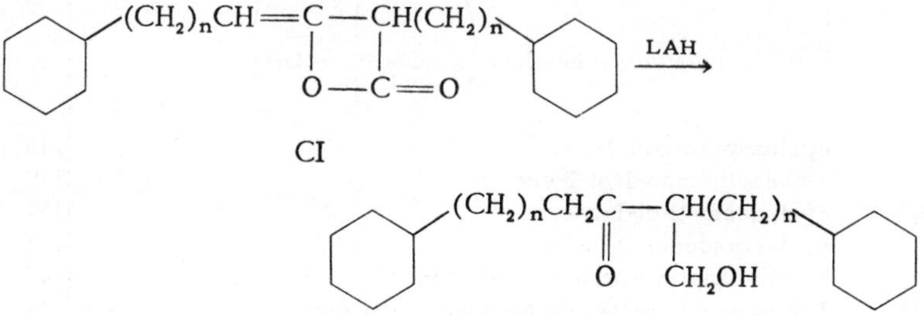

CI

$$(7\text{-}64)$$

CII

7.2.1.i *α,β-Unsaturated ketones including polycyclic ketones with aromatic or heterocyclic nuclei.* The LAH reduction of α,β-unsaturated ketones generally yields the corresponding unsaturated carbinol, although departures from this behavior due to the presence of various structural components have been observed. The reduction of α,β-unsaturated ketones is summarized in Table XV.

The reduction of conjugated alkenyl ketones to yield the corresponding alkenyl carbinols may be complicated by the sensitivity of the product. Attempts to prepare diisobutenyl carbinol by the reduction of phorone (CIII) with LAH yield, mainly, the triene (CIV) due to the sensitivity of the carbinol to traces of acidic impurities, resulting in rearrangement, and the ease of dehydration of the isomeric carbinol (156).

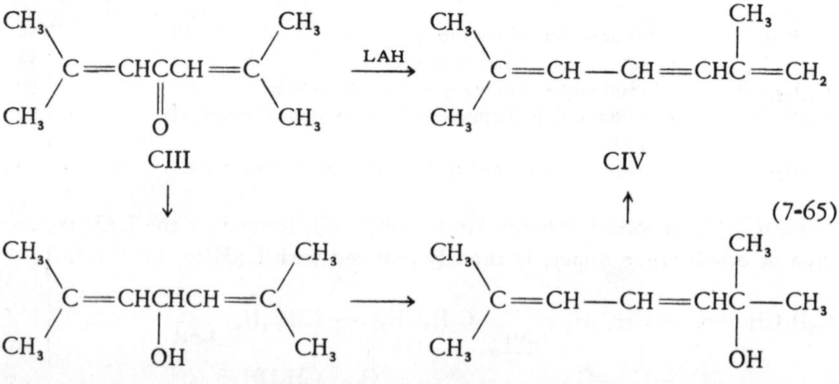

$$(7\text{-}65)$$

An analogous rearrangement has been observed in the hydrolysis of the reaction product from the reduction of various highly conjugated unsaturated ketones. In the presence of acids, allylic rearrangement occurs, while no rearrangement occurs in the presence of ammonium chloride solution (14).

$$C_6H_5(CH=CH)_2\overset{\overset{\displaystyle O}{\|}}{C}(CH=CH)_2C_6H_5 \xrightarrow{\text{LAH}}$$

$$C_6H_5(CH=CH)_2\overset{\overset{\displaystyle OH}{|}}{C}H(CH=CH)_2C_6H_5 \xrightarrow{\text{H}^{\oplus}}$$

$$C_6H_5(CH=CH)_2(CH=CH)_2\overset{\overset{\displaystyle OH}{|}}{C}HC_6H_5 \quad (7\text{-}66)$$

The LAH reduction of compounds which contain the styryl ketone grouping can be controlled to yield either the saturated or unsaturated alcohol.

$$C_6H_5CH=CH\overset{\overset{\displaystyle OH}{|}}{C}HCHR \quad (7\text{-}67)$$

$$C_6H_5CH=CH\overset{\overset{\displaystyle O}{\|}}{C}R \underset{\text{CV}}{}$$

$$C_6H_5CH_2CH_2\overset{\overset{\displaystyle OH}{|}}{C}HR \quad (7\text{-}68)$$

Thus, benzalacetone (CV : R = CH_3) (29,157,158), benzalacetophenone (CV : R = C_6H_5) (159,160) and dibenzalacetone (CV : R = $-CH=CHC_6H_5$) (14,29) have been reduced to both saturated and unsaturated carbinols while various highly conjugated unsaturated ketones have been reduced to the corresponding unsaturated carbinols (14,161).

$$C_6H_5(CH=CH)_m\overset{\overset{\displaystyle O}{\|}}{C}(CH=CH)_nC_6H_5 \xrightarrow{\text{LAH}}$$

$$C_6H_5(CH=CH)_m\overset{\overset{\displaystyle OH}{|}}{C}H(CH=CH)_nC_6H_5 \quad (7\text{-}69)$$

$$C_6H_5(CH\rightarrow CH)_m\overset{\overset{\displaystyle O}{\|}}{C}R \xrightarrow{\text{LAH}} C_6H_5(CH=CH)_m\overset{\overset{\displaystyle OH}{|}}{C}HR \quad (7\text{-}70)$$

$$C_6H_5(CH=CH)_m\overset{\overset{\displaystyle O}{\|}}{C}\!-\!\overset{\overset{\displaystyle O}{\|}}{C}(CH=CH)_nC_6H_5 \xrightarrow{\text{LAH}}$$

$$C_6H_5(CH=CH)_m\overset{\overset{\displaystyle OH}{|}}{C}H\!-\!\!-\!\overset{\overset{\displaystyle OH}{|}}{C}H(CH=CH)_nC_6H_5 \quad (7\text{-}71)$$

TABLE XV

LAH Reduction of α,β-Unsaturated Ketones

$$\text{A.} \qquad \text{—CH=CHCR} \;(\text{C=O}) \;\longrightarrow\; \text{—CH=CHCHR} \;(\text{CH–OH})$$

1. Exocyclic Double Bond RCH=CHCR(=O)

	Ketone	Product	% Yield	Ref.
$C_6H_{10}O$	2-Methyl-2-penten-4-one (mesityl oxide)	2-Methyl-2-penten-4-ol	90	1
$C_9H_{14}O$	2,6-Dimethylhepta-2,5-dien-4-one	Product not indicated	...	2
$C_9H_{16}O$	4,4-Dimethyl-3-ethylidene-2-pentanone	2,6-Dimethylhepta-1,3,5-triene	63	3
$C_{10}H_{10}O$	Benzalacetone	Product not indicated	...	2
		4-Phenyl-3-buten-2-ol	99	4
$C_{10}H_{16}O$	4-Cyclohexyl-3-buten-2-one	4-Cyclohexyl-3-buten-2-ol	85–93	5
$C_{12}H_{12}O$	Cinnamalacetone	6-Phenylhexa-3,5-dien-2-ol	80[6]	7
$C_{12}H_{14}O_2$	4,6,8,10-Dodecatetraen-2,3-dione	4,6,8,10-Dodecatetraen-2,3-diol	77[6]	8
$C_{13}H_{18}O$	4-(2',6',6'-Trimethylcyclohexa-1',3'-dienyl)-2-buten-2-one (3-dehydro-β-ionone)	4-(2',6',6'-Trimethylcyclohexa-1',3'-dienyl)-3-buten-2-ol (3-dehydro-β-ionol)	64	9
$C_{13}H_{18}O_2$	5-Keto-α-ionone	5-Hydroxy-α-ionol	...	10
$C_{13}H_{20}O$	β-Ionone	β-Ionol	86	11
$C_{15}H_{12}O$	Benzalacetophenone	1,3-Diphenyl-2-propen-1-ol	...	12
$C_{15}H_{14}O_2$	9-Phenyl-4,6,8-nonatrien-2,3-dione	9-Phenyl-4,6,8-nonatrien-2,3-diol	65	13
$C_{16}H_{14}O_5$	2,2',4'-Trihydroxy-3-methoxychalcone	1-(2',4'-Dihydroxyphenyl)-3-(2-hydroxy-3-methoxyphenyl)-2-propen-1-ol	75[6]	7
	2',4,4'-Trihydroxy-3-methoxychalcone	1-(2',4'-Dihydroxyphenyl)-3-(3-methoxy-4-hydroxyphenyl)-2-propen-1-ol	...	14

$C_{17}H_{14}O$	Dibenzalacetone	1,5-Diphenylpenta-1,4-dien-3-ol	73^6	7
	Cinnamalacetophenone	1,5-Diphenylpenta-2,4-dien-1-ol	80^6	7
$C_{17}H_{16}O_6$	2',4,4'-Trihydroxy-3,5-dimethoxychalcone	1-(2',4,4'-Dihydroxyphenyl)-3-(3,5-dimethoxy-4-hydroxyphenyl)-2-propen-1-ol	...	15
$C_{18}H_{16}O_2$	trans-Dibenzoyldimethylethylene	1,4-Diphenyl-2,3-dimethyl-2-buten-1,4-diol (equal amounts racemic and meso)	...	16
$C_{18}H_{26}O$	8-(2',2',6'-Trimethylcyclohex-6'-enyl)-6-methylocta-3,5,7-trien-2-one	8-(2',2',6'-Trimethylcyclohex-6'-enyl)-6-methylocta-3,5,7-trien-2-ol	...	11
$C_{19}H_{16}O$	1,7-Diphenylhepta-1,4,6-trien-3-one	1,7-Diphenylhepta-1,4,6-trien-3-ol	$...^6$	7
$C_{19}H_{18}O_5$	2',4,4'-Trihydroxy-3-methoxy-5-propenylchalcone	1-(2',4,4'-Dihydroxyphenyl)-3-(3-methoxy-4-hydroxy-5-propenylphenyl)-2-propen-1-ol	...	14,15
$C_{19}H_{20}O_5$	2',4'-Dihydroxy-3-methoxy-4-isopropoxychalcone	1-(2',4'-Dihydroxyphenyl)-3-(3-methoxy-4-isopropoxyphenyl)-2-propen-1-ol	...	14
$C_{19}H_{20}O_6$	3',4-Dihydroxy-3,4',5-trimethoxy-6'-methylchalcone	1-(2'-Methyl-4'-methoxy-5'-hydroxyphenyl)-3-(3,5-dimethoxy-4-hydroxyphenyl)-2-propen-1-ol	...	15
$C_{19}H_{22}O$	Nonadeca-2,4,6,8,11,13,15,17-octaen-10-one	Nonadeca-2,4,6,8,11,13,15,17-octaen-10-ol	$...^6$	7
$C_{19}H_{28}O$	1-Methyl-2-(decahydro-1-naphthylideneacetyl)-1-cyclohexene	1-(α-Naphthyl)-2-(o-tolyl)ethane	$...^6$ } 17	18
		1-Methylchrysene	$...^6$	8
$C_{20}H_{22}O_2$	Eicosa-2,4,6,8,12,14,16,18-octaen-10,11-dione	Eicosa-2,4,6,8,12,14,16,18-octaen-10,11-diol	$...^6$	8
$C_{21}H_{18}O$	Dicinnamalacetone	1,9-Diphenyl-1,3,6,8-nonatetraen-5-ol	70^6	7
$C_{21}H_{24}O_6$	2',4-Dihydroxy-3',3,5-trimethoxypropylchalcone	1-(2'-Hydroxy-3'-methoxy-5'-propylphenyl)-3-(3,5-dimethoxy-4-hydroxyphenyl)-2-propen-1-ol	...	15
$C_{22}H_{18}O_2$	1,10-Diphenyldeca-1,3,7,9-tetraen-5,6-dione	1,10-Diphenyldeca-1,3,7,9-tetraen-5,6-diol	$...^6$	8
$C_{22}H_{26}O_7$	3',4-Dihydroxy-2',3,4',5-tetramethoxy-6'-propylchalcone	1-(2',4'-Dimethoxy-3'-hydroxy-6'-propylphenyl)-3-(3,5-dimethoxy-4-hydroxyphenyl)-2-propen-1-ol	...	15
$C_{25}H_{22}O$	1,13-Diphenyltrideca-1,3,5,8,10,12-hexaen-7-one	1,13-Diphenyltrideca-1,3,5,8,10,12-hexaen-7-ol	75^6	7

(Continued)

TABLE XV (Continued)

Ketone	Product	% Yield	Ref.
	1. Exocyclic Double Bond RCH=CHCR (Continued)		
$C_{26}H_{22}O_2$	1,14-Diphenyltetradeca-1,3,5,9,11,13-hexaen-7,8-dione	1,14-Diphenyltetradeca-1,3,5,9,11,13-hexaen-7,8-diol	25[6]	8

2. Alicyclic Double Bond

Ketone	Product	% Yield	Ref.
$C_7H_{10}O$	1-Acetyl-1-cyclopentene	1-(1'-Cyclopentenyl)ethanol	60–80	19
$C_8H_{12}O$	1-Acetyl-1-cyclohexene	1-(1'-Cyclohexenyl)ethanol	88	19
		1-(1'-Cyclohexenyl)ethanol	...	20,21
		1-Cyclohexylethanol	...	
$C_{10}H_{16}O$	1-Acetyl-4,4-dimethyl-1-cyclohexene	1-(4',4'-Dimethyl-1'-cyclohexenyl)ethanol	84	22
$C_{11}H_{18}O$	2-Acetyl-1,3,3-trimethyl-1-cyclohexene	1-(2',6',6'-Trimethyl-1'-cyclohexenyl)ethanol	80	23
$C_{19}H_{26}O_2$	1-Methyl-2-(5-keto-1,2,3,4,5,6,7,8-octahydro-1-naphthylacetyl)-1-cyclohexene	1-(α-Naphthyl)-2-(o-tolyl)ethane	...[17]	18
		1-Methylchrysene	...[17]	
$C_{19}H_{28}O$	1-Methyl-2-(decahydro-1-naphthylideneacetyl)-1-cyclohexene	1-(α-Naphthyl)-2-(o-tolyl)ethane	...[17]	18
		1-Methylchrysene	...[17]	

3. Alicyclic Carbonyl Group and Double Bond

Ketone	Product	% Yield	Ref.
C_6H_8O	1-Cyclohexen-3-one	1-Cyclohexen-3-ol	70	20,21
$C_7H_{10}O$	1-Methyl-1-cyclohexen-3-one	1-Methyl-1-cyclohexen-3-ol	....	20,21,24
			68	25

			Yield	Ref.
$C_9H_{14}O$	4-Methyl-3-cyclohexen-1-one	4-Methyl-3-cyclohexen-1-ol	54	25
	(-)-4-Isopropyl-2-cyclohexen-1-one ((-)-cryptone)	(+)-cis-Cryptol 25} / (-)-trans-Cryptol 75}	95	26
$C_{10}H_{14}O$	3-Keto-1,2,3,4,5,6,7,8-octahydroazulene	3-Hydroxy-1,2,3,4,5,6,7,8-octahydroazulene	85	27
	4-Keto-1,2,3,4,5,6,7,8-octahydroazulene	4-Hydroxy-1,2,3,4,5,6,7,8-octahydroazulene	100	28
$C_{10}H_{16}O$	(-)-3-Methyl-6-isopropyl-2-cyclohexen-1-one ((-)-piperitone)	(-)-cis-Piperitol 36} / (+)-trans-Piperitol 64}	90	26
	1-Cyclodecen-3-one	1-Cyclodecen-3-ol	……	29
$C_{11}H_{16}O$	1-Methyl-3-ketooctahydroazulene	1-Methyl-3-hydroxyoctahydroazulene	85	27
$C_{12}H_{14}O_3$	trans-1,4-Diketo-2-methoxy-10-methyl-$\Delta^{2,6}$-hexahydronaphthalene	trans-1,4-Dihydroxy-2-methoxy-10-methyl-$\Delta^{2,6}$-hexahydronaphthalene	64 }	30,31
		trans-1,4-Dihydroxy-2-methoxy-$\Delta^{2,6}$-hexahydronaphthalene	…… }	
	cis-1,4-Diketo-2-methoxy-10-methyl-$\Delta^{2,6}$-hexahydronaphthalene	cis-1,4-Dihydroxy-2-methoxy-10-methyl-$\Delta^{2,6}$-hexahydronaphthalene	96	31
$C_{12}H_{16}O_2$	1-Keto-6-methoxy-5-methyl-1,2,3,4,5,8-hexahydronaphthalene[32]	2-Keto-1-methyl-2,3,4,6,7,8-hexahydronaphthalene	……[33]	34
$C_{12}H_{16}O_3$	trans-1,4-Diketo-2-methoxy-10-methyl-Δ^2-octahydronaphthalene	trans-1,4-Dihydroxy-2-methoxy-10-methyl-Δ^2-octahydronaphthalene	46	31
$C_{13}H_{18}O_2$	5-Keto-α-ionone	5-Hydroxy-α-ionol	……	10
$C_{14}H_{24}O$	1-Cyclotetradecen-3-one	1-Cyclotetradecen-3-ol	100	35
$C_{17}H_{24}O_3$	Ketolactone, m.p. 187°	Triol, m.p. 116°	……	36
$C_{18}H_{18}BrNO_3$	1-Bromocodeinone	Codeine	……[37]	38

(Continued)

TABLE XV (*Continued*)

3. Alicyclic Carbonyl Group and Double Bond $\underbrace{\text{—(CH}_2)_x\text{C}=\text{CC—}}$ (*Continued*)

(product structure: $\text{R—C(}\overset{\text{O}}{\underset{\text{H}}{\parallel}}\text{)—(CH}_2)_x\text{C}=\text{CC—}$)

Ketone	Product	% Yield	Ref.
C$_{18}$H$_{32}$O 1-Cyclooctadecen-3-one	1-Cyclooctadecen-3-ol	83.7	35
C$_{19}$H$_{26}$O$_2$ 1-Methyl-2-(5-keto-1,2,3,4,5,6,7,8-octahydro-1-naphthylacetyl)-1-cyclohexene	1-(α-Naphthyl)-2-(o-tolyl)ethane	...[17]	18
	1-Methylchrysene	...[17]	18
C$_{19}$H$_{28}$O$_2$ 1-Methyl-2-(5-keto-1,2,3,4,5,6,7,8-octahydronaphthylacetyl)cyclohexane	1-(α-Naphthyl)-2-(o-tolyl)ethane		
C$_{38}$H$_{26}$O 2-Keto-1,1,9,10-tetraphenyl-1,2-dihydroanthracene	2-Hydroxy-1,1,9,10-tetraphenyl-1,2-dihydroanthracene	....	39

4. Alicyclic Carbonyl Group and Semi-cyclic Double Bond $\underbrace{\text{—(CH}_2)_x\text{C—}}$

(product structure: $\text{R—HC}=\text{C}\overset{\text{O}}{\underset{}{\parallel}}\text{C—(CH}_2)_x\text{C—}$)

Ketone	Product	% Yield	Ref.
C$_7$H$_{10}$O 2-Ethylidenecyclopentanone	2-Ethylidene-1-cyclopentanol	50	19
C$_8$H$_{12}$O 2-Methylenecyclohexanone	2-Methylene-1-cyclohexanol	....	40
2-Ethylidenecyclohexanone	2-Ethylidene-1-cyclohexanol	55	19
C$_{10}$H$_{16}$O (+)-2-Isopropylidene-5-methyl-1-cyclohexanone ((+)-pulegone)	(+)-*trans*-Pulegol ; (−)-*cis*-Pulegol	} 90	41

$$\text{B.}\qquad -CH{=}CH\overset{\displaystyle O}{\overset{\|}{C}}R \;\longrightarrow\; -CH_2CH_2\overset{\displaystyle OH}{\overset{|}{C}}HR$$

Formula	Ketone	Product	Yield (%)	Ref.
$C_8H_{12}O$	1-Acetyl-1-cyclohexene	1-(1'-Cyclohexenyl)ethanol	....	20,21
		1-Cyclohexylethanol	....	1
$C_{10}H_{10}O$	Benzalacetone	4-Phenyl-2-butanol	87, 80	42
$C_{15}H_{11}ClO$	Benzal-p-chloroacetophenone	1-p-Chlorophenyl-3-phenyl-1-propanol	95	43
	p-Chlorobenzalacetophenone	1-Phenyl-3-p-chlorophenyl-1-propanol	88	43
$C_{15}H_{12}O$	Benzalacetophenone	1,3-Diphenyl-1-propanol	....	12
$C_{16}H_{14}O$	Benzal-p-methylacetophenone	1-p-Tolyl-3-phenyl-1-propanol	97	43
$C_{16}H_{14}O_2$	Anisalacetophenone	1-Phenyl-3-p-anisyl-1-propanol	88	43
	Benzal-p-methoxyacetophenone	1-p-Anisyl-3-phenyl-1-propanol	90	43
$C_{17}H_{14}O$	Dibenzalacetone	1,5-Diphenyl-3-pentanone	94	1

References—Table XV

[1]E. Larsson, *Trans. Chalmers Univ. Technol., Gothenburg,* 94, 15 (1950).

[2]W. A. Mosher and J. C. Cox, Jr., *J. Am. Chem. Soc.,* 72, 3701 (1950).

[3]E. A. Braude and J. A. Coles, *J. Chem. Soc.,* 1952, 1425.

[4]J. S. Meek, F. J. Lorenzi, and S. J. Cristol, *J. Am. Chem. Soc.,* 71, 1830 (1949).

[5]O. Grummitt and J. Splitter, *ibid.,* 74, 3924 (1952).

[6]Reduction carried out in a benzene-ether mixture.

[7]F. Bohlmann, *Chem. Ber.,* 85, 1144 (1952).

[8]F. Bohlmann, *ibid.,* 85, 386 (1952).

[9]H. B. Henbest, *J. Chem. Soc.,* 1951, 1074.

[10]V. Prelog and M. Osgan, *Helv. Chim. Acta,* 35, 986 (1952).

[11]H. H. Inhoffen, F. Bohlmann, and M. Bohlmann, *Ann.,* 565, 35 (1949).

[12]W. G. Brown, in *Organic Reactions,* Vol. VI, p. 482.

[13]F. A. Hochstein, *J. Am. Chem. Soc.,* 71, 305 (1949).

[14]J. C. Pew, *ibid.,* 73, 1678 (1951).

[15]J. C. Pew, *ibid.,* 74, 2850 (1952).

[16]R. E. Lutz and J. S. Gillespie, Jr., *Abstracts of Papers,* 116th Meeting American Chemical Society, Atlantic City, N. J., September 1949, p. 8M.

[17]Isolated after dehydration and dehydrogenation.

[18]W. S. Johnson, J. Szmuszkovicz, and M. Miller, *J. Am. Chem. Soc.,* 72, 3726 (1950).

[19]J. English, Jr. and V. Lamberti, *ibid.,* 74, 1909 (1952).

[20]M. Mousseron, R. Jacquier, M. Mousseron-Canet, and R. Zagdoun, *Compt. rend.,* 235, 177 (1952); *Bull. soc. chim. France,* [5] 19, 1042 (1952).

[21]R. Jacquier and R. Zagdoun, *ibid.,* [5] 19, 698 (1952).

[22]H. B. Henbest, B. L. Shaw, and G. Woods, *J. Chem. Soc.,* 1952, 1154.

[23]H. B. Henbest and G. Woods, *ibid.,* 1952, 1150.

[24]R. Jacquier and R. Zagdoun, *Bull. soc. chim. France,* [5] 18, 792 (1951).

[25]M. I. Bowman, C. C. Ketterer, and G. Dinga, *J. Org. Chem.,* 17, 563 (1952).

[26]A. K. Macbeth and J. S. Shannon, *J. Chem. Soc.,* 1952, 2852.

[27]E. A. Braude and W. F. Forbes, *Nature,* 168, 874 (1951).

[28]A. G. Anderson, Jr., and J. A. Nelson, *J. Am. Chem. Soc.,* 73, 232 (1951).

[29]V. Prelog and K. Schenker, *Helv. Chim. Acta,* 35, 2044 (1952).

[30]R. B. Woodward, F. Sondheimer, D. Taub, K. Heusler, and W. M. McLamore, *J. Am. Chem. Soc.,* 73, 2403 (1951).

[31]R. B. Woodward, F. Sondheimer, D. Taub, K. Heusler, and W. M. McLamore, *ibid.,* 74, 4223 (1952).

[32]Present as impurity in mixture with 1-keto-6-methoxy-9-methyl-1,2,3,4,8,9-hexahydronaphthalene.

[33]Isolated after acid hydrolysis of reduction product.

[34]A. J. Birch, J. A. K. Quartey, and H. Smith, *J. Chem. Soc.,* 1952, 1768.

[35]R. B. Ingraham, D. M. MacDonald, and K. Wiesner, *Can. J. Research,* 28B, 453 (1950).

[36]C. Collin-Asselineau, *Compt. rend.,* 235, 634 (1952).

[37]Reduction carried out in tetrahydrofuran.

[38]M. Gates and G. Tschudi, *J. Am. Chem. Soc.,* 74, 1109 (1952).

[39]A. Étienne and J. Weill-Raynal, *Compt. rend.,* 235, 301 (1952).

[40]A. S. Dreiding and J. A. Hartman, *J. Am. Chem. Soc.,* 75, 939 (1953).

[41]A. K. Macbeth and J. S. Shannon, *J. Chem. Soc.,* 1952, 4748.

[42]P. P. T. Sah, *Z. Vitamin-, Hormon- u. Fermentforsch.,* 3, 324 (1949); through M. Ferles, and J. Rudinger, *Chem. Listy,* 47, 129 (1953).

[43]C. S. Rondestvedt, Jr., *J. Am. Chem. Soc.,* 73, 4509 (1951).

The simultaneous reduction of the double bond and the carbonyl group is postulated as proceeding through the complex CVI as discussed in Section 15.1.1.b.1.

$$
\begin{array}{c}
\text{CH}_2\text{---CHR} \\
| \qquad\qquad | \\
\text{C}_6\text{H}_5\text{CH} \qquad \text{O} \\
\diagdown \quad \diagup \\
\text{Al} \\
\diagup \quad \diagdown \\
\text{O} \qquad\quad \text{CHC}_6\text{H}_5 \\
| \qquad\qquad | \\
\text{CH}_2\text{---CHR} \\
\text{CVI}
\end{array}
$$

The O-methyl derivative of dibenzoylmethane (CVII) has been reported to be resistant to reduction with LAH (135).

$$
\begin{array}{cc}
\text{OCH}_3 & \text{O} \\
| & \| \\
\text{C}_6\text{H}_5\text{C}=\text{CHCC}_6\text{H}_5 \\
\text{CVII}
\end{array}
$$

Rondestvedt reported that the treatment of various chalcones in ether with 0.6 mole of LAH per mole of chalcone by the Soxhlet extraction technique gives high yields of the corresponding saturated carbinols (162).

(7-72)

R	R'	% Yield
H	OCH₃	88
H	Cl	88
CH₃	H	97
OCH₃	H	90
Cl	H	95

Pew reported that the addition of 0.05 millimole of LAH to 0.02 millimole of chalcone in ether followed by a period of one hour in which the reaction mixture apparently is maintained at ambient temperatures gives the corresponding unsaturated carbinol (163,164).

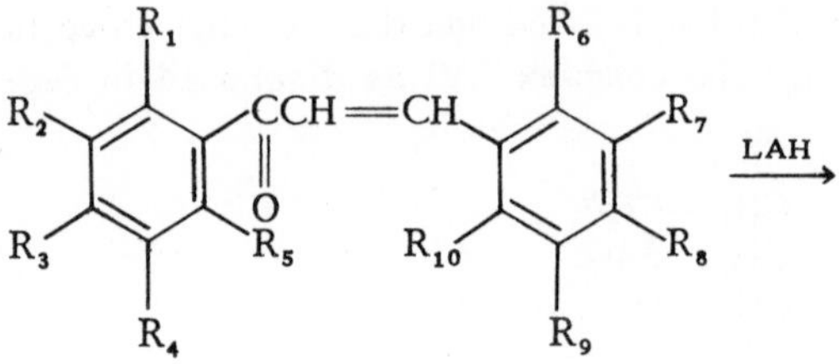

CIX

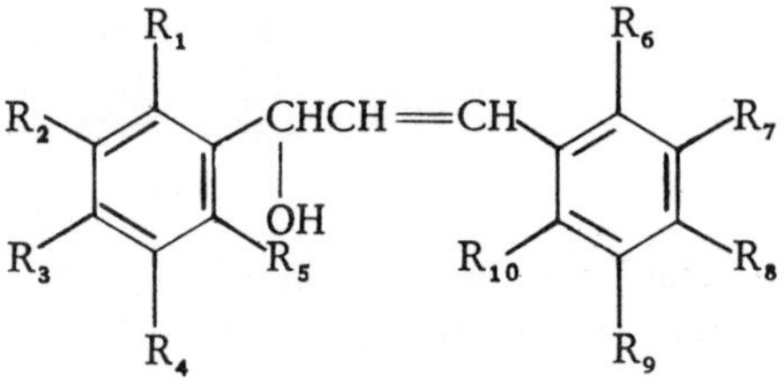

(7-73)

R_1	R_2	R_3	R_4	R_5	R_6	R_7	R_8	R_9	R_{10}
OH	H	OH	H	H	H	OCH_3	$OCH(CH_3)_2$	H	H
OH	H	OH	H	H	OH	OCH_3	H	H	H
OH	H	OH	H	H	H	OCH_3	OH	$CH=CHCH_3$	H
OH	H	OH	H	H	H	OCH_3	OH	H	H
OH	H	OH	H	H	H	OCH_3	OH	OCH_3	H
OH	OCH_3	H	C_3H_7	H	H	OCH_3	OH	OCH_3	H
OCH_3	OH	OCH_3	H	C_3H_7	H	OCH_3	OH	OCH_3	H
H	OH	OCH_3	H	CH_3	H	OCH_3	OH	OCH_3	H

Lutz and Gillespie (165) reported that the LAH reduction of *cis*- and *trans*-dibenzoylethylene (CX) gives the same two products in identical yield ratios in each case apparently due to *cis*- to *trans*- isomerization occurring prior to reduction.

$$C_6H_5CCH=CHCC_6H_5 \xrightarrow{\text{LAH}}$$

with O double bonds below the two C groups

CX

$$C_6H_5CHCH_2CH_2CC_6H_5 + C_6H_5CHCH=CHCHC_6H_5 \quad (7\text{-}74)$$

OH   O   OH   OH

CXI   CXII

The formation of *trans*-1,4-diphenyl-2-buten-1,4-diol (CXII) in 10% yield is the expected result of successive 1,2-additions to the two carbonyl groups. The hydroxyketone (CXI) (88% yield) must have been stabilized in the form of an enolate and liberated upon hydrolysis of the reaction mixture. This result is explained by the postulation of a 1,4-addition of the reagent to the α,β-unsaturated ketone (b) with prior or subsequent 1,2-addition (a) independently of the other carbonyl group.

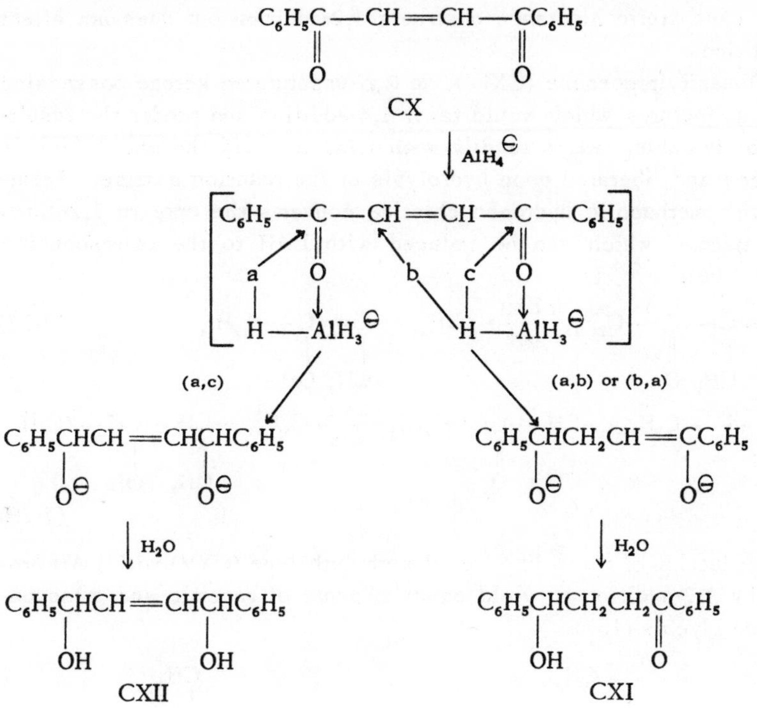

$$C_6H_5C-CH=CH-CC_6H_5$$

(with $\|$ O groups)

CX

$$\downarrow AlH_4^{\ominus}$$

$$\left[C_6H_5-\overset{a}{C}-CH=CH-\overset{c}{C}-C_6H_5 \right]$$

positions a, b, c; O; H—AlH$_3^{\ominus}$; H—AlH$_3^{\ominus}$

(7-75)

(a,c)

(a,b) or (b,a)

$$C_6H_5CHCH=CHCHC_6H_5$$
$$O^{\ominus} \qquad O^{\ominus}$$

$$C_6H_5CHCH_2CH=CC_6H_5$$
$$O^{\ominus} \qquad O^{\ominus}$$

$$\downarrow H_2O$$

$$\downarrow H_2O$$

$$C_6H_5CHCH=CHCHC_6H_5$$
$$OH \qquad OH$$
CXII

$$C_6H_5CHCH_2CH_2CC_6H_5$$
$$OH \qquad O$$
CXI

Failure to isolate any saturated diketone excludes the possibility of enolization at the second carbonyl group, after initial 1,4-addition, to yield the diene-diolate.

Reduction of *trans*-dimesitoylethylene (CXIII) yields the hydroxyketone as the only product.

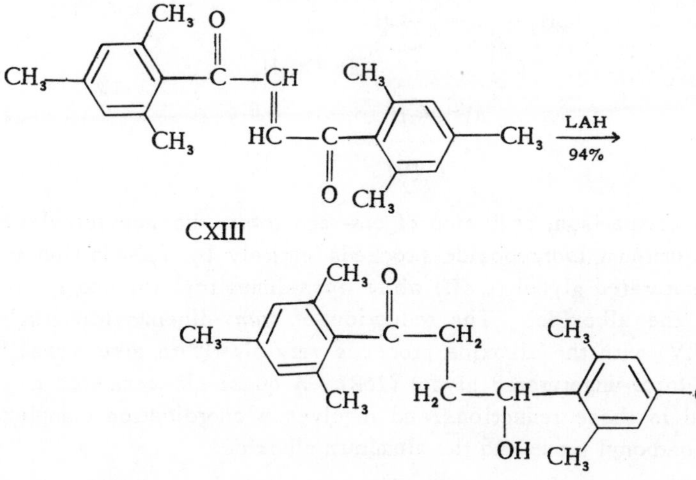

CXIII

$$\xrightarrow[94\%]{LAH}$$

(7-76)

In this case steric hindrance obstructs 1,2-addition but does not affect 1,4-addition.

1,2-Dimesitylpropenone (CXIV), an α,β-unsaturated ketone possessing structural features which would favor 1,4-addition and render the resulting enol isolable, reacts readily with LAH to yield the enol which is stabilized and liberated upon hydrolysis of the reaction mixture. Treatment with methanolic hydrogen chloride converts the enol to 1,2-dimesitylpropanone which can be reduced with LAH to the corresponding alcohol (166).

$$C_9H_{11}-\overset{\overset{\displaystyle \parallel}{CH_2}}{C}-\overset{\overset{\displaystyle \parallel}{O}}{C}-C_9H_{11} \xrightarrow[90\%]{LAH} C_9H_{11}-\overset{\overset{\displaystyle |}{CH_3}}{C}=\overset{\overset{\displaystyle |}{OH}}{C}-C_9H_{11} \qquad (7\text{-}77)$$

$$\xrightarrow{CH_3OH-HCl} C_9H_{11}-\overset{\overset{\displaystyle |}{CH_3}}{CH}-\overset{\overset{\displaystyle \parallel}{O}}{C}-C_9H_{11} \xrightarrow[80\%]{LAH} C_9H_{11}-\overset{\overset{\displaystyle |}{CH_3}}{CH}-\overset{\overset{\displaystyle |}{OH}}{CH}-(C_9H_{11})$$

$$(7\text{-}78)$$

The reduction of trans-dibenzoyldimethylethylene (CXV) with LAH proceeds by 1,2-addition to yield equal amounts of racemic and meso unsaturated glycols (167).

$$C_6H_5\overset{\overset{\displaystyle \parallel}{O}}{C}-\overset{\overset{\displaystyle |}{CH_3}}{C}=\overset{\overset{\displaystyle |}{CH_3}}{C}-\overset{\overset{\displaystyle \parallel}{O}}{C}C_6H_5 \xrightarrow{LAH} C_6H_5\overset{\overset{\displaystyle |}{OH}}{CH}-\overset{\overset{\displaystyle |}{CH_3}}{C}=\overset{\overset{\displaystyle |}{CH_3}}{C}-\overset{\overset{\displaystyle |}{OH}}{CH}C_6H_5$$

CXV   (7-79)

Lutz (165) has advanced the postulation of an intermediate cyclic resonating transition state in the case of 1,4-additions, analogous to those proposed for Grignard reactions and aluminum alkoxide reduction.

$$C_6H_5-C \longrightarrow CH$$
$$O \qquad CHCOC_6H_5$$
$$Al^{\ominus}-H$$
$$H_3$$

CXVI

By way of comparison, reduction of cis- and trans- dibenzoylethylene (CX) with aluminum isopropoxide proceeds entirely by 1,2-addition to yield the unsaturated glycol (CXII) while trans-dimesitoylethylene is not attacked by the alkoxide. The reduction of trans-dibenzoyldimethylethylene (CXV) with the alkoxide proceeds very slowly to give a small yield of the trans-unsaturated glycol (168). A quasi six-membered ring is postulated in these reductions and involves a coordination complex between the carbonyl group and the aluminum alkoxide.

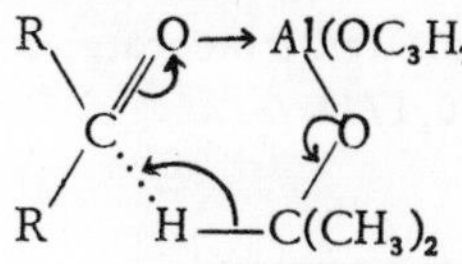

CXVII

The action of phenylmagnesium bromide on dibenzoylethylene (CX) involves chiefly 1,4-addition as the first step, but differs from the LAH reaction in the second step by causing enolization at the remaining carbonyl group.

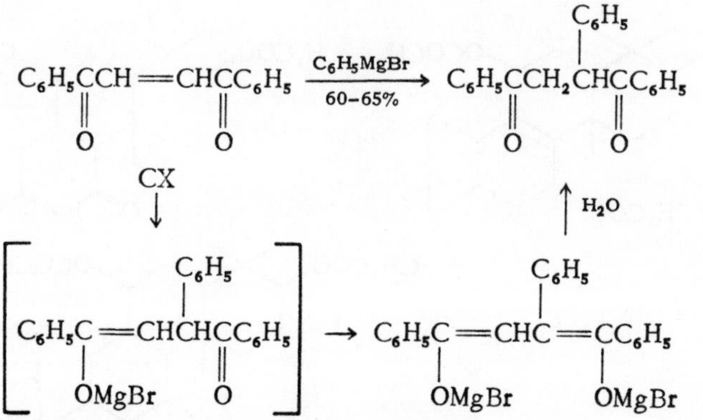

$$(7\text{-}80)$$

This difference is accounted for by the influence of the phenyl group and the hydrogen, which enter alpha to the second carbonyl group, on the ability of this second carbonyl group subsequently to add and to enolize (169).

In the LAH reduction of chalcones to saturated carbinols (equation (7-72), Rondestvedt (162) obtained a small quantity of p-anisylpropiophenone in the reduction of anisalacetophenone (CXVIII).

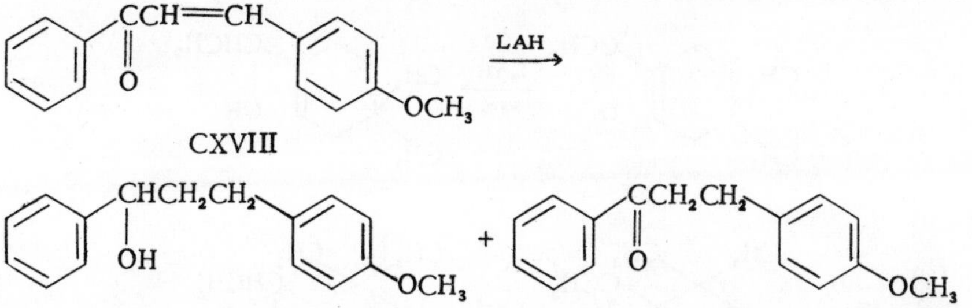

CXVIII

$$(7\text{-}81)$$

It was postulated that the initial addition is 1,4- to the conjugated system. The isolation of the saturated carbinol in 88% yield would therefore require further reduction of the enolate. It is more likely that a complex such as has been postulated in the reduction of cinnamyl type compounds, e.g., styryl ketones is involved. This is discussed more fully in Section 15.1.1.b.1.

The LAH reduction of diketolanostenyl acetate (CXIX), followed by acetylation, yields an unsaturated triacetate, a ketodiacetate and a saturated diacetoxy carbinol (170,171).

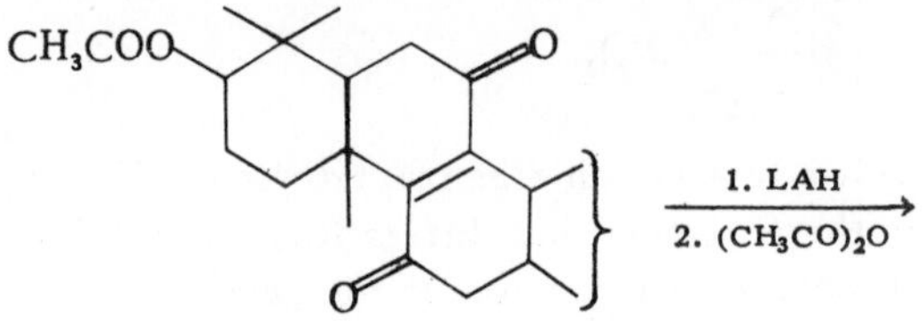

CXIX

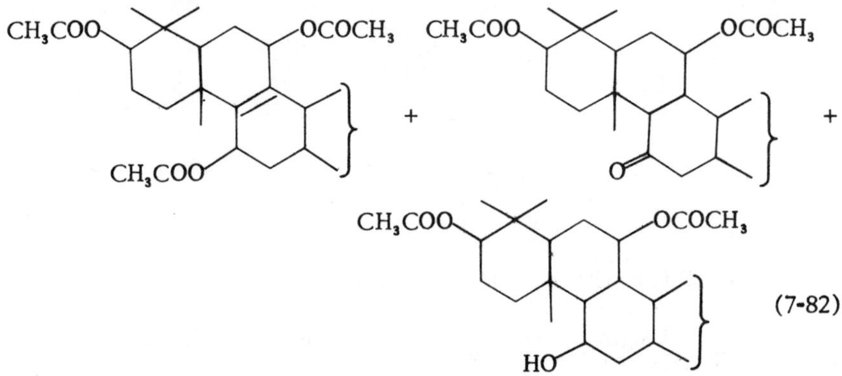

(7-82)

The isolation of the ketodiacetate is indicative of 1,4-addition to the unsaturated 1,4-diketone grouping.

The reduction of α,β-unsaturated ketones containing alicyclic double bonds has been reported in most cases to yield the corresponding α-ethylenic alcohol (Table XV). Thus, 1-acetyl-4,4-dimethylcyclohexene (CXX) and 2-acetyl-1,3,3-trimethylcyclohexene (CXXI) are reduced with LAH in refluxing ether to the cyclohexenyl ethanols (172,173).

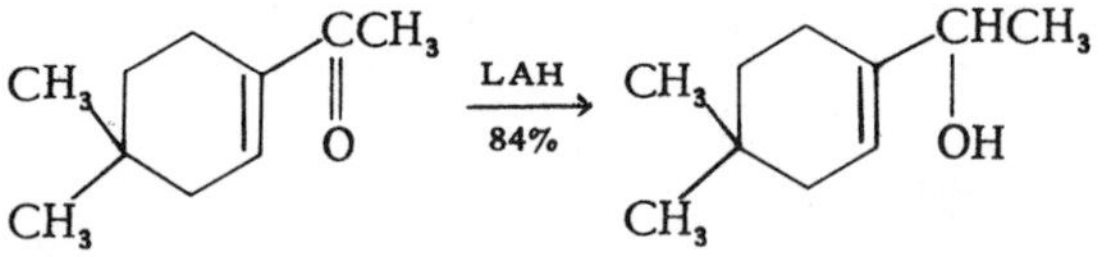

(7-83)

CXX

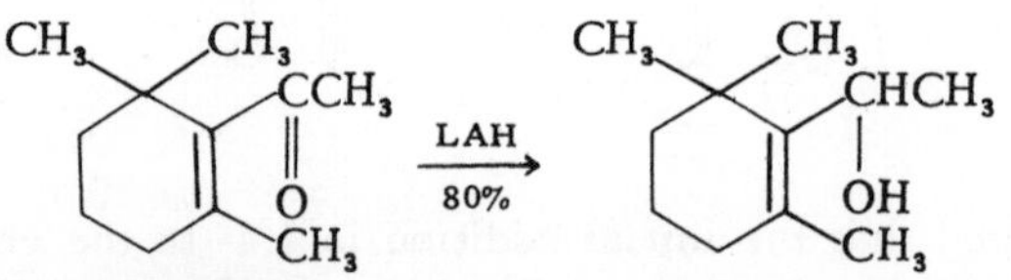

(7-84)

CXXI

English and Lamberti (174) reported that treatment of 1-acetylcyclohexene (CXXII) with a slight excess of LAH in refluxing ether gives 1-(1'-cyclohexenyl)ethanol contaminated with about 20% of unchanged ketone. A second reduction of the crude product with LAH reduces the ketone content. Considerable difficulties are encountered in isolating characteristic derivatives. Mousseron and his coworkers (10,11,175) reported that the addition of CXXII to an excess of LAH at ambient temperatures gives a mixture of the saturated and unsaturated carbinols, in which the saturated carbinol is the predominant product.

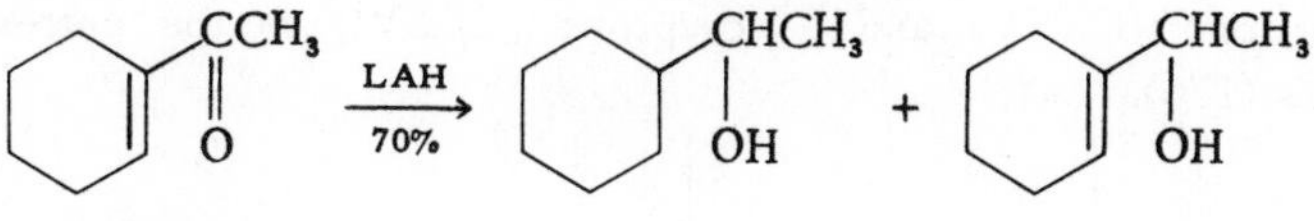

CXXII

Inverse addition at $-10°$ of a decreased amount of the hydride gives the same mixture with a reversal of the relative proportions of saturated and unsaturated alcohols. Because of the difficulty in obtaining satisfactory derivatives, the products were identified after oxidation to the corresponding ketones and fractionation of the 2,4-dinitrophenylhydrazones. It was suggested that English and Lambert may have overlooked the saturated carbinol due to the extreme conditions necessary to obtain derivatives. The formation of the saturated carbinol has been interpreted as arising through a complex (CXXIII) analogous to that proposed for the reduction of cinnamyl-type compounds:

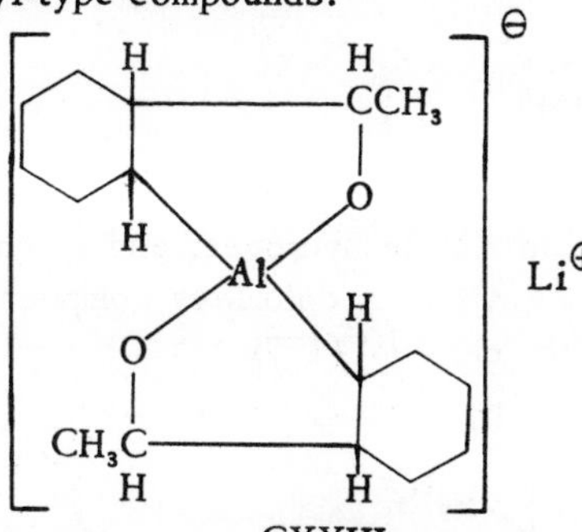

CXXIII

English and Lamberti (174) reported that the attempted reduction of CXXII with aluminum isopropoxide results in extensive isopropyl ether formation. Mousseron et al. (10,11,175) obtained practically equal quantities of the saturated and unsaturated carbinols by the reduction of CXXII with the aluminum alkoxide. This 1,4-addition is interpreted by the formation of the aluminum complex CXXIV via the migration of two hydrogen ions.

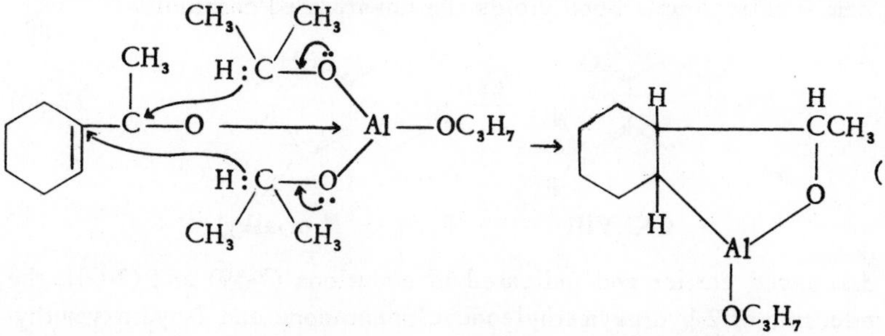

CXXIV

The LAH reduction of unsaturated ketones in which the double bond and the ketone group are both part of an alicyclic system yields the corresponding unsaturated carbinol. As in the reduction of the methylcyclohexanones the *trans*-isomer is the predominant product in the reduction of (–)-piperitone (CXXV) and (–)-cryptone (CXXVI) to the corresponding carbinols (176).

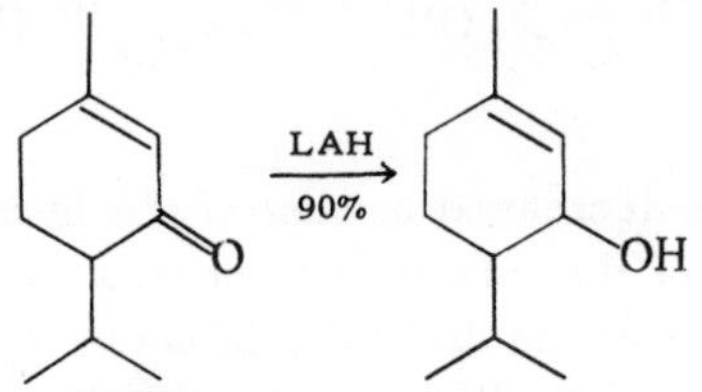

$$\xrightarrow[90\%]{\text{LAH}}$$

(–)-*cis* 36%
(+)-*trans* 64%   (7-87)

CXXV

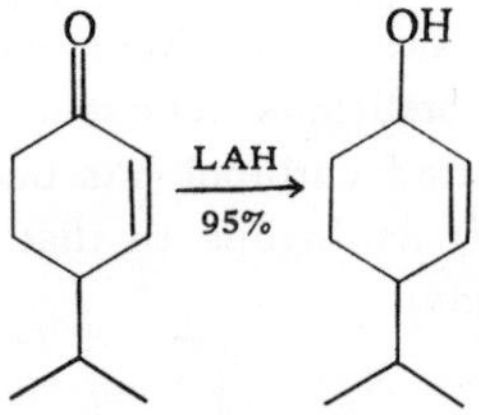

$$\xrightarrow[95\%]{\text{LAH}}$$

(+)-*cis* 25%
(–)-*trans* 75%   (7-88)

CXXVI

The ketone group in CXXVII resists all the usual reagents for carbonyls, does not contain mobile hydrogen, and is not enolizable. However, it is reduced by LAH to a colorless compound containing active hydrogen, presumably the carbinol (177).

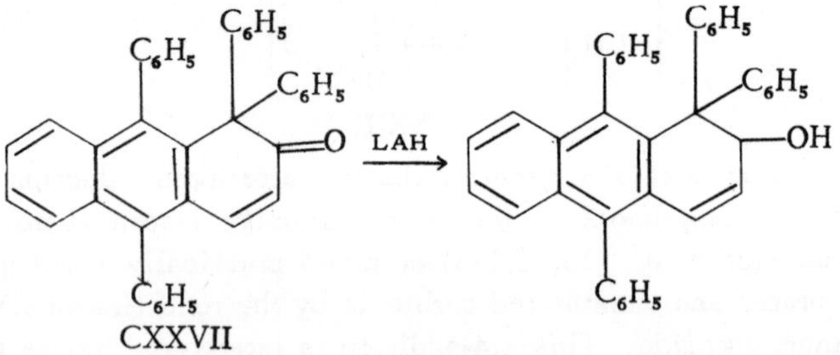

$$\xrightarrow{\text{LAH}}$$ (7-89)

CXXVII

The LAH reduction of ketones containing an alicyclic carbonyl group and a semi-cyclic double bond yields the unsaturated carbinol.

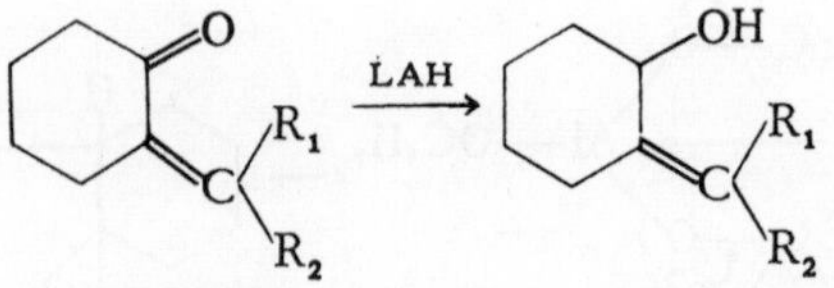

$$\xrightarrow{\text{LAH}}$$ (7-90)

CXXVIII R_1, R_2 = H or alkyl

As discussed earlier and indicated in equations (7-59) and (7-60), the LAH reduction of 2-hydroxymethylenecyclopentanone and 2-hydroxymethylenecyclohexanone (CXXIX) yields a mixture of 2-methylenecycloalkanol, 1-hydroxymethylcycloalkane and 2-hydroxymethylcycloalkanol (137).

$$(7\text{-}91)$$

Vonderwahl and Schinz (178) reported that treatment of 1,1,5,5-tetra-methyl-4-hydroxymethylene-3-cyclohexanone (CXXX) with LAH in refluxing ether, followed by the addition of sulfuric acid, gives 49% of a mixture of saturated (67%) and unsaturated aldehydes (33%) as well as a quantity of glycol.

$$(7\text{-}92)$$

Seifert and Schinz (179) carried out the reduction of various substituted and unsubstituted 2-alkoxymethylenecyclohexanones (CXXXI) with LAH in refluxing ether. Hydrolysis with water gives the 2-alkoxymethylenecyclohexanol which is saponified and dehydrated with cold, concentrated sulfuric acid to yield the 1-cyclohexenecarboxaldehyde.

$$(7\text{-}93)$$

	R	R_1	R_2	R_3	R_4	% Aldehyde
$C_{10}H_{16}O_2$	CH_3	CH_3	CH_3	H	H	60
$C_{11}H_{18}O_2$	i-C_4H_9	H	H	H	H	23
$C_{12}H_{20}O_2$	i-C_4H_9	CH_3	H	H	H	80
$C_{13}H_{22}O_2$	i-C_4H_9	H	H	CH_3	CH_3	46

Similar to the cyclohexanone derivatives, treatment of 2-isobutoxymethy-lenecyclopentanone in an analogous manner gives a 29% yield of 1-cyclo-pentenecarboxaldehyde.

Vonderwahl and Schinz (178) reported that when the 2-alkoxymethy-lenecyclohexanone is substituted in the beta position to the carbonyl the procedure of Seifert and Schinz yields a mixture of saturated and unsatu-rated aldehydes in which the saturated aldehyde is the major product.

$$(7\text{-}94)$$

When the reduction is carried out at $-15°$ the dominant products are the isomeric unsaturated aldehydes.

Reduction Temp.	R	R_1	% CXXXIII + CXXXIV	% CXXXIII	% CXXXIV	
					α	β
$-15°$	CH_3	CH_3	52	20	55	25
$35°$	CH_3	CH_3	72	dominant		
$35°$	CH_3	H	52	dominant		

The LAH reduction of the enol ether of a β-diketone followed by hy-drolysis yields an α,β-unsaturated ketone.

$$(7\text{-}95)$$

By this method the 5-isopropyl (CXXXV: R = H,R_1 = $CH(CH_3)_2$) (64%) (135), 5-methyl (CXXXV: R = H,R_1 = CH_3) (49–92%) (180) and 5,5-di-methyl (CXXXV: R = R_1 = CH_3) (48%) (135) compounds have been con-verted to the 5-alkyl-2-cyclohexen-1-ones. Analogously, cis-5-ethoxy-8-methylhydrind-5-ene-7-one (CXXXVI) is reduced and hydrolyzed to cis-8-methylhydrind-6-ene-5-one (181).

CXXXVI (7-96)

Although inverse addition and excess ketone were originally proposed for the reduction of CXXXV (135), it has been found that normal addition gives a higher conversion.

The LAH reduction of *cis*- and *trans*-1,4-diketo-2-methoxy-10-methyl-$\Delta^{2,6}$-hexahydronaphthalene (CXXXVII) yields the corresponding 1,4-diol which on treatment with sulfuric acid in dioxane is converted to *cis*- and *trans*-1-hydroxy-2-keto-10-methyl-$\Delta^{3,6}$-hexahydronaphthalene, respectively.

CXXXVII   CXXXVIII   (7-97)

The reduction of the *trans*-Δ^2-octahydronaphthalene analogue of CXXXVII yields the corresponding *trans*-1,4-diol which is hydrolyzed to the *trans*-bicyclic ketol (182,183).

The LAH reduction of *trans*-CXXXVII yields a by-product, $C_{11}H_{16}O_2$, m.p. 167–168°, as well as CXXXVIII. The by-product is postulated as the glycol formed by initial 1,4-addition, ketonization, elimination and reduction (183).

CXXXVII   (7-98)

Attempts to reduce 3-chloro-5,5-dimethyl-2-cyclohexen-1-one (CXXXIX) with LAH in ether have been reported to result in recovery of starting material (135).

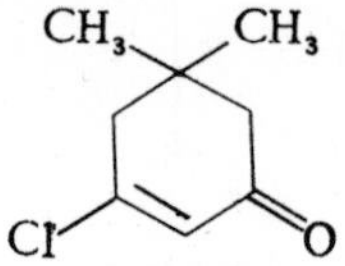

$$C_6H_5CC \equiv CCC_6H_5$$

CXXXIX

CXL

The attempted reduction of dibenzoylacetylene (CXL) with ethereal LAH has given dark red resinous products which have not been further characterized (165).

Various polycyclic ketones in which the carbonyl group is conjugated with an aromatic nucleus have been subjected to the reducing action of LAH, to yield in most cases the corresponding carbinol.

Although 1,4-diketo-1,2,3,4-tetrahydronaphthalene (CXLI) and its 2-methyl homologue exhibit few ketonic properties, and under most reaction conditions enolize and yield only naphthol derivatives, reductions with LAH and aluminum isopropoxide yield the corresponding 1,4-dihydroxy-naphthalenes (184).

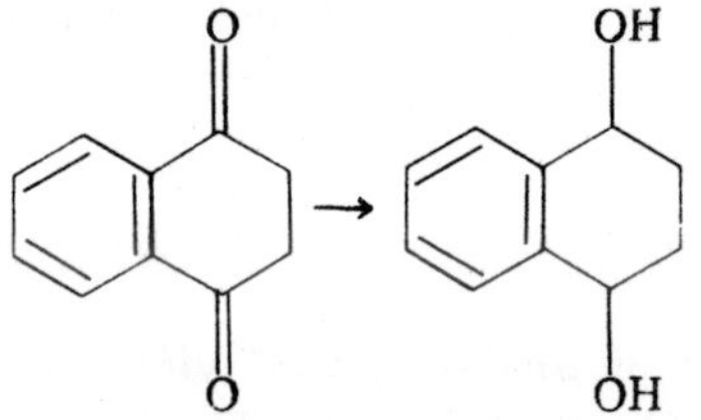

(7-99)

CXLI   CXLII

The dihydroxy compounds (CXLII) are the only products isolated from the Grignard and Reformatsky reactions.

Reduction of 1,4-acepleiadanedione (CXLIII) with LAH in an ether-benzene mixture gives, after a four hour reflux period, a mixture of isomeric glycols, m.p. 208° and 149–150°. The former is obtained in 46% yield under these conditions while the latter is favored by shorter reaction times and has been isolated in 31% yield from runs of one hour or less (185).

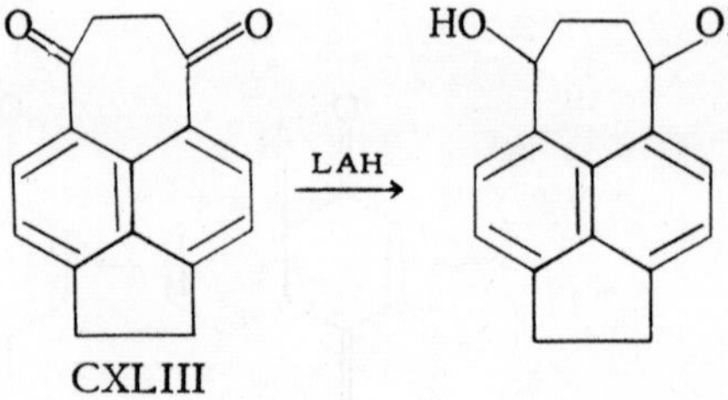

(7-100)

CXLIII

The two isomeric ketones, 1-keto-2-methyl-1,2,2a,3,4,5-hexahydro-pyrene (CXLIV), in which the methyl group in position 2 and the hydrogen at 2a exist in *cis* and *trans* configurations, have been treated with LAH to yield isomeric carbinols. Although reduction forms a new asymmetric center and introduces the possibility of two stereoisomeric alcohols from each ketone, only one sterically homogeneous compound is formed from each ketone (186).

$$(7\text{-}101)$$

CXLIV

ketone A, colorless, m.p. 141–142° $\xrightarrow[84\%]{}$ alcohol A, m.p. 188–189°

ketone B, yellow, m.p. 140–142° $\xrightarrow[79\%]{}$ alcohol B, m.p. 172–174°

mixture ketones A and B $\longrightarrow$ mixture alcohols A and B

Clemo *et al.* reported that attempts to reduce 1,2,3,8-tetrahydro-1-keto-cyclopent[a]indene (CXLV) by the Meerwein-Ponndorf, Clemmensen or Wolff-Kishner methods as well as with LAH were not encouraging (187).

CXLV   CXLVI

Orchin and Reggel reported that the reduction of 3-keto-12c,1,2,3-tetra-hydrobenz[j]fluoranthene (CXLVI) with LAH gave a product which was dehydrogenated over palladium-on-charcoal. Chromatography gave small amounts of two products which were not identified but were shown not to be the aromatic hydrocarbon benz[j]fluoranthene (188).

Hochstein obtained 9-fluorenol (CXLVIII) in 99% yield by the LAH reduction of fluorenone (CXLVII) in ether (159). Wender, Greenfield, and Orchin (189) also obtained 9-fluorenol by the reduction of CXLVII

whereas 2-methyl-, 3-methyl-, and 2,7-dimethylfluorenone have been reduced with ethereal LAH to the corresponding fluorenols (190).

Bergmann and his co-workers (191) have carried out the LAH reduction
of fluorenone (CXLVII) in dioxane and, upon hydrolysis of the reaction
product, obtained fluorenol (CXLVIII), dibiphenyleneethane (CXLIX) and
fluorene (CL).

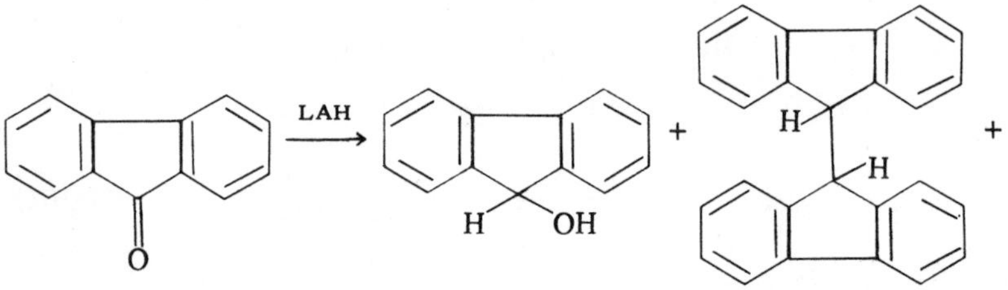

CXLVII   CXLVIII   CXLIX

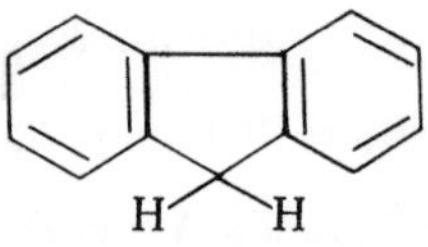

                                                             (7-102)

                                   CL

Treatment of the reduction product with *p*-chlorobenzyl chloride gives 9-
(*p*-chlorobenzyl)fluorene (CLI) and 9,9′-di-(*p*-chlorobenzyl)dibiphenylene-
ethane (CLII).

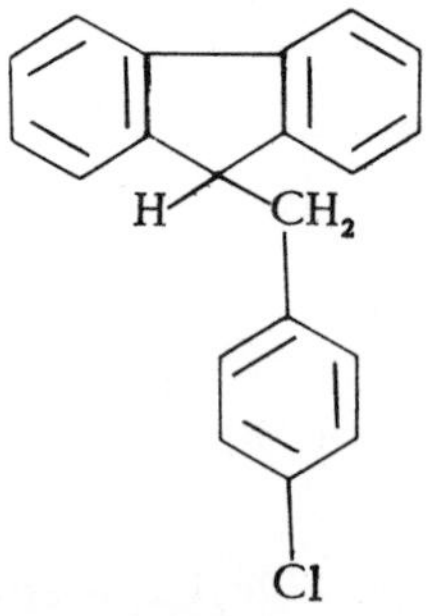

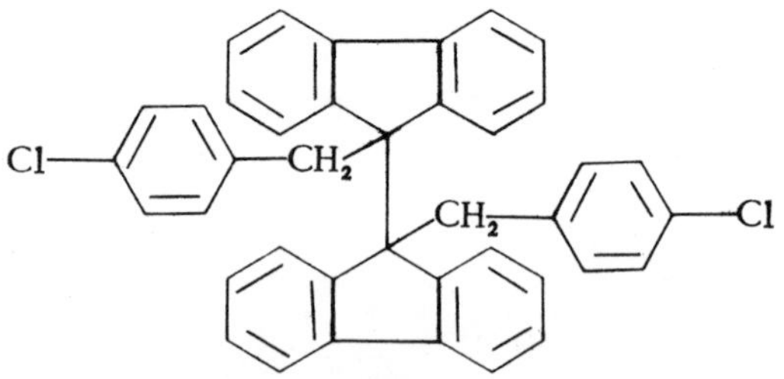

          CLI   CLII

The passage of air into a dioxane solution of the reduction product gives
upon hydrolysis fluorenol (CXLVIII) and dibiphenyleneethane (CXLIX).
It has been postulated that the primary attack on fluorenone gives a lithium compound A which reacts according to one of the following schemes:
rearrangement to B or hydrogenolysis to C and D by excess LAH.

The reaction of fluorenone with *p*-chlorobenzylmagnesium chloride yields 9-(*p*-chlorobenzyl)fluorenol by 1,2-addition to the carbonyl group (191).

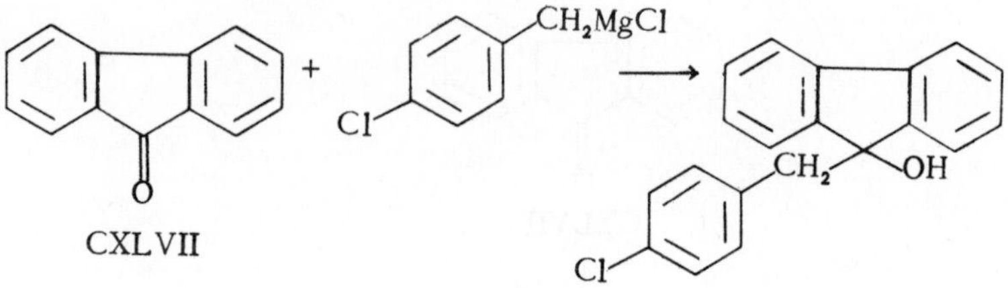

CXLVII

(7-104)

Julian *et al.* (98) reported that reduction of benzalanthrone (CLIII) with aluminum isopropoxide gives 9-hydroxy-10-benzylidene-9,10-dihydroan-thracene which on warming with dilute sulfuric acid rearranges to 9-(1-hydroxybenzyl)anthracene.

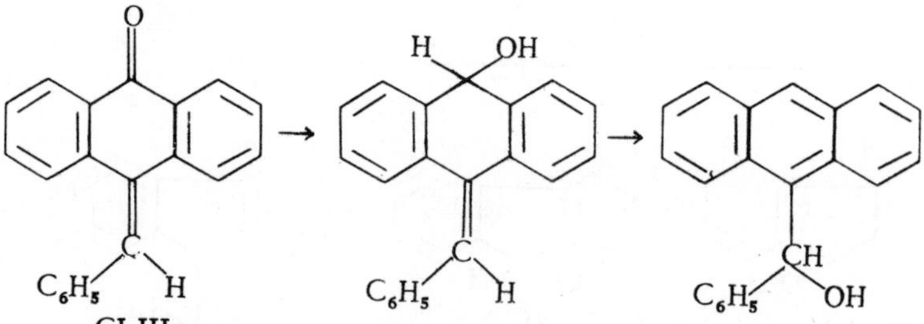

CLIII

(7-105)

Treatment of CLIII with LAH gave a mixture of products which were not separated (98). Bergmann, Hirshberg, and Lavie (192) have carried out the LAH reduction of CLIII in dioxane and isolated anthraquinone as the only product. The same result is obtained when the reduction is carried out under nitrogen.

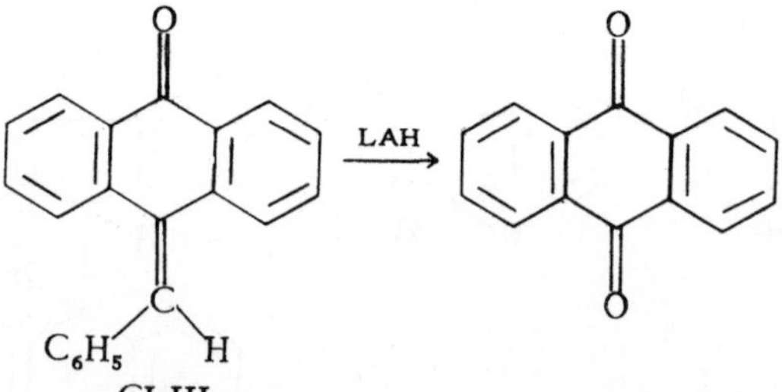

CLIII

(7-106)

The reaction of CLIII with organomagnesium compounds similarly yields anthraquinone (193) as well as 1,2-addition products (194).

The reduction of benzhydrylideneanthrone (CLIV) with LAH in dioxane yields a dimeric product, *sym*-tetraphenyl-bis-(9,10-dihydro-9-anthryl)-ethane (192). The reaction is postulated as proceeding by a 1,6-addition to yield a free radical which is stabilized by dimerization. Subsequent hydrogenolysis yields the dimeric oxygen-free product.

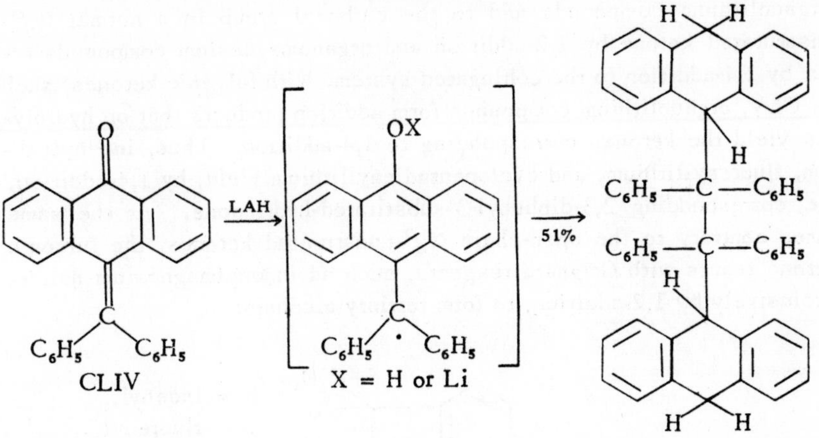

(7-107)

The reaction between CLIV and phenylmagnesium bromide yields the 1,2-addition product, 9-benzhydrylidene-10-phenyl-10-hydroxy-9,10-dihydroanthracene (193).

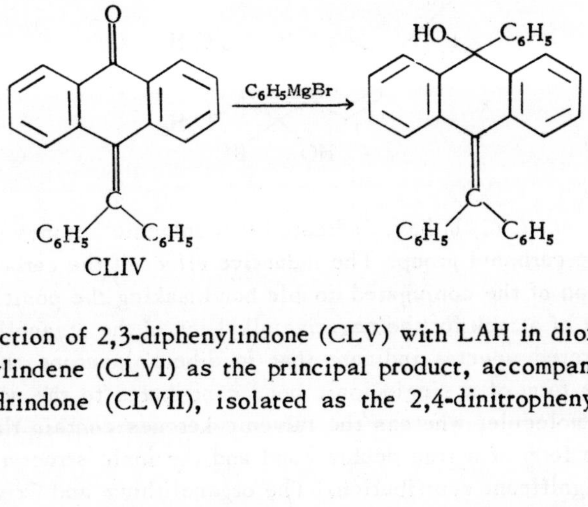

(7-108)

The reduction of 2,3-diphenylindone (CLV) with LAH in dioxane yields 2,3-diphenylindene (CLVI) as the principal product, accompanied by 2,3-diphenylhydrindone (CLVII), isolated as the 2,4-dinitrophenylhydrazone (191).

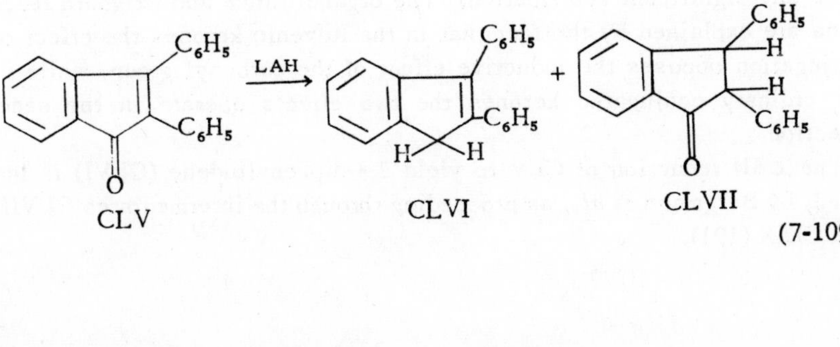

(7-109)

Organolithium compounds add to the carbonyl group in a normal α,β-unsaturated ketone by 1,2-addition and organomagnesium compounds react by 1,4-addition to the conjugated system. With fulvenic ketones, such as CLV, organolithium compounds form addition products that on hydrolysis yield the ketones corresponding to 1,4-addition. Thus, indenyllithium, fluorenyllithium, and cyclopentadienyllithium yield, by 1,4-addition, the corresponding 2,3-diphenyl-3-substituted-hydrindone. At the same time, contrary to the open-chain α,β-unsaturated ketones, the fulvenic ketone reacts with Grignard reagents, such as indenylmagnesium halide, exclusively by 1,2-addition, to form tertiary alcohols.

Bergmann *et al.* (191) have indicated that fulvenic ketones do not contain an ionic carbonyl group. The inductive effect of the carbonyl causes a polarization of the conjugated double bond making the positive extremity the point of attack for the negative alkyl ion of the organolithium compound. Infrared spectra indicate that in dibenzalacetone the carbonyl group in the form of a single ionic bond contributes to the actual structure of the molecule, whereas the fulvenic ketones contain the carbonyl group in the form of a true double bond and the ionic structure does not make any significant contribution. The organolithium and Grignard reactions are explained by the fact that in the fulvenic ketones the effect of conjugation opposes the inductive effect of the carbonyl group, while in the ordinary conjugated ketones the two effects operate in the same direction.

The LAH reduction of CLV to yield 2,3-diphenylindene (CLVI) is implied, by Bergmann *et al.*, as proceeding through the intermediates CLVIII and CLIX (191).

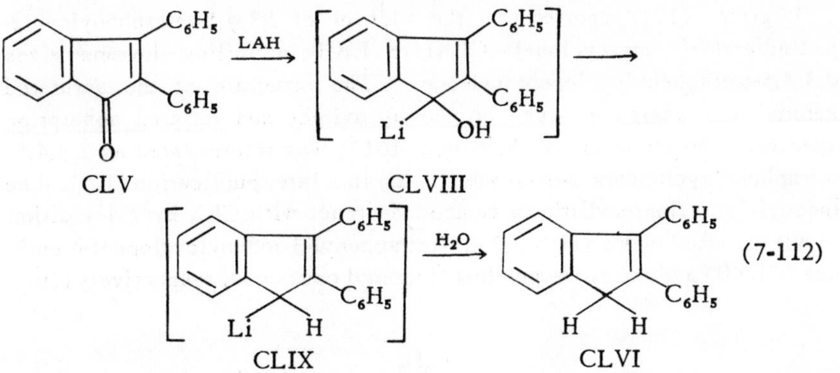

(7-112)

However, as discussed in Section 16.1, the course of the reaction may be due to the presence of a polarized double bond alpha to the carbonyl group, resulting in hydrogenolysis. Although the formation of 2,3-diphenylhydrindone (CLVII) may be the result of 1,4-addition, the extreme polarization of the double bond resulting from the double bond character of the carbonyl group may have led to its direct reduction. A further possible course leading to CLVI and CLVII may be postulated as follows:

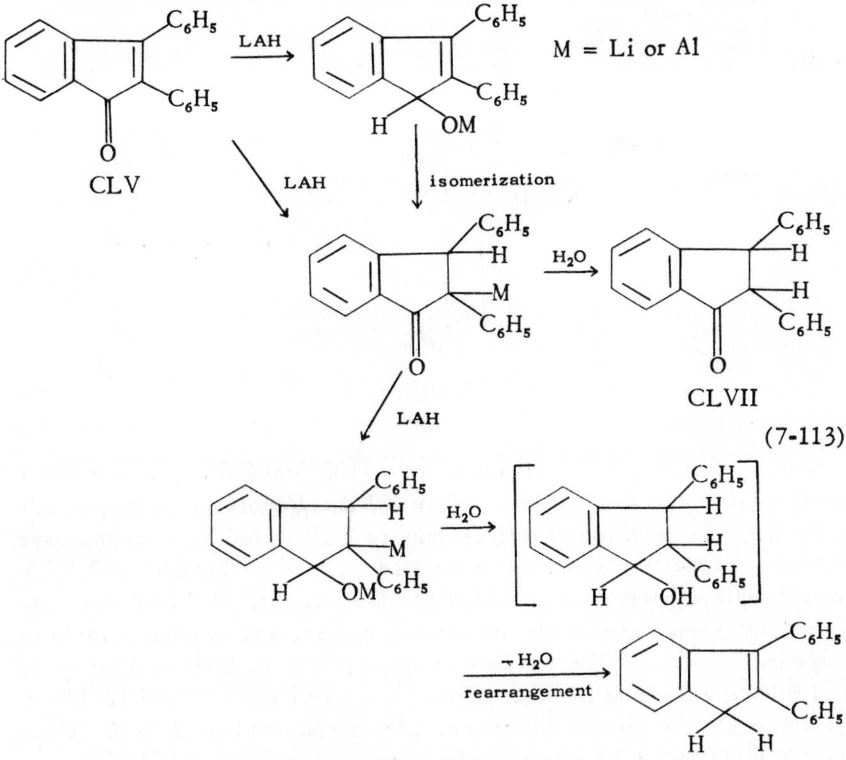

M = Li or Al

(7-113)

Bergmann (191) reported that the addition of 2,3,4,5-tetraphenylcyclo-pentadienone (tetracyclone) (CLX) to LAH in boiling dioxane gives 2,3,4,5-tetraphenylcyclopentan-1-one.   The structure of the saturated ketone was assigned based on the ultraviolet and infrared absorption spectra.   The reduction product, m.p. 161°, was reformulated as 2,3,4,5-tetraphenylcyclopenta-2-en-1-one (CLXI) in a later publication (195). The indenyl- and fluorenyllithium compounds react with CLX by 1,4-addition to yield, after hydrolysis, 2,3,4,5-tetraphenyl-3-indenylcyclopent-4-en-1-one (CLXII) and the corresponding fluorenyl compound, respectively (191).

$$ (7\text{-}114) $$

$$ R = \text{indenyl, fluorenyl} $$
$$ (7\text{-}115) $$

Becker, Spoerri, and their co-workers (196) carried out an extensive study of the reduction of tetracyclone (CLX). Repetition of Bergmann's procedure, i.e. addition of tetracyclone to LAH in boiling dioxane, gave 65% of 2,3,4,5-tetraphenylcyclopenta-2-en-1-one (CLXI) and 3% of 2,3,4,5-tetraphenylcyclopentadiene (CLXIII).   The identity of CLXI was confirmed by comparison of the absorption spectra and melting point with authentic material.   The addition of tetracyclone to LAH in a refluxing 1:1 dibutyl ether-diethyl ether mixture gives 73% of CLXI and 12-17% of CLXIII while the inverse addition of LAH to tetracyclone at 0-10° gives an 81% yield of 2,3,4,5-tetraphenylcyclopenta-2,4-dien-1-ol (CLXIV).

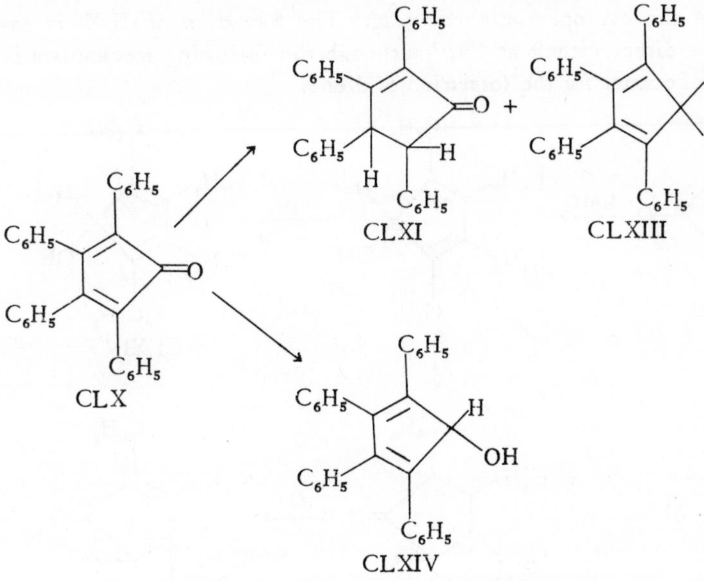

C_6H_5

C_6H_5 C_6H_5 O + C_6H_5 H (7-116)

C_6H_5 H C_6H_5 H

C_6H_5 C_6H_5

H C_6H_5

C_6H_5 CLXI CLXIII

C_6H_5 O

C_6H_5

C_6H_5

CLX

C_6H_5

C_6H_5 H (7-117)

OH

C_6H_5

C_6H_5

CLXIV

Becker, Spoerri, *et al.* proposed that Bergmann had not isolated any CLXIV presumably because inverse addition is required and in refluxing dioxane CLXIV would probably isomerize to CLXI. They further cited the work of Hochstein and Brown (13) relating to the change in the course of the reaction with the order of addition.

The same considerations advanced in the reduction of 2,3-diphenylindone are applicable to the reduction of tetracyclone. Polarization of the double bond may be responsible for the formation of the unsaturated ketone (CLXI) as well as for the hydrogenolysis product (CLXIII). The cyclic mechanism (CXVI) proposed for the reduction of open-chain α,β-unsaturated ketones with LAH by 1,4-addition was considered by Becker *et al.* as not operative in tetracyclone since atoms 1,2,3,4 must lie in a plane. Applying the C—C distances for cyclopentadiene, the 1,4-distance is 3.5 A while the Al—H distance is 1.63 A.

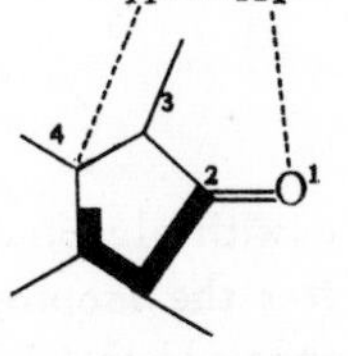

H—Al

CLXV

In addition to the fact that these dimensions appear to be too small to close the ring, the plane of the cycle would have to lie perpendicular to the plane of the cyclopentadienone ring. The formation of CLXI is explained by a direct attack at "4," although the following mechanism is advanced to account for the formation of diene:

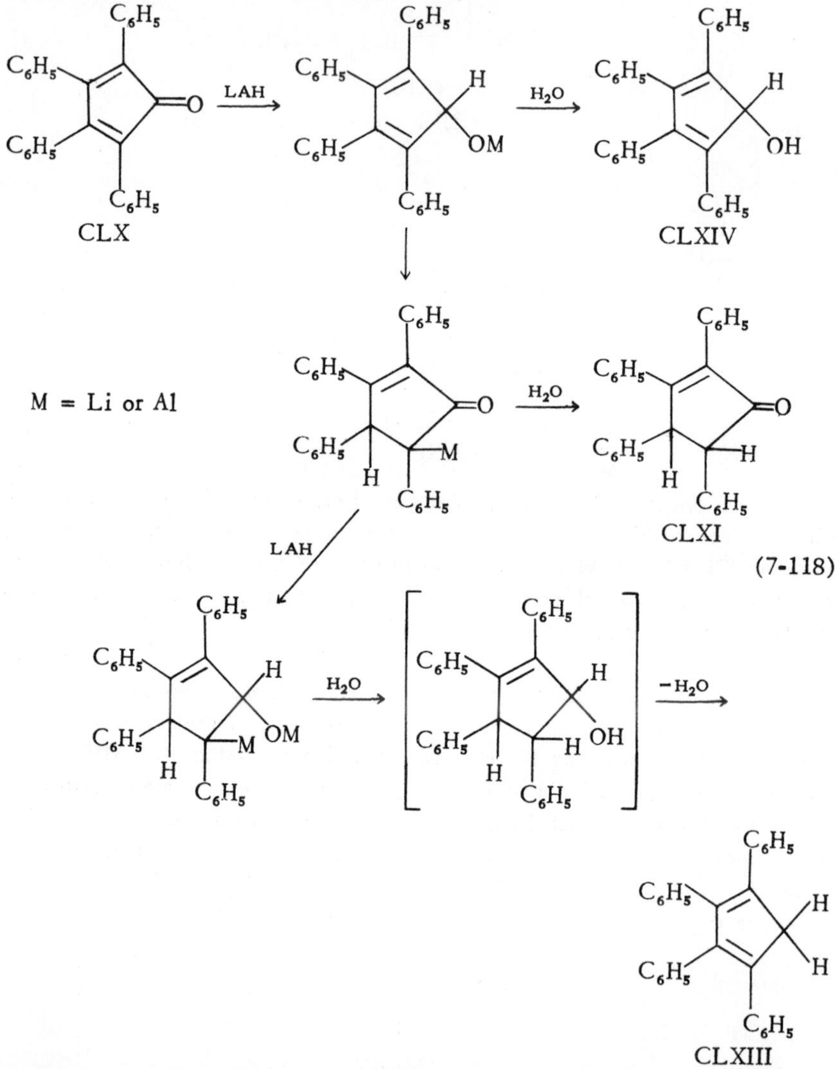

CLX

CLXIV

M = Li or Al

CLXI

(7-118)

LAH

CLXIII

The reduction of tetracyclone with aluminum isopropoxide in isopropyl alcohol-toluene gives CLXI, after the isopropyl alcohol is distilled. It appears that tetracyclone is converted to CLXIV which is isomerized to CLXI (196).

The LAH reduction of perinaphthanone-7 (CLXVI) (197) and 1-, 3-, 8-, and 9-methylperinaphthanone-7 (198) proceeds in high yield to the corresponding perinaphthanols.

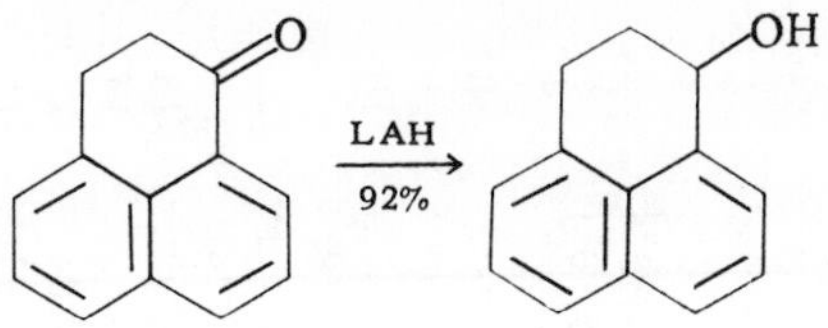

$$\text{CLXVI} \xrightarrow[92\%]{\text{LAH}} \qquad\qquad\qquad (7\text{-}119)$$

CLXVI

Hochstein (159) reported that the reduction of perinaphthenone (CLXVII) with LAH in refluxing ether gives a 23% yield of perinaphthene (CLXVIII). Boekelheide and Larrabee (197) reported that the reaction proceeds with the evolution of hydrogen and gives 65% of perinaphthanone-7 (CLXVI), 14% of perinaphthene (CLXVIII) and 12% of phenolic material.

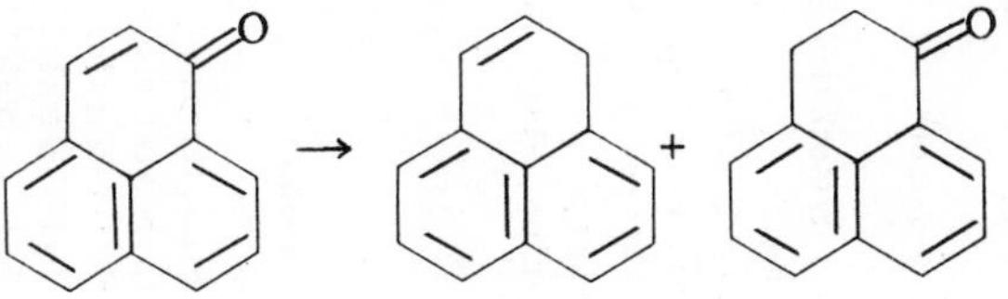

$$(7\text{-}120)$$

CLXVII   CLXVIII   CLXVI

It was postulated that the initial reduction product (CLXIX) may undergo further reaction to give either perinaphthene (CLXVIII) or a second inter-mediate, CLXX. On hydrolysis CLXX would be converted to perinaphtha-none-7 (CLXVI), a phenol or perinaphthenol, depending on the position on the perinaphthenyl nucleus taken by the incoming hydrogen. Addition of the hydrogen at the 7-position would give the enolic form of CLXVI, addition at the 9-position would yield perinaphthenol, and addition at any of the other possible positions would yield a phenol.

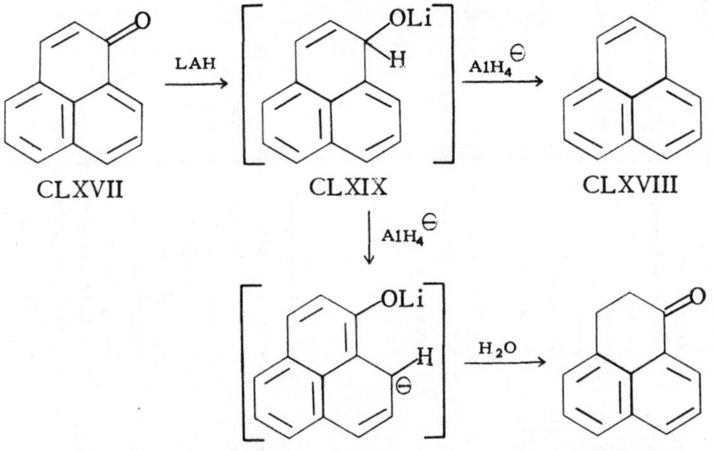

$$(7\text{-}121)$$

CLXVII   CLXIX   CLXVIII

CLXX   CLXVI

TABLE XVI

LAH Reduction of Benzenoid Polycyclic Ketones in Which Carbonyl Group Is Conjugated with Aromatic Nucleus

	Ketone	No.	Product	% Yield	Ref.
$C_{10}H_8O_2$	1,4-Diketo-1,2,3,4-tetrahydronaphthalene	I	1,4-Dihydroxy-1,2,3,4-tetrahydronaphthalene	...	1
$C_{10}H_{10}O$	α-Tetralone	II	1-Tetralol	79	2
$C_{11}H_{10}O_2$	1,4-Diketo-2-methyl-1,2,3,4-tetrahydronaphthalene	III	1,4-Dihydroxy-2-methyl-1,2,3,4-tetrahydronaphthalene	...	1
$C_{11}H_{12}O_2$	1-Hydroxy-2-keto-2-methyl-1,2,3,4-tetrahydronaphthalene	IV	1,4-Dihydroxy-2-methyl-1,2,3,4-tetrahydronaphthalene	78	3
$C_{11}H_{12}O_3$	5,6-Dimethoxy-1-indanone	V	5,6-Dimethoxy-1-indanol		4
$C_{12}H_6O_2$	Acenaphthenequinone	VI	cis-Acenaphthene glycol	15,13[5]	6
			trans-Acenaphthene glycol	45,50[5]	
$C_{12}H_{10}O$	1,2,3,8-Tetrahydro-1-ketocyclopent[a]indene	VII	product not specified	...	7
$C_{12}H_{14}O$	1,2-Benzocyclooct-1-en-3-one	VIII	1,2-Benzocyclooct-1-en-3-ol	90	8
$C_{13}H_8O$	Fluorenone	IX	9-Fluorenol	99	9
			9-Fluorenol	...	10
			Fluorene	18	11
			Dibiphenyleneethane	26	12
$C_{13}H_{10}O$	Perinaphthanone-7	X	Perinaphthanol-7	92	13
$C_{13}H_{14}O$	3,4-Cyclopentanotetralone	XI	3,4-Cyclopentanotetralol	...	14
$C_{13}H_{16}O$	4,5,7-Trimethyl-1-tetralone	XII	4,5,7-Trimethyl-1-tetralol	84	15
	4,5,8-Trimethyl-1-tetralone	XII	4,5,8-Trimethyl-1-tetralol	93.5	15
	4,6,7-Trimethyl-1-tetralone	XII	4,6,7-Trimethyl-1-tetralol	68	15
	4,6,8-Trimethyl-1-tetralone	XII	4,6,8-Trimethyl-1-tetralol	91	15
$C_{14}H_{10}O$	2-Methylfluorenone	XIII	2-Methyl-9-fluorenol	82.5	16
	3-Methylfluorenone	XIII	3-Methyl-9-fluorenol	92	16
$C_{14}H_{12}O$	1-Methylperinaphthanone-7	XIV	1-Methylperinaphthanol-7	97	17
	3-Methylperinaphthanone-7	XIV	3-Methylperinaphthanol-7	94	17
	8-Methylperinaphthanone-7	XV	8-Methylperinaphthanol-7	96	17

	Ketone	No.	Product	%	Ref.
$C_{14}H_{16}O$	9-Methylperinaphthanone-7	XV	9-Methylperinaphthanol-7	88	17
	7-Keto-1,2,3,7,8,9,10,10a-octahydro-cycloheptal[de]naphthalene	XVI	7-Hydroxy-1,2,3,7,8,9,10,10a-octahydro-cycloheptal[de]naphthalene	....	18
$C_{15}H_{12}O$	2,7-Dimethylfluorenone	XVII	2,7-Dimethylfluorenol	82.5	16
$C_{15}H_{20}O$	4,5,6,7,8-Pentamethyl-1-tetralone	XVIII	4,5,6,7,8-Pentamethyl-1-tetralol	100	15
	3,5-Dimethyl-8-isopropyl-1-tetralone	XIX	3,5-Dimethyl-8-isopropyl-1-tetralol	96	19
	2,5-Dimethyl-8-isopropyl-1-tetralone	XIX	2,5-Dimethyl-8-isopropyl-1-tetralol	....	20
$C_{16}H_{12}O_2$	1,4-Acepleiadanedione	XX	1,4-Acepleidanediol (mixture of cis and trans isomers)	....[21]	22
$C_{17}H_{16}O$	1-Keto-2-methyl-1,2,2a,3,4,5-hexahydropyrene isomer, m.p. 141–142°	XXI	1-Hydroxy-2-methyl-1,2,2a,3,4,5-hexahydropyrene isomer, m.p. 188–189°	84	23
	isomer, m.p. 140–142°		isomer, m.p. 172–174°	79	23
	mixture of isomers		mixture of isomers	....[21]	23
$C_{18}H_{14}O_2$	9-Methoxy-7,8-benzoperinaphthan-1-one	XXII	9-Methoxy-7,8-benzoperinaphthan-1-ol	....[21]	24
$C_{18}H_{18}O$	9-Keto-4,5,6,7,9,10,11,12-octahydro-cyclohepta[jk]phenanthrene	XXIII	4,5,6,7,9,10,11,12-Octahydrohepta[jk]-9-phenanthrol	88	25
$C_{19}H_{14}O$	2'-Methylbenzanthrone	XXIV	2'-Methylbenzanthrol	38	26
$C_{19}H_{16}O_2$	3'-Methyl-3,4,9,10,11,12-hexahydro-1,2-benzanthracene-1,10-dione	XXV	3'-Methyl-3,4,9,10,11,12-hexahydro-1,2-benzanthracene-3,10-diol	100	26
	6-Methyl-3,4,9,10,11,12-hexahydro-1,2-benzanthracene-3,10-dione	XXV	6-Methyl-3,4,9,10,11,12-hexahydro-1,2-benzanthracene-3,10-diol	100	26
	8-Methyl-3,4,9,10,11,12-hexahydro-1,2-benzanthracene-3,10-dione	XXV	8-Methyl-3,4,9,10,11,12-hexahydro-1,2-benzanthracene-3,10-diol	....	26
	5,6,6a,7,8,12b-Hexahydro-1-methylbenzo[c]-phenanthrene-5,8-dione	XXVI	5,6,6a,7,8,12b-Hexahydro-1-methylbenzo[c]-phenanthrene-5,8-diol	93	27
$C_{19}H_{18}O$	6-Methyl-3,4,9,10,11,12-hexahydro-1,2-benzanthracene-3-one	XXVII	6-Methyl-3,4,9,10,11,12-hexahydro-1,2-benzanthracene-3-ol	96	26
	8-Methyl-3,4,9,10,11,12-hexahydro-1,2-benzanthracene-3-one	XXVI	8-Methyl-3,4,9,10,11,12-hexahydro-1,2-benzanthracene-3-ol	100	26
$C_{19}H_{20}O_5$	9,12,13,14-Tetramethoxy-3,4,5,6-dibenzocyclohepta-3,5-dien-2-one	XXVIII	(±)-9,12,13,14-Tetramethoxy-3,4,5,6-dibenzocyclohepta-3,5-dien-2-ol	....	28

(Continued)

TABLE XVI (Continued)

Ketone	No.	Product	% Yield	Ref.
C$_{20}$H$_{14}$O 3-Keto-12c,1,2,3,4-tetrahydrobenzl[j]-fluoranthene	XXIX	product not specified	....	29
C$_{20}$H$_{18}$O$_2$ 5,6,6a,8,12b-Hexahydro-1,2-dimethylbenzo-[c]phenanthrene-5,8-dione	XXVI	5,6,6a,7,8,12b-Hexahydro-1,2-dimethylbenzo-[c]phenanthrene-5,8-diol	100	27
C$_{21}$H$_{14}$O Benzalanthrone	XXX	Mixture of compounds Anthraquinone	....[11]	30 31
2,3-Diphenylindone	XXXI	2,3-Diphenylindene 2,3-Diphenylhydrindone	....[11]	12
C$_{24}$H$_{16}$O 9-Phenylnaphthacen-12-one	XXXII	9-Phenylnaphthacen-12-ol	....	32
C$_{24}$H$_{22}$O 5-Keto-2,9-dimethyl-5,6,6a,13,14,14a-hexahydropicene	XXXIII	5-Hydroxy-2,9-dimethyl-5,6,6a,13,14,14a-hexahydropicene[33]	....	34
C$_{27}$H$_{18}$O Benzhydrylideneanthrone	XXXIV	sym-Tetraphenyl-bis-(9,10-dihydro-9-anthryl)ethane	51	31

CHART TO TABLE XVI

(continued)

CHART TO TABLE XVI (*continued*)

CHART TO TABLE XVI (continued)

XXVIII

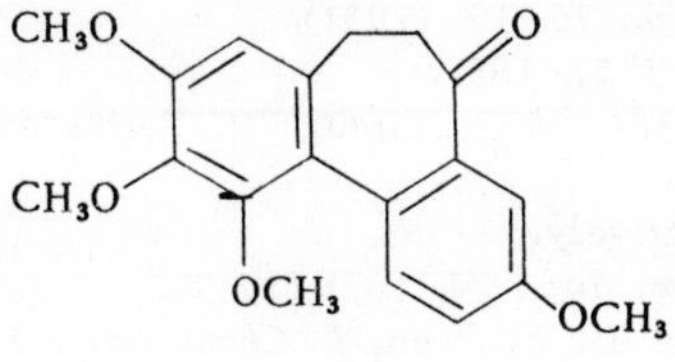

XXIX

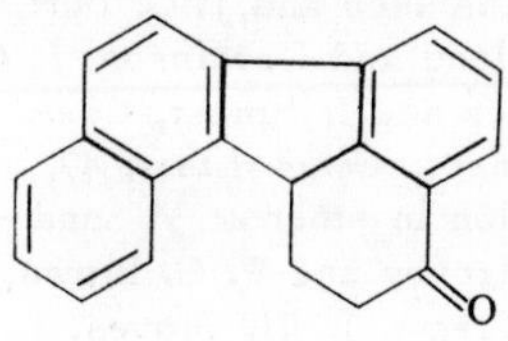

XXX

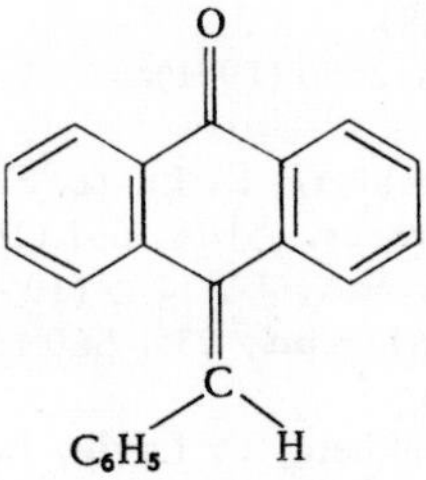

XXXI

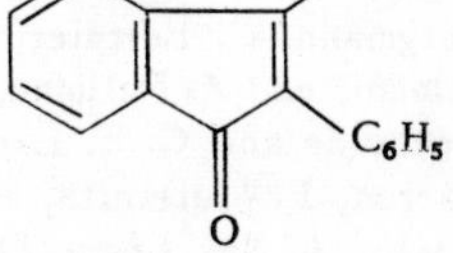

XXXII

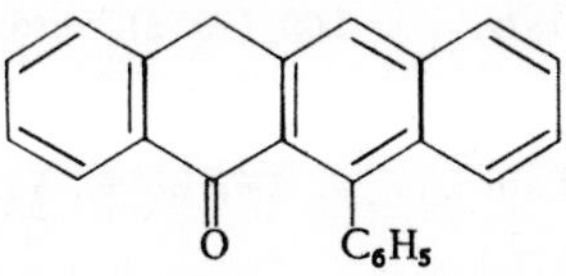

XXXIII

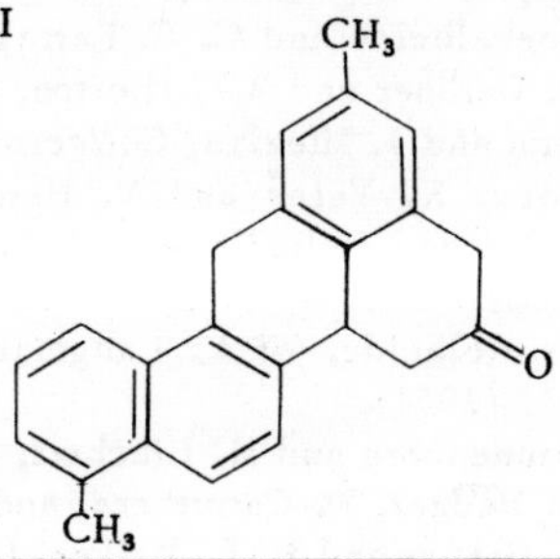

XXXIV

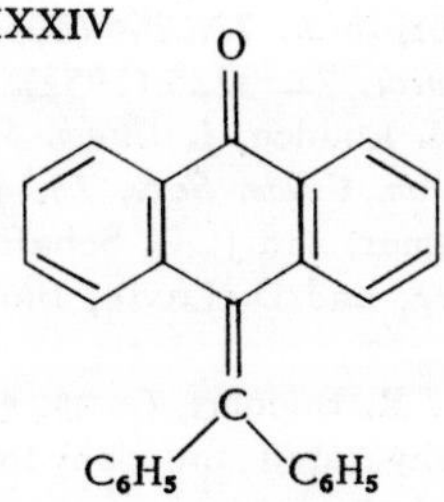

References—Table XVI

[1] R. H. Thomson, *J. Chem. Soc., 1950*, 1737.
[2] M. S. Kharasch and J. G. Burt, *J. Org. Chem.*, 16, 156 (1951).
[3] E. Boyland and D. Manson, *J. Chem. Soc., 1951*, 1837.
[4] R. Lukeš and I. Ernest, *Chem. Listy*, 46, 361 (1952); through M. Ferles and J. Rudinger, *Chem. Listy*, 47, 113 (1953).
[5] Reduction in ether at 35° and −80°, respectively.
[6] L. W. Trevoy and W. G. Brown, *J. Am. Chem. Soc.*, 71, 1675 (1949).
[7] G. R. Clemo, L. H. Groves, L. Munday, and G. A. Swan, *J. Chem. Soc., 1951*, 863.
[8] R. Huisgen and W. Rapp, *Chem. Ber.*, 85, 826 (1952).
[9] F. A. Hochstein, *J. Am. Chem. Soc.*, 71, 305 (1949).
[10] I. Wender, H. Greenfield, and M. Orchin, *ibid.*, 73, 2656 (1951).
[11] Reduction carried out in dioxane.
[12] E. D. Bergmann, G. Berthier, D. Ginsburg, Y. Hirshberg, D. Lavie, S. Pinchas, B. Pullman, and A. Pullman, *Bull. soc. chim. France*, [5] 18, 661 (1951).
[13] V. Boekelheide and C. E. Larrabee, *J. Am. Chem. Soc.*, 72, 1245 (1950).
[14] M. Mousseron, F. Winternitz, and G. Rouzier, *Compt. rend.*, 235, 660 (1952).
[15] W. L. Mosby, *J. Am. Chem. Soc.*, 74, 2564 (1952).
[16] E. D. Bergmann, G. Berthier, E. Fischer, Y. Hirshberg, D. Lavie, E. Loewenthal, and B. Pullman, *Bull. soc. chim. France*, [5] 19, 78 (1952).
[17] V. Boekelheide and C. E. Larrabee, *J. Am. Chem. Soc.*, 72, 1240 (1950).
[18] P. D. Gardner and W. J. Horton, *ibid.*, 74, 657 (1952).
[19] F. Šorm and J. Mleziva, *Collection Czechoslov. Chem. Communs.*, 14, 98 (1949).
[20] F. Šorm, K. Vereš and V. Herout, *Chem. Listy*, 46, 100 (1952), through M. Ferles and J. Rudinger, *Chem. Listy*, 47, 115 (1953).
[21] Reduction carried out in benzene-ether mixture.
[22] V. Boekelheide, W. E. Langeland, and Chu-Tsin Liu, *J. Am. Chem. Soc.*, 73, 2432 (1951).
[23] H. Dannenberg and H. Brachert, *Chem. Ber.*, 84, 504 (1951).
[24] G. M. Badger, W. Carruthers, and J. W. Cook, *J. Chem. Soc., 1952*, 4996.
[25] W. J. Horton and F. E. Walker, *J. Am. Chem. Soc.*, 74, 758 (1952).
[26] M. S. Newman and R. Gaertner, *ibid.*, 72, 264 (1950).
[27] M. S. Newman and M. Wolf, *ibid.*, 74, 3225 (1952).
[28] J. W. Cook, J. Jack, and J. D. Loudon, *J. Chem. Soc., 1952*, 607.
[29] M. Orchin and L. Reggel, *J. Am. Chem. Soc.*, 73, 436 (1951).
[30] P. L. Julian, W. Cole, G. Diemer, and J. G. Schafer, *ibid.*, 71, 2058 (1949).
[31] E. D. Bergmann, Y. Hirshberg, and D. Lavie, *Bull. soc. chim. France*, [5] 19, 268 (1952).
[32] C. Dufraisse, A. Étienne, and R. Bucourt, *Comp. rend.*, 233, 1401 (1951).
[33] Carbinol not isolated but dehydrated and dehydrogenated over sulfur at 230–270° to yield 25% 2,9-dimethylpicene.
[34] M. S. Newman and W. K. Cline, *J. Org. Chem.*, 16, 934 (1951).

The formation of CLXVI may be indicative of the polarization of the double bond in CLXVII, analogous to the situation with tetracyclone and 2,3-diphenylindone. The hydrogenolysis product, CLXVIII, would therefore also be formed analogously. The hydrogenolysis reaction is discussed in Section 16.1.

The reaction of methylmagnesium iodide with CLXVII is analogous to the LAH reaction, yielding 1-(or 6-) methylperinaphthene, methane and a compound having the correct analysis for a methylperinaphthenone (198).

The reduction of various benzenoid polycyclic ketones in which the carbonyl group is conjugated with an aromatic nucleus is summarized in Table XVI.

Mustafa and Hilmy (199) have shown that the reduction of xanthone (CLXXI) with LAH in ether yields xanthene.

$$\text{CLXXI} \xrightarrow[90\%]{\text{LAH}} \qquad (7\text{-}122)$$

The LAH reduction of 3,4-benzoxanthone (CLXXII) and 1,2-benzoxanthone (CLXIII) similarly yields the hydrogenolysis products, 3,4-benzoxanthene (85% yield) and 1,2-benzoxanthene (82% yield), respectively. This is discussed more fully in Section 16.1.

CLXXII   CLXXIII

The reaction of CLXXII and CLXXIII with phenylmagnesium bromide yields the expected 1,2-addition products, 9-phenyl-3,4-(or 1,2-) benzoxanthydrol.

Mirza and Robinson reported that γ-pyrones are reduced by LAH in tetrahydrofuran to γ-pyranols, which afford pyrylium salts on treatment with acids. Anthocyanidins are produced in this way from the appropriate flavones. Thus, kaempferol(3,5,7,4′-tetrahydroxyflavone)(CLXXXIV : R = H) is converted in 32% yield to pelargondin chloride while quercitin (3,5,7, 3′,4′-pentahydroxyflavone) (CLXXIV : R = OH) yields 28% of cyanidin chloride (200,201).

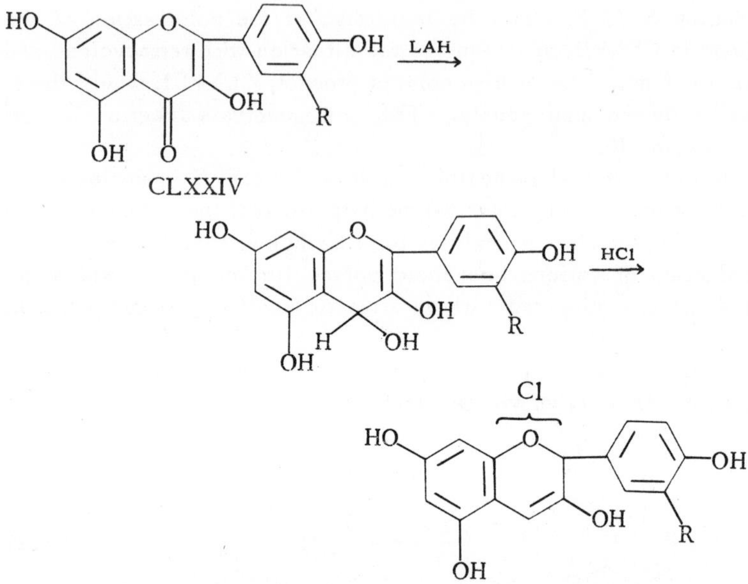

CLXXIV

(7-123)

The reaction is reported to proceed well with methoxylated flavones and is stated to be applicable to the reduction of xanthones to xanthhydrols and thence to xanthylium salts (200). No details or examples of the reduction of xanthones were given and it is therefore difficult to reconcile this statement with the results reported by Mustafa and Hilmy wherein hydrogenolysis products were formed by the reduction of xanthones.

The reaction of 2,6-di-*tert*-butyl-*p*-cresol (CLXXV) with *tert*-butyl hydroperoxide yields 1-methyl-1-*tert*-butylperoxy-3,5-di-*tert*-butylcyclohexadien-4-one (CLXXVI). The peroxy ketone is reduced to the starting phenol with LAH (202).

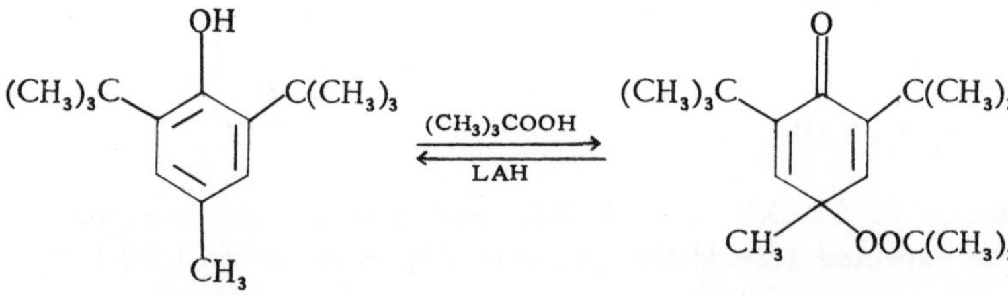

(7-124)

CLXXV　　　　　　　　　CLXXVI

Cook *et al.* reported that the reduction of tropolone (CLXXVII) with LAH in ether gives a product which resinifies on hydrolysis. Distillation of the tar gives a very small amount of liquid which readily gives a bis-2,4-dinitrophenylhydrazone. It is postulated that the product is cyclohept-4-ene-1,2-dione produced by 1,4- or 1,6-addition of LAH to the dienone system of the initially formed lithium tropolone derivative (203,204).

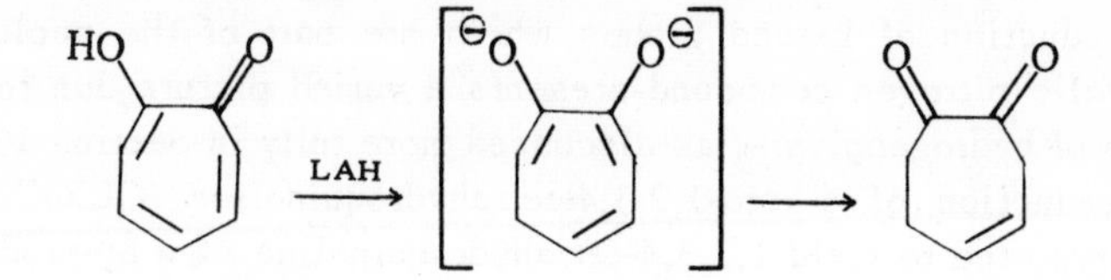

(7-125)

CLXXVII

The LAH reduction of tropolone methyl ether (CLXXVIII) gives a substantial yield of benzaldehyde, postulated as proceeding through anionotropy of the primary reduction product with concomitant Wagner-Meerwein rearrangement of the resulting 7-membered carbonium ion to the stable benzenoid ion (204).

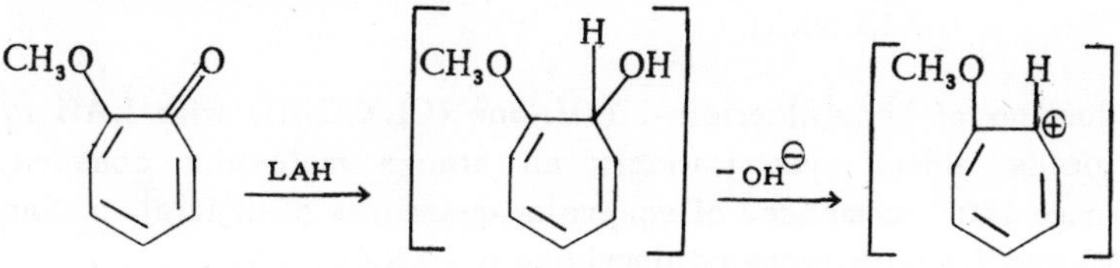

CLXXVIII

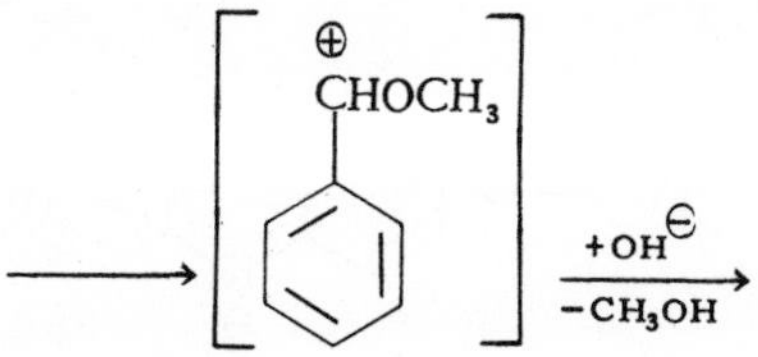

(7-126)

Several examples of the reduction of alicyclic ketones in which the ring is fused to an indole nucleus have been reported. In all cases, the corresponding hydroxy compound is formed. Thus, 1-keto-1,2,3,4-tetrahydrocarbazole (CLXXIX) (205), 2-keto-1,2,3,4,5,6-hexahydrocyclooctindole (CLXXX) (206) and 5-keto-1,3,4,5-tetrahydrobenz[c,d]indole (CLXXXI) (207) are reduced to the corresponding carbinols.

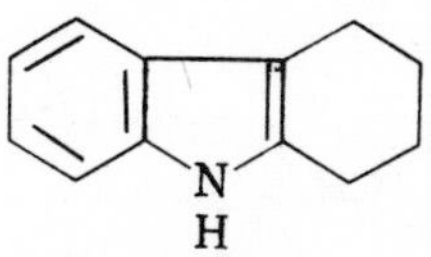

CLXXIX 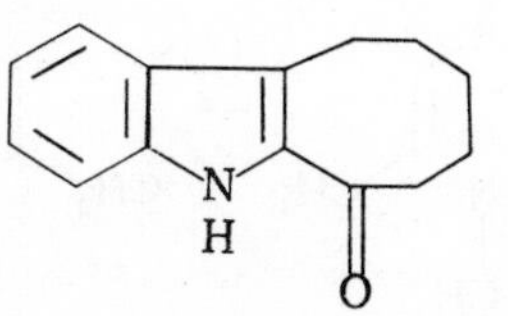   CLXXX 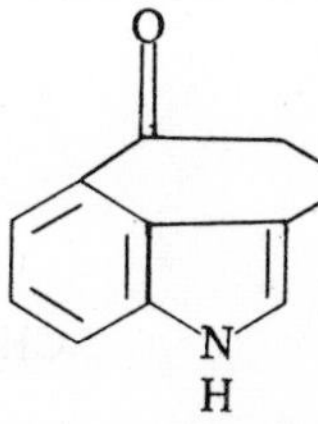   CLXXXI

The reduction of CLXXXI with aluminum isopropoxide in isopropanol yields the isopropyl ether of the corresponding hydroxy compound (207).

The reduction of ketone groups which are part of the nucleus of a heterocyclic nitrogen compound presents a varied picture due to the occurrence of hydrogenolysis, as discussed more fully in Section 16.1.

The reduction of 4-keto-1,2,3,4-tetrahydroquinoline (CLXXXII) with LAH is reported to yield 1,2,3,4-tetrahydroquinoline as a by-product. No indication of the major product was given (208).

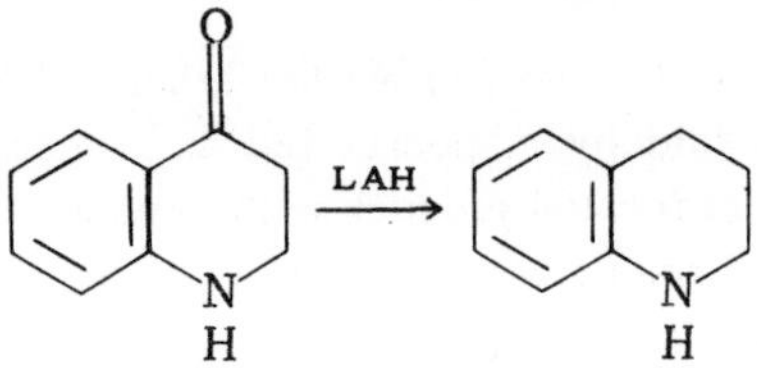

(7-127)

CLXXXII

The reduction of benz[a]acridin-12(7H)-one (CLXXXIII) with LAH in dioxane yields almost quantitatively an orange molecular complex, $C_{34}H_{24}N_2$, m.p. 140°, composed of equimolar quantities of benz[a]acridine (CLXXXIV) and 7,12-dihydrobenz[a]acridine (CLXXXV) (209).

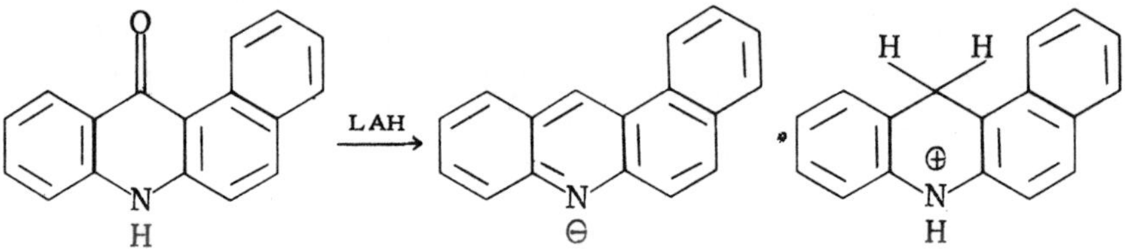

CLXXXIII   CLXXXIV   CLXXXV

(7-128)

Treatment of 1,2,6-trimethyl-4-pyridone (CLXXXVI) with LAH in ether results in no reduction, possibly due to the low solubility of the pyridone in ether. Catalytic hydrogenation over prereduced platinum oxide or palladium-on-charcoal similarly fails to reduce CLXXXVI. However, the following reduction methods yield 1,2,6-trimethyl-4-piperidinol (210):

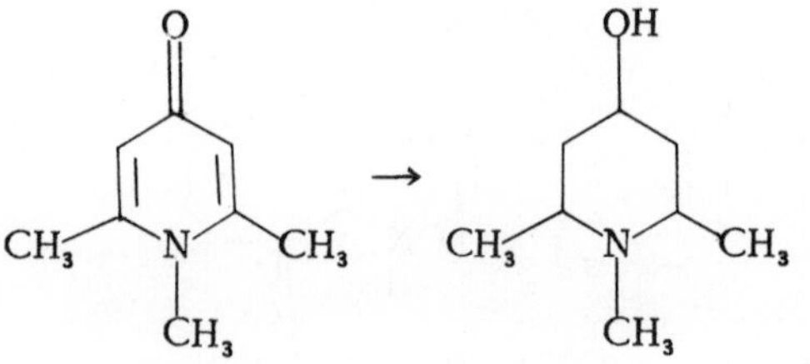

(7-129)

CLXXXVI

	Yield
Sodium in liquid ammonia	40%
Raney nickel, 125°, 1500 p.s.i.	85
Nickel on silicon dioxide, 125°, 1500 p.s.i.	83
Copper chromite, 140°, 1600 p.s.i.	80

Witkop and his co-workers have carried out the LAH reduction of a number of gem-disubstituted pseudoindoxyls and have observed the occurrence of reduction, hydrogenolysis and rearrangement. Treatment of quinamine (CLXXXVII) with alcoholic alkali yields isoquinamine (CLXXXVIII) (211,212).

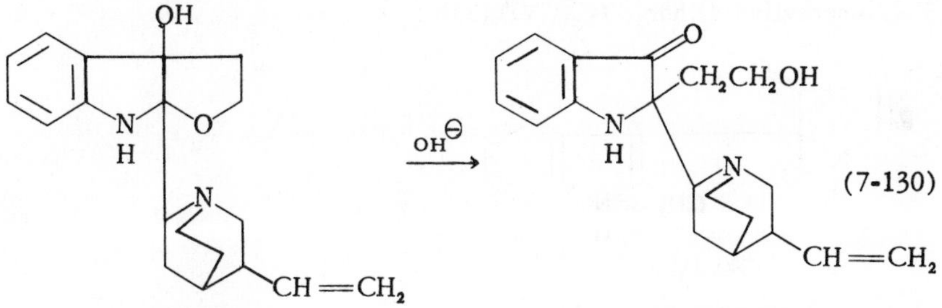

(7-130)

CLXXXVII   CLXXXVIII

The reaction of CLXXXVIII with LAH yields the reduction product, allodihydroisoquinamine (211).

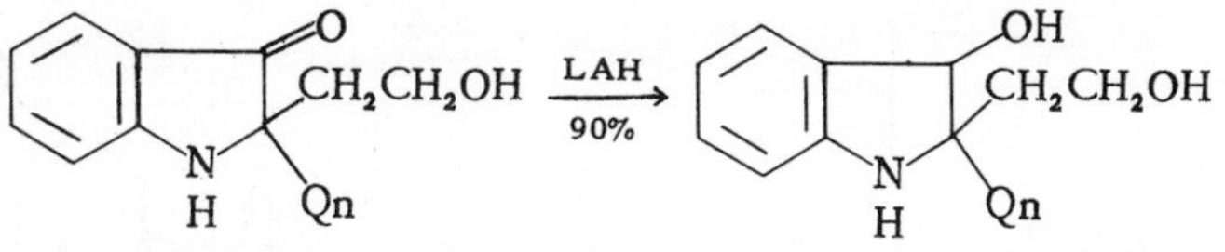

(7-131)

CLXXXVIII

The reduction of 1-methyl-2,2-diphenyl-ψ-indoxyl (CLXXXIX) with LAH also yields a carbinol, 1-methyl-2,2-diphenyl-3-hydroxyindoline (CXC) (213).

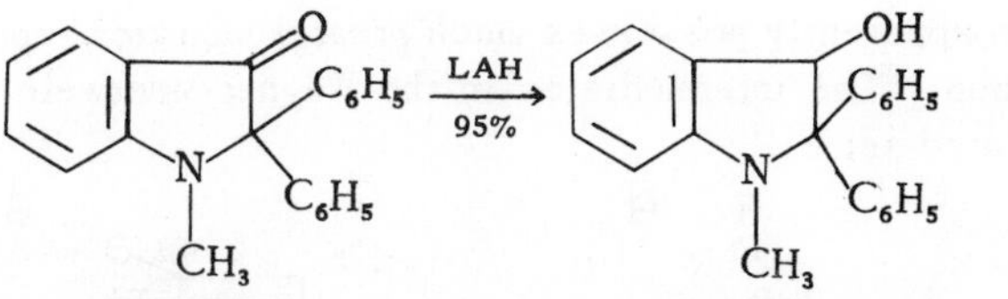

(7-132)

CLXXXIX   CXC

The reduction of spiro-[cyclopentane-1,2'-ψ-indoxyl] (CXCI) yields 47% of the reduction product, spiro-[cyclopentane-1,2'-dihydroindoxyl] (CXCII), and 34% of the hydrogenolysis product, *spiro*-[cyclopentane-1,2'-dihydro-indole] (CXCIII) (214,215).

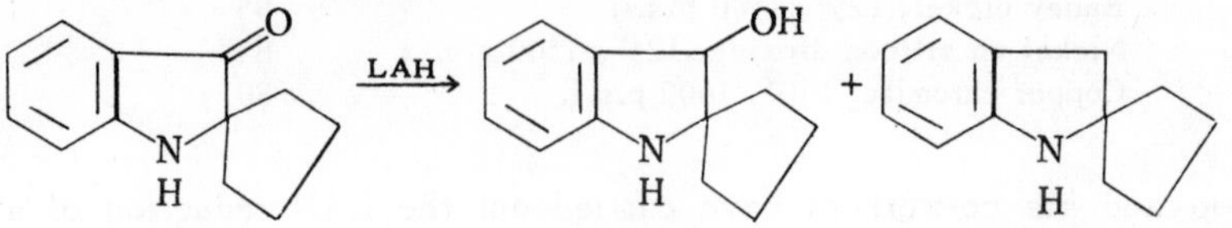

CXCI   CXCII   CXCIII   (7-133)

The reduction of 2-methyl-2,3'-[2'-methylindyl]-ψ-indoxyl (CXCIV) yields 23% of the hydrogenolysis product, 2-methyl-2,3'-[2'-methylindyl]-2,3-dihydroindole (CXCV), and 42% of a rearrangement product, 2-methyl-3,3'-[2'-methylindyl]indole (CXCVI) (216).

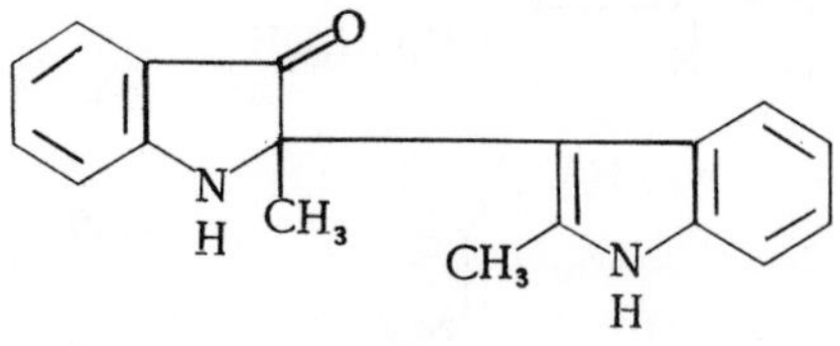

CXCIV

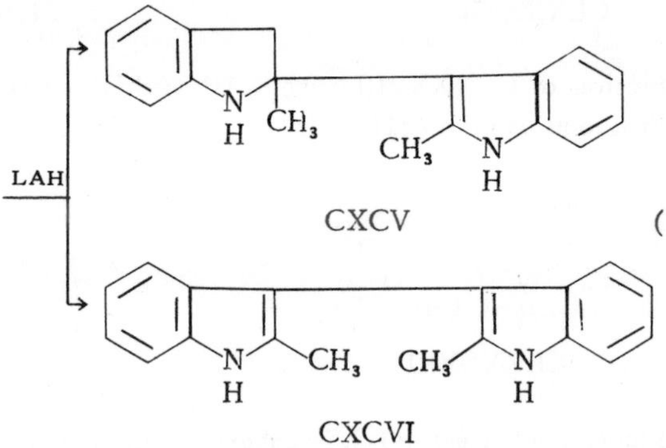

CXCV   (7-134)

CXCVI

It has been postulated that the aluminum compound formed in the initial reaction acts like an acid, resulting in migration of the methyl-ketyl residue, which apparently possesses much greater migratory aptitude than the methyl group. The intermediates in the Wagner-Meerwein rearrangement are postulated as:

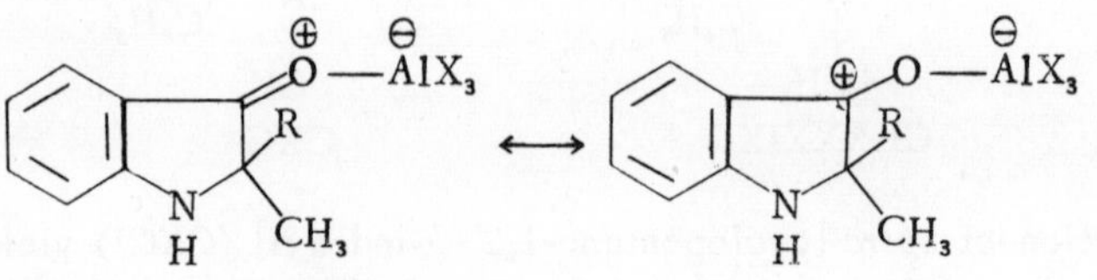

CXCVII   (7-135)

The treatment of indole with dilute peracetic acid yields a trimeric condensation product, 2,2-bis-[3′-indyl]-ψ-indoxyl (CXCVIII), in two different crystalline modifications, m.p. 204° and 245°. Both forms, on reduction with LAH, fail to yield the corresponding carbinol but, with the loss of water, give directly the rearranged compound, 2,3-di-[3′-indyl]indole (CXCIX) (216).

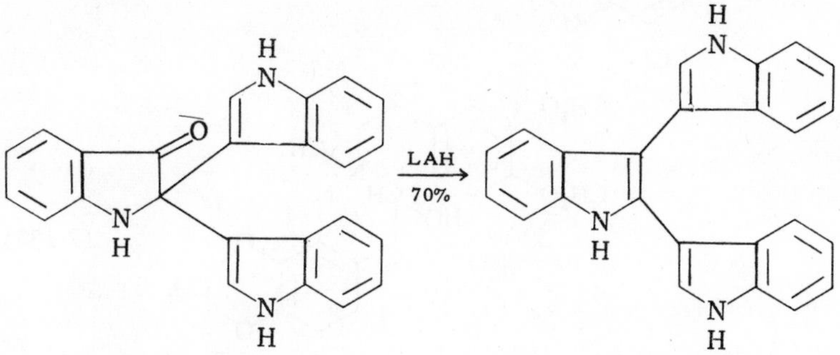

CXCVIII CXCIX (7-136)

It has been concluded that gem-disubstituted ψ-indoxyls with two bulky substituents next to the carbonyl group, such as two indyl or phenyl groups or a quinuclidine and β-hydroxyethyl chain as in the case of isoquinamine, do not undergo hydrogenolysis but rather form carbinols that can either be isolated or, if the migrating group possesses unusually high migrational aptitude, undergo rearrangement directly in the process of reduction (213).

Attempts to reduce 7-methoxy-1-methylisatin (CC) with LAH in ether are reported (217) to give only a small quantity of a steam-volatile indole and an unidentified, non-volatile material which after passage through an alumina column yields prisms of m.p. 208-210°.

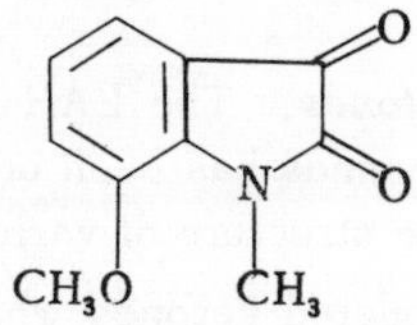

CC

7.2.1.j. *Alkaloid ketones.* In addition to those alkaloids, such as isoquinamine, discussed in previous sections, various other alkaloid ketones have been reduced with LAH.

Mirza reported that the alkaloid cryptopine (CCI), which is reduced with difficulty due to steric hindrance, is readily reduced with LAH in an ether-benzene solution to dihydrocryptopine (218).

(7-137)

Lycopodine, an alkaloid of unknown structure with the empirical formula $C_{16}H_{25}NO$, does not react with phenylmagnesium bromide but the presence of a carbonyl group has been shown by the formation of a hydrazone, by conversion to a tertiary carbinol with phenyllithium and by reduction of the keto group to an alcohol, dihydrolycopodine, $C_{16}H_{27}NO$, by LAH (219).

Among the alkaloids isolated from *Lycopodium annotinum* L. have been annotin and annotinin. Annotin, $C_{16}H_{23}NO_4$, m.p. 172–173°, is a tertiary base which, similar to lycopodine, does not react with the Grignard reagent. It does not form a hydrazone but reacts with LAH to form a base, $C_{16}H_{23}NO_3$, m.p. 162–163°, the reaction being postulated as proceeding through the "addition of two hydrogens and splitting out of water." Annotinin, $C_{16}H_{21}NO_3$, neither reacts with the Grignard reagent nor LAH (220).

7.2.1.k. *Triterpenoid ketones.* The LAH reduction of ketones to the corresponding hydroxy compounds has been utilized to a considerable extent in the elucidation of the structure of various triterpenoids.

The ability to reduce hindered ketones which are not attacked by the usual reagents is amply illustrated among the triterpenoids. Reduction of a keto group in the 2- or 8-positions yields a carbinol which is readily acetylated. However, reduction of the hindered ketone in the 11-position yields a carbinol which is not acetylated. Thus, LAH reduction of lanostan-8,11-dione (221) and lanostan-8,11-dione-2-yl acetate (CCII) (222) yields the 8,11-diol and 2,8,11-triol, respectively. Acetylation of the reduction products yields the 8-monoacetate and 2,8-diacetate, respectively.

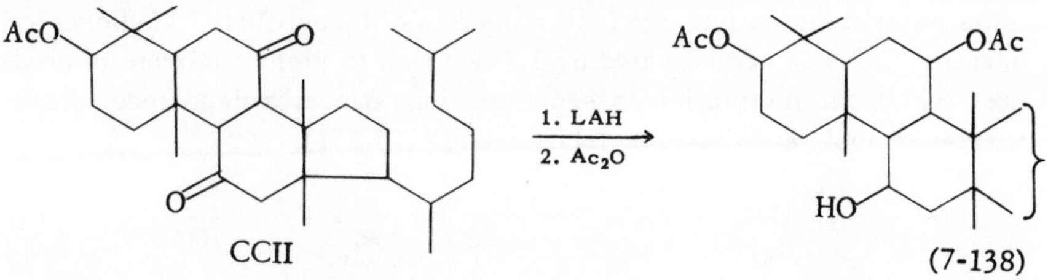

CCII   (7-138)

Extensive work by both British (170,171,223) and Swiss (222,224) workers has resulted in the elucidation of the above structure for the lanostane skeleton.

In addition to the 11-position, a ketone group in the 19-position is reducible with LAH but the resultant carbinol does not form an acetate (225,226).

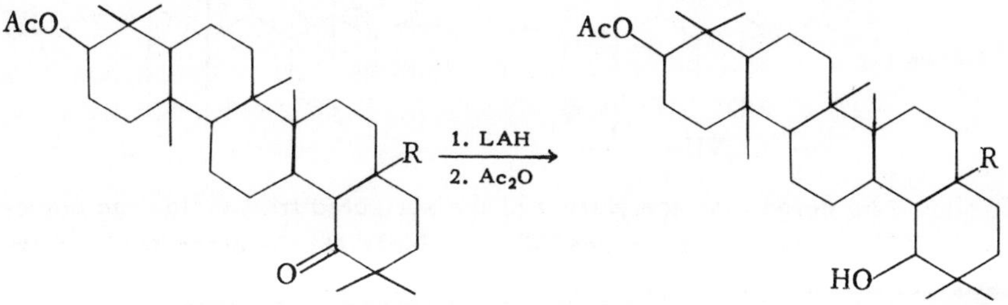

CCIII   (7-139)

In contrast, in trisnorlupanoyl acetate (CCIV) the ketone group, which would correspond to the 19-position in CCIII, does not form carbonyl derivatives but is reduced with LAH to the carbinol which is readily acetylated (227).

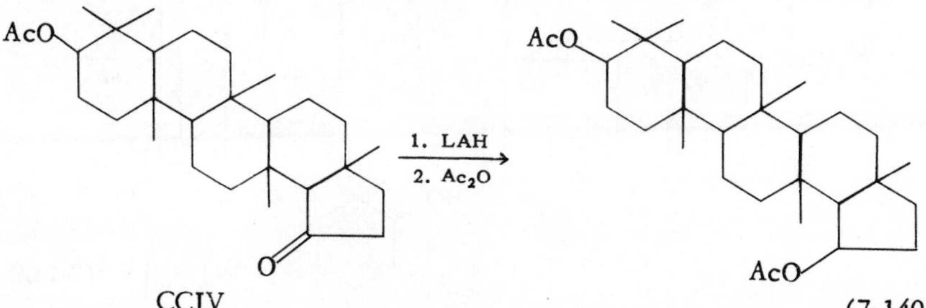

CCIV   (7-140)

Barton and Holness (225) have pointed out that the LAH reduction of a keto group which is not hindered sterically affords the equatorial hydroxyl group whereas similar reduction of keto groups which are subject to marked hindrance, e.g., C-11 and C-19 in the triterpenoid series, gives the polar hydroxyl group.

As pointed out earlier, the LAH reduction of lanost-9-en-8,11-dione-2-yl acetate (CCV) is accompanied by 1,4-addition to yield a mixture of products which on acetylation is separated into triacetoxylanostene, diacetoxylanostanol, and diacetoxylanostanone (170,171).

$$(7\text{-}141)$$

It should be noted that acetylation of the saturated triol yields the diacetate (CCVII) retaining the intact C-11 carbinol. On the other hand, acetylation of the unsaturated triol yields the triacetate (CCVI).

The LAH reduction of α,β-unsaturated triterpene ketones is complicated by the instability of the allylic alcohol formed. In the reduction of lanost-9-en-8-one-2-yl acetate (CCVIII) attempts to isolate the intermediate diol result in dehydration yielding γ-lanostadienol (170,228).

$$(7\text{-}142)$$

The reduction of methyl 11-ketooleanolate acetate (CCIX) yields a triol which on refluxing two hours with acetic anhydride is converted to a diene diacetate (225).

$$\text{CCIX} \xrightarrow[\text{2. Ac}_2\text{O}]{\text{1. LAH}} \quad (7\text{-}143)$$

Treatment of 2-acetoxynorolean-17-en-19-one (CCX) with LAH in ether yields a product whose melting point remains indefinite after repeated recrystallization. The reduction product is converted to norolean-16,18-dienol acetate (CCXI) after heating with an acetic anhydride-pyridine mixture (229).

$$\text{CCX} \xrightarrow{\text{LAH}} \quad \xrightarrow{\text{Ac}_2\text{O}} \quad (7\text{-}144)$$

CCXI

Acorone, a sesquiterpene with the empirical formula $C_{15}H_{24}O_2$, isolated from oil of sweet flag, is a saturated diketone in which one carbonyl group is apparently sterically protected since reaction with methylmagnesium bromide yields a ketoalcohol, methylacorolone, $C_{16}H_{28}O_2$. Reduc-

TABLE XVII

LAH Reduction of Triterpene Ketones

	Ketone	No.	Product	% Yield	Ref.
$C_{29}H_{46}O_3$	Trisnorlupanonyl acetate	I	Trisnorlupanediol	90	1
$C_{30}H_{46}O_3$	Betulinic acid lactone	II	triol, $C_{30}H_{52}O_3$, m.p. 296°	81[2]	3,4
$C_{30}H_{48}O$	β-Amyrenone	III	β-Amyrin	55[2]	5
	Lupenone	IV	Lupeol	60[2]	5
	Lupenone-I	V	Lupenol-I	60[2]	5
	Lupenone-II (δ-amyrenone)	VI	Lupenol-II (δ-amyrenol)	74[2]	5
	Taraxerone	?	Taraxerol, $C_{30}H_{50}O$	97	6
	Euphorbadienone	?	Euphorbadienol, $C_{30}H_{50}O$	95	7
$C_{30}H_{50}O$	Deoxyzeorinone	?	Epi-deoxyzeorin, $C_{30}H_{52}O$, m.p. 209°	...[9,10]	8
$C_{30}H_{50}O_2$	Lanostan-8,11-dione	VII	Lanostane-8,11-diol	...	11
	18α-Oleanan-19-one-2β-ol	VIII	18α-Oleanane-2β,19β-diol	...	12
$C_{30}H_{50}O_3$	Euphorbendiolone	?	Euphorbentriol, $C_{30}H_{52}O_3$, m.p. 197°	92	7
$C_{30}H_{50}O_4$	ketone ozonide	IX	Trisnor-diketone[13]	...	14
$C_{30}H_{52}O_2$	Lanostan-11-one-2-ol	X	Lanostane-2,11-diol	...	15,16
$C_{30}H_{52}O_3$	Lanostan-11-one-2,8-diol	XI	Lanostanetriol[17]	63	18,19
$C_{31}H_{40}O_2$	8,11-diketone	XII	diol, $C_{31}H_{44}O_2^{10}$	...[9]	20
$C_{31}H_{48}O_3$	Methyl elemadienonate	?	Epielemadienediol, $C_{30}H_{50}O_2$	78	21
$C_{31}H_{50}O_3$	2-Acetoxynorolean-17-en-19-one	XIII	Norolean-17-en-2,19-diol	...	22
$C_{32}H_{48}O_3$	Lupenone formate	XIV	18α-Oleanane-2β,19α-diol	63[2]	23
$C_{32}H_{50}O_4$	iso-β-Amyradienonyl acetate	XV	diene-diol, $C_{34}H_{52}O_4$, m.p. 168°[17]	60	24
	2-Acetoxylanost-9-en-8,11-dione	XVI	Lanostene-2,8,11-triol[25]	51	18,19
			Lanostane-2,8,11-triol[17]	4	
			Lanostan-11-one-2,8-diol[17]	18	

Formula	Compound	No.	Reduction product	Yield	Ref.
$C_{32}H_{52}O_3$	2-Acetoxylanost-9-en-8-one	XVII	Lanosta-8,10-dien-2-ol	80	26
$C_{32}H_{52}O_4$	2β-Acetoxy-18α-oleanan-19-one	XVIII	18α-Oleanane-2β,19β-diol	57[9]	23,27
$C_{32}H_{54}O_3$	2-Acetoxylanostan-8,11-diol[17]	XIX	Lanostane-2,8,11-triol[17]	78	16,18,19
	2-Acetoxylanostan-11-one	XX	Lanostane-2,11-diol	100	16
					15
$C_{33}H_{49}O_5$	Methyl 11-ketooleanolate acetate	XXI	2,28-Diacetoxyolean-11,13(18)-diene[28]	⋯	29
$C_{33}H_{52}O_5$	Methyl 11-ketooleananolate acetate	XXII	Oleanane-2,11,28-triol	⋯	29
	Methyl 19-keto-18-isooleananolate acetate	XXIII	18-Isoolean-2,19,28-triol[17]	⋯	29,30
$C_{34}H_{54}O_5$	2,28-Diacetoxy-18-isooleanan-19-one	XXIV	18-Isoolean-2,19,28-triol[17]	⋯	29
$C_{34}H_{56}O_5$	2,8-Diacetoxylanostan-11-one	XXV	Lanostane-2,8,11-triol[17]	75	18,19

CHART TO TABLE XVII

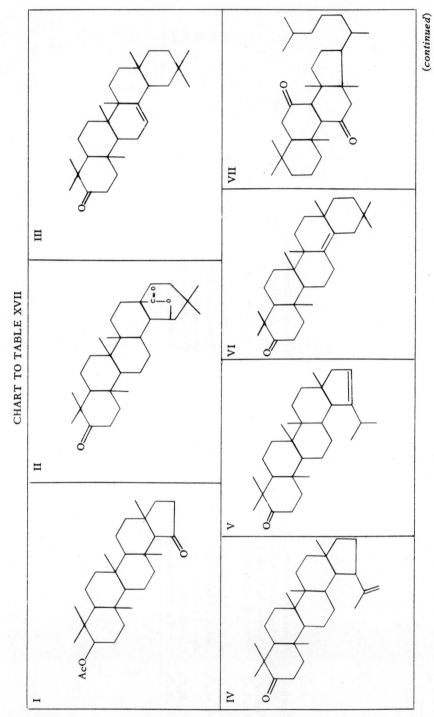

(continued)

CHART TO TABLE XVII (*continued*)

CHART TO TABLE XVII (continued)

(continued)

CHART TO TABLE XVII (*continued*)

References—Table XVII

[1]G. S. Davy, E. R. H. Jones and, T. G. Halsall, Rec. trav. chim., 69, 368 (1950).
[2]Reduction carried out in tetrahydrofuran.
[3]G. S. Davy, T. G. Halsall, and E. R. H. Jones, Chemistry and Industry, 1951, 233; J. Chem. Soc., 1951, 2696.
[4]G. S. Davy, T. G. Halsall, E. R. H. Jones, and G. D. Meakins, J. Chem. Soc., 1951, 2702.
[5]T. R. Ames, T. G. Halsall, and E. R. H. Jones, ibid., 1951, 450.
[6]E. Koller, A. Hiestand, P. Dietrich, and O. Jeger, Helv. Chim. Acta, 33, 1050 (1950).
[7]C. Vogel, O. Jeger, and L. Ruzicka, ibid., 35, 510 (1952).
[8]D. H. R. Barton and T. Bruun, J. Chem. Soc., 1952, 1683.
[9]Reduction carried out in ether-benzene mixture.
[10]Isolated as monoacetate.
[11]E. Kyburz, M. V. Mićović, W. Voser, H. Heusser, O. Jeger, and L. Ruzicka, Helv. Chim. Acta, 35, 2073 (1952).
[12]T. R. Ames, G. S. Davy, T. G. Halsall, E. R. H. Jones, and G. D. Meakins, Chemistry and Industry, 1952, 443.
[13]Isolated after oxidation of reduction product with chromic oxide in glacial acetic acid.
[14]W. Voser, D. E. White, H. Heusser, O. Jeger, and L. Ruzicka, Helv. Chim. Acta, 35, 830 (1952).
[15]J. F. McGhie, M. K. Pradhan, and J. F. Cavalla, J. Chem. Soc., 1952, 3176.
[16]W. Voser, M. Montavon, H. H. Günthard, O. Jeger, and L. Ruzicka, Helv. Chim. Acta, 33, 1893 (1950).
[17]Isolated as diacetate.
[18]J. F. McGhie and J. F. Cavalla, Chemistry and Industry, 1950, 744.
[19]J. F. Cavalla and J. F. McGhie, J. Chem. Soc., 1951, 834.
[20]W. Voser, H. H. Günthard, O. Jeger, and L. Ruzicka, Helv. Chim. Acta, 35, 66 (1952).
[21]R. Bhuvanendram, W. Manson, and F. S. Spring, J. Chem. Soc., 1950, 3472.
[22]D. H. R. Barton and C. J. W. Brooks, ibid., 1951, 257.
[23]T. R. Ames, G. S. Davy, T. G. Halsall, and E. R. H. Jones, ibid., 1952, 2868.
[24]R. Budziarek, J. D. Johnston, W. Manson, and F. S. Spring, ibid., 1951, 3019.
[25]Isolated as triacetate.
[26]J. F. Cavalla and J. F. McGhie, J. Chem. Soc., 1951, 744.
[27]T. R. Ames, G. S. Davy, T. G. Halsall, E. R. H. Jones, and G. D. Meakins, Chemistry and Industry, 1951, 741.
[28]Isolated after refluxing reduction product with acetic anhydride.
[29]D. H. R. Barton and N. J. Holness, J. Chem. Soc., 1952, 78.
[30]D. H. R. Barton and N. J. Holness, Chemistry and Industry, 1951, 233.

tion of the diketone with LAH yields acordiol, $C_{15}H_{28}O_2$, while reduction of methylacorolone yields methylacordiol, $C_{16}H_{30}O_2$ (230).

The LAH reduction of various triterpenoid ketones is summarized in Table XVII.

7.2.1.1. *Steroidal ketones.* The LAH reduction of steroidal ketones yields hydroxy derivatives whose spatial arrangement is dependent upon the configuration of neighboring groups.

The reduction of various steroid ring A ketones, particularly 3-keto steroids, is summarized in Table XVIII.

The LAH reduction of 3-ketosteroids with the 5-normal configuration (CCXII) yields the 3α-hydroxy compound as the principal product while 5-allo isomers (CCXIII) yield 3β-hydroxy epimers.

$$(7\text{-}145)$$

CCXII

$$(7\text{-}146)$$

CCXIII

Shoppee and Summers (231) have reasoned that steric hindrance by the angular methyl group at C_{10} arising from repulsion by the electrons of the three carbon-hydrogen bonds might impede frontal as compared with rearward attack by the aluminohydride ion on the 3-keto group. The production of cholestanol, the 3β-epimer, as the principal product from the reduction of cholestan-3-one is consistent with the lesser hindrance in the allo series. The predominant formation of epicoprostanol, the 3α-epimer, from the reduction of coprostan-3-one, is favored by the steric hindrance present in the normal series.

Paddock (63) has postulated that in the transition state the carbon-oxygen bond will be converted to a single bond with two directions open to it, corresponding to the α- and β-isomers. That configuration should be favored, whether ring A is the boat form (coprostan-3-one) or the chair form (cholestan-3-one), in which the carbon-oxygen bond is *trans* to at least one of the C_1C_2 and C_4C_5 bonds. Sparke (116) has stated that the orientation of the hydroxyl group is consistent with that predicted on the basis of the polar-equatorial bond concept whereby the hydroxyl group is usually obtained in the more thermodynamically stable equatorial form.

TABLE XVIII

LAH Reduction of Steroid Ring A Ketones

Ketone	No.	Product	% Yield	Ref.
C$_{19}$H$_{26}$O$_2$ 16,17α-Oxidoandrost-4-en-3-one	I	Androst-4-en-3β,17α-diol[1]	73	2
C$_{19}$H$_{32}$O$_2$ Androst-4-en-3-one-17α-ol	II	Androst-4-en-3β,17α-diol[1]	57[3]	2
Testosterone	III	Mixture of isomeric androst-5-en-3,17β-diols	53[4]	5
C$_{21}$H$_{26}$O$_3$ Methyl 3-keto-Δ$^{4,9(11),16}$-etiocholatrienate	IV	not specified	....	6
C$_{21}$H$_{30}$O$_2$ Progesterone	V	4-Pregnenediol	....	7
17,20-Oxido-4-pregnen-3-one	VI	unsaturated diol, m.p. 150°	....	8
17,17aα-Oxido-17aβ-methyl-D-homo-4,5-androsten-3-one	VII	17aβ-Methyl-D-homo-4,5-androsten-3β,17a-diol[1]	99	9
C$_{21}$H$_{30}$O$_3$ Allopregnan-3,11,20-trione	VIII	Allopregnan-3β,11β,20β-triol[1]	74	10
C$_{23}$H$_{32}$O$_6$ 21-Acetoxyallopregnan-3,11,20-trione-17α-ol	IX	Allopregnan-3β,11β,17α,20β,21-pentol[1]	39[11]	12
C$_{23}$H$_{34}$O$_2$S Progesterone-20-ethylenehemithioketal	X	4-Pregnen-3-ol-20-one 20-ethylenehemithioketal[1]	78	13
C$_{25}$H$_{38}$O$_3$ Methyl 3-keto-9(11)-cholenate	XI	9(11)-Lithocholenyl alcohol	86	14,15
C$_{25}$H$_{38}$O$_4$ Methyl 3-keto-9α,11α-oxidocholanate	XII	3α-Hydroxy-9α,11α-oxidocholanyl alcohol	80	14
C$_{27}$H$_{38}$O$_3$ 22-Isospirosta-4,6-dien-3-one	XIII	22-Isospirosta-4,6-dien-3β-ol[1]	75	16
22-Isospirosta-7,9(11)-dien-3-one	XIV	22-Isospirosta-7,9(11)-dien-3α-ol	69	17
C$_{27}$H$_{40}$O$_2$ 5β-Methyl-19-norcoprosta-1(10),8(9)-dien-3,6-dione	XV	non-crystalline mixture of diols, m.p. 70–80°	....	18
5β-Methyl-19-norcoprosta-1,9(10)-dien-3,6-dione	XVI	non-crystalline mixture of diols, m.p. 60–70°	....	18
C$_{27}$H$_{40}$O$_3$ 22-Isospirost-8(9)-en-3-one	XVII	22-Isospirost-8(9)-en-3α-ol	73	19
C$_{27}$H$_{40}$O$_4$ 22-Isoallospirostan-3,11-dione	XVIII	22-Isoallospirostan-3β,11β-diol	63	20
C$_{27}$H$_{42}$O Hecogenone	XIX	22-Isoallospirostan-3β,12β-diol[21]	....	22
Cholesta-4,6-dien-3-one	XX	Cholesta-4,6-dien-3β-ol	93	23
C$_{27}$H$_{42}$O$_3$ 22-Isospirostan-3-one	XXI	22-Isospirostan-3α-ol	73	19
C$_{27}$H$_{44}$O Cholest-4-en-3-one	XXII	Cholest-4-en-3-ol	....	24
		Cholest-4-en-3β-ol (allocholesterol)	44	25
		Cholest-4-en-3α-ol (epiallocholesterol)	44	

Formula	No.	Ketone	Products	%		Ref.
			Cholest-4-en-3β-ol	49 } $_{26}$		27
			Cholest-4-en-3α-ol	11 }		28
			Cholest-4-en-3β-ol	56 }		
			Cholest-4-en-3α-ol	25 }		
			1:1 Molecular compound of cholest-4-en-3α- and 3β-ols			
			Cholest-4-en-3β-ol	70 }		29
			Cholest-4-en-3α-ol	24 }		
			Cholest-4-en-3β-ol	72 } $_{30}$		29
			Cholest-4-en-3α-ol	16 }		
	XXIII	Cholest-5-en-3-one	Cholest-5-en-3β-ol (cholesterol)	90 }		31
			Cholest-5-en-3α-ol (epicholesterol)	4 }		
			Cholest-5-en-3β-ol	75		32
$C_{27}H_{44}O_2$	XXIV	4β,5-Oxidocoprostan-3-one	Coprostan-3α,5-diol	71 }		8
			Coprostan-3β,5-diol	26 }		
			Coprostan-3α,5-diol	68 } $_{33}$		28
			Coprostan-3β,5-diol	23 }		
	XXV	Cholestan-3,6-dione	Cholestan-3β,6β-diol	...		34,35
$C_{27}H_{46}O$	XXVI	Cholestan-3-one	Cholestanol	...		7
			Cholestan-3β-ol	91 }		31
			Cholestan-3α-ol	4 }		
			Cholestan-3β-ol	88]	82–90	36
			Cholestan-3α-ol	12]		
			Cholestan-3β-ol	82 } $_{30}$		29
			Cholestan-3α-ol	12 }		
	XXVII	Coprostan-3-one	Coprostanol	...		7
			Coprostan-3β-ol	4 }		31
			Coprostan-3α-ol	94 }		
			Coprostan-3β-ol	7 } $_{30}$		29
			Coprostan-3α-ol	87 }		
$C_{27}H_{46}O_2$	XXVIII	Cholestan-3-one-6β-ol	Cholestan-3β,6β-diol	...		34

(*Continued*)

TABLE XVIII (Continued)

Ketone	No.	Product	% Yield	Ref.
$C_{28}H_{43}NO_3$ Methyl solanidane-3-one-13-carboxylate	XXIX	Solanidane-3β,18-diol (dihydroisorubijervine) unidentified compound, m.p. 190–210° postulated as 3α-ol	28	37
$C_{29}H_{44}O_3$ 6β-Acetoxy-5β-methyl-19-norcoprosta-9(10), 11-dien-3-one	XXX	5β-Methyl-19-norcoprosta-9(10),11-dien-3β,6β-diol	27[3]	18

CHART TO TABLE XVIII

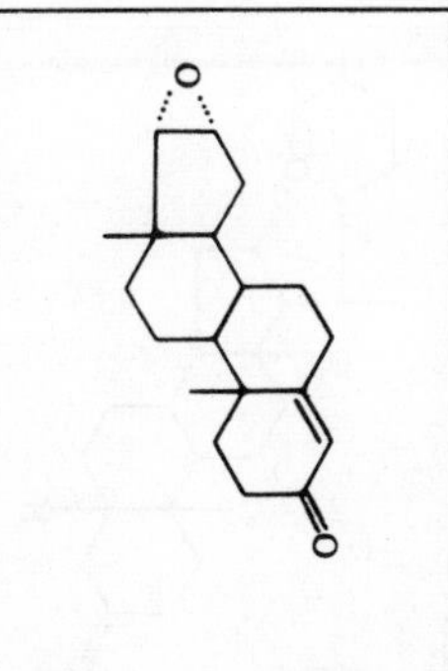

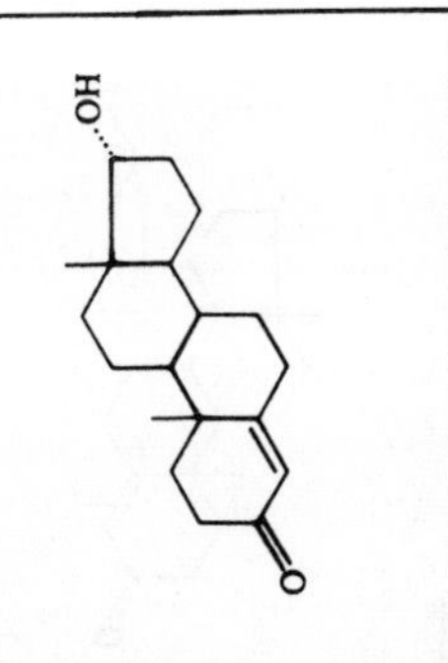

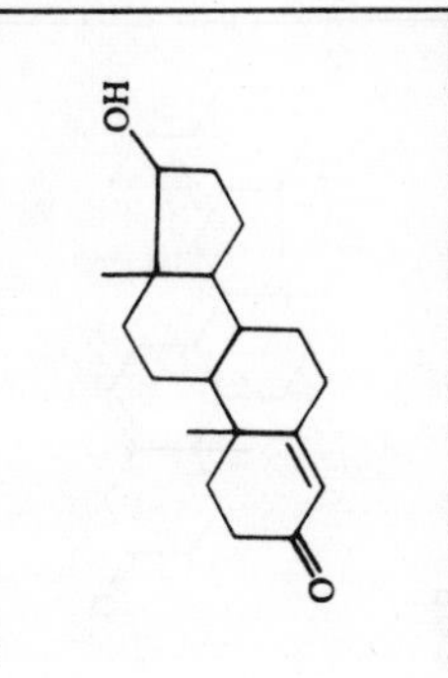

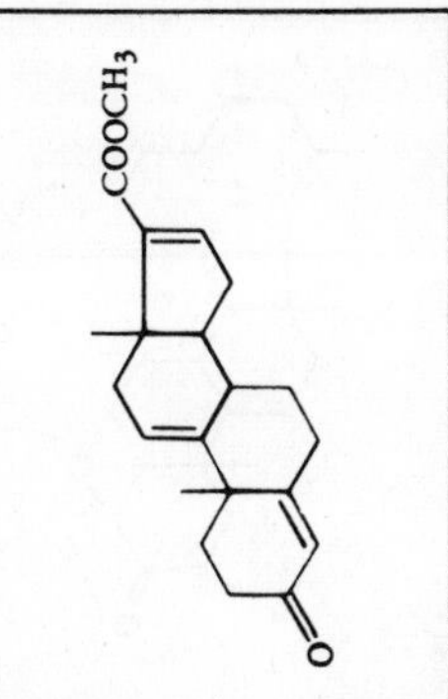

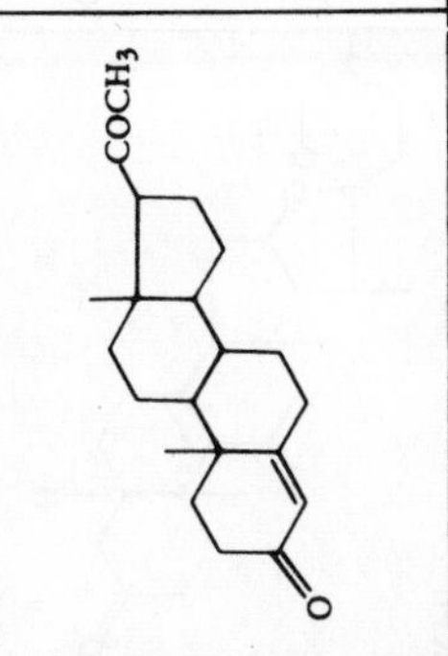

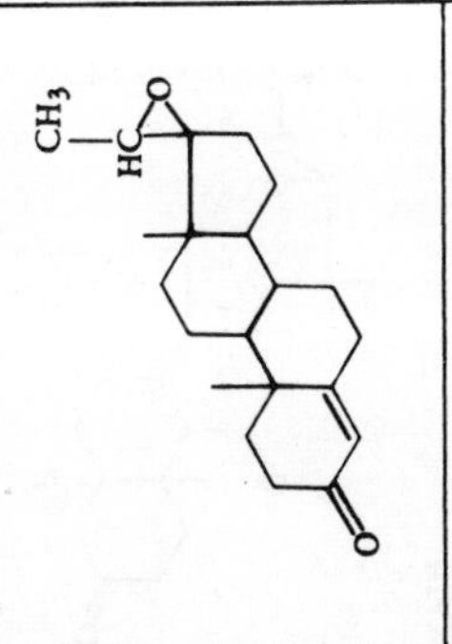

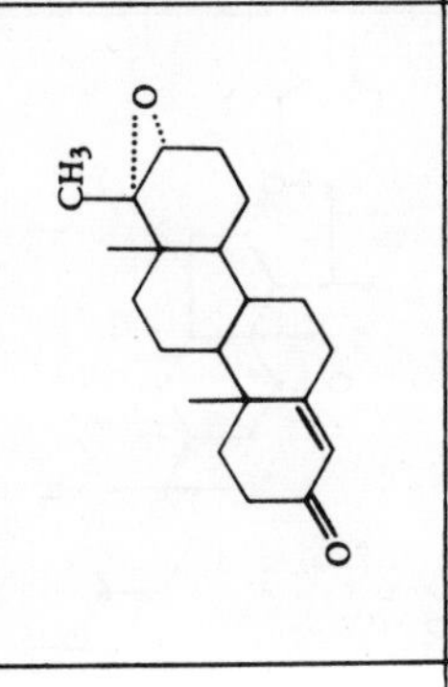

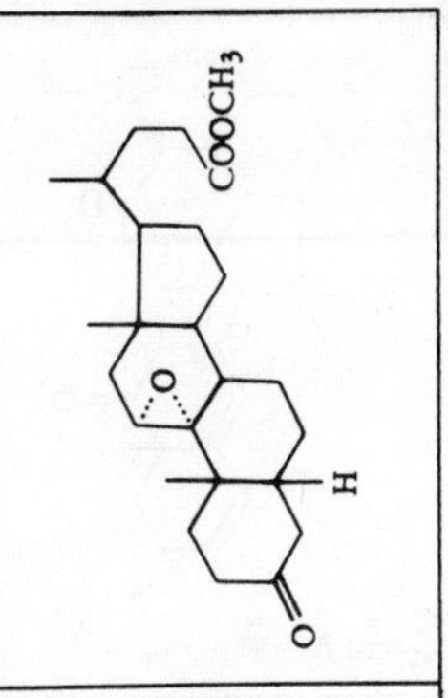

(continued)

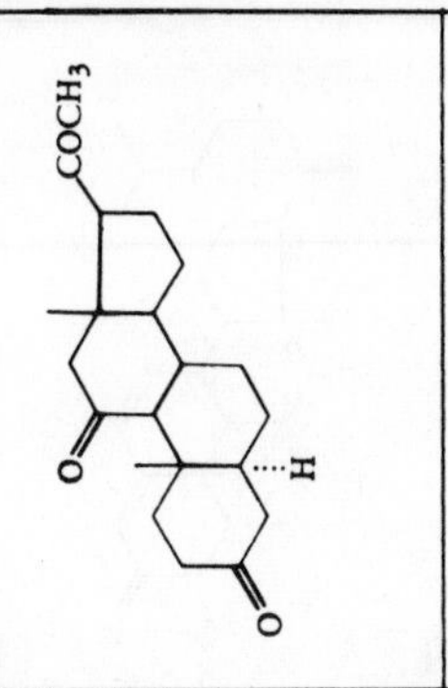

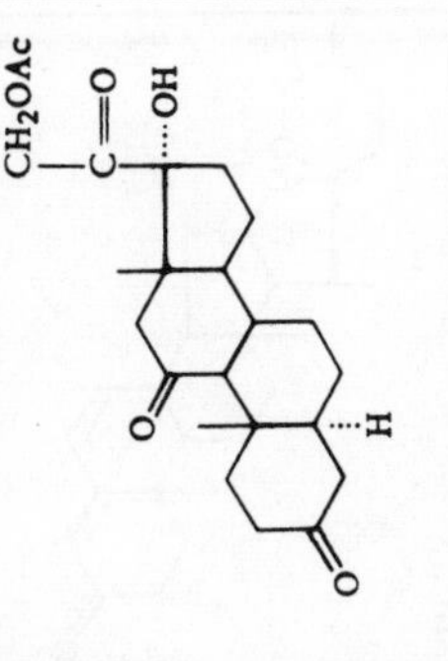

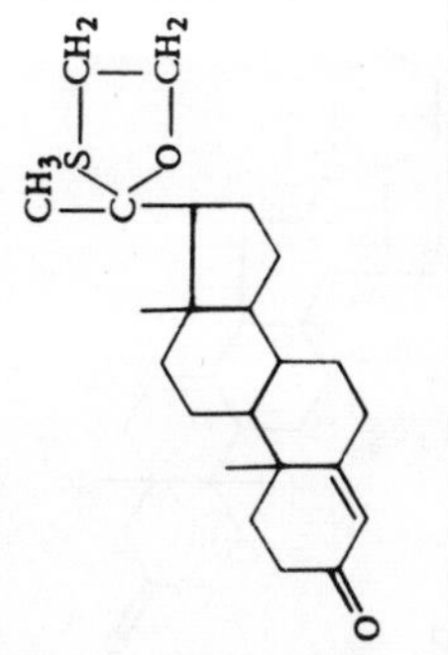

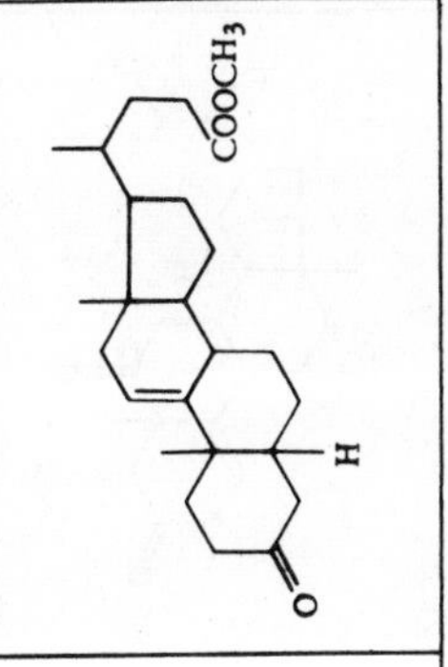

CHART TO TABLE XVIII (continued)

(continued)

CHART TO TABLE XVIII (*continued*)

References—Table XVIII

[1]Reduction carried out in tetrahydrofuran.
[2]H. Heusser, M. Feurer, K. Eichenberger, and V. Prelog, *Helv. Chim. Acta*, 33, 2243 (1950).
[3]Isolated as diacetate.
[4]Isolated as androsta-3,5-dien-17β-ol after refluxing with ethanol and hydrochloric acid.
[5]G. Rosenkranz, S. Kaufmann, and J. Romo, *J. Am. Chem. Soc.*, 71, 3689 (1949).
[6]R. B. Woodward, F. Sondheimer, D. Taub, K. Heusler, and W. M. McLamore, *ibid.*, 74, 4223 (1952).
[7]H. I. Schlesinger and A. E. Finholt, U. S. Pat. 2,576,311 (November 27, 1951).
[8]Ciba S. A., Fr. Pat. 994,615 (August 8, 1951); Ciba Ltd., Brit. Pat. 665,254 (January 16, 1952); P. Plattner, Ger. Pat. 834,848 (May 15, 1952), U. S. Pat. 2,599,481 (June 3, 1952).
[9]L. Ruzicka, N. Wahba, P. T. Herzig, and H. Heusser, *Chem. Ber.*, 85, 491 (1952).
[10]J. Romo, G. Stork, G. Rosenkranz, and C. Djerassi, *J. Am. Chem. Soc.*, 74, 2918 (1952).
[11]Isolated as 3,10,21-triacetate.
[12]C. Djerassi, G. Rosenkranz, J. Pataki, and S. Kaufmann, *J. Biol. Chem.*, 194, 115 (1952).
[13]J. Romo, G. Rosenkranz, and C. Djerassi, *J. Am. Chem. Soc.*, 73, 4961 (1951).
[14]L. F. Fieser and S. Rajagopalan, *ibid.*, 73, 118 (1951).
[15]J. C. Babcock and L. F. Fieser, *ibid.*, 74, 5472 (1952).
[16]J. Romo, H. J. Ringold, G. Rosenkranz, and C. Djerassi, *J. Org. Chem.*, 16, 1873 (1951).
[17]R. Yashin, G. Rosenkranz, and C. Djerassi, *J. Am. Chem. Soc.*, 73, 4654 (1951).
[18]B. Ellis and V. Petrow, *J. Chem. Soc.*, 1952, 2246.
[19]C. Djerassi, R. Yashin, and G. Rosenkranz, *J. Am. Chem. Soc.*, 74, 422 (1952).
[20]C. Djerassi, E. Batres, M. Velasco, and G. Rosenkranz, *ibid.*, 74, 1712 (1952).
[21]Reduction carried out in a tetrahydrofuran-ether mixture.
[22]N. L. Wendler, H. L. Slates, and M. Tishler, *J. Am. Chem. Soc.*, 74, 4894 (1952).
[23]J. Schmutz, H. Schaltegger, and M. Sanz, *Helv. Chim. Acta*, 34, 1111 (1951).
[24]A. C. Ott and M. F. Murray, *Abstracts of Papers*, 113th Meeting American Chemical Society, Chicago, Ill., April 1948, p. 17K.
[25]H. McKennis, Jr., and G. W. Gaffney, *J. Biol. Chem.*, 175, 217 (1948).
[26]Isolated as the oxidoacetate after treatment with phthalic monoperacid and acetylation.
[27]P. A. Plattner, H. Heusser, and A. B. Kulkarni, *Helv. Chim. Acta*, 32, 1070 (1949).
[28]P. A. Plattner, H. Heusser, and A. B. Kulkarni, *ibid.*, 32, 265 (1949).
[29]W. G. Dauben, R. A. Micheli, and J. F. Eastham, *J. Am. Chem. Soc.*, 74, 3852 (1952).
[30]Inverse addition.
[31]C. W. Shoppee and G. H. R. Summers, *J. Chem. Soc.*, 1950, 687.
[32]A. J. Birch, *ibid.*, 1950, 2325.
[33]Isolated as monoacetate.
[34]C. W. Shoppee and G. H. R. Summers, *J. Chem. Soc.*, 1952, 3361.
[35]C. W. Shoppee and G. H. R. Summers, *ibid.*, 1952, 3374.
[36]H. R. Nace and G. L. O'Connor, *J. Am. Chem. Soc.*, 73, 5824 (1951).
[37]Y. Sato and W. A. Jacobs, *J. Biol. Chem.*, 191, 63 (1951).

Nace and O'Connor (232) postulated that in the reduction of cholestan-3-one (CCXIII) to cholestan-3α-ol and cholestan-3β-ol, there is more hindrance on the rear (α) side of the molecule than on the frontal (β) side, mainly due to the 5-hydrogen.

CCXIII   (7-147)

Therefore, as the size of the reducing group is increased attack on the unhindered (β) side would be favored, resulting in a higher percentage of the α-epimer. This hypothesis was examined by carrying out a number of reductions with LAH and various aluminum alkoxides. The yield of α-cholestanol increased from 12% with LAH to 28% for aluminum isopropoxide, 35% for the aluminum salt of diethyl carbinol, 45% for the aluminum salt of diisopropyl carbinol and 55% for the aluminum salt of di-*t*-butyl carbinol. The α-cholestanol, whose formation is favored by the hindrance, is not produced in greater quantity than the β-isomer because the α-producing transition states may rearrange to produce the more favorable β-producing transition states since the β-isomer is the more stable form. With inverse addition, the LAH reduction of CCXIII gives an increased yield of the α-epimer (233).

Catalytic hydrogenation of coprostan-3-one over platinum oxide in an ether-alcohol solution at room temperature, proceeds analogously to the LAH reduction, yielding *epi*coprostanol, the 3α-epimer, accompanied by less than 5% of the β-epimer (234). A slightly increased yield of the β-epimer is obtained by the inverse addition of LAH (233) as compared to the normal procedure (231).

The LAH reduction of 4β,5-oxidocoprostan-3-one (CCXIV) yields 71% of the 3α,5-diol and 26% of the 3β,5-diol (235,236). Here the β-oxide, analogous to the 5-normal hydrogen, favors the 3α-epimer as the predominant product.

CCXIV   (7-148)

The reduction of 6β-acetoxy-5β-methyl-19-norcoprosta-9(10),11-dien-3-one (CCXV) is reported to yield the 3β,6β-diol, isolated in 27% yield as the diacetate (237).

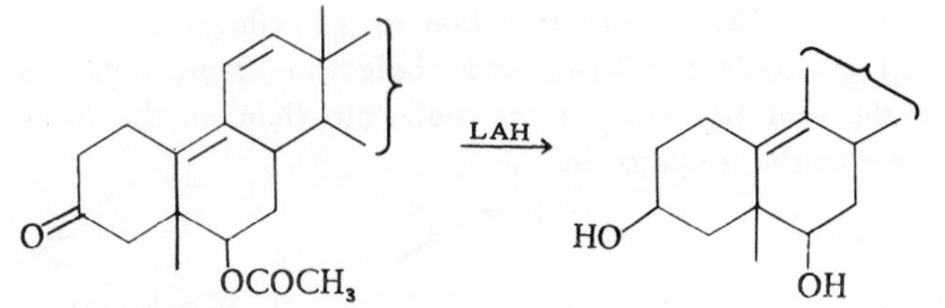

(7-149)

CCXV

The decreased steric hindrance due to the absence of the angular C_{10}-methyl group is apparently of greater influence than the 5β-methyl group resulting in the formation of the 3β-epimer.

The LAH reduction of cholest-5-en-3-one (CCXVI) yields 90% of the 3β-epimer, cholesterol, and less than 5% of *epi*cholesterol (231,238).

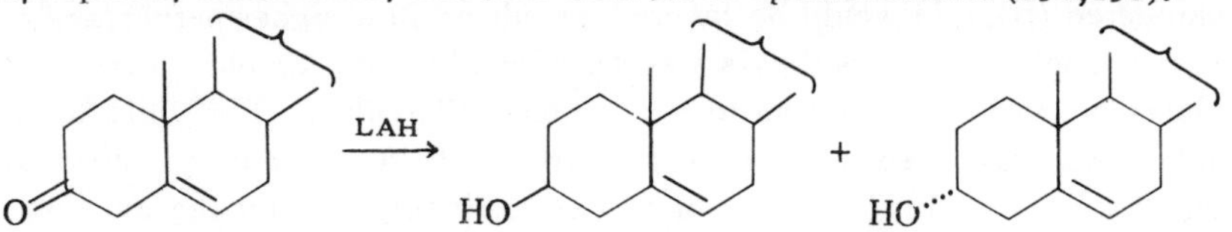

CCXVI   (7-150)

Shoppee and Summers (231) point out that the presence of the double bond at the bridgehead ensures that the lower portions of rings A and B are essentially flat. Therefore, nucleophilic attack on the 3-keto group should form the α and β epimers in equal quantities. However, the steric hindrance by the angular methyl group may impede frontal attack and favor the formation of the 3β-epimer. Paddock (63) has postulated that since the β-form yields a transition state in which the carbon-oxygen bond is most nearly *trans* to C_1C_2 and C_4C_5 it should be the predominant form, as is experimentally verified.

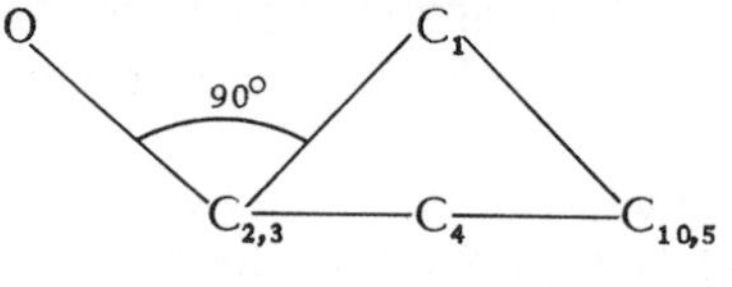

α β

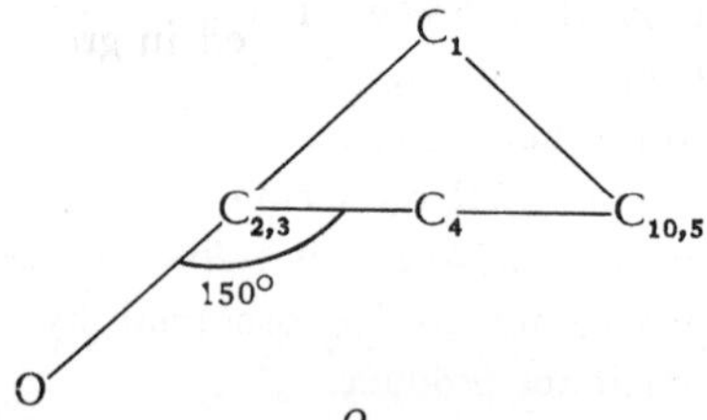

The reduction of cholest-5-en-3-one can generally be carried out without alteration of the double bond only in neutral media, since this compound is readily isomerized to cholest-4-en-3-one. Partial catalytic hydrogenation with Raney nickel yields considerable quantities of *epi*cholestrol (239).

McKennis and Gaffney (240) reported that the LAH reduction of cholest-4-en-3-one (CCXVII) gives a quantitative yield of a mixture of equal parts of the 3α- and 3β-diastereoisomers, *epi*allocholesterol and allocholesterol, respectively.

CCXVII   (7-151)

The mixture of epimers is obtained even in the presence of a fivefold excess of LAH.

Plattner *et al.* reported that the LAH reduction of CCXVII gives a 56% yield of allocholesterol and a 25% yield of an addition compound containing a 1:1 ratio of allocholesterol and *epi*allocholesterol (236). In additional work, the reduction mixture of α- and β-epimers was treated with phthalic monoperacid and the crude mixture of oxides was acetylated to yield 49% of the 3β-acetoxy-4,5-oxide and 11% of the 3α-acetoxy-4,5-oxide (241). Dauben, Micheli, and Eastham (233) found that in the LAH reduction of CCXVII either normal or inverse addition gives a 70–72% yield of the 3β-ol.

The reaction between cholest-4-en-3-one (CCXVII) and methylmagnesium iodide yields a molecular compound of 3α-methylcholest-4-en-3β-ol and 3β-methylcholest-4-en-3α-ol, analogous to the addition compound formed by reduction with LAH (242).

The 3β-hydroxy derivative is reported as the product of the LAH reduction of 17,17aα-oxido-17aβ-methyl-D-homoandrost-4-en-3-one (CCXVIII) (243), 16,17α-oxidoandrost-4-en-3-one (CCXIX) (244) and androst-4-en-3-one-17α-ol (17-*epi*testosterone) (CCXX) (244).

CCXVIII   CCXIX

CCXX

Heusser *et al.* (244) point out that as in the cholestene series it is possible that the androstenediol contains an addition compound between the

4-en-3α- and 4-en-3β-ol forms. In addition, the crude reduction mixture may contain the epimeric androst-4-en-3α,17α-diol which could not be obtained in crystalline form.

The LAH reduction of cholesta-4,6-dien-3-one (CCXXI) yields the 3β-ol in 93% yield (245). The reduction of 22-isospirosta-4,6-dien-3-one yields 75% of the 3β-ol (246). In contrast, reduction of CCXXI with aluminum isopropoxide yields equimolar amounts of the 3α- and 3β-isomerides as an addition complex (247).

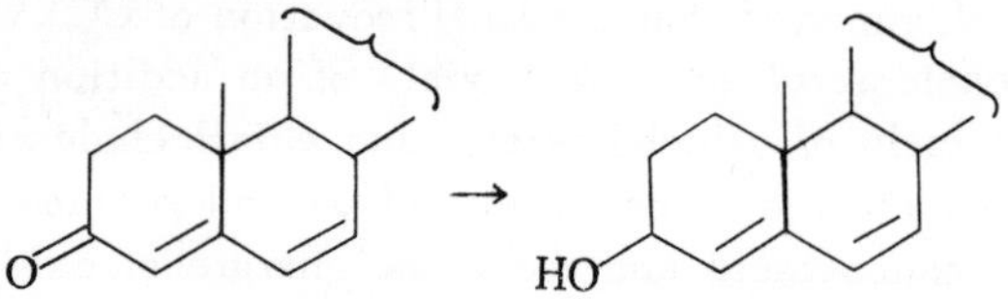

CCXXI

(7-152)

The LAH reduction of the enol acetates of 3-keto steroids yields the 3α- and 3β-ols in a different ratio from that obtained with the free ketones. The enol acetates of cholestanone (CCXXII) and coprostanone (CCXXIII) yield 3 to 4 times as much *epi*cholestanol (α-epimer) and coprostanol (β-epimer), respectively, with normal or inverse addition of LAH, as in the reduction of the ketone. The parent ketone is present in the reduction mixture from the enol acetates (233).

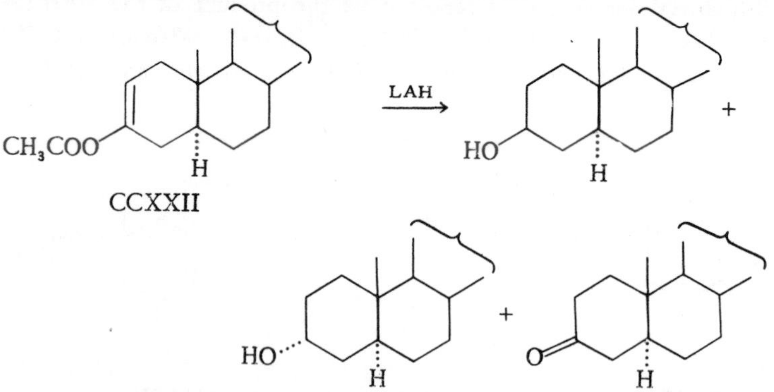

CCXXII

(7-153)

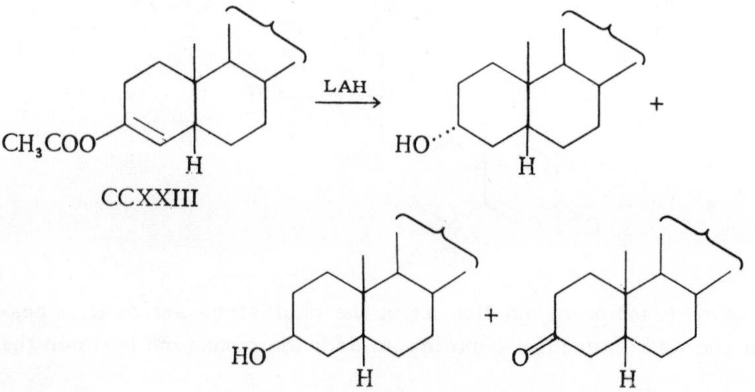

CCXXIII

(7-154)

The enol acetate of cholest-4-en-3-one, 3-acetoxycholesta-3,5-diene (CCXXIV), is reduced with LAH to cholest-4-en-3-one and a mixture of cholest-5-en-3β-ol (cholesterol) and 3α-ol (*epi*cholesterol) and small amounts of cholest-4-en-3α- and 3β-ols (248).

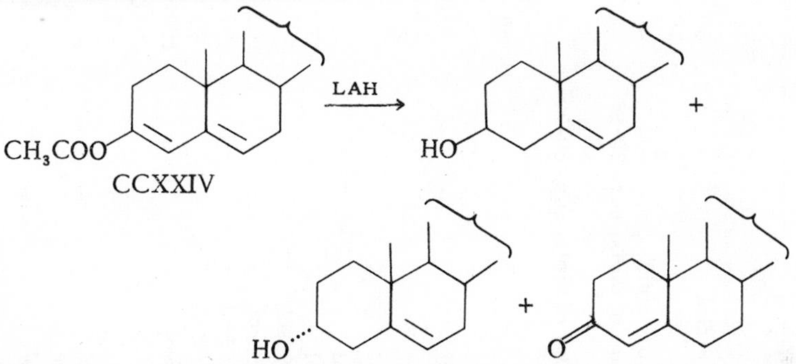

CCXXIV

(7-155)

The LAH reduction of the enol acetates is discussed more fully in Section 9.3.

The LAH reduction of steroid ring B ketones, i.e., 6- and 7-keto steroids, is summarized in Table XIX.

The reduction of 3-substituted cholestan-6-ones (CCXXV) with LAH yields the corresponding cholestan-6β-ol as the predominant or only product (249).

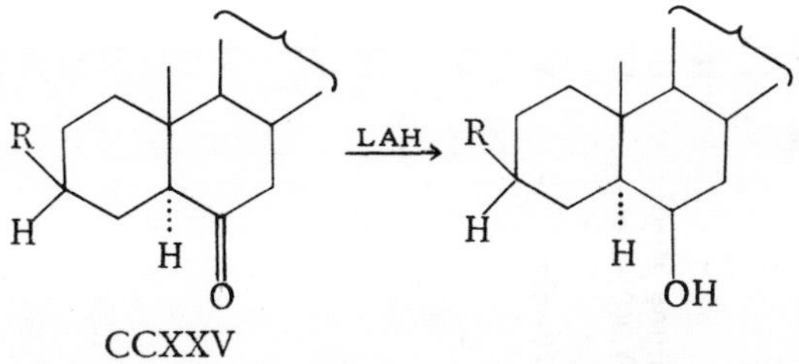

CCXXV   (7-156)

R = H, α-OH, β-OH, α-Br, β-Br, α-Cl, β-I

Similarly, cholestan-3,6-dione, 2α,3α-oxidocholestan-6-one and cholest-2-en-6-one are reduced to the corresponding 6β-ols. In contrast, reduction with sodium in ethanol converts cholestan-6-one (CCXXVI) to the 6α-ol derivative.

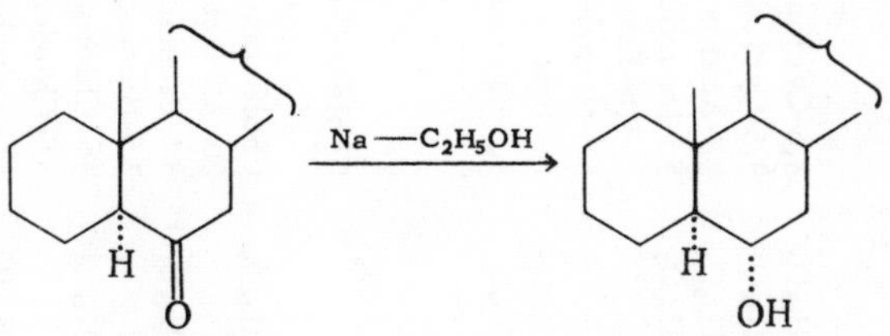

CCXXVI   (7-157)

TABLE XIX

LAH Reduction of Steroid Ring B Ketones

Ketones	No.	Product	% Yield	Ref.
A. 6-Keto Steroids				
$C_{19}H_{26}O_2$ 3,5-Cycloandrostan-6,17-dione	I	epi-i-Androstan-6,17β-diol	89	1
$C_{19}H_{28}O$ 3,5-Cycloandrostan-6-one	II	epi-i-Androstan-6-ol	79	1
$C_{26}H_{46}O_4$ 3β-Acetoxyergosta-7,22-dien-6-one-5α-ol	III	Cerevisterol (3β,5α,6β-triol)	....	2
$C_{27}H_{40}O_2$ 5β-Methyl-19-norcoprosta-1(10),8(9)-dien-3,6-dione	IV	non-crystalline mixture of diols, m.p. 70–80°	....	3
5β-Methyl-19-norcoprosta-1,9(10)-dien-3,6-dione	V	non-crystalline mixture of diols, m.p. 60–70°	....	3
$C_{27}H_{44}O$ 3,5-Cyclocholestan-6-one	VI	epi-i-Cholestanol	86	1
		epi-i-Cholestanol	34 }	4
		i-Cholestanol	10 }	
Cholest-2-en-6-one	VII	Cholest-2-en-6β-ol	95 }	5,6
		Cholest-2-en-6α-ol	5 }	
$C_{27}H_{44}O_2$ Cholestan-3,6-dione	VIII	Cholestan-3β,6β-diol	....	8
2α,3α-Oxidocholestan-6-one	IX	Cholestan-3α,6β-diol	77[7]	8
$C_{27}H_{45}BrO$ 3α-Bromocholestan-6-one	X	3α-Bromocholestan-6β-ol	....	9
3β-Bromocholestan-6-one	XI	3β-Bromocholestan-6β-ol	100	8
$C_{27}H_{45}ClO$ 3α-Chlorocholestan-6-one	X	3α-Chlorocholestan-6β-ol	97	9
3β-Chlorocholestan-6-one	XI	3β-Chlorocholestan-6β-ol	91	9
$C_{27}H_{45}IO$ 3β-Iodocholestan-6-one	XII	3β-Iodocholestan-6β-ol	100	9
$C_{27}H_{46}O$ Cholestan-6-one	XII	Cholestan-6β-ol	95 }	5
		Cholestan-6α-ol	5 }	
$C_{27}H_{46}O_2$ Cholestan-6-one-3α-ol	XIII	Cholestan-3α,6β-diol	....	8
Cholestan-6-one-3β-ol	XIV	Cholestan-3β,6β-diol	86 }	8
		Cholestan-3β,6α-diol	.... }	

B. 7-Keto Steroids

Formula	No.	Name	Product	%	Ref.
$C_{25}H_{38}O_5$	XV	3β,20β-Diacetoxyallopregnan-7-one	Allopregnan-3β,7,20β-triol	....	10
$C_{27}H_{42}O_2$	XVI	3,7-Diketocholestene	unidentified gum	....	11
$C_{27}H_{44}O_2$	XVII	7-Ketocholesterol	Mixture of 7α- and 7β-hydroxy cholesterols	100	12,13
$C_{28}H_{44}O_2$	XVIII	3-Methoxycholesta-3,5-dien-7-one	Cholesta-4,6-dien-3-one[14]	60	11
$C_{29}H_{42}O_5$	XIX	3β-Acetoxy-Δ5-22-isospirosten-7-one	Δ5-22-Isospirosten-3β,7β-diol	100	15
$C_{29}H_{42}O_6$	XX	3β-Acetoxy-9α,11α-oxido-22-isoallospirostan-7-one	9α,11α-Oxido-22-isoallospirostan-3β,7(β?)-diol[14]	78	16
$C_{29}H_{46}O_2$	XXI	7-Ketostigmasterol	7-Hydroxystigmasterol	100	13
$C_{29}H_{46}O_3$	XXII	7-Ketocholesteryl acetate	7α-Hydroxycholesterol 7β-Hydroxycholesterol	5[17] 59[17]	18
$C_{29}H_{48}O_2$	XXIII	7-Ketositosterol	Mixture of 7α- and 7β-hydroxy cholesterols 7-Hydroxysitosterol	100 100	13 13
$C_{29}H_{48}O_3$	XXIV	7-Ketocholestanyl acetate	Cholestan-3β,7α-diol Cholestan-3β,7β-diol Cholestan-3β,7α-diol Cholestan-3β,7β-diol	33 37.5 23 35	18 19
$C_{31}H_{48}O_3$	XXV	7-Ketostigmasteryl acetate	7α-Hydroxystigmasterol 7β-Hydroxystigmasterol	5,5[17] 56[17]	18

CHART TO TABLE XIX

I

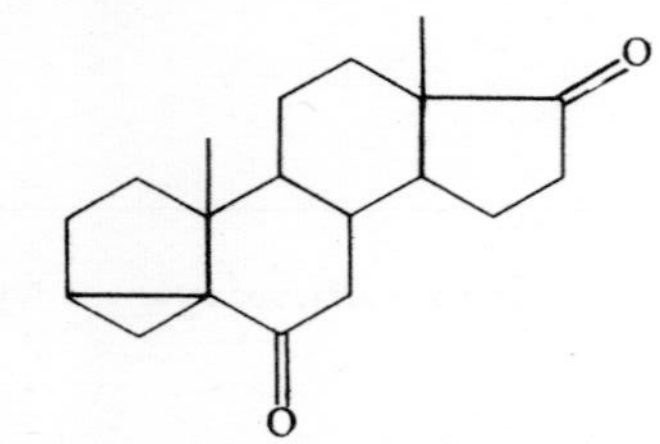

II

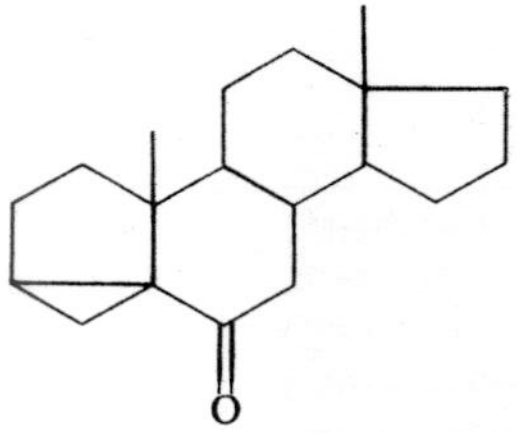

III

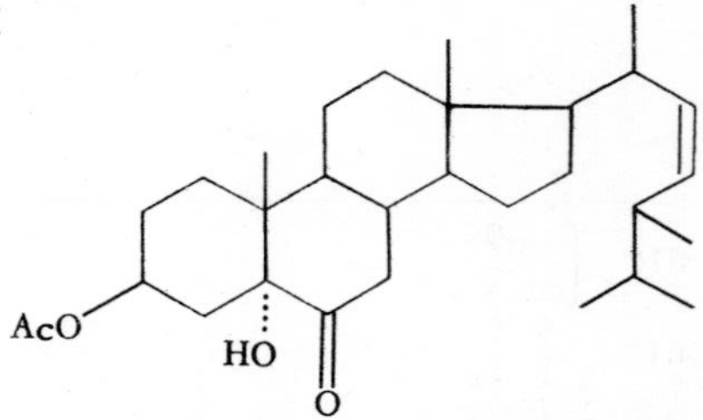

IV

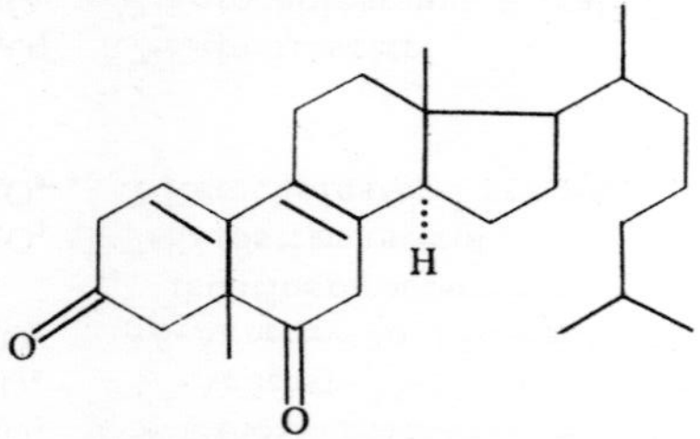

V

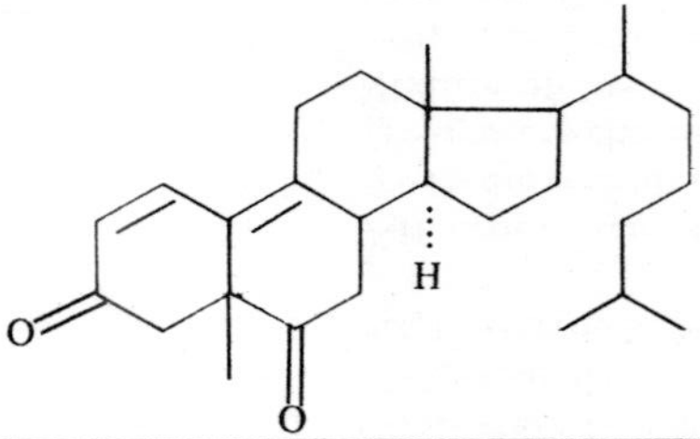

VI

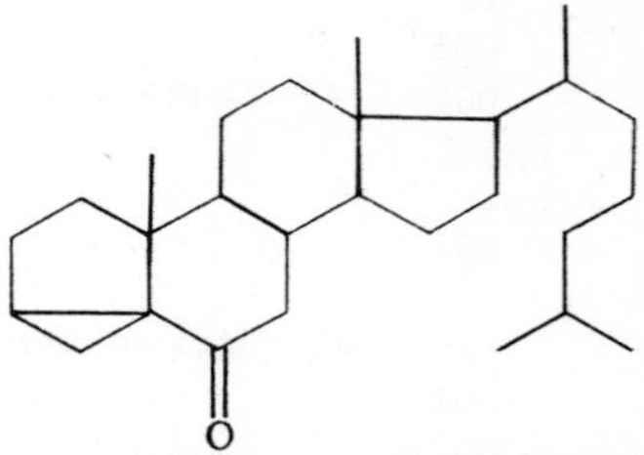

VII

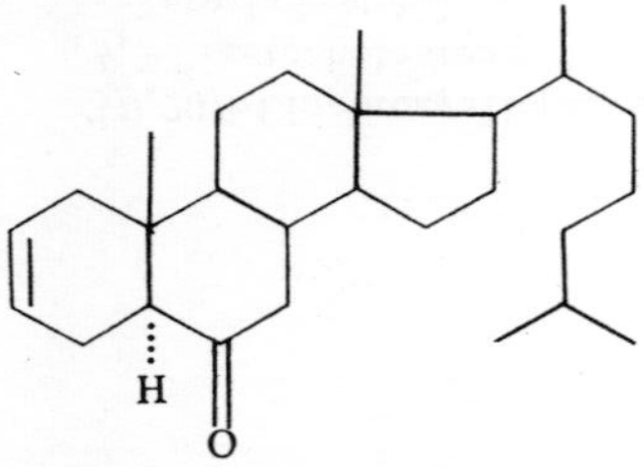

VIII

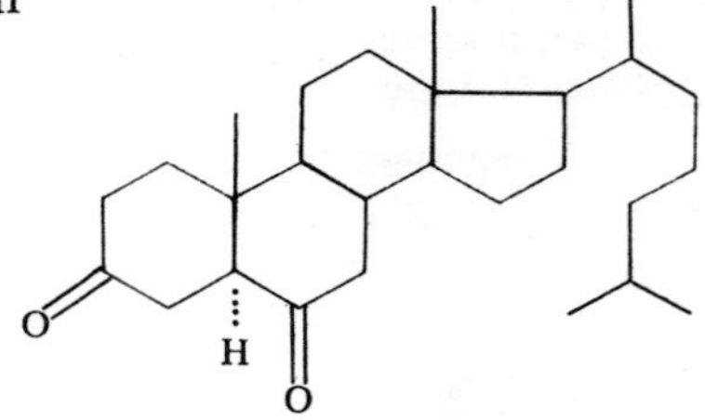

IX

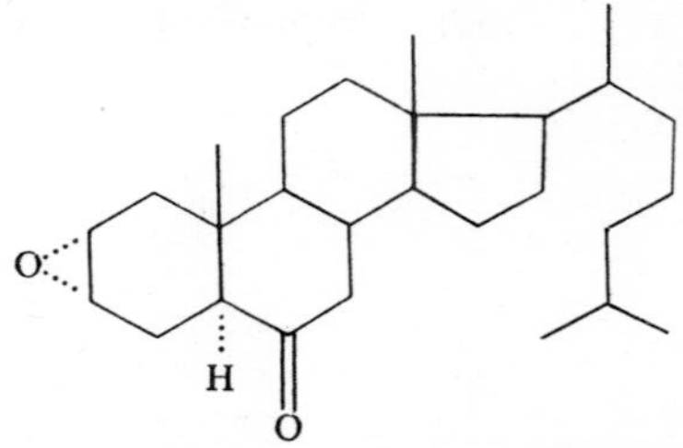

(*continued*)

CHART TO TABLE XIX (*continued*)

(*continued*)

CHART TO TABLE XIX (*continued*)

References—Table XIX

[1]A. F. Wagner, N. E. Wolff, and E. S. Wallis, *J. Org. Chem.*, 17, 529 (1952).
[2]G. H. Alt and D. H. R. Barton, *Chemistry and Industry*, 1952, 1103.
[3]B. Ellis and V. Petrow, *J. Chem. Soc.*, 1952, 2246.
[4]A. F. Wagner and E. S. Wallis, *J. Am. Chem. Soc.*, 72, 1047 (1950).
[5]C. W. Shoppee and G. H. R. Summers, *J. Chem. Soc.*, 1952, 3361.
[6]C. W. Shoppee and G. H. R. Summers, *ibid.*, 1952, 3374.
[7]Isolated as diacetate.
[8]C. W. Shoppee and G. H. R. Summers, *J. Chem. Soc.*, 1952, 1790.
[9]C. W. Shoppee and G. H. R. Summers, *ibid.*, 1952, 1786.
[10]J. Romo, G. Rosenkranz, and C. Djerassi, *J. Org. Chem.*, 17, 1413 (1952).
[11]C. W. Greenhalgh, H. B. Henbest, and E. R. H. Jones, *J. Chem. Soc.*, 1952, 2375.
[12]E. Y. Spencer and M. Lambert, unpublished work; through R. H. Cox, and E. Y. Spencer, *Can. J. Chem.*, 29, 398 (1951).
[13]K. Abildgaard-Elling, Brit. Pat. 656,388 (August 22, 1951); *Chem. Abstracts*, 46, 10213 (1952).
[14]Reduction carried out in tetrahydrofuran.
[15]H. J. Ringold, G. Rosenkranz, and C. Djerassi, *J. Am. Chem. Soc.*, 74, 3318 (1952).
[16]C. Djerassi, E. Batres, M. Velasco, and G. Rosenkranz, *ibid.*, 74, 1712 (1952).
[17]Isolated as dibenzoate.
[18]L. F. Fieser, M. Fieser, and R. N. Chakravarti, *J. Am. Chem. Soc.*, 71, 2226 (1949).
[19]L. F. Fieser, J. E. Herz, M. W. Klohs, M. A. Romero, and T. Utne, *ibid.*, 74, 3309 (1952).

Catalytic hydrogenation of cholestan-6-one over platinum oxide in methanol yields cholestan-6β-ol. While the reduction of cholest-2-en-6-one with LAH and sodium in ethanol yields cholest-2-en-6β- and 6α-ol, respectively, catalytic hydrogenation over palladium in acetic acid yields cholestan-6-one.

The LAH reduction of 3β-acetoxyergosta-7,22-dien-5α-ol-6-one (CCXXVII) yields cerevisterol, the 3β, 5α, 6β-triol (250).

CH₃COO   OH   O   CCXXVII   →(LAH)→   HO   OH   OH   (7-158)

Ellis and Petrow (237) have reported that the LAH reduction of 5β-methyl-19-norcoprosta-1(10),8(9)-dien-3,6-dione (CCXXVIII) and the 1,9(10)-diene (CCXXIX) yields a non-crystalline mixture of diols which fail to crystallize before or after acetylation followed by chromatography.

CCXXVIII   CCXXIX

In a preliminary communication Wagner and Wallis reported that the LAH reduction of i-cholestan-6-one (CCXXX) gives epi-i-cholestan-6-ol (CCXXX), with no trace of i-cholestan-6-ol (251).

CCXXX   →(LAH)→   OH   CCXXXI   (7-159)

In a more detailed report (252) Wagner et al. described the preparation of epi-i-androstan-6,17β-diol and epi-i-androstan-6-ol as well as epi-i-cholestan-6-ol by the LAH reduction of i-androstan-6,17-dione, i-androstan-6-one and i-cholestan-6-one, respectively. On the basis of a rate study of the rearrangement of i-cholestan-6-ol and epi-i-cholestan-6-ol to isomeric

3,5,6-tribromocholestanes by the action of a 1% ethereal solution of bromine, the solubility properties of the epimeric 3,5-cyclodiols and the dielectric constants of the epimeric diol-diacetates, a 6α-configuration was assigned to the *i*-sterols and a 6β-configuration to the *epi-i*-sterols. Hence the *epi-i*-sterols obtained by the LAH reduction of the 3,5-cyclostan-6-ones are assigned the 3,5-cyclostan-6β-ol structure.

Shoppee and Summers (253) reported that the LAH reduction of *i*-cholestan-6-one (CCXXX) gives 10% of *i*-cholestan-6-ol, 34% of *epi-i*-cholestan-6-ol and a considerable quantity of uncrystallizable oil. In order to assign configurations to the epimeric 6-ols they were converted to the corresponding cholestan-6-ols. The 6β-ol was synthesized by a number of independent methods as summarized in Flow Sheet I. These transformations and the agreement shown between the observed molecular rotations and those calculated for the epimeric cholestan-6-ols led to the proposal that *i*-cholestanol is 3,5-cyclocholestan-6β-ol. Therefore the major product of the LAH reduction, the *epi-i*-cholestan-6-ol, is assigned the 3,5-cyclocholestan-6α-ol structure.

There appears to be little question that the predominant product of the LAH reduction of *i*-cholestan-6-one is the *epi-i*-cholestan-6-ol. However, the conflicting assignments of the configuration of the 6-ol can only be resolved by an evaluation of the evidence presented in support of the postulated structure. Similar considerations pertain to the structures of the *epi-i*-androstan-6-ols obtained by the LAH reduction of the *i*-androstan-6-ones.

Fieser *et al.* reported that the LAH reduction of 7-ketocholestanyl acetate (CCXXXII) gives a mixture of cholestan-3β,7α-diol and 3β,7β-diol containing a slight excess of the 3β,7β-diol (254,255).

CCXXXII

(7-160)

Djerassi and his co-workers (256) reported that the LAH reduction of 3β-acetoxy-9α,11α-oxido-22-isoallospirostan-7-one (CCXXXIII) gives a 78% yield of a 3β,7-diol in which the 7β-configuration has been postulated.

FLOW SHEET I

STRUCTURE PROOF OF i-CHOLESTANOL AND epi-i-CHOLESTANOL (253)

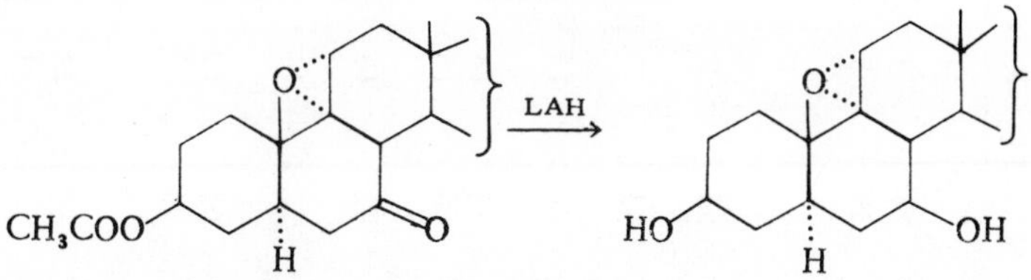

$$(7\text{-}161)$$

CCXXXIII

The LAH reduction of 7-ketocholesteryl acetate and 7-ketostigmasteryl acetate (CCXXXIV) yields approximately 60% of the 7β-hydroxy and 5% of the 7α-hydroxy epimers (254).

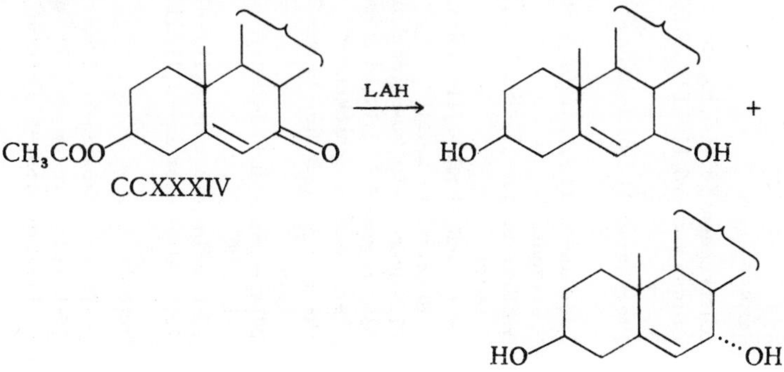

$$(7\text{-}162)$$

The 7β-ol is also the principal product of the reduction of 7-ketocholesteryl acetate with aluminum isopropoxide, although the yield is reported as less than 30% (257,258).

Mixtures of the 7α- and 7β-ols are reported from the LAH reduction of 7-ketocholesterol, 7-ketostigmasterol and 7-ketositosterol. The reduction of 3-acetoxy-Δ⁵-22-isospirosten-7-one quantitatively yields the 3β,7-diol postulated as the 3β,7β-diol (259).

The reduction of "3,7-diketocholestene" (CCXXXV) with LAH in ether yields an unidentified non-ketonic gum while reduction with LAH in tetrahydrofuran yields a ketonic gum (260). The structure of the "3,7-diketocholestene" is actually that of an enol ketone and can be represented as either of the two forms.

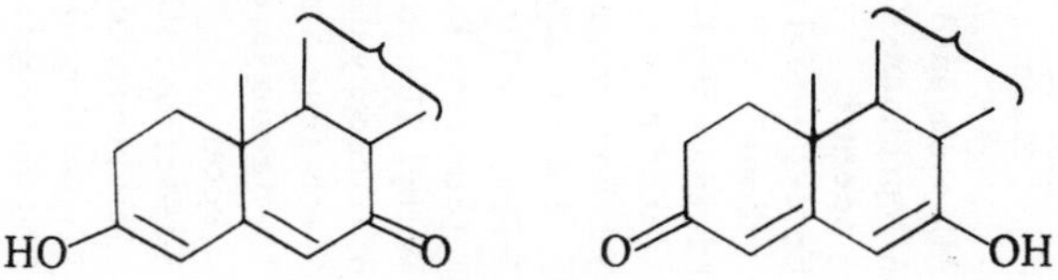

CCXXXV

TABLE XX

LAH Reduction of Steroid Ring C Ketones

Ketone	No.	Product	% Yield	Ref.
A. 11-Keto Steroids				
$C_{21}H_{30}O_3$				
Allopregnan-3,11,20-trione	I	Allopregnan-3β,11β,20β-triol[1]	74[2]	3
$C_{23}H_{32}O_6$				
Allopregnan-17α,21-diol-3,11,20-trione-21-acetate	II	Allopregnan-3β,11β,17α,20β,21-pentol[1]	39[4]	5
$C_{23}H_{36}O_3$				
Enol-20-ethyl ether of pregnan-3α-ol-11,20-dione[6]	III	Pregnan-3α,11β-diol-20-one[7]	....	8
$C_{24}H_{38}O_5$				
Pregnan-3α,17α,20β,21-tetrol-11-one-20,21-acetonide[1]	IV	Pregnan-3α,11β,17α,20β,21-pentol-20,21-acetonide	54	9
$C_{25}H_{34}O_6$				
3-Ethoxypregna-3,5-dien-17α,21-diol-11,20-dione-21-acetate	V	3-Ethoxypregna-3,5-dien-11β,17α,20β,21-tetrol	43[10]	9,11
$C_{25}H_{36}O_7$				
5-Pregnen-17α,21-diol-3,11,20-trione-3,20-di-(ethylene ketal)	VI	5-Pregnen-11β,17α,21-triol-3,20-dione-3,20-di-(ethylene ketal)[12]	48	13
$C_{25}H_{38}O_4$				
Methyl 11-keto-3α,9α-oxidocholanate	VII	11β-Hydroxy-3α,9α-oxidocholanyl alcohol	73	14
$C_{25}H_{38}O_4S$				
3β-Acetoxyallopregnan-11,20-dione-20-ethylene hemithioketal	VIII	Allopregnan-3β,11β-diol-20-one-20-ethylene hemithioketal[15]	96	16
$C_{25}H_{38}O_5$				
3α-Acetoxypregnan-11,20-dione-20-ethylene ketal	IX	Pregnan-3α,11β-diol-20-one-20-ethylene ketal	92[17]	18
3β-Acetoxyallopregnan-11,20-dione-20-ethylene ketal	X	Allopregnan-3β,11β-diol-20-one-20-ethylene ketal[15]	....	16
B. 12-Keto Steroids				
$C_{27}H_{40}O_4$				
22-Isoallospirostan-3,11-dione	XI	22-Isoallospirostan-3,11β-diol	63	19
$C_{27}H_{42}O_5$				
22-Isoallospirostan-3β,12β-diol-11-one	XII	22-Isoallospirostan-3β,11β,12β-triol[1]	94	20
$C_{27}H_{40}O_4$				
2α,3α-Oxido-22-isoallospirostan-12-one	XIII	22-Isoallospirostan-3α,12-diol	95	21
22-Isoallospirostan-3,12-dione (hecogenone)	XIV	22-Isoallospirostan-3β,12-diol[15]	....	21
22-Isoallospirost-9(11)-en-3β-ol-12-one	XV	22-Isoallospirost-9(11)-en-3β,12-diol[1]	86	20

C₂₇H₄₂O₄	22-Isoallospirostan-3β-ol-12-one (hecogenin)	XVI	22-Isoallospirostar-3β,12β-diol (rockogenin)	22
			22-Isoallospirostar-3β,12α-diol	23
			Rockogenin	23
	Saponin acetate	XVII	Rockogenin[1] [24]	

[1] Reduction carried out in tetrahydrofuran solution.

[2] Isolated as 3,20-diacetate.

[3] J. Romo, G. Stork, G. Rosenkranz, and C. Djerassi, *J. Am. Chem. Soc.*, 74, 2918 (1952).

[4] Isolated as 3,20,21-triacetate.

[5] C. Djerassi, G. Rosenkranz, J. Pataki, and S. Kaufmann, *J. Biol. Chem.*, 194, 115 (1952).

[6] Mixture of $\Delta^{17,20}$ and $\Delta^{20,21}$ enol ethers.

[7] Isolated after acid hydrolysis of reduction mixture.

[8] B. Belleau and T. F. Gallagher, *J. Am. Chem. Soc.*, 74, 2816 (1952).

[9] L. H. Sarett, M. Feurer, and K. Folkers, *ibid.*, 73, 1777 (1951).

[10] Isolated as 20β,21-diacetoxy-Δ^4-pregnen-11β,17α-diol-3-one after acid hydrolysis and acetylation.

[11] P. L. Julian, E. W. Meyer, W. J. Karpel, and W. Cole, *J. Am. Chem. Soc.*, 73, 1982 (1951).

[12] Reduction carried out in tetrahydrofuran-di-*n*-butyl ether mixture.

[13] S. Bernstein, R. M. Antonucci, and M. D. Heller, U. S. Pat. 2,622,081 (December 16, 1952).

[14] L. F. Fieser and S. Rajagopalan, *J. Am. Chem. Soc.*, 73, 118 (1951).

[15] Reduction carried out in tetrahydrofuran-ether mixture.

[16] C. Djerassi, E. Batres, J. Romo, and G. Rosenkranz, *J. Am. Chem. Soc.*, 74, 3634 (1952).

[17] Isolated as pregnan-3α,11β-diol-20-one after treatment with *p*-toluenesulfonic acid and acetone.

[18] G. Rosenkranz, J. Pataki, and C. Djerassi, *J. Org. Chem.*, 17, 290 (1952).

[19] C. Djerassi, E. Batres, M. Velasco, and G. Rosenkranz, *J. Am. Chem. Soc.*, 74, 1712 (1952).

[20] C. Djerassi, H. Martinez, and G. Rosenkranz, *J. Org. Chem.*, 16, 1278 (1951).

[21] N. L. Wendler, H. L. Slates, and M. Tishler, *J. Am. Chem. Soc.*, 74, 4894 (1952).

[22] R. Hirschmann, C. S. Snoddy, Jr., and N. L. Wendler, *ibid.*, 74, 2693 (1952).

[23] E. S. Rothman, M. E. Wall, and C. R. Eddy, *ibid.*, 74, 4013 (1952).

[24] Isolated after hydrolysis of reduction product with ethanolic hydrochloric acid.

CHART TO TABLE XX

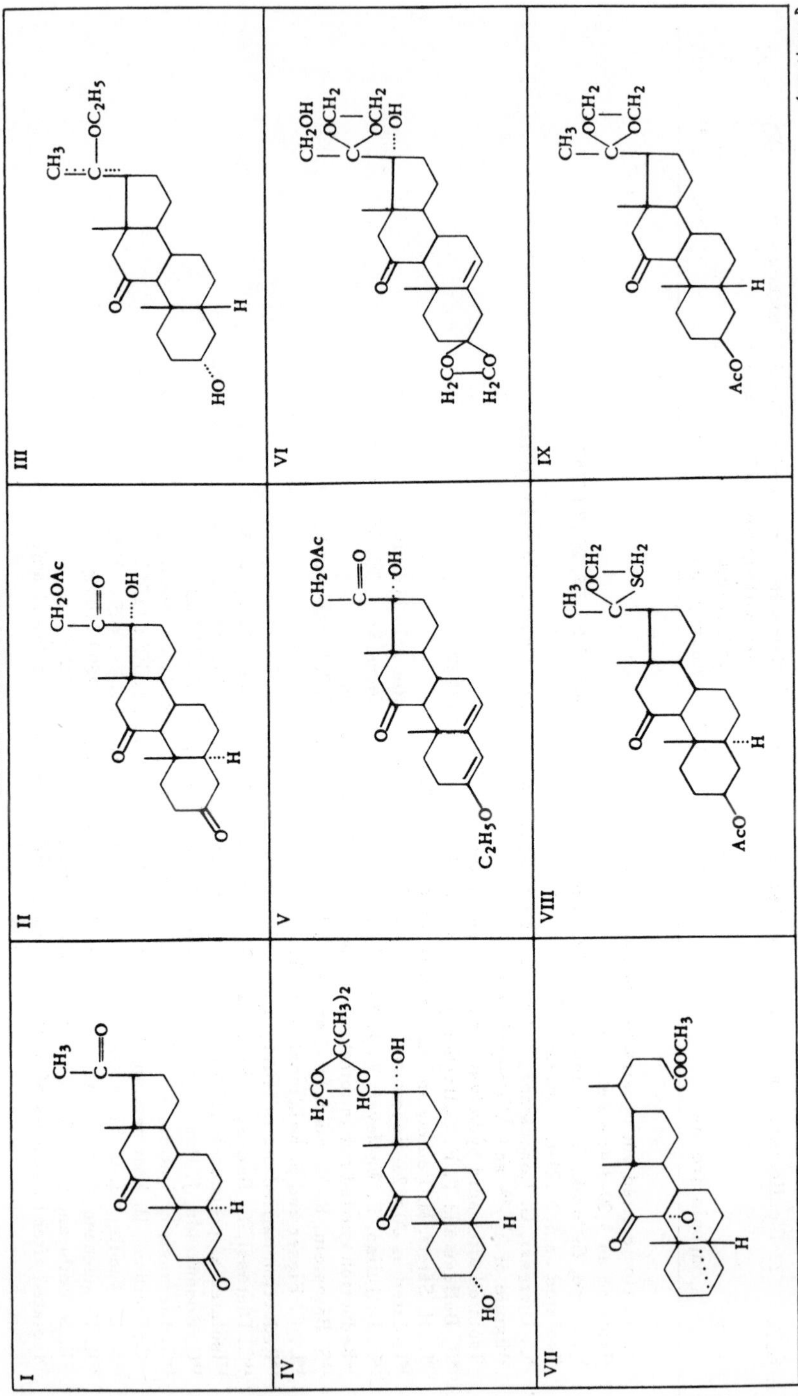

(continued)

CHART TO TABLE XX (continued)

The LAH reduction of 3-methoxycholesta-3,5-dien-7-one (CCXXXVI), followed by the hydrolysis of the reduction mixture with aqueous tartaric acid, yields 60% of cholesta-4,6-dien-3-one. The initial product of the reduction is probably a mixture of the two epimeric 7-ols. As a result of the hydrolysis anionotropic rearrangement takes place to position 3 followed by the loss of methanol to give the dienone (260).

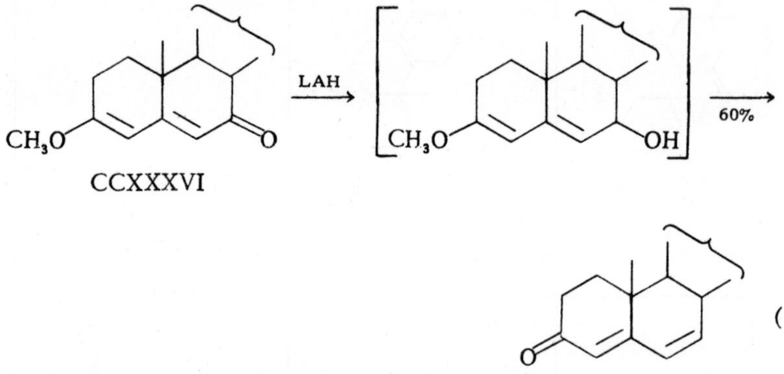

(7-163)

The LAH reduction of steroid ring C ketones, i.e., 11- and 12-keto steroids, is summarized in Table XX.

The carbonyl group at C_{11} is resistant to catalytic hydrogenation in neutral medium but is reduced to the 11β-hydroxy steroid over platinum in acetic acid solution. Reduction with LAH also yields exclusively the hindered 11β-ol (261).

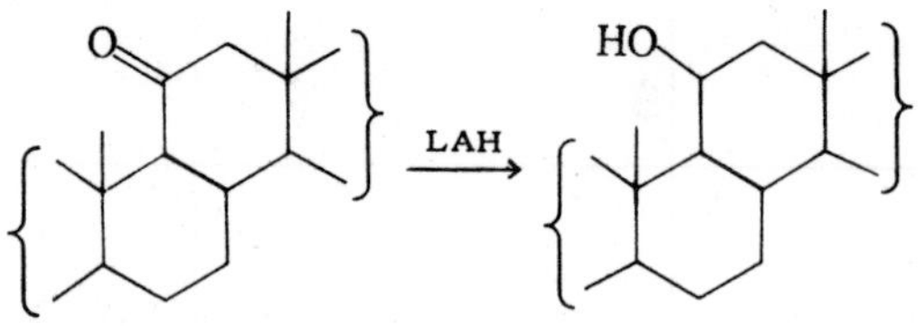

(7-164)

The stereospecific course of the reduction is indicative of attack from the rear to open the rear member of the double bond. Fieser (262) has pointed out that at position 11 both the extra and intraradial effects operate to make the rear side (α) the more accessible to attack. The presence of a 12β-hydroxy group does not affect the stereochemical course of the reaction (263). Reduction of the 11-keto group with sodium in propanol yields the 11α-hydroxy derivative which is readily acetylatable in contrast to the 11β-ol (264).

$$(7\text{-}165)$$

The LAH reduction of 12-keto steroids yields a 12-hydroxy derivative which, in the case of the reduction of hecogenin (CCXXXIX), has been shown to be a mixture of C_{12}-epimeric diols (265).

$$(7\text{-}166)$$

In only one case has the reduction of a 12-keto steroid with α,β-unsaturation been reported (263). However, the configuration of the resultant 12-ol has not been demonstrated.

CCXL   (7-167)

The LAH reduction of various steroid ring D ketones, i.e., 16- and 17-keto steroids, is summarized in Table XXI.

The reduction of *trans*-16-equilenone (CCXLI) yields a 16-hydroxy-*trans*-equilenane, m.p. 183.5-184.5°.

CCXLI   (7-168)

The reduction of 14,15-dehydro-16-equilenone (CCXLII) yields 16-hydroxy-14,15-dehydroequilenane (CCXLIII), which is catalytically reduced over palladium-on-charcoal to an isomeric 16-hydroxy-*trans*-equilenane, m.p. 123.5°-124° (266).

CCXLII   CCXLIII

(7-169)

The 16-keto steroids apparently give essentially a single stereoisomeric alcohol with LAH but with the favored configuration reversed by the presence of a 14,15-double bond.

The LAH reduction of 3β,26-diacetoxycholest-4-en-16,22-dione (CCXLIV) yields the corresponding 3β,16,22,26-tetrol. The reduction of 3β,26-diacetoxycholesta-5,17(20)-dien-16,22-dione (CCXLV) similarly yields the corresponding tetrol. Since hydrogenation of the 17(20)-bond was not carried out and no configuration was assigned to the 16-ol, it is not possible to determine whether the 17(20)-double bond affects the reduction of the 16-one (267).

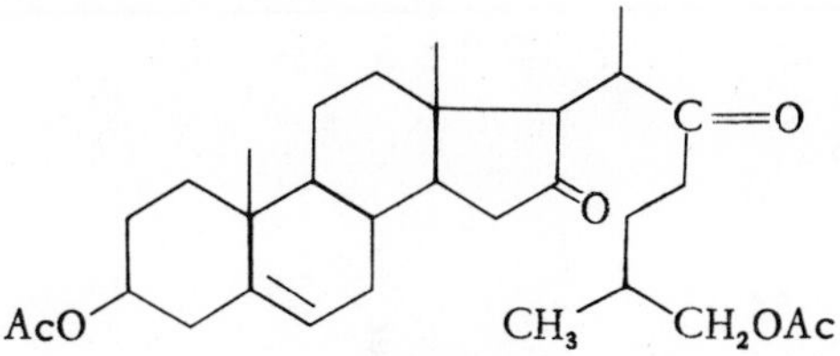

AcO — C=O — O — CH$_3$ — CH$_2$OAc

CCXLIV

AcO — C=O — O — CH$_3$ — CH$_2$OAc

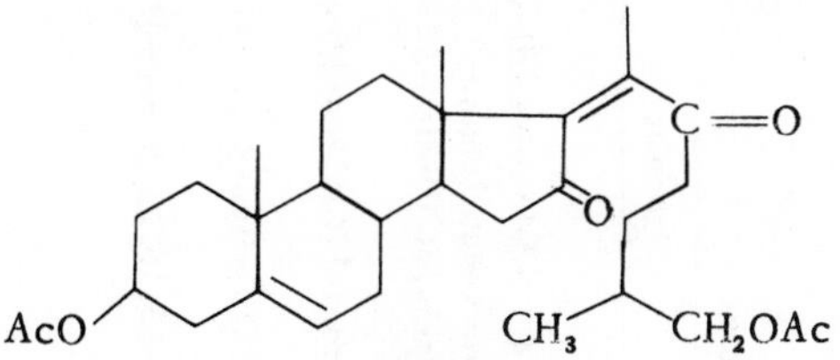

CCXLV

The LAH reduction of 22,26-oxidocholest-17(20)-en-3β,22-diol-16-one (CCXLVI) yields 22-isoallospirost-17(20)-en-3β-ol (CCXLVII) (268). The analogous cholesta-5,17(20)-diene similarly yields 22-isospirosta-5,17(20)-dien-3β-ol (267). The expected initial products, 22,26-oxidocholest-17(20)-en- and 5,17(20)-dien-3β,16,22-triol, respectively, apparently dehydrate very readily.

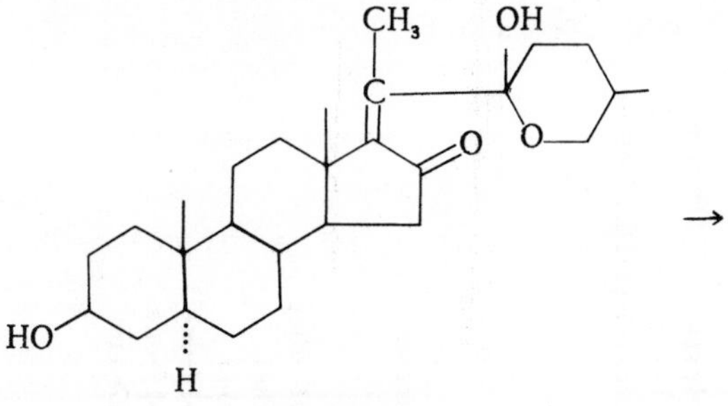

CH$_3$ OH   C — O — O — HO — H

CCXLVI

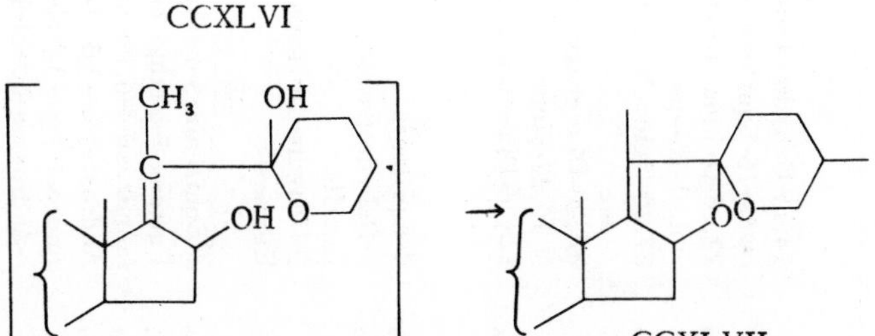

→

[CH$_3$ OH   C — OH   O —] → O — O   (7-170)

CCXLVII

The LAH reduction of 17-ketosteroids with the normal configuration at C$_{14}$ affords largely or exclusively the β-oriented empimeride.

TABLE XXI

LAH Reduction of Steroid Ring D Ketones

	Ketone	No.	Product	% Yield	Ref.
	A. 16-Keto Steroids				
$C_{18}H_{16}O$	14,15-Dehydro-16-equilenone	I	16-Hydroxy-14,15-dehydroequilenane[1]	97	2
$C_{18}H_{18}O$	trans-16-Equilenone	II	16-Hydroxy-trans-equilenane	95	2
$C_{27}H_{40}O_4$	22,26-Oxidocholesta-5,17(20)-dien-3β,22-diol-16-one	III	22-Isospirosta-5,17(20)-dien-3β-ol[3]	82	4
$C_{27}H_{42}O_4$	22,26-Oxidocholest-17(20)-en-3β,22-diol-16-one	IV	22-Isoallospirost-17(20)-en-3β-ol[3]	67–73	5
$C_{31}H_{44}O_6$	3β,26-Diacetoxycholesta-5,17(20)-dien-16,22-dione	V	Cholesta-5,17(20)-dien-3β,16,22,26-tetrol[3]	52[6]	4
$C_{31}H_{46}O_6$	3β,26-Diacetoxycholest-5-en-16,22-dione	VI	Cholest-5-en-3β,16,22,26-tetrol[3]	76	4
	B. 17-Keto Steroids				
$C_{18}H_{18}O_2$	d-Equilenin	VII	No reduction	...	7
$C_{18}H_{20}O_2$	6-Dehydroestrone	VIII	6-Dehydroestradiol-17β	...	8
	Equilin	IX	17-Dihydroequilin-17β	...	9
$C_{18}H_{22}O_2$	9-Dehydro-14-isoestrone	X	"β",9-Dehydro-14-isoestradiol	73	10
	Estrone	XI	Estradiol-17β	90–95	11–13
$C_{19}H_{20}O_2$	d-Equilenin 3-methyl ether	XII	Dihydroequilenin-17β-3-methyl ether	97	7
$C_{19}H_{24}O_2$	Estrone 3-methyl ether	XIII	Estradiol-17β-3-methyl ether	...	11
$C_{19}H_{26}O_2$	i-Androstan-6,17-dione	XIV	epi-i-Androstan-6,17β-diol	89	15
$C_{19}H_{28}O_2$	Androst-5-en-3β-ol-17-one[16]	XV	Androst-5-en-3β,17β-diol	...	12,13
	Androst-7-en-3β-ol-17-one	XVI	Androst-7-en-3β,17β-diol[3]	80	17
	i-Androstan-6α-ol-17-one	XVII	3,5-Cycloandrostan-6α,17β-diol (i-androstanediol)	50	15
$C_{20}H_{20}O_3$	Equilenin acetate	XVIII	17-Dihydroequilenin-17β[3]	...	8

Formula	Ketone		Product	Yield	Ref.
$C_{20}H_{22}O_3$	6-Dehydroestrone acetate	XIX	6-Dehydroestradiol	84	18
$C_{20}H_{24}O_3$	Estrone acetate	XX	Estradiol-17β	"almost quant."	19,20
$C_{20}H_{30}O_2$	Androst-5-en-3β-ol-17-one 3-methyl ether	XXI	Androst-5-en-3β,17-diol 3-methyl ether	95	21
$C_{21}H_{22}O_3$	1-Methylequilenin acetate	XXII	1-Methyl-17-dihydroequilenin-17β	....	11
$C_{21}H_{24}O_3$	1-Methyl-6-dehydroestrone acetate	XXIII	1-Methyl-6-dehydroestradiol	88	22
$C_{21}H_{26}O_3$	Estrone propionate	XX	Estradiol-17β	"almost quant."	19,20
$C_{21}H_{28}O_2$	3-Ethoxyandrosta-3,5,11-trien-17-one	XXIV	3-Ethoxyandrosta-3,5,11-trien-17β-ol	29[23]	24
$C_{21}H_{30}O_2$	3-Ethoxyandrosta-3,5-dien-17-one	XXV	3-Ethoxyandrosta-3,5-dien-17β-ol	"almost quant."	{12,13, 25-27}
$C_{21}H_{30}O_2S$	3-(β-Hydroxythioethoxy)androsta-3,5-dien-17-one	XXVI	3-(β-Hydroxythioethoxy)androsta-3,5-dien-17β-ol	66	28-29
$C_{21}H_{30}O_3$	3β-Acetoxyandrost-5-en-17-one[30]	XXVII	3β-Acetoxyandrost-5-en-17-ol	80[31]	21
$C_{21}H_{30}O_4$	3β-Acetoxy-5,6α-oxidoandrostan-17-one	XXVIII	Androstan-3β,5,17β-triol[32]	85	33
$C_{21}H_{32}O_3$	3β-Acetoxyandrostan-17-one	XXIX	Androstan-3β,17β-diol	....[34]	35
$C_{23}H_{30}O_3$	Estrone trimethylacetate	XX	Estradiol-17β	100	36
$C_{23}H_{34}O_3$	Dehydroepiandrosterone trimethylacetate	XXX	3-Trimethylacetoxy-5-androstene-17-ol	83	37
$C_{24}H_{36}O_3$	Dehydroepiandrosterone-3-(2'-tetrahydropyranyl)ether	XXXI	3β-(2'-Tetrahydropyranyloxy)androst-5-en-17β-ol	96	38,39
$C_{25}H_{36}O_2$	3-Cyclohexyloxyandrosta-3,5-dien-17-one	XXXII	3-Cyclohexyloxyandrosta-3,5-dien-17β-ol	"almost quant."	12,13
$C_{26}H_{32}OS$	3-Thiobenzyloxyandrosta-3,5-dien-17-one	XXXIII	3-Thiobenzyloxyandrosta-3,5-dien-17β-ol	66	28,29
$C_{26}H_{32}O_2$	3-Benzyloxyandrosta-3,5-dien-17-one	XXXII	3-Benzyloxyandrosta-3,5-dien-17β-ol	"almost quant."	12,13
$C_{26}H_{32}O_2S$	Androst-4-en-3,17-dione 3-benzylsulfoxidoenol ether	XXXIV	3-Thiobenzyloxyandrosta-3,5-dien-17β-ol[3]	57	40

CHART TO TABLE XXI

I

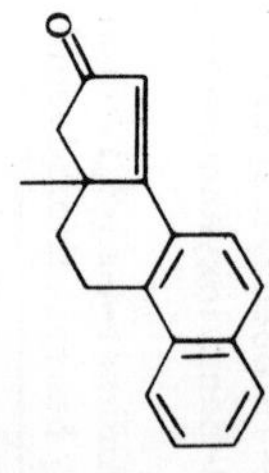

II

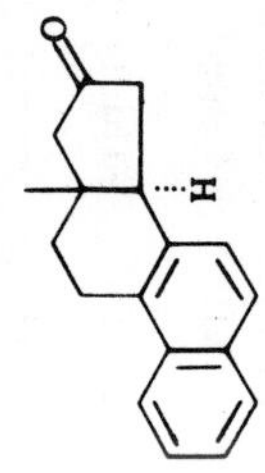

III

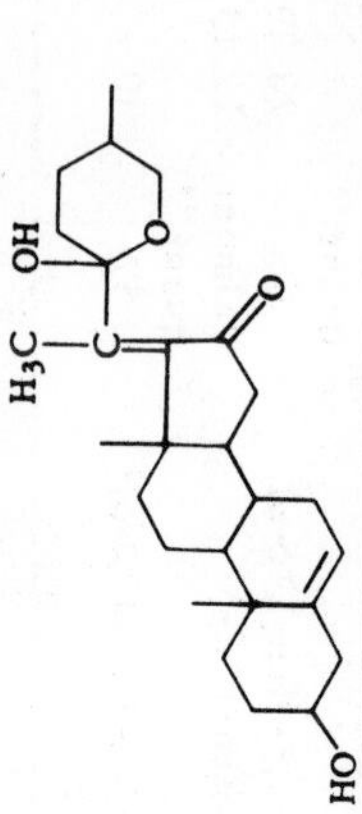

IV

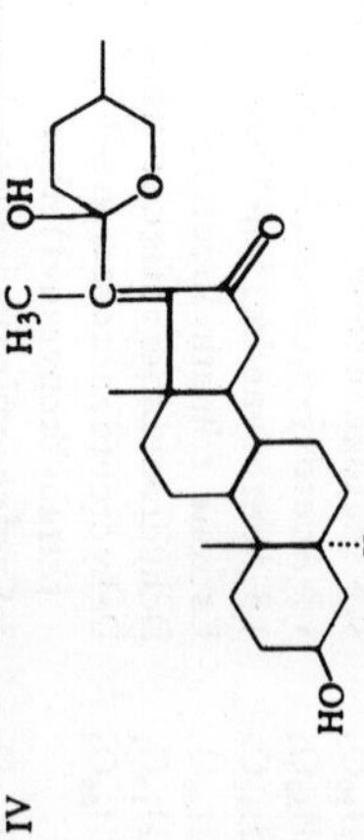

V

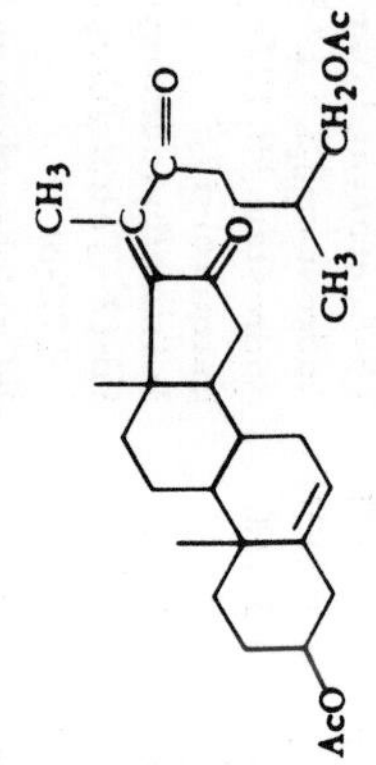

VI

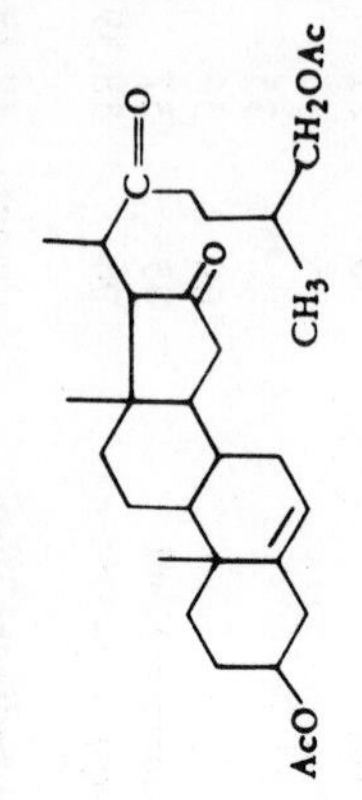

VII

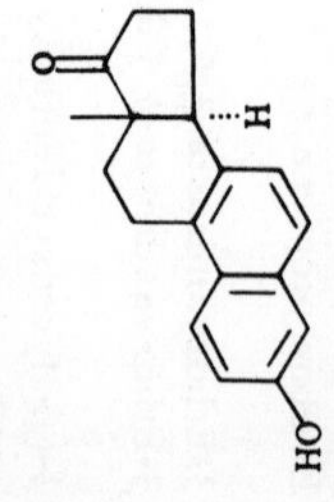

VIII

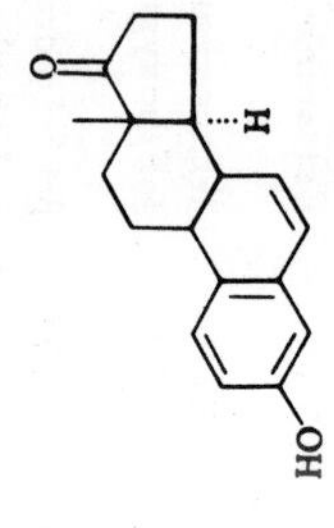

IX

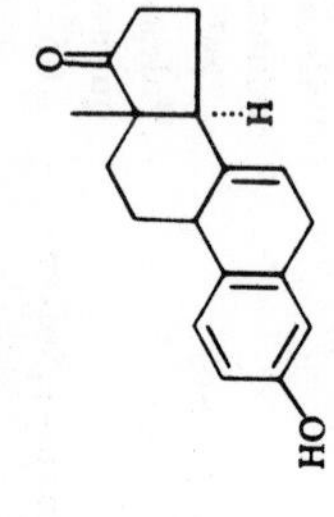

X

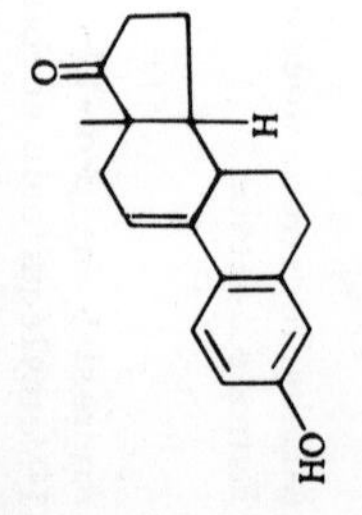

XI

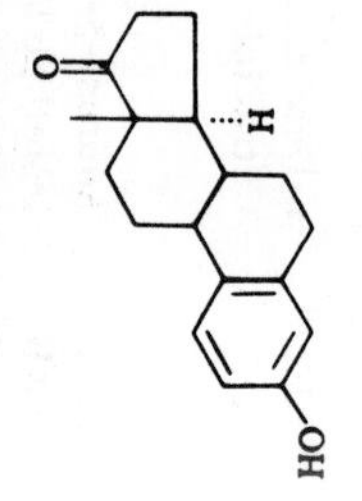

XII

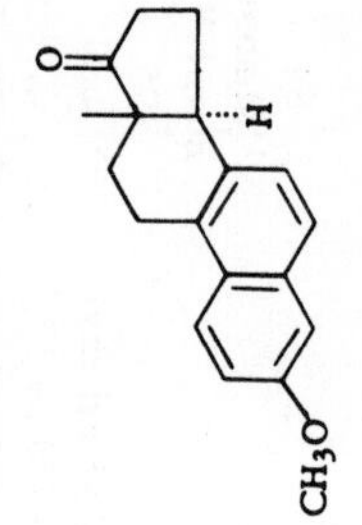

(continued)

CHART TO TABLE XXI (continued)

(continued)

CHART TO TABLE XXI (*continued*)

References—Table XXI

[1] Reduction carried out in a benzene-ether mixture.

[2] A. L. Wilds, J. A. Johnson, Jr., and R. E. Sutton, *J. Am. Chem. Soc.*, 72, 5524 (1950).

[3] Reduction carried out in tetrahydrofuran.

[4] A. Sandoval, J. Romo, G. Rosenkranz, S. Kaufmann, and C. Djerassi, *J. Am. Chem. Soc.*, 73, 3820 (1951).

[5] A. L. Nussbaum, A. Sandoval, G. Rosenkranz, and C. Djerassi, *J. Org. Chem.*, 17, 426 (1952).

[6] Isolated as tetraacetate.

[7] W. E. Bachmann and A. S. Dreiding, *J. Am. Chem. Soc.*, 72, 1323 (1950).

[8] C. Djerassi, G. Rosenkranz, J. Romo, S. Kaufmann, and J. Pataki, *ibid.*, 72, 4534 (1950).

[9] J. Carol, E. O. Haenni, and D. Banes, unpublished work, through *J. Biol. Chem.*, 185, 267 (1950).

[10] D. Banes, J. Carol, and E. O. Haenni, *ibid.*, 187, 557 (1950).

[11] A. C. Ott and M. F. Murray, *Abstracts of Papers*, 113th Meeting American Chemical Society, Chicago, Ill., April 1948, p. 17K.

[12] Syntex, S. A., Brit. Pat. 646,979 (November 29,1950); *Chem. Abstracts*, 45, 8050 (1951).

[13] G. Rosenkranz and S. Kaufmann, U. S. Pat. 2,588,294 (March 4, 1952); *Chem. Abstracts*, 46, 9628 (1952).

[14] E. B. Hershberg, unpublished work, through L. F. Fieser and M. Fieser, "Natural Products Related to Phenanthrene," 3rd Edition, Reinhold Publishing Corp., New York, 1949, p. 327.

[15] A. F. Wagner, N. E. Wolff, and E. S. Wallis, *J. Org. Chem.*, 17, 529 (1952).

[16] Referred to as dehydroisoandrosterone. Fieser and Fieser, ref. 14, p. 364, have proposed dehydroepiandrosterone.

[17] F. Neumann, G. Rosenkranz, J. Romo and C. Djerassi, *J. Am. Chem. Soc.*, 73, 5478 (1951).

[18] S. Kaufmann, S. Pataki, G. Rosenkranz, J. Romo, and C. Djerassi, *ibid.*, 72, 4531 (1950).

[19] S. Kaufmann and G. Rosenkranz, U. S. Pat. 2,555,344 (June 5, 1951).

[20] Syntex, S. A., Brit. Pat. 661,805 (November 28, 1951).

[21] G. Papineau-Couture, E. M. Richardson, and G. A. Grant, *Can. J. Research*, 27B, 902 (1949).

[22] C. Djerassi, G. Rosenkranz, J. Romo, J. Pataki, and S. Kaufmann, *J. Am. Chem. Soc.*, 72, 4540 (1950).

[23] Isolated as 11-dehydrotestosterone acetate after acid hydrolysis and acetylation.

[24] C. Meystre and A. Wettstein, *Helv. Chim. Acta*, 32, 1978 (1949).

[25] Ciba, Akt., Swiss Pat. 274,087 (June 1, 1951).

[26] Ciba Ltd., Brit. Pat. 665,337 (January 23, 1952).

[27] K. Miescher and C. Meystre, U. S. Pat. 2,623,885 (December 30, 1952).

[28] G. Rosenkranz, S. Kaufmann, and J. Romo, *J. Am. Chem. Soc.*, 71, 3689 (1949); U. S. Pat. 2,609,378 (September 2, 1952).

[29] Syntex, S. A., Brit. Pat. 662,400 (December 5, 1951).

[30] Inverse addition of one-quarter mole of LAH.

[31] Isolated as 17-benzoate.

[32] Reduction carried out in tetrahydrofuran-ether mixture.

[33] S. A. Julia, P. A. Plattner, and H. Heusser, *Helv. Chim. Acta*, 35, 665 (1952).

[34] Isolated as diacetate.

[35]D. K. Patel, V. Petrow, R. Royer, and I. A. Stuart-Webb, *J. Chem. Soc.*, *1952*, 161.

[36]J. H. Biel, *J. Am. Chem. Soc.*, *73*, 847 (1951).

[37]F. Šorm and M. Vraný, unpublished work, through J. Rudinger, M. Ferles and M. Protiva, *Chem. Listy*, *45*, 346 (1951).

[38]A. C. Ott, M. F. Murray, and R. L. Pederson, *J. Am. Chem. Soc.*, 74, 1239 (1952).

[39]A. C. Ott and M. F. Murray, U. S. Pat. 2,625,556 (January 13, 1953).

[40]J. Romo, M. Romero, C. Djerassi, and G. Rosenkranz, *J. Am. Chem. Soc.*, *73*, 1528 (1951).

$$(7\text{-}171)$$

CCXLVIII

Apparently the attack of the aluminohydride ion proceeds more readily from the α or rear face to preferentially open the rear member of the double bond (262,269). The rule of rear attack at C_{17} applies to a wide variety of reagents wherein products are formed in which the hydroxyl group is oriented to the front (β-OH). Thus, in addition to LAH reduction, hydrogenation, the addition of Grignard reagents and the addition of potassium acetylide yield the 17β-ol (262,270,271). It is of interest to note that in the reaction of 17-ketosteroids with the ethyl Grignard reagent the 17α-ethyl-17β-ol is accompanied by the 17β-ol arising from direct reduction of the 17-keto group. With n-propylmagnesium iodide reduction of the carbonyl group is the main reaction, while the methyl and allyl Grignard reagents yield the 17α-alkyl-17β-ol (271).

Ott and Murray reported that the LAH reduction of estrone (CCXLIX : R = H) affords natural estradiol in excellent yield (272).

$$(7\text{-}172)$$

CCXLIX

Although the product is the so-called α-estradiol its production in the LAH reduction is indicative of the 17β configuration. The same product, estradiol-17β, is obtained by the LAH reduction of estrone esters (R = CH$_3$CO, CH$_3$CH$_2$CO, (CH$_3$)$_3$CCO) while the dehydroestradiol-17β containing ring B unsaturation is obtained from the corresponding dehydroestrone and its esters. In contrast, the reduction of estrone and its esters with aluminum isopropoxide yields a mixture of the 17α- and 17β-epimers (272) while catalytic hydrogenation over a nickel-aluminum alloy yields a mixture in which the 17β-isomer is the predominant form (274).

Bachmann and Dreiding (275) reported that although attempts to reduce d-equilenin with LAH in refluxing ether resulted in the recovery of the starting material, the reduction of d-equilenin methyl ether (CCL) gives the methyl ether of the so-called α-dihydroequilenin which actually contains the 17-hydroxyl group in the β-configuration (276).

CCL   (7-173)

The 17β-ol is also obtained by catalytic hydrogenation and is the predominant product in aluminum isopropoxide reduction. The LAH reduction of equilenin acetate analogously yields 17-dihydroequilenin-17β (277).

The LAH reduction of equilin (CCLI) is reported to yield α-dihydroequilin which should contain the 17β-hydroxy group (278).

CCLI   (7-174)

The reduction of CCLI with aluminum isopropoxide yields a mixture of the 17α- and 17β-epimers.

The LAH reduction of the 3-enol ethers of androst-4-en-3,17-dione (CCLII) yields the 3-enol ethers of androst-4-en-17β-ol-3-one which can be hydrolyzed with dilute mineral acids to testosterone.

CCLII   (7-175)

Testosterone acyl esters are readily produced by the following scheme, starting with dehydroepiandrosterone (CCLIII) (279).

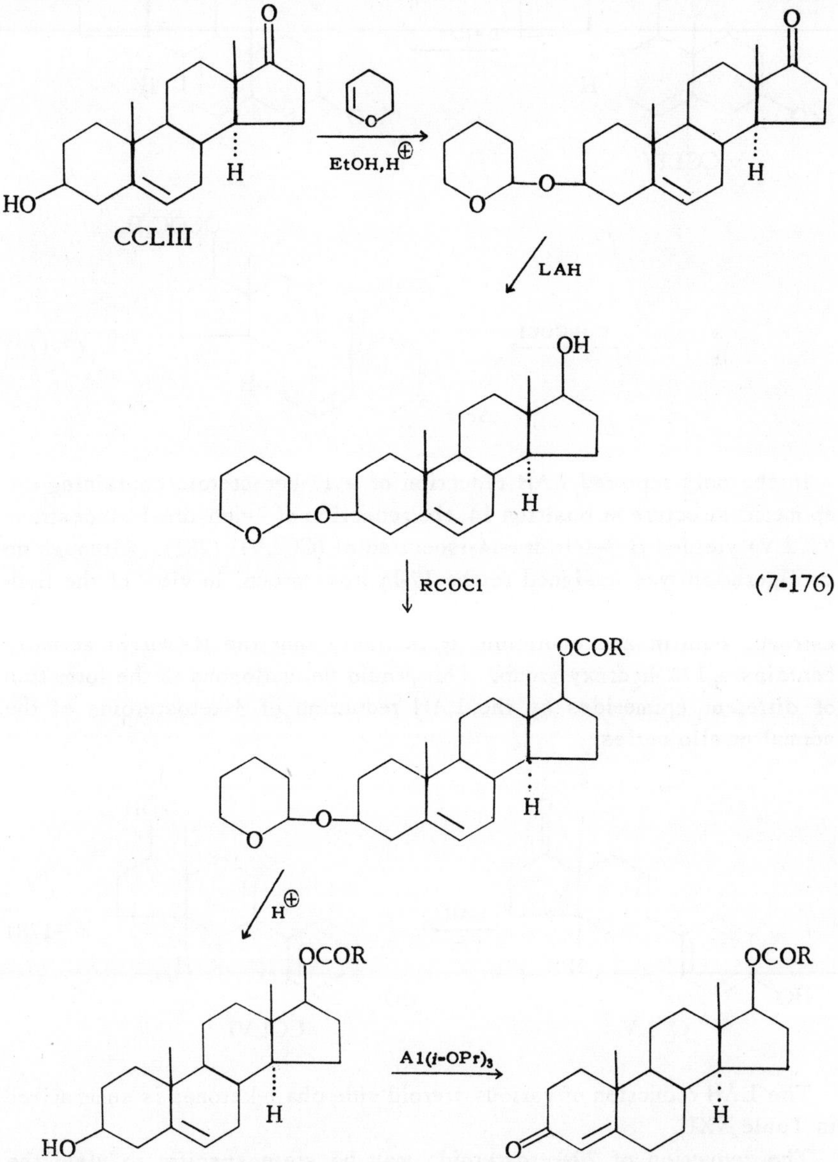

(7-176)

The inverse addition of one-quarter mole of LAH to dehydroepiandrosterone acetate (CCLIV), followed by the benzoylation of the crude reduction product is reported to yield 80% of 3β-acetoxy-17β-benzoxy-5-androstene (280).

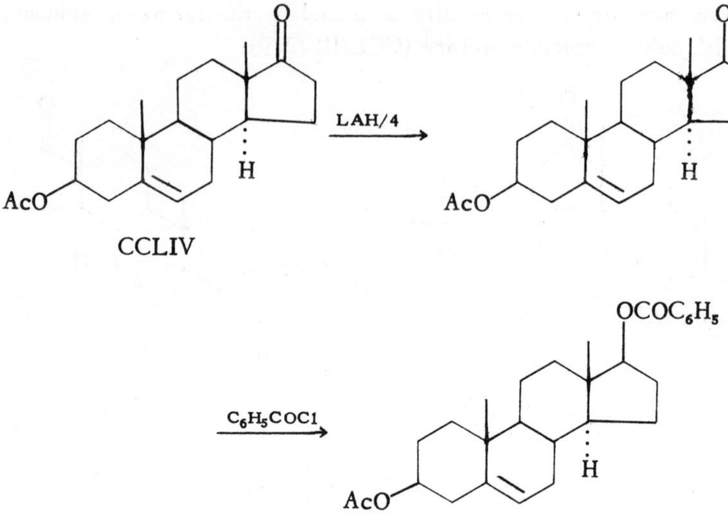

(7-177)

In the only reported LAH reduction of a 17-ketosteroid containing the epimeric structure at position 14, the reduction of 9-dehydro-14-isoestrone (CCLV) yielded β-9-dehydro-14-isoestradiol (CCLVI) (281). Although no configuration was assigned to the 17-hydroxy group, in view of the findings relative to the configuration of the 17-ol group in "α"- and "β"-estrone, equilin and equilenin, it is likely that the β-CCLVI actually contains a 17α-hydroxy group. This would be analogous to the formation of different epimerides by the LAH reduction of 3-ketosteroids of the normal or allo series.

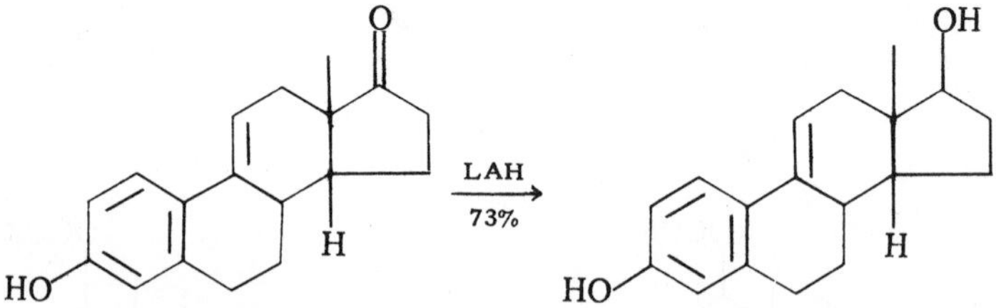

(7-178)

The LAH reduction of various steroid side chain ketones is summarized in Table XXII.

The reduction of 20-ketosteroids may be stereospecific to yield the 20β-ol. However, in many cases a mixture of epimers is formed. The epimeric mixture may contain equivalent amounts of the 20α- and 20β-hydroxy compounds although in most cases the 20β-ol is the predominant form.

$$(7\text{-}179)$$

CCLVII

The effect of α,β-unsaturation, e.g., $\Delta^{16(17)}$-20-ketosteroids, has not been ascertained since the configuration of the 20-hydroxy group was not proved in the only two cases recorded.

The LAH reduction of various 22- and 24-ketosteroids has given the corresponding hydroxy compounds, usually in the form of epimeric mixtures.

Heer and Miescher have reported that a permanganate oxidation of $3\beta,21$-diacetoxy-20-cyanopregna-5,17-diene ($C_{26}H_{35}NO_4$) and $3\beta,21$-diacetoxy-5,6-dibromo-20-cyano-17-pregnene ($C_{26}H_{35}Br_2NO_4$) yields, among other products, a ketol diacetate, $C_{25}H_{36}O_6$, m.p. 172–174°, which is possibly a hydrochrysene derivative. Reduction of the ketol diacetate with LAH followed by acetylation yields a tetrol triacetate, $C_{27}H_{40}O_7$, m.p. 175°, indicating reduction of the ketone to a carbinol. Catalytic hydrogenation of the ketol diacetate in alcohol over platinum oxide yields a tetrol diacetate which on acetylation yields the same tetrol triacetate, m.p. 175°, obtained by acetylation of the LAH reduction product (282).

7.2.1.m. *Protection of the keto group.* Where the retention of a carbonyl group is desired, it can be converted to a form which is not attacked by LAH and then regenerated by appropriate means. By the same means other functional groups can be reduced while the highly reactive ketone group remains intact. Thus, cyclic ketals are formed by reaction with ethylene glycol in the presence of an acid such as p-toluenesulfonic acid and can readily be transformed to the ketone.

CCLVIII $(7\text{-}180)$

Among the ketosteroids, selective protection is possible. Reaction of an unconjugated steroidal carbonyl group such as a 3-, 17-, or 20-keto group with ethylene glycol yields the corresponding ethylene ketal. However, the 11-keto group is not attacked and can subsequently be reduced with

TABLE XXII

LAH Reduction of Steroid Side Chain Ketones

A. 20-Keto Steroids

	Ketone	No.	Product	% Yield	Ref.
$C_{21}H_{30}O_2$	Progesterone	I	4-Pregnen-3,20-diol	...	1
$C_{21}H_{30}O_3$	Allopregnan-3,11,20-trione	II	Allopregnan-3β,11β,20β-triol[2]	74[3]	4
$C_{21}H_{32}O_2$	5-Pregnen-3β-ol-20-one	III	5-Pregnen-3β,20-diol	...	5
			5-Pregnen-3β,20β-diol[6]	68	7
$C_{21}H_{32}O_3$	16,17α-Oxido-5-allopregnan-3β-ol-20-one	IV	5-Allopregnan-3β,17α,20α-triol	...⎫	8
			5-Allopregnan-3β,17α,20β-triol	...⎭	
$C_{22}H_{32}O_2$	16,17-Methylene-5-pregnen-3β-ol-20-one	V	16,17-Methylene-5-pregnen-3β,20β-diol[2]	85	9
$C_{23}H_{32}O_2$	3β-Acetoxyallopregna-7,9(11)-dien-20-one	VI	Allopregna-7,9(11)-dien-3β,20β-diol	71	10
$C_{23}H_{32}O_3$	3β-Acetoxyallopregna-7,16-dien-20-one	VII	Allopregna-7,16-dien-3β,20β-diol	70	10
$C_{23}H_{32}O_4$	3β-Acetoxy-16,17-oxido-5-pregnen-20-one	VIII	5-Pregnen-3β,17,20-triol[11]	...	12
	3β-Acetoxy-14,15β-oxidoallo-16-pregnen-20-one	IX	compound, $C_{21}H_{34}O_3$, m.p. 223-224°	...⎫	8
			compound, $C_{21}H_{32}O_3$, m.p. 174°	...⎭	
$C_{23}H_{32}O_6$	21-Acetoxyallopregnan-17α-ol-3,11,20-trione	X	Allopregnan-3β,11β,17α,20β,21-pentol[2]	39[13]	14
$C_{23}H_{34}O_3$	3β-Acetoxy-5-pregnen-20-one	XI	5-Pregnen-3β,20β-diol	36[3]⎫	15
			5-Pregnen-3β,20α-diol	5[3]⎭	
			5-Pregnen-3β,20β-diol	.[3]⎫	
			1:1 molecular compound of C20-epimers	.[3]⎭	16
	3β-Acetoxy-5-allo-7-pregnen-20-one	XII	5-Allo-7-pregnen-3β,20β-diol	63	10
$C_{23}H_{34}O_4$	3β-Acetoxy-16α,17α-oxido-5-allopregnan-20-one	XIII	5-Allopregnan-3β,17α,20β-triol	40⎫	17
			5-Allopregnan-3β,17α,20α-triol	20 ⎬[5,6]	
			16α,17α-Oxido-5-allopregnan-3β,20β-diol	25⎭	
	3β-Acetoxy-5-pregnen-17α-ol-20-one	XIV	5-Allopregnan-3β,17α,20α-triol[11]	...	8,12
			5-Pregnen-3β,17α,20α-triol	39[3]⎫	18
			5-Pregnen-3β,17α,20β-triol	20[3]⎭	
	3β-Acetoxy-5-allo-7-pregnen-17α-ol-20-one	XV	5-Allo-7-pregnen-3β,17α,20-triol	83	19
$C_{25}H_{34}O_5$	21-Acetoxy-3-ethoxy-16,17-oxidopregna-3,5-dien-20-one	XVI	3-Ethoxypregna-3,5-dien-17α,20α,21-triol	36⎫	21
			3-Ethoxypregna-3,5-dien-17α,20β,21-triol	51 ⎭[6,20]	

Formula	Compound	No.	Product	Yield %	Ref.
$C_{25}H_{34}O_6$	21-Acetoxy-3-ethoxypregna-3,5-dien-17α-ol-11,20-dione	XVII	3-Ethoxypregna-3,5-dien-11β,17α,20β,21-tetrol	....[22]	23
$C_{25}H_{36}O_5$	21-Acetoxy-3-ethoxypregna-3,5-dien-17α-ol-20-one	XVIII	3-Ethoxypregna-3,5-dien-17α,20β,21-triol[6]	43[5,24] 74[24]	21 21
$C_{25}H_{36}O_6$	3β,21-Diacetoxy-16,17α-oxido-5-allopregnan-20-one	XIX	5-Allopregnan-3β,17α,20,21-tetrol	....	8
$C_{28}H_{36}OS$	3-Thiobenzyloxypregna-3,5-dien-20-one	XX	3-Thiobenzyloxypregna-3,5-dien-20β-ol	60	25
$C_{28}H_{36}O_2S$	3-Thiobenzyloxypregna-3,5-dien-17α-ol-20-one	XXI	3-Thiobenzyloxypregna-3,5-dien-17α,20β-diol	62	25
$C_{28}H_{40}O_4S$	5-Pregnen-3-ol-20-one tosylate	XXII	5-Pregnen-20-ol[6,11]	....	26
$C_{30}H_{40}O_4$	3β-Acetoxy-16α-benzyloxy-5-pregnen-20-one	XXIII	16α-Benzyloxy-5-pregnen-3β,20-diol[11]	100	27
$C_{59}H_{62}O_3$	3β,16α-Ditritoxy-5-allopregnan-20-one	XXIV	3β,16α-Ditritoxy-5-allopregnan-20α-ol 3β,16α-Ditritoxy-5-allopregnan-20β-ol	51[28] 49	29

B. 22-Keto Steroids

Formula	Compound	No.	Product	Yield %	Ref.
$C_{28}H_{38}O_2$	22-Phenylbisnor-5-cholen-3β-ol-22-one	XXV	22-Phenylbisnor-5-cholen-3β,22-diol[11] High melting epimer 30 Low melting epimer 70	....	30
$C_{31}H_{44}O_6$	3β,26-Diacetoxycholesta-5,17(20)-dien-16,22-dione	XXVI	Cholesta-5,17(20)-dien-3β,16,22,26-tetrol[2]	52[31]	32
$C_{31}H_{46}O_6$	3β,26-Diacetoxy-5-cholestene-16,22-dione	XXVII	5-Cholesten-3β,16,22,26-tetrol[2]	76	32

C. 24-Keto Steroids

Formula	Compound	No.	Product	Yield %	Ref.
$C_{29}H_{46}O_3$	24-Ketocholesteryl acetate	XXVIII	24-Hydroxycholesterol	96	33
$C_{31}H_{44}O_4$	24-p-Anisyl-5-cholene-3β-ol-24-one	XXIX	24-p-Anisyl-5-cholene-3β,24-diol[11]	71	34
$C_{32}H_{44}O_3$	3β-Acetoxy-24-phenyl-5-cholene-24-one	XXX	24-Phenyl-5-cholene-3β,24-diol[11]	88	35

CHART TO TABLE XXII

I

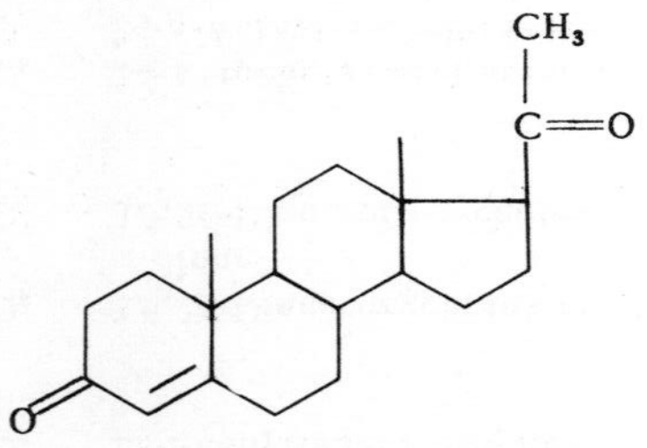

II

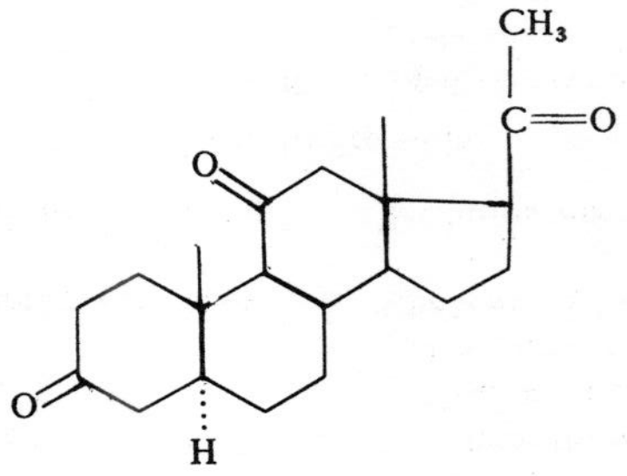

III

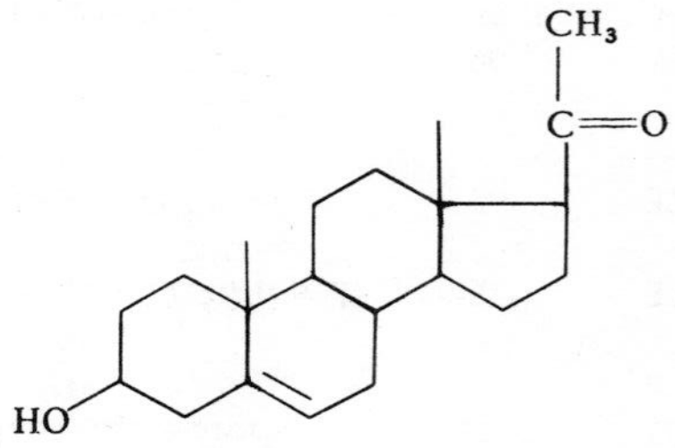

IV

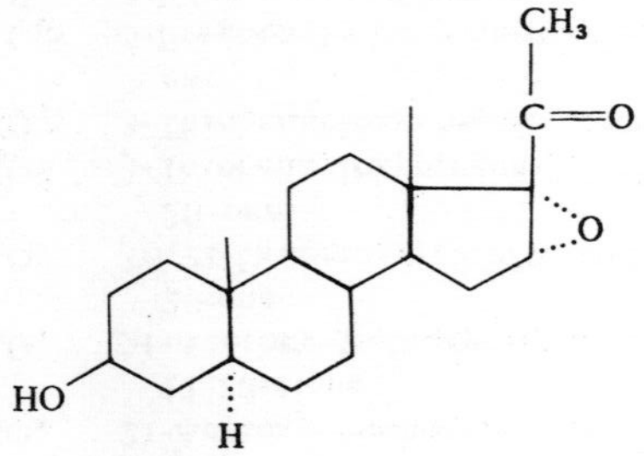

V

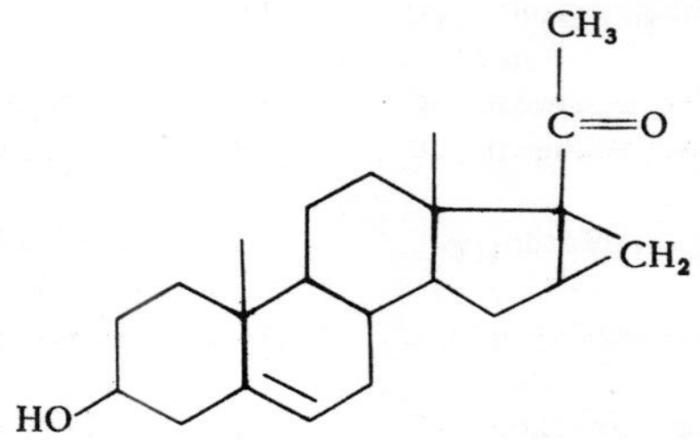

VI

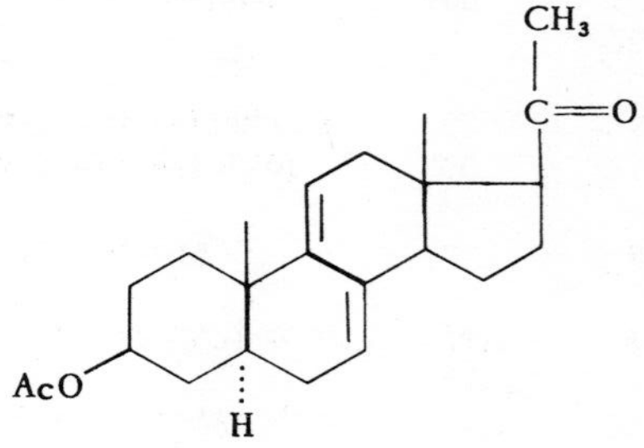

(continued)

CHART TO TABLE XXII (*continued*)

VII

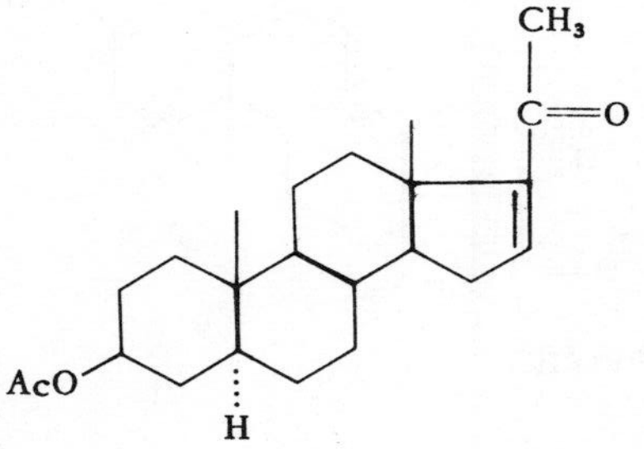

VIII

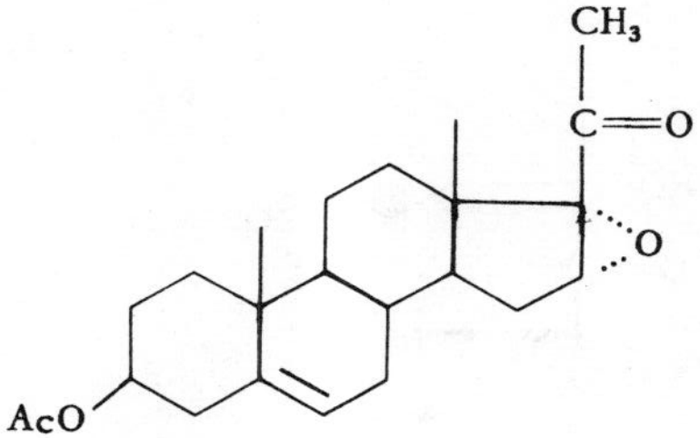

IX

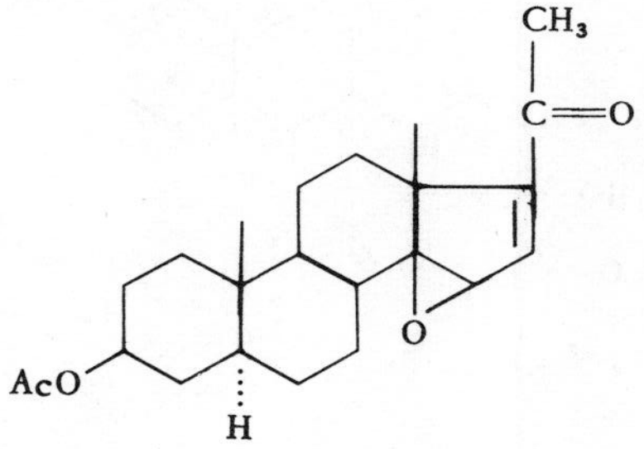

X

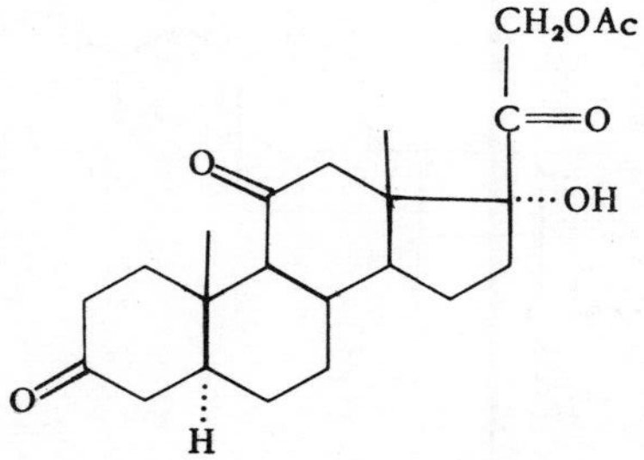

XI

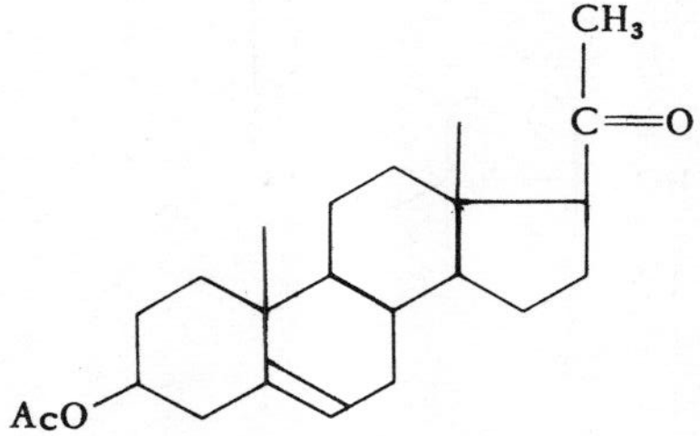

XII

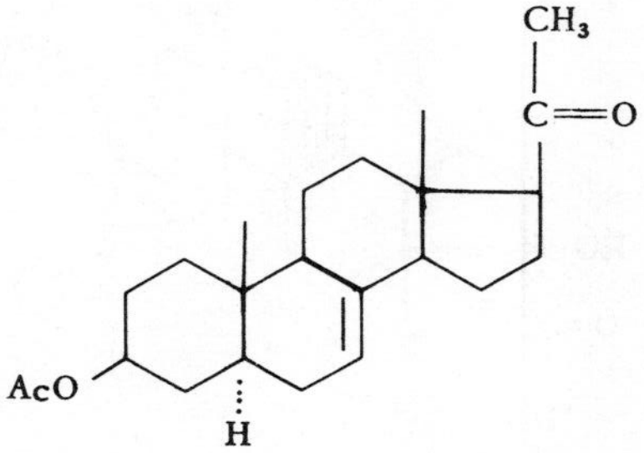

(*continued*)

CHART TO TABLE XXII (*continued*)

XIII

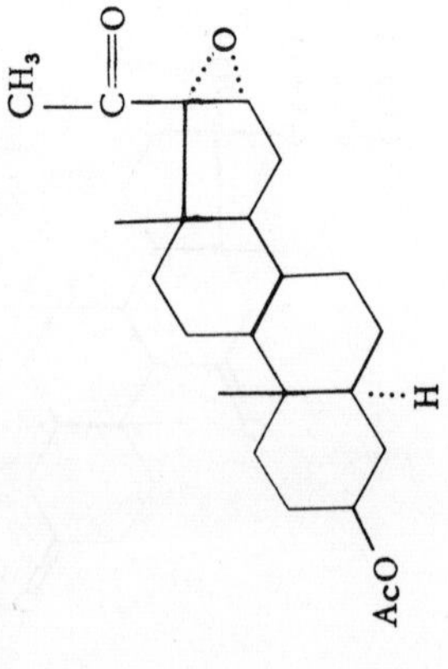

XIV

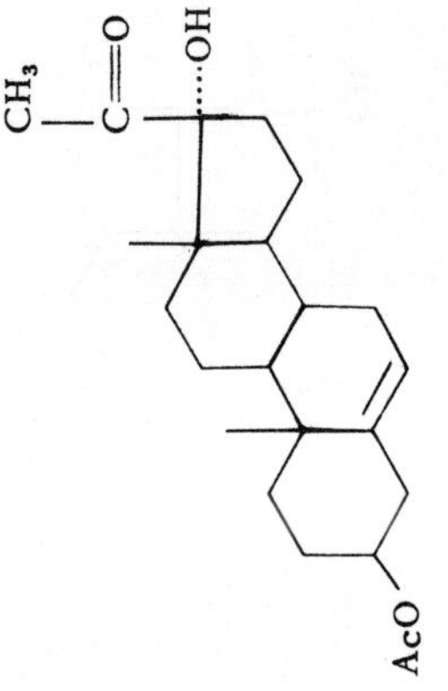

XV

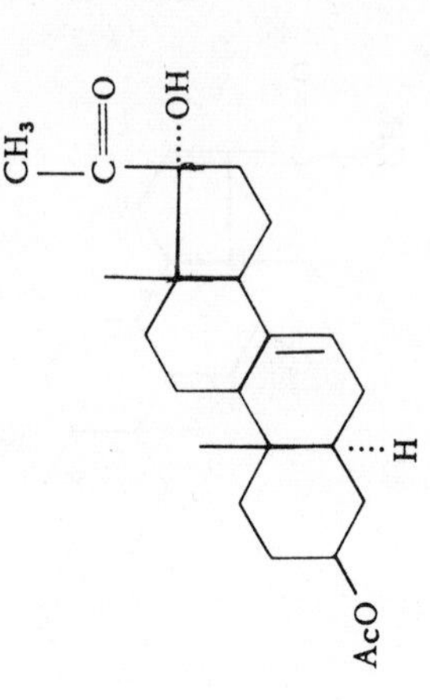

XVI

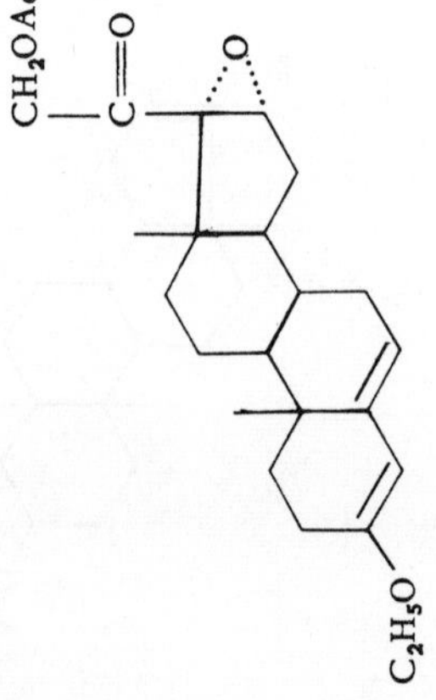

XVII

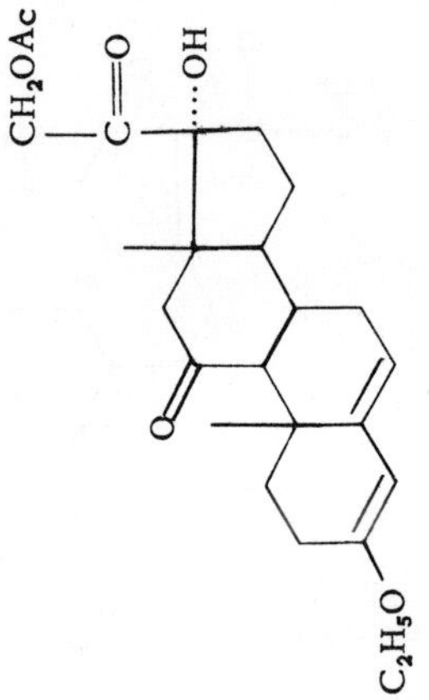

XVIII

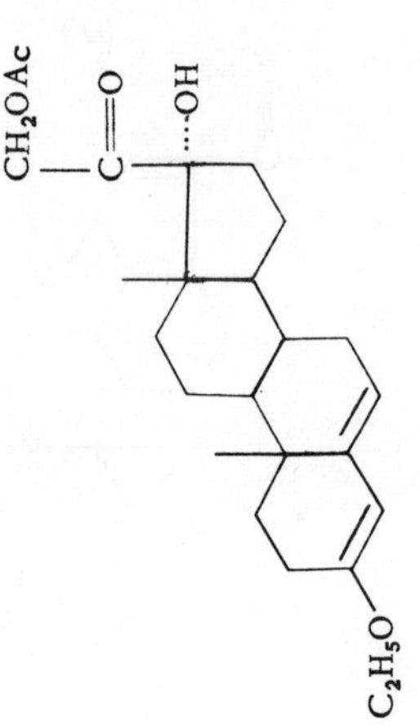

(*continued*)

CHART TO TABLE XXII (continued)

(continued)

CHART TO TABLE XXII (*continued*)

XXV

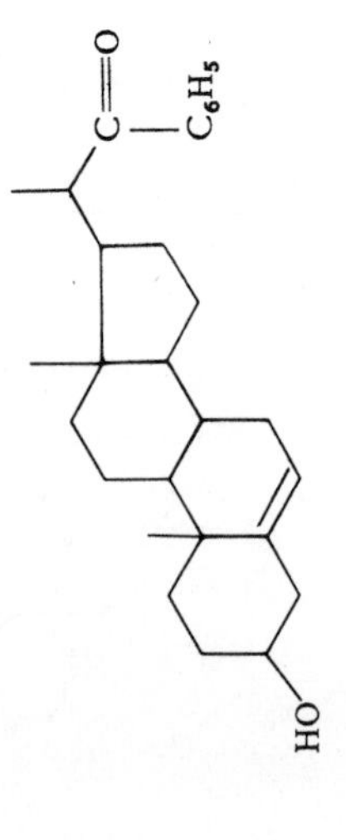

XXVI

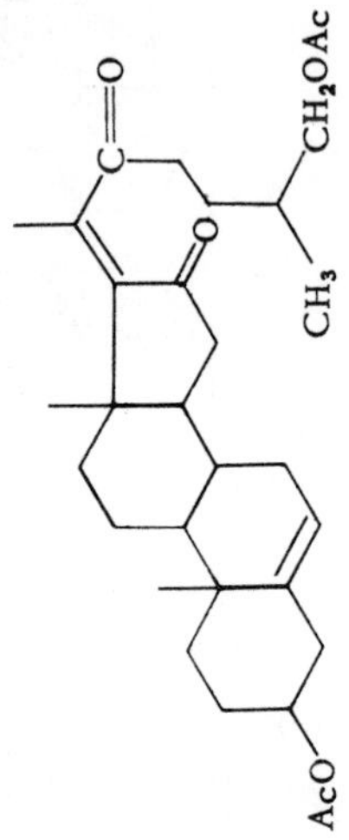

XXVII

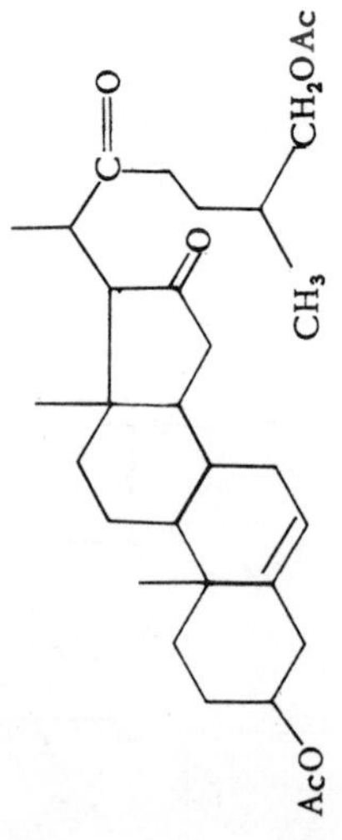

XXVIII

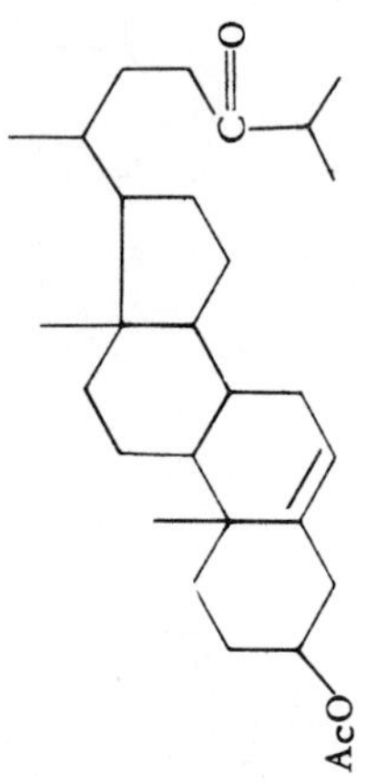

(*continued*)

CHART TO TABLE XXII (*continued*)

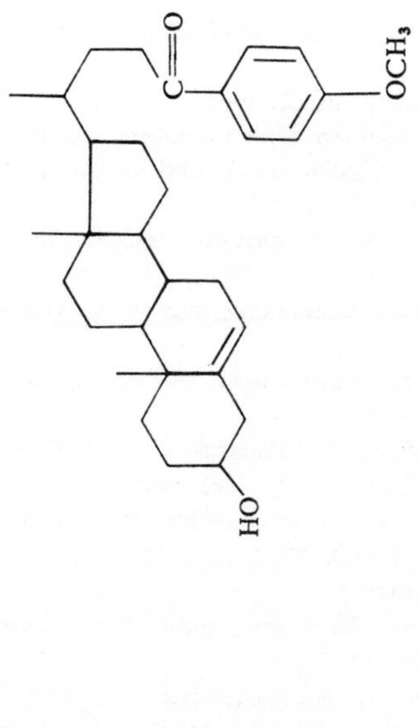

XXX

XXIX

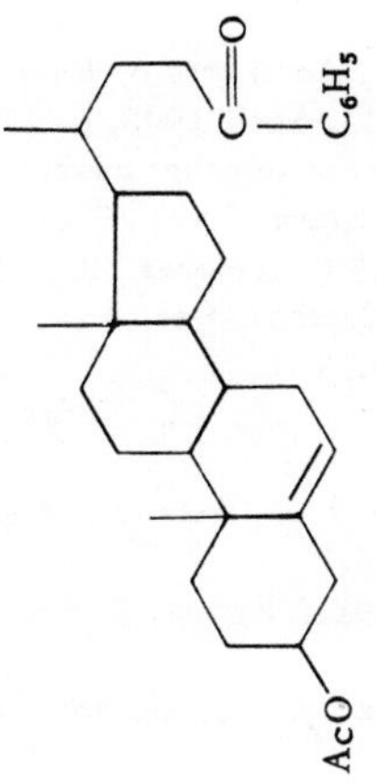

References—Table XXII

[1]H. I. Schlesinger and A. E. Finholt, U. S. Pat. 2,576,311 (November 27, 1951).

[2]Reduction carried out in tetrahydrofuran.

[3]Isolated as diacetate.

[4]J. Romo, G. Stork, G. Rosenkranz, and C. Djerassi, J. Am. Chem. Soc., 74, 2918 (1952).

[5]A. C. Ott and M. F. Murray, Abstracts of Papers, 113th Meeting American Chemical Society, Chicago, Ill., April 1948, p. 17K.

[6]Reduction carried out in benzene-ether mixture.

[7]W. Klyne and E. Miller, J. Chem. Soc., 1950, 1972.

[8]Ciba S. A., Fr. Pat. 994,615 (November 20, 1951); Ciba Ltd., Brit. Pat. 665,254 (January 16, 1952); P. Plattner, Ger. Pat. 834,848 (May 15, 1952); U. S. Pat. 2,599,481 (June 3, 1952).

[9]A. Sandoval, G. Rosenkranz, and C. Djerassi, J. Am. Chem. Soc., 73, 2383 (1951).

[10]J. Romo, G. Rosenkranz, and C. Djerassi, ibid., 73, 5489 (1951).

[11]Mixture of epimers.

[12]P. L. Julian, E. W. Meyer, and I. Ryden, J. Am. Chem. Soc., 71, 756 (1949).

[13]Isolated as triacetate.

[14]C. Djerassi, G. Rosenkranz, J. Pataki, and S. Kaufmann, J. Biol. Chem., 194, 115 (1952).

[15]H. Hirschmann and F. B. Hirschmann, ibid., 184, 259 (1950); H. Hirschmann, M. A. Daus, and F. B. Hirschmann, ibid., 192, 115 (1951).

[16]R. B. Turner and D. M. Voitle, J. Am. Chem. Soc., 73, 2283 (1951).

[17]P. A. Plattner, H. Heusser, and M. Feurer, Helv. Chim. Acta, 31, 2210 (1948).

[18]H. Hirschmann and F. B. Hirschmann, J. Biol. Chem., 187, 137 (1950).

[19]J. Pataki, G. Rosenkranz, and C. Djerassi, J. Am. Chem. Soc., 74, 3436 (1952).

[20]Isolated as 4-pregnen-17α,20α,21-triol-3-one 20,21-diacetate and the 20β-epimer after acid cleavage of the enol ether and acetylation.

[21]P. L. Julian, E. W. Meyer, W. J. Karpel, and W. Cole, J. Am. Chem. Soc., 73, 1982 (1951).

[22]Isolated as 4-pregnen-11β,17α,20β,21-tetrol-3-one after acid cleavage of enol ether.

[23]L. H. Sarett, M. Feurer, and K. Folkers, J. Am. Chem. Soc., 73, 1777 (1951).

[24]Isolated as 20,21-diacetate after treatment as in ref. 22.

[25]J. Romo, M. Romero, C. Djerassi, and G. Rosenkranz, J. Am. Chem. Soc., 73, 1528 (1951).

[26]P. Karrer, H. Asmis, K. N. Sareen, and R. Schwyzer, Helv. Chim. Acta, 34, 1022 (1951).

[27]H. Hirschmann, F. B. Hirschmann, and M. A. Daus, J. Am. Chem. Soc., 74, 539 (1952).

[28]Isolated as 3β,16α,20-triacetoxy-5-allopregnane after acid hydrolysis and acetylation.

[29]H. Hirschmann and F. B. Hirschmann, J. Biol. Chem., 184, 259 (1950).

[30]R. H. Levin, G. B. Spero, A. V. McIntosh, Jr., F. W. Heyl, and J. L. Thompson, Abstracts of Papers, 115th Meeting American Chemical Society, San Francisco, California, March 1949, p. 33L.

[31]Isolated as tetraacetate.

[32]A. Sandoval, J. Romo, G. Rosenkranz, S. Kaufmann, and C. Djerassi, J. Am. Chem. Soc., 73, 3820 (1951).

[33]D. H. Hey, J. Honeyman, and W. J. Peal, J. Chem. Soc., 1952, 4836.

[34]R. H. Levin, A. V. McIntosh, Jr., and G. B. Spero, U. S. Pat. 2,575,351 (November 20, 1951); Chem. Abstracts, 46, 6164 (1952).

[35]R. H. Levin, G. B. Spero, A. V. McIntosh, Jr., and D. E. Rayman, J. Am. Chem. Soc., 70, 2958 (1948).

LAH. In the case of a Δ^4-3-ketosteroid the reaction with ethylene glycol proceeds with rearrangement of the $C_{4,5}$ double bond to afford a Δ^5-steroid (283). The influence of steric factors in ketal formation is seen in the report that desoxycorticosterone acetate (CCLIX) reacts with ethylene glycol to form a monoketal while progesterone (CCLX) yields a diketal (284).

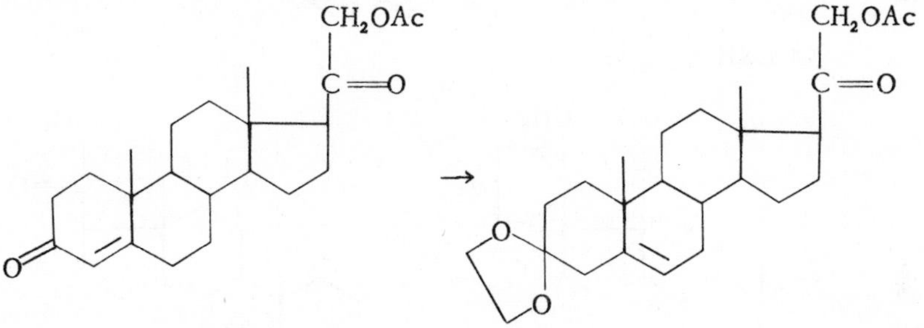

CCLIX   (7-181)

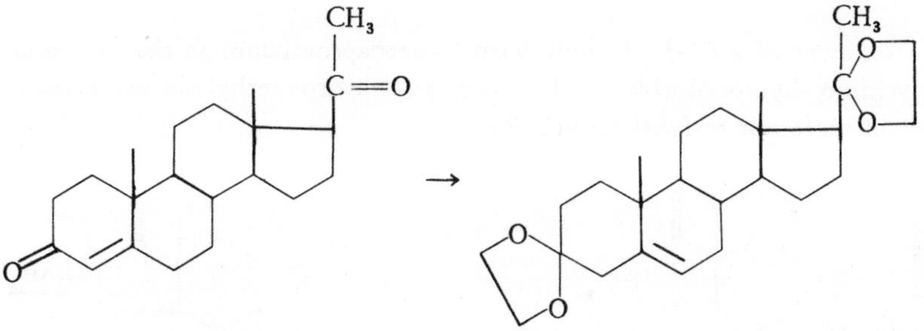

CCLX   (7-182)

In contrast to the reaction with ethylene glycol, the reaction of a Δ^4-3-ketosteroid with ethanedithiol and zinc chloride yields the Δ^4-3-keto-ethylene thioketal (283).

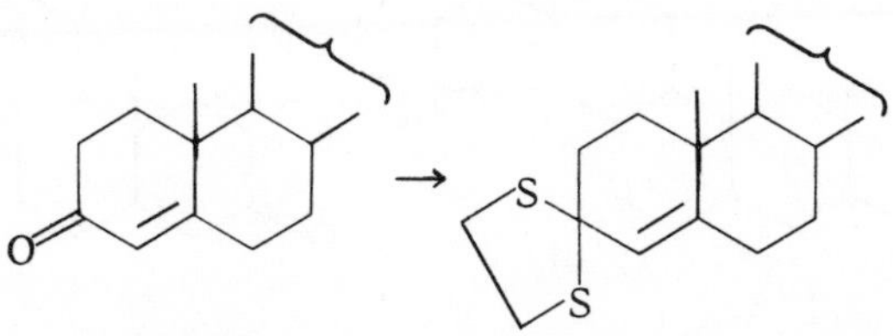

(7-183)

CCLXI

The selective protection of an isolated carbonyl group in the presence of a Δ^4-3-keto group can be achieved using β-mercaptoethanol and zinc chloride (285).

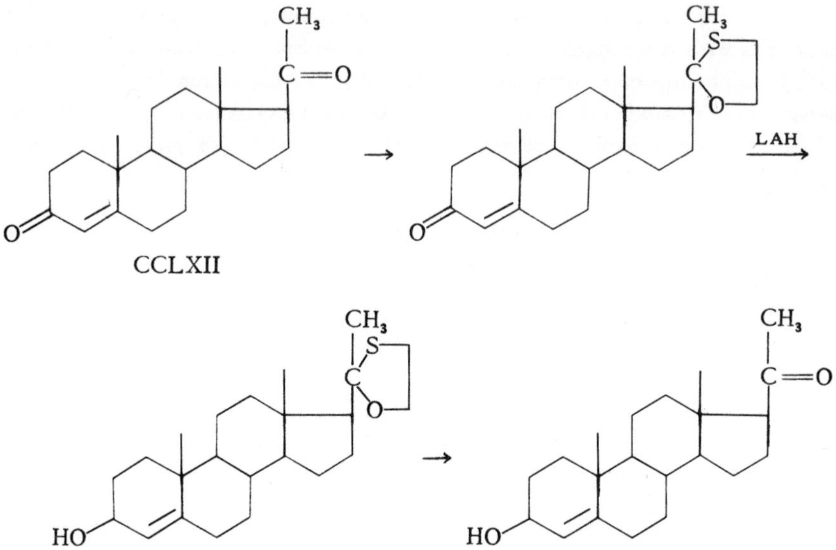

CCLXII

(7-184)

The treatment of a Δ^4-3,17-dione with β-mercaptoethanol in the presence of pyridine hydrochloride yields the 3-(β-hydroxyethyl)thioenol ether which is resistant to LAH attack (286).

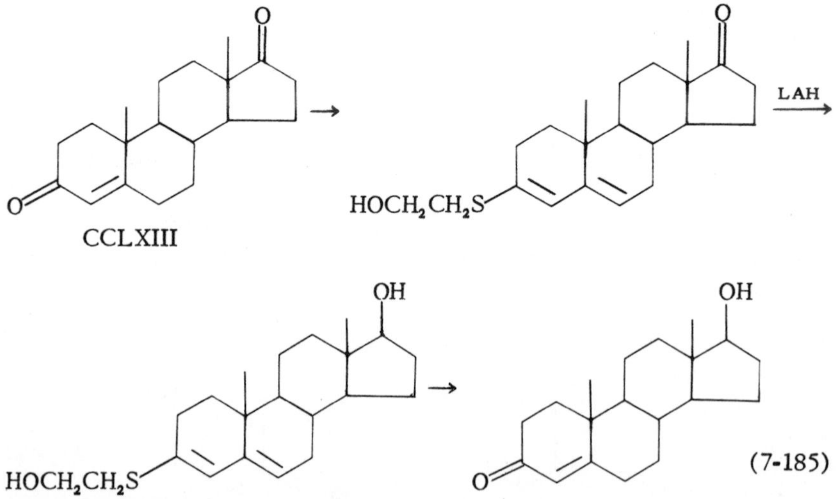

CCLXIII

(7-185)

The 11-keto group is not attacked by β-mercaptoethanol. In contrast to the sequence in equation (7-184), the reaction of a Δ^4-3,17- or 3,20-dione with benzyl mercaptan in the presence of zinc chloride yields a 3-benzyl-thioenol ether, the isolated keto group remaining untouched and reducible with LAH (286).

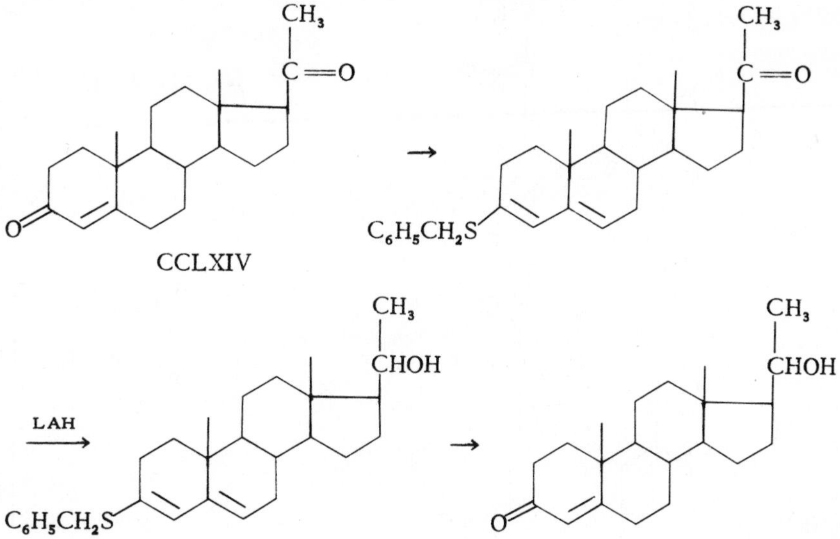

CCLXIV

(7-186)

The reaction of a Δ^4-3-ketosteroid with ethyl orthoformate yields the enol ether which is resistant to attack by LAH (287).

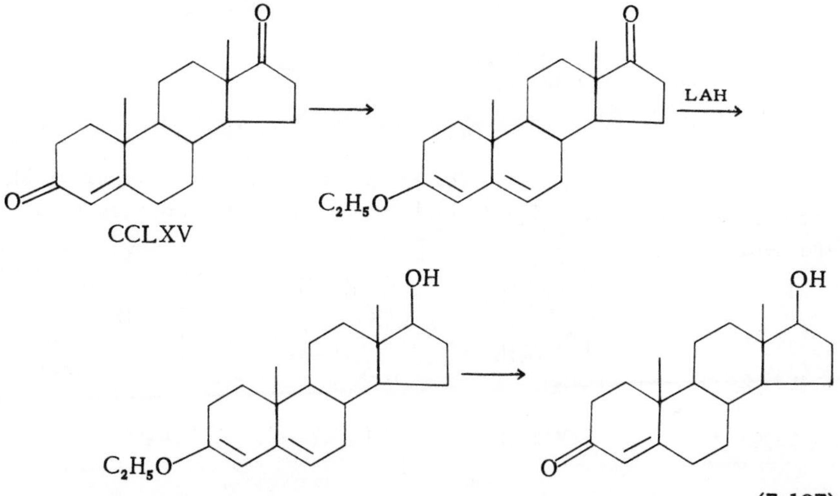

CCLXV

(7-187)

The 3-benzylenol ether and the 3-cyclohexylenol ether have been utilized as well as the 3-ethylenol ether. The treatment of 3α-acetoxypregnane-11,20-dione (CCLXVI) with ethyl orthoformate in absolute ethanol with one drop of concentrated sulfuric acid followed by heating in a xylene solution yields a mixture of $\Delta^{17,20}$- and $\Delta^{20,21}$-enol ethers. Reduction of the mixture with LAH followed by mild acid hydrolysis gives the 3α,11β-diol-20-one (288).

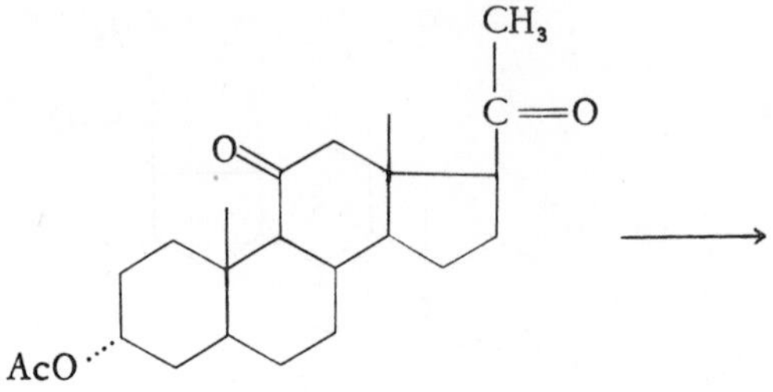

CCLXVI

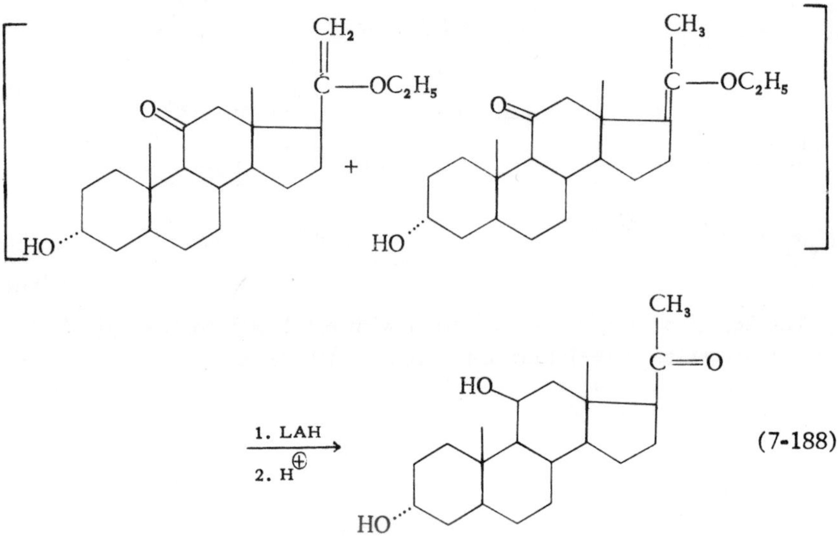

(7-188)

The treatment of a non-steroidal ketone with ethyl orthoformate yields the corresponding diethyl ketal which is resistant to LAH but regenerates the ketone (289).

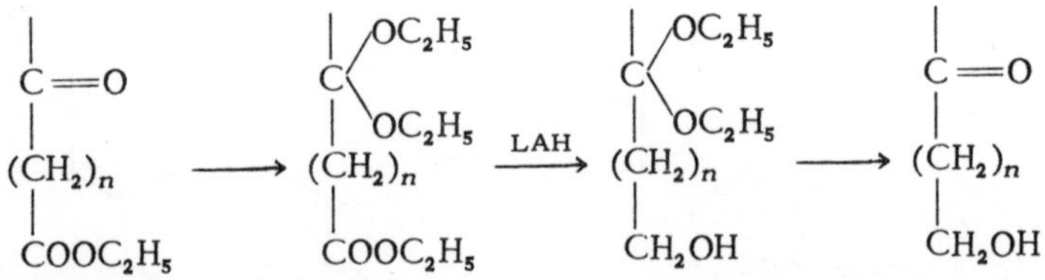

(7-189)

CCLXVII

7.2.1.n *Oxidation.* A recent patent (290) has described a process for oxidizing steroid alcohols with the use of LAH. The process is similar to the Oppenauer oxidation with aluminum alkoxides and involves the formation of a "lithium aluminum organic radical complex" by the reaction of LAH with an alcohol, aldehyde, ketone, amine, etc. The steroid alcohol, containing a hydroxyl group capable of oxidation to a ketone, is subjected to the action of a hydrogen acceptor containing a keto or aldehyde group in the presence of the "lithium aluminum organic radical complex." The following combinations of ketones have been used in the formation of the complex and as hydrogen acceptors.

Complexing agents	Hydrogen acceptors
acetone	cyclohexanone
2-butanone	2-butanone
3-pentanone	cyclopentanone
cyclohexanone	cyclohexanone
cyclopentanone	acetone

This oxidation reaction is discussed more fully in Section 16.2.

7.2.2 Reductions with Aluminum Hydride

The aluminum hydride-aluminum chloride addition compound (AlH_2Cl + $AlHCl_2$) has been utilized in the reduction of 2-butanone to 2-butanol in 67% yield. However, benzophenone is reported to resist reduction (38).

7.2.3 Reductions with Magnesium Aluminum Hydride

The only reported reduction of a ketone with magnesium aluminum hydride involves the reduction of acetone in ethereal solution to 2-propanol in 84% yield (39,40,291).

7.2.4 Reductions with Sodium Borohydride

The reduction of various ketones has been carried out with sodium borohydride in order to selectively reduce the carbonyl group in the presence of other reactive functional groups or where ether-insolubility made LAH reduction impractical.

7.2.4.a *Non-steroidal ketones.* Schlesinger *et al.* (292) have proposed the following scheme in the reduction of acetone.

$$4\ CH_3COCH_3 + NaBH_4 \longrightarrow NaB[OCH(CH_3)_2]_4 \xrightarrow{H_2O} 4\ (CH_3)_2CHOH$$

$$(7-190)$$

The ketone group has been reduced in the presence of halogen, nitro, nitrile, amide, ester and carboxylic acid groups, as summarized in Table XXIII for non-steroidal ketones.

In the reduction of 1,1,1-trifluoro-3-bromo-2-propanone with sodium borohydride the yield is only about half that obtained with LAH due to the probable formation of a stable hydrate or hemiacetal in the presence of water or alcohol, respectively, reducing the concentration of free carbonyl groups (293).

Chaikin and Brown reported that on treatment of pyruvic acid (CCLXVIII) with sodium borohydride reduction occurred but boron-free products were not isolated. In addition, attempted reduction of acetylacetone (CCLXIX)

TABLE XXIII

Reduction of Non-Steroidal Ketones with Sodium Borohydride

	Ketone	Medium[1]	Product	% Yield	Ref.
C_3HCl_5O	Pentachloroacetone	M	1,1,1,3,3-Pentachloro-2-propanol	.....	2
$C_3H_2BrF_3O$	1,1,1-Trifluoro-3-bromo-2-propanone	W	1,1,1-Trifluoro-3-bromo-2-propanol	48.4	3
C_3H_6O	Acetone	ST	2-Propanol	....	4
$C_4H_6O_2$	Biacetyl	W	2,3-Butanediol	62	5
C_4H_8O	2-Butanone	W	2-Butanol	87	5
C_5H_8O	Cyclopentanone	W	Cyclopentanol	90	5
$C_5H_8O_3$	Levulinic acid	W	γ-Valerolactone	81	5
$C_5H_8N_2O_5$	5,5-Dinitro-2-pentanone	WM	5,5-Dinitro-2-pentanol	48.5	6
$C_5H_9NO_3$	5-Nitro-2-pentanone	WM	5-Nitro-2-pentanol	86.6,61.2	6
$C_6H_{10}O$	Mesityl oxide	W	4-Methyl-3-penten-2-ol	77	5
$C_6H_{10}O_2$	2,5-Hexanedione	W	2,5-Hexanediol	86	5
$C_6H_{10}N_2O_5$	5,5-Dinitro-2-hexanone	WM	5,5-Dinitro-2-hexanol	78.2,54.5	6
$C_6H_{11}NO_3$	5-Nitro-2-hexanone	WM	5-Nitro-2-hexanol	50.7	6
$C_6H_{12}O_6$	d-Fructose	W	Sorbitol 50}7 d-Mannitol 50}	75	8
$C_7H_{13}NO_3$	5-Methyl-5-nitro-2-hexanone	WM	5-Methyl-5-nitro-2-hexanol	98.7	6
C_7H_7BrO	ω-Bromoacetophenone	M	1-Phenyl-2-bromoethanol	71	5
C_8H_7ClO	α-Chloro-3,4-dihydroxyacetophenone	M	1-(3,4-Dihydroxyphenyl)-2-chloroethanol	....	9
$C_8H_{10}N_2O$	N-Cyanonortropinone	W	N-Cyanonortropine N-Cyanopseudotropine }	79	10
$C_9H_9Cl_2NO_3S$	dl-1-(2-Thienyl)-2-dichloroacetamidopropan-3-ol-1-one	M	dl-erythro-1-(2-Thienyl)-2-dichloro-acetamido-1,3-propanediol dl-threo form }	"high"	11
$C_9H_{11}NO_3$	Adrenalone	M	Adrenaline 50}	98.3	9
$C_9H_{11}NO_3S$	dl-1-(2-Thienyl)-2-acetamidopropan-3-ol-1-one	M	dl-erythro-1-(2-Thienyl)-2-acetamido-1,3-propanediol dl-threo form } 50}	94	11

Formula	Compound	Solvent	Derivative	mp	Ref.
$C_{11}H_{10}Cl_2NO_5$	1-p-Nitrophenyl-2-dichloroacetamidopropan-3-ol-1-one	E	dl-erythro-1-p-Nitrophenyl-2-dichloroacetamido-1,3-propanediol	27	12
			dl-threo form	39	
$C_{11}H_{12}NO_5$	1-p-Nitrophenyl-2-acetamidopropan-3-ol-1-one	E	dl-erythro-1-p-Nitrophenyl-2-acetamido-1,3-propanediol	47	12
			dl-threo form	25	
$C_{12}H_{14}NO_6$	1-p-Nitrophenyl-2-methoxyacetamidopropan-3-ol-1-one	E	dl-erythro-1-p-Nitrophenyl-2-methoxyacetamido-1,3-propanediol	28	12
			dl-threo form	33	
$C_{12}H_{20}O_4S$	Ethyl 9-thiaundecan-6,10-dione-1-oate	M	8-Thiol-6-hydroxyoctanoic acid[13]	...	14
$C_{13}H_{10}Cl_4NO_6$	1-p-Nitrophenyl-2-dichloroacetamido-3-dichloroacetoxy-1-propanone	E	dl-erythro-1-p-Nitrophenyl-2-dichloroacetamido-1,3-propanediol	...	12
$C_{13}H_{12}Cl_2NO_6$	1-p-Nitrophenyl-2-dichloroacetamido-3-acetoxy-1-propanone	E	dl-erythro-1-p-Nitrophenyl-2-dichloroacetamido-1,3-propanediol	40–45	12
$C_{13}H_{14}NO_6$	1-p-Nitrophenyl-2-acetamido-3-acetoxy-1-propanone	E	dl-erythro-1-p-Nitrophenyl-2-acetamido-1,3-propanediol	47.6	12
$C_{13}H_{12}O$	Dicyclohexyl ketone	M	Dicyclohexylmethanol	88	5
$C_{14}H_{10}O_2$	Benzil	M	meso-Hydrobenzoin	89	5
			dl-Hydrobenzoin	56 / ...	
$C_{14}H_{16}O_4$	4-Carboxymethyl-5-methoxy-8-methyl-1-tetralone	.....	4-Carboxymethyl-5-methoxy-8-methyl-1-tetralol	...	15
$C_{15}H_{12}O_3$	p-Benzoylphenylacetic acid	W	p-(α-Hydroxybenzyl)phenylacetic acid	91	16
$C_{16}H_{13}BrNO_5$	1-p-Nitrophenyl-2-p'-bromobenzamidopropan-3-ol-1-one	E	dl-1-p-Nitrophenyl-2-p'-bromobenzamido-1,3-propanediol[17]	...	12
$C_{16}H_{14}NO_5$	1-p-Nitrophenyl-2-benzamidopropan-3-ol-1-one	E	dl-erythro-1-p-Nitrophenyl-2-benzamido-1,3-propanediol	41	12
			dl-threo form	32	
$C_{17}H_{16}NO_5$	1-p-Nitrophenyl-2-phenylacetamidopropan-3-ol-1-one	E	dl-erythro-1-p-Nitrophenyl-2-phenylacetamido-1,3-propanediol	24	12
			dl-threo form	28	
	1-p-Nitrophenyl-2-p'-methylbenzamidopropan-3-ol-1-one	E	dl-1-p-Nitrophenyl-2-p'-methylbenzamido-1,3-propanediol[17]	...	12

(Continued)

TABLE XXIII (*Continued*)

Ketone		Medium[1]	Product	% Yield	Ref.
1-p-Nitrophenyl-2-m'-methoxybenzamido-propan-3-ol-1-one	$C_{17}H_{16}NO_6$	E	dl-1-p-Nitrophenyl-2-m'-methoxybenzamido-1,3-propanediol[17]	....	12
Methyl 2-n-hexyl-3-ketodecanoate	$C_{17}H_{32}O_3$	DM	2-n-Hexyl-3-hydroxydecanoic acid[13]	36	18
2β,4b-Dimethyl-2-methallyl-1-carboxy-methylene-7-ethylenedioxy-1,2,3,4,4aα,4b,5,6,7,8,10,10aβ-dodecahydro-phenanthren-4-one	$C_{23}H_{30}O_5$	....	2β,4b-Dimethyl-2-methallyl-1-carboxy-methylene-7-ethylenedioxy-1,2,3,4,4aα,5,6,7,8,10,10aβ-dodecahydrophenanthren-4α-ol	....	19
Methyl 2-n-hexadecyl-3-ketoeicosanoate	$C_{37}H_{72}O_3$	DM	2-n-Hexadecyl-3-hydroxyeicosanoic acid	78.5	18
Mycolonic acid	$C_{87}H_{172}O_4$	....	$R_2CH\!-\!CH\!-\!CH\!-\!CHCOOH$ OH R_1 OH $C_{24}H_{49}$	....	20

Ketone structure: $R_2C\!-\!CH\!-\!CH\!-\!CHCOOH$, O R_1 OH $C_{24}H_{49}$

References—Table XXIII

[1] Reaction medium: M = methanol, W = water, WM = water-methanol mixture, E = ethanol, DM = dioxane-methanol mixture, ST = sealed tube, no solvent.

[2] Ciba Ltd., Australian Pat. Appln. 9261/52.

[3] E. T. McBee and T. M. Burton, *J. Am. Chem. Soc.*, 74, 3022 (1952).

[4] H. I. Schlesinger, H. C. Brown, H. R. Hoekstra, and L. R. Rapp, *ibid.*, 75, 199 (1953).

[5] S. W. Chaikin and W. G. Brown, *ibid.*, 71, 122 (1949).

[6] H. Shechter, D. E. Ley, and L. Zeldin, *ibid.*, 74, 3664 (1952).

[7] Isolated as the hexaacetate.

[8] M. Abdel-Akher, J. K. Hamilton, and F. Smith, *J. Am. Chem. Soc.*, 73, 4691 (1951).

[9] A. L. P. Coll, *Afinidad*, 27, 549 (1950); *Chem. Abstracts*, 45, 7981 (1951).

[10] A. Nickon and L. F. Fieser, *J. Am. Chem. Soc.*, 74, 5566 (1952).

[11] E. C. Hermann and A. Kreuchunas, *ibid.*, 74, 5168 (1952).

[12] Parke, Davis and Co., Australian Pat. Appln. 13,395/52 (October 15, 1952).

[13] Isolated after hydrolysis of the reduction product.

[14] M. W. Bullock, J. A. Brockman, Jr., E. L. Patterson, J. V. Pierce, and E. L. R. Stokstad, *J. Am. Chem. Soc.*, 74, 3455 (1952).

[15] A. S. Dreiding and A. J. Tomasewski, *Abstracts of Papers*, 121st Meeting American Chemical Society, Milwaukee, Wisconsin, April 1952, p. 82K.

[16] R. P. Zelinski, B. W. Turnquest, and E. C. Martin, *J. Am. Chem. Soc.*, 73, 5521 (1951).

[17] Mixture of *erythro* and *threo* forms.

[18] E. Lederer, V. Portelance, and K. Serck-Hanssen, *Bull. soc. chim. France*, [5] 19, 413 (1952).

[19] L. H. Sarett, G. E. Arth, R. M. Lukes, R. E. Beyler, G. I. Poos, W. F. Johns, and J. M. Constantin, *J. Am. Chem. Soc.*, 74, 4974 (1952).

[20] H. Demarteau and E. Lederer, *Compt. rend.*, 235, 265 (1952).

gave a 63% yield of isopropyl alcohol as a result of cleavage prior to or during reduction (42).

$$CH_3COCOOH \qquad\qquad CH_3COCH_2COCH_3$$

$$\text{CCLXVIII} \qquad\qquad\qquad \text{CCLXIX}$$

It has been reported that no difficulty is encountered in the reduction of 5-nitro-2-pentanone, 5-nitro-2-hexanone, 5-methyl-5-nitro-2-hexanone and 5,5-dinitro-2-hexanone with sodium borohydride in aqueous methanol solution. However, 5,5-dinitro-2-pentanone (CCLXX) is reduced slowly to the pentanol and even with a 300% excess of reducing agent and a long reaction time the reduction is incomplete and the product contains unreacted *gem*-dinitro compound (294).

$$CH_3COCH_2CH_2CH\!\!\begin{array}{c}NO_2\\[-2pt]\\NO_2\end{array} \xrightarrow[48.5\%]{NaBH_4} CH_3\underset{OH}{C}HCH_2CH_2CH\!\!\begin{array}{c}NO_2\\[-2pt]\\NO_2\end{array} \qquad (7\text{-}191)$$

$$\text{CCLXX}$$

It has been suggested that the slow reduction is related to a ring-chain tautomerism in which the effective concentration of the carbonyl group is diminished by the participation of the primary nitro-nitronate anion with the formation of a pseudo nitronic ester.

$$(7\text{-}192)$$

$$\text{CCLXXI}$$

The reduction of sugars with sodium borohydride in aqueous solution has been applied to the ketoses, fructose and sorbose. The reduction of *d*-fructose yields a mixture of equal parts of sorbitol and mannitol, isolated as the hexaacetates (47). As discussed in Section 5.1, a quantitative method for the analysis of aldoses and ketoses involves reduction in aqueous solution with excess borohydride, followed by decomposition and measurement of the evolved hydrogen. This method has been applied to the analysis of both fructose and sorbose (51).

7.2.4.b *Steroidal ketones.* The reduction of 3-ketosteroids with sodium borohydride is stereospecific, reduction in the normal series (CCLXXII) yielding the 3α-ol as the sole or major product while reduction in the allo series (CCLXXIII) yields the 3β-ol.

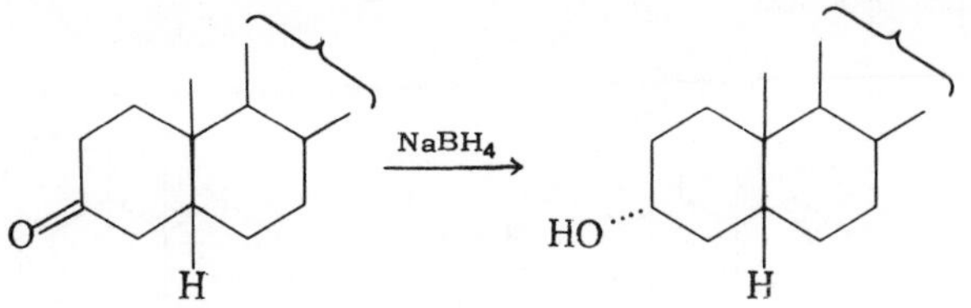

(7-193)

CCLXXII

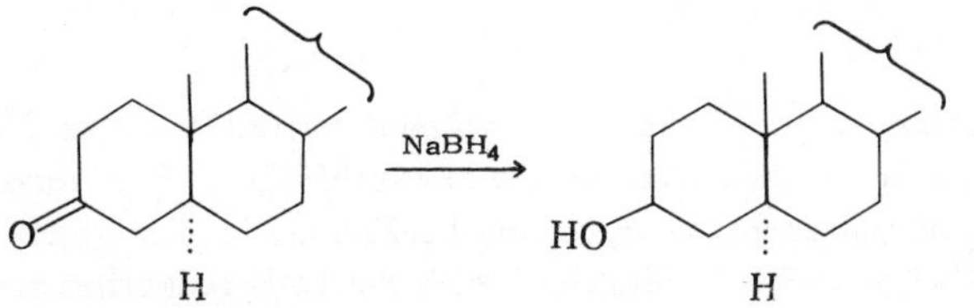

(7-194)

CCLXXIII

The stereospecificity of the reduction is illustrated by the formation of methyl 3α-hydroxyetiocholanate and methyl 3β-hydroxyetioallocholanate by the reduction of a mixture of methyl 3-ketoetiocholanate and methyl 3-ketoetioallocholanate (183). A similar result is reported in the reduction of the analogous $\Delta^{9(11)}$ compounds (183,295). In the reduction of the saturated 3-ketoetiocholanate and 3-ketoetioallocholanate, a "3-desoxy material" is reported among the reduction products (183). The yields in the reduction of cholestanone (CCLXXIII) and coprostanone (CCLXXII) with LAH and sodium borohydride are similar although the less available isomer is formed to a slightly greater amount when the borohydride is used (233).

Elisberg, Vanderhaeghe, and Gallagher (296) reported that the rate of reaction of the 3-ketone of the allo series is slower than that for the normal series. Thus, the reduction of etiocholane-3,17-dione (CCLXXIV) with sodium borohydride in methanol after 20 minutes gives a mixture of products corresponding to a 91% reduction of the 3-ketone group to a carbinol. Under the same conditions more than 30% of androstane-3,17-dione (CCLXXV) is recovered unchanged after treatment with the borohydride.

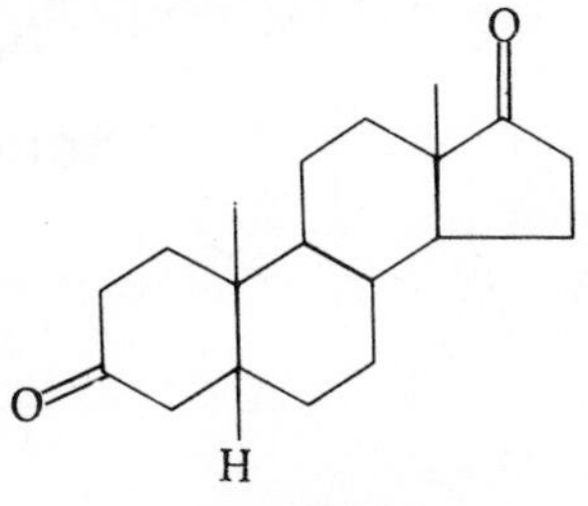

CCLXXIV

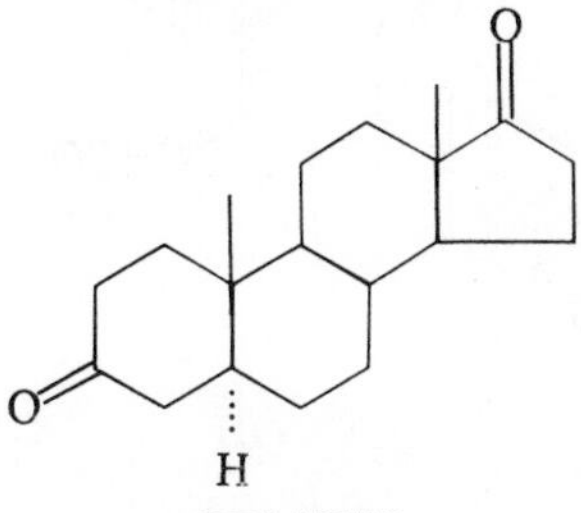

CCLXXV

The reduction of Δ^4-3-ketosteroids with sodium borohydride yields a mixture of the corresponding Δ^4-3-hydroxy epimers in which the 3β-ol is the principal product.

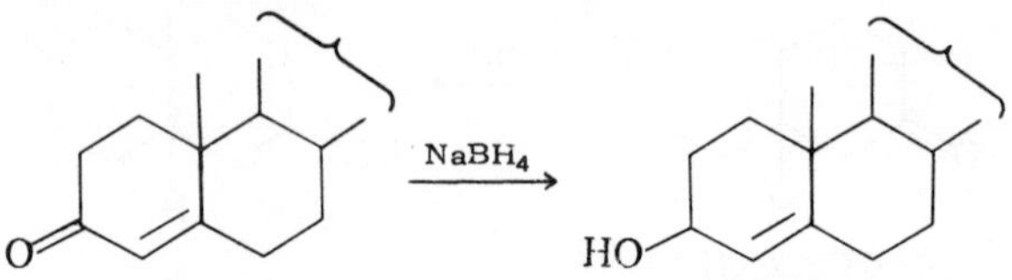

(7-195)

CCLXXVI

The configuration of the 7-ol obtained on reduction of 7-ketosteroids with sodium borohydride has not been established. It is reported that the reduction of 3β-acetoxy-9α,11α-oxido-22-isoallospirostane-7-one yields a 3β,7(β?)-diol which is identical with the LAH reduction product (256).

The reduction of 11-ketosteroids with sodium borohydride is stereospecific yielding 11β-hydroxy steroids. Under mild conditions the 11-keto group may not be attacked but under more drastic conditions such as in refluxing aqueous alcohol the 11β-ol is formed (183,295,297).

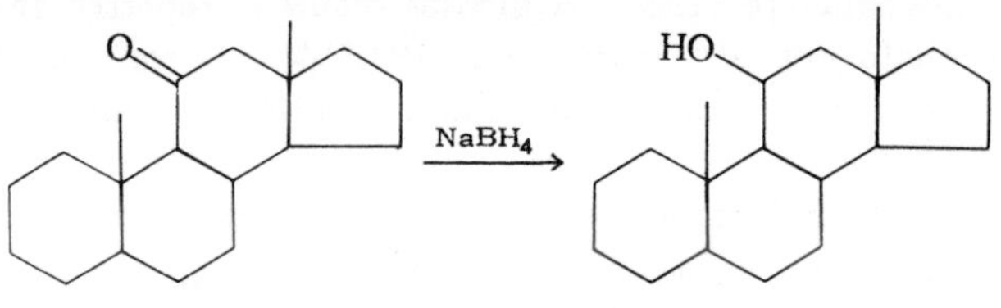

(7-196)

CCLXXVII

It is of interest to note that the reduction of the 4-one (CCLXXVIII) which contains a partial structure analogous to the 11-ketosteroid, is reported to yield the 4α-hydroxy compound (298).

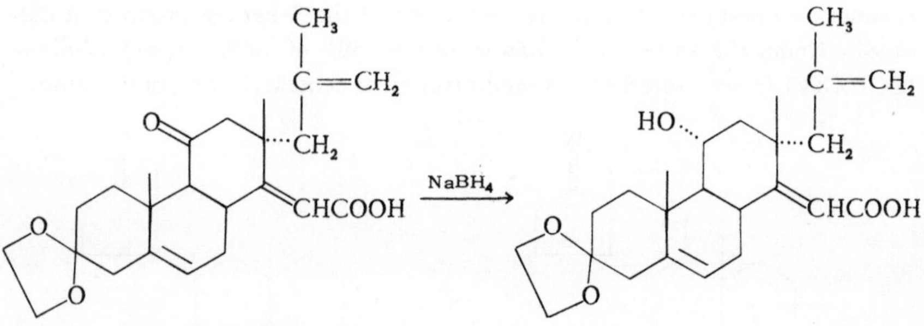

CCLXXVIII

(7-197)

Heymann and Fieser (297) reported that an attempt to reduce methyl 3α-hydroxy-12-keto-$\Delta^{9(11)}$-cholenate (CCLXXIX) with sodium borohydride resulted in attack on the carbomethoxy group rather than the ketone.

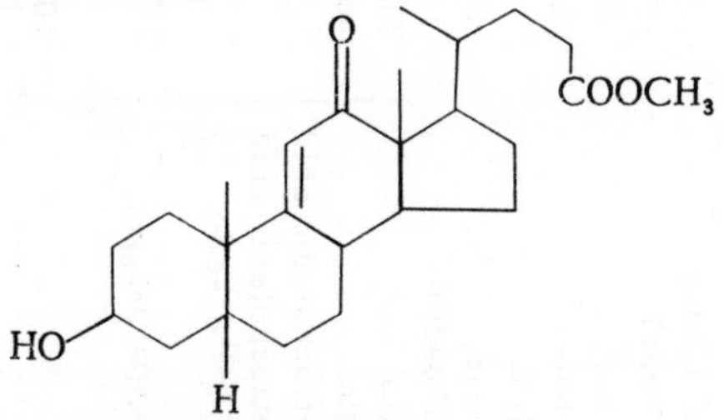

CCLXXIX

The C_{17} carbonyl group is somewhat resistant to attack by sodium borohydride. Thus, the C_3 ketone in androstane-3,17-dione and etiocholane-3,17-dione has been selectively reduced in dilute methanol solution to yield the corresponding 3-ol-17-one accompanied by a small amount of the 3,17β-diol (296). The use of pyridine instead of methanol as a solvent results in a sluggish reaction and smaller yields of the same product.

The C_{17} ketosteroid containing the normal configuration in the C_{14} position is reduced mainly to the 17β-hydroxy epimer while in 14-iso compounds reduction of the 17-ketone yields the 17α-hydroxy epimer (299).

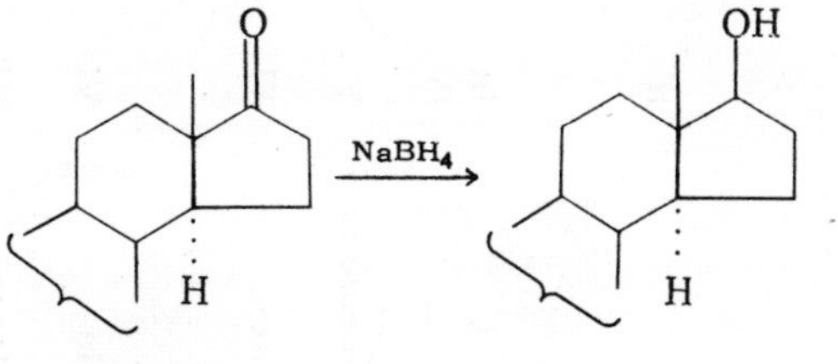

(7-198)

CCLXXX

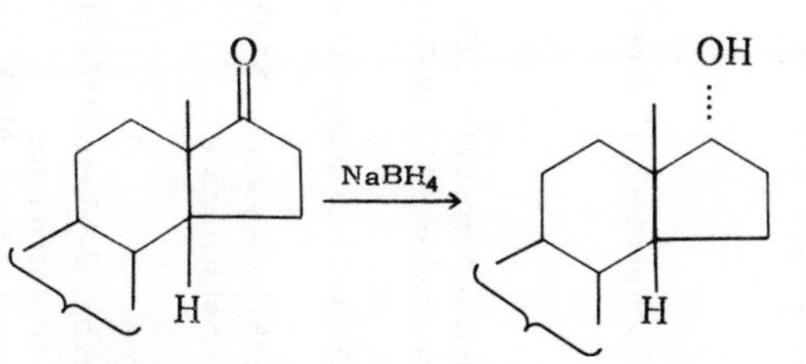

(7-199)

CCLXXXI

The presence of a 14,15-double bond results in the formation of the 17β epimer.

TABLE XXIV

Reduction of Steroidal Ketones with Sodium Borohydride

Ketone	No.	Medium[1]	Product	% Yield	Ref.
A. 3-Ketosteroids					
$C_{19}H_{28}O_2$ Androstane-3,17-dione	I	M	Epiandrosterone(3β-ol-17-one)	45⎫ 2	3
			Androstane-3β,17β-diol	5⎭	3
		P	Epiandrosterone (3β-ol-17-one)	55⎫	3
			Androsterone(3α-ol-17-one)	4⎭	3
Etiocholane-3,17-dione	II	M	Etiocholane-3α-ol-17-one	69⎫	3
			Etiocholane-3β-ol-17-one	17⎬	3
			Etiocholane-3α,17β-diol	5⎭	3
		P	Etiocholane-3α-ol-17-one	25[4]	3
14-Isoandrostane-3,17-dione	III	M	14-Isoandrostane-3β,17α-diol	....	5
Etiocholane-17β-ol-3-one	IV	P	Etiocholane-3α,17β-diol	"almost	5
			Etiocholane-3β,17β-diol	quant."	6
$C_{20}H_{28}O_4$ 3-Keto-19-hydroxy-Δ^4-etiocholenic acid	V	W	3β,19-Dihydroxy-Δ^4-etiocholenic acid[7]	97	8
			3α,19-Dihydroxy-Δ^4-etiocholenic acid		
$C_{21}H_{26}O_3$ Methyl dl-3-keto-$\Delta^{4,9(11),16}$-etio-cholatrienate	VI	E	Methyl 3α-hydroxy-$\Delta^{4,9(11),16}$-etio-cholatrienate	100	9,10
			Methyl 3β-hydroxy-$\Delta^{4,9(11),16}$-etio-cholatrienate		
Methyl d-3-keto-$\Delta^{4,9(11),16}$-etio-cholatrienate	VI	E	as above	100	10
$C_{21}H_{30}O_3$ ⎧Methyl 3-keto-$\Delta^{9(11)}$-etiocholenate⎫[11] ⎩Methyl 3-keto-$\Delta^{9(11)}$-etioallocholenate⎭	VII VIII	E	Methyl 3α-hydroxy-$\Delta^{9(11)}$-etiocholenate Methyl 3β-hydroxy-$\Delta^{9(11)}$-etioallocholenate	....⎫ ....⎭	10,12 10,12
$C_{21}H_{30}O_4$ Methyl 3,11-diketoetiocholanate	IX	E	Methyl 3α-hydroxy-11-keto-etiocholanate	61[13]	10,12
$C_{21}H_{32}O_3$ Methyl 3-ketoetioallocholanate	X	E	Methyl 3β-hydroxyetioallocholanate Methyl 3α-hydroxyetioallocholanate	65⎫ ....⎭	10,14

Molecular formula	Ketone	No.	Solvent	Product (alcohol)	Yield (%)	Ref.
	Methyl 3-ketoetiocholanate	XI		Methyl 3α-hydroxyetiocholanate	40	
	Methyl 3-ketoetioallocholanate [15]	X	E	Methyl 3β-hydroxyetioallocholanate	14	10
				"3-Desoxy material"	30	
	17β-Acetoxyetiocholane-3-one	XII	M	17β-Acetoxyetiocholane-3α-ol	80	3
				17β-Acetoxyetiocholane-3β-ol	15	
$C_{22}H_{32}O_4$	Ethyl 3-keto-19-hydroxy-Δ⁴-etiocholenate	XIII	E	Ethyl 3β,19-dihydroxy-Δ⁴-etiocholenate	31	8
$C_{24}H_{36}O_4$	3,11-Diketocholanic acid	XIV	WE	3α-Hydroxy-11-ketocholanic acid	85	17
				3β-Hydroxy-11-ketocholanic acid [16]	11	17
			WE	3α,11β-Dihydroxycholanic acid	...[16]	
$C_{27}H_{44}O$	Cholest-4-en-3-one	XV	M	Cholest-4-en-3α-ol	24	18
				Cholest-4-en-3β-ol	69	
	Cholest-5-en-3-one	XVI	M	Cholest-5-en-3α-ol	23	18
				Cholest-5-en-3β-ol	72	
$C_{27}H_{46}O$	Cholestan-3-one	XVII	M	Cholestan-3α-ol	13	18
				Cholestan-3β-ol	84	
	Coprostan-3-one	XVIII	M	Coprostan-3α-ol	76	18
				Coprostan-3β-ol	16	
B. 7-Ketosteroids						
$C_{27}H_{40}O_5$	Methyl 3α-acetoxy-7-keto-Δ⁹(11)-cholenate	XIX	...	Methyl 3α-acetoxy-7-hydroxy-Δ⁹(11)-cholenate	...	19
$C_{29}H_{42}O_6$	3β-Acetoxy-9α,11α-oxido-22-isoallospirostan-7-one	XX	M	9α,11α-Oxido-22-isoallospirostan-3,7(3β)-diol	...	20
C. 11-Ketosteroids						
$C_{20}H_{30}O_4$	3α-Hydroxy-11-ketoetiocholanic acid	XXI	W	3α,11β-Dihydroxyetiocholanic acid	74.5[21]	22
$C_{21}H_{30}O_4$	Methyl 3,11-diketoetiocholanate	IX	E	Methyl 3α-hydroxy-11-ketoetiocholanate	61[21]	10,12
				Methyl 3α,11-dihydroxyetiocholanate		
$C_{24}H_{35}NO_4$	3,3-Dimethoxy-20-cyano-17-pregnene-21-ol-11-one	XXII	WT	3,3-Dimethoxy-20-cyano-17-pregnene-11β,21-diol	79[23]	24
$C_{24}H_{36}O_4$	3,11-Diketocholanic acid	XIV	WE	3α-Hydroxy-11-ketocholanic acid	85[16]	17
				3β-Hydroxy-11-ketocholanic acid	11	17
			WE	3α,11β-Dihydroxycholanic acid	...[16]	

(Continued)

TABLE XXIV (Continued)

	Ketone	No.	Medium[1]	Product	% Yield	Ref.
$C_{24}H_{36}O_5$	3β-Hydroxy-3α,9α-oxido-11-ketocholanic acid[25]	XXIII	W	3α,9α,11β-Trihydroxycholanic acid 3β,9α,11β-Trihydroxycholanic acid	80}16 9}	17
$C_{24}H_{38}O_4$	3α-Hydroxy-11-ketocholanic acid[25]	XXIV	M	3α,11β-Dihydroxycholanic acid	80[16]	17
$C_{24}H_{38}O_5$	3α,9α-Dihydroxy-11-ketocholanic acid[25]	XXV	WE	3α,9α,11β-Trihydroxycholanic acid	78	17
$C_{25}H_{38}O_5$	3β-Methoxy-3α,9α-oxido-11-ketocholanic acid[25]	XXVI	WE	3β-Methoxy-3α,9α-oxido-11β-hydroxycholanic acid	94	17
$C_{27}H_{42}O_6$	Methyl 3β-acetoxy-9α-hydroxy-11-ketocholanate	XXVII	M	Methyl 3β-acetoxy-9α,11β-dihydroxy-cholanate	98	17
			D. 12-Ketosteroids			
$C_{25}H_{38}O_4$	Methyl 3α-hydroxy-12-keto-$\Delta^{9(11)}$-cholenate	XXVIII		Product not completely specified	....	17
			E. 17-Ketosteroids			
$C_{18}H_{22}O_2$	Estrone	XXIX	M	Estradiol-17β	90	26
$C_{19}H_{28}O_2$	Androstane-3,17-dione	I	M	Epiandrosterone(3β-ol-17-one) Androstane-3β,17β-diol	45}2 5}	3
			P	Epiandrosterone(3β-ol-17-one) Androsterone(3α-ol-17-one)	55} 4}	3
	Etiocholane-3,17-dione	II	M	Etiocholane-3α-ol-17-one Etiocholane-3β-ol-17-one Etiocholane-3α,17β-diol	69} 17} 5}	3
		III	P	Etiocholane-3α-ol-17-one	25[4]	3
$C_{20}H_{24}O_3$	14-Isoandrostane-3,17-dione	III	M	14-Isoandrostane-3β,17α-diol	....	5
$C_{21}H_{26}O_3$	Estrone acetate	XXIX	M	Estradiol-17β	....	26
$C_{21}H_{26}O_3$	Estrone propionate	XXIX	M	Estradiol-17β	....	26
$C_{21}H_{28}O_3$	3β-Acetoxyandrosta-5,14-dien-17-one	XXX	M	Androsta-5,14-dien-3β,17β-diol	68	5
$C_{21}H_{30}O_3$	3β-Acetoxy-14-androsten-17-one	XXXI	M	14-Androstene-3β,17β-diol	57	5

Formula	Compound	Product			Yield	Ref.
$C_{21}H_{30}O_4$	3β-Acetoxy-14ξ-hydroxy-5-androsten-17-one	5-Androstene-3β,17β,14ξ-triol	XXXII	M	....[27]	5
$C_{21}H_{32}O_3$	3β-Acetoxy-14-isoandrostane-17-one	14-Isoandrostane-3β,17α-diol	XXXIII	M	....	5
$C_{21}H_{32}O_4$	3β-Acetoxy-14ξ-hydroxyandrostane-17-one	Androstane-3β,14ξ,17β-triol	XXXIV	M	44[27]	5
$C_{22}H_{28}O_3$	Estrone butyrate	Estradiol-17β	XXIX	M	....	26
$C_{23}H_{30}O_3$	Estrone trimethylacetate	Estradiol-17β 3-trimethylacetate	XXIX	M	89	26
$C_{24}H_{32}O_3$	Estrone t-butylacetate	Estradiol-17β 3-t-butylacetate	XXIX	M	70	26
$C_{25}H_{26}O_3$	Estrone benzoate	Estradiol-17β	XXIX	M	....	26

F. 17a-Ketosteroids

Formula	Compound	Product			Yield	Ref.
$C_{22}H_{32}O_3$	3β-Acetoxy-D-homoandrost-5-en-17a-one	3β-Acetoxy-D-homoandrost-17aβ-ol	XXXV	WD	85[28]	29

G. 20-Ketosteroids

Formula	Compound	Product			Yield	Ref.
$C_{23}H_{32}O_4$	3β-Acetoxy-14,15β-oxido-5-allo-16-pregnene-20-one	compound, $C_{23}H_{34}O_4$, m.p. 149-150°[30]	XXXVI	WD	....	31

CHART TO TABLE XXIV

I

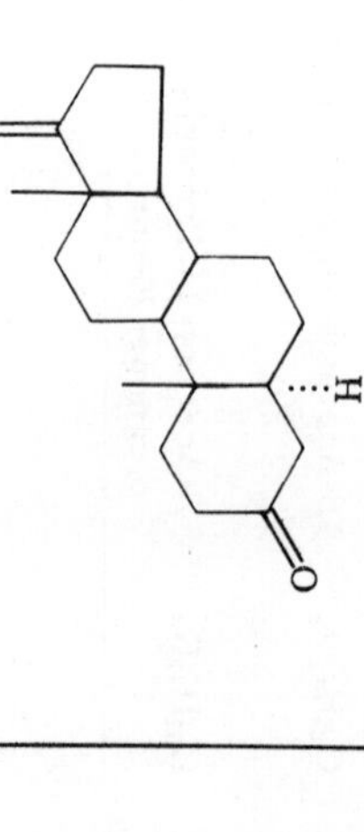

II

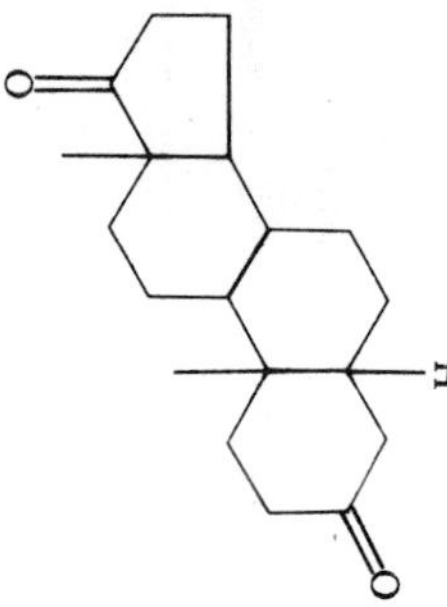

III

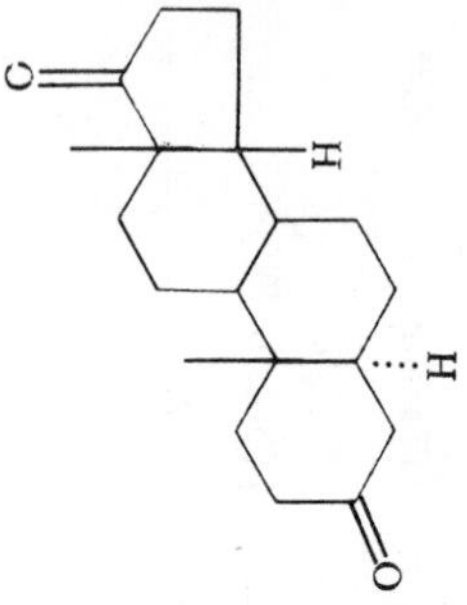

IV

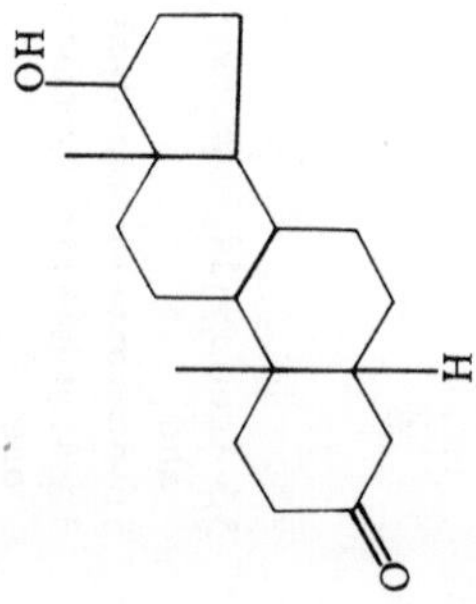

V

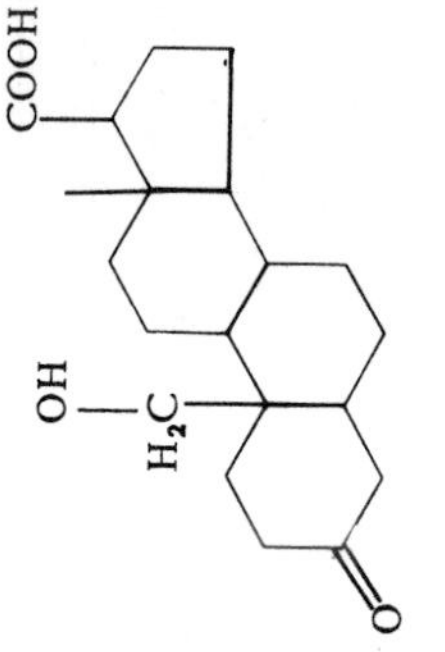

VI

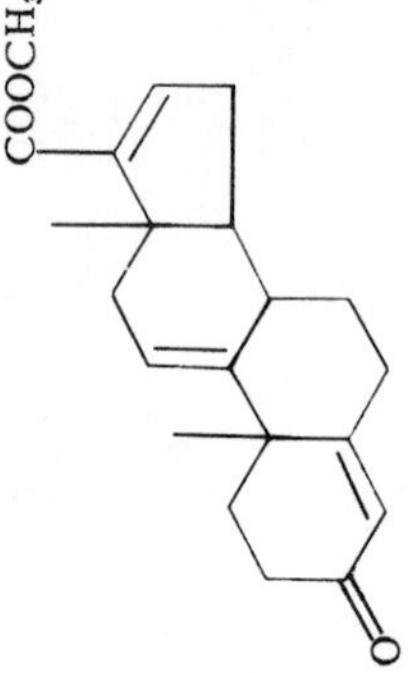

(*continued*)

CHART TO TABLE XXIV (*continued*)

(continued)

CHART TO TABLE XXIV (continued)

(continued)

CHART TO TABLE XXIV (continued)

(continued)

CHART TO TABLE XXIV (continued)

(continued)

CHART TO TABLE XXIV (continued)

References—Table XXIV

[1] Reaction medium: M = methanol, P = pyridine, W = water, E = ethanol, WE = water-ethanol mixture, WT = water-tetrahydrofuran mixture, WD = water-dioxane mixture.

[2] 30% starting material recovered.

[3] E. Elisberg, H. Vanderhaeghe, and T. F. Gallagher, *J. Am. Chem. Soc.*, *74*, 2814 (1952).

[4] 42% starting material recovered.

[5] A. F. St. André, H. B. MacPhillamy, J. A. Nelson, A. C. Shabica, and C. R. Scholz, *J. Am. Chem. Soc.*, *74*, 5506 (1952).

[6] B. Belleau and T. F. Gallagher, *ibid.*, *73*, 4458 (1951).

[7] Predominant product.

[8] P. T. Herzig and M. Ehrenstein, *J. Org. Chem.*, *17*, 713 (1952).

[9] R. B. Woodward, F. Sondheimer, and D. Taub, *J. Am. Chem. Soc.*, *73*, 3547 (1951).

[10] R. B. Woodward, F. Sondheimer, D. Taub, K. Heusler, and W. M. McLamore, *ibid.*, *74*, 4223 (1952).

[11] Mixture of equal parts.

[12] R. B. Woodward, F. Sondheimer, and D. Taub, *J. Am. Chem. Soc.*, *73*, 4057 (1951).

[13] Isolated as 3α-acetoxy derivative after acetylation and chromic acid oxidation of reduction product.

[14] R. B. Woodward, F. Sondheimer, and D. Taub, *J. Am. Chem. Soc.*, *73*, 3548 (1951).

[15] Mixture containing methyl 3-ketoetiocholanate as predominant material.

[16] Isolated as methyl ester acetate.

[17] H. Heymann and L. F. Fieser, *J. Am. Chem. Soc.*, *73*, 5252 (1951).

[18] W. G. Dauben, R. A. Micheli, and J. F. Eastham, *ibid.*, *74*, 3852 (1952).

[19] L. F. Fieser, J. C. Babcock, J. E. Herz, Wei-Yuan Huang, and W. P. Schneider, *ibid.*, *73*, 4053 (1951).

[20] C. Djerassi, E. Batres, M. Velasco, and G. Rosenkranz, *ibid.*, *74*, 1712 (1952).

[21] Isolated as monoacetate.

[22] H. Heymann and L. F. Fieser, *J. Am. Chem. Soc.*, *74*, 5938 (1952).

[23] Isolated as 3-one after hydrolysis of ketal.

[24] N. L. Wendler, R. P. Graber, R. E. Jones, and M. Tishler, *J. Am. Chem. Soc.*, *74*, 3630 (1952).

[25] As sodium salt.

[26] J. H. Biel, *J. Am. Chem. Soc.*, *73*, 847 (1951).

[27] Isolated as diacetate.

[28] Isolated as 17aβ-benzoate.

[29] H. Heusser, P. T. Herzig, A. Fürst, and P. A. Plattner, *Helv. Chim. Acta*, *33*, 1093 (1950).

[30] Isolated after oxidation of reduction product with chromic acid.

[31] Ciba S. A., Fr. Pat. 994,615 (November 20, 1951); Ciba Ltd., Brit. Pat. 665,254 (January 16, 1952); P. Plattner, Ger. Pat. 834,848 (May 15, 1952); U. S. Pat. 2,599,481 (June 3, 1952).

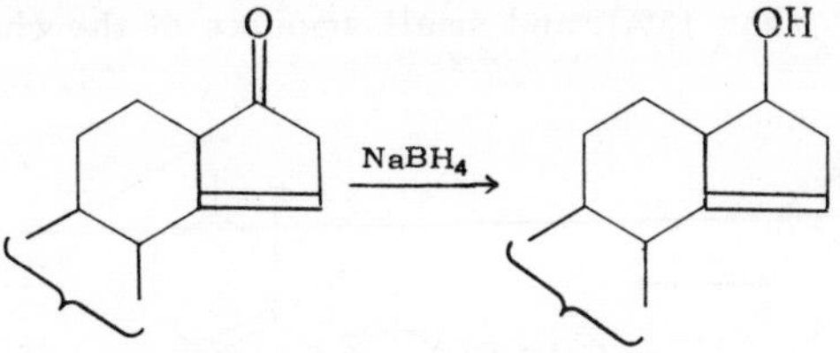

(7-200)

CCLXXXII

The reduction of a 17a-ketone is reported to yield a 17aβ-ol (300).

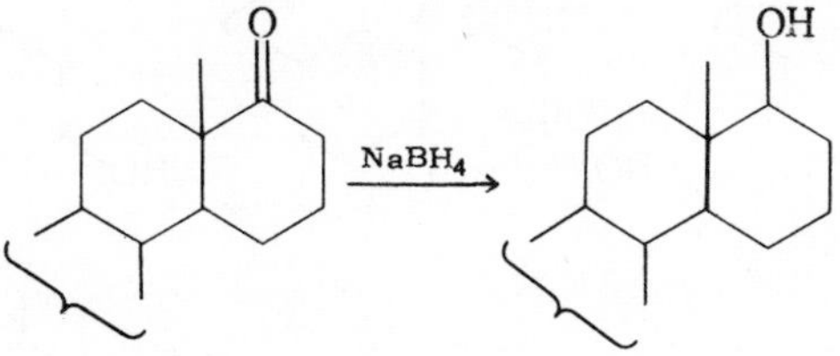

(7-201)

CCLXXXIII

The reduction of various steroidal ketones with sodium borohydride is summarized in Table XXIV.

The ratio of isomers obtained in the reduction of the enol acetate of cholestan-3-one (CCLXXXIV) with sodium borohydride is similar to the ratio obtained from the parent ketone (233).

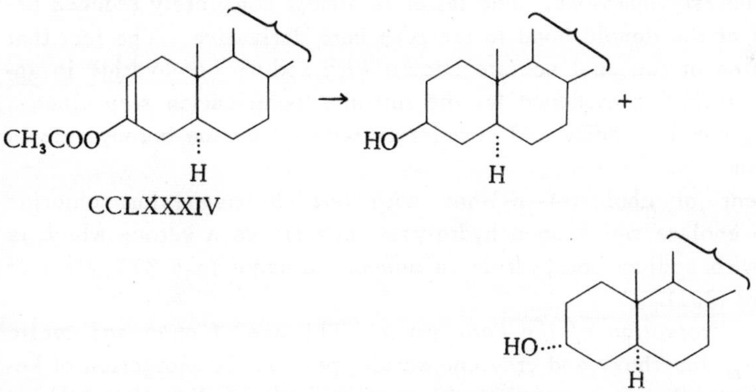

(7-202)

This is in contrast to the results obtained with LAH where the parent ketone is also found in the reduction mixture. The initial step in the borohydride reduction apparently involves solvolysis of the enol acetate to the enol form of the ketone which rearranges to the free ketone.

The conversion of cholest-4-en-3-one to the enol acetate (CCLXXXV) followed by sodium borohydride reduction in alcoholic solution, results in the formation of a mixture of products containing the 3β-ol, cholesterol, as the major product (60–75%), accompanied by the 3α-epimer, *epi-*

cholesterol (less than 15%), and small amounts of the cholest-4-en-3-ols (301-303).

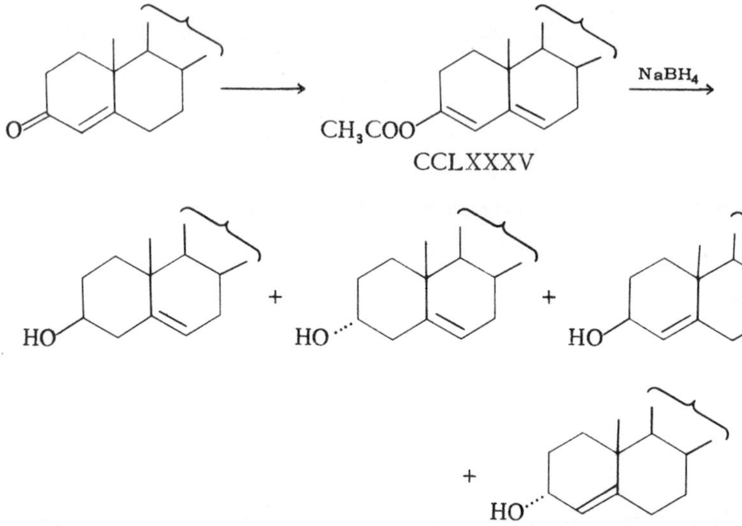

CCLXXXV

NaBH₄

CH₃COO

(7-203)

The ratio of the major products is similar to that obtained in the reduction of cholest-5-en-3-one rather than the parent ketone. It has been proposed that the initial step in the reaction involves the solvolysis of the enol acetate to the enol form of the ketone which rearranges to the free ketone, cholest-5-en-3-one. The latter is almost completely reduced before shift of the double bond to the Δ⁴-3 keto derivative. The fact that no reduction of the enol acetate occurs with sodium borohydride in anhydrous pyridine is evidence for the initial saponification step since a carbonyl group is readily and completely reduced by the borohydride in this solvent.

Treatment of cholest-4-en-3-one with *tert*-butylmagnesium chloride yields an enolate which upon hydrolysis regenerates a ketone which is reduced with sodium borohydride in aqueous ethanol to a 37% yield of cholesterol (301).

7.2.4.c   *Protection of the keto group.* The use of open and cyclic ketals, i.e., dimethoxy and ethylene ketals, permits the protection of ketones, especially the reactive 3-ketosteroid, in sodium borohydride reductions.

7.2.5 Reductions with Potassium Borohydride

Only a limited number of ketones have been reduced with potassium borohydride. The reduction of 1-*p*-nitrophenyl-2-dichloroacetamidopropan-3-ol-1-one (CCLXXXVI) in a water-methanol mixture yields 23% of the *dl-erythro* form and 35% of the *dl-threo* form of 1-*p*-nitrophenyl-2-dichloroacetamido-1,3-propanediol (304).

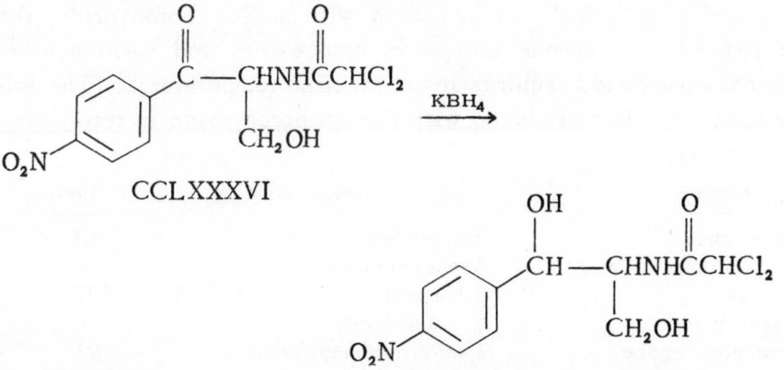

$$\text{(7-204)}$$

CCLXXXVI

The reduction of 2,2-diphenylene-1-indanone (CCLXXXVII) with potassium borohydride in methanol yields the indanol (305).

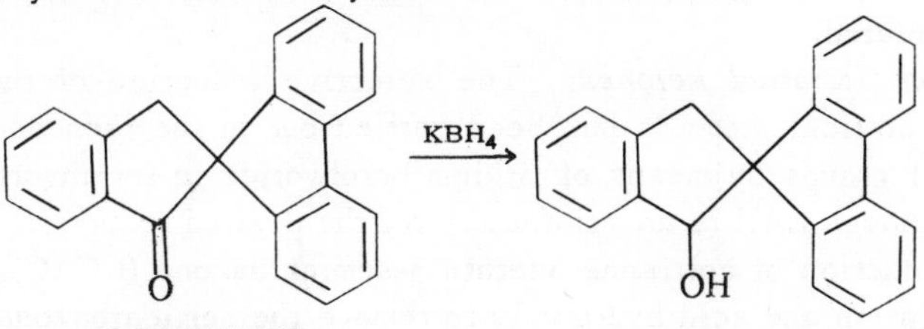

$$\text{(7-205)}$$

CCLXXXVII

The reduction of hecogenin (CCLXXXVIII) and manogenin (CCLXXXIX) with potassium borohydride yields mixtures of the epimeric C_{12}-hydroxy compounds (306).

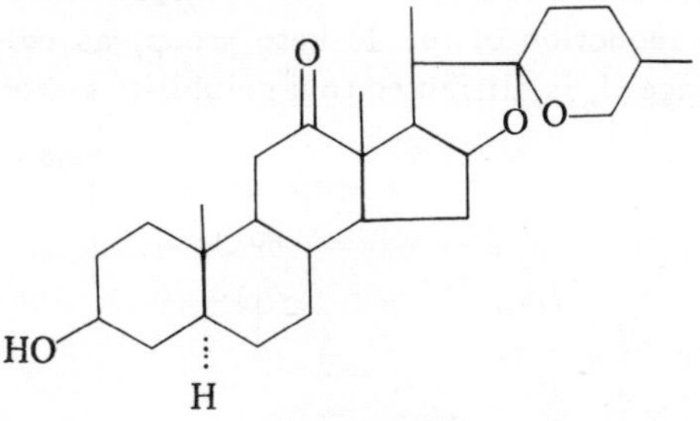

CCLXXXVIII

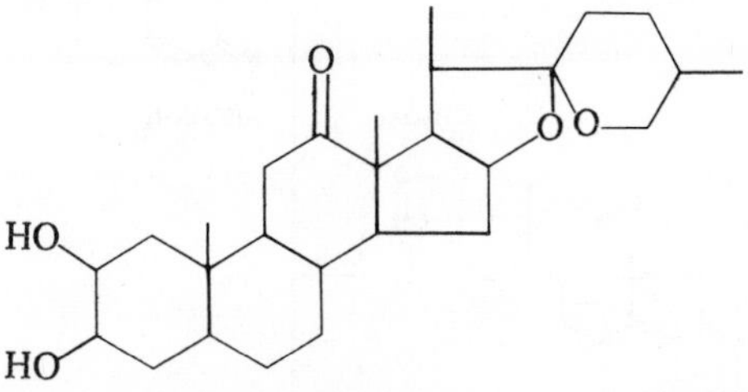

CCLXXXIX

7.2.6   Reductions with Lithium Borohydride

7.2.6.a   *Non-steroidal ketones.* The reduction of various ketones has been carried out at normal temperatures with lithium borohydride. Due to the greater reducing action, as compared with sodium borohydride, the selective reduction of ketone groups in keto esters and various other polyfunctional compounds requires lower reaction temperatures. The following ketones have been reduced with lithium borohydride in tetrahydrofuran solution (54).

Ketone	Product	% Yield
benzophenone	benzhydrol	81
β-benzoylpropionic acid	γ-phenylbutyrolactone	78
2-butanone	2-butanol	77
ethyl levulinate	γ-valerolactone	44
m-nitroacetophenone	1-(m-nitrophenyl)ethanol	93

The attempted selective reduction of ethyl acetoacetate has been reported to yield a borate complex from which the reduction product could not be isolated.

7.2.6.b   *Steroidal ketones.*   The selective reduction of the 11-keto group in cortical steroids has been carried out in the presence of other functional groups by means of lithium borohydride in tetrahydrofuran solution although LAH is unsatisfactory for the desired reduction.

The reduction of cortisone acetate 3-semicarbazone (CCXC), followed by acetylation and acid hydrolysis to remove the semicarbazone grouping yields 4-pregnene-11,17,20,21-tetrol-3-one-20,21-diacetate (Reichstein's substance E 20,21-diacetate), 4-pregnene-11,17,20,21-tetrol-3-one-21-acetate (Reichstein's substance E 21-acetate) and 4-pregnene-17,20,21-triol-3,11-dione-20,21-diacetate (Reichstein's substance U 20,21-diacetate) (307,308). The incomplete reduction of the 11-keto group, as evidenced by the formation of substance U, is attributed to a solubility factor.

(7-206)

The reduction of cortisone-3,20-bis-semicarbazone (CCXCI: R = OH) and 11-dehydrocorticosterone-3,20-bis-semicarbazone (CCXCI: R = H) with lithium borohydride in a mixture of dimethylformamide and tetrahydrofuran, followed by acetylation and hydrolysis, yields 17α-hydroxycorticosterone acetate (CCXCII: R = OH) and corticosterone acetate (CCXCII: R = H), respectively (307).

$$(7\text{-}207)$$

The 3-semicarbazone (307,309), 3-dimethylketal (309) and 3-diethylketal (310) of 20-cyano-17-pregnene-21-ol-3,11-dione (CCXCIII) are reduced with lithium borohydride to the corresponding derivative of 20-cyano-17-pregnene-11β,21-diol-3-one.

$$(7\text{-}208)$$

R = H$_2$NCONHN, (CH$_3$O)$_2$, (C$_2$H$_5$O)$_2$

The reduction of the 3-ethyl enol ether of 4-androstene-3,17-dione (CCXCIV) with lithium borohydride yields the 17β-hydroxy epimer which upon acid hydrolysis is converted to testosterone (311).

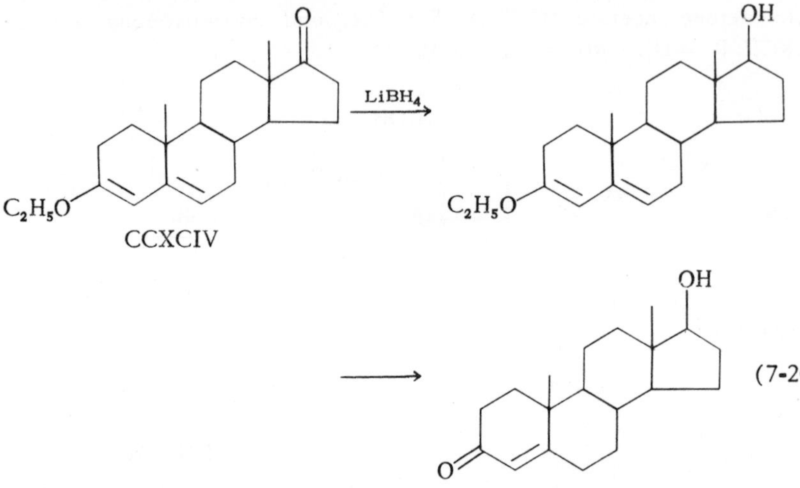

CCXCIV

(7-209)

The reduction of the 20-ketone group with lithium borohydride yields the 20β-ol, as shown in the reduction of cortisone acetate 3-semicarbazone (equation 7-206).

As indicated in the previous examples, the ketone group has been protected from reduction with lithium borohydride by the formation of the semicarbazone, ketal or enol ether.

7.2.7 Reductions with Lithium Gallium Hydride

Although acetone is reduced by lithium gallium hydride in ether solution to 2-propanol, benzophenone is not attacked by the complex metal hydride (56).

7.3 QUINONES

7.3.1 Reductions with Lithium Aluminum Hydride

The reduction of quinones with LAH is analogous in many respects to that of ketones.

7.3.1.a *o-Quinones*. Booth, Boyland and Turner (312) have examined the reduction of a number of o-quinones with LAH. While reduction of o-benzoquinone (CCXCV) yields pyrocatechol, the reduction of 1,2-naphthaquinone (CCXCVI) gives a mixture of alkali soluble material which may be 1,2-dihydroxynaphthalene (CCXCVII) and *trans*-1,2-dihydroxy-1,2-dihydronaphthalene (CCXCVIII).

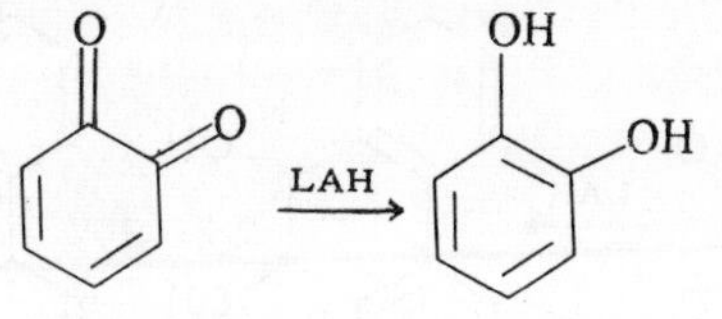

(7-210)

CCXCV

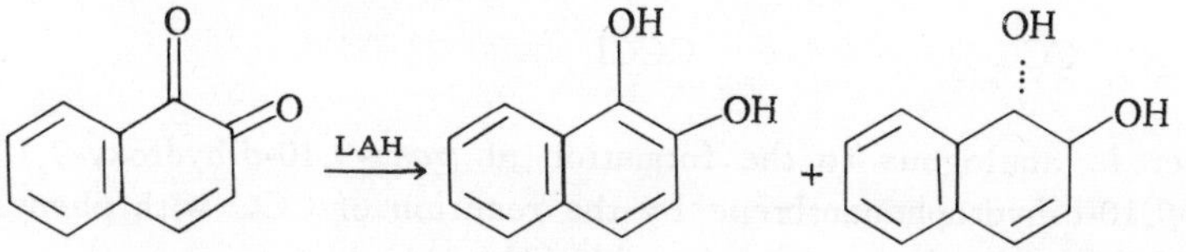

(7-211)

CCXCVI   CCXCVII   CCXCVIII

A summary of the relative quantities of CCXCVII and CCXCVIII formed in the reduction of CCXCVI with various amounts of LAH is given in Table XXV.

TABLE XXV

Reduction of 1,2-Naphthaquinone[a] with LAH (312)

LAH	CCXCVII		CCXCVIII	
g.	g.	Yield	g.	Yield
0.5	0.42	10.4	1.0	24.4
1.0	1.36	33.5	1.80	43.8
2.0	1.54	38.0	1.52	37.1
4.0	1.35	33.3	1.9	46.3

[a] Four grams quinone reduced by Soxhlet technique.

The LAH reduction of 1,2-anthraquinone (CCXCIX) yields *trans*-1,2-dihydroxy-1,2-dihydroanthracene (312).

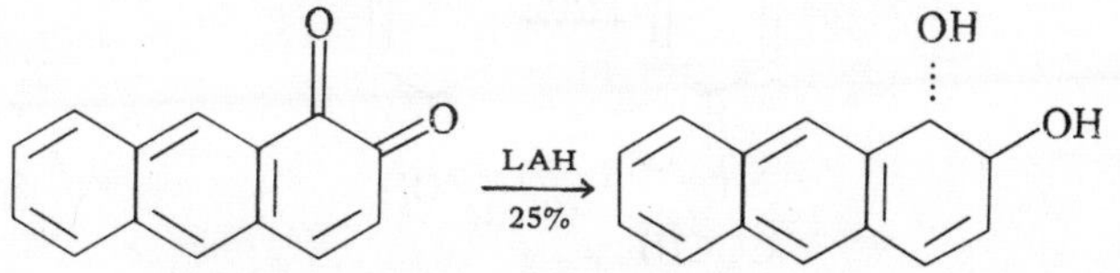

(7-212)

CCXCIX

Nystrom and Brown (12) and Schlesinger and Finholt (2) reported that the reduction of 9,10-phenanthraquinone (CCC) with LAH gives 9,10-di-hydroxyphenanthrene in 98% yield. Booth, Boyland and Turner (312) found that the reduction yields only traces of this product and over 80% of racemic *trans*-9,10-dihydroxy-9,10-dihydrophenanthrene (CCCI).

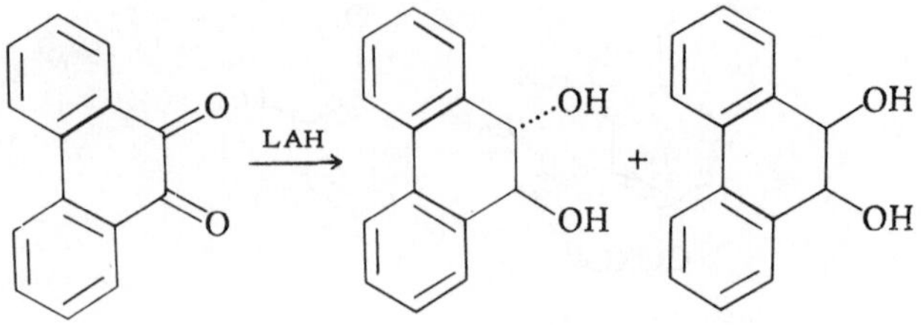

$$(7\text{-}213)$$

CCC   CCCI

The latter is analogous to the formation of *trans*-9,10-dihydroxy-9,10-diphenyl-9,10-dihydrophenanthrene by the reaction of CCC with phenyllithium (313) or phenylmagnesium bromide (314,315).

Trevoy and Brown (61) reported that the reduction of acenaphthenequinone (CCCII) with LAH in ether at $35°$ gives 45% of *trans*-acenaphthene glycol and 15% of the *cis*-glycol. At $-80°$ the yield of the *trans*-glycol is 50% and that of the *cis*-glycol is 13%.

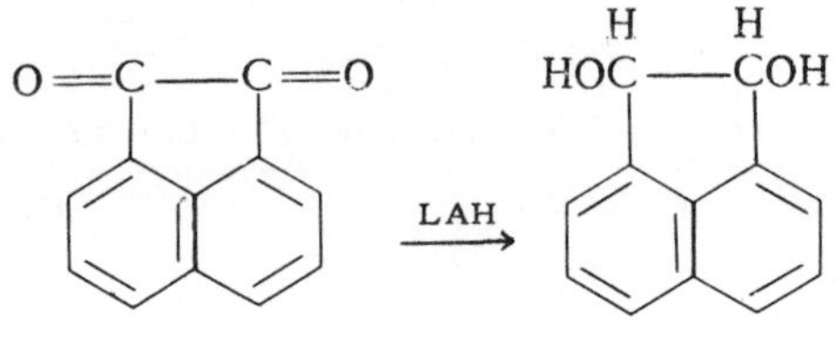

$$(7\text{-}214)$$

CCCII

7.3.1.b *p-Quinones.* The reduction of benzoquinone (CCCIII) with LAH yields 70% hydroquinone (2,12).

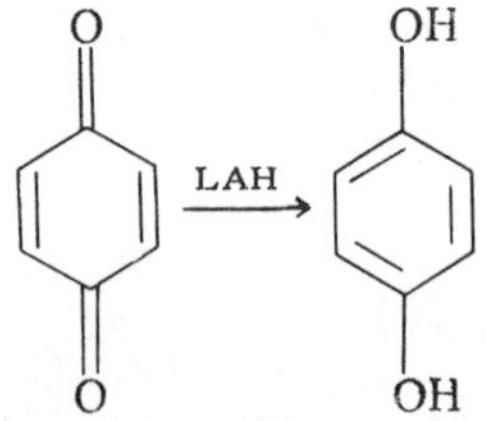

$$(7\text{-}215)$$

CCCIII

Boyland and Manson (316) found that the LAH reduction of 1,4-naphthaquinone (CCCIV) gives the phenolic derivative, 1,4-dihydroxynaphthalene (CCCV), as well as two neutral products isolated as benzoates. The neutral products contain saturated 2,3-bonds and have been identified as 1,2,3,4-tetrahydro-1,4-dihydroxynaphthalene (CCCVI) and 1,2,3,4-tetrahydro-4-hydroxy-1-ketonaphthalene (CCCVII).

$$(7\text{-}216)$$

CCCIV   CCCV   CCCVI   CCCVII

The reduction of 2-methyl-1,4-naphthaquinone (CCCVIII) gives different neutral alcoholic products according to the reaction conditions although the main product of the reaction is the phenolic 1,4-dihydroxy-2-methyl-naphthalene (CCCIX). The reduction of 10 g. (0.058 mole) of CCCVIII with 2 g. (0.053 mole) of LAH in refluxing ether gives CCCIX and 1,2,3,4-tetrahydro-1,4-dihydroxy-2-methylnaphthalene (CCCX). When the reduction is carried out with 1 g. (0.026 mole) of LAH in an attempt to avoid the hydrogenation of the 2,3-bond the only neutral product isolated is the keto-alcohol, 1,2,3,4-tetrahydro-1-hydroxy-4-keto-2-methylnaphthalene (CCCXI). When twice as much LAH is employed the main neutral product of the reaction depends on the temperature and solvent employed. The reduction of CCCVIII under different conditions is summarized in Table XXVI.

$$(7\text{-}217)$$

CCCVIII   CCCIX   CCCX

CCCXI

The saturation of the 2,3-bond is postulated as analogous to the 1,4-addition of hydrogen discussed in Section 7.2.1.i. The keto-alcohol (CCCXI) can be reduced to CCCX with LAH in refluxing ether.

Nystrom and Brown (12) reported that reduction of 9,10-anthraquinone (CCCXII) with LAH by the Soxhlet technique gives a 95% yield of "anthra-

TABLE XXVI

LAH Reduction of 2-Methyl-1,4-Naphthaquinone (316)

Quinone/LAH Molar Ratio	Solvent	Temp.	% Yield[a,b]	
			Dialcohol CCCX	Keto-Alcohol CCCXI
2/1	Ether	$-10°$		4.0
	Tetrahydrofuran	$-10°$		2.9
	Ether	$25°$		4.2
	Ether	$35°$		1.2
1/1	Ether	$-10°$	1.7	6.2
	Tetrahydrofuran	$-10°$	2.0	"small amount"
	Ether	$25°$	1.9	"small amount"
	Ether	$35°$	1.9	"small amount"
			4.4[c]	
	Tetrahydrofuran	$65°$	2.2	"small amount"

[a]Main product is 1,4-dihydroxy-2-methylnaphthalene.
[b]LAH in ethereal solution added to a solution of the quinone.
[c]Ethereal solution of quinone added to ethereal LAH solution.

hydroquinone'' presumably 9,10-dihydroxyanthracene. Boyland and Manson (316) found that the reaction product is 9,10-dihydroxy-9,10-dihydroanthracene (CCCXIII), in 13% yield in ethereal solution (72% based on unrecovered quinone) and 45% yield in tetrahydrofuran (67% based on unrecovered quinone).

$$\text{CCCXII} \xrightarrow{\text{LAH}} \text{CCCXIII} \qquad (7\text{-}218)$$

The reduction of 1-o-methoxyphenylanthraquinone in benzene with an ethereal LAH solution is reported to give 9,10-dihydroxy-9,10-dihydro-1-o-methoxyphenylanthracene (317).

7.3.2 Reductions with Other Complex Metal Hydrides

Benzoquinone is reduced to hydroquinone by the use of an ethereal solution of the aluminum hydride-aluminum chloride complex (318) as well as with lithium gallium hydride (56) and magnesium aluminum hydride (40).

Chaikin and Brown (42) reported that in the reaction of anthraquinone with sodium borohydride reduction occurred but boron-free products were not isolated.

REFERENCES

1. Schlesinger, H. I., and A. E. Finholt, U. S. Pat. 2,567,972 (September 18, 1951).
2. Schlesinger, H. I., and A. E. Finholt, U. S. Pat. 2,576,311 (November 27, 1951).
3. Nystrom, R. F., and W. G. Brown, *J. Am. Chem. Soc.*, 69, 1197 (1947).
4. Hayes, K., and G. Drake, *J. Org. Chem.*, 15, 873 (1950).
5. Arens, J. F., and D. A. van Dorp, *Rec. trav. chim.*, 68, 604 (1949).
6. Meunier, P., J. Jouanneteau, and G. Swingelstein, *Compt. rend.*, 231, 1170 (1950).
7. Wendler, N. L., C. Rosenblum, and M. Tishler, *J. Am. Chem. Soc.*, 72, 234 (1950).
8. van Dorp, D. A., and J. F. Arens, *Nature*, 160, 189 (1947).
9. Mellier, M. T., and M. Servent, *Oléagineux*, 6, 473 (1951); *Chem. Abstracts*, 46, 7081 (1952).
10. Jacquier, R., and R. Zagdoun, *Bull. soc. chim. France*, [5] 19, 698 (1952).
11. Mousseron, M., R. Jacquier, M. Mousseron-Canet, and R. Zagdoun, *Bull. soc. chim. France*, [5] 19, 1042 (1952).
12. Nystrom, R. F., and W. G. Brown, *J. Am. Chem. Soc.*, 70, 3738 (1948).
13. Hochstein, F. A., and W. G. Brown, *J. Am. Chem. Soc.*, 70, 3484 (1948).
14. Bohlmann, F., *Chem. Ber.*, 85, 1144 (1952).
15. Eiter, K., and E. Sackl, *Monatsh.*, 83, 123 (1952).
16. Petuely, F., and H. F. Bauer, *Monatsh.*, 83, 758 (1952).
17. Wille, F., and F. Knörr, *Chem. Ber.*, 85, 841 (1952).
18. Elphimoff-Felkin, I., H. Felkin, B. Tchoubar, and Z. Welvart, *Bull. soc. chim. France*, [5] 19, 252 (1952).
19. Abdel-Akher, M., and F. Smith, *Nature*, 166, 1037 (1950).
20. Hardegger, E., H. J. Leemann, and F. G. Robinet, *Helv. Chim. Acta*, 35, 825 (1952), footnote 1.
21. Prins, D. A., *J. Am. Chem. Soc.*, 70, 3955 (1948).
22. Marvel, C. S., and H. W. Hill, Jr., *J. Am. Chem. Soc.*, 73, 481 (1951).
23. Swoboda, W., *Monatsh.*, 82, 388 (1951).
24. Hurd, C. D., and W. H. Saunders, Jr., *J. Am. Chem. Soc.*, 74, 5324 (1952).
25. Finn, S. R., and J. W. G. Musty, *J. Appl. Chem. (London)*, 1, 182 (1951).
26. Finn, S. R., and J. W. G. Musty, *Chemistry and Industry*, 1950, 677.
27. Wessely, F., K. Benedikt, H. Benger, G. Friedrich, and F. Prillinger, *Monatsh.*, 81, 1071 (1950).
28. Schieler, L., and R. D. Sprenger, *J. Am. Chem. Soc.*, 73, 4045 (1952).
29. Larsson, E., *Trans. Chalmers Univ. Technol., Gothenburg*, 94, 15 (1950); *Chem. Abstracts*, 45, 1494 (1951).
30. Clemo, G. R., and J. M. Smith, *J. Chem. Soc.*, 1928, 2423.
31. Hass, H. B., and M. L. Bender, *J. Am. Chem. Soc.*, 71, 1767 (1949).
32. Conover, L. H., and D. S. Tarbell, *J. Am. Chem. Soc.*, 72, 3586 (1950).
33. Avison, A. W. D., *J. Appl. Chem. (London)*, 1, 469 (1951).
34. Badger, G. M., J. E. Campbell, J. W. Cook, R. A. Raphael and A. I. Scott, *J. Chem. Soc.*, 1950, 2326.
35. Newman, M. S., and H. S. Whitehouse, *J. Am. Chem. Soc.*, 71, 3664 (1949).
36. Treibs, A., and H. Scherer, *Ann.*, 577, 139 (1952).
37. Wiberg, E., and A. Jahn, *Z. Naturforsch.*, 7b, 581 (1952).
38. Wiberg, E., and A. Jahn, *Z. Naturforsch.*, 7b, 580 (1952).
39. Wiberg, E., and R. Bauer, *Z. Naturforsch.*, 5b, 397 (1950).

40. Wiberg, E., and R. Bauer, Z. Naturforsch., 7b, 131 (1952).
41. Wiberg, E., through European Scientific Notes, No. 7-1 (January 1, 1953).
42. Chaikin, S. W., and W. G. Brown, J. Am. Chem. Soc., 71, 122 (1949).
43. Societe des Usines Chimiques Rhone Poulenc, Australian Pat. Appln. 955/51 (February 21, 1951).
44. Hunger, A., and T. Reichstein, Helv. Chim. Acta, 35, 1073 (1952).
45. Hunger, A., and T. Reichstein, Chem. Ber., 85, 635 (1952).
46. Edwards, O. E., and L. Marion, Can. J. Chem., 30, 627 (1952).
47. Abdel-Akher, M., J. K. Hamilton, and F. Smith, J. Am. Chem. Soc., 73, 4691 (1951).
48. Wolfrom, M. L., and K. Anno, J. Am. Chem. Soc., 74, 5583 (1952).
49. Meller, A., Tappi, 36, 366 (1953).
50. Zief, M., and J. R. Stevens, J. Am. Chem. Soc., 74, 2126 (1952).
51. Lindberg, B., and A. Misiorny, Svensk Papperstidn., 55, 13 (1952); Chem. Abstracts, 46, 7942 (1952).
52. Abdel-Akher, M., J. K. Hamilton, R. Montgomery, and F. Smith, J. Am. Chem. Soc., 74, 4970 (1952).
53. Parke, Davis and Co., Australian Pat. Appln. 10904/52 (June 24, 1952).
54. Nystrom, R. F., S. W. Chaikin, and W. G. Brown, J. Am. Chem. Soc., 71, 3245 (1949).
55. Brown, W. G., L. Kaplan, and K. E. Wilzbach, J. Am. Chem. Soc., 74, 1343 (1952).
56. Wiberg, E., and M. Schmidt, Z. Naturforsch., 6b, 171 (1951).
57. Leo, A., and F. H. Westheimer, J. Am. Chem. Soc., 74, 4383 (1952).
58. Shiner, V. J., Jr., J. Am. Chem. Soc., 74, 5285 (1952).
59. Logan, A. V., and J. Murray, J. Am. Chem. Soc., 74, 2436 (1952).
60. Condon, F. E., J. Am. Chem. Soc., 73, 4675 (1951).
61. Trevoy, L. W., and W. G. Brown, J. Am. Chem. Soc., 71, 1675 (1949).
62. Paddock, N. L., Nature, 167, 1070 (1951).
63. Paddock, N. L., Chemistry and Industry, 1953, 63.
64. Cram, D. J., and F. A. Abd Elhafez, J. Am. Chem. Soc., 74, 5828 (1952).
65. Geiger, M., E. Usteri and C. Gränacher, Helv. Chim. Acta, 34, 1335 (1951).
66. Schlenk, H., and B. Lamp, J. Am. Chem. Soc., 73, 5493 (1951).
67. Henne, A. L., M. A. Smook, and R. L. Pelley, J. Am. Chem. Soc., 72, 4756 (1950).
68. Henne, A. L., and R. L. Pelley, J. Am. Chem. Soc., 74, 1426 (1952).
69. Skerrett, E. J., and D. Woodcock, J. Chem. Soc., 1952, 3308.
70. Winstein, S., B. K. Morse, E. Grunwald, K. C. Schreiber, and J. Corse, J. Am. Chem. Soc., 74, 1113 (1952).
71. Cromwell, N. H., and Kwan-Chung Tsou, J. Org. Chem., 15, 1219 (1950).
72. May, E. L., and E. Mosettig, J. Org. Chem., 13, 459 (1948).
73. Speeter, M. E., W. M. Byrd, L. C. Cheney, and S. B. Binkley, J. Am. Chem. Soc., 71, 57 (1949).
74. Pohland, A., F. J. Marshall, and T. P. Carney, J. Am. Chem. Soc., 71, 460 (1949).
75. May, E. L., and E. Mosettig, J. Org. Chem., 13, 663 (1948).
76. Eddy, N. B., E. L. May, and E. Mosettig, J. Org. Chem., 17, 321 (1952).
77. May, E. L., and N. B. Eddy, J. Org. Chem., 17, 1210 (1952).
78. Bockmühl, M., and G. Ehrhart, Ann., 561, 52 (1948).
79. Speeter, M. E., L. C. Cheney, and S. B. Binkley, J. Am. Chem. Soc., 72, 1659 (1950).
80. Bothner-By, A. A., J. Am. Chem. Soc., 73, 846 (1951).

81. Backer, H. J., J. Strating, and J. Drenth, *Rec. trav. chim.*, 70, 365 (1951).
82. Slabey, V. A., and P. H. Wise, *J. Am. Chem. Soc.*, 71, 3252 (1949).
83. Van Volkenburgh, R., K. W. Greenlee, J. M. Derfer, and C. E. Boord, *J. Am. Chem. Soc.*, 71, 3595 (1949).
84. Johnson, W. S., J. Szmuszkovicz, and M. Miller, *J. Am. Chem. Soc.*, 72, 3726 (1950).
85. Shirley, D. A., and G. A. Schmidt, *J. Am. Chem. Soc.*, 73, 5507 (1951).
86. Normant, H., *Compt. rend.*, 232, 1358 (1951).
87. Asselineau, J., E. Ganz, and E. Lederer, *Compt. rend.*, 232, 2050 (1951).
88. Smith, L. I., and R. R. Holmes, *J. Am. Chem. Soc.*, 73, 3851 (1951).
89. Cromwell, N. H., and F. W. Starks, *J. Am. Chem. Soc.*, 72, 4108 (1950).
90. Boekelheide, V., and E. J. Agnello, *J. Am. Chem. Soc.*, 72, 5005 (1950).
91. May, E. L., and E. Mosettig, *J. Am. Chem. Soc.*, 73, 1301 (1951).
92. May, E. L., and E. Mosettig, *J. Am. Chem. Soc.*, 70, 686 (1951).
93. Williams, A. L., and A. R. Day, *J. Am. Chem. Soc.*, 74, 3875 (1952).
94. Price, C. C., and G. H. Schilling, *J. Am. Chem. Soc.*, 70, 4265 (1948).
95. Price, C. C., and Sing-Tuh Voong, *J. Org. Chem.*, 14, 111 (1949).
96. Coll, A. L. P., *Afinidad*, 27, 549 (1950); *Chem Abstracts*, 45, 7981 (1951).
97. Newman, M. S., and N. C. Deno, *J. Am. Chem. Soc.*, 73, 3644 (1951).
98. Julian, P. L., W. Cole, G. Diemer, and J. G. Schafer, *J. Am. Chem. Soc.*, 71, 2058 (1949).
99. Cairns, T. L., and B. C. McKusick, *J. Org. Chem.*, 15, 790 (1950).
100. Hayes, K., and G. Gever, *J. Org. Chem.*, 16, 269 (1951).
101. Morrison, A. L., and H. Rinderknecht, *J. Chem. Soc.*, 1950, 1467.
102. Newman, M. S., and W. L. Mosby, *J. Am. Chem. Soc.*, 73, 3738 (1951).
103. Blood, C. T., and R. P. Linstead, *J. Chem. Soc.*, 1952, 2255.
104. Winternitz, F., and R. M. Thakker, *Bull. soc. chim. France*, [5] 18, 792 (1951); 19, 471 (1952).
105. Noyce, D. S., and D. B. Denney, *J. Am. Chem. Soc.*, 72, 5743 (1950).
106. Goering, H. L., and C. Serres, Jr., *J. Am. Chem. Soc.*, 74, 5908 (1952).
107. Sarett, L. H., R. M. Lukes, G. I. Poos, J. M. Robinson, R. E. Beyler, J. M. Vandergrift, and G. E. Arth, *J. Am. Chem. Soc.*, 74, 1393 (1952).
108. Beyler, R. E., and L. H. Sarett, *J. Am. Chem. Soc.*, 74, 1406 (1952).
109. Roberts, J. D., and W. F. Gorham, *J. Am. Chem. Soc.*, 74, 2278 (1952).
110. Sternbach, L. H., and S. Kaiser, *J. Am. Chem. Soc.*, 74, 2215 (1952).
111. Leonard, N. J., S. Swann, Jr., and J. Figueras, Jr., *J. Am. Chem. Soc.*, 74, 4620 (1952).
112. Mirza, R., *Nature*, 170, 630 (1952).
113. Leonard, N. J., S. Swann, Jr., and H. L. Dryden, Jr., *J. Am. Chem. Soc.*, 74, 2871 (1952).
114. Witkop, B., *J. Am. Chem. Soc.*, 70, 3712 (1948).
115. Clemo, G. R., and K. H. Jack, *Chemistry and Industry*, 1953, 195.
116. Sparke, M. B., *Chemistry and Industry*, 1953, 749.
117. Burger, A., and E. D. Hornbaker, *J. Am. Chem. Soc.*, 74, 5514 (1952).
118. Avison, A. W. D., *J. Appl. Chem. (London)*, 1, 469 (1951).
119. Dornow, A., and G. Petsch, *Arch. pharm.*, 285, 323 (1952).
120. Mousseron, M., and M. Canet, *Bull. soc. chim. France*, [5] 19, 247 (1952).
121. Mousseron, M., and M. Canet, *Bull. soc. chim. France*, [5] 18, 792 (1951).
122. Reynaud, P., and J. Matti, *Bull. soc. chim. France*, [5] 18, 612 (1951).
123. Nystrom, R. F., and W. G. Brown, *J. Am. Chem. Soc.*, 69, 2548 (1947).
124. Gruber, W., and H. Renner, *Monatsh.*, 81, 751 (1950).
125. Boyer, J. H., *J. Am. Chem. Soc.*, 73, 5865 (1951).

126. Felkin, H., *Compt. rend.*, *230*, 304 (1950).
127. Gregory, G. I., and T. Malkin, *J. Chem. Soc.*, *1951*, 2453.
128. Fisher, N., *Chemistry and Industry*, *1952*, 130.
129. Viscontini, M., and K. Adank, *Helv. Chim. Acta*, *35*, 1342 (1952).
130. Viscontini, M., *Helv. Chim. Acta*, *35*, 1803 (1952).
131. Buchta, E., and H. Bayer, *Ann.*, *573*, 227 (1951).
132. Viscontini, M., and C. Ebnöther, *Helv. Chim. Acta*, *34*, 116 (1951).
133. Helg, R., and H. Schinz, *Helv. Chim. Acta*, *35*, 2406 (1952).
134. Carrara, G., V. D'Ameto, and M. Bellenghi, *Gazz. chim. ital.*, *80*, 822 (1950).
135. Frank, R. L., and H. K. Hall, Jr., *J. Am. Chem. Soc.*, *72*, 1645 (1950).
136. Höfling, E., and W. Schöninger, private communication; through F. Petuely, and W. Künssberg, *Monatsh.*, *83*, 86 (1952).
137. Dreiding, A. S., and J. A. Hartman, *J. Am. Chem. Soc.*, *75*, 939 (1953).
138. Voltman, A., unpublished results; through ref. 137.
139. Reid, W. B., Jr., U. S. Pat. 2,605,266 (July 29, 1952).
140. Protiva, M., and J. O. Jílek, *Chem. Listy*, in press; through M. Ferles, and J. Rudinger, *Chem. Listy*, *47*, 113 (1953).
141. Browne, C. L., and R. E. Lutz, *J. Org. Chem.*, *17*, 1187 (1952).
142. Colonna, M., and C. Runti, *Ann. chim. (Rome)*, *41*, 740 (1951); through M. Ferles, and J. Rudinger, *Chem. Listy*, *47*, 115 (1953).
143. Wishingsky, H., and M. Rubin, *Abstracts of Papers*, XIIth International Congress of Pure and Applied Chemistry, New York, N. Y., September 1951, p. 307.
144. Winternitz, F., and N. J. Antia, *Bull. soc. chim. France*, [5] *19*, 248 (1952).
145. Cromwell, N. H., and N. G. Barker, *J. Am. Chem. Soc.*, *72*, 4110 (1950).
146. Barker, N. G., and N. H. Cromwell, *J. Am. Chem. Soc.*, *73*, 1051 (1951).
147. Sculley, J. D., and N. H. Cromwell, *J. Org. Chem.*, *16*, 94 (1951).
148. Knight, J. D., and D. J. Cram, *J. Am. Chem. Soc.*, *73*, 4136 (1951).
149. Lynn, J. W., and J. English, Jr., *J. Am. Chem. Soc.*, *73*, 4284 (1951).
150. Blomquist, A. T., R. E. Burge, Jr., and A. C. Sucsy, *J. Am. Chem. Soc.*, *74*, 3636 (1952).
151. Ingraham, R. B., D. M. MacDonald, and K. Wiesner, *Can. J. Research*, *28B*, 453 (1950).
152. Wear, R. L., *J. Am. Chem. Soc.*, *73*, 2390 (1951).
153. Findlay, S. P., and L. F. Small, *J. Am. Chem. Soc.*, *73*, 4001 (1951).
154. Proštenik, M., and J. Bišćan, *Arhiv. Kemi*, *22*, 177 (1951); through *Chem. Abstracts*, *46*, 3951 (1952).
155. Spriggs, A. S., C. M. Hill, and G. W. Senter, *J. Am. Chem. Soc.*, *74*, 1555 (1952).
156. Braude, E. A., and J. A. Coles, *J. Chem. Soc.*, *1952*, 1425.
157. Meek, J. S., F. J. Lorenzi, and S. J. Cristol, *J. Am. Chem. Soc.*, *71*, 1830 (1949).
158. Sah, P. P. T., Z. *Vitamin-, Hormon- u. Fermentforsch*, *3*, 324 (1949–1950); through M. Ferles and J. Rudinger, *Chem. Listy*, *47*, 129 (1953).
159. Hochstein, F. A., *J. Am. Chem. Soc.*, *71*, 305 (1949).
160. Brown, W. G., in *Organic Reactions*, Vol. VI, p. 482.
161. Bohlmann, F., *Chem. Ber.*, *85*, 386 (1952).
162. Rondestvedt, C. S., Jr., *J. Am. Chem. Soc.*, *73*, 4509 (1951).
163. Pew, J. C., *J. Am. Chem. Soc.*, *73*, 1678 (1951).
164. Pew, J. C., *J. Am. Chem. Soc.*, *74*, 2850 (1952).
165. Lutz, R. E., and J. S. Gillespie, Jr., *J. Am. Chem. Soc.*, *72*, 2002 (1950).

166. Lutz, R. E., and D. F. Hinkley, *J. Am. Chem. Soc.,* 72, 4091 (1950).
167. Lutz, R. E., and J. S. Gillespie, Jr., *Abstracts of Papers,* 116th Meeting American Chemical Society, Atlantic City, N. J., September 1949, p. 8M.
168. Lutz, R. E., and J. S. Gillespie, Jr., *J. Am. Chem. Soc.,* 72, 344 (1950).
169. Lutz, R. E., and W. R. Tyson, *J. Am. Chem. Soc.,* 56, 1341 (1934).
170. McGhie, J. F., and J. F. Cavalla, *Chemistry and Industry, 1950,* 744.
171. Cavalla, J. F., and J. F. McGhie, *J. Chem. Soc., 1951,* 834.
172. Henbest, H. B., and G. Woods, *J. Chem. Soc., 1952,* 1150.
173. Henbest, H. G., B. L. Shaw, and G. Woods, *J. Chem. Soc., 1952,* 1154.
174. English, J., Jr., and V. Lamberti, *J. Am. Chem. Soc.,* 74, 1909 (1952).
175. Mousseron, M., R. Jacquier, M. Mousseron-Canet, and R. Zagdoun, *Compt. rend.,* 235, 177 (1952).
176. Macbeth, A. K., and J. S. Shannon, *J. Chem. Soc., 1952,* 2852.
177. Étienne, A., and J. Weill-Raynal, *Compt. rend.,* 235, 301 (1952).
178. Vonderwahl, R., and H. Schinz, *Helv. Chim. Acta,* 35, 2368 (1952).
179. Seifert, P., and H. Schinz, *Helv. Chim. Acta,* 34, 728 (1951).
180. Blanchard, J. P., and H. L. Goering, *J. Am. Chem. Soc.,* 73, 5863 (1951).
181. Conroy, H., *J. Am. Chem. Soc.,* 74, 3046 (1952).
182. Woodward, R. B., F. Sondheimer, D. Taub, K. Heusler, and W. M. McLamore, *J. Am. Chem. Soc.,* 73, 2403 (1951).
183. Woodward, R. B., F. Sondheimer, D. Taub, K. Heusler, and W. M. McLamore, *J. Am. Chem. Soc.,* 74, 4223 (1952).
184. Thomson, R. H., *J. Chem. Soc., 1950,* 1737.
185. Boekelheide, V., W. E. Langeland and Chu-Tsin Liu, *J. Am. Chem. Soc.,* 73, 2432 (1951).
186. Dannenberg, H., and H. Brachert, *Chem. Ber.,* 84, 504 (1951).
187. Clemo, G. R., L. H. Groves, L. Munday, and G. A. Swan, *J. Chem. Soc., 1951,* 863.
188. Orchin, M., and L. Reggel, *J. Am. Chem. Soc.,* 73, 436 (1951).
189. Wender, I., H. Greenfield, and M. Orchin, *J. Am. Chem. Soc.,* 73, 2656 (1951).
190. Bergmann, E. D., G. Berthier, E. Fischer, Y. Hirshberg, D. Lavie, E. Loewenthal, and B. Pullman, *Bull. soc. chim. France,* [5] 19, 78 (1952).
191. Bergmann, E. D., G. Berthier, D. Ginsburg, Y. Hirshberg, D. Lavie, S. Pinchas, B. Pullman, and A. Pullman, *Bull. soc. chim. France,* [5] 18, 661 (1951).
192. Bergmann, E. D., Y. Hirshberg, and D. Lavie, *Bull. soc. chim. France,* [5] 19, 268 (1952).
193. Bergmann, E., *Ber.,* 63, 1037 (1930).
194. Julian, P. L., and A. Magnani, *J. Am. Chem. Soc.,* 56, 2174 (1934); P. L. Julian and W. Cole, *ibid.,* 57, 1607 (1935).
195. Bergmann, E. D., *Bull. soc. chim. France,* [5] 19, 703 (1952).
196. Sonntag, N. O. V., S. Linder, E. I. Becker, and P. E. Spoerri, *J. Am. Chem. Soc.,* 75, 2283 (1953).
197. Boekelheide, V., and C. E. Larrabee, *J. Am. Chem. Soc.,* 72, 1245 (1950).
198. Boekelheide, V., and C. E. Larrabee, *J. Am. Chem. Soc.,* 72, 1240 (1950).
199. Mustafa, A., and M. K. Hilmy, *J. Chem. Soc., 1952,* 1343.
200. Mirza, R., and R. Robinson, *Nature,* 166, 997 (1950).
201. Robinson, R., and R. Mirza, *Nature,* 166, 929 (1950).
202. Campbell, T. W., and G. M. Coppinger, *J. Am. Chem. Soc.,* 74, 1469 (1952).
203. Cook, J. W., A. R. Gibb, R. A. Raphael, and A. R. Somerville, *J. Chem. Soc., 1951,* 503.

204. Cook, J. W., R. A. Raphael, and A. I. Scott, *J. Chem. Soc.*, *1952*, 4416.
205. Beer, R. J. S., L. McGrath, and A. Robertson, *J. Chem. Soc.*, *1950*, 2118.
206. Witkop, B., J. B. Patrick, and M. Rosenblum, *J. Am. Chem. Soc.*, *73*, 2641 (1951).
207. Uhle, F. C., *J. Am. Chem. Soc.*, *71*, 761 (1949).
208. Johnson, W. S., and B. G. Buell, *J. Am. Chem. Soc.*, *74*, 4517 (1952).
209. Badger, G. M., J. H. Seidler, and B. Thomson, *J. Chem. Soc.*, *1951*, 3207.
210. Campbell, K. N., J. F. Ackerman and B. K. Campbell, *J. Org. Chem.* *15*, 337 (1950).
211. Witkop, B., *J. Am. Chem. Soc.*, *72*, 2311 (1950).
212. Bendz, G., C. C. J. Culvenor, L. J. Goldsworthy, K. S. Kirby and R. Robinson, *J. Chem. Soc.*, *1950*, 1130; C. C. J. Culvenor, L. J. Goldsworthy, K. S. Kirby, and R. Robinson, *Nature*, *166*, 105 (1950).
213. Witkop, B., and A. Ek, *J. Am. Chem. Soc.*, *73*, 5664 (1951).
214. Witkop, B., and J. B. Patrick, *Experientia*, *6*, 183 (1950).
215. Witkop, B., *J. Am. Chem. Soc.*, *72*, 614 (1950).
216. Witkop, B., and J. B. Patrick, *J. Am. Chem. Soc.*, *73*, 713 (1951).
217. Cook, J. W., J. D. Loudon, and P. McCloskey, *J. Chem. Soc.*, *1952*, 3904.
218. Mirza, R., *Experientia*, *8*, 258 (1952).
219. MacLean, D. B., R. H. F. Manske, and L. Marion, *Can. J. Research*, *28B*, 460 (1950).
220. Bertho, A., and A. Stoll, *Chem. Ber.*, *85*, 663 (1952).
221. Kyburz, E., M. V. Mićović, W. Voser, H. Heusser, O. Jeger and L. Ruzicka, *Helv. Chim. Acta*, *35*, 2073 (1952).
222. Voser, W., M. Montavon, H. H. Günthard, O. Jeger, and L. Ruzicka, *Helv. Chim. Acta*, *33*, 1893 (1950).
223. Barnes, C. S., D. H. R. Barton, J. S. Fawcett, S. K. Knight, J. F. McGhie, M. K. Pradhan, and B. R. Thomas, *Chemistry and Industry*, *1951*, 1067; C. S. Barnes, D. H. R. Barton, A. R. H. Cole, J. S. Fawcett, and B. R. Thomas, *ibid.*, *1952*, 426; J. F. Cavalla, J. F. McGhie, and M. K. Pradhan, *J. Chem. Soc.*, *1951*, 3142; D. H. R. Barton, J. S. Fawcett, and B. R. Thomas, *ibid.*, *1951*, 3147; C. S. Barnes, D. H. R. Barton, J. S. Fawcett, and B. R. Thomas, *ibid.*, *1952*, 2339; J. F. McGhie, M. K. Pradhan, and J. F. Cavalla, *ibid.*, *1952*, 3176.
224. Voser, W., H. H. Günthard, O. Jeger, and L. Ruzicka, *Helv. Chim. Acta*, *35*, 66 (1952).
225. Barton, D. H. R., and N. J. Holness, *Chemistry and Industry*, *1951*, 233; *J. Chem. Soc.*, *1952*, 78.
226. Ames, T. R., G. S. Davy, T. G. Halsall, E. R. H. Jones, and G. D. Meakins, *Chemistry and Industry*, *1951*, 741.
227. Davy, G. S., E. R. H. Jones, and T. G. Halsall, *Rec. trav. chim.*, *69*, 368 (1950).
228. Cavalla, J. F., and J. F. McGhie, *J. Chem. Soc.*, *1951*, 744.
229. Barton, D. H. R., and C. J. W. Brooks, *J. Chem. Soc.*, *1951*, 257.
230. Šorm, F., and V. Herout, *Collection Czech. Chem. Communs.*, *14*, 723 (1949).
231. Shoppee, C. W., and G. H. R. Summers, *J. Chem. Soc.*, *1950*, 687.
232. Nace, H. R., and G. L. O'Connor, *J. Am. Chem. Soc.*, *73*, 5824 (1951).
233. Dauben, W. G., R. A. Micheli, and J. F. Eastham, *J. Am. Chem. Soc.*, *74*, 3852 (1952).
234. Ruzicka, L., H. Brüngger, E. Eichenberger, and J. Meyer, *Helv. Chim. Acta*, *17*, 1407 (1934).

235. Ciba S. A., Fr. Pat. 994,615; Ciba Ltd., Brit. Pat. 665,254; P. Plattner, Ger. Pat. 834,848; U. S. Pat. 2,599,481.
236. Plattner, P. A., H. Heusser, and A. B. Kulkarni, *Helv. Chim. Acta*, 32, 265 (1949).
237. Ellis, B., and V. Petrow, *J. Chem. Soc.*, 1952, 2246.
238. Birch, A. J., *J. Chem. Soc.*, 1950, 2325.
239. Ruzicka, L., and M. W. Goldberg, *Helv. Chim. Acta*, 19, 1407 (1936).
240. McKennis, H., Jr., and G. W. Gaffney, *J. Biol. Chem.*, 175, 217 (1948).
241. Plattner, P. A., H. Heusser, and A. B. Kulkarni, *Helv. Chim. Acta*, 32, 1070 (1949).
242. Musgrave, O. C., *J. Chem. Soc.*, 1951, 3121.
243. Ruzicka, L., N. Wahba, P. T. Herzig, and H. Heusser, *Chem. Ber.*, 85, 491 (1952).
244. Heusser, H., M. Feurer, K. Eichenberger, and V. Prelog, *Helv. Chim. Acta*, 33, 2243 (1950).
245. Schmutz, J., H. Schaltegger, and M. Sanz, *Helv. Chim. Acta*, 34, 1111 (1951).
246. Romo, J., H. J. Ringold, G. Rosenkranz, and C. Djerassi, *J. Org. Chem.*, 16, 1873 (1951).
247. Petrow, V. A., *J. Chem. Soc.*, 1940, 66.
248. Dauben, W. G., and J. F. Eastham, *J. Am. Chem. Soc.*, 72, 2305 (1950); 73, 3260 (1951).
249. Shoppee, C. W., and G. H. R. Summers, *J. Chem. Soc.*, 1952, 1786, 1790, 3361, 3374.
250. Alt, G. H., and D. H. R. Barton, *Chemistry and Industry*, 1952, 1103.
251. Wagner, A. F., and E. S. Wallis, *J. Am. Chem. Soc.*, 72, 1047 (1950).
252. Wagner, A. F., N. E. Wolff, and E. S. Wallis, *J. Org. Chem.*, 17, 529 (1952).
253. Shoppee, C. W., and G. H. R. Summers, *J. Chem. Soc.*, 1952, 3361.
254. Fieser, L. F., M. Fieser, and R. N. Chakravarti, *J. Am. Chem. Soc.*, 71, 2226 (1949).
255. Fieser, L. F., J. E. Herz, M. W. Klohs, M. A. Romero, and T. Utne, *J. Am. Chem. Soc.*, 74, 3309 (1952).
256. Djerassi, C., E. Batres, M. Velasco, and G. Rosenkranz, *J. Am. Chem. Soc.*, 74, 1712 (1952).
257. Windaus, A., H. Lettré, and F. Schenck, *Ann.*, 520, 98 (1935).
258. Buser, W., *Helv. Chim. Acta*, 30, 1379 (1947).
259. Ringold, H. J., G. Rosenkranz, and C. Djerassi, *J. Am. Chem. Soc.*, 74, 3318 (1952).
260. Greenhalgh, C. W., H. B. Henbest, and E. R. H. Jones, *J. Chem. Soc.*, 1952, 2375.
261. Sarett, L. H., M. Feurer, and K. Folkers, *J. Am. Chem. Soc.*, 73, 1777 (1951).
262. Fieser, L. F., *Experientia*, 6, 312 (1950).
263. Djerassi, C., H. Martinez, and G. Rosenkranz, *J. Org. Chem.*, 16, 1278 (1951).
264. Heusser, H., R. Anliker, and O. Jeger, *Helv. Chim. Acta*, 35, 1537 (1952).
265. Hirschmann, R., C. S. Snoddy, Jr., and N. L. Wendler, *J. Am. Chem. Soc.*, 74, 2693 (1952).
266. Wilds, A. L., J. A. Johnson, Jr., and R. E. Sutton, *J. Am. Chem. Soc.*, 72, 5524 (1950).
267. Sandoval, A., J. Romo, G. Rosenkranz, S. Kaufmann, and C. Djerassi, *J. Am. Chem. Soc.*, 73, 3820 (1951).

320   REDUCTION OF CARBONYL DERIVATIVES

268. Nussbaum, A. L., A. Sandoval, G. Rosenkranz, and C. Djerassi, *J. Org. Chem.*, *17*, 426 (1952).
269. Shoppee, C. W., *Nature*, *166*, 107 (1950).
270. Gallagher, T. F., and T. H. Kritchevsky, *J. Am. Chem. Soc.*, *72*, 882 (1950).
271. Greenhalgh, C. W., H. B. Henbest, and E. R. H. Jones, *J. Chem. Soc.*, *1951*, 1190.
272. Ott, A. C., and M. F. Murray, *Abstracts of Papers*, 113th Meeting American Chemical Society, Chicago, Ill., April 1948, p. 17K.
273. Marker, R. E., *J. Am. Chem. Soc.*, *60*, 1879 (1938); R. E. Marker and E. Rohrmann, *ibid.*, *60*, 2927 (1938).
274. Whitman, B., O. Wintersteiner, and E. Schwenk, *J. Biol. Chem.*, *118*, 789 (1937).
275. Bachmann, W. E., and A. S. Dreiding, *J. Am. Chem. Soc.*, *72*, 1323 (1950).
276. Shoppee, C. W., *Chemistry and Industry*, *1950*, 810.
277. Djerassi, C., G. Rosenkranz, J. Romo, S. Kaufmann, and J. Pataki, *J. Am. Chem. Soc.*, *72*, 4534 (1950).
278. Carol, J., E. O. Haenni, and D. Banes, unpublished work, through *J. Biol. Chem.*, *185*, 267 (1950).
279. Ott, A. C., M. F. Murray, and R. L. Pederson, *J. Am. Chem. Soc.*, *74*, 1239 (1952).
280. Papineau-Couture, G., E. M. Richardson, and G. A. Grant, *Can. J. Research*, *27B*, 902 (1949).
281. Banes, D., J. Carol, and E. O. Haenni, *J. Biol. Chem.*, *187*, 557 (1950).
282. Heer, J., and K. Miescher, *Helv. Chim. Acta*, *34*, 359 (1951).
283. Antonucci, R., S. Bernstein, R. Littell, K. J. Sax, and J. H. Williams, *J. Org. Chem.*, *17*, 1341 (1952).
284. Antonucci, R., S. Bernstein, R. Lenhard, K. J. Sax, and J. H. Williams, *J. Org. Chem.*, *17*, 1369 (1952).
285. Romo, J., G. Rosenkranz, and C. Djerassi, *J. Am. Chem. Soc.*, *73*, 4961 (1951).
286. Rosenkranz, G., S. Kaufmann, and J. Romo, *J. Am. Chem. Soc.*, *71*, 3689 (1949).
287. Meystre, C., and K. Miescher, *Helv. Chim. Acta*, *32*, 1758 (1949).
288. Belleau, B., and T. F. Belleau, *J. Am. Chem. Soc.*, *74*, 2816 (1952).
289. Schmid, L., W. Swoboda, and M. Wichtl, *Monatsh.*, *83*, 185 (1952).
290. Ott, A. C., and M. F. Murray, U. S. Pat. 2,625,556 (January 13, 1953).
291. Wiberg, E., R. Bauer, and P. Buchheit, *Angew. Chem.*, *62*, 448 (1950).
292. Schlesinger, H. I., H. C. Brown, H. R. Hoekstra and L. R. Rapp, *J. Am. Chem. Soc.*, *75*, 199 (1953).
293. McBee, E. T., and T. M. Burton, *J. Am. Chem. Soc.*, *74*, 3022 (1952).
294. Shechter, H., D. E. Ley, and L. Zeldin, *J. Am. Chem. Soc.*, *74*, 3664 (1952).
295. Woodward, R. B., F. Sondheimer, and D. Taub, *J. Am. Chem. Soc.*, *73*, 4057 (1951).
296. Elisberg, E., H. Vanderhaeghe, and T. F. Gallagher, *J. Am. Chem. Soc.*, *74*, 2814 (1952).
297. Heymann, H., and L. F. Fieser, *J. Am. Chem. Soc.*, *73*, 5252 (1951).
298. Sarett, L. H., G. E. Arth, R. M. Lukes, R. E. Beyler, G. I. Poos, W. F. Johns, and J. M. Constantin, *J. Am. Chem. Soc.*, *74*, 4974 (1952).
299. St. André, A. F., H. B. MacPhillamy, J. A. Nelson, A. C. Shabica, and C. R. Scholz, *J. Am. Chem. Soc.*, *74*, 5506 (1952).

300. Heusser, H., P. T. Herzig, A. Fürst, and P. A. Plattner, *Helv. Chim. Acta,* 33, 1093 (1950).

301. Belleau, B., and T. F. Gallagher, *J. Am. Chem. Soc.,* 73, 4458 (1951).

302. Dauben, W. G., and J. F. Eastham, *J. Am. Chem. Soc.,* 73, 4463 (1951).

303. Schwenk, E., M. Gut, and J. Belisle, *Arch. Biochem. Biophys.,* 31, 456 (1951).

304. Parke, Davis and Co., Australian Pat. Appln. 13,395/52 (October 15, 1952).

305. Vaillant, M., *Compt. rend.,* 234, 534 (1952).

306. Sannié, C., and H. Lapin, *Bull. soc. chim. France,* [5] 19, 1080 (1952).

307. Wendler, N. L., Huang-Minlon, and M. Tishler, *J. Am. Chem. Soc.,* 73, 3818 (1951).

308. Huang-Minlon and R. H. Pettebone, *J. Am. Chem. Soc.,* 74, 1562 (1952).

309. Wendler, N. L., R. P. Graber, R. E. Jones, and M. Tishler, *J. Am. Chem. Soc.,* 74, 3630 (1952).

310. Wendler, N. L., R. P. Graber, Rl E. Jones, and M. Tishler, *J. Am. Chem. Soc.,* 72, 5793 (1950).

311. Ciba Akt., Swiss Pat. 274,087 (June 1, 1951); Ciba Ltd., Brit. Pat. 665,337 (January 23, 1952).

312. Booth, J., E. Boyland, and E. E. Turner, *J. Chem. Soc.,* 1950, 1188.

313. Crawford, H. M., M. Lumpkin, and M. McDonald, *J. Am. Chem. Soc.,* 74, 4087 (1952).

314. Bachmann, W. E., *J. Am. Chem. Soc.,* 54, 1969 (1932).

315. Acree, S. F., *Am. Chem. J.,* 33, 186 (1905).

316. Boyland, E., and D. Manson, *J. Chem. Soc.,* 1951, 1837.

317. Braude, E. A., and J. S. Fawcett, *J. Chem. Soc.,* 1952, 1528.

318. Wiberg, E., and M. Schmidt, *Z. Naturforsch.,* 6b, 333 (1951).

CHAPTER 8

Reduction of
OXYGEN-CONTAINING ORGANIC COMPOUNDS
II. Carboxylic Acid Derivatives
(Acids, Anhydrides, Acyl Halides)

8.1 CARBOXYLIC ACIDS

8.1.1 Reductions with Lithium Aluminum Hydride

The reduction of carboxylic acids consumes three-quarters of a mole of LAH per mole of acid (1) according to the equation:

$$4\ RCOOH + 3\ LiAlH_4 \rightarrow (RCH_2O)_4\ LiAl + 2\ LiAlO_2 + 4\ H_2 \qquad (8\text{-}1)$$

The acidic hydrogen consumes one-quarter mole of hydride while hydroxyl and amino groups in hydroxy and amino acids consume an equivalent amount of LAH.

The reduction generally proceeds satisfactorily although in some cases an insoluble derivative is formed, in the initial active hydrogen reaction, which is slowly reduced. In such cases the reduction of the corresponding ester or acid chloride is more satisfactory.

The reduction of ether-soluble acids is carried out by the usual procedure of adding an ethereal solution of the acid to one of the hydride. In the case of slightly soluble acids, the latter, in the thimble of a Soxhlet extractor, is continuously extracted with solvent from a refluxing LAH solution.

8.1.1.a *Aliphatic carboxylic acids*. The LAH reduction of α,β-saturated aliphatic carboxylic acids yields the corresponding alcohol without undue difficulty.

The LAH reduction of mono-, di-, and trichlorosubstituted aliphatic acids yields the corresponding chloroalcohol (2,3). A patent on the use of fluorinated aliphatic phosphates reported the synthesis of heptafluorobutanol, in 26% yield, by the LAH reduction of heptafluorobutyric acid (4). However, Husted and Ahlbrecht reported that the products of the reduction of perfluoroaliphatic carboxylic acids (I) are mixtures of the perfluoroalcohol and the corresponding aldehydrol (5-8).

$$C_nF_{2n+1}COOH \xrightarrow{\text{LAH}} C_nF_{2n+1}CH_2OH + C_nF_{2n+1}CH(OH)_2 \qquad (8\text{-}2)$$

I

The aldehydrol, i.e., the aldehyde monohydrate, is dehydrated to the aldehyde by means of sulfuric acid or phosphorous pentoxide. The fluorocarbon aldehydes are sensitive to moisture, forming aldehydrols almost instantaneously in the presence of water, and polymerize rapidly at room temperature, while the aldehydrols are quite stable. The patents claim the aldehydrols from three to eighteen carbon atoms with specific claims for the two, three, and four carbon compounds and the corresponding aldehydes. Utilizing a 1:1 ratio of LAH to acid, the yields of aldehyde are reported as ranging from 20–40% while McBee and his co-workers found that a 0.75:1 ratio gives yields of aldehyde from 40–49% and 40–50% of the accompanying perfluoroalcohol (9).

Reid and Smith reported (10) that trifluoroacetic acid as well as various perfluoroamides form unstable complexes with LAH which decompose violently upon heating on a hot plate. The production of free carbon indicates the deep-seated nature of the decomposition.

Although the LAH reduction of amino acids to amino alcohols generally proceeds satisfactorily, the attempted reduction of glycine in tetrahydrofuran reportedly gives no ethanolamine (11). The attempted LAH reduction of glutamyl-γ-glycine (II) in morpholine has been reported to give only a 5% yield of diol while esterification of the diacid prior to reduction increases the yield to 31% (12).

$$H_2NCHCH_2CH_2CONHCH_2COOH \xrightarrow{\text{LAH}} H_2NCHCH_2CH_2CONHCH_2CH_2OH$$

$$\underset{\text{COOH}}{|} \qquad\qquad\qquad \underset{\text{CH}_2\text{OH}}{|}$$

$$\text{II}$$

(8-3)

Attempts to reduce glutathione (III) and N-carbobenzoxyglutathione have been similarly unsatisfactory until the two acid functions of the tripeptide were esterified (12).

$$H_2NCHCH_2CH_2CONHCHCONHCH_2COOH$$

$$\underset{\text{COOH}}{|} \qquad\qquad \underset{\text{CH}_2\text{SH}}{|}$$

$$\text{III}$$

The LAH reduction of N-substituted succinamic acids yields the expected amino alcohols (13–15). Similarly succinamic acid itself yields 4-amino-1-butanol (14). However, the reduction of 2-dodecylsuccinamic acid (IV) is accompanied by ring closure to yield 3-dodecylpyrrolidine.

$$C_{12}H_{25}CHCOOH \qquad\qquad C_{12}H_{25}CH - CH_2$$

$$\underset{\text{CH}_2\text{CONH}_2}{|} \xrightarrow{\text{LAH}} \quad H_2C \quad CH_2$$

$$\text{IV} \qquad\qquad\qquad N$$

$$H$$

(8-4)

The reduction of 2-dodecyl-3-methylsuccinamic acid (V) yields a mixture of the amino alcohol and pyrrolidine (13).

$$\begin{matrix} CH_3CHCONH_2 \\ | \\ C_{12}H_{25}CHCOOH \\ V \end{matrix} \xrightarrow{LAH} \begin{matrix} CH_3CHCH_2NH_2 \\ | \\ C_{12}H_{25}CHCH_2OH \end{matrix} + \begin{matrix} C_{12}H_{25}CH-CHCH_3 \\ | \qquad | \\ H_2C \qquad CH_2 \\ \diagdown N \diagup \\ H \end{matrix} \quad (8\text{-}5)$$

The LAH reduction, in tetrahydrofuran, of a mixture of the two ammonium succinamates, VI and VII, containing less VI than VII, has been reported to yield 16% of an amino alcohol which is converted, with hydrobromic acid, to 27% 1-bromo-3,3-dimethyl-4-aminobutane, as the only isolable product (16).

$$\left. \begin{matrix} (CH_3)_2CCONH_2 \\ | \\ CH_2COONH_4 \\ VI \\ \\ (CH_3)_2CCOONH_4 \\ | \\ CH_2CONH_2 \\ VII \end{matrix} \right\} \xrightarrow{LAH} \begin{matrix} (CH_3)_2CCH_2NH_2 \\ | \\ CH_2CH_2OH \end{matrix} \xrightarrow{HBr} \begin{matrix} (CH_3)_2CCH_2NH_2 \\ | \\ CH_2CH_2Br \end{matrix} \quad (8\text{-}6)$$

The reduction of dicarboxylic acids provides a satisfactory route to the corresponding diols. Thus, substituted succinic acids and sebacic acids are converted to the corresponding butane- and decanediols, respectively. Marvel and Fuller (17) reported that while preliminary experiments indicated that good yields of diols could be obtained by LAH reduction of substituted succinic acids, in larger scale reductions appreciable amounts of the acids containing isopropyl or n-butyl substituents are converted to γ-butyrolactones. The exact structure of the lactones has not been further investigated. Noyce and Denney (18) reported that with normal addition in refluxing ether the LAH reduction of 2-ethyl-2-n-butylglutaric acid (VIII) gives a 75% yield of the disubstituted 1,5-pentanediol. With inverse addition at lower temperatures an 11% yield of the diol is accompanied by 39% of 2-ethyl-2-n-butyl-δ-valerolactone (IX) and 14% of unreacted acid.

$$\begin{matrix} C_2H_5 \diagdown \\ \qquad CCOOH \\ n\text{-}C_4H_9 \diagup | \\ CH_2 \\ | \\ CH_2COOH \\ VIII \end{matrix} \xrightarrow{LAH} \begin{matrix} C_2H_5 \diagdown \\ \qquad CCH_2OH \\ n\text{-}C_4H_9 \diagup | \\ CH_2 \\ | \\ CH_2CH_2OH \end{matrix} + \begin{matrix} C_2H_5 \diagdown \\ \qquad C-C=O \\ n\text{-}C_4H_9 \diagup | \qquad | \\ CH_2 \quad O \\ | \qquad | \\ CH_2-CH_2 \\ IX \end{matrix} \quad (8\text{-}7)$$

The structure of IX and the apparent effect of steric hindrance indicates that the γ-butyrolactones obtained by Marvel and Fuller probably have structures X and XI.

$(CH_3)_2CHCHCOOH$
|
$CH_3CHCOOH$
$\xrightarrow{LAH}$
$(CH_3)_2CHCHCH_2OH$
|
CH_3CHCH_2OH
+
$(CH_3)_2CHCH\!-\!C\!=\!O$
| |
CH_3CH O
\ /
C
H_2

X   (8-8)

$C_4H_9CHCOOH$
|
$CH_3CHCOOH$
$\xrightarrow{LAH}$
$C_4H_9CHCH_2OH$
|
CH_3CHCH_2OH
+
$C_4H_9CH\!-\!C\!=\!O$
| |
CH_3CH O
\ /
C
H_2

(8-9)

XI

Nystrom and Brown (1) reported that sebacic acid is reduced to the diol in 97% yield by excess LAH. Attempts to carry out a selective reduction by the addition of a quantity of LAH sufficient to reduce one carboxyl group, to the ethereal acid solution (inverse addition) gave a mixture of the diol and unchanged acid. The same products were obtained by the reduction of the half ethyl ester of sebacic acid under similar conditions.

The reduction of hexuronic acids with LAH to the corresponding hexitols (19,20) has recently been reported.

The reduction of a carboxyl group next to an asymmetric carbon atom proceeds without loss of activity since little or no racemization accompanies the reductions.

The LAH reduction of various α,β-saturated aliphatic acids, including halo, hydroxy, amino and alicyclic substituted compounds, is summarized in Table XXVII.

Although phenyl-, diphenyl-, and other aryl substituted aliphatic acids are generally reduced in good yield, trisubstituted acids introduce steric factors. Thus, Nystrom and Brown reported (1) that triphenylacetic acid is not reduced in diethyl ether at 25°. However, reduction in tetrahydrofuran at a higher temperature gives the carbinol in good yield (21). Baker reported that the reduction of highly hindered acids such as 2-benzyl-2,4-diphenylbutanoic and 2-benzyl-2,3-diphenylpropionic acids is accomplished satisfactorily in di-n-butyl ether (22).

Eliel and Freeman have reported that the LAH reduction of 2-chloro-2-phenylpropionic acid yields 2-phenyl-1-propanol, 2-phenyl-1,2-propanediol as well as small amounts of 2-phenylpropanal and acetophenone (23). Since an excess of LAH was employed in the reduction, the carbonyl compounds were presumed to have originated during the isolation process.

TABLE XXVII

LAH Reductions of α,β-Saturated Aliphatic Carboxylic Acids

	Acid	Product	% Yield	Ref.
C$_2$HCl$_3$O$_2$	Trichloroacetic acid	2,2,2-Trichloroethanol	31	1
C$_2$HF$_3$O$_2$	Trifluoroacetic acid	2,2,2-Trifluoroethanol	...	2,3,4
		Trifluoroacetaldehydrol		
C$_2$H$_2$Cl$_2$O$_2$	Dichloroacetic acid	2,2-Dichloroethanol	65	1
C$_2$H$_3$ClO$_2$	Chloroacetic acid	2-Chloroethanol	13	1
			...	5
C$_2$H$_4$O$_2$	Acetic acid	Ethanol	100	6
	Acetic-1-C^{14} acid	Ethanol-1-C^{14}	...	7
	Acetic-2-C^{14} acid	Ethanol-2-C^{14}	...[8]	9
			...[8]	9
	Acetic-1-C^{14}-2-C^{13} acid	Ethanol-1-C^{14}-2-C^{13}	40	10
C$_3$HF$_5$O$_2$	Perfluoropropionic acid	2,2,3,3,3-Pentafluoropropanol	...	11
		Pentafluoropropionaldehydrol	...	2,3,4
		2,2,3,3,3-Pentafluoropropanol	40-50	12
		Pentafluoropropionaldehyde	40-49	
C$_3$H$_5$ClO$_2$	3-Chloropropionic-1-C^{14} acid	3-Chloropropanol-1-C^{14}	25-35	13
C$_3$H$_6$O$_2$	Propionic-1-C^{13} acid	Propanol-1-C^{13}	75[15]	14
C$_3$H$_7$O$_2$N	L(+)-Alanine	L(+)-Alaninol	26	16
C$_4$HF$_7$O$_2$	Perfluorobutyric acid	2,2,3,3,4,4,4-Heptafluorobutanol	...	17
		Heptafluorobutanol	...	2,3,4
		Heptafluorobutyraldehydrol		
C$_4$H$_6$O$_6$	Erythraric acid (I)	Erythritol	18[15]	18
C$_4$H$_7$ClO$_2$	2-Chloro-n-butyric acid	2-Chloro-1-butanol	...	19
C$_4$H$_7$NO$_3$	Succinamic acid	4-Amino-1-butanol	...	20
C$_4$H$_8$O$_2$	Isobutyric-1-C^{14} acid	Isobutanol-1-C^{14}	...	21,22
	Isobutyric-2-C^{14} acid	Isobutanol-2-C^{14}	...	21
C$_5$H$_8$O$_2$	Pent-4-en-1-oic acid	Pent-4-en-1-ol	60	23

Formula	Acid	Alcohol	Yield	Ref
$C_5H_9NO_4$	N-Carbomethoxysarcosine	Dimethylaminoethanol	87	24
$C_5H_{10}O_2$	Valeric acid	1-Pentanol	...	25
	(+)-2-Methylbutanoic acid	2-Methyl-1-butanol	83	26
	Trimethylacetic acid	Neopentyl alcohol	...	27
			92	28
			83	29
$C_5H_{11}NO_2$	DL-Valine	DL-Valinol	83[15]	16
$C_6H_{10}O_2$	trans-Hex-3-en-1-oic acid	trans-Hex-3-en-1-ol	66	30
$C_6H_{11}NO_3$	N,N-Dimethylsuccinamic acid	4-Dimethylamino-1-butanol	81	31
$C_6H_{12}O_2$	Caproic-1-C^{14} acid	Hexanol-1-C^{14}	60	32
			89.5	33
			...	34
$C_6H_{12}O_3$	(+)-4-Methoxyvaleric acid	(+)-4-Methoxy-1-pentanol	80-85	35
$C_6H_{13}NO_2$	L-(+)-Leucine	L-(+)-Leucinol	79[15]	16
$C_6H_{14}N_2O_3$	Ammonium 3,3-dimethylsuccinamate[36]	4-Amino-3,3-dimethyl-1-butanol	16	37
$C_7H_{10}O_2$	1-Cyclopentenylacetic acid	2-(1-Cyclopentenyl) ethanol	88.5	38
$C_7H_{12}O_2$	5-Methylhex-5-en-1-oic acid	5-Methylhex-5-en-1-ol	91	39
	DL-2-Isopropylsuccinic acid	DL-2-Isopropyl-1,4-butanediol	...	40
	(+)-2-Isopropylsuccinic acid	(+)-2-Isopropyl-1,4-butanediol	...	40
$C_8H_{12}O_4$	2-Methyl-3-ethylsuccinic acid	2-Methyl-3-ethyl-1,4-butanediol	93	41
$C_7H_{12}N_2O_5$	Glutamyl-γ-glycine (II)	dipetide diol (III)	5[42]	43
$C_7H_{14}O_2$	Heptanoic-1-C^{14} acid	n-Heptanol-1-C^{14}	...	34
	4-Methylcaproic acid	4-Methyl-1-hexanol	...	44
$C_8H_{14}O_2S$	Cyclohexylthioacetic acid (IV)	2-Cyclohexylthioethanol	50	45
$C_8H_{14}O_3$	Cyclohexyloxyacetic acid	2-Cyclohexyloxyethanol	65 ⎱	45
		Cyclohexanol	10 ⎰	
$C_8H_{14}O_4$	2-Methyl-3-isopropylsuccinic acid	2-Methyl-3-isopropyl-1,4-butanediol	51 ⎱	41
		Methylisopropyl-γ-butyrolactone[46]	... ⎰	
	2,3-Diethylsuccinic acid	2,3-Diethyl-1,4-butanediol	...	47
	Suberic acid	1,8-Octanediol	...	47
$C_8H_{14}D_2O_2$	2,2-d-η-Octanoic acid	2,2-d-η-Octanol	...	48

(Continued)

TABLE XXVII (*Continued*)

	Acid	Product	% Yield	Ref.
$C_8H_{18}N_2O_2$	Bis-(dimethylaminomethyl)acetic acid	2,2-Bis-(dimethylaminomethyl)ethanol	76	49
$C_9H_{16}O_2$	trans-n-Non-5-en-1-oic acid	trans-n-Non-5-en-1-ol	93	50
$C_9H_{16}O_4$	2-Methyl-3-n-butylsuccinic acid	2-Methyl-3-n-butyl-1,4-butanediol Methylbutyl-γ-butyrolactone[46]	56 }	41
$C_9H_{18}O_2$	Pelargonic acid	1-Nonanol	55	51
	2,4-Dimethyl-2-ethylpentanoic acid	2,4-Dimethyl-2-ethyl-1-pentanol	87	52
$C_{10}H_{16}O_2$	Lavandulic acid (V)	Lavandulol	75	53
$C_{10}H_{11}NO_3$	Succinanilic acid	N-Hydroxybutylaniline	42	54
$C_{10}H_{18}O_4$	Sebacic acid	1,10-Decanediol	97	27,28
$C_{10}H_{20}O_2$	3-Methylnonanoic acid [55]	3-Methyl-1-nonanol	....	56
	Homocamphenilanic acid (VI)[57]	Homocamphenilanol	80	58
$C_{11}H_{16}O_2$	Homoisocamphenilanic acid (VI)[59]	Homoisocamphenilanol	87	58
$C_{11}H_{17}NO_3$	1-Carboxymethyl-5-methyl-2-azabicyclo [3.3.1] nonan-3-one	1-Hydroxyethyl-5-methyl-2-azabicyclo [3.3.1] nonan-3-one	....	60
$C_{11}H_{20}O_2$	10-Undecen-1-oic acid	10-Undecen-1-ol	95 80–90	61 62
$C_{11}H_{20}O_4$	2-Ethyl-2-n-butylglutaric acid	2-Ethyl-2-butyl-1,5-pentanediol α-Ethyl-α-butyl-δ-valerolactone 2-Ethyl-2-butyl-1,5-pentanediol	11] [63,64] 39] 75	26 26
$C_{12}H_{20}O_3$	trans-β-Decahydronaphthyloxyacetic acid	2-(β-Decahydronaphthyloxy) ethanol β-Decalol	65] [45] 10]	45
$C_{12}H_{22}O_3$	(−)-Menthoxyacetic acid (VII)	(−)-2-Menthoxyethanol	55	65
$C_{12}H_{22}O_4$	Ethyl hydrogen sebacate	1,10-Decanediol	91	27,28
$C_{12}H_{24}O_2$	Dineopentylacetic acid	2,2-Dineopentylethanol	....	66
$C_{13}H_{24}O_4$	2-Nonylsuccinic acid	2-Nonyl-1,4-butanediol	....	67
$C_{14}H_{26}O_4$	2,2,9,9-Tetramethylsebacic acid	2,2,9,9-Tetramethyl-1,10-decanediol	82	68
$C_{15}H_{13}NO_2S$	3-(10-Phenothiazine)propionic acid	10-Hydroxypropylphenothiazine	50	69
$C_{15}H_{24}O_2$	Sesquilavandulyl acid (VIII)	Sesquilavandulol	87	70
	Allobicyclofarnesyl acid (IX)	Allobicyclofarnesol	....	71

Formula	Acid	Alcohol (reduction product)	M.P., °C	Ref.
$C_{15}H_{28}O_4$	2-Decylglutaric acid	2-Decyl-1,5-pentanediol	...	67
$C_{16}H_{26}O_2$	Bicyclohomofarnesyl acid (X)	Bicyclohomofarnesol	72	72
$C_{16}H_{28}O_3$	5-[1,1,4a,6-Tetramethyl-6-hydroxydecahydronaphthyl]acetic acid (XI)	2-(5-[1,1,4a,6-Tetramethyl-6-hydroxydecahydronaphthyl]ethanol	94.5	73
$C_{16}H_{31}NO_3$	2-Dodecylsuccinamic acid	3-Dodecylpyrrolidine	...	20
$C_{17}H_{31}NO_2$	2-Dodecyl-4-cyanobutyric acid	2-Dodecyl-5-amino-1-pentanol	...	67
$C_{17}H_{33}NO_3$	2-Dodecyl-3-methylsuccinamic acid	2-Dodecyl-3-methyl-4-amino-1-butanol; 3-Methyl-4-dodecylpyrrolidine	...	67
$C_{17}H_{42}O_4$	2-Methyl-3-dodecylsuccinic acid	2-Methyl-3-dodecyl-1,4-butanediol	...	67
$C_{18}H_{14}O_8$	Dibenzoylerythraric acid (XII)	Erythritol	27[15]	18
$C_{18}H_{30}O_2$	α-Eleostearic acid (XIII)	α-Eleostearyl alcohol	82.5	74
	β-Eleostearic acid (XIII)	β-Eleostearyl alcohol	87	74
	Ximenynic acid (XIV)	Ximenynyl alcohol	97	74
$C_{18}H_{30}O_4$	5-(1,1,4a,6-Tetramethyl-6-acetoxydecahydronaphthyl)acetic acid	2-(5-[1,1,4a,6-Tetramethyl-6-hydroxydecahydronaphthyl]ethanol	100	73
$C_{18}H_{32}O_2$	Stearolic acid (XV)	Stearolyl alcohol	87-91	75
$C_{18}H_{32}Br_2O_2$	9,10-Dibromooleic acid	9,10-Dibromooleyl alcohol	89	75
$C_{18}H_{34}O_2$	Oleic acid	Oleyl alcohol	87	76
$C_{18}H_{34}O_3$	Ricinoleic acid	Ricinoleyl alcohol	92.5	74
$C_{18}H_{36}O_2$	Stearic acid	1-Octadecanol	91	27,28
$C_{18}H_{44}O_4$	2-Ethyl-3-dodecylsuccinic acid	2-Ethyl-3-dodecyl-1,4-butanediol	...	67
$C_{19}H_{24}O_5$	Methoxymarianolic acid (XVI)	diol from XVI	...	77
$C_{19}H_{34}O_2$	Sterculic acid (XVII)	Sterculyl alcohol	...	78
$C_{20}H_{38}O_4$	2-Hexadecylsuccinic acid	2-Hexadecyl-1,4-butanediol	...	67
$C_{21}H_{41}NO_3$	N,N-Diethyl-2-dodecyl-3-methylsuccinamic acid	2-Dodecyl-3-methyl-4-diethylamino-1-butanol	...	20,67
$C_{22}H_{34}O_3$	3β-Hydroxy-bisnor-Δ⁵-cholenic acid (XVIII)	20-Hydroxymethyl-5-pregnen-3β-ol	...	79
$C_{22}H_{44}O_3$	21-Methoxyheneicosanoic acid	21-Methoxyheneicosanol	88[80]	81

(Continued)

TABLE XXVII (*Continued*)

Acid	Product	% Yield	Ref.
$C_{23}H_{34}O_5$ 2β,4b-Dimethyl-1β-carboxymethyl-2-methallyl-7-ethylenedioxy-1,2,3,4,4aβ,4b,5,6,7,8,10,10aβ-dodecahydrophenanthrene-4α-ol (XIX)	2β,4b-Dimethyl-1-1β-(β-hydroxyethyl)-2-methallyl-7-ethylenedioxy-1,2,3,4,4aβ,4b,5,6,7,8,10,10aβ-dodecahydrophenanthrene-4α-ol	....	82
$C_{24}H_{36}O_4$ 3β-Acetoxy-bisnor-Δ⁵-cholenic acid	20-Hydroxymethyl-5-pregnen-3β-ol	....	79
$C_{24}H_{39}NO_3$ N,3-Dimethyl-N-phenyl-2-dodecylsuccinamic acid	2-Dodecyl-3-methyl-4-(N-methylanilino)-1-butanol	....	67
$C_{24}H_{40}O_2$ Cholenic acid (XX: R,R₁,R₂ = H)	24-Hydroxycholane	94	83
$C_{24}H_{40}O_3$ Lithocholic acid (XX: R = OH, R₁,R₂ = H)	Lithocholanyl alcohol (cholane-3,24-diol)	87.5 "excellent"	83 84 85
$C_{24}H_{40}O_4$ Desoxycholic acid (XX: R,R₁ = OH, R₂ = H)	Cholane-3,12,24-triol	98 84	83 27
$C_{24}H_{40}O_5$ Cholic acid (XX: R,R₁,R₂ = OH)	Cholane-3,7,12,24-tetrol	76	83 27
$C_{24}H_{48}O_2$ D(+)-3-Methyltricosanoic acid	D(+)-3-Methyl-1-tricosanol	96	86
$C_{25}H_{50}O_2$ D(−)-21-Methyltetracosanoic acid	D(−)-21-Methyl-1-tetracosanol	82	87
$C_{32}H_{64}O_3$ Corynomycolic acid (XXI)	Corynomycolyl alcohol	71	88
$C_{88}H_{176}O_4$ α-Mycolic acid, m.p. 55–56° (XXII)	α-Mycolyl alcohol, m.p. 50–52°	80	89
β-Mycolic acid, m.p. 71–73° (XXII)	β-Mycolyl alcohol, m.p. 60–63°	80	89

CHART TO TABLE XXVII

I	II	III
COOH | HCOH | HCOH | COOH	CONHCH₂COOH | CH₂ | CH₂ | H₂NCHCOOH	CONHCH₂CH₂OH | CH₂ | CH₂ | H₂NCHCH₂OH

IV	V	VI

VII	VIII	IX

X	XI	XII

XIII, XIV, XV	XVI
XIII $CH_3(CH_2)_5(CH=CH)_3(CH_2)_7COOH$ XIV $CH_3(CH_2)_5CH=CHC\equiv C(CH_2)_7COOH$ XV $CH_3(CH_2)_7C\equiv C(CH_2)_7COOH$	

(*continued*)

CHART TO TABLE XXVII (*continued*)

XVII

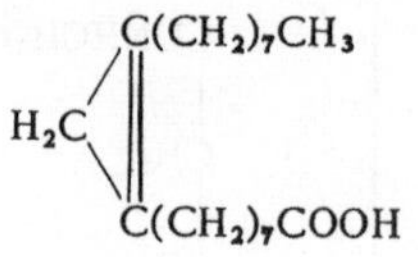

$C(CH_2)_7CH_3$

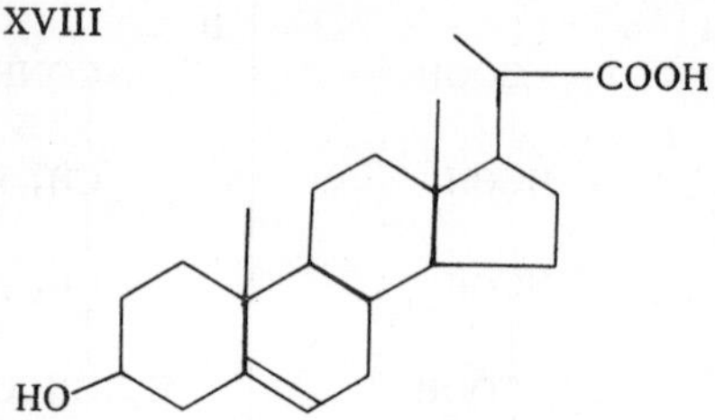

H_2C

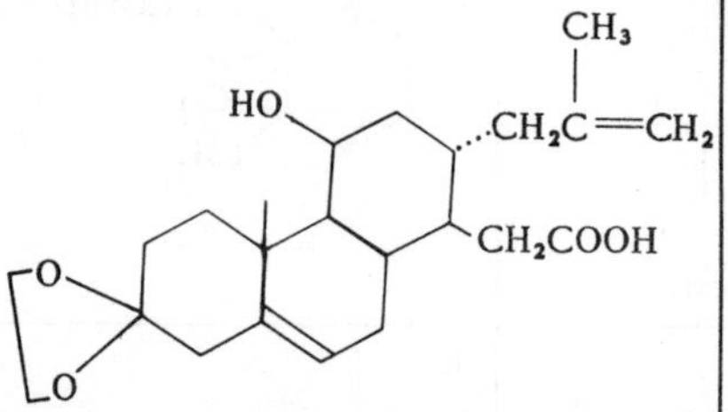

$C(CH_2)_7COOH$

XVIII

—COOH

HO—

XIX

CH_3

HO—

—CH_2C=CH_2

CH_2COOH

XX

R_1

COOH

R R_2

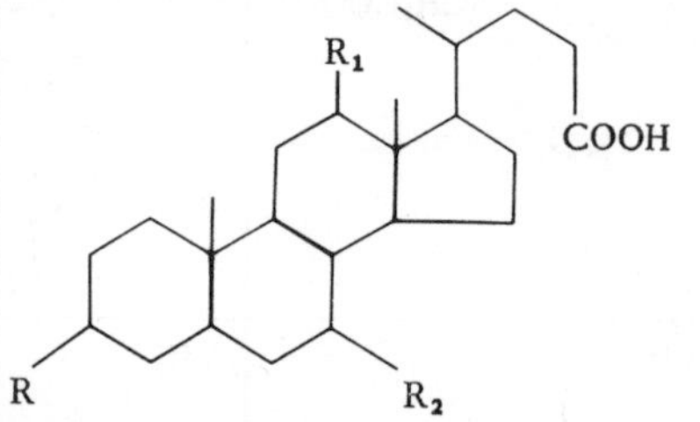

XXI

$CH_3(CH_2)_{14}CHOH$

$CH_3(CH_2)_{13}CHCOOH$

XXII

CH_3O—$C_{60}H_{120}CHOH$

$CH_3(CH_2)_{23}CHCOOH$

References—Table XXVII

[1] C. E. Sroog, C. M. Chih, F. A. Short, and H. M. Woodburn *J. Am. Chem. Soc.,* 71, 1710 (1949).

[2] D. R. Husted and A. H. Ahlbrecht, U. S. Pat. 2,568,500 (September 18, 1951).

[3] Minnesota Mining and Manufacturing Co., Brit. Pat. 676,273 (July 23, 1952).

[4] D. R. Husted and A. H. Ahlbrecht, *J. Am. Chem. Soc.,* 74, 5422 (1952).

[5] L. S. Nelson, D. E. Laskowski, and H. A. Porte, *J. Chem. Educ.,* 28, 648 (1951).

[6] R. F. Nystrom, unpublished work, through W. G. Brown, *Organic Reactions,* Vol. VI, p. 504.

[7] J. D. Roberts and J. A. Yancey, *J. Am. Chem. Soc.,* 74, 5943 (1952).

[8] Reduction carried out in diethyl carbitol. Reaction mixture decomposed with *n*-butyl carbitol.

[9] R. Ostwald, P. T. Adams, and B. M. Tolbert, *J. Am. Chem. Soc.,* 74, 2425 (1952).

[10] J. D. Cox and H. S. Turner, *J. Chem. Soc.,* 1950, 3176.

[11] G. Ehrensvärd, L. Reio, E. Saluste, and R. Stjernholm, *J. Biol. Chem.,* 189, 93 (1951).

[12] E. T. McBee, J. F. Higgins, and O. R. Pierce, *J. Am. Chem. Soc.,* 74, 1387 (1952).

[13] J. P. Ryan and P. R. O'Connor, *ibid.,* 74, 5866 (1952).

[14] A. S. Gordon and S. Heimel, *ibid.,* 73, 2942 (1951); Document 3210, American Documentation Institute, Washington, D. C.

[15] Reduction carried out in tetrahydrofuran solution.

[16]O. Vogl and M. Pöhm, *Monatsh.*, *83*, 541 (1952).

[17]A. F. Benning, U. S. Pat. 2,559,749 (July 10, 1951).

[18]R. K. Ness, H. G. Fletcher, Jr., and C. S. Hudson, *J. Am. Chem. Soc.*, *73*, 4759 (1951).

[19]B. I. Halperin, H. B. Donahoe, J. Kleinberg, and C. A. Vander Werf, *J. Org. Chem.*, *17*, 623 (1952).

[20]V. C. Barry and D. Twomey, *Abstracts of Papers*, XIIth International Congress of Pure and Applied Chemistry, New York, N.Y., September 1951, p. 308.

[21]M. J. Coon and S. Gurin, *J. Biol. Chem.*, *180*, 1159 (1949).

[22]H. Gottlieb and J. Sorden, *Abstracts of Papers*, 121st Meeting American Chemical Society, Milwaukee, Wis., April 1952, p. 91K.

[23]R. L. Rowland, *J. Am. Chem. Soc.*, *73*, 2381 (1951).

[24]F. Wessely and W. Swoboda, *Monatsh.*, *82*, 621 (1951).

[25]H. Pines, A. Rudin, and V. N. Ipatieff, *J. Am. Chem. Soc.*, *74*, 4063 (1952).

[26]D. S. Noyce and D. B. Denney, *ibid.*, *72*, 5743 (1950).

[27]H. I. Schlesinger and A. E. Finholt, U. S. Pat. 2,576,311 (November 27, 1951).

[28]R. F. Nystrom and W. G. Brown, *J. Am. Chem. Soc.*, *69*, 2548 (1947).

[29]D. Y. Curtin and S. M. Gerber, *ibid.*, *74*, 4052 (1952).

[30]L. Crombie and S. H. Harper, *J. Chem. Soc.*, *1950*, 873.

[31]D. R. Howton and R. H. Davis, *J. Org. Chem.*, *16*, 1405 (1951).

[32]A. W. D. Avison, *J. Appl. Chem. (London)*, *1*, 469 (1951).

[33]E. O. Weinman, I. L. Chaikoff, W. G. Dauben, M. Gee, and C. Entenman, *J. Biol. Chem.*, *184*, 735 (1950).

[34]R. P. Geyer, M. Cunningham, and J. Pendergast, *ibid.*, *185*, 461 (1950).

[35]W. von E. Doering and R. W. Young, *J. Am. Chem. Soc.*, *74*, 2997 (1952).

[36]Mixture containing ammonium 2,2-dimethylsuccinamate obtained from ammonolysis of 2,2-dimethylsuccinic anhydride.

[37]R. F. Brown, private communication.

[38]R. T. Arnold, R. W. Amidon, and R. M. Dodson, *J. Am. Chem. Soc.*, *72*, 2871 (1950).

[39]A. Eschenmoser and A. Frey, *Helv. Chim. Acta*, *35*, 1660 (1952).

[40]A. Fredga, *Acta Chem. Scand.*, *3*, 208 (1949).

[41]C. S. Marvel and J. A. Fuller, *J. Am. Chem. Soc.*, *74*, 1506 (1952).

[42]Reaction carried out in morpholine solution.

[43]P. Jollès and C. Fromageot, *Biochim. et Biophys. Acta*, *9*, 287 (1952).

[44]H. E. Heller, *J. Am. Chem. Soc.*, *74*, 4858 (1952).

[45]M. Mousseron, R. Jacquier, M. Mousseron-Canet, and R. Zagdoun, *Bull. soc. chim. France*, [5] *19*, 1042 (1952).

[46]Exact structure of butyrolactone not determined.

[47]M. S. Kharasch, F. S. Arimoto, and W. Nudenberg, *J. Org. Chem.*, *16*, 1556 (1951).

[48]D. G. Hill, W. A. Judge, P. S. Skell, S. W. Kantor, and C. R. Hauser, *J. Am. Chem. Soc.*, *74*, 5599 (1952).

[49]S. W. Pelletier and J. E. Franz, *J. Org. Chem.*, *17*, 855 (1952).

[50]L. Crombie, *J. Chem. Soc.*, *1952*, 2997.

[51]E. A. Braude and E. S. Waight, *ibid.*, *1952*, 1116.

[52]W. von E. Doering, M. Farber, M. Sprecher, and K. B. Wiberg, *J. Am. Chem. Soc.*, *74*, 3000 (1952).

[53]W. Kuhn and H. Schinz, *Helv. Chim. Acta*, *35*, 2008 (1952).

[54]R. E. Holman and D. D. Carroll, *J. Am. Chem. Soc.*, *73*, 1859 (1951).

[55]Mixture of aldehyde and acid obtained by ozonization of (+)-4-methyl-1-decene.

[56]R. L. Letsinger and J. G. Traynham, *J. Am. Chem. Soc.*, *72*, 849 (1950).

[57]High melting isomer, m.p. 76–77°, exo or trans structure.
[58]J. C. LoCicero and R. T. Johnson, J. Am. Chem. Soc., 74, 2094 (1952).
[59]Low melting isomer, m.p. 56–57°, endo or cis structure.
[60]M. W. Cronyn and G. H. Riesser, Abstracts of Papers. 121st Meeting American Chemical Society, Milwaukee, Wis., April 1952, p. 87K.
[61]W. J. Gensler, E. M. Behrmann, and G. R. Thomas, J. Am. Chem. Soc., 73, 1071 (1951).
[62]R. H. Bunnell and D. A. Shirley, J. Org. Chem., 17, 1545 (1952).
[63]Inverse addition.
[64]14% dicarboxylic acid recovered.
[65]J. Glazer, M. M. Harris, and E. E. Turner, J. Chem. Soc., 1950, 1753.
[66]W. H. Hickinbottom and D. G. M. Wood, ibid., 1951, 1600.
[67]V. C. Barry, J. G. Belton, R. M. Kelly, and D. Twomey, Nature, 166, 303 (1950).
[68]R. Adams and J. L. Anderson, J. Am. Chem. Soc., 73, 136 (1951).
[69]R. Dahlbom, Acta Chem. Scand., 6, 310 (1952).
[70]W. Kuhn and H. Schinz, Helv. Chim. Acta, 35, 2395 (1952).
[71]A. Caliezi and H. Schinz, ibid., 35, 1637 (1952).
[72]M. Stoll and M. Hinder, ibid., 33, 1251 (1950).
[73]M. Hinder and M. Stoll, ibid., 33, 1308 (1950).
[74]S. P. Ligthelm, E. von Rudloff, and D. A. Sutton, J. Chem. Soc., 1950, 3187.
[75]N. A. Khan, F. E. Deatherage, and J. B. Brown, J. Am. Oil Chemists' Soc., 28, 27 (1951).
[76]V. M. Mićović and M. L. Mikhailović, Bull. soc. chim. Belgrade, 14, 256 (1949); through Chem. Abstracts, 46, 6407 (1952).
[77]J. Jacques, A. Horeau, and R. Courrier, Compt. rend., 229, 321 (1949).
[78]J. R. Nunn, J. Chem. Soc., 1952, 313.
[79]A. C. Ott and M. F. Murray, Abstracts of Papers, 113th Meeting American Chemical Society, Chicago, Ill. April 1948 p. 17K.
[80]Reduction carried out in ether-toluene solution.
[81]R. E. Bowman and R. G. Mason, J. Chem. Soc., 1952, 4151.
[82]L. H. Sarett, G. E. Arth, R. M. Lukes, R. E. Beyler, G. I. Poos, W. F. Johns, and J. M. Constantin, J. Am. Chem. Soc., 74, 4974 (1952).
[83]F. Wessely and W. Swoboda, Monatsh., 82, 437 (1951).
[84]L. F. Fieser and S. Rajagopalan, J. Am. Chem. Soc., 73, 118 (1951).
[85]L. F. Fieser, J. E. Herz, M. W. Klohs, M. A. Romero, and T. Utne, ibid., 74, 3309 (1952).
[86]S. Ställberg-Stenhagen, Arkiv Kemi, 3, 117 (1951); Chem. Abstracts, 45, 10193 (1951).
[87]S. Ställberg-Stenhagen and E. Stenhagen, J. Biol. Chem., 183, 223 (1950).
[88]E. Lederer and J. Pudles, Bull. soc. chim. biol., 33, 1003 (1951).
[89]J. Asselineau and E. Lederer, Biochim. et Biophys. Acta, 7, 126 (1951).

In a further extension of the work on the reduction of α-chloro acids, Eliel and Herrmann reported that chlorohydrins are isolated in the reduction of chloroacetic acid, 2-chloropropionic acid and 2-chlorobutyric acid with excess LAH in ether. Under ordinary conditions 2-chloroisobutyric acid gives isobutanol. 2-Chloro-2-phenylacetic acid, 2-chloro-2-phenylpropionic acid and 2-chloro-2,2-diphenylacetic acid are reduced to a mixture of the alcohol and the glycol, the latter increasing with increasing bulk of substituent, H < CH₃ < C₆H₅.

$$C_6H_5\overset{R}{\underset{Cl}{C}}COOH \xrightarrow{LAH} C_6H_5\overset{R}{C}HCH_2OH + C_6H_5\overset{R}{\underset{OH}{C}}CH_2OH \quad (8\text{-}10)$$

XII

R = H, CH₃, C₆H₅

The chlorohydrins are intermediates in the reduction to the alcohols since they can be isolated by the inverse addition of a limited amount of LAH and can be further reduced to the alcohols (24).

The LAH reduction of various aryl substituted α,β-saturated aliphatic acids is summarized in Table XXVIII.

The LAH reduction of various α,β-saturated aliphatic acids substituted with heterocyclic nuclei is summarized in Table XXIX. These include furan, thiophene, pyrrole, indole, and thianaphthene nuclei. The attempted reduction of 2-amino-4-hydroxy-6-methyl-5-pyrimidylacetic acid with LAH has been reported to be unsuccessful and no reduction product could be isolated (25).

The LAH reduction of carboxyl groups has been utilized in the characterization of various proteins. The latter is treated with LAH in N-ethylmorpholine whereby the free carboxyl groups are reduced to primary alcohol groups. After hydrolysis and extraction of the amino alcohols they are identified by paper chromatography. This method has been applied to the characterization of insulin (26–29) and ovomucoid (29,30).

Mousseron et al. reported that the reduction of cyclohexyloxyacetic acid (XIII), in ethereal solution, utilizing 0.5 mole of LAH per mole of acid, gives 65% 2-cyclohexyloxyethanol and 10% cyclohexanol (31).

XIII   (8-11)

The LAH reduction of trans-β-decahydronaphthyloxyacetic acid analogously gives 65% 2-(β-decahydronaphthyloxy)ethanol and 10% β-decalol.

TABLE XXVIII

LAH Reduction of Aryl Substituted α,β-Saturated Aliphatic Carboxylic Acids

	Acid	Product	% Yield	Ref.
$C_8H_6O_3$	Phenylglyoxylic acid	Phenylethylene glycol	80	1
$C_8H_8O_2$	Phenylacetic acid	2-Phenylethanol	...	2
			92	1
			...	2
			85	3
	Phenylacetic-2-C^{14} acid	2-Phenylethanol-2-C^{14}	85.6	4
$C_9H_9ClO_2$	2-Chloro-2-phenylpropionic acid	2-Phenyl-1-propanol ⎫ 2-Phenyl-1,2-propanediol ⎬ 2-Phenylpropionaldehyde ⎪ Acetophenone ⎭	...[5]	6
$C_9H_9NO_3$	2-Formylaminophenylacetic acid	2-Methylamino-2-phenylethanol	42[7]	8
$C_9H_{10}O_2$	(−)-2-Phenylpropionic acid	(+)-2-Phenyl-1-propanol	90	6
$C_9H_{10}O_3$	DL-2-Phenyllactic acid	DL-2-Phenyl-1,2-propanediol	76	6
	(+)-2-Phenyllactic acid	(+)-2-Phenyl-1,2-propanediol	69	6
	2-Methoxyphenylacetic acid	2-Methoxy-2-phenylethanol	55	9
	m-Methoxyphenylacetic acid	2-(m-Methoxyphenyl) ethanol	90	9
$C_9H_{11}NO_2$	DL-Phenylalanine	DL-Phenylalaninol	...	10
			74[7]	11
$C_{10}H_{11}NO_3$	N-Formyl-DL-β-phenylalanine	N-Methyl-DL-β-phenylalaninol	73	12
$C_{10}H_{12}O_2$	3-p-Tolylpropionic acid	3-p-Tolyl-1-propanol	96.2	13
			90	14
$C_{11}H_{14}O_2$	2-Methyl-3-phenylpropionic acid	2-Methyl-3-phenyl-1-propanol	90	15
	(−)-3-Phenylbutanoic acid	(−)-3-Phenyl-1-butanol	84	16
	4-Phenylbutanoic acid	4-Phenyl-1-butanol	71.5	17
	2-Methyl-4-phenylbutanoic acid	2-Methyl-4-phenyl-1-butanol	100	18
$C_{12}H_9ClO_2$	1-(7-Chloronaphthyl) acetic acid	2-(1-[7-Chloronaphthyl]) ethanol	75	19
$C_{12}H_{10}O_3$	1-(2-Hydroxynaphthyl) acetic acid	2-(1-[2-Hydroxynaphthyl]) ethanol	90	20

Formula	Acid	Alcohol	Yield (%)	Ref.
$C_{12}H_{16}O_3$	2-(2-Methoxybenzyl) butanoic acid	2-(2-Methoxybenzyl)-1-butanol	90	21
$C_{12}H_{16}O_3$	2-(4-Methoxybenzyl) butanoic acid	2-(4-Methoxybenzyl)-1-butanol	94	21
	3-(3,4,5-Trimethoxyphenyl) propionic acid	3-(3,4,5-Trimethoxyphenyl)-1-propanol	88	22
$C_{12}H_{17}NO_2$	m-Diethylaminophenylacetic acid	2-(m-Diethylaminophenyl) ethanol	81	23
$C_{13}H_{12}O_3$	1-(6-Methoxynaphthyl) acetic acid	2-(1-[6-Methoxynaphthyl]) ethanol	90	24
$C_{13}H_{14}O_3$	1-(6-Methoxy-3,4-dihydronaphthyl)acetic acid	2-(1-[6-Methoxy-3,4-dihydronaphthyl])-ethanol	78[25]	24
$C_{14}H_{10}Cl_2O_2$	Di-p-chlorophenylacetic acid	2,2-Di-p-chlorophenylethanol	91[26]	27
$C_{14}H_{12}O_2$	Diphenylacetic acid	2,2-Diphenylethanol	93	28
			88	29
			84	30
			77	31
$C_{14}H_{12}O_3$	2-p-Hydroxyphenyl)-2-phenylacetic acid	2-(p-Hydroxyphenyl)-2-phenylethanol	44	32
$C_{14}H_{14}O_3$	1-(5-Methoxy-8-methylnaphthyl)acetic acid	2-(1-[5-Methoxy-8-methylnaphthyl])-ethanol	79	33
	1-(5-Methyl-8-methoxynaphthyl)acetic acid	2-(1-[5-Methyl-8-methoxynaphthyl])-ethanol	...	34
$C_{15}H_{14}O_2$	2-Phenyl-2-(p-tolyl) acetic-1-C^{14} acid	2-Phenyl-2-(p-tolyl) ethanol-1-C^{14}	93	35
	2-Phenyl-2-(m-tolyl) acetic-1-C^{14} acid	2-Phenyl-2-(m-tolyl) ethanol-1-C^{14}	92	35
	(+)-2-Methylbenzilic acid	(+)-1-Phenyl-1-(o-tolyl) ethylene glycol	76	36
$C_{15}H_{14}O_3$	2-Phenyl-2-(p-methoxyphenyl)acetic-1-C^{14} acid	2-Phenyl-2-(p-methoxyphenyl)ethanol-1-C^{14}	93	35
	2,2-Diphenyl-3-hydroxypropionic acid	2,2-Diphenyl-1,3-propanediol	96	37
$C_{15}H_{14}O_4$	2-Phenoxy-2-(p-methoxyphenyl)acetic acid	2-Phenoxy-2-(p-methoxyphenyl)ethanol	79	38
$C_{15}H_{15}NO_2$	3-Phenyl-3-anilinopropionic acid	3-Phenyl-3-anilino-1-propanol	...[26]	39
$C_{15}H_{20}O_5$	(5-Methoxy-2,4-dimethylbenzyl)ethylmalonic acid	2-(5-Methoxy-2,4-dimethylbenzyl)-2-ethyl-1,3-propanediol	...	40
$C_{16}H_{12}O_2$	2-Phenanthrylacetic acid	2-(2-Phenanthryl) ethanol	86	41
	3-Phenanthrylacetic acid	2-(3-Phenanthryl) ethanol	86	41
$C_{16}H_{16}O_2$	(+)-2,4-Diphenylbutanoic acid	(+)-2,4-Diphenyl-1-butanol	96	42
	(-)-2,4-Diphenylbutanoic acid	(-)-2,4-Diphenyl-1-butanol	77	42

(Continued)

TABLE XXVIII (Continued)

Acid	Product	%Yield	Ref.
C₁₆H₁₆O₂ (cont.)			
2-Phenyl-2-(3,4-dimethylphenyl)acetic-1-C¹⁴ acid	2-Phenyl-2-(3,4-dimethylphenyl)-ethanol-1-C¹⁴	90	35
2-Phenyl-2-(p-ethylphenyl)acetic 1-C¹⁴ acid	2-Phenyl-2-(p-ethylphenyl) ethanol-1-C¹⁴	95	35
C₁₇H₁₆O₂			
Allyldiphenylacetic acid	2,2-Diphenylpent-4-en-1-ol	95	43
C₁₇H₁₈O₂			
2-Phenyl-2-(p-[2-propyl] phenyl)acetic-1-C¹⁴ acid	2-Phenyl-2-(p-[2-propyl] phenyl)-ethanol-1-C¹⁴	92	35
C₁₈H₁₄O₃			
2-Phenyl-2-(2-naphthyloxy)acetic acid	2-Phenyl-2-(2-naphthyloxy) ethanol	68.4	44
C₁₈H₂₀O₂			
2-Phenyl-2-(p-[t-butyl] phenyl)acetic-1-C¹⁴ acid	2-Phenyl-2-(p-[t-butyl] phenyl)ethanol-1-C¹⁴	100	35
C₁₉H₂₂O₄			
(3-[1-{p-Methoxyphenyl} propyl]-4-methoxy) phenylacetic acid	2-(3-[1-{p-Methoxyphenyl} propyl]-4-methoxy) phenylethanol	....	45
C₁₉H₂₃NO₂			
2,2-Diphenyl-4-dimethylaminovaleric acid	2,2-Diphenyl-4-dimethylamino-1-pentanol	"poor"	46
C₂₀H₁₆O₂			
2-Phenyl-2-(p-xenyl) acetic-1-C¹⁴ acid	2-Phenyl-2-(p-xenyl) ethanol-1-C¹⁴	88	35
Triphenylacetic acid	2,2,2-Triphenylethanol	0	1
		"good"[7]	47
C₂₀H₂₄O₄			
3-(3-[1-{p-Methoxyphenyl}propyl]-4-methoxy)-phenylpropionic acid	3-(3-[1-{p-Methoxyphenyl} propyl]-4-methoxy) phenyl-1-propanol	....	45
C₂₀H₂₆O₂			
2,2-Diethyl-3-(2-naphthyl)hexanoic acid	2,2-Diethyl-3-(2-naphthyl)-1-hexanol	....	48
C₂₂H₂₀O₂			
2-Benzyl-2,3-diphenylpropanoic acid	2-Benzyl-2,3-diphenyl-1-propanol	57[49]	50
C₂₃H₂₂O₂			
2-Benzyl-2,4-diphenylbutanoic acid	2-Benzyl-2,4-diphenyl-1-butanol	62[49]	50

References—Table XXVIII

[1] R. F. Nystrom and W. G. Brown, *J. Am. Chem. Soc.,* 69, 2548 (1947).
[2] H. I. Schlesinger and A. E. Finholt, U. S. Pat. 2,576,311 (November 27, 1951).
[3] J. Mahé, J. Rollet, and A. Willemart, *Bull. soc. chim. France,* [5] 16, 481 (1949).
[4] W. G. Dauben and P. Coad, *J. Am. Chem. Soc.,* 71, 2928 (1949).
[5] See text.
[6] E. L. Eliel and J. P. Freeman, *J. Am. Chem. Soc.,* 74, 923 (1952).
[7] Reduction carried out in tetrahydrofuran.
[8] A. Dornow, G. Messwarb, and H. H. Frey, *Chem. Ber.,* 83, 445 (1950).
[9] W. Reeve and I. Christoffel, *J. Am. Chem. Soc.,* 72, 1480 (1950).
[10] J. H. Hunter and J. A. Hogg, *ibid.,* 71, 1922 (1949).
[11] P. Karrer, P. Portmann, and M. Suter, *Helv. Chim. Acta,* 31, 1617 (1948).
[12] O. Vogl and M. Pöhm, *Monatsh.,* 83, 541 (1952).
[13] F. Wessely and W. Swoboda, *ibid.,* 82, 621 (1951).
[14] C. J. Collins, *J. Am. Chem. Soc.,* 73, 1038 (1951).
[15] P. P. T. Sah, *Z. Vitamin-, Hormon- u. Fermentforsch.,* 3, 324 (1949); through M. Ferles and J. Rudinger, *Chem. Listy,* 47, 129 (1953).
[16] D. J. Cram, *J. Am. Chem. Soc.,* 74, 2137 (1952).
[17] W. E. Truce and J. P. Milionis, *ibid.,* 74, 974 (1952).
[18] L. Bateman, J. I. Cunneen, and J. A. Lyons, *J. Chem. Soc.,* 1951, 2290.
[19] C. C. Price and Sing Tuh Voong, *J. Org. Chem.,* 14, 111 (1949).
[20] C. O. Guss, *J. Am. Chem. Soc.,* 74, 608 (1951).
[21] O. Brunner, E. Müllner, and G. Weinwurm, *Monatsh.,* 83, 1477 (1952).
[22] H. Rapoport and J. E. Campion, *J. Am. Chem. Soc.,* 73, 2239 (1951).
[23] R. L. Bent, J. C. Dessloch, F. C. Duennebier, D. W. Fassett, D. B. Glass, T. H. James, D. B. Julian, W. R. Ruley, J. M. Small, J. H. Sterner, J. R. Thirtle, P. W. Vittum, and A. Weissberger, *ibid.,* 73, 3125 (1951).
[24] E. Buchta, M. Klisch, S. Maier, and H. Bayer, *Ann.,* 576, 7 (1952).
[25] Reduction carried out in dioxane-ether mixture.
[26] Reduction carried out in tetrahydrofuran-ether mixture.
[27] E. J. Skerrett and D. Woodcock, *J. Chem. Soc.,* 1952, 3308.
[28] K. E. Hamlin, A. W. Weston, F. E. Fischer, and R. J. Michaels, Jr., *J. Am. Chem. Soc.,* 71, 2734 (1949).
[29] D. O. Dean, W. B. Dickinson, O. R. Quayle, and C. T. Lester, *ibid.,* 72, 1740 (1950).
[30] S. Winstein, B. K. Morse, E. Grunwald, K. C. Schreiber, and J. Corse, *ibid.,* 74, 1113 (1952).
[31] J. H. Biel, H. L. Friedman, H. A. Leiser, and E. P. Sprengeler, *ibid.,* 74, 1485 (1952).
[32] C. O. Guss, H. R. Williams, and L. H. Jules, *ibid.,* 73, 1257 (1951).
[33] J. Herran, O. Mancera, G. Rosenkranz, and C. Djerassi, *J. Org. Chem.,* 16, 899 (1951).
[34] A. S. Dreiding and A. J. Tomasewski, *Abstracts of Papers,* 121st Meeting American Chemical Society, Milwaukee, Wis., April 1952, p. 82K.
[35] J. G. Burr, Jr., and L. S. Ciereszko, *J. Am. Chem. Soc.,* 74, 5426 (1952).
[36] K. Mislow and M. Siegel, *ibid.,* 74, 1060 (1952).
[37] F. F. Blicke and H. Raffelson, *ibid.,* 74, 1740 (1952).
[38] C. O. Guss, *ibid.,* 74, 2561 (1952).
[39] M. E. Speeter and W. H. Maroney, unpublished work.

[40]W. Cocker, B. E. Cross, A. K. Fateen, C. Lipman, E. R. Stuart, W. H. Thompson, and D. R. A. Whyte, *J. Chem. Soc.*, *1950*, 1781.

[41]C. C. Price and B. D. Halpern, *J. Am. Chem. Soc.*, *73*, 818 (1951).

[42]R. H. Baker and S. H. Jenkins, Jr., *ibid.*, *71*, 3969 (1949).

[43]R. L. Rowland, *ibid.*, *73*, 2381 (1951).

[44]C. O. Guss and L. H. Jules, *ibid.*, *72*, 3878 (1950).

[45]J. M. Vander Zanden and G. de Vries, *Rec. trav. chim.*, *71*, 879 (1952).

[46]M. E. Speeter, W. M. Byrd, L. C. Cheney, and S. B. Binkley, *J. Am. Chem. Soc.*, *71*, 57 (1949).

[47]F. A. Hochstein, unpublished work, through W. G. Brown in *Organic Reactions*, Vol. VI, p. 478.

[48]Ciba Ltd., Brit. Pat. 666,051 (February 6, 1952).

[49]Reduction carried out in di-*n*-butyl ether.

[50]R. H. Baker, *J. Am. Chem. Soc.*, *70*, 3857 (1948).

TABLE XXIX

LAH Reduction of Heterocyclic Substituted α, β-Saturated Aliphatic Carboxylic Acids

	Acid	Product	% Yield	Ref.
$C_6H_6O_3$	3-Furylacetic acid	2-(3-Furyl) ethanol	96.5	1
$C_7H_8O_2S$	3-(2-Methylthienyl) acetic acid	2-(3-[2-Methylthienyl]) ethanol	89	2
$C_9H_{13}NO_2$	Kryptopyrrolecarboxylic acid	2,4-Dimethyl-3-hydroxypropylpyrrole	"good"	3
$C_{10}H_9NO_2$	3-Indoleacetic acid	2-(3-Indolyl)ethanol	65.2	4
$C_{11}H_{10}O_2S$	2-(3-Methylthianaphthenyl)acetic acid	2-(2-[3-Methylthianaphthenyl])ethanol	89	5
	3-(3-Thianaphthenyl) propionic acid	3-Hydroxypropylthianaphthene	83	5

[1] E. Sherman and E. D. Amstutz, *J. Am. Chem. Soc.*, **72**, 2195 (1950).
[2] R. Gaertner, *ibid.*, **73**, 3934 (1951).
[3] A. Treibs and H. Scheret, *Ann.*, **577**, 139 (1952).
[4] H. R. Snyder and F. J. Pilgrim, *J. Am. Chem. Soc.*, **70**, 3770 (1948).
[5] R. Gaertner, *ibid.*, **74**, 2185 (1952).

On the other hand, the reduction of cyclohexylthioacetic acid (XIV) gives 50% 2-cyclohexylthioethanol without cleaving the thioether grouping (31).

$$\text{(8-12)}$$

XIV

The following acids containing an α-ether grouping have been sub-jected to LAH reduction without the reported isolation of cleavage products: (–)-Menthoxyacetic acid (32), α-Methoxyphenylacetic acid (33), α-(2-Naphthyloxy)phenylacetic acid (34), α-Phenoxy-p-methoxyphenyl-acetic acid (35).

8.1.1.b *Alicyclic carboxylic acids.* The reduction of α,β-saturated alicyclic acids proceeds in the same manner as in the case of other acids. The solubility of the acid in the reaction medium plays an important role in the yield of carbinol. The degree of substitution of the ring carbon atom to which the carboxyl group is attached does not appear to be sig-nificant since carboxyl groups located at a bridgehead position are readily reduced.

The LAH reduction of triterpene acids such as oleanolic, ursolic and betulic acids is carried out satisfactorily in a tetrahydrofuran-ether mix-ture (36). Morolic acid is reduced in ether solution (37).

Asiatic acid, the aglycone of asiaticoside, is a triterpene acid for which structure XV has been elucidated (38,39).

XV

Reduction of XV with LAH in ether yields the corresponding tetrol, asiati-col. Asiaticoside, which on hydrolysis with acid or dilute alkali yields glucose, rhamnose and asiatic acid, is reduced with LAH in N-ethyl-morpholine solution to asiaticol (39,40).

Quinovaic acid, a triterpene monohydroxy dicarboxylic acid for which structure XVI has been advanced, contains two carboxyl groups of differ-ent reactivity since only one can be readily transformed to an aldehyde or methylol group.

XVI

The desoxy derivative, 2-desoxyquinovaic acid, is reduced with LAH in dioxane to a hydroxy acid. The second carboxyl group remains unchanged although both groups can be reduced using the diacid chloride (41).

The LAH reduction of various α,β-saturated alicyclic carboxylic acids is summarized in Table XXX.

8.1.1.c α,β-*Unsaturated carboxylic acids.* The LAH reduction of unconjugated unsaturated acids proceeds without attacking the double bond to yield the unsaturated alcohol, as shown in Tables XXVII–XXX. The reduction of sterculic acid (XVII) leaves the cyclopropene ring intact (42).

$$CH_3(CH_2)_7C \overset{\overset{\displaystyle CH_2}{\diagup\!\!\diagdown}}{=\!=} C(CH_2)_7COOH \xrightarrow{\text{LAH}} CH_3(CH_2)_7C \overset{\overset{\displaystyle CH_2}{\diagup\!\!\diagdown}}{=\!=} C(CH_2)_7CH_2OH \quad (8\text{-}13)$$

XVII

Reduction of dibromooleic acid (XVIII) yields dibromooleyl alcohol (43).

$$CH_3(CH_2)_7\overset{\overset{\displaystyle Br}{|}}{C} =\!= \overset{\overset{\displaystyle Br}{|}}{C}(CH_2)_7COOH \xrightarrow[89\%]{\text{LAH}} CH_3(CH_2)_7\overset{\overset{\displaystyle Br}{|}}{C} =\!= \overset{\overset{\displaystyle Br}{|}}{C}(CH_2)_7CH_2OH \quad (8\text{-}14)$$

XVIII

Ximenynic acid which has been shown to be heptadec-10-en-8-yne-1-carboxylic acid (XIX) (44,45) is reduced with LAH to ximenynyl alcohol retaining the conjugated double and triple bonds (45).

$$CH_3(CH_2)_5CH =\!= CH - C \equiv C(CH_2)_7COOH \rightarrow$$

                      XIX

$$CH_3(CH_2)_5CH =\!= CH - C \equiv C(CH_2)_7CH_2OH \quad (8\text{-}15)$$

When the acid (XIX) is heated with potassium hydroxide in ethylene glycol at 180–190° isomerization yields isomeric heptadecatriene-1-carboxylic acids (XX) which are reduced with LAH to the corresponding alcohols (46).

TABLE XXX

LAH Reduction of α,β-Saturated Alicyclic Carboxylic Acids

Acid	No.	Product	% Yield	Ref.
C$_4$H$_6$O$_2$ Cyclopropanecarboxylic acid		Hydroxymethylcyclopropane	95	1
C$_5$H$_8$O$_2$ Cyclobutanecarboxylic acid		Hydroxymethylcyclobutane	68	2
C$_6$H$_{10}$O$_2$ Cyclopentanecarboxylic acid		Hydroxymethylcyclopentane	69	3
C$_7$H$_{10}$O$_4$ trans-Cyclopentane-1,2-dicarboxylic acid		trans-1,2-Bis-(hydroxymethyl)cyclopentane	....	4
C$_8$H$_{12}$O$_2$ Cyclohexanecarboxylic acid		Hexahydrobenzyl alcohol	76	5
C$_8$H$_{12}$O$_3$ cis-3-Hydroxycyclohexanecarboxylic acid		cis-3-Hydroxyhexahydrobenzyl alcohol	79	6
trans-3-Hydroxycyclohexanecarboxylic acid		trans-3-Hydroxyhexahydrobenzyl alcohol	56	7
(+)-cis-3-Hydroxycyclohexanecarboxylic acid		(-)-cis-3-Hydroxyhexahydrobenzyl alcohol	73	8
(-)-cis-3-Hydroxycyclohexanecarboxylic acid		(+)-cis-3-Hydroxyhexahydrobenzyl alcohol	86	8
C$_9$H$_{12}$O$_4$ 4-Methyl-4-cyclohexene-1,2-dicarboxylic acid[9]		1,2-Bis-(hydroxymethyl)-4-methyl-4-cyclohexene	86	10
C$_{10}$H$_{16}$O$_2$ Apocamphane-1-carboxylic acid	I	10-Hydroxycamphane	....	11
C$_{10}$H$_{16}$O$_4$ Camphoric acid	II	1,2,2-Trimethyl-1,3-bis-(hydroxymethyl)-cyclopentane	....	12
C$_{11}$H$_{18}$O$_2$ 5-Methylcyclolavandulic acid	III	5-Methylcyclolavandulol	67	13
C$_{12}$H$_{20}$O$_2$ 5,5-Dimethylcyclolavandulic acid	IV	5,5-Dimethylcyclolavandulol	72	14
C$_{15}$H$_{24}$O$_2$ α-Bicyclofarnesyl acid (liquid)	V	α-Bicyclofarnesol (liquid)	18.7	15
C$_{17}$H$_{22}$O$_3$ Podocarpic acid	VI R = H	Podocarpinol	56	17,18
C$_{18}$H$_{14}$O$_3$ 9-Formyl-9,10-dihydro-9,10-ethano-anthracene-12-carboxylic acid	VII	9,10-Dihydro-9,12-bis-(hydroxymethyl)-9,10-ethanoanthracene	55	19

Formula	Acid		Derivative	m.p.	Ref.
$C_{18}H_{24}O_3$	O-Methylpodocarpic acid	VI R = CH$_3$	O-Methylcarpinol	....	18
$C_{19}H_{24}O_5$	Methoxymarrianolic acid	VIII	glycol, m.p. 142–143°	....	20
$C_{20}H_{32}O_2$	Dihydro-dextro-pimaric acid	IX	Dihydrodextropimarol	99[21]	22
$C_{28}H_{46}O_2$	3 α-Cholesterylcarboxylic acid	X	3α-Hydroxymethylcholest-5-ene	85[23]	24
$C_{30}H_{46}O_4$	2-Desoxyquinovaic acid $C_{28}H_{44}$ {COOH, COOH		hydroxy acid $C_{28}H_{44}$ {COOH, CH$_2$OH	86[25]	26
$C_{30}H_{48}O_3$	Morolic acid	XI	Moradiol	49	27
	Oleanolic acid	XII	Erythrodiol	77–86[28]	29
	Ursolic acid		Ursolic diol	60–72[28]	29
$C_{30}H_{48}O_5$	Asiatic acid	XIII	Asiaticol	62	30,31
$C_{30}H_{50}O_4$	Dihydrosiaresinolic acid	XIV	triol, m.p. 255°	....	32
$C_{36}H_{54}O_6$	Betulic acid		Betulin	68[28]	29
$C_{54}H_{88}O_{23}$	Asiaticoside		Asiaticol	....[33]	30,31

CHART TO TABLE XXX

(*continued*)

CHART TO TABLE XXX (*continued*)

References—Table XXX

[1] R. F. Nystrom, unpublished work, through W. G. Brown, in *Organic Reactions,* Vol. VI, p. 504.

[2] J. D. Roberts and R. H. Mazur, *J. Am. Chem. Soc.,* 73, 2509 (1951).

[3] C. G. Bergstrom and S. Siegel, *ibid.,* 74, 145 (1952).

[4] H. G. Kuivila and W. L. Masterton, *ibid.,* 74, 4953 (1952).

[5] H. S. Turner, *Nature,* 168, 73 (1951).

[6] J. O. Halford and B. Weissman, *J. Org. Chem.,* 17, 1276 (1952).

[7] P. A. S. Smith and D. R. Baer, *J. Am. Chem. Soc.,* 74, 6135 (1952).

[8] D. S. Noyce and D. B. Denney, *ibid.,* 74, 5912 (1952).

[9] Abstract shows no double bond in starting material but text indicates presence of double bond.

[10] W. J. Bailey, J. Rosenberg, and L. J. Young, *Abstracts of Papers,* 119th Meeting American Chemical Society, Cleveland, Ohio, April 1951, p. 68M.

[11] M. Levitz, Ph.D. Dissertation, Columbia University, 1951, through W. von E. Doering, M. Farber, M. Sprecher, and K. B. Wiberg, *J. Am. Chem. Soc.,* 74, 3000 (1952).

[12] D. S. Noyce and D. B. Denney, *ibid.,* 72, 5743 (1950).

[13] R. Vonderwahl and H. Schinz, *Helv. Chim. Acta,* 35, 1997 (1952).

[14] R. Vonderwahl and H. Schinz, *ibid.,* 35, 2368 (1952).

[15] A. Caliezi and H. Schinz, *ibid.,* 32, 2556 (1949).

[16] A. Caliezi and H. Schinz, *ibid.,* 35, 1637 (1952).

[17] H. H. Zeiss, C. E. Slimowicz, and V. Z. Pasternak, *J. Am. Chem. Soc.,* 70, 1981 (1948).

[18] H. H. Zeiss and C. E. Slimowicz, Fr. Pat. 979,346 (April 25, 1951).

[19] J. S. Meek, B. T. Poon, and S. J. Cristol, *J. Am. Chem. Soc.,* 74, 761 (1952).

[20] J. Jacques, A. Horeau, and R. Courrier, *Compt. rend.,* 229, 321 (1949).

[21] Reduction carried out in ether-dioxane mixture.

[22] A. Brossi and O. Jeger, *Helv. Chim. Acta,* 34, 2446 (1951).

[23] Reduction carried out in di-*n*-butyl ether.

[24] R. H. Baker and Q. R. Petersen, *J. Am. Chem. Soc.,* 73, 4080 (1951).

[25] Reduction carried out in dioxane.

[26] H. Diener, O. Jeger, and L. Ruzicka, *Helv. Chim. Acta,* 33, 896 (1950).

[27] D. H. R. Barton and C. J. W. Brooks, *J. Chem. Soc.,* 1951, 257.

[28] Reduction carried out in tetrahydrofuran-ether mixture.

[29] B. Y. T. Wu and L. M. Parks, *J. Am. Pharm. Assoc., Sci. Ed.,* 39, 475 (1950).

[30] J. Polonsky, *Compt. rend.,* 230, 485 (1950).

[31] J. Polonsky, *Bull. soc. chim. France,* [5] 19, 649 (1952).

[32] D. H. R. Barton and N. J. Holness, *Chemistry & Industry,* 1951, 233.

[33] Reduction carried out in N-ethylmorpholine.

$$CH_3(CH_2)_x(CH=\!\!=\!\!CH)_3(CH_2)_yCOOH \xrightarrow{\text{LAH}}$$

$$\text{XX}$$

$$CH_3(CH_2)_x(CH=\!\!=\!\!CH)_3(CH_2)_yCH_2OH \qquad\qquad (8\text{-}16)$$

The reduction of unsaturated acids in which the double bond is conjugated with the carboxylic group generally yields the corresponding unsaturated alcohol.

$$CH_2=\!\!=\!\!CHCOOH \xrightarrow[68\%]{\text{LAH}} CH_2=\!\!=\!\!CHCH_2OH \qquad\qquad (8\text{-}17)$$

The LAH reduction of various α,β-unsaturated aliphatic and alicyclic acids involving non-reduction of the double bond is summarized in Table XXXI.

The reduction of *trans*-4-carboxy-vitamin A acid (XXI) with excess LAH (2.2 moles LAH/0.005 moles acid) is reported to yield a product, $C_{21}H_{30}O_3$ (47).

$$\text{XXI}$$

The analysis of the product indicates reduction of one carboxyl group to the hydroxymethyl derivative with retention of unsaturation and one carboxyl group.

The LAH reduction of 2,4-pentadienoic acid (XXII) to 2,4-pentadienol proceeds in low yield (48,49) due to the polymerization of XXII (48).

$$CH_2=\!\!=\!\!CHCH=\!\!=\!\!CHCOOH \xrightarrow{\text{LAH}} CH_2=\!\!=\!\!CHCH=\!\!=\!\!CHCH_2OH \qquad (8\text{-}18)$$

$$\text{XXII}$$

Freedman and Becker reported that the reduction of 0.80 moles of 2-hexenoic acid (XXIII) with 1.18 moles of LAH gives a 59% yield of a mixture of alcohols which has been shown by quantitative bromination to contain 25.0 to 28.5% of the saturated alcohol (50).

$$CH_3CH_2CH_2CH=\!\!=\!\!CHCOOH \xrightarrow{\text{LAH}}$$

$$\text{XXIII}$$

$$CH_3CH_2CH_2CH=\!\!=\!\!CHCH_2OH + CH_3CH_2CH_2CH_2CH_2CH_2OH \qquad (8\text{-}19)$$

Dornow, Messwarb, and Frey reported that the reduction of 0.0087 moles of 2-cyano-5,9-dimethyldeca-2,4,8-trienoic acid (XXIV) with 0.019 moles of LAH at room temperature gives an 82% yield of 2-aminomethyl-5,9-dimethyldeca-4,8-dien-1-ol (51).

TABLE XXXI

LAH Reduction of α,β-Unsaturated Carboxylic Acids Involving Non-Reduction of the Double Bond

	Acid	Product	% Yield	Ref.
	A. Aliphatic			
$C_3H_4O_2$	Acrylic acid	Allyl alcohol	68.3	1
$C_4H_4O_4$	Fumaric acid	2-Butene-1,4-diol	78	1
$C_4H_6O_2$	cis-2-Buten-1-oic acid	cis-Crotyl alcohol	....	2
$C_6H_6O_2$	trans-Penta-2,4-dienoic acid	trans-Penta-2,4-dien-1-ol	17.5	3
	Penta-2,4-dienoic acid	Penta-2,4-dien-1-ol	35	4
$C_6H_8O_2$	2-Methyl-2-buten-1-oic acid	2-Methyl-2-buten-1-ol	80	5
	3-Methyl-2-buten-1-oic acid	3-Methyl-2-buten-1-ol	43	6
$C_6H_8O_2$	Sorbic acid	Sorbyl alcohol	92	7
			....	8
$C_8H_{14}O_2$	2-Octen-1-oic acid	2-Octen-1-ol	59	9
$C_9H_8O_3$	p-Hydroxycinnamic acid	p-Hydroxycinnamyl alcohol	....	10
$C_{10}H_{10}O_2$	2-Methylcinnamic acid	2-Methylcinnamyl alcohol	83	11
	p-Methylcinnamic acid	p-Methylcinnamyl alcohol	90	12
$C_{11}H_{12}O_5$	4-Hydroxy-3,5-dimethoxycinnamic acid	4-Hydroxy-3,5-dimethoxycinnamyl alcohol	....	10
$C_{11}H_{18}O_2$	3,7-Dimethyl-6-methylene-2-octen-1-oic acid	3,7-Dimethyl-6-methylene-2-octen-1-ol	....	13
$C_{15}H_{22}O_2$	β-Ionylideneacetic acid	β-Ionylideneethanol	96	14
$C_{20}H_{28}O_2$	Vitamin A acid (I)	Vitamin A	80	15–17, 18,19
$C_{21}H_{30}O_3$	Pregna-5,17-dien-3β-ol-21-oic acid (II)	Pregna-5,17-dien-3β,21-diol	....	20
$C_{87}H_{170}O_2$	2,x-Mycoldienoic acid (III)	2,x-Mycoldien-1-ol	....	21
$C_{87}H_{172}O_3$	x-Hydroxy-2-mycolenoic acid (IV)	x-Hydroxy-2-mycolen-1-ol[22]	....	21
$C_{88}H_{174}O_3$	Anhydromycolic acid (V)	Anhydromycolvl alcohol	....	23

B. Alicyclic

$C_6H_8O_2$	1-Cyclopentenecarboxylic acid	1-Hydroxymethylcyclopentene	83	24
$C_7H_{10}O_2$	1-Cyclohexenecarboxylic acid	1-Hydroxymethylcyclohexene	70	25,26
			91	24
			...	27,28
$C_{10}H_{16}O_2$	β-Cyclolavandulylic acid (VI)	β-Cyclolavandulol	56	29
			72	30
$C_{11}H_{18}O_2$	β-Isocyclolavandulylic acid (VII)	β-Isocyclolavandulol	75	29
	6-Methylcyclolavandulylic acid (VIII)	6-Methylcyclolavandulol	68	31
$C_{13}H_{24}O_2$	β-Bicyclosesquilavandulylic acid (IX)	β-Bicyclosesquilavandulol	70	32

CHART TO TABLE XXXI

I

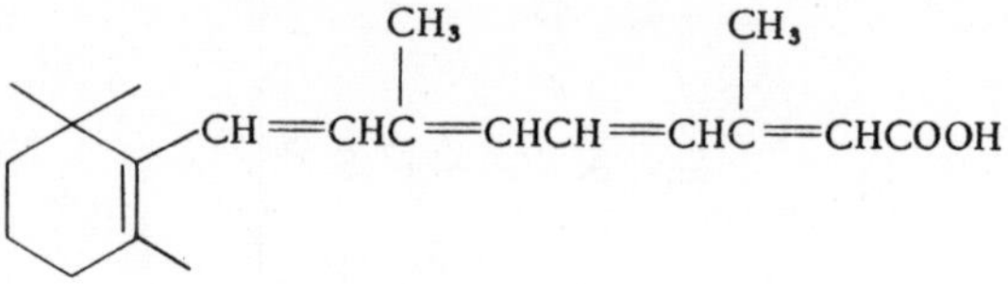

$$CH=CHC(CH_3)=CHCH=CHC(CH_3)=CHCOOH$$

II

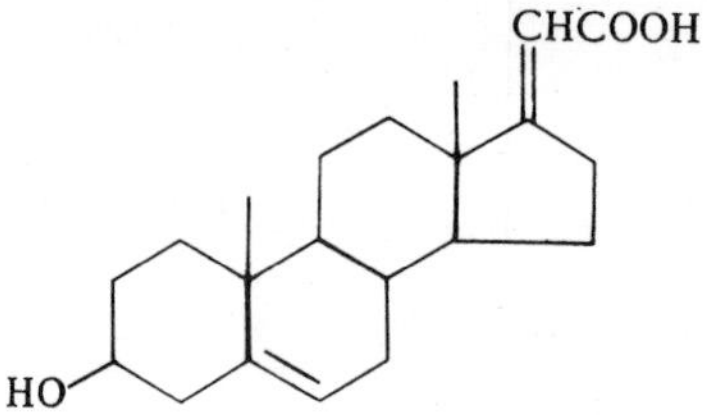

CHCOOH

HO

III

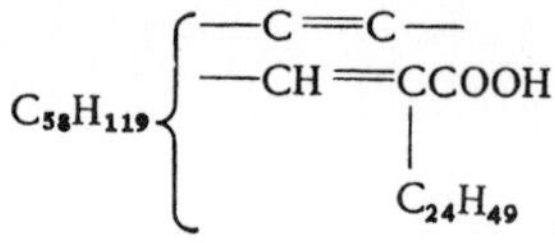

$$C_{58}H_{119}\left\{\begin{array}{l}-C=C-\\-CH=CCOOH\\\quad\quad\quad|\\\quad\quad\quad C_{24}H_{49}\end{array}\right.$$

IV

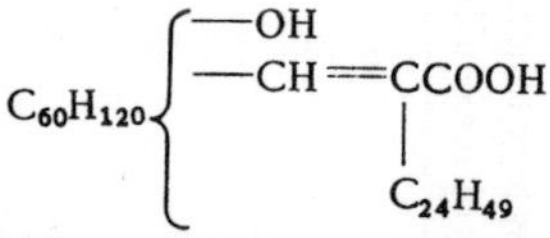

$$C_{60}H_{120}\left\{\begin{array}{l}-OH\\-CH=CCOOH\\\quad\quad\quad|\\\quad\quad\quad C_{24}H_{49}\end{array}\right.$$

V

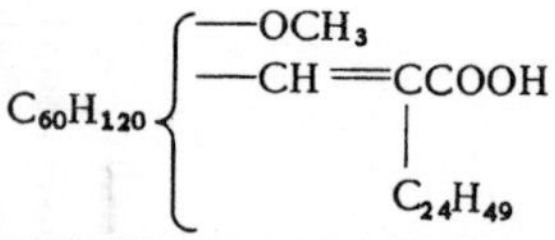

$$C_{60}H_{120}\left\{\begin{array}{l}-OCH_3\\-CH=CCOOH\\\quad\quad\quad|\\\quad\quad\quad C_{24}H_{49}\end{array}\right.$$

VI

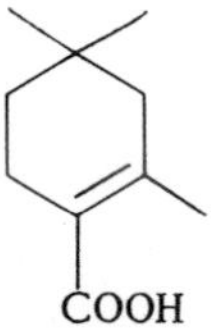

COOH

VII

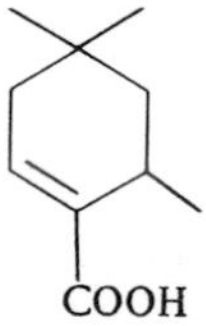

COOH

VIII

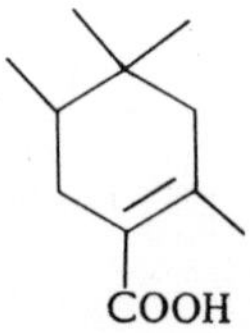

COOH

IX

COOH

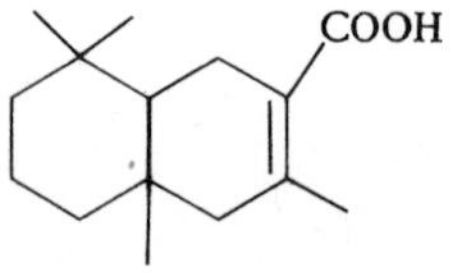

References—Table XXXI

[1] G. E. Benedict and R. R. Russell, *J. Am. Chem. Soc.*, 73, 5444 (1951).
[2] L. F. Hatch and S. S. Nesbitt, *ibid.*, 72, 727 (1950).
[3] L. Crombie, S. H. Harper, and D. Thompson, *J. Chem. Soc.*, 1951, 2906.
[4] A. D. Mebane, *J. Am. Chem. Soc.*, 74, 5227 (1952).
[5] E. A. Braude and C. J. Timmons, *J. Chem. Soc.*, 1950, 2007.
[6] A. Bolleter, K. Eiter, and H. Schmid, *Helv. Chim. Acta*, 34, 186 (1951).
[7] R. F. Nystrom and W. G. Brown, *J. Am. Chem. Soc.*, 69, 2548 (1947).
[8] H. I. Schlesinger and A. E. Finholt, U. S. Pat. 2,576,311 (November 27, 1951).
[9] M. Jacobson, *Abstracts of Papers,* 122nd Meeting American Chemical Society, Atlantic City, N. J., September 1952, p. 57M.
[10] K. Freudenberg and F. Bittner, *Chem. Ber.*, 83, 600 (1950).
[11] Liang Li and W. H. Elliott, *J. Am. Chem. Soc.*, 74, 4089 (1952).
[12] C. J. Collins, unpublished work, through W. G. Brown, in *Organic Reactions,* Vol. VI, p. 504.
[13] H. Favre and H. Schinz, *Helv. Chim. Acta*, 35, 1627 (1952).
[14] H. O. Huisman, A. Smit, S. Vromen, and L. G. M. Fisscher, *Rec. trav. chim.*, 71, 899 (1952).
[15] J. F. Arens and D. A. van Dorp, *ibid.*, 68, 604 (1949).
[16] I. Heilbron, *J. Chem. Soc.*, 1948, 386.
[17] C. D. Robeson, Ger. Pat. 855,992 (November 17, 1952).
[18] N. L. Wendler, H. L. Slates, and M. Tishler, *J. Am. Chem. Soc.*, 71, 3267 (1949).
[19] N. L. Wendler, H. L. Slates, N. R. Trenner, and M. Tishler, *ibid.*, 73, 719 (1951).
[20] D. Magrath, D. S. Morris, V. Petrow, and R. Royer, *J. Chem. Soc.*, 1950, 2393.
[21] J. Asselineau, *Bull. soc. chim. France* [5] 19, 557 (1952).
[22] Mixture of *cis*- and *trans*-isomers.
[23] J. Asselineau and E. Lederer, *Biochim. et Biophys. Acta*, 7, 126 (1951).
[24] A. S. Dreiding and J. A. Hartman, *J. Am. Chem. Soc.*, 75, 939 (1953).
[25] R. Jacquier and R. Zagdoun, *Bull. soc. chim. France* [5] 18, 487 (1951).
[26] M. Mousseron, R. Jacquier, M. Mousseron-Canet and R. Zagdoun, *ibid.* [5] 19, 1042 (1952).
[27] T. J. King, *J. Chem. Soc.*, 1951, 898.
[28] R. Jacquier and R. Zagdoun, *Bull. soc. chim. France* [5] 19, 698 (1952).
[29] A. Brenner and H. Schinz, *Helv. Chim. Acta*, 35, 1615 (1952).
[30] W. Kuhn and H. Schinz, *ibid.*, 35, 2008 (1952).
[31] R. Vonderwahl and H. Schinz, *ibid.*, 35, 2005 (1952).
[32] W. Kuhn and H. Schinz, *ibid.*, 35, 2395 (1952).

$$CH_3C\!=\!CHCH_2CH_2C\!=\!CHCH\!=\!C\overset{\displaystyle COOH}{\underset{\displaystyle CN}{\big\langle}} \quad\overset{LAH}{\longrightarrow}$$

with CH_3 substituents above each $C\!=\!C$

XXIV

$$CH_3C\!=\!CHCH_2CH_2C\!=\!CHCH_2C\overset{\displaystyle CH_2OH}{\underset{\displaystyle CH_2NH_2}{H\big\langle}} \qquad (8\text{-}20)$$

with CH_3 substituents above each $C\!=\!C$

The reduction of 0.016 moles of isoamylidene cyanoacetic acid (XXV) with 0.025 moles of LAH at room temperature gives 38% of the saturated amino alcohol (51).

$$(CH_3)_2CHCH_2CH\!=\!C\overset{\displaystyle COOH}{\underset{\displaystyle CN}{\big\langle}} \quad\overset{LAH}{\longrightarrow}\quad (CH_3)_2CHCH_2CH_2C\overset{\displaystyle CH_2OH}{\underset{\displaystyle CH_2NH_2}{H\big\langle}} \qquad (8\text{-}21)$$

XXV

Nystrom and Brown reported that the LAH reduction of cinnamic acid (XXVI) gives hydrocinnamyl alcohol (1,52).

$$C_6H_5CH\!=\!CHCOOH \overset{LAH}{\longrightarrow} C_6H_5CH_2CH_2CH_2OH \qquad (8\text{-}22)$$

XXVI

The reduction of the double bond in compounds such as XXVII wherein the ethylenic group is substituted on one side by a phenyl group and the other by a reducible group is dependent upon the reaction conditions (53). Thus, the reduction of 2-methylcinnamic acid (XXVII) with LAH at 0–5° yields the unsaturated alcohol in 83% yield. At higher temperatures a mixture of allylic and saturated alcohols is obtained (54). Refluxing p-methylcinnamic acid (XXVIII) with excess LAH in ether yields a mixture of the saturated and unsaturated alcohols (55).

XXVII

XXVIII

Freudenberg and Bittner have reported the reduction of p-hydroxycinnamic acid and 4-hydroxy-3,5-dimethylcinnamic acid to the corresponding cinnamyl alcohol. However, no experimental details were given (56).

The LAH reduction of α-dimethylaminoacrylic acid is reported to yield a non-homogeneous product which could not be satisfactorily characterized (57).

The attempted reduction of *l*-ascorbic acid (XXIX), isoascorbic acid (XXX) and reductic acid (XXXI) with LAH in refluxing ether is unsuccessful, apparently due to the difficult polarizability of the mesomeric system (58).

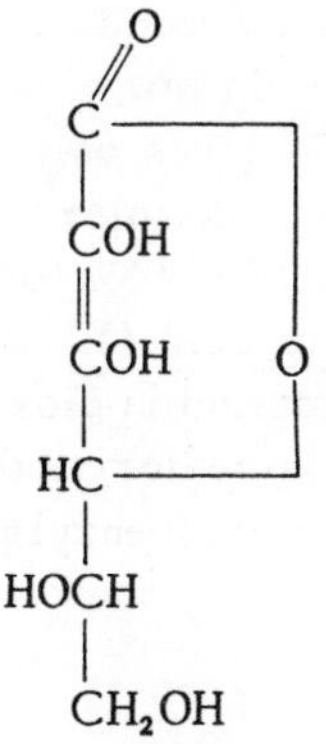

XXIX 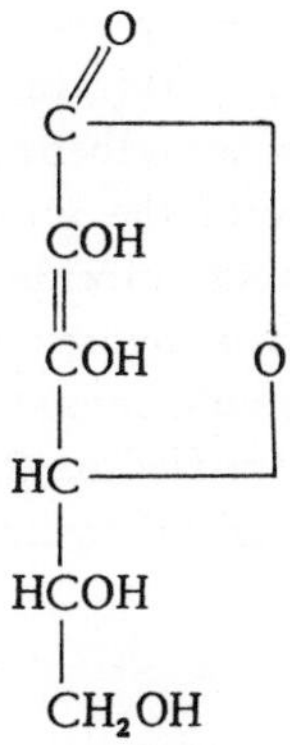   XXX 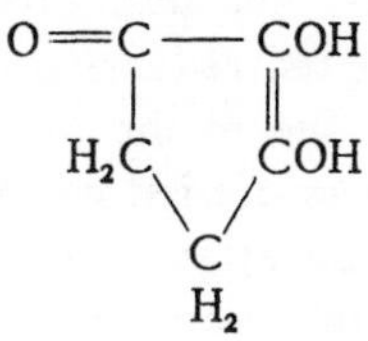   XXXI

8.1.1.d *Acetylenic carboxylic acids.* The LAH reduction of unconjugated acetylenic acids results in the formation of acetylenic carbinols. Thus, the acetylenic bonds are retained in the reduction of ximenynic acid (45) (equation 8–15) and stearolic acid (XXXII)) (43).

$$CH_3(CH_2)_7C \equiv C(CH_2)_7COOH \xrightarrow[87-91\%]{LAH} CH_3(CH_2)_7C \equiv C(CH_2)_7CH_2OH$$

XXXII   (8-23)

The reduction of propiolic acid (XXXIII) (59–61) and acetylenedicarboxylic acid (XXXIV) (59) yields allyl alcohol and 2-butene-1,4-diol, respectively.

$$HC \equiv CCOOH \xrightarrow[65-85\%]{LAH} CH_2 = CHCH_2OH \qquad (8-24)$$

XXXIII

$$HOOCC \equiv CCOOH \xrightarrow[84\%]{LAH} HOCH_2CH = CHCH_2OH \qquad (8-25)$$

XXXIV

While cyclohexanepropiolic acid (XXXV) is reduced to 3-cyclohexyl-2-propen-1-ol, the LAH reduction of phenylpropiolic acid (XXXVI) yields a mixture of phenylpropargyl alcohol (XXXVII) and cinnamyl alcohol (60,61).

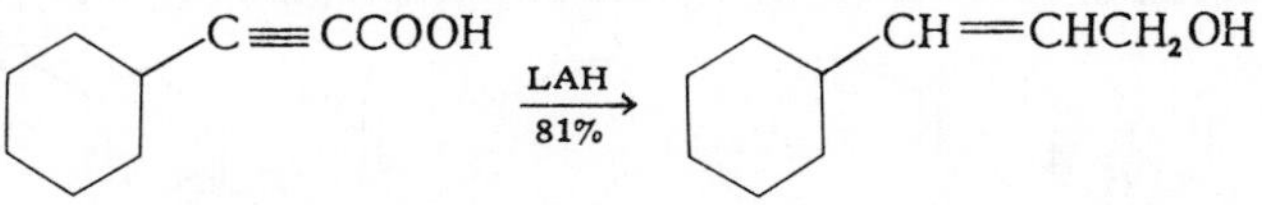

XXXV

$$C_6H_5C \equiv CCOOH \xrightarrow{LAH} C_6H_5C \equiv CCH_2OH + C_6H_5CH = CHCH_2OH$$

XXXVI   XXXVII   (8-27)

Although a recent patent (52) indicates only the isolation of XXXVII, a mixture of products is reported even when an excess of LAH sufficient for complete hydrogenation of the triple bond is employed (60).

8.1.1.e   *Aromatic carboxylic acids.*   The reduction of unsubstituted aromatic acids proceeds satisfactorily under the usual conditions. While mono-, di-, and trimethylbenzoic acids are reduced in fair yields (62,63) the attempted reduction of pentamethylbenzoic acid gives only 8% of the carbinol, due to the insolubility of the intermediate complex. When the reduction is carried out on the acid chloride the yield is 95% (62).

While the attempted reduction of hydroxytrimesic acid (XXXVIII) with LAH in ether was reported to be unsuccessful, reduction in dioxane gives a 12% yield of a crude resin identified as 2,4,6-tris-hydroxymethylphenol (XXXIX) by conversion to 2,4,6-tri-(2′-hydroxy-5′-methylbenzyl)phenol by reaction with *p*-cresol (64).

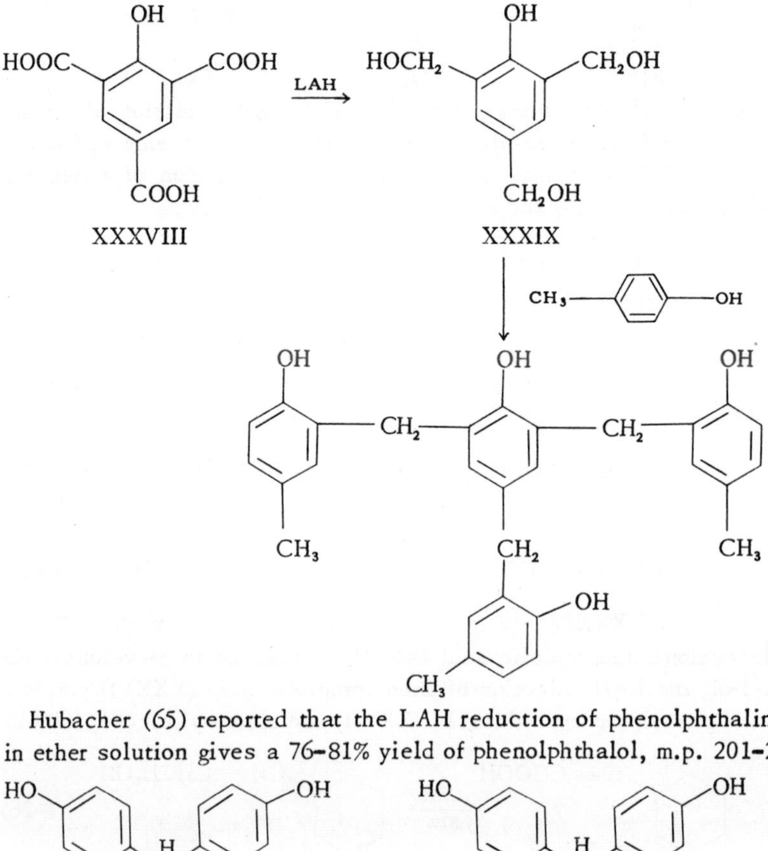

(8-28)

XXXVIII   XXXIX

Hubacher (65) reported that the LAH reduction of phenolphthalin (XL) in ether solution gives a 76–81% yield of phenolphthalol, m.p. 201–202°.

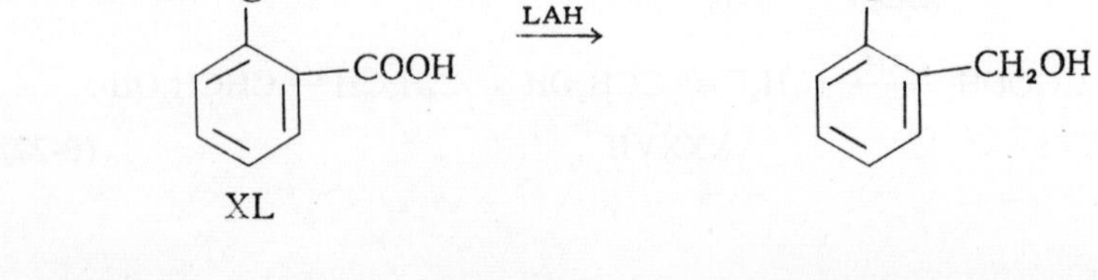

(8-29)

XL

Baeyer reported (66) that reduction of XL with sodium amalgam gives a product melting at 190° which he called phenolphthalol. This compound is oxidized to phenolphthalein by potassium ferricyanide and gives a red, water-insoluble condensation product on treatment with concentrated sulfuric acid. Hubacher reported that the phenolphthalol obtained by LAH reduction of XL neither produces Baeyer's red product, nor does it yield phenolphthalein on oxidation. This product gives a mono as well as a triacetyl derivative. Repetition of Baeyer's procedure gave a crude product which melted at about 190° and on recrystallization from water melted at 198–199° and was identical to the LAH reduction product.

The greater ease of reduction of the ester and ketone groups as compared to the acid, as well as the influence of steric factors have been observed. Newman and Gaertner (67) found that the LAH reduction of 2-(o-toluyl)-1-naphthoic acid (XLI) gives only 16% the expected diol (XLII) and 57% of the lactone (XLIII).

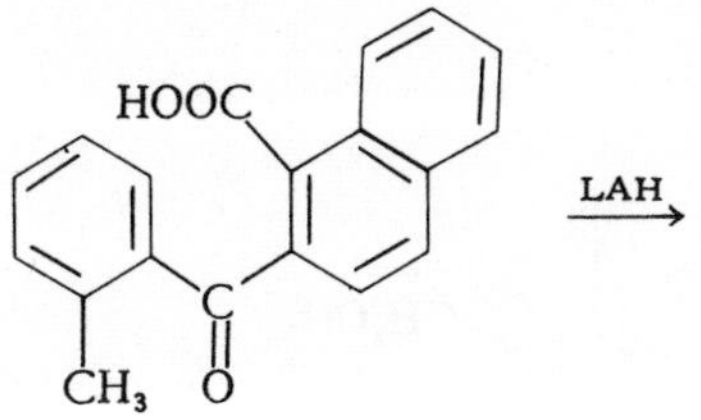

XLI

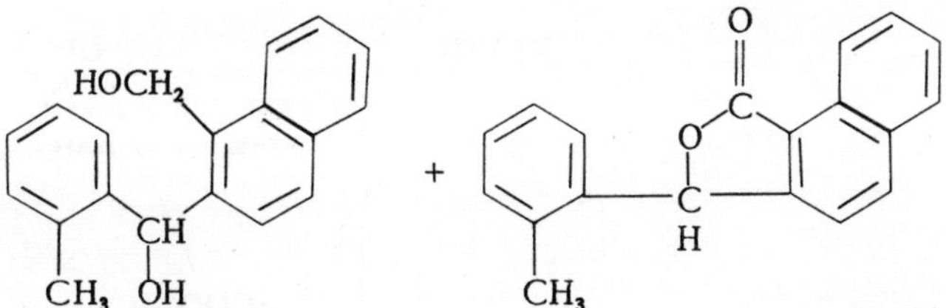

XLII   XLIII

(8-30)

The selective reduction of monomethylphthalate (XLIV) with 0.75 mole of LAH (0.25 mole required for the active hydrogen of the free carboxyl group) is reported to yield the lactone phthalide (XLV) (68).

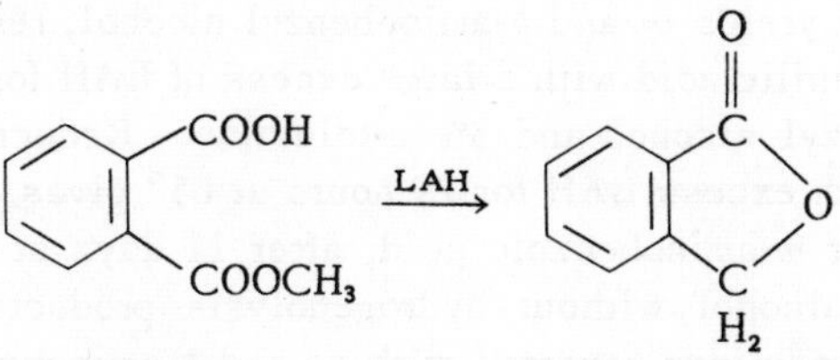

XLIV   XLV

(8-31)

Bird and Turner have carried out an interesting study of the LAH reduction of 3-chlorophthalic acid and its esters (69). The reduction of
3-chlorophthalic acid (XLVI) and 1-methyl-2-hydrogen-3-chlorophthalate
(XLVII) with 120% of the quantity of LAH calculated for conversion to
the glycol, in boiling ether gives 7-chlorophthalide (XLVIII). The reduction of methyl 3-chlorophthalate (XLIX) and 2-methyl-1-hydrogen-3-chloro-
phthalate (L) under the same conditions gives 3-chloro-o-xylylene gylcol
(LI). The reduction of the phthalide (XLVIII) to the glycol (LI) requires
five moles of LAH.

(8-32)

The reduction of anthranilic acid and p-aminobenzoic acid under the
usual conditions yields o- and p-aminobenzyl alcohol, respectively. Reduction of anthranilic acid with a large excess of LAH for 22 hours gives
83% o-aminobenzyl alcohol and 3% o-toluidine. Reduction of p-aminobenzoic acid with excess LAH for 29 hours at 65° gives 47% p-toluidine.
The reduction of m-aminobenzoic acid, after 11 days at 85°, gives 72%
m-aminobenzyl alcohol without hydrogenolysis products (70). These
hydrogenolysis reactions reported with o- and p-aminobenzoic acids are
discussed in Section 16.1.

The LAH reduction of various aromatic carboxylic acids is summarized in Table XXXII.

8.1.1.f *Heterocyclic carboxylic acids*. The LAH reduction of heterocyclic carboxylic acids provides a satisfactory method for the synthesis of heterocyclic carbinols.

Furan, tetrahydropyran, benzofuran, and chroman carboxylic acids have been reduced to the corresponding carbinols. Aldobiuronic acid, a degradation product of the xylan isolated from the cell-wall material of ripe pears, identified as 2-methyl-3-(2,3,4-trimethyl-α-D-glucuronosido)-D-xylose (LII) is reduced with LAH to yield a syrup which on hydrolysis with dilute hydrochloric acid is converted to 2-methylxylose and 2,3,4-trimethylglucose in equimolar proportion (20). The reduction and hydrolysis reactions are represented as follows:

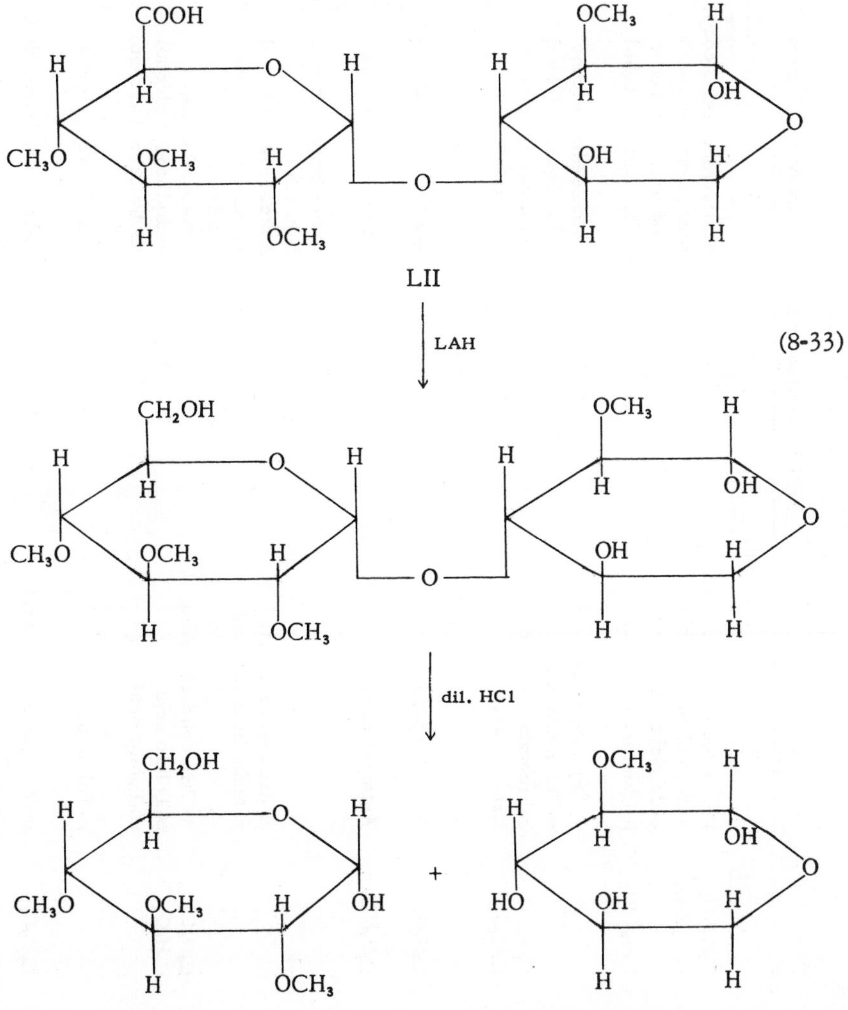

LII

LAH (8-33)

dil. HCl

TABLE XXXII

LAH Reduction of Aromatic Carboxylic Acids

	Acid	Product	% Yield	Ref.
$C_7HF_5O_2$	Pentafluorobenzoic acid	Pentafluorobenzyl alcohol	77[1]	2
$C_7H_3BrO_2$	m-Bromobenzoic acid	m-Bromobenzyl alcohol	92	3
	p-Bromobenzoic acid	p-Bromobenzyl alcohol	82	3
$C_7H_5ClO_2$	o-Chlorobenzoic acid	o-Chlorobenzyl alcohol	97	4
			...	5
	m-Chlorobenzoic acid	m-Chlorobenzyl alcohol	85	6
	p-Chlorobenzoic acid	p-Chlorobenzyl alcohol	85	6
$C_7H_5FO_2$	o-Fluorobenzoic acid	o-Fluorobenzyl alcohol	81	7
$C_7H_6O_2$	Benzoic acid	Benzyl alcohol	81	4
			75	8
			...	5
$C_7H_6O_3$	Salicylic acid	o-Hydroxybenzyl alcohol	99	4
			...	5,9
$C_7H_7NO_2$	Anthranilic acid	o-Aminobenzyl alcohol	97	4
			...	5,10
		o-Aminobenzyl alcohol	83[11,12]	9
		o-Toluidine	3	
	m-Aminobenzoic acid	m-Aminobenzyl alcohol	72[11,13]	9
	p-Aminobenzoic acid	p-Aminobenzyl alcohol	20	14
		p-Toluidine	47[11,15]	9
$C_8H_5ClO_4$	3-Chlorophthalic acid	7-Chlorophthalide	70	16
$C_8H_8O_2$	o-Toluic acid	o-Methylbenzyl alcohol	97	17
	m-Toluic acid	m-Methylbenzyl alcohol	85	6
			87	18
	p-Toluic acid	p-Methylbenzyl alcohol	85	6
			64	18
$C_9H_8O_3$	m-Methoxybenzoic acid	m-Methoxybenzyl alcohol	75	18

Formula	Acid	Product	Yield	Ref.
	p-Methoxybenzoic acid	p-Methoxybenzyl alcohol	85	6
$C_9H_6O_7$	Hydroxytrimesic acid	2,4,6-Tris-(hydroxymethyl)phenol	0	19
			12[20]	19
$C_9H_7ClO_4$	2-Carbomethoxy-3-chlorobenzoic acid	2-Hydroxymethyl-3-chlorobenzyl alcohol	85	16
	2-Carbomethoxy-6-chlorobenzoic acid	7-Chlorophthalide	80	16
$C_9H_8O_4$	Monomethyl phthalate	Phthalide	....[21]	22
$C_9H_{10}O_4$	2,4-Dimethoxybenzoic acid	2,4-Dimethoxybenzyl alcohol	....	23
	2,6-Dimethoxybenzoic acid	2,6-Dimethoxybenzyl alcohol	....	23
	3,5-Dimethoxybenzoic acid	3,5-Dimethoxybenzyl alcohol	93	24
$C_{10}H_{12}O_2$	2,4,6-Trimethylbenzoic acid	2,4,6-Trimethylbenzyl alcohol	53	25
$C_{10}H_{12}O_3$	2,4-Dimethyl-5-methoxybenzoic acid	2,4-Dimethyl-5-methoxybenzyl alcohol	41	18
	2,4,5-Trimethyl-6-hydroxybenzoic acid	2,4,5-Trimethyl-6-hydroxybenzyl alcohol	100	26
$C_{10}H_{12}O_5$	3,4,5-Trimethoxybenzoic acid	3,4,5-Trimethoxybenzyl alcohol	....	27
$C_{10}H_{16}O_2$	Isocamphenilanic acid	Isocamphenilanol	88	28
$C_{11}H_8O_2$	2-Naphthoic acid	2-Hydroxymethylnaphthalene	99	29
	2-Naphthoic acid-carboxyl-C^{14}	2-Hydroxymethyl-C^{14}-naphthalene	....	30
$C_{11}H_8O_3$	3-Hydroxy-2-naphthoic acid	3-Hydroxymethyl-2-naphthol	97	31
			....	32
$C_{11}H_{12}O_3$	6-Hydroxy-5,6,7,8-tetrahydro-2-naphthoic acid	2-Hydroxymethyl-6-hydroxy-5,6,7,8-tetrahydronaphthalene	23	33
			40	34
$C_{11}H_{14}O_2$	p-t-Butylbenzoic acid	p-t-Butylbenzyl alcohol	88	18
$C_{11}H_{14}O_5$	2,4-Dimethoxy-3-ethoxybenzoic acid	2,4-Dimethoxy-3-ethoxybenzyl alcohol	82	35
$C_{12}H_{16}O_2$	Pentamethylbenzoic acid	Pentamethylbenzyl alcohol	8	25
$C_{13}H_{10}O_2$	2-Phenylbenzoic acid	2-Phenylbenzyl alcohol	85	36
$C_{13}H_{11}NO_4S$	2-Benzenesulfonamidobenzoic acid	2-Benzenesulfonamidobenzyl alcohol	85	37
$C_{14}H_{12}O_4$	3-(p-Hydroxybenzyl)-4-hydrobenzoic acid	3-(p-Hydroxybenzyl)-4-hydroxybenzyl alcohol	38	19
$C_{14}H_{12}N_2O_2$	2-Methyl-3-carboxyazobenzene	2-Methyl-3'-hydroxymethylazobenzene	....	38
$C_{14}H_{13}NO_4S$	2-(p'-Toluenesulfonamido)benzoic acid	2-(p'-Toluenesulfonamido)benzyl alcohol	81	37
$C_{15}H_{14}O_3$	2-Hydroxy-2'-carboxydibenzyl	2-Hydroxy-2'-hydroxymethyldibenzyl	76	39
$C_{15}H_{16}O_4$	Mono-[1-(1'-cyclopentenylethyl)]phthalate	(−)-1-(1'-Cyclopentenyl) ethanol	....	40

(Continued)

TABLE XXXII (*Continued*)

Acid	Product	% Yield	Ref.
C₁₆H₁₈O₄			
Mono-[1-(1'-cyclohexenylethyl)]phthalate	(−)-1-(1'-Cyclohexenyl) ethanol	....	40
C₁₆H₂₂O₄			
(+)-Mono-[4-(2,4-dimethylhexyl)]phthalate	(−)-2,4-Dimethylhexan-4-ol Phthalalcohol	80–85	41
(−)-Mono-[4-(2,4-dimethylhexyl)]phthalate	(+)-2,4-Dimethylhexan-4-ol Phthalalcohol	83	41
C₁₇H₁₃NO₄S			
2-(2'-Naphthalenesulfonamido)benzoic acid	2-(2'-Naphthalenesulfonamido)benzyl alcohol	....	37
C₁₈H₁₈O₄			
(−)-Mono-[2-(2-phenylbutyl)]phthalate	(+)-2-Phenylbutan-2-ol	77	42
(+)-Mono-[2-(2-phenylbutyl)]phthalate	(−)-2-Phenylbutan-2-ol	66	42
C₁₈H₂₀O₄			
3-(α-p-Methoxyphenylpropyl)-4-methoxy-benzoic acid	3-(α-p-Methoxyphenylpropyl)-4-methoxy-benzyl alcohol	100	43
C₁₉H₁₄O₃			
2-(o-Toluyl)-1-naphthoic acid	Lactone of 2-(α-hydroxy-o-methylbenzyl)-1-naphthoic acid	57	44
	1-Hydroxymethyl-2-(α-hydroxy-o-methylbenzyl)-naphthalene	16	44
C₂₀H₁₆O₂			
o-Carboxytriphenylmethane	o-Hydroxymethyltriphenylmethane	95	45
C₂₀H₁₆O₄			
Phenolphthalin	Phenolphthalol	76–81	46

References—Table XXXII

[1]Isolated as p-nitrobenzoate.

[2]E. T. McBee and E. Rapkin, *J. Am. Chem. Soc.*, 73, 1366 (1951).

[3]C. G. Swain and W. P. Langsdorf, Jr., *ibid.*, 73, 2813 (1951).

[4]R. F. Nystrom and W. G. Brown, *ibid.*, 69, 2548 (1947).

[5]H. I. Schlesinger and A. E. Finholt, U. S. Pat. 2,576,311 (November 27, 1951).

[6]Neville, unpublished work, through W. G. Brown, in *Organic Reactions*, Vol. VI, p. 504.

[7]A. Sveinbjornsson and C. A. Vander Werf, *J. Am. Chem. Soc.*, 73, 1378 (1951).

[8]J. Mahé, J. Rollet and A. Willemart, *Bull. soc. chim. France* [5] 16, 481 (1949).

[9]L. H. Conover and D. S. Tarbell, *J. Am. Chem. Soc.*, 72, 3586 (1950).

[10]B. Witkop, J. B. Patrick, and H. M. Kissman, *Chem. Ber.*, 85, 949 (1952).

[11]Reaction carried out in diethyl ether-di-n-butyl ether mixture.

[12]Four equivalents excess LAH, 22 hours, 25°.

[13]Twelve equivalents excess LAH, 11 days, 85°.

[14]A. P. Phillips and A. Maggiolo, *J. Org. Chem.*, 15, 659 (1950).

[15]Four equivalents excess LAH, 29 hours, 65°.

[16]R. F. Bird and E. E. Turner, *J. Chem. Soc.*, 1952, 5050.

[17]S. W. Kantor and C. R. Hauser, *J. Am. Chem. Soc.*, 73, 4122 (1951).

[18]I. Wender, H. Greenfield, S. Metlin, and M. Orchin, *ibid.*, 74, 4079 (1952).

[19]A. T. Carpenter and R. F. Hunter, *J. Appl. Chem. (London)*, 1, 217 (1951).

[20]Reduction carried out in dioxane gave indicated crude yield of resin identified by preparation of 2,4,6-tri-(2′-hydroxy-5′-methylbenzyl)phenol by reaction with p-cresol.

[21]Reduction carried out with 0.75 mole LAH.

[22]G. Papineau-Couture, E. M. Richardson, and G. A. Grant, *Can. J. Research*, 27B, 902 (1949).

[23]E. R. Shepard, H. D. Porter, J. F. Noth, and C. K. Simmans, *J. Org. Chem.*, 17, 568 (1952).

[24]R. Adams, M. Harfenist, and S. Loewe, *J. Am. Chem. Soc.*, 71, 1624 (1949).

[25]M. S. Newman and N. C. Deno, *ibid.*, 73, 3644 (1951).

[26]W. Cocker, B. E. Cross, A. K. Fateen, C. Lipman, E. R. Stuart, W. H. Thompson, and D. R. A. Whyte, *J. Chem. Soc.*, 1950, 1781.

[27]F. Wessely, K. Benedikt, H. Benger, G. Friedrich and F. Prillinger, *Monatsh.*, 81, 1071 (1950).

[28]A. Dornow and G. Petsch, *Arch. pharm.*, 285, 323 (1952).

[29]W. R. Vaughan and R. Perry, Jr., *J. Am. Chem. Soc.*, 74, 5355 (1952).

[30]M. S. Newman and J. R. Mangham, *ibid.*, 71, 3342 (1949).

[31]R. V. Phillips, L. W. Trevoy, L. B. Jaques, and J. W. T. Spinks, *Can. J. Chem.*, 30, 844 (1952).

[32]L. E. Miller, W. W. Hanneman, W. L. St. John, and R. R. Smeby, *Abstracts of Papers*, 118th Meeting American Chemical Society, Chicago, Ill., September 1950, p. 59N.

[33]W. T. Smith, Jr. and L. Campamaro, *J. Am. Chem. Soc.*, 74, 1107 (1952).

[34]W. G. Dauben, C. F. Hiskey, and A. H. Markhart, Jr., *ibid.*, 73, 1393 (1951).

[35]A. Critchlow, R. D. Haworth, and P. L. Pauson, *J. Chem. Soc.*, 1951, 1318.

[36]S. Goldschmidt and W. L. C. Veer, *Rec. trav. chim.*, 67, 489 (1948).

[37]A. Mustafa, *J. Chem. Soc.*, 1952, 2435.

[38]D. H. Smith, J. R. Schwartz, and G. W. Wheland, *J. Am. Chem. Soc.*, 74, 2282 (1952).

[39]W. Baker, W. D. Ollis, and T. S. Zealley, *J. Chem. Soc.*, *1952*, 1447.
[40]J. English, Jr., and V. Lamberti, *J. Am. Chem. Soc.*, *74*, 1909 (1952).
[41]W. von E. Doering and H. H. Zeiss, *ibid.*, *72*, 147 (1950).
[42]H. H. Zeiss, *ibid.*, *73*, 2391 (1951).
[43]J. M. Van der Zanden and G. de Vries, *Rec. trav. chim.*, *71*, 879 (1952).
[44]M. S. Newman and R. Gaertner, *J. Am. Chem. Soc.*, *72*, 264 (1950).
[45]van Dyken, unpublished work, through W. G. Brown, in *Organic Reactions*, loc. cit.
[46]M. H. Hubacher, *J. Am. Chem. Soc.*, *74*, 5216 (1952).

The LAH reduction of various heterocyclic nitrogen carboxylic acids including pyrrolidine, indole, and pyridine nuclei have been carried out successfully. Attempts to reduce 3-carboxy-6-methyl-2(1)-pyridone (LIII) in ether have not been successful. However, LAH reduction of LIII in di-*n*-butyl ether gives 3-hydroxymethyl-6-methyl-2-pyridol as well as considerable unreacted acid (71).

$$\qquad \xrightarrow{\text{LAH}} \qquad \qquad \qquad (8\text{-}34)$$

LIII

Attempts to reduce 4-acetoxymethyl-3-carboxy-6-methyl-2-pyridol have been reported to be unsuccessful (72).

Thiophene and thianaphthene carboxylic acids are reduced with LAH in good yield to the corresponding hydroxymethyl derivatives (73-76).

The LAH reduction of various carboxylic acids containing heterocyclic oxygen, nitrogen and sulfur nuclei is summarized in Table XXXIII.

8.1.1.g *Labeled carboxylic acids.* The LAH reduction of isotopically labeled carboxylic acids permits the synthesis of carbinols labeled in the 1- and 2-positions with C^{13} and C^{14}. Various labeled acids treated in this manner are summarized in Table XXXIV. In the case of acetic acid, reported procedures have utilized diethyl carbitol (77,78) and ethylene glycol diethyl ether (79) as the reaction media with *n*-butyl carbitol and ethylene glycol monophenyl ether for the alcoholysis of the organometallic complex. In the reduction in diethyl carbitol the labeled ethanol has been found to be contaminated with inactive material arising from cleavage of the ether linkages of the diethyl carbitol.

The LAH reduction of 2,2-*d*-octanoic acid has been utilized in the synthesis of 2,2-*d*-*n*-octanol (80).

8.1.2 Reductions with Aluminum Hydride

The reduction of benzoic acid has been carried out with the aluminum hydride-aluminum chloride addition compound to yield 61% benzyl alcohol (81). The course of the reaction has been postulated as follows:

$$-\text{CH}=\text{O} \xrightarrow{+\text{alH}} -\text{CH}_2\text{Oal} \xrightarrow{+\text{H}_2\text{O}} -\text{CH}_2\text{OH} \quad (8\text{-}35)$$

al = 1 equiv. Al

TABLE XXXIII

LAH Reduction of Heterocyclic Carboxylic Acids

	Acid	Product	% Yield	Ref.
A. Heterocyclic Oxygen Compounds				
$C_5H_4O_3$	2-Furoic acid (I)	Furfuryl alcohol	85	1
$C_6H_6O_3$	3-Furoic acid	3-Hydroxymethylfuran	....	2
	3-Methyl-2-furoic acid	3-Methylfurfuryl alcohol	86.2–91.5	3
$C_6H_{10}O_3$	Tetrahydropyran-4-carboxylic acid (II)	4-Hydroxymethyltetrahydropyran	90.3	3
$C_9H_6O_3$	Benzofuran-2-carboxylic acid (III)	2-Hydroxymethylbenzofuran	55[4]	5
$C_{11}H_{10}O_3$	2-Methyl-3-methylene-2,3-dihydrobenzofuran-2-carboxylic acid (IV)	2-Methyl-2-hydroxymethyl-3-methylene-2,3-dihydrobenzofuran	85	6
			78	7
$C_{14}H_{18}O_3$	2,4,4,7-Tetramethylchroman-2-carboxylic acid (V)	2-Hydroxymethyl-2,4,4,7-tetramethylchroman	47	8
$C_{15}H_{24}O_{10}$	2-Methyl-3-(2,3,4-trimethyl-α-D-glucuronosido)-D-xylose	2,3,4-Trimethylglucose	....[9]	10
		2-Methylxylose	....[9]	
B. Heterocyclic Nitrogen Compounds				
$C_5H_9NO_2$	DL-Proline (VI)	DL-Prolinol	81[11]	12
$C_6H_5NO_2$	Isonicotinic acid (VII)	4-Hydroxymethylpyridine	46	13
$C_7H_7NO_3$	3-Carboxy-6-methyl-2(1)-pyridone (VIII)	3-Hydroxymethyl-6-methyl-2-pyridol	17[15,16]	14
$C_{10}H_9NO_2$	1-Methylindole-2-carboxylic acid (IX)	1-Methyl-2-hydroxymethylindole	86[11]	17
$C_{10}H_{11}NOS$	4-Acetoxymethyl-3-carboxy-6-methyl-2-pyridol (X)	None	....	18
$C_{13}H_{16}N_2O_6$	5-Amino-2,3-dicarbethoxy-6-methylpyridine-4-carboxylic acid	5-Amino-6-methyl-2,3,4-trihydroxymethylpyridine	47	19
$C_{16}H_{16}N_2O_2$	Lysergic acid (XI)	Lysergol	....	20
C. Heterocyclic Sulfur Compounds				
$C_6H_6O_2S$	2-Methylthiophene-3-carboxylic acid (XII)	2-Methyl-3-hydroxymethylthiophene	85	21
$C_9H_6O_2S$	Thianaphthene-2-carboxylic acid (XIII)	2-Hydroxymethylthianaphthene	99	22–24
	Thianaphthene-3-carboxylic acid	3-Hydroxymethylthianaphthene	96	22–24
$C_{10}H_8O_2S$	3-Methylthianaphthene-2-carboxylic acid	2-Hydroxymethyl-3-methylthianaphthene	95	25
	2-Methylthianaphthene-3-carboxylic acid	3-Hydroxymethyl-2-methylthianaphthene	43[26]	27

CHART TO TABLE XXXIII

References—Table XXXIII

[1]R. F. Nystrom and W. G. Brown, *J. Am. Chem. Soc.*, 69, 2548 (1947).
[2]H. I. Schlesinger and A. E. Finholt, U. S. Pat. 2,576,311 (November 27, 1951).
[3]E. Sherman and E. D. Amstutz, *J. Am. Chem. Soc.*, 72, 2195 (1950).
[4]Based on starting material consumed in reaction.
[5]A. Burger, L. B. Lennox, and J. G. Dinwiddie, Jr., *J. Am. Chem. Soc.*, 72, 5512 (1950).
[6]R. Gaertner, *ibid.*, 73, 4400 (1951).
[7]R. Gaertner, *ibid.*, 74, 5319 (1952).
[8]W. Baker, R. F. Curtis, and J. F. W. McOmie, *J. Chem. Soc.*, 1951, 76.
[9]LAH reduction product hydrolyzed with dilute hydrochloric acid to yield indicated products.
[10]S. K. Chanda, E. L. Hirst, and E. G. V. Percival, *J. Chem. Soc.*, 1951, 1240.
[11]Reduction carried out in tetrahydrofuran.
[12]O. Vogl and M. Pöhm, *Monatsh.*, 83, 541 (1952).
[13]H. S. Mosher and J. E. Tessieri, *J. Am. Chem. Soc.*, 73, 4925 (1951).
[14]R. P. Mariella and A. J. Havlik, *ibid.*, 74, 1915 (1952).
[15]Reduction carried out in di-*n*-butyl ether.
[16]44% unreacted acid recovered.
[17]K. Eiter and O. Svierak, *Monatsh.*, 83, 1453 (1952).
[18]R. P. Mariella and E. P. Belcher, *J. Am. Chem. Soc.*, 74, 4049 (1952).
[19]R. G. Jones, *ibid.*, 74, 1489 (1952).
[20]Sandoz Ltd., Brit. Pat. 674,061 (June 18, 1952).
[21]R. Gaertner, *J. Am. Chem. Soc.*, 73, 3934 (1951).
[22]F. F. Blicke and D. G. Sheets, *ibid.*, 71, 2856 (1949).
[23]F. F. Blicke, U. S. Pat. 2,533,086 (December 5, 1950).
[24]F. F. Blicke, U. S. Pat. 2,533,087 (December 5, 1950).
[25]R. Gaertner, *J. Am. Chem. Soc.*, 74, 2185 (1952).
[26]38.5% unreacted acid recovered.
[27]R. Gaertner, *J. Am. Chem. Soc.*, 74, 766 (1952).

TABLE XXXIV

LAH Reduction of Isotopically Labeled Carboxylic Acids

	Acid	Product	% Yield	Ref.
C_2H_4O	Acetic-1-C^{14} acid	Ethanol-1-C^{14}	...[1]	2
	Acetic-2-C^{14} acid	Ethanol-2-C^{14}	...	3
			...[1]	2
	Acetic-1-C^{14}-2-C^{13} acid	Ethanol-1-C^{14}-2-C^{13}	40[4]	5
$C_3H_5ClO_2$	3-Chloropropionic-1-C^{14} acid	3-Chloropropanol-1-C^{14}	...[1]	6
$C_3H_6O_2$	Propionic-1-C^{13} acid	Propanol-1-C^{13}	25–35	7
$C_4H_8O_2$	Isobutyric-1-C^{14} acid	Isobutanol-1-C^{14}	...	8
	Isobutyric-2-C^{14} acid	Isobutanol-2-C^{14}	...	9,10
$C_6H_{12}O_2$	Caproic-1-C^{14} acid	n-Hexanol-1-C^{14}	89.5	9
$C_7H_{14}O_2$	Heptanoic-1-C^{14} acid	n-Heptanol-1-C^{14}	...	11
$C_8H_8O_2$	Phenylacetic-2-C^{14} acid	2-Phenylethanol-2-C^{14}	85.6	12
$C_{11}H_8O_2$	2-Naphthoic acid-carboxyl-C^{14}	1-(2-Naphthalene) methanol-1-C^{14}	97	12
$C_{15}H_{14}O_2$	2-Phenyl-2-m-tolylacetic-1-C^{14} acid	2-Phenyl-2-m-tolylethanol-1-C^{14}	92	13
	2-Phenyl-2-p-tolylacetic-1-C^{14} acid	2-Phenyl-2-p-tolyethanol-1-C^{14}	93	14
$C_{15}H_{14}O_3$	2-Phenyl-2-p-methoxyphenylacetic-1-C^{14} acid	2-Phenyl-2-p-methoxyphenylethanol-1-C^{14}	93	15
$C_{16}H_{16}O_2$	2-Phenyl-2-p-ethylphenylacetic-1-C^{14} acid	2-Phenyl-2-p-ethylphenylethanol-1-C^{14}	95	15
	2-Phenyl-2-(3,4-dimethylphenyl)acetic-1-C^{14} acid	2-Phenyl-2-(3,4-dimethylphenyl)ethanol-1-C^{14}	90	15
$C_{17}H_{18}O_2$	2-Phenyl-2-p-(2-propyl) phenylacetic-1-C^{14} acid	2-Phenyl-2-p-(2-propyl) phenylethanol-1-C^{14}	92	15
$C_{18}H_{20}O_2$	2-Phenyl-2-p-(t-butyl) phenylacetic-1-C^{14} acid	2-Phenyl-2-p-(t-butyl) phenylethanol-1-C^{14}	100	15
$C_{20}H_{16}O_2$	2-Phenyl-2-p-xenylacetic-1-C^{14} acid	2-Phenyl-2-p-xenylethanol-1-C^{14}	88	15

References—Table XXXIV

[1]Reduction carried out in diethyl carbitol, decomposed with n-butyl carbitol.

[2]R. Ostwald, P. T. Adams, and B. M. Tolbert, *J. Am. Chem. Soc.*, 74, 2425 (1952).

[3]J. D. Roberts and J. A. Yancey, *ibid.*, 74, 5943 (1952).

[4]Reduction carried out in ethylene glycol diethyl ether, decomposed with ethylene glycol monophenyl ether.

[5]J. D. Cox and H. S. Turner, *J. Chem. Soc.*, 1950, 3176.

[6]G. Ehrensvärd, L. Reio, E. Saluste, and R. Stjernholm, *J. Biol. Chem.*, 189, 93 (1951).

[7]J. P. Ryan and P. R. O'Connor, *J. Am. Chem. Soc.*, 74, 5866 (1952).

[8]Document 3210, American Documentation Institute, through A. S. Gordon and S. Heimel, *ibid.*, 73, 2942 (1951).

[9]M. J. Coon and S. Gurin, *J. Biol. Chem.*, 180, 1159 (1949).

[10]H. Gottlieb and J. Sorden, *Abstracts of Papers*, 121st Meeting American Chemical Society, Milwaukee, Wis., April 1952, p. 91K.

[11]E. O. Weinman, I. L. Chaikoff, W. G. Dauben, M. Gee, and C. Entenman, *J. Biol. Chem.*, 184, 735 (1950).

[12]R. P. Geyer, M. Cunningham, and J. Pendergast, *ibid.*, 185, 461 (1950).

[13]W. G. Dauben and P. Coad, *J. Am. Chem. Soc.*, 71, 2928 (1949).

[14]R. V. Phillips, L. W. Trevoy, L. B. Jaques, and J. W. T. Spinks, *Can. J. Chem.*, 30, 844 (1952).

[15]J. G. Burr, Jr. and L. S. Ciereszko, *J. Am. Chem. Soc.*, 74, 5426 (1952).

8.1.3   Reductions with Magnesium and Zinc Aluminum Hydrides

Magnesium aluminum hydride in ethereal solution reduces carboxylic acids to the corresponding alcohols, analogous to the behavior of LAH (82,83). Thus, reduction of benzoic acid yields a white precipitate which, on hydrolysis, yields 86% benzyl alcohol. Similarly, cinnamic acid yields cinnamyl alcohol. The reaction is postulated (82) as follows:

$$
-C\underset{OH}{\overset{O}{\big\langle}} \xrightarrow{+2H} -C\underset{OH}{\overset{OH}{H}} \xrightarrow{-H_2O} -CH{=}O \xrightarrow{+2H} -CH_2OH \qquad (8\text{-}36)
$$

Zinc aluminum hydride is reported to reduce acids to alcohols although no specific examples have been recorded (83).

8.1.4   Reductions with Sodium Borohydride

The non-reduction of carboxylic acids with sodium borohydride permits the selective reduction of other functional groups in the presence of acid groups (84). The following compounds have been treated with sodium borohydride with the carboxylic acid group being retained intact:

Compound	Ref.
Maleic acid	84
p-Benzoylphenylacetic acid	85
4-Carboxymethyl-5-methoxy-8-methyl-1-tetralone	86
2β,4β-Dimethyl-2-methallyl-1-carboxymethylene-7-ethylenedioxy-1,2,3,4,4aα,4b,5,6,7,8,10,10aβ-decahydrophenanthrene-4-one	87
3β,11β-Dihydroxy-3α,9α-oxidocholanic acid	88
3,11-Diketocholanic acid	88
3α-Hydroxy-11-ketoetiocholanic acid	89
19-Hydroxy-3-keto-Δ^4-etiocholenic acid	90
Sodium 3α,9α-dihydroxy-11-ketocholanate	88
Sodium 3α-hydroxy-11-ketocholanate	88
Sodium 3β-hydroxy-3α,9α-oxido-11-ketocholanate	88
Sodium 3β-methoxy-3α,9α-oxido-11-ketocholanate	88

The β-mycolic acid isolated from a bovine *Mycobacterium* tuberculosis and called β-mycolic acid Marmorek, $C_{87}H_{172}O_4$, is postulated as LIV and on treatment with sodium borohydride yields the expected dihydroxycarboxylic acid (91).

$$
\underset{O\;\;R_1\;\;OH\;\;C_{24}H_{49}}{R_2C-CH-CH-CHCOOH}
\qquad\qquad
\underset{SH}{HSCH_2(CH_2)_x CH(CH_2)_{5-x}COOH}
$$

$$\text{LIV} \qquad\qquad\qquad \text{LV}$$

Protogen-B, a growth factor for *Tetrahymena geleii*, on treatment with sodium borohydride yields the dithiol carboxylic acid (LV) (92). Presumably the Protogen-B contains a carboxylic acid group which is recovered intact. DL-6-Thioctic acid (LVI) is oxidized to a sulfoxide carboxylic acid which on treatment with sodium borohydride yields 6,8-dithioloctanoic acid (93).

$$CH_2CH_2CH(CH_2)_4COOH$$
$$\quad |\qquad\qquad |$$
$$\quad S\text{------}S$$

LVI

Reduction of 10-formylpteroylglutamic acid (LVII) with sodium borohydride yields a product with increased biological activity. Although the structure of the product has not been determined it is probable that the acid groups are unattacked (94).

HOOCCHNHCO—⟨⟩—NCH₂— [pteridine ring] —NH₂
with CHO, OH substituents

$$\quad CH_2$$
$$\quad |$$
$$HOOCCH_2$$

LVII

Chaikin and Brown reported that treatment of pyruvic acid with sodium borohydride results in reduction but that boron-free products are not isolated. It has not been indicated whether the ketone or acid groups are reduced. Butyric acid undergoes partial reduction under the influence of sodium borohydride (84).

Reduction of levulinic acid (LVIII) with sodium borohydride in aqueous solution yields γ-valerolactone (84).

$$CH_3CCH_2CH_2COOH \xrightarrow[81\%]{NaBH_4} CH_3CHCH_2CH_2 \qquad (8\text{-}37)$$
$$\quad \|\qquad\qquad\qquad\qquad\qquad |\qquad\quad |$$
$$\quad O\qquad\qquad\qquad\qquad\qquad O\text{----}C\!=\!O$$

LVIII

Lactones are obtained in the reduction of some carbohydrate acids. Thus, the reduction of sodium D-glucuronate monohydrate yields γ-L-gulonolactone while the hexahydrated sodium calcium salt of D-galacturonic acid yields γ-L-galactonolactone (95). A polyuronide hemicellulose isolated from wheat straw, after methylation and hydrolysis, yields a methylated aldobiuronic acid identified as 2-methyl-3-(2,3,4-trimethyl-D-glucuronosido)-D-xylose. This compound, after reduction with sodium borohydride and subsequent hydrolysis, gives equimolar quantities of 2-methyl-D-xylose and 2,3,4-trimethyl-D-glucose (96).

Meller reported (97) that the sodium borohydride reduction of the aldonic acid groups present in gluconic acid oxycelluloses may proceed to aldehyde groups (acid reduction) or alcohol groups (alkaline reduction). No reduction products were isolated but the presence of carbonyl or alcohol groups was determined by measurement of the "hot alkali stability."

8.1.5 Reductions with Potassium Borohydride

In the only reported case of the reduction of a compound containing a carboxylic acid group with potassium borohydride, nicotinic acid methiodide (LIX) has been reduced to arecaidine (LX) (98).

$$(8\text{-}38)$$

LIX   LX

8.1.6 Reductions with Lithium Borohydride

The free carboxyl group does not seriously interfere in the reduction of other functional groups with lithium borohydride (99). Reduction of β-benzoylpropionic acid (LXI) yields γ-phenylbutyrolactone.

$$C_6H_5COCH_2CH_2COOH \xrightarrow[78\%]{LiBH_4} C_6H_5CHCH_2CH_2$$

LXI

Treatment of benzoic acid with lithium borohydride results in decomposition of the hydride and the evolution of diborane but the benzoic acid is recovered unchanged. The reaction between butyric acid and lithium borohydride, after one-half hour, results in a 75% recovery of the acid but an 8% yield of n-butanol. The reaction between crotonic acid and the borohydride, after two hours, yields a 45% recovery of crotonic acid accompanied by 10% of butyric acid and 4% n-butanol (99).

8.1.7 Reductions with Lithium Gallium Hydride

The complex gallium hydride is reported to reduce acids to alcohols. Reduction of butyric acid with lithium gallium hydride yields n-butanol (100).

8.2 ACID ANHYDRIDES

8.2.1 Reductions with Lithium Aluminum Hydride

The reaction between carboxylic acid anhydrides and LAH usually proceeds to yield primary alcohols. The following stoichiometric relationship, indicating the consumption of one mole of LAH per mole of anhydride, is based on the determination of hydride consumed (101).

$$(RCO)_2O + LiAlH_4 \rightarrow LiAlO(OCH_2R)_2 \qquad (8\text{-}40)$$

8.2.1.a *Anhydrides of monobasic acids.* The only reported reduction of the anhydride of a monobasic acid involves the reduction of benzoic anhydride to benzyl alcohol in 87% yield (52,101).

8.2.1.b *Anhydrides of dibasic acids.* Among the non-aromatic anhydrides, 2,2-dimethylsuccinic anhydride (LXII) has been converted to 2,2-dimethyl-1,4-butanediol (102).

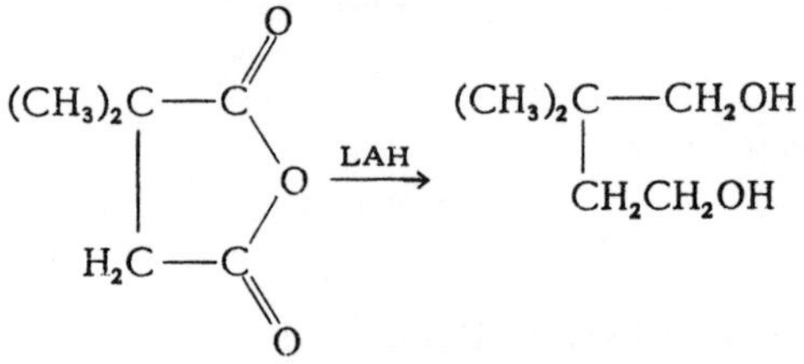

$$(8\text{-}41)$$

LXII

The maleic anhydride adduct of $\Delta^{16,20\,(22)}$-allofurostadiene-3β,26-diol diacetate (LXIII) is reduced with LAH in tetrahydrofuran solution to the tetrol (LXIV) (103).

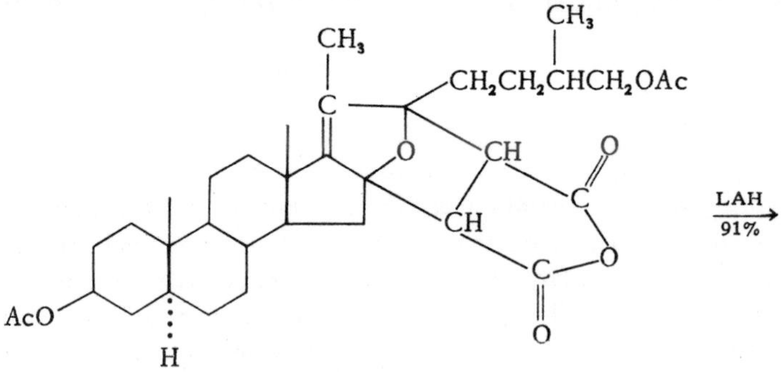

LXIII

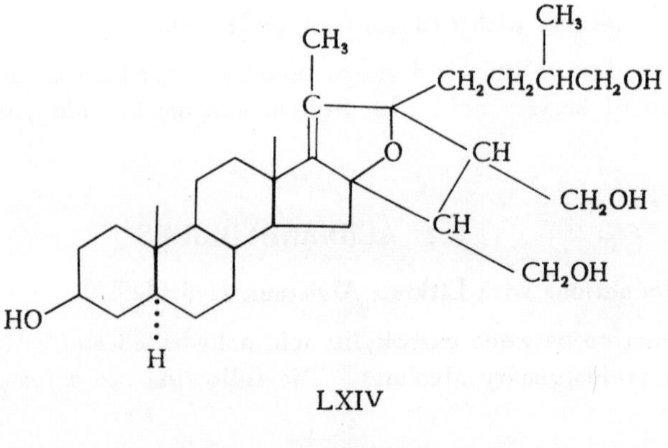

$$(8\text{-}42)$$

LXIV

The reduction of diacetyl-L-threaric anhydride (LXV) with LAH in a tetrahydrofuran-ether mixture followed by deionization gives an 18% yield of L-threitol (LXVI) on decomposition of the reaction product with water and a 32% yield on decomposition with ethanol. The low yield is attributed to the removal of starting material or some intermediate from the reaction as an insoluble complex (104).

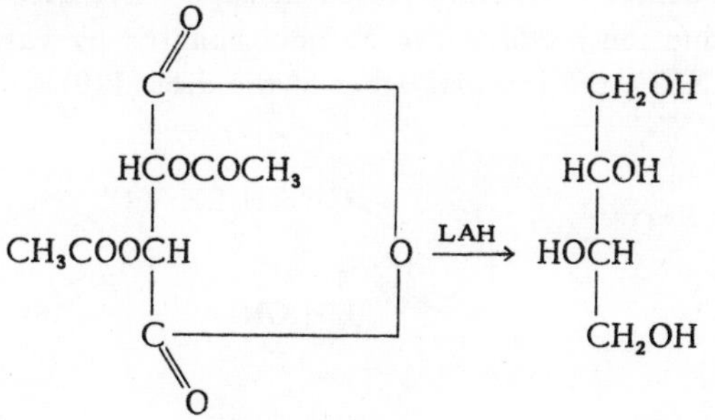

$$
\begin{array}{c}
\overset{O}{\underset{\parallel}{C}} \\
| \\
\text{HCOCOCH}_3 \\
| \\
\text{CH}_3\text{COOCH} \\
| \\
\underset{\underset{O}{\parallel}}{C} \\
\end{array}
O \xrightarrow{\text{LAH}}
\begin{array}{c}
\text{CH}_2\text{OH} \\
| \\
\text{HCOH} \\
| \\
\text{HOCH} \\
| \\
\text{CH}_2\text{OH}
\end{array}
\qquad (8\text{-}43)
$$

LXV   LXVI

The anhydrides of 1-cyclohexene-4,5-dicarboxylic acid (LXVII) (105) and 1,2-dimethyl-1-cyclohexene-4,5-dicarboxylic acid (LXVIII) (106) are also reduced to the corresponding diols. (The double bond in LXVIII is erroneously omitted in the abstract literature.)

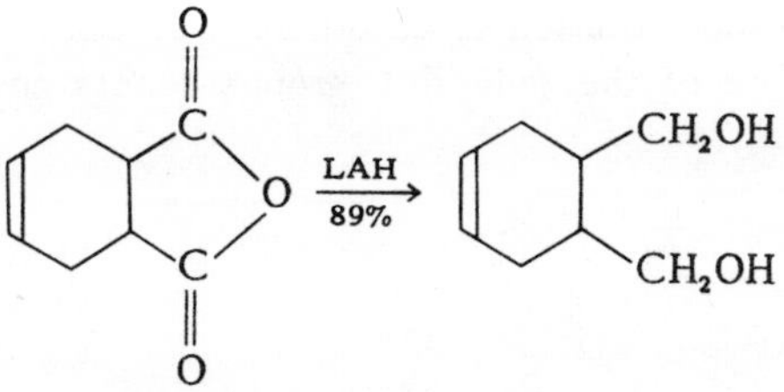

$$(8\text{-}44)$$

LXVII

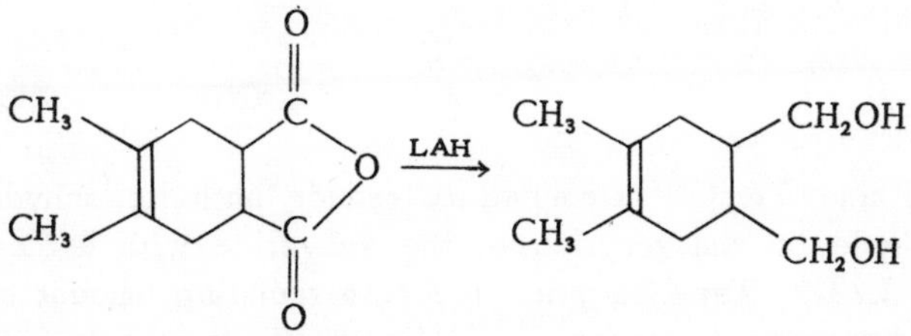

$$(8\text{-}45)$$

LXVIII

By comparison with LAH reduction it is of interest to note that the reaction of one mole of succinic anhydride and six moles of phenylmagnesium bromide in boiling toluene yields 1,1,4,4-tetraphenyl-1,4-butanediol, i.e., the product normally given by succinic esters (107). The anhydride and phenyllithium in refluxing ether or in dioxane at room temperature or at $-80°$ afford only a small yield of diphenyl and a large amount of a thick viscous oil (108).

The LAH reduction of homophthalic anhydride (LXIX) by the method used for compounds with low ether solubility, i.e., extraction from the thimble of a Soxhlet extractor, yields homophthalyl alcohol (LXX) (109, 110). The reduction product may be accompanied by varying amounts of isochroman (LXXI), the internal ether of the diol (110).

$$(8\text{-}46)$$

LXIX   LXX   LXXI

The reduction of phthalic anhydride with LAH by the extraction technique yields over 80% phthalyl alcohol (52,101,111,112). Papineau-Couture, Richardson, and Grant carried out the selective reduction of phthalic anhydride to phthalide (LXXII) (68). By the addition of one-half mole of LAH in ether solution to an ethereal solution of one mole of the anhydride only one of the reducible groups reacts to yield 45% of the lactone (LXVII).

$$(8\text{-}47)$$

LXXII

Weygand and Tietjen attempted to reduce phthalic anhydride to o-phthalaldehyde by the reaction of the anhydride with a "calculated" amount of LAH. They obtained the corresponding amount of phthalyl alcohol and recovered unreacted phthalic anhydride without isolating any of the expected aldehyde (113).

The LAH reduction of the anhydride of naphthalene-2,3-dicarboxylic acid (LXXIII) by the Soxhlet technique yields 2,3-di-(hydroxymethyl)-naphthalene (114,115).

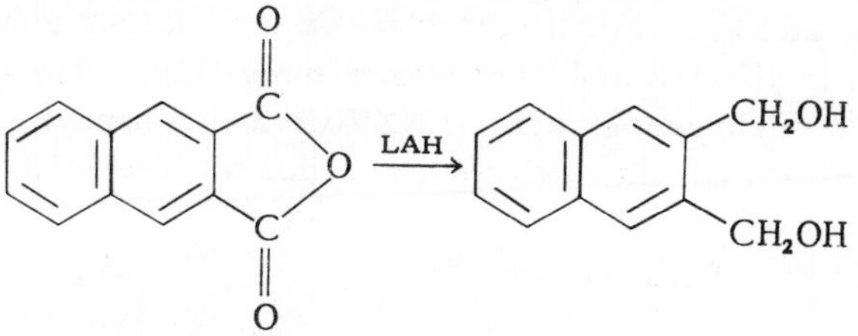

(8-48)

LXXIII

In a similar manner, the reduction of naphthalic anhydride (LXXIV) yields the 1,8-di-(hydroxymethyl) compound (116,117).

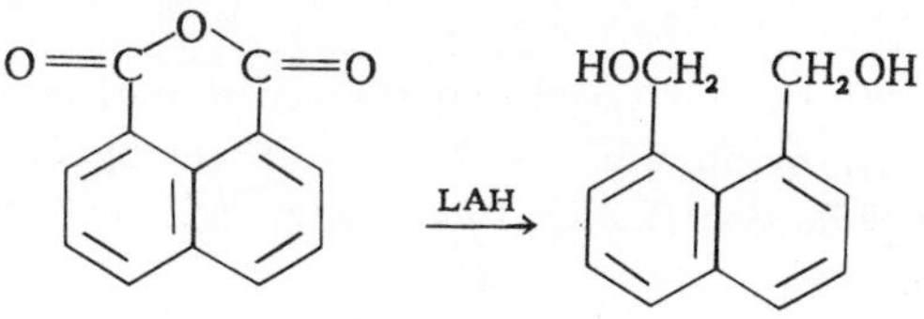

(8-49)

LXXIV

In contrast, the reduction of the anhydride of naphthalene-1,2-dicarboxylic acid (LXXV) with LAH in diethyl ether yields the naphthalide (LXXVI). Further reaction of the naphthalide (LXXVI) with LAH under the same conditions, i.e., reflux six hours in diethyl ether, does not give further reduction. When the reaction of the anhydride with LAH is carried out by refluxing three hours in di-n-butyl ether the product is the diol (LXXVII) (115).

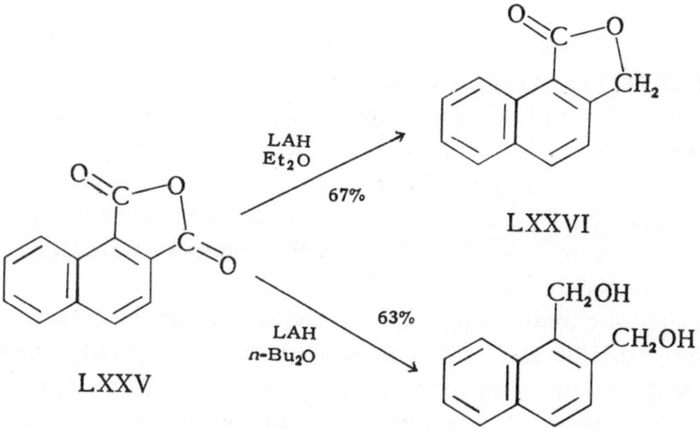

LAH
Et$_2$O
67%

(8-50)

LXXVI

LAH
n-Bu$_2$O
63%

LXXV

CH$_2$OH
CH$_2$OH

(8-51)

LXXVII

The reduction yielding LXXVI as the final product strongly suggests the influence of steric hindrance on the reduction of the carbonyl in the

1-position of LXXV. While triphenylacetic acid is not reduced at 25°
(1) reduction is effected at higher temperatures (118). The reduction of
2-benzyl-2,4-phenylbutanoic acid (LXXVIII) and 2-benzyl-2,3-diphenyl-
propanoic acid (LXXIX) is carried out in refluxing di-n-butyl ether (22).

$$C_6H_5CH_2CH_2\underset{\underset{CH_2C_6H_5}{|}}{\overset{\overset{C_6H_5}{|}}{C}}COOH$$

LXXVIII

$$C_6H_5CH_2\underset{\underset{CH_2C_6H_5}{|}}{\overset{\overset{C_6H_5}{|}}{C}}COOH$$

LXXIX

Becker (119,120) has observed that the addition of tetraphenylphthalic
anhydride (LXXX) to an ethereal LAH solution by Soxhlet extraction
yields only the phthalide (LXXXI) even with three moles of LAH to one
of the anhydride.

LXXX   LXXXI   (8-52)

However, in contrast to the behavior of the naphthalide (LXXVI), the
phthalide (LXXXI) is readily reduced to the corresponding diol in a second reaction. The failure of the first reaction to proceed beyond the
phthalide stage might be attributed to the insolubility of the complex
formed in the course of the reduction, except that no appreciable precipitation occurs (119). An alternative explanation is based on steric
factors of the type indicated by Fuchs and Vander Werf (121). Further,
the anhydride is highly hindered.

The reaction of phthalic anhydride and phenyllithium in dioxane yields
α,α-diphenylphthalide (LXXXII) indicating reaction with only one of the
carbonyl groups of the anhydride (108). The nature of the reaction between the anhydride and a Grignard reagent is controversial. Bauer (122)
obtained dialkylphthalides with alkylmagnesium bromides and claimed
to have obtained diphenylphthalide with the phenyl Grignard reagent. On
the other hand, Howell (123) claimed to have obtained 3-hydroxy-1,1,3-
triphenylbenzo[c]furan (LXXXIII) by the action of phenylmagnesium
bromide.

LXXXII   LXXXIII

8.2.1.c *N-Carboxyanhydrides*. The reduction of the N-carboxyanhydride of DL-phenylalanine (LXXXIV) with LAH by the Soxhlet extraction
technique yields phenylalaninol (LXXXV) as the major product accompanied by N-methylphenylalaninol (LXXXVI) and N-formylphenylalanine
(LXXXVII) (124).

LXXXIV   LXXXV

$$(8\text{-}53)$$

LXXXVI   LXXXVII

The formation of phenylalaninol involves the cleavage of the carbamate
grouping at the nitrogen-carbon bond although the N-methyl compound
(LXXXVI) should be the expected product (Section 10.4).

8.2.2 Reductions with Sodium Borohydride

Anhydrides show only slight reduction on prolonged heating with sodium borohydride in dioxane or diethyl carbitol. Phthalic and succinic
anhydrides are partially reduced under these conditions (84). Therefore
the selective reduction of more active groups can be carried out without
interference from anhydrides.

8.3 ACYL HALIDES

8.3.1 Reductions with Lithium Aluminum Hydride

The reduction of acyl halides with LAH consumes one-half mole of
hydride per mole of acyl halide to yield, on hydrolysis, primary alcohols
(52,101,125).

$$2\ RCOCl + LiAlH_4 \rightarrow LiAlCl_2(OCH_2R)_2 \qquad (8\text{-}54)$$

Phosgene, ClCOCl, is reduced to methanol (52,126). Aliphatic and aromatic acyl halides are equally readily reduced to the corresponding alcohols. Halogen substituted acid chlorides such as mono-, di-, and trichloroacetyl chloride (2) and di- (127) and trifluoroacetyl (128) chloride have been reduced to the corresponding chloro- and fluoroethanols. Isotopically labeled acetyl chloride has been utilized in the synthesis of ethanol-2-C^{14} (79,129). Cox and Turner (79) have carried out the almost quantitative reduction of acetyl chloride-2-C^{14} utilizing diethylene glycol diethyl ether as solvent for the LAH and ethylene glycol monophenyl ether for the alcoholysis of the intermediate complex. Attempts to reduce acetic acid by the same technique failed to yield over 40% ethanol and resulted in the evolution of hydrogen.

As indicated above, reduction of the acid chloride is of great utility where direct reduction of the carboxylic acid is difficult or troublesome. Thus, while chloro- and trichloroacetyl chlorides are reduced to the chloroethanols in over 60% yield, LAH reduction of chloroacetic and trichloroacetic acid proceeds in 13 and 31% yield, respectively (2). Similarly, triphenylacetic acid is not reduced with LAH in ether at 25° (1) while the acid chloride is readily reduced under these conditions (1,130).

The fact that LAH reduction does not cause a change in the configuration of the α-carbon has been utilized in the reduction of L(+)-α-chloropropionyl chloride to L(+)-2-chloro-1-propanol without loss of optical activity (131).

The reduction of various acid halides with LAH is summarized in Table XXXV.

LAH reduction of acid chlorides has been utilized in the degradation studies of various triterpenes. Thus, in studies on the structure of elemadienolic acid, elemonoyl chloride (LXXXVIII) has been reduced to the carbinol with LAH in ether in 91% yield (132).

$$C_{20}H_{35}\left\{\begin{array}{l}-CH_2\overset{|}{C}HCOCl\\ {}^{\diagdown}CH_2\\ {}^{\diagup}\\ {}^{\diagdown}C=C{}^{\diagup}\\ -CH_2CH(CH_3)_2\end{array}\right. \xrightarrow{\text{LAH}} C_{20}H_{35}\left\{\begin{array}{l}-CH_2\overset{|}{C}HCH_2OH\\ {}^{\diagdown}CH_2\\ {}^{\diagup}\\ {}^{\diagdown}C=C{}^{\diagup}\\ -CH_2CH(CH_3)_2\end{array}\right.\qquad(8\text{-}55)$$

LXXXVIII

Quinovaic acid, a triterpene monohydroxy dicarboxylic acid, has been examined by Ruzicka and co-workers (41) and illustrates the utility of acid chloride reduction in structural analysis. Of the two carboxyl groups one can be readily transformed into an aldehyde or carbinol group while

TABLE XXXV
LAH Reduction of Acyl Halides

	Acyl Halide	Product	% Yield	Ref.
	Aliphatic and Alicyclic			
C_2HCl_3O	Dichloroacetyl chloride	2,2-Dichloroethanol	63	1
C_2HClF_2O	Difluoroacetyl chloride	2,2-Difluoroethanol	69	2
$C_2H_2Cl_2O$	Chloroacetyl chloride	2-Chloroethanol	62	1
	Chloroacetyl chloride-2-C[14]	2-Chloroethanol-2-C[14]	...	3
C_2H_3ClO	Acetyl chloride-2-C[14]	Ethanol-2-C[14]	100[a]	5
			...	6
C_2Cl_4O	Trichloroacetyl chloride	2,2,2-Trichloroethanol	64	1
C_2ClF_3O	Trifluoroacetyl chloride	2,2,2-Trifluoroethanol	85	7
			...	8
$C_3H_4Cl_2O$	L(+)-2-Chloropropionyl chloride	L(+)-2-Chloro-1-propanol	67–72	9
C_5H_9ClO	Trimethylacetyl chloride	Neopentyl alcohol	86	10
			...	11,12
C_6H_7ClO	Sorboyl chloride	Sorbyl alcohol	98	10,11
$C_6H_{11}ClO$	Isocaproyl chloride	4-Methyl-1-pentanol	95	10,11
$C_{16}H_{31}ClO$	Palmitoyl chloride	1-Hexadecanol	99	10,11
$C_{18}H_{23}ClO_2$	O-Methylpodocarpoyl chloride	O-Methylpodocarpinol	92	13,14
	Aromatic			
C_7H_5ClO	Benzoyl chloride	Benzyl alcohol	72	10,11
$C_8H_4Cl_2O_2$	o-Phthaloyl chloride	Phthalyl alcohol	95	10,11
			94	15
$C_8H_6ClFO_2$	2-Fluoro-4-methoxybenzoyl chloride	2-Fluoro-4-methoxybenzyl alcohol	100	16
$C_{10}H_{11}ClO$	2,4,6-Trimethylbenzoyl chloride	2,4,6-Trimethylbenzyl alcohol	62	17
$C_{12}H_{15}ClO$	Pentamethylbenzoyl chloride	Pentamethylbenzyl alcohol	95	18
$C_{20}H_{15}ClO$	Triphenylacetyl chloride	2,2,2-Triphenylethanol	...	19,20
	Triphenylacetyl chloride-1-C*	2,2,2-Triphenylethanol-1-C*	...	21,22
			97	23

References—Table XXXV

[1] C. E. Sroog, C. M. Chih, F. A. Short, and H. M. Woodburn, *J. Am. Chem. Soc.*, 71, 1710 (1949).

[2] A. L. Henne and R. L. Pelley, *ibid.*, 74, 1426 (1952).

[3] H. R. V. Arnstein, *Biochem. J.*, 48, 27 (1951).

[4] Reaction carried out in diethylene glycol diethyl ether; alcoholysis with ethylene glycol monophenyl ether.

[5] J. D. Cox and H. S. Turner, *J. Chem. Soc.*, 1950, 3176

[6] I. Siegel and V. Lorber, *J. Biol. Chem.*, 189, 571 (1951).

[7] A. L. Henne, R. M. Alm, and M. Smook, *J. Am. Chem. Soc,*, 70, 1968 (1948).

[8] A. L. Henne, R. L. Pelley, and R. M. Alm, *ibid.*, 72, 3370 (1950).

[9] W. Fickett, H. K. Garner, and H. J. Lucas, *ibid.*, 73, 5063 (1951).

[10] R. F. Nystrom and W. G. Brown, *ibid.*, 69, 1197 (1947).

[11] H. I. Schlesinger and A. E. Finholt, U. S. Pat. 2,576,311 (November 27, 1951).

[12] S. Winstein, B. K. Morse, E. Grunwald, K. C. Schreiber, and J. Corse, *J. Am. Chem. Soc.*, 74, 1113 (1952).

[13] H. H. Zeiss, C. E. Slimowicz, and V. Z. Pasternak, *ibid.*, 70, 1981 (1948).

[14] H. H. Zeiss and C. E. Slimowicz, French Pat. 979,346 (April 25, 1951).

[15] J. Entel, C. H. Ruof, and H. C. Howard, *J. Am. Chem. Soc.*, 74, 441 (1952).

[16] E. L. Bennett and C. Niemann, *ibid.*, 72, 1806 (1950).

[17] I. Wender, H. Greenfield, S. Metlin, and M. Orchin, *ibid.*, 74, 4079 (1952).

[18] M. S. Newman and N. C. Deno, *ibid.*, 73, 3644 (1951).

[19] R. F. Nystrom and W. G. Brown, *ibid.*, 69, 2548 (1947).

[20] R. F. Nystrom, unpublished work; through W. G. Brown in *Organic Reactions*, Vol. VI, p. 469.

[21] W. G. Brown, *Symposium on The Use of Isotopes in Biological Research*, University of Chicago, March 1947; through W. W. Miller and T. D. Price, *Nucleonics*, 1, 4 (November 1947).

[22] C. Heidelberger, personal communication; through W. W. Miller and T. D. Price, *loc. cit.*

[23] L. Pichat and M. Audinot, *Bull. soc. chim. France*, [5] 19, 466 (1952).

catalytic reduction causes one carboxyl group to be split off. Quinovaic acid (LXXXIX) is readily transformed into 2-desoxyquinovaic acid or quinovene dicarboxylic acid (XC). LAH reduction of XC reduces one carboxyl group to the carbinol and leaves the other unchanged. The reduction of both carboxyl groups in LXXXIX or XC can be carried out using the diacid chloride. Flow Sheet II summarizes the various transformations carried out and indicates the conversions made possible by the reducibility of the acid chloride group with LAH in dioxane solution.

Flow Sheet II

$$C_{28}H_{43} \begin{cases} OH \\ COOH \\ COOH \end{cases} \longrightarrow C_{28}H_{43} \begin{cases} OCOC_6H_5 \\ COCl \\ COCl \end{cases} \xrightarrow[78\%]{LAH} C_{28}H_{43} \begin{cases} OH \\ CH_2OH \\ CH_2OH \end{cases}$$

LXXXIX

$$\downarrow$$

$$C_{28}H_{44} \begin{cases} COOH \\ COOH \end{cases} \xrightarrow[86\%]{LAH} C_{28}H_{44} \begin{cases} COOH \\ CH_2OH \end{cases} \longrightarrow C_{28}H_{44} \begin{cases} COOH \\ CH_2OCOCH_3 \end{cases}$$

XC

$$\downarrow \qquad\qquad\qquad\qquad\qquad\qquad\qquad\qquad \downarrow$$

$$C_{28}H_{44} \begin{cases} COCl \\ COCl \end{cases} \xrightarrow[62\%]{LAH} C_{28}H_{44} \begin{cases} CH_2OH \\ CH_2OH \end{cases} \xleftarrow[73\%]{LAH} C_{28}H_{43} \begin{cases} COCl \\ CH_2OCOCH_3 \end{cases}$$

The LAH reduction of a phosphinyl chloride has been carried out to yield a phosphine oxide (133). Treatment of di-*n*-octylphosphinic acid with phosphorus pentachloride in benzene yields the phosphinyl chloride (XCI). Reduction of XCI with LAH in ether at low temperatures yields 54% (based on the acid) of di-*n*-octylphosphine oxide.

$$(C_8H_{17})_2\overset{\overset{\displaystyle O}{\uparrow}}{P}\!-\!OH \xrightarrow{PCl_5} (C_8H_{17})_2\overset{\overset{\displaystyle O}{\uparrow}}{P}\!-\!Cl \xrightarrow{LAH} (C_8H_{17})_2\overset{\overset{\displaystyle O}{\uparrow}}{P}H \qquad (8\text{-}56)$$

XCI

8.3.2   Reductions with Aluminum Hydride

Acetyl chloride has been reduced to ethanol in 54% yield by means of the aluminum hydride-aluminum chloride addition compound (81).

8.3.3   Reductions with Sodium Borohydride

The reduction of acid chlorides with sodium borohydride is generally carried out in dioxane. The reaction is vigorous with aliphatic acid chlorides but aromatic acid chlorides require heating. Simple acid chlorides are converted to the alcohols in good yield but unsaturated acid chlorides such as crotonyl and cinnamoyl chloride undergo reaction at the carbon-carbon double bond. The fact that in the latter cases unsaturated alcohols could not be isolated is considered by Chaikin and Brown as indicating addition of the borohydride to the double bond forming a carbon-boron bond with the β-carbon atom. This bond, in contrast with the compounds formed from LAH, is apparently resistant to hydrolytic fission (84).

While phthaloyl chloride (XCII) is reduced to phthalyl alcohol in 94% yield with LAH (134), on reduction with sodium borohydride the major product is phthalide (84).

$$(8\text{-}57)$$

$$(8\text{-}58)$$

Henne, Pelley, and Alm (135) have reported that while trifluoroacetyl chloride is reduced to 2,2,2-trifluoroethanol with LAH, no reduction occurs with sodium hydride or sodium borohydride. No conditions are given for the latter attempts.

Various acid chlorides reduced with sodium borohydride are summarized in Table XXXVI.

TABLE XXXVI

Reduction of Acid Chlorides with Sodium Borohydride (84)

Acid chloride	Product	% Yield
Benzoyl chloride	Benzyl alcohol	76
n-Butyryl chloride	n-Butanol	81
Cinnamoyl chloride	Hydrocinnamyl alcohol[a]	12
Crotonyl chloride	[b]	
Monoethyl succinate acid chloride	Butyrolactone	40
Palmitoyl chloride	Cetyl alcohol	87
o-Phthaloyl chloride	Phthalide	49
	Phthalyl alcohol	15

[a] Major product unhydrolyzable organo-boron material.
[b] Reduction occurred but boron-free product not isolated.

The selective reducing action of sodium borohydride has been utilized in the reduction of acid chlorides containing hydantoin rings. Wilk and Close have shown that with LAH at least one carbonyl group in the hydantoin ring is reduced (136). Wessely, Schlögl, Korger, and Wawersich (137-141) have utilized sodium borohydride in the reduction of the acid chloride group in determining the constitution of hydantoin peptides.

$$(8\text{-}59)$$

R_1	R_2	Ref.
H	$CH_2C_6H_5$	140
CH_3	$CH_2CH(CH_3)_2$	141
$(CH_3)_2CHCH_2$	CH_3	140
$C_6H_5CH_2$	H	137,139
$(p)HOC_6H_4CH_2$	CH_3	140

$$(8\text{-}60)$$

8.3.4 Reductions with Potassium Borohydride

Acid chlorides are reportedly reduced in inert solvents in high yields by means of potassium borohydride (142).

8.3.5 Reductions with Lithium Borohydride

Lithium borohydride reacts rapidly at room temperature with acid chlorides according to the equation (143):

$$2\,LiBH_4 + 4\,RCOCl \rightarrow LiCl + BCl_3 + LiB(OCH_2R)_4$$

$$\downarrow H_2O$$

$$4\,RCH_2OH + LiBO_2$$

(8-61)

8.3.6 Reductions with Aluminum Borohydride

Phosgene reacts violently with aluminum borohydride to yield diborane, carbon monoxide and hydrogen, among the identifiable products (144).

REFERENCES

1. Nystrom, R. F., and W. G. Brown, *J. Am. Chem. Soc.*, *69*, 2548 (1947).
2. Sroog, C. E., C. M. Chih, F. A. Short, and H. M. Woodburn, *J. Am. Chem. Soc.*, *71*, 1710 (1949).
3. Halperin, B. I., H. B. Donahoe, J. Kleinberg, and C. A. Vander Werf, *J. Org. Chem.*, *17*, 623 (1952).
4. Benning, A. F., U. S. Pat. 2,559,749 (July 10, 1951).
5. Husted, D. R., and A. H. Ahlbrecht, U. S. Pat. 2,568,500 (September 18, 1951).
6. Minnesota Mining and Manufacturing Co., Brit. Pat. 676,273 (July 23, 1952).
7. Kauck, E. A., and A. R. Diesslin, *Ind. Eng. Chem.*, *43*, 2332 (1951).
8. Husted, D. R., and A. H. Ahlbrecht, *J. Am. Chem. Soc.*, *74*, 5422 (1952).
9. McBee, E. T., J. F. Higgins, and O. R. Pierce, *J. Am. Chem. Soc.*, *74*, 1387 (1952).
10. Reid, T. S., and G. H. Smith, through *Chem. Eng. News*, *29*, 3042 (1951).
11. Vogl, O., and M. Pöhm, *Monatsh.*, *83*, 541 (1952).
12. Jollès, P., and C. Fromageot, *Biochim. et Biophys. Acta*, *9*, 287 (1952).
13. Barry, V. C., J. G. Belton, R. M. Kelley, and D. Twomey, *Nature*, *166*, 303 (1950).
14. Barry, V. C., and D. Twomey, *Abstracts of Papers*, XIIth International Congress of Pure and Applied Chemistry, New York, N.Y., September 1951, p. 308.
15. Holman, R. E., and D. D. Carroll, *J. Am. Chem. Soc.*, *73*, 1859 (1951).
16. Brown, R. F., private communication; R. F. Brown and N. van Gulick, *Abstracts of Papers*, 122nd Meeting American Chemical Society, Atlantic City, N.J., September 1952, p. 7M.
17. Marvel, C. S., and J. A. Fuller, *J. Am. Chem. Soc.*, *74*, 1506 (1952).
18. Noyce, D. S., and D. B. Denney, *J. Am. Chem. Soc.*, *72*, 5743 (1950).
19. Hardegger, E., H. J. Leemann, and F. G. Robinet, *Helv. Chim. Acta*, *35*, 824 (1952).
20. Chanda, S. K., E. L. Hirst, and E. G. V. Percival, *J. Chem. Soc.*, *1951*, 1240.
21. Hochstein, F. A., unpublished work; through W. G. Brown, in *Organic Reactions*, Vol. VI, p. 478.
22. Baker, R. H., *J. Am. Chem. Soc.*, *70*, 3857 (1948).
23. Eliel, E. L., and J. P. Freeman, *J. Am. Chem. Soc.*, *74*, 923 (1952).

24. Eliel, E. L., and M. C. Herrmann, *Abstracts of Papers*, 122nd Meeting American Chemical Society, Atlantic City, N. J., September, 1952, p. 46M.
25. Schrage, A., and G. H. Hitchings, *J. Org. Chem.*, 16, 1153 (1951).
26. Fromageot, C., M. Jutisz, D. Meyer, and L. Pénasse, *Biochim. et Biophys. Acta*, 6, 283 (1950).
27. Fromageot, C., M. Jutisz, D. Meyer, and L. Pénasse, *Compt. rend.*, 230, 1905 (1950).
28. Jollès, P., and C. Fromageot, *Biochim. et Biophys. Acta*, 9, 416 (1952).
29. Jutisz, M., *Bull. soc. chim. France*, [5] 19, 821 (1952).
30. Pénasse, L., M. Jutisz, C. Fromageot, and H. Fraenkel-Conrat, *Biochim. et Biophys. Acta*, 9, 551 (1952).
31. Mousseron, M., R. Jacquier, M. Mousseron-Canet, and R. Zagdoun, *Bull. soc. chim. France*, [5] 19, 1042 (1952).
32. Glazer, J., M. M. Harris, and E. E. Turner, *J. Chem. Soc.*, 1950, 1753.
33. Reeve, W., and I. Christoffel, *J. Am. Chem. Soc.*, 72, 1480 (1950).
34. Guss, C. O., and L. H. Jules, *J. Am. Chem. Soc.*, 72, 3878 (1950).
35. Guss, C. O., *J. Am. Chem. Soc.*, 74, 2561 (1952).
36. Wu, B. Y. T., and L. M. Parks, *J. Am. Pharm. Assoc., Sci. Ed.*, 39, 475 (1950).
37. Barton, D. H. R., and C. J. W. Brooks, *J. Chem. Soc.*, 1951, 257.
38. Polonsky, J., *Compt. rend.*, 233, 671 (1951).
39. Polonsky, J., *Bull. soc. chim. France*, [5] 19, 649 (1952).
40. Polonsky, J., *Compt. rend.*, 230, 485 (1950).
41. Diener, H., O. Jeger, and L. Ruzicka, *Helv. Chim. Acta*, 33, 896 (1950).
42. Nunn, J. R., *J. Chem. Soc.*, 1952, 313.
43. Khan, N. A., F. E. Deatherage, and J. B. Brown, *J. Am. Oil Chemists' Soc.*, 28, 27 (1951).
44. Ligthelm, S. P., and H. M. Schwartz, *J. Am. Chem. Soc.*, 72, 1868 (1950).
45. Ligthelm, S. P., E. von Rudloff, and D. A. Sutton, *J. Chem. Soc.*, 1950, 3187.
46. Ligthelm, S. P., H. M. Schwartz, and M. M. von Holdt, *J. Chem. Soc.*, 1952, 1088.
47. Petrow, V., and O. Stephenson, *J. Chem. Soc.*, 1950, 1310.
48. Crombie, L., S. H. Harper, and D. Thompson, *J. Chem. Soc.*, 1951, 2906.
49. Mebane, A. D., *J. Am. Chem. Soc.*, 74, 5227 (1952).
50. Freedman, R. W., and E. I. Becker, *J. Am. Chem. Soc.*, 73, 2366 (1951).
51. Donrow, A., G. Messwarb, and H. H. Frey, *Chem. Ber.*, 83, 445 (1950).
52. Schlesinger, H. I., and A. E. Finholt, U. S. Pat. 2,576,311 (November 27, 1951).
53. Hochstein, F. A., and W. G. Brown, *J. Am. Chem. Soc.*, 70, 3484 (1948).
54. Liang Li and W. H. Elliott, *J. Am. Chem. Soc.*, 74, 4089 (1952).
55. Collins, C. J., unpublished work; through W. G. Brown, in *Organic Reactions*, Vol. VI, p. 482, 504.
56. Freudenberg, K., and F. Bittner, *Chem. Ber.*, 83, 600 (1950).
57. Pelletier, S. W., and J. E. Franz, *J. Org. Chem.*, 17, 855 (1952).
58. Petuely, F., and H. F. Bauer, *Monatsh.*, 83, 758 (1952).
59. Benedict, G. E., and R. R. Russell, *J. Am. Chem. Soc.*, 73, 5444 (1951).
60. Mitchovitch, V., and M. L. Mihailovic, *Compt. rend.*, 231, 1238 (1950).
61. Mićović, V. M., and M. L. Mikhailović, *Glasnik Khem. Drushtva Beograd*, 16, 19 (1951); through *Chem. Abstracts*, 46, 8609 (1952).
62. Newman, M. S., and N. C. Deno, *J. Am. Chem. Soc.*, 73, 3644 (1951).

388   REDUCTION OF CARBOXYLIC ACID DERIVATIVES

63. Wender, I., H. Greenfield, S. Metlin, and M. Orchin, *J. Am. Chem. Soc.*, 74, 4079 (1952).
64. Carpenter, A. T., and R. F. Hunter, *J. Appl. Chem. (London)*, 1, 217 (1951).
65. Hubacher, H. M., *J. Am. Chem. Soc.*, 74, 5216 (1952).
66. Baeyer, A., *Ann.*, 202, 87 (1880).
67. Newman, M. S., and R. Gaertner, *J. Am. Chem. Soc.*, 72, 264 (1950).
68. Papineau-Couture, G., E. M. Richardson, and G. A. Grant, *Can. J. Research*, 27B, 902 (1949).
69. Bird, R. F., and E. E. Turner, *J. Chem. Soc.*, 1952, 5050.
70. Conover, L. H., and D. S. Tarbell, *J. Am. Chem. Soc.*, 72, 3586 (1950).
71. Mariella, R. P., and A. J. Havlik, *J. Am. Chem. Soc.*, 74, 1915 (1952).
72. Mariella, R. P., and E. P. Belcher, *J. Am. Chem. Soc.*, 74, 4049 (1952).
73. Gaertner, R., *J. Am. Chem. Soc.*, 73, 3934 (1951).
74. Gaertner, R., *J. Am. Chem. Soc.*, 74, 766 (1952).
75. Gaertner, R., *J. Am. Chem. Soc.*, 74, 2185 (1952).
76. Blicke, F. F., and D. G. Sheets, *J. Am. Chem. Soc.*, 71, 2856 (1949).
77. Ostwald, R., P. T. Adams, and B. M. Tolbert, *J. Am. Chem. Soc.*, 74, 2425 (1952).
78. Ehrensvärd, G., L. Reio, E. Saluste, and R. Stjernholm, *J. Biol. Chem.*, 189, 93 (1951).
79. Cox, J. D., and H. S. Turner, *J. Chem. Soc.*, 1950, 3176.
80. Hill, D. G., W. A. Judge, P. S. Skell, S. W. Kantor, and C. R. Hauser, *J. Am. Chem. Soc.*, 74, 5599 (1952).
81. Wiberg, E., and A. Jahn, *Z. Naturforsch.*, 7b, 580 (1952).
82. Wiberg, E., and R. Bauer, *Z. Naturforsch.*, 7b, 131 (1952).
83. Wiberg, E., *et al.*, through *European Scientific Notes*, No. 7-1, January 1, 1953.
84. Chaikin, S. W., and W. G. Brown, *J. Am. Chem. Soc.*, 71, 122 (1949).
85. Zelinski, R. P., B. W. Turnquest, and E. C. Martin, *J. Am. Chem. Soc.*, 73, 5521 (1951).
86. Dreiding, A. S., and A. J. Tomasewski, *Abstracts of Papers*, 121st Meeting American Chemical Society, Milwaukee, Wis., April 1952, p. 82K.
87. Sarett, L. H., G. E. Arth, R. M. Lukes, R. E. Beyler, G. I. Poos, W. F. Johns, and J. M. Constantin, *J. Am. Chem. Soc.*, 74, 4974 (1952).
88. Heymann, H., and L. F. Fieser, *J. Am. Chem. Soc.*, 73, 5252 (1951).
89. Heymann, H., and L. F. Fieser, *J. Am. Chem. Soc.*, 74, 5938 (1952).
90. Herzig, P. T., and M. Ehrenstein, *J. Org. Chem.*, 17, 713 (1952).
91. Demarteau, H., and E. Lederer, *Compt. rend.*, 235, 265 (1952).
92. Brockman, J. A., Jr., E. L. R. Stokstad, E. L. Patterson, J. V. Pierce, M. Macchi, and F. P. Day, *J. Am. Chem. Soc.*, 74, 1868 (1952).
93. Bullock, M. W., J. A. Brockman, Jr., E. L. Patterson, J. V. Pierce, and E. L. R. Stokstad, *J. Am. Chem. Soc.*, 74, 3455 (1952).
94. Roth, B., M. E. Hultquist, M. J. Fahrenbach, D. B. Cosulich, H. P. Broquist, J. A. Brockman, Jr., J. M. Smith, Jr., R. P. Parker, E. L. R. Stokstad, and T. H. Jukes, *J. Am. Chem. Soc.*, 74, 3247 (1952).
95. Wolfrom, M. L., and K. Anno, *J. Am. Chem. Soc.*, 74, 5583 (1952).
96. Adams, G. A., *Can. J. Chem.*, 30, 698 (1952).
97. Meller, A., *Tappi*, 36, 366 (1953).
98. Panouse, J. J., *Compt. rend.*, 233, 1200 (1951).
99. Nystrom, R. F., S. W. Chaikin, and W. G. Brown, *J. Am. Chem. Soc.*, 71, 3245 (1949).
100. Wiberg, E., and M. Schmidt, *Z. Naturforsch.*, 6b, 171 (1951).

101. Nystrom, R. F., and W. G. Brown, *J. Am. Chem. Soc.*, 69, 1197 (1947).
102. Brown, R. F., private communication.
103. Nussbaum, A. L., A. Sandoval, G. Rosenkranz, and C. Djerassi, *J. Org. Chem.*, 17, 426 (1952).
104. Ness, R. K., H. G. Fletcher, Jr., and C. S. Hudson, *J. Am. Chem. Soc.*, 73, 4759 (1951).
105. Bailey, W. J., and J. Rosenberg, *Abstracts of Papers*, XIIth International Congress of Pure and Applied Chemistry, New York, N. Y., September 1951, p. 422.
106. Bailey, W. J., J. Rosenberg, and L. J. Young, *Abstracts of Papers*, 119th Meeting American Chemical Society, Cleveland, Ohio, April 1951, p. 68M.
107. Houben, J., and A. Hahn, *Ber.*, 41, 1580 (1908).
108. Wilson, J. M., *J. Chem. Soc.*, 1951, 2297.
109. Siegel, S., and S. Coburn, *J. Am. Chem. Soc.*, 73, 5494 (1951).
110. Anderson, E. L., and F. G. Holliman, *J. Chem. Soc.*, 1950, 1037.
111. Mahé, J., J. Rollet, and A. Willemart, *Bull. soc. chim. France*, [5] 16,.481 (1949).
112. Ratouis, R., and A. Willemart, *Compt. rend.*, 233, 1124 (1951).
113. Weygand, F., and D. Tietjen, *Chem. Ber.*, 84, 625 (1951).
114. Weygand, F., *Angew. Chem.*, 61, 441 (1949).
115. Weygand, F., K. G. Kinkel, and D. Tietjen, *Chem. Ber.*, 83, 394 (1950).
116. Ghilardi, G., and G. Kalopissis, *Bull. soc. chim. France*, [5] 19, 217 (1952).
117. Beyler, R. E., and L. H. Sarett, *J. Am. Chem. Soc.*, 74, 1406 (1952).
118. Brown, W. G., address before the Chicago Section of the American Chemical Society; through ref. 22.
119. Becker, E. I., private communication.
120. Bonner, E. F., A. G. Finkensieper, and E. I. Becker, *J. Org. Chem.*, 18, 426 (1953).
121. Fuchs, R., and C. A. Vander Werf, *J. Am. Chem. Soc.*, 74, 5917 (1952).
122. Bauer, H., *Ber.*, 37, 735 (1904).
123. Howell, L. B., *J. Am. Chem. Soc.*, 42, 2333 (1920).
124. Wessely, F., and W. Swoboda, *Monatsh.*, 82, 621 (1951).
125. Schlesinger, H. I., and A. E. Finholt, U. S. Pat. 2,567,972 (September 18, 1951).
126. Brown, W. G., A. E. Finholt, R. F. Nystrom, and H. I. Schlesinger, *Abstracts of Papers*, 110th Meeting American Chemical Society, Chicago, Ill., September, 1946, p. 27P.
127. Henne, A. L., and R. L. Pelley, *J. Am. Chem. Soc.*, 74, 1426 (1952).
128. Henne, A. L., R. M. Alm, and M. Smook, *J. Am. Chem. Soc.*, 70, 1968 (1948).
129. Siegel, I., and V. Lorber, *J. Biol. Chem.*, 189, 571 (1951).
130. Nystrom, R. F., unpublished work; through W. G. Brown, in *Organic Reactions*, Vol. VI, p. 469.
131. Fickett, W., W. K. Garner, and H. J. Lucas, *J. Am. Chem. Soc.*, 73, 5063 (1951).
132. Arnold, R. T., E. Koller, and O. Jeger, *Helv. Chim. Acta*, 34, 555 (1951).
133. Williams, R. H., and L. A. Hamilton, *J. Am. Chem. Soc.*, 74, 5418 (1952).
134. Engel, J., C. H. Ruof, and H. C. Howard, *J. Am. Chem. Soc.*, 74, 441 (1952).
135. Henne, A. L., R. L. Pelley, and R. M. Alm, *J. Am. Chem. Soc.*, 72, 3370 (1950).
136. Wilk, I. J., and W. J. Close, *J. Org. Chem.*, 15, 1020 (1950).

137. Schlögl, K., F. Wessely, and G. Korger, *Monatsh.*, *83*, 493 (1952).
138. Wessely, F., K. Schlögl, and G. Korger, *Nature*, *169*, 708 (1952).
139. Wessely, F., K. Schlögl, and G. Korger, *Monatsh.*, *83*, 1156 (1952).
140. Wessely, F., K. Schlögl, and E. Wawersich, *Monatsh.*, *83*, 1426 (1952).
141. Wessely, F., K. Schlögl, and E. Wawersich, *Monatsh.*, *83*, 1439 (1952).
142. Metal Hydrides Inc., Beverly, Mass., Bulletin, "Potassium Borohydride."
143. Metal Hydrides Inc., Beverly, Mass., Bulletin 402-B, "Lithium Borohydride."
144. Gerstein, M., R. A. Lad, and H. I. Schlesinger, *Abstracts of Papers*, 110th Meeting American Chemical Society, Chicago, Ill., September, 1946, p. 26P.

CHAPTER 9

Reduction of
OXYGEN-CONTAINING ORGANIC COMPOUNDS
III. Carboxylic Acid Derivatives
(Esters, Lactones, Enol Esters)

9.1 ESTERS

9.1.1 Reductions with Lithium Aluminum Hydride

The conversion of esters to primary alcohols represents probably the area of greatest application of LAH reductions. The reduction consumes one-half mole of the hydride for each mole of ester reduced, according to the equation (1,2):

$$2\ RCOOR' + LiAlH_4 \longrightarrow (RCH_2O)_2(R'O)_2LiAl \qquad (9\text{-}1)$$

$$\xrightarrow{H_2O} 2\ RCH_2OH + 2\ R'OH + LiAlO_2$$

The yields of alcohols are generally good, the quantitative nature of the reduction having been established by the work of Nystrom and Brown (1) and Hochstein (3).

An insight into the influence of adjacent groups has been obtained by the work of Eliel and Freeman (4). In the LAH reduction of optically active methyl 2-chloro-2-phenylpropionate (I) the ester group is reduced to the carbinol, as expected. However, the product of the reduction is partially racemized 2-phenyl-2-propanol. It is proposed that the reduction of the ester leads to the chlorohydrin anion which undergoes a hydride shift with loss of chloride ion to form 2-phenylpropanal. Reduction of the latter yields the carbinol.

$$C_6H_5CCl(CH_3)COOCH_3 \xrightarrow{LAH} C_6H_5CCl(CH_3)CH_2O^{\ominus}$$

$$\text{I}$$

$$-Cl^{\ominus} \bigg| \ H^{\ominus} \qquad (9\text{-}2)$$

$$CH_3CH(C_6H_5)CHO \xrightarrow{LAH} CH_3CH(C_6H_5)CH_2OH$$

Actually reduction of the chloroester (I) with one-half mole of LAH yields 11% of 2-phenylpropanal on acid hydrolysis, and 18% of α-methylstyrene, on basis hydrolysis. Both of these products are presumed to have been formed from the primary reduction product, the chlorohydrin, during the isolation process.

9.1.1.a *Reduction of carbinol esters to the parent carbinols.* The LAH reduction of the esters of various carbinols has been utilized where the parent carbinols were the desired products.

$$R'O\overset{\displaystyle O}{\overset{\|}{C}}R \xrightarrow{LAH} R'OH \qquad (9\text{-}3)$$

Thus, acetoxy derivatives have been employed where the presence of the original hydroxyl group results in the formation of an intermediate complex whose ether insolubility reduces yields or even further reaction. In addition, acetates or benzoates have been used where the parent carbinols are insoluble in the reaction medium.

The reduction of the esters, i.e., formates, acetates, trimethylacetates, menthoxyacetates, benzoates, p-nitrobenzoates, p-bromobenzoates, and hydrogen phthalates, of various alkanols, substituted alkanols, phenols and sugar, steroid, alkaloid and triterpene alcohols, to the parent carbinols is summarized in Table XXXVII.

The attempted reduction of triethyl hydroxytrimesate (II) and dimethyl 2-hydroxy- and 4-hydroxyisophthalates (III) to the corresponding polymethylolphenols has been reported to yield only trace amounts of products. By acetylation of the phenolic group, the ether solubility is maintained enabling the LAH reduction to proceed smoothly (5).

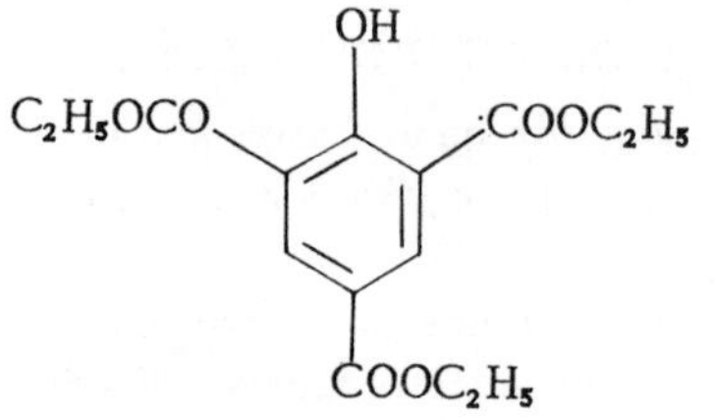

II

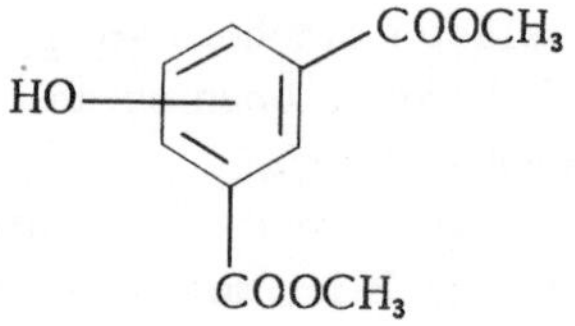

III

The reduction of II with LAH in dioxane has been reported to give 2,4,6-tris-(hydroxymethyl)phenol (IV) in a crude yield of 18.5%. While the reduction of the free acid in ether has been unsuccessful reduction in a dioxane solution gives a 12% yield of crude IV. The attempted reduction of 2,4,6-tris-(acetoxymethyl)-2-acetoxybenzene (V) to IV with LAH in ether solution has also been unsuccessful (6).

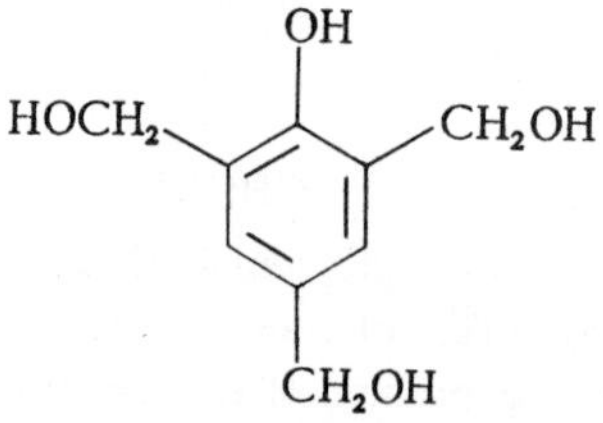

IV

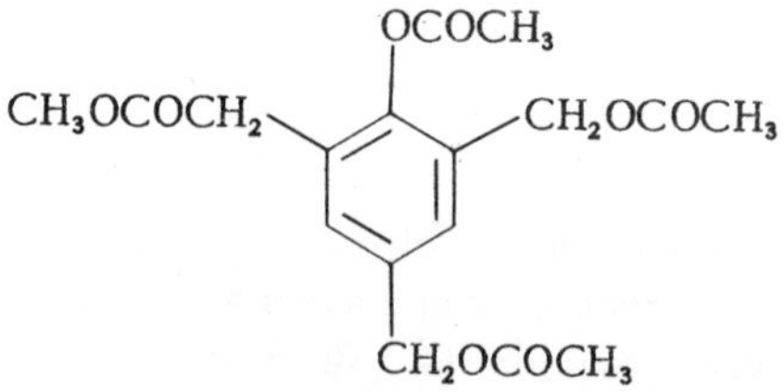

V

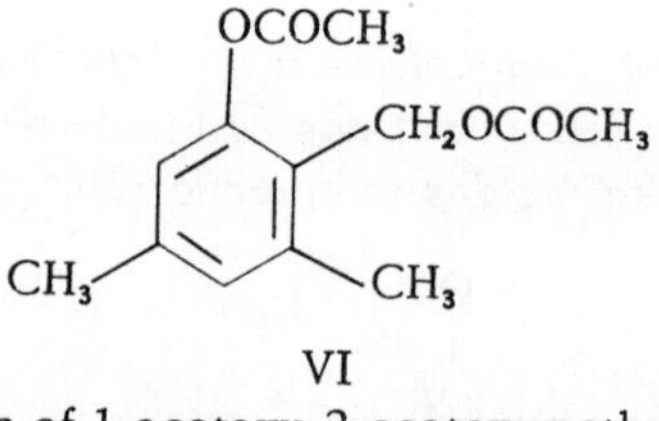

VI

Similarly, the reduction of 1-acetoxy-2-acetoxymethyl-3,5-dimethylbenzene (VI) in ether solution gives only a 15% yield of 2-hydroxymethyl-3,5-dimethylphenol (7,8).

The reduction of the acetyl derivative has been utilized for the purification of a hydroxy compound. Thus, terranaphthol (VII), a phenolic by-product from the alkaline degradation of terramycin, has been purified through the triacetate by the reductive cleavage of the acetyl groups with LAH (9,10).

$$(9\text{-}4)$$

VII

Cram has carried out a study of the solvolysis of the tosylates of the stereoisomers of 3-phenyl-2-butanol, 2-phenyl-3-butanol and 2-phenyl-3-pentanol. The reaction of the tosylates with acetic acid yields a mixture of olefins and acetoxy compounds which are converted by LAH to mixtures of alcohols and olefins. These two classes of components are then quantitatively separated by chromatographic methods (11). The solvolysis of *threo*-3,4-dimethyl-4-phenyl-3-hexyl-*p*-bromobenzoate yields an olefinic mixture resulting from intramolecular rearrangement. The mixture is treated with LAH and the fact that the olefin isolated after the reduction has the same refractive index as the material which is obtained in the solvolysis demonstrates that no acetate is formed in the solvolysis (12).

The attempted LAH reduction of 4-acetoxymethyl-3-carboxy-6-methyl-2-pyridol (VIII) has been unsuccessful as has been the reduction of the lactone of 3-carboxy-6-methyl-4-hydroxymethyl-2(1)-pyridone (IX) (13). 10-Acetoxy-9-methyl-1,2-benzanthracene (X) is not reduced by LAH, zinc dust-sodium hydroxide or aluminum isopropoxide (14).

VIII   IX   X

The LAH reduction of N-(α-acetoxybenzyl)acetanilide (XI) yields the cleavage products N-ethylaniline and benzyl alcohol as well as N-ethyl-N-phenylbenzylamine (XII) (15). The formation of XII rather than the hydroxy compound is due to the cleavage of the $-\overset{|\ |}{N}\overset{}{C}O-$ linkage as discussed in Section 12.17.

TABLE XXXVII

$$\overset{O}{\underset{\|}{}}$$

LAH Reduction of $ROCR'$ to ROH

	Ester	Product	% Yield	Ref.
	I. Formates (ROCH $\rightarrow$ ROH) $\overset{O}{\underset{\|}{}}$			
$C_{11}H_{14}O_2$	2-Formoxy-3-phenylbutane ⎫ 3-Formoxy-2-phenylbutane ⎭[1]	3-Phenyl-2-butanol ⎫ 2-Phenyl-3-butanol ⎭	...	2
$C_{31}H_{50}O_3$	19α-Formoxy-18α-oleanan-2-one (lupenone formate)	18α-Oleanane-2β,19α-diol	63[3]	4
	II. Acetates (ROCCH$_3$ $\rightarrow$ ROH) $\overset{O}{\underset{\|}{}}$			
	A. Alkyl, Arylalkyl and Heterocyclic Alkyl Acetates			
$C_9H_{14}O_6$	Diethyl acetoxymalonate-1-C^{14}	Glycerol-1-C^{14}	85	5
	Diethyl acetoxymalonate-2-C^{14}	Glycerol-2-C^{14}	85	5
	2,3-Diacetoxy-DL-glycerate-1-C^{14}	Glycerol-1-C^{14}	...	6
$C_{11}H_{18}O_5$	1,3-Diacetoxyheptan-2-one	1,2,3-Heptanetriol	85	7
$C_{12}H_{16}O_2$	2-Acetoxy-2-phenylbutane	2-Phenyl-2-butanol	...	8
	3-Acetoxy-2-phenylbutane ⎫[9] 2-Acetoxy-2-phenylbutane ⎭	2-Phenyl-3-butanol ⎫ 2-Phenyl-2-butanol ⎭	...	8
	2-Acetoxy-3-phenylbutane	3-Phenyl-2-butanol ⎫ 3-Phenyl-3-butanol ⎭	...	2,10
	2-Acetoxy-3-phenylbutane ⎫[11] 3-Acetoxy-2-phenylbutane ⎭	2-Phenyl-2-butanol ⎫ 2-Phenyl-3-butanol ⎭	...	2
$C_{13}H_{13}NO_3$	3-(2-Acetoxyethyl)-2-indolecarboxaldehyde	2-(Hydroxymethyl)-3-(2-hydroxyethyl)indole	...	12

Formula	Ester	Parent compound		Ref.
$C_{13}H_{16}O_4$	1-Acetoxy-2-acetoxymethyl-3,5-dimethylbenzene	2-Hydroxymethyl-3,5-dimethylphenol	15	13
$C_{13}H_{18}O_2$	3-Acetoxy-2-phenylpentane / 2-Acetoxy-3-phenylpentane}[14]	2-Phenyl-3-pentanol / 3-Phenyl-2-pentanol}	...	15
$C_{14}H_{18}O_5$	Ethyl 2-acetoxy-3-benzyloxypropionate-1-C[14]	1-Benzyloxy-2,3-propanediol-3-C[14]	...	16
$C_{15}H_{16}Cl_2N_2O_7$	Ethyl 2-dichloroacetamido-3-acetoxy-3-p-nitrophenylpropionate	2-Dichloroacetamido-1-p-nitrophenyl-1,3-propanediol	...[17]	18
$C_{15}H_{19}NO_5$	Ethyl 2-acetamido-3-phenyl-3-acetoxypropionate	2-Acetamido-1-phenyl-1,3-propanediol	...	19
	Ethyl threo-2-acetamido-3-phenyl-3-acetoxypropionate	threo-1-Phenyl-1-acetoxy-2-acetamidopropan-3-ol	58	20
$C_{15}H_{26}O_5$	1,3-Diacetoxyundecan-2-one	1,2,3-Undecanetriol	76	7
$C_{16}H_{13}NO_4$	N-(2-Acetoxyethyl)naphthalimide	2-β-Hydroxyethyl-2,3-dihydro-1-benz[de]isoquinoline	68.5[21]	22
$C_{16}H_{20}O_8$	Methyl 2,3-diacetoxy-3-(3,4-dimethoxyphenyl)propionate	1-(3,4-Dimethoxyphenyl)glycerol	70	23
$C_{17}H_{17}NO_3$	N-(α-Acetoxybenzyl)acetanilide	N-Ethyl-N-phenylbenzylamine / N-Ethylaniline / Benzyl alcohol	8.5 } 79 } ...	24
$C_{18}H_{18}O_6$	1,8-Diacetoxy-3-acetoxymethyl-4-methyl-naphthalene (terranaphthol triacetate)	1,8-Dihydroxy-3-hydroxymethyl-4-methyl-naphthalene (terranaphthol)[25]	87	26
$C_{19}H_{21}NO_6S$	cis-2-Benzamido-3-acetoxy-1-methanesulphonyloxy-1-phenylpropane	Uncrystallizable gum	...[27]	28
$C_{22}H_{25}NO_3$	1,3-Diphenyl-3-piperidino-2-acetoxy-1-propanone	1,3-Diphenyl-3-piperidino-1,2-propanediol	63	29
$C_{25}H_{25}NO_3$	1,3-Diphenyl-2-acetoxy-3-(N-methylbenzylamino)-1-propanone	1,3-Diphenyl-3-(N-methylbenzylamino)-1,2-propanediol	45	29

B. Alicyclic Acetates

Formula	Ester	Parent compound		Ref.
$C_8H_{12}O_3$	1-Acetoxy-1,2-epoxycyclohexane	cis-Cyclohexane-1,2-diol 75 } / trans-Cyclohexane-1,2-diol 25 }	50	30

(Continued)

TABLE XXXVII (*Continued*)

Ester	Product	% Yield	Ref.
B. Alicyclic Acetates (Contd.)			
$C_9H_{14}O_2$			
endo-Norbornyl acetate	*endo*-Norborneol	...	31
exo-Norbornyl acetate	*exo*-Norborneol	...	31,32
exo-Norbornyl-2,3-C_2^{14} acetate	*exo*-Norbornyl-2,3-C_2^{14} alcohol	...	33
$C_{10}H_{11}NO_2$			
6-Acetoxy-6-cyanobicyclo[3.2.0]-2-heptene	6-Aminomethylbicyclo[3.2.0]-2-hepten-6-ol	...	34
$C_{12}H_{16}O_6$			
Acetyl acetonequinide	Acetone quinalcohol	80[35]	36
$C_{18}H_{30}O_4$			
1,1,4a,6-Tetramethyl-6-acetoxydecahydro-5-naphthaleneacetic acid	1,1,4a,6-Tetramethyl-5-hydroxyethyl-6-hydroxynaphthalene	100	37
C. Phenolic Acetates			
$C_{12}H_{12}O_4$			
Methyl *p*-acetoxycinnamate	*p*-Hydroxycinnamyl alcohol	84	38
$C_{12}H_{12}O_6$			
Dimethyl 2-acetoxyisophthalate	2,6-Di-(hydroxymethyl)phenol	70	39
Dimethyl 4-acetoxyisophthalate	2,4-Di-(hydroxymethyl)phenol	79	39
$C_{12}H_{13}NO_4$			
N,N,O-Triacetyl-*o*-aminophenol	*o*-Ethylaminophenol	57	40
	Red oil (3,5-dinitrobenzoate, m.p. 128.5–130°)	...	
$C_{12}H_{15}ClO_3$			
2-Chloromethyl-C^{14}-3,5,6-trimethyl-4-acetoxyphenol	Durohydroquinone-α-C^{14}	89	41
$C_{13}H_{14}O_4$			
Ethyl *p*-acetoxycinnamate	*p*-Hydroxycinnamyl alcohol	84	38
$C_{13}H_{16}O_4$			
1-Acetoxy-2-acetoxymethyl-3,5-dimethylbenzene	2-Hydroxymethyl-3,5-dimethylphenol	15	13
$C_{14}H_{14}O_6$			
Methyl 3,4-diacetoxycinnamate	3,4-Dihydrocinnamyl alcohol	...[43]	42
$C_{14}H_{16}O_5$			
Ethyl 3-methoxy-4-acetoxycinnamate (ethyl acetoferulate)	3-Methoxy-4-hydroxycinnamyl alcohol (coniferyl alcohol)	42.6,67.3[43] 73.7,57[43] ...[45]	44 42 42
Ethyl 3-acetoxy-4-methoxycinnamate	3-Hydroxy-4-methoxycinnamyl alcohol	...	42

Formula	Acetate	Alcohol or phenol	Yield, %	Ref.
$C_{15}H_{13}NO_3$	2-Acetoxybenzanilide		...	40
	Oil (phenyl isocyanate reaction product, m.p. 192–195°)		...	42
$C_{15}H_{18}O_5$	Ethyl 3-ethoxy-4-acetoxycinnamate		...	46
$C_{15}H_{18}O_6$	Ethyl acetylsinapate	Sinapyl alcohol	40–47	47
			55–58	48
$C_{17}H_{20}O_8$	Triethyl acetoxytrimesate	2,4,6-Tris-(hydroxymethyl)phenol	27	39
$C_{18}H_{18}O_6$	1,8-Diacetoxy-3-acetoxymethyl-4-methyl-naphthalene (terranaphthol triacetate)	Terranaphthol[25]	87	26
	D. Heterocyclic Acetates			
$C_{12}H_{13}NO_6$	2-Methyl-3-acetoxy-4,5-dicarbomethoxy-pyridine	2-Methyl-3-hydroxy-4,5-di-(hydroxymethyl)-pyridine	84[21]	49
	E. Sugar Acetates			
$C_8H_8O_5$	Diacetyl-L-threaric anhydride	L-Threitol[50]	18,32	51
$C_{12}H_{17}BrO_7$	Triacetyl-α-L-rhamnopyranosyl bromide	1,5-Anhydro-L-rhamnitol	87[52]	53
$C_{14}H_{18}O_6$	Tetraacetyl-D-gulono-γ-lactone	L-Glucitol[50]	47	51
$C_{14}H_{19}BrO_9$	Tetraacetyl-α-D-glucopyranosyl bromide	1,5-Anhydro-D-glucitol	67[54]	53
	Tetraacetyl-α-D-mannopyranosyl bromide	1,5-Anhydro-D-mannitol	74[55]	53
$C_{14}H_{19}ClO_9$	Tetraacetyl-D-galactofuranosyl chloride	1,4-Anhydro-D-galacitol	41	56
$C_{16}H_{22}O_{11}$	D-Galactofuranose pentaacetate	Galactitol	72[50]	56
	F. Steroid Acetates			
$C_{20}H_{20}O_3$	Equilenin acetate	17-Dihydroequilenin-17β[3]	...	57
$C_{20}H_{22}O_3$	6-Dehydroestrone acetate	6-Dehydroestradiol	84	58
$C_{20}H_{24}O_3$	Estrone acetate	α-Estradiol	95	59
			"almost quant."	60
$C_{21}H_{22}O_3$	1-Methylequilenin acetate	1-Methyl-17-dihydroequilenin-17β[3]	...	61

(Continued)

TABLE XXXVII (Continued)

F. Steroid Acetates (Contd.)

	Ester	Product	% Yield	Ref.
$C_{21}H_{24}O_3$	1-Methyl-6-dehydroestrone	1-Methyl-6-dehydroestradiol	88	61
$C_{21}H_{26}O_3$	Estrone propionate	α-Estradiol	:::	60
$C_{21}H_{30}O_4$	3β-Acetoxy-5,6α-oxidoandrostan-17-one	Androstane-3β,5,17β-triol[50]	85	62
$C_{21}H_{32}O_3$	3β-Acetoxyandrostan-17-one	Androstane-3β,17β-diol	...[63]	64
$C_{21}H_{31}NO_2$	3β-Acetoxy-20-cyanopregna-5,17-diene	21-Aminopregna-5,17-dien-3β-ol[65]	66	64
$C_{23}H_{32}O_3$	3β-Acetoxyallopregna-7,9(11)-dien-20-one	Allopregna-7,9(11)-dien-3β,20β-diol	71	66
	3β-Acetoxyallopregna-7,16-dien-20-one	Allopregna-7,16-dien-3β,20β-diol	70	66
$C_{23}H_{32}O_4$	3β-Acetoxy-16,17-oxido-5-pregnen-20-one	5-Pregnene-3β,17,20-triol	...[67]	68
	3β-Acetoxy-14,15β-oxido-16(17)allopregnen-20-one	Compound, $C_{21}H_{32}O_3$, m.p. 174°	...[27]	69,70
		Compound, $C_{21}H_{34}O_3$, m.p. 223–224°	...[27]	
$C_{23}H_{32}O_6$	21-Acetoxyallopregnane-17α-ol-3,11,20-trione	Allopregnane-3β,11β,17α,20β,21-pentol[3]	39[71]	72
$C_{23}H_{34}O_3$	3β-Acetoxy-7-allopregnene-20-one	7-Allopregnen-3β,20β-diol	63	66
	3β-Acetoxy-5-pregnene-20-one	5-Pregnene-3β,20α-diol	5 }	73
		5-Pregnene-3β,20β-diol	36 }	
		5-Pregnene-3β,20α-diol[74]	...[63] }	75
		5-Pregnene-3β,20β-diol	::: }	
$C_{23}H_{34}O_4$	3β-Acetoxy-5-pregnene-17α-ol-20-one	5-Pregnene-3β,17α,20α-triol	39[63] }	76
		5-Pregnene-3β,17α,20β-triol	20[63] }	
	3β-Acetoxy-7-allopregnene-17α-ol-20-one	7-Allopregnene-3β,17α,20-triol	83	77
	3β-Acetoxy-16,17α-oxidoallopregnane-20-one	Allopregnane-3β,17α,20α-triol (Reichstein's Substance O)	20	77
		Allopregnane-3β,17α,20β-triol (Reichstein's Substance J)	40[27,63] }	78
		16,17α-Oxidoallopregnane-3β,20β-diol	25 }	
		Reichstein's Substance O	::: }	
		Reichstein's Substance J	::: }	68

Formula	Acetate	Product	Value	Refs
C₂₃H₃₆O₄	3β-Acetoxy-20β,21-oxido-17-isoallopregnane-17β-ol	Reichstein's Substance O	...[63]	69,70
		Reichstein's Substance J 17-Isoallopregnane-3β,17β,20β-triol	97[27]	79
C₂₄H₃₃NO₄	3β,17β-Diacetoxy-17α-cyano-5-androstene	17α-Aminomethyl-5-androstene-3β,17β-diol[27]	80,5,98[80]	81
C₂₄H₃₄O₄	Methyl 3β-acetoxypregna-5,17-dien-21-oate	Pregna-5,17-dien-3β,21-diol	91	82
C₂₄H₃₆O₄	3β-Acetoxy-5-bisnorcholenic acid	5-Bisnorcholene-3β,22-diol	....	83
C₂₅H₃₄O₅	3-Ethoxy-16,17-oxido-21-acetoxypregna-3,5-dien-20-one	4-Pregnene-17α,20α,21-triol-3-one 4-Pregnene-17α,20β,21-triol-3-one	36[84] 51	85
C₂₅H₃₄O₆	3-Ethoxy-21-acetoxypregna-3,5-dien-17α-ol-11,20-dione	4-Pregnene-11β,17α,20β,21-tetrol-3-one	43[27,84] [84]	85 86
C₂₅H₃₆O₄	Ethyl 3β-acetoxypregna-5,17-dien-21-oate	Pregna-5,17-dien-3β,21-diol	93	82
C₂₅H₃₆O₅	3-Ethoxy-21-acetoxypregna-3,5-dien-17α-ol-20-one	4-Pregnene-17α,20β,21-triol-3-one	74[27,84]	85
C₂₅H₃₆O₆	3β-Acetoxy-16,17-oxido-5-pregnene-20-one-20-ethylene ketal	5-Pregnene-3β,17α-diol-20-one-20-ethylene ketal	80,5[27]	68,87
	3β,21-Diacetoxy-16,17α-oxidoallopregnane-20-one	Allopregnane-3β,17α,20,21-tetrol	....	69,70
C₂₅H₃₈O₄S	ketol diacetate, m.p. 172-174°[88]	tetrol, C₂₁H₃₄O₄, m.p. 180-186°	...[71]	89
	3β-Acetoxyallopregnane-11,20-dione-20-ethylene hemithioketal	Allopregnane-3β,11β-diol-20-one-20-ethylene hemithioketal	96[80]	90
C₂₅H₃₈O₅	3β-Acetoxyallopregnane-11,20-dione-20-ethylene ketal	Allopregnane-3β,11β-diol-20-one-20-ethylene ketal	....	90
	3α-Acetoxypregnane-11,20-dione-20-ethylene ketal	Pregnane-3α,11β-diol-20-one-20-ethylene ketal	92	91
	Ethyl 3β-acetoxy-17-isopregn-5-ene-17β-ol-21-oate	17-Isopregn-5-ene-3β,17β,21-triol	82	82
	3β,20β-Diacetoxyallopregnane-7-one	Allopregnane-3β,7,20β-triol	....	92
	3β,20β-Diacetoxy-16α,17α-oxido-allopregnane	Allopregnane-3β,17α,20β-triol	30[63]	78

(Continued)

TABLE XXXVII (Continued)

F. Steroid Acetates (Contd.)

	Ester	Product	% Yield	Ref.
$C_{26}H_{40}O_4$	3β-Acetoxy-20-hydroxyallocholanic acid lactone	Allocholane-3β,20,24-triol	79[9,63]	93
$C_{26}H_{46}O_4$	3β-Acetoxyergosta-7,22-dien-5α-ol-6-one	Cerevisterol (3β,5α,6β-triol)	....	94
$C_{27}H_{41}NO_4$	N-Acetyldimethyloxazolidine of 17α-aminomethyl-3β-acetoxy-5-androstene-17β-ol	17α-N-Ethyl-N-isopropylaminomethyl-5-androstene-3β,17β-diol	85[27]	81
$C_{27}H_{42}O_4$	Methyl 3α-acetoxychol-11-enate	Chol-11-ene-3α,24-diol	100	95
$C_{27}H_{42}O_5$	Methyl 3α-acetoxy-11,12β-oxidocholanate	Cholane-3α,11β,24-triol	.96	69,70
	Methyl 3α-acetoxy-11,12α-oxidocholanate	Cholane-3α,11α,24-triol	....	69,70
$C_{27}H_{44}O_5$	Methyl 3α-acetoxy-11β-hydroxycholanate	Cholane-3α,11β,24-triol	....	69,70
$C_{28}H_{44}O_5$	Ethyl 3α-acetoxy-11,12α-oxidocholanate	Cholane-3α,11α,24-triol	....	70
$C_{29}H_{42}O_5$	3β-Acetoxy-22-isospirost-5-en-7-one	22-Isospirost-5-en-3β,7β-diol	100	97
$C_{29}H_{42}O_6$	3β-Acetoxy-9α,11α-oxido-22-isoallospirostan-7-one	9α,11α-Oxido-22-isoallospirostan-3β,7β-diol	78[3]	98
$C_{29}H_{44}O_3$	6β-Acetoxy-5β-methyl-19-norcoprosta-9(10),11-dien-3-one	5β-Methyl-19-norcoprosta-9(10),11-dien-3β,6β-diol	27[63]	99
$C_{29}H_{46}O_3$	3β-Acetoxycholest-5-ene-7-one	Cholest-5-ene-3β,7α-diol	5 } 100	101
		Cholest-5-ene-3β,7β-diol	59 }	102
		Cholest-5-ene-3β,7α-diol[62]	100	103
	3β-Acetoxycholest-5-ene-24-one	Cholest-5-ene-3β,24-diol	96	70
$C_{29}H_{46}O_5$	n-Propyl 3α-acetoxy-11,12α-oxidocholanate	Cholane-3α,11α,24-triol	....	69,70
$C_{29}H_{46}O_6$	Methyl 3α,11α-diacetoxycholanate	Cholane-3α,11α,24-triol	....	101
$C_{29}H_{48}O_3$	3β-Acetoxycholestan-7-one	Cholestane-3β,7α-diol	33 }	
		Cholestane-3β,7β-diol	37.5 }	104
		Cholestane-3β,7α-diol	23 }	
		Cholestane-3β,7β-diol	35 }	105
	3α-Acetoxy-4α,5-oxidocholestane	Cholestane-3α,5-diol	22	69,70
			....	

Formula	Acetate	Product	Yield (%)	Reference
$C_{29}H_{48}O_3$	3β-Acetoxy-4α,5-oxidocholestane	Cholestane-3β,5-diol	100	105
			...	69,70
	3α-Acetoxy-4β,5-oxidocoprostane	Coprostane-3α,5-diol	92	106
			...	69,70
	3β-Acetoxy-4β,5-oxidocoprostane	Coprostane-3β,5-diol	71	106
			...	69,70
	3β-Acetoxy-5,6α-oxidocholestane	Cholestane-3β,5-diol	95	107
			...	69,70
	3β-Acetoxy-5,6β-oxidocholestane	Cholestane-3β,6β-diol	61[63]	107
		Cholestane-3β,5-diol	15	69,70
		Cholestane-3β,6β-diol	57[63]	
$C_{30}H_{40}O_4$	3β-Acetoxy-16α-benzyloxy-5-pregnen-20-one[109]	16α-Benzyloxy-5-pregnene-3β,20-diol[67]	100	108
$C_{30}H_{46}O_3$	Ergosteryl-D acetate epoxide	Ergosterol-D epoxide	...[3]	110
$C_{30}H_{48}O_5$	Butyl 3α-acetoxy-11,12α-oxidocholanate	Cholane-3α,11α,24-triol		70
$C_{31}H_{44}O_6$	3β,26-Diacetoxycholesta-5,17(20)-dien-16,22-dione	Cholesta-5,17(20)-dien-3β,16,22,26-tetrol	52[3,111]	112
$C_{31}H_{46}O_6$	3β,26-Diacetoxy-5-cholestene-16,22-dione	5-Cholestene-3β,16,22,26-tetrol	76[3]	112
$C_{31}H_{48}O_3$	7-Ketostigmasteryl acetate	7α-Hydroxystigmasterol	5.5 }[100]	101
		7β-Hydroxystigmasterol	56	
$C_{31}H_{44}O_3$	3β-Acetoxy-24-phenyl-5-cholen-24-one	24-Phenyl-5-cholen-3β,24-diol[67]	88	113
$C_{32}H_{52}O_4$	3β,11α-Diacetoxy-22(23)-ergostene	22(23)-Ergostene-3β,11α-diol	95	114
$C_{33}H_{45}NO_6$	Triacetyl-5,6-oxidoveratramine	N-Ethyldihydroveratramine-3,5,23-triol	...[115]	116
		N-Ethyldihydroveratramine-3,5,6,23-tetrol	...	117
$C_{35}H_{46}O_8$	Maleic anhydride adduct of 3β,26-diacetoxyallofurosta-16,20(22)-diene	Tetrol, $C_{31}H_{50}O_5$	91[3]	117
$C_{36}H_{49}NO_6$	3β-p-Nitrobenzoxy-6(α and β)-acetoxy-cholesta-7,9(11)-diene[118]	Cholesta-7,9(11)-dien-3β,6-diol[67]	...	119

G. Triterpene Acetates

Formula	Acetate	Product	Yield (%)	Reference
$C_{29}H_{46}O_3$	Trisnorlupanonyl acetate	Trisnorlupanediol	96[50]	120

(Continued)

TABLE XXXVII (Continued)

G. Triterpene Acetates (Contd.)

	Ester	Product	% Yield	Ref.
C$_{31}$H$_{48}$O$_3$	2-Acetoxynorolean-17-ene-19-one	Norolean-17-ene-2,19-diol[121]	...	122
	Iso-β-amyradienonyl acetate	diene-diol, isolated as diacetate, C$_{34}$H$_{52}$O$_4$, m.p. 167-168°	60	123
C$_{32}$H$_{49}$ClO$_3$	Acetoxyquinovenecarboxylic acid chloride	Quinovenediol	73[124]	125
C$_{32}$H$_{50}$O$_4$	Betulinic acid "lactone A" acetate	Triol, C$_{30}$H$_{52}$O$_3$	...	126
	8,11-Diketolanostenyl acetate	Lanostene-2,8,11-triol	51[71]	127,128
		Lanostane-2,8,11-triol	4[63]	
		Lanostane-8-one-2,11-diol	18[63]	
C$_{32}$H$_{52}$O$_3$	8-Ketolanostenyl acetate	Lanosta-8,10-dien-2-ol (dihydroagnosterol) Diol?	...	127
		Lanosta-8,10-dien-2-ol	80	129
C$_{32}$H$_{52}$O$_4$	2β-Acetoxy-19-keto-18α-oleanane[27]	18α-Oleanane-2β,19β-diol	57[130]	4,131
	8,11-Diketolanostanyl acetate	Lanostane-2,8,11-triol	...[63]	127
		Lanost-10(11)-ene-2,8-diol	...[63]	128
		Lanostane-2,8,11-triol	78[63]	132
C$_{32}$H$_{54}$O$_3$	11-Ketolanostanyl acetate	Lanost-10(11)-ene-2,8-diol	31[63]	128
		Lanostane-2,11-diol	100	132
				133
C$_{33}$H$_{50}$O$_4$	Methyl dehydrooleanolate acetate	Olean-11,13(18)-diene-2,28-diol[134]	63	135
C$_{33}$H$_{50}$O$_5$	Methyl 11-ketooleanolate acetate	Olean-11,13(18)-diene-2,28-diol[134]	63	135
C$_{33}$H$_{52}$O$_4$	Methyl olean-10-enolate acetate	Olean-10-ene-2,28-diol	63	135
	Methyl morolate acetate	Moradiol	60-70	136,137
	Methyl olean-13(18)-enolate acetate	Olean-13(18)-ene-2,28-diol	...	137
	Methyl acetylelemadienolate	Elemadienediol	100	138
	Methyl acetyleburicoate	Eburicodiol	...	139
C$_{33}$H$_{52}$O$_5$	Methyl morolate acetate oxide	Norolean-16,18-dien-2-ol[134]	...[130]	136

Formula	Compound	Parent (ROH)	Yield %	Ref.
$C_{33}H_{54}O_5$	Methyl 19-keto-18-isooleananolate acetate	Norolean-16,18-dien-2-ol[134]	36[130] }	137
$C_{34}H_{54}O_4$	Methyl 11-ketoolecananolate acetate	Moradiol oxide[134]	...[63]	135,140
$C_{34}H_{54}O_5$	Methyl dihydrosiaresinolate 2-acetate	18-Isooleanan-2,19,28-triol	...[63]	135
	Moradiol diacetate	Oleanane-2,11,28-triol	...	135
	Moradiol diacetate oxide	Oleanan-2,19,28-triol	64[27]	141
		Moradiol	19[130] }	137
		Norolean-16,18-dien-2-ol[134]		
		13(18)-ene-19,20-oxide-2-ol[134]		
$C_{34}H_{56}O_5$	2,28-Diacetoxy-18-isooleanan-19-one	18-Isooleanan-2,19,28-triol	...[63]	137
$C_{34}H_{58}O_4$	2,8-Diacetoxylanostane-11-one	Lanostane-2,8,11-triol	75[63]	127,128
	2,11-Diacetoxylanostane	Lanostane-2,11-diol	...	142
$C_{39}H_{58}O_5S$	Moradiol-2-acetate-28-p-toluenesulfonate	Moradiol	...	137

H. Alkaloid Acetates

Formula	Compound	Parent (ROH)	Yield %	Ref.
$C_{24}H_{37}O_3$	O,N-diacetate of tetrahydro base, $C_{20}H_{30}NO$[143]	Oily base, $C_{22}H_{37}NO$	...	144
$C_{27}H_{39-41}NO_9$	Lycoctonam acetate	Lycoctonine, $C_{25}H_{41}NO_7$	83[124]	145
$C_{33}H_{45}NO_6$	Triacetyl-5,6-oxidoveratramine	N-Ethyldihydroveratramine-3,5,23-triol	...[115] }	116
		N-Ethyldihydroveratramine-3,5,6,23-tetrol	...	

III. Trimethylacetates (ROC(=O)C(CH₃)₃ → ROH)

Formula	Compound	Parent (ROH)	Yield %	Ref.
$C_{23}H_{30}O_3$	Estrone trimethylacetate	β-Estradiol	100	146

IV. Menthoxyacetates (ROC(=O)CH₂OC₁₀H₁₉ → ROH)

Formula	Compound	Parent (ROH)	Yield %	Ref.
$C_{38}H_{52}O_6$	Di-(−)-menthoxyacetate of (−)-trans-9,10-dihydrophenanthrene-9,10-diol	(−)-trans-9,10-Dihydrophenanthrene-9,10-diol	...	147

(Continued)

TABLE XXXVII (Continued)

IV. Menthoxyacetates (ROCCH$_2$OC$_{10}$H$_{19}$ → ROH) (Contd.)

Ester	Product	% Yield	Ref.
C$_{38}$H$_{52}$O$_6$ (contd.)			
Di-(−)-menthoxyacetate of (+)-trans-9,10-dihydrophenanthrene-9,10-diol	(+)-trans-9,10-Dihydrophenanthrene-9,10-diol	....	147

V. Benzoates (ROCC$_6$H$_5$ → ROH)

Ester	Product	% Yield	Ref.
C$_{18}$H$_{14}$O$_8$	Dibenzoylerythraric acid	Erythritol	27[35]	51
C$_{25}$H$_{26}$O$_3$	3-Benzoxy-16,17α-oxidoestra-1,3,5(10)-triene	Estra-1,3,5(10)-triene-3,17α-diol (17-epiestradiol)	58[35]	148
C$_{26}$H$_{21}$BrO$_7$	1-Bromo-2,3,5-tribenzoyl-d-ribose	1,4-Anhydro-d-ribitol	....	149
C$_{27}$H$_{27}$NO$_3$	1,3-Diphenyl-2-benzoxy-3-piperidino-1-propanone	1,3-Diphenyl-3-piperidino-1,2-propanediol	63	29
C$_{28}$H$_{38}$O$_4$	3β-Benzoxy-20α,21-oxido-17-isoallopregnane-17β-ol	17-Isoallopregnane-3β,17β,20α-triol	88[63]	79
C$_{34}$H$_{49}$BrO$_2$	7-Bromocholesteryl benzoate[150]	7-D-Cholesterol	....	151
C$_{35}$H$_{46}$O$_2$	14-Dehydroergosteryl benzoate	14-Dehydroergosterol	....	152
C$_{35}$H$_{50}$O$_2$	7-Dehydro-3-methylcholesteryl benzoate	7-Dehydro-3-methylcholesterol	93	153
C$_{37}$H$_{48}$Cl$_2$O$_4$	Benzoylquinovayl dichloride	Quinovenetriol	78[129]	125

VI. p-Nitrobenzoates (ROCC$_6$H$_4$NO$_2$ → ROH)

Ester	Product	% Yield	Ref.
C$_{17}$H$_{21}$NO$_4$	(−)-Pulegyl p-nitrobenzoate	(−)-Pulegol	35	154
C$_{36}$H$_{49}$NO$_6$	3β-p-Nitrobenzoxy-6 (α and β)-acetoxy-cholesta-7,9(11)-diene[118]	Cholesta-7,9(11)-diene-3β,6-diol[67]	....	119

VII. p-Bromobenzoates (ROCC₆H₄Br → ROH)

$$\overset{\text{O}}{\underset{\|}{\text{VII. } p\text{-Bromobenzoates (ROCC}_6\text{H}_4\text{Br} \rightarrow \text{ROH)}}}$$

$C_{21}H_{25}BrO_2$	(+)-*erythro*-3,4-Dimethyl-4-phenyl-3-hexyl-p-bromobenzoate	(+)-*erythro*-3,4-Dimethyl-4-phenyl-3-hexanol	19	155
	(+)-*threo*-3,4-Dimethyl-4-phenyl-3-hexyl-p-bromobenzoate	(+)-*threo*-3,4-Dimethyl-4-phenyl-3-hexanol	57	155
	(−)-*threo*-3,4-Dimethyl-4-phenyl-3-hexyl-p-bromobenzoate	(−)-*threo*-3,4-Dimethyl-4-phenyl-3-hexanol	81	155
	(−)-*erythro*-3,4-Dimethyl-4-phenyl-3-hexyl-p-bromobenzoate	(−)-*erythro*-3,4-Dimethyl-4-phenyl-3-hexanol	54	155

VIII. Hydrogen Phthalates (ROCC₆H₄COH → ROH)

$$\text{VIII. Hydrogen Phthalates (RO}\overset{\text{O}}{\underset{\|}{\text{C}}}\text{C}_6\text{H}_4\overset{\text{O}}{\underset{\|}{\text{C}}}\text{OH} \rightarrow \text{ROH)}$$

$C_{15}H_{16}O_4$	Hydrogen 1-(1-cyclopentenyl)ethyl-1-phthalate	(−)-1-(1-Cyclopentenyl)ethanol	...[156]	157
$C_{16}H_{18}O_4$	Hydrogen 1-(1-cyclohexenyl)ethyl-1-phthalate	(−)-1-(1-Cyclohexenyl)ethanol	...[156]	157
$C_{16}H_{22}O_4$	Hydrogen (+)-2,4-dimethylhexyl-4-phthalate	(+)-2,4-Dimethyl-4-hexanol	63[156]	158
	Hydrogen (−)-2,4-dimethylhexyl-4-phthalate	(+)-2,4-Dimethyl-4-hexanol	83[156]	158
$C_{18}H_{18}O_4$	Hydrogen (−)-2-phenylbutyl-2-phthalate	(+)-2-Phenyl-2-butanol	77[156]	159
	Hydrogen (+)-2-phenylbutyl-2-phthalate	(−)-2-Phenyl-2-butanol	66[156]	159

References—Table XXXVII

[1]Mixture from reaction of p-toluenesulfonates of stereoisomers of 3-phenyl-2-butanol with sodium formate and formic acid.
[2]D. J. Cram, J. Am. Chem. Soc., 74, 2129 (1952).
[3]Reduction carried out in tetrahydrofuran.
[4]T. R. Ames, G. S. Davy, T. G. Halsall, and E. R. H. Jones, J. Chem. Soc., 1952, 2868.
[5]L. I. Gidez and M. L. Karnovsky, J. Am. Chem. Soc., 74, 2413 (1952).
[6]A. P. Doerschuk, ibid., 73, 821 (1951); 74, 4202 (1952).
[7]M. Proštenik and J. Biščan, Arkiv Kemi, 22, 177 (1951); Chem. Abstracts, 46, 3951 (1952).
[8]D. J. Cram, J. Am. Chem. Soc., 74, 2137 (1952).
[9]Mixture from acetolysis of p-toluenesulfonates or p-bromobenzenesulfonates of stereoisomers of 3-phenyl-2-butanol.
[10]D. J. Cram, J. Am. Chem. Soc., 71, 3863 (1949).
[11]Mixture from acetolysis of p-toluenesulfonates of stereoisomers of 3-phenyl-2-butanol at 75°.
[12]R. Goutarel, M. M. Janot, V. Prelog, and W. I. Taylor, Helv. Chim. Acta, 33, 150 (1950).
[13]S. R. Finn and J. W. G. Musty, Chemistry and Industry, 1950, 677; J. Applied Chem. (London), 1, 182 (1951).
[14]Mixture from acetolysis of p-toluenesulfonates of stereoisomers of D-threo- and D-erythro-2-phenyl-3-pentanol and D-threo- and D-erythro-3-phenyl-2-pentanol.
[15]D. J. Cram, J. Am. Chem. Soc., 74, 2159 (1952).
[16]Chem. Eng. News, 30, 1872 (1952).
[17]Product was syrup containing indicated material as major component.
[18]C. F. Huebner and C. R. Scholz, J. Am. Chem. Soc., 73, 2089 (1951).
[19]G. Carrara and G. Weitnauer, Gazz. chim. ital., 79, 856 (1949).
[20]Lepetit S. A., Brit. Pat. 679,028 (September 10, 1952).
[21]Isolated as hydrochloride.
[22]W. L. Garbrecht, J. H. Hunter, and J. B. Wright, J. Am. Chem. Soc., 72, 1359 (1950).
[23]E. Adler and K. J. Bjorkqvist, Acta Chem. Scand., 5, 241 (1951).
[24]A. W. Burgstahler, J. Am. Chem. Soc., 73, 3021 (1951).
[25]Isolated and purified as triacetate from alkaline degradation of terramycin.
[26]R. Pasternack, A. Bavley, R. L. Wagner, F. A. Hochstein, P. P. Regna, and K. J. Brunings, J. Am. Chem. Soc., 74, 1926 (1952); F. A. Hochstein, C. R. Stephens, L. H. Conover, P. P. Regna, R. Pasternack, P. N. Gordon, F. J. Pilgrim, K. J. Brunings, and R. B. Woodward, ibid., 75, 5455 (1953).
[27]Reduction carried out in benzene-ether mixture.
[28]G. Fodor, J. Kiss, and I. Sallay, J. Chem. Soc., 1951, 1858.
[29]N. H. Cromwell and F. W. Starks, J. Am. Chem. Soc., 72, 4108 (1950).
[30]M. Mousseron-Canet and R. Jacquier, Bull. soc. chim. France, [5] 19, 698 (1952); M. Mousseron, R. Jacquier, M. Mousseron-Canet, and R. Zagdoun, ibid., [5] 19, 1042 (1952); Compt. rend., 235, 177 (1952).
[31]S. Winstein and D. Trifan, J. Am. Chem. Soc., 74, 1147 (1952).
[32]S. Winstein and D. Trifan, ibid., 74, 1154 (1952).
[33]J. D. Roberts and C. C. Lee, ibid., 73, 5009 (1951).
[34]J. D. Roberts and W. F. Gorham, ibid., 74, 2278 (1952).
[35]Reduction carried out in dioxane-ether mixture.
[36]R. Grewe and E. Nolte, Ann., 575, 1 (1951).

[37]M. Hinder and M. Stoll, *Helv. Chim. Acta*, *33*, 1308 (1950).

[38]K. Freudenberg and G. Gehrke, *Chem. Ber.*, *84*, 443 (1951).

[39]J. H. Freeman, *J. Am. Chem. Soc.*, *74*, 6257 (1952).

[40]B. Witkop and J. B. Patrick, *ibid.*, *74*, 3861 (1952).

[41]A. A. Bothner-By, *ibid.*, *73*, 4228 (1951).

[42]C. F. H. Allen and J. R. Byers, Jr., U. S. Pat. 2,545,439 (March 20, 1951).

[43]Isolated as benzoate after treatment of lithium salt with benzoic anhydride.

[44]C. F. H. Allen and J. R. Byers, Jr., *Science*, *107*, 269 (1948); *J. Am. Chem. Soc.*, *71*, 2683 (1949).

[45]Isolated as acetate and phenylacetate after treatment of lithium salt with acetic anhydride and phenylacetic anhydride, respectively.

[46]K. Freudenberg and R. Dillenburg, *Chem. Ber.*, *84*, 67 (1951).

[47]K. Freudenberg, R. Kraft, and W. Heimberger, *ibid.*, *84*, 472 (1951).

[48]K. Freudenberg and H. H. Hübner, *ibid.*, *85*, 1181 (1952).

[49]R. G. Jones and E. C. Kornfeld, *J. Am. Chem. Soc.*, *73*, 107 (1951).

[50]Reduction carried out in a tetrahydrofuran-ether mixture.

[51]R. K. Ness, H. G. Fletcher, Jr., and C. S. Hudson, *J. Am. Chem. Soc.*, *73*, 4759 (1951).

[52]Based on starting β-L-rhamnopyranose tetraacetate.

[53]R. K. Ness, H. G. Fletcher, Jr., and C. S. Hudson, *J. Am. Chem. Soc.*, *72*, 4547 (1950).

[54]Based on starting β-D-glucopyranose pentaacetate.

[55]Based on starting α-D-mannopyranose pentaacetate.

[56]R. K. Ness, H. G. Fletcher, Jr., and C. S. Hudson, *J. Am. Chem. Soc.*, *73*, 3742 (1951).

[57]C. Djerassi, G. Rosenkranz, J. Romo, S. Kaufmann, and J. Pataki, *ibid.*, *72*, 4534 (1950).

[58]S. Kaufmann, J. Pataki, G. Rosenkranz, J. Romo, and C. Djerassi, *ibid.*, *72*, 4531 (1950).

[59]G. Papineau-Couture, E. M. Richardson, and G. A. Grant, *Can. J. Research*, *27B*, 902 (1949).

[60]S. Kaufmann and G. Rosenkranz, U. S. Pat. 2,555,344 (June 5, 1951); Syntex, S. A., Brit. Pat. 661,805 (November 28, 1951).

[61]C. Djerassi, G. Rosenkranz, J. Romo, J. Pataki, and S. Kaufmann, *J. Am. Chem. Soc.*, *72*, 4540 (1950).

[62]A. S. Julia, P. A. Plattner, and H. Heusser, *Helv. Chim. Acta*, *35*, 665 (1952).

[63]Isolated as diacetate.

[64]D. K. Patel, V. Petrow, R. Royer, and I. A. Stuart-Webb, *J. Chem. Soc.*, *1952*, 161.

[65]Isolated as 3β,21-diacetoxypregna-5,17-diene after treatment with nitrous acid and acetylation.

[66]J. Romo, G. Rosenkranz, and C. Djerassi, *J. Am. Chem. Soc.*, *73*, 5489 (1951).

[67]Mixture of epimers.

[68]P. L. Julian, E. W. Meyer, and I. Ryden, *J. Am. Chem. Soc.*, *71*, 756 (1949).

[69]Ciba Ltd., Brit. Pat. 665,254 (January 16, 1952); Ciba, S. A., Fr. Pat. 994,615 (November 20, 1951); P. Plattner, Ger. Pat. 834,848 (May 15, 1952).

[70]P. Plattner, U. S. Pat. 2,599,481 (June 3, 1952).

[71]Isolated as triacetate.

[72]C. Djerassi, G. Rosenkranz, J. Pataki, and S. Kaufmann, *J. Biol. Chem.*, *194*, 115 (1952).

[73]H. Hirschmann and F. B. Hirschmann, *ibid.*, *184*, 259 (1950); H. Hirschmann, M. A. Daus, and F. B. Hirschmann, *ibid.*, *192*, 115 (1951).

[74]Isolated as molecular compound of two epimeric diacetates.

[75]R. B. Turner and D. M. Voitle, *J. Am. Chem. Soc.*, 73, 2283 (1951).

[76]H. Hirschmann and F. B. Hirschmann, *J. Biol. Chem.*, 187, 137 (1950).

[77]J. Pataki, G. Rosenkranz, and C. Djerassi, *J. Am. Chem. Soc.*, 74, 3436 (1952).

[78]P. A. Plattner, H. Heusser, and M. Feurer, *Helv. Chim. Acta, 31,* 2210 (1948).

[79]I. Salamon, *Helv. Chim. Acta, 32,* 1306 (1949).

[80]Isolated as acetone condensation product (spiro-oxazolidene).

[81]H. Heusser, P. T. Herzig, A. Fürst, and P. A. Plattner, *Helv. Chim. Acta, 33,* 1093 (1950).

[82]D. Magrath, D. S. Morris, V. Petrow, and R. Royer, *J. Chem. Soc., 1950,* 2393.

[83]A. C. Ott and M. F. Murray, *Abstracts of Papers,* 113th Meeting American Chemical Society, Chicago, Ill., April 1948, p. 17K.

[84]Isolated as diacetate after acid cleavage of the enol ether and acetylation.

[85]P. L. Julian, E. W. Meyer, W. J. Karpel, and W. Cole, *J. Am. Chem. Soc.,* 73, 1982 (1951).

[86]L. H. Sarett, M. Feurer, and K. Folkers, *ibid.,* 73, 1777 (1951).

[87]P. L. Julian, E. W. Meyer, and I. Ryden, *ibid.,* 72, 367 (1950).

[88]Product from permanganate oxidation of 3β,21-diacetoxy-20-cyanopregna-5,17-diene, $C_{26}H_{35}NO_4$, and 3β,21-diacetoxy-5,6-dibromo-20-cyano-17-pregnene, $C_{26}H_{35}Br_2NO_4$.

[89]J. Heer and K. Miescher, *Helv. Chim. Acta, 34,* 359 (1951).

[90]C. Djerassi, E. Batres, J. Romo, and G. Rosenkranz, *J. Am. Chem. Soc.,* 74, 3634 (1952).

[91]G. Rosenkranz, J. Pataki, and C. Djerassi, *J. Org. Chem.,* 17, 290 (1952).

[92]J. Romo, G. Rosenkranz, and C. Djerassi, *ibid.,* 17, 1413 (1952).

[93]A. I. Ryer and W. H. Gebert, *J. Am. Chem. Soc.,* 74, 4336 (1952).

[94]G. H. Alt and D. H. R. Barton, *Chemistry and Industry, 1952,* 1103.

[95]P. Bladon, H. B. Henbest, and G. W. Wood, *J. Chem. Soc., 1952,* 2737.

[96]Reduction carried out in ether, dioxane or tetrahydrofuran.

[97]H. J. Ringold, G. Rosenkranz, and C. Djerassi, *J. Am. Chem. Soc.,* 74, 3318 (1952).

[98]C. Djerassi, E. Batres, M. Velasco, and G. Rosenkranz, *ibid.,* 74, 1712 (1952).

[99]B. Ellis and V. Petrow, *J. Chem. Soc., 1952,* 2246.

[100]Isolated as dibenzoate.

[101]L. F. Fieser, M. Fieser, and R. N. Chakravarti, *J. Am. Chem. Soc.,* 71, 2226 (1949).

[102]K. Abildgaard-Elling, Brit. Pat. 656,388 (August 22, 1951).

[103]D. H. Hey, J. Honeyman, and W. J. Peal, *J. Chem. Soc., 1952,* 4836.

[104]L. F. Fieser, J. E. Herz, M. W. Klohs, M. A. Romero, and T. Utne, *J. Am. Chem. Soc.,* 74, 3309 (1952).

[105]P. A. Plattner, H. Heusser, and A. B. Kulkarni, *Helv. Chim. Acta, 32,* 1070 (1949).

[106]P. A. Plattner, H. Heusser, and A. B. Kulkarni, *ibid.,* 31, 1885 (1948).

[107]P. A. Plattner, H. Heusser, and M. Feurer, *ibid.,* 32, 587 (1949).

[108]H. Hirschmann, F. B. Hirschmann, and M. A. Daus, *J. Am. Chem. Soc.,* 74, 539 (1952).

[109]Postulated as 3β-acetoxy-9α,11α-oxidoergosta-7,22-diene (Heusser, Eichenberger, Kurath, Dällenbach, and Jeger, *Helv. Chim. Acta, 34,* 2106 (1951) or 3β-acetoxy-7ξ,8ξ-oxidoergosta-9(11),22-diene (Budziarek, Newbold, Stevenson, and Spring, *Chemistry and Industry, 1951,* 1035).

[110]R. Budziarek, G. T. Newbold, R. Stevenson, and F. S. Spring, *J. Chem. Soc., 1952,* 2892.

[111] Isolated as tetraacetate.
[112] A. Sandoval, J. Romo, G. Rosenkranz, S. Kaufmann, and C. Djerassi, *J. Am. Chem. Soc.*, *73*, 3820 (1951).
[113] R. H. Levin, G. B. Spero, A. V. McIntosh, Jr., and D. E. Rayman, *ibid.*, *70*, 2958 (1948).
[114] H. Heusser, R. Anliker, K. Eichenberger, and O. Jeger, *Helv. Chim. Acta*, *35*, 936 (1952).
[115] Isolated as 3,23-diacetate.
[116] W. A. Jacobs and Y. Sato, *J. Biol. Chem.*, *191*, 71 (1951).
[117] A. L. Nussbaum, A. Sandoval, G. Rosenkranz, and C. Djerassi, *J. Org. Chem.*, *17*, 426 (1952).
[118] Products of the reaction between isodehydrocholesteryl *p*-nitrobenzoate and mercuric acetate.
[119] D. H. R. Barton and W. J. Rosenfelder, *J. Chem. Soc.*, *1951*, 2381.
[120] G. S. Davy, E. R. H. Jones, and T. G. Halsall, *Rec. trav. chim.*, *69*, 368 (1950).
[121] Isolated as 2-acetoxynorolean-16,18-diene after treatment of reduction product with acetic anhydride and pyridine.
[122] D. H. R. Barton and C. J. W. Brooks, *J. Chem. Soc.*, *1951*, 257.
[123] R. Budziarek, J. D. Johnston, W. Manson, and F. S. Spring, *ibid.*, *1951*, 3019.
[124] Reduction carried out in dioxane or dioxane-ether mixture.
[125] H. Diener, O. Jeger, and L. Ruzicka, *Helv. Chim. Acta*, *33*, 896 (1950).
[126] G. S. Davy, T. G. Halsall, and E. R. H. Jones, *Chemistry and Industry*, *1950*, 732.
[127] J. F. McGhie and J. F. Cavalla, *ibid.*, *1950*, 744.
[128] J. F. Cavalla and J. F. McGhie, *J. Chem. Soc.*, *1951*, 834.
[129] J. F. Cavalla and J. F. McGhie, *ibid.*, *1951*, 744.
[130] Isolated as acetate.
[131] T. R. Ames, G. S. Davy, T. G. Halsall, E. R. H. Jones, and G. D. Meakins, *Chemistry and Industry*, *1951*, 741.
[132] W. Voser, M. Montavon, H. H. Günthard, O. Jeger, and L. Ruzicka, *Helv. Chim. Acta*, *33*, 1893 (1950).
[133] J. F. McGhie, M. K. Pradhan, and J. F. Cavalla, *J. Chem. Soc.*, *1952*, 3176.
[134] Isolated after treatment of reduction product with acetic anhydride.
[135] D. H. R. Barton and N. J. Holness, *J. Chem. Soc.*, *1952*, 78.
[136] D. H. R. Barton and C. J. W. Brooks, *J. Am. Chem. Soc.*, *72*, 3314 (1950).
[137] D. H. R. Barton and C. J. W. Brooks, *J. Chem. Soc.*, *1951*, 257.
[138] R. Bhuvanendram, W. Manson, and F. S. Spring, *ibid.*, *1950*, 3472.
[139] F. N. Lahey and P. H. A. Strasser, *ibid.*, *1951*, 873.
[140] D. H. R. Barton and N. J. Holness, *Chemistry and Industry*, *1951*, 233.
[141] G. S. Davy, T. G. Halsall, and E. R. H. Jones, *J. Chem. Soc.*, *1951*, 2696.
[142] M. V. Mijović, W. Voser, H. Heusser, and O. Jeger, *Helv. Chim. Acta*, *35*, 964 (1952).
[143] Base formed by LAH reduction of $C_{20}H_{29}NO$, product of selenium dehydrogenation of veatchine.
[144] M. F. Bartlett, W. I. Taylor, and K. Wiesner, *Chemistry and Industry*, *1953*, 173.
[145] O. E. Edwards and L. Marion, *Can. J. Chem.*, *30*, 627 (1952).
[146] J. H. Biel, *J. Am. Chem. Soc.*, *73*, 847 (1951).
[147] J. Booth, E. Boyland, and E. E. Turner, *J. Chem. Soc.*, *1950*, 2808.
[148] H. Heusser, M. Feurer, K. Eichenberger, and V. Prelog, *Helv. Chim. Acta*, *33*, 2243 (1950).
[149] F. Weygand and F. Wirth, *Chem. Ber.*, *85*, 1000 (1952).

[150]Reduction carried out with lithium aluminum deuteride.
[151]D. K. Fukushima, S. Lieberman, and B. Praetz, *J. Am. Chem. Soc.*, *72*, 5205 (1950).
[152]D. H. R. Barton and T. Bruun, *J. Chem. Soc.*, *1951*, 2728.
[153]J. Strating, *Rec. trav. chim.*, *71*, 822 (1952).
[154]A. K. Macbeth and J. S. Shannon, *J. Chem. Soc.*, *1952*, 4748.
[155]D. J. Cram and J. D. Knight, *J. Am. Chem. Soc.*, *74*, 5835 (1952).
[156]Inverse addition.
[157]J. English, Jr., and V. Lamberti, *J. Am. Chem. Soc.*, *74*, 1909 (1952).
[158]W. von E. Doering and H. H. Zeiss, *ibid.*, *72*, 147 (1950).
[159]H. H. Zeiss, *ibid.*, *73*, 2391 (1951).

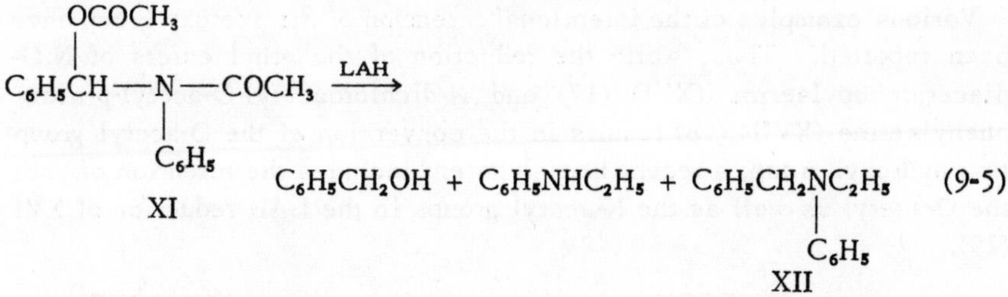

$$\underset{XI}{\overset{\displaystyle OCOCH_3}{\underset{\displaystyle C_6H_5}{C_6H_5CH-N-COCH_3}}} \xrightarrow{LAH}$$

$$C_6H_5CH_2OH + C_6H_5NHC_2H_5 + \underset{\underset{XII}{C_6H_5}}{C_6H_5CH_2NC_2H_5} \quad (9\text{-}5)$$

The LAH reduction of moradiol diacetate oxide (XIII), followed by acetylation, is reported to yield a mixture of unexpected products, i.e., 2-acetoxynorolean-16,18-diene (XIV) and a 13(18)-ene-19,28-oxide-2-acetate (XV). The reaction is postulated as proceeding according to the following scheme (16):

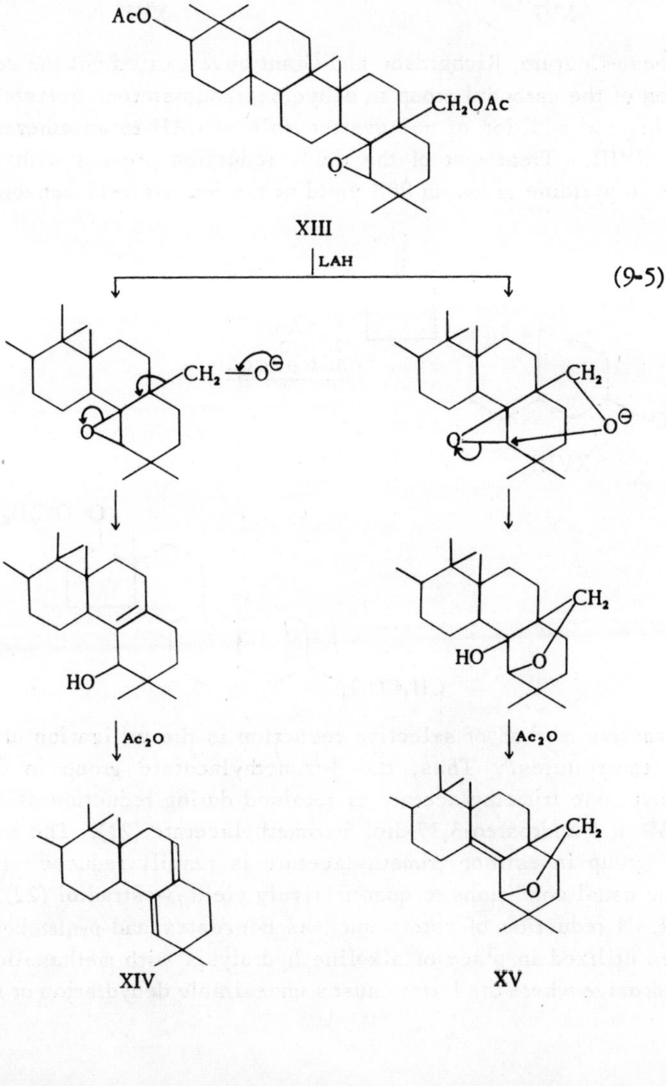

Various examples of the intentional retention of the acetoxy group have been reported. Thus, while the reduction of the ethyl esters of N,O-diacetylphenylserine (XVI) (17) and N-dichloroacetyl-O-acetyl-*p*-nitrophenylserine (XVII) (18) results in the conversion of the O-acetyl group to a hydroxyl group, a recent British patent includes the retention of both the O-acetyl as well as the N-acetyl groups in the LAH reduction of XVI (19).

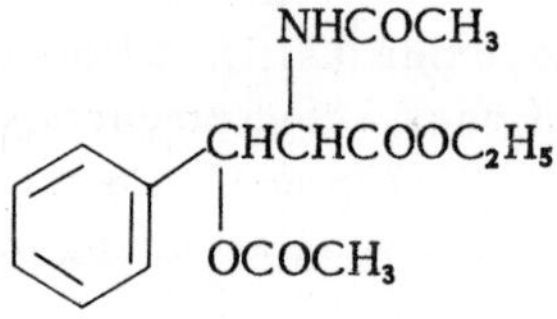

XVI 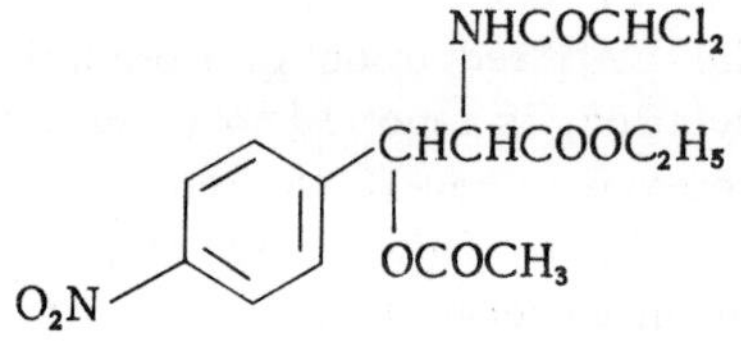   XVII

Papineau-Couture, Richardson and Grant have carried out the selective reduction of the carbonyl group in dehydroepiandrosterone acetate (XVIII) by the inverse addition of one-quarter mole of LAH to an ethereal solution of XVIII. Treatment of the crude reduction product with benzoyl chloride in pyridine gives an 80% yield of the 3-acetate-17-benzoate (20).

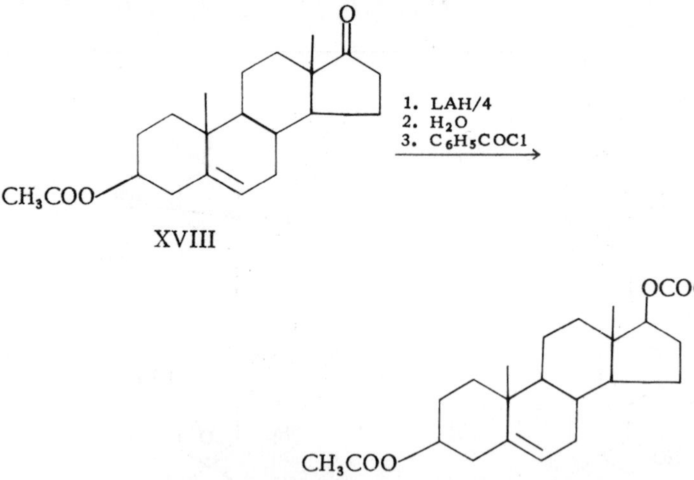

1. LAH/4
2. H₂O
3. C₆H₅COCl

XVIII

(9-6)

An alternative method of selective reduction is the utilization of low reaction temperatures. Thus, the 3-trimethylacetate group in dehydroepiandrosterone trimethylacetate is retained during reduction at $-15°$ to yield 83% of 5-androsten-3,17-diol 3-trimethylacetate (21). The trimethylacetoxy group in estrone trimethylacetate is readily reduced with LAH under the usual conditions to quantitatively yield β-estradiol (22).

The LAH reduction of esters such as benzoates and *p*-nitrobenzoates has been utilized in place of alkaline hydrolysis with methanolic potassium hydroxide where the latter causes undesirable dehydration or resinification. This reductive hydrolysis has been applied after the separation of mixtures of isomeric compounds by fractional or other prolonged recrystallizations. Thus, ergosterol and 14-dehydroergosterol have been separated by recrystallization of the mixed benzoates and the parent sterols have been isolated after LAH reduction (23). The LAH reduction of (+)-pulegone affords a mixture of isomeric pulegols which have been converted to the corresponding p-nitrobenzoates. The latter, after separation by recrystallization, have been cleaved by LAH to yield the individual pulegols (24). The LAH reduction of the p-bromobenzoates of the stereoisomeric 3,4-dimethyl-4-phenyl-3-hexanols has permitted the isolation and characterization of the parent carbinols (25).

The resolution of several carbinols has been carried out by means of the hydrogen phthalates by the following scheme (26–28):

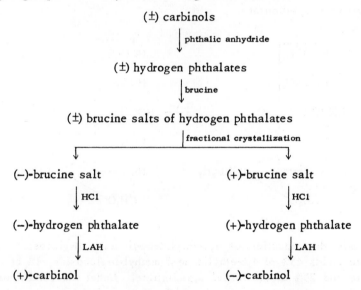

(±) carbinols

| phthalic anhydride

(±) hydrogen phthalates

| brucine

(±) brucine salts of hydrogen phthalates

| fractional crystallization

(–)-brucine salt   (+)-brucine salt

| HCl | HCl

(–)-hydrogen phthalate   (+)-hydrogen phthalate

| LAH | LAH

(+)-carbinol   (–)-carbinol

The attack of the nucleophilic LAH on the carbonyl group permits regeneration of the optically active alcohol from the hydrogen phthalate without racemization.

Soffer, Parrotta, and Di Domenico (29) reported that the LAH reduction of nitrates initially yields nitrous oxide and hydrogen. Hydrolysis of the reduction product yields ammonia, hydrogen and the parent alcohol in excellent yield. Although the Gilman-Schulze color test indicates that two moles of LAH react per mole of nitrate, under these conditions yields of alcohols are low and considerable amounts of unreacted esters are recovered. From a plot of the moles of gas evolved during the reduction step per mole of ester it has been determined that 3.3 moles of LAH per mole of nitrate are required for complete reaction. Four moles of gas are evolved in the reduction step per mole of nitrate.

The following nitrates have been reduced to the parent alcohols in 87–98% yield (29): *n*-hexyl nitrate, 2-octyl nitrate, cyclohexyl nitrate, *cis*-cyclohexane-1,2-diol dinitrate, *trans*-cyclohexane-1,2-diol dinitrate. The reduction of nitrocellulose, containing 13.0 to 13.9% nitrogen, with LAH in tetrahydrofuran results in complete denitration as evidenced by the absence of a nitrate absorption band in the infrared and by a negative diphenylamine sulfonic acid test. Viscosity measurements in cuprammonium solution have revealed, however, that extensive degradation of the polymer has occurred (29).

Ansell and Honeyman (30,31) have carried out the LAH reduction of sugar nitrates in refluxing ether. Thus, the reduction of 4,6-propylidene-α-methyl-D-glucoside 2,3-dinitrate (XIX) yields 45% of 4,6-propylidene-α-methyl-D-glucoside (XX) accompanied by 19% of the 3-nitrate and 31% of the initial 2,3-dinitrate.

$$
\begin{array}{ccc}
\overset{\displaystyle|}{\text{HCOCH}_3} & & \overset{\displaystyle|}{\text{HCOCH}_3} \\
\overset{\displaystyle|}{\text{HCONO}_2} & & \overset{\displaystyle|}{\text{HCOH}} \\
\overset{\displaystyle|}{\text{O}_2\text{NOCH}} & \xrightarrow{\text{LAH}} & \overset{\displaystyle|}{\text{HOCH}} \\
\overset{\displaystyle|}{\text{HCO}} & & \overset{\displaystyle|}{\text{HCO}} \\
\overset{\displaystyle|}{\text{HCO}}\!\!-\!\!\text{CHC}_2\text{H}_5 & & \overset{\displaystyle|}{\text{HCO}}\!\!-\!\!\text{CHC}_2\text{H}_5 \\
\text{CH}_2\text{O} & & \text{CH}_2\text{O} \\
\text{XIX} & & \text{XX}
\end{array}
\qquad (9\text{-}7)
$$

Similarly the reduction of 4,6-ethylidene-β-methyl-D-glucoside 2,3-dinitrate yields 45% of 4,6-ethylidene-β-methyl-D-glucoside, 3% of the 3-nitrate and 25% of the initial 2,3-dinitrate. Under the conditions employed, i.e., less than two moles of LAH per mole of ester, unchanged nitrate is recovered even after refluxing for two days.

The LAH reduction of nitrites produces relatively more nitrous oxide and less ammonia than the reduction of nitrates. The alcohols are obtained in 87–98% yield. Although the Gilman-Schulze test indicates the reaction of one mole of LAH per mole of nitrite, measurement of the evolved gases, 2.6 moles per mole of nitrite, indicates that 1.8 moles of LAH per mole of nitrite are required for complete reaction (29).

The following nitrites have been reduced to the alcohols (29): *n*-hexyl nitrite, 2-octyl nitrite, cyclohexyl nitrite.

Karrer and Jucker (32) reported that cetyl phosphate (XXI) is reduced with LAH in ether to 58% cetyl alcohol, phosphoric acid and phosphine.

$$CH_3(CH_2)_{15}O\overset{\overset{\displaystyle OH}{|}}{\underset{\underset{\displaystyle OH}{|}}{P}}=O \xrightarrow{\text{LAH}} CH_3(CH_2)_{15}OH + H_3PO_4 + PH_3 \qquad (9\text{-}8)$$

XXI

The reduction of lecithin (XXII) yields fatty alcohols, glycerol, choline, phosphoric acid and phosphine.

$$\begin{array}{l} CH_2OCOC_nH_{2n+1} \\ | \\ HCOCOC_mH_{2m+1} \\ | \\ \qquad\qquad\qquad \overset{\displaystyle O}{\underset{\displaystyle }{|}} \\ CH_2O\!-\!\!P\!-\!OCH_2CH_2N(CH_3)_3 \\ \qquad\quad | \\ \qquad\quad O\underline{\qquad\qquad\quad} \end{array} \xrightarrow{\text{LAH}}$$

XXII

$$\begin{array}{l} CH_2OH \\ | \\ CHOH \quad + \ C_nH_{2n+1}CH_2OH \ + \ C_mH_{2m+1}CH_2OH \\ | \\ CH_2OH \end{array}$$

$$+ \ \underset{OH^{\ominus}}{HOCH_2CH_2\overset{\oplus}{N}(CH_3)_3} + H_3PO_4 + PH_3 \qquad (9\text{-}9)$$

9.1.1.b   *Reduction of esters to alcohols.* The LAH reduction of esters to the corresponding primary alcohols has been widely used for the synthesis of monofunctional as well as difunctional compounds.

$$RCOOR' \xrightarrow{\text{LAH}} RCH_2OH \qquad (9\text{-}10)$$

$$(CH_2)_n\!\!\begin{array}{l} \diagup COOR' \\[4pt] \diagdown COOR' \end{array} \xrightarrow{\text{LAH}} (CH_2)_n\!\!\begin{array}{l} \diagup CH_2OH \\[4pt] \diagdown CH_2OH \end{array} \qquad (9\text{-}11)$$

1. *Aliphatic carboxylates.* The reduction of the esters of various aliphatic acids yields alkanols while malonic esters (33) and succinic esters (34) are converted to 1,3-propanediol and 1,4-butanediol, respectively. Substituted 1,3-propanediols are prepared by reduction of the corresponding malonic ester (XXIII). Satisfactory yields have been reported where R is hydrogen or alkyl and R′ is alkyl or aryl. Yields are poorer when R′ is an alkoxy or aryloxy group or an arylmercapto group.

$$\underset{\text{XXIII}}{\underset{R'}{\overset{R}{>}}C\underset{\text{COOC}_2H_5}{\overset{\text{COOC}_2H_5}{<}}} \xrightarrow{\text{LAH}} \underset{R'}{\overset{R}{>}}C\underset{\text{CH}_2\text{OH}}{\overset{\text{CH}_2\text{OH}}{<}} \qquad (9\text{-}12)$$

Reduction of diethyl 2-ethyl-2-ethylmercaptomalonate (XXIII: R = C_2H_5; R′ = SC_2H_5) appeared to proceed normally although none of the desired diol could be isolated (33).

Overberger and Roberts have prepared 2-alkyl-1,4-butanediols in 85–96% yield by the LAH reduction of the corresponding succinic esters (33). Catalytic hydrogenation of the substituted succinic ester over copper chromite at 300 atmospheres pressure at 250° is reported to proceed in less than 30% yield (35,36).

An interesting comparison in the effects of various reduction methods has been reported in the case of diethyl 2-(2-pyridylethyl)malonate (XXIV). While LAH reduction yields the expected 1,3-propanediol (XXV), catalytic hydrogenation over Raney nickel at 200 atmospheres at 145° yields 3-carbethoxy-4-ketoquinolizidine (XXVI) and hydrogenation over copper chromite at 250 atmospheres at 260° yields a mixture of quinolizidine (XXVII) and 4-ketoquinolizidine (XXVIII) (37).

Several examples of cyclization occurring in the course of the LAH reduction of esters have been reported. Thus, the reduction of triethyl ethane-1,1,1-triacetate (XXIX) at 18° yields the *tris*-(2-hydroxyethyl)-ethane (XXX) while reduction at 35° yields 4-methyl-4-(2-hydroxyethyl)-tetrahydropyran (XXXI) as the major product (38).

$$CH_3C(CH_2COOC_2H_5)_3 \xrightarrow{LAH}$$

XXIX

$$\xrightarrow{18°} CH_3C(CH_2CH_2OH)_3 \qquad (9\text{-}16)$$

XXX

$$\xrightarrow{35°}$$

CH₃, CH₂CH₂OH

+ XXX

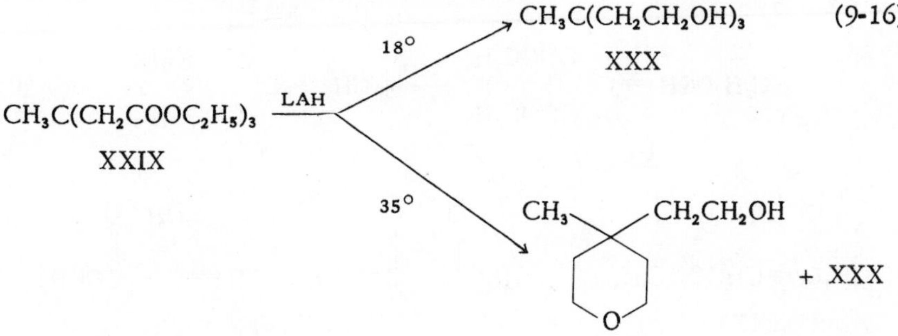

XXXI   (9-17)

The reduction of diethyl L-glutamate (XXXII) yields L-2-amino-1,5-pentanediol accompanied by L-2-hydroxymethylpyrrolidine (39).

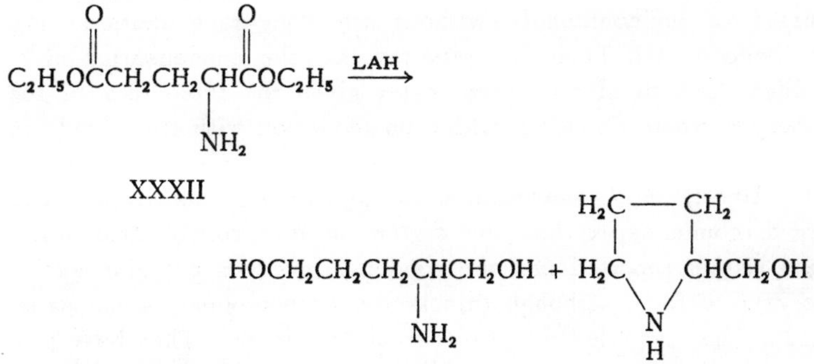

$$C_2H_5OCCH_2CH_2CHCOC_2H_5 \xrightarrow{LAH}$$

(O, O double bonds shown; NH₂ substituent)

XXXII

$$HOCH_2CH_2CH_2CHCH_2OH + H_2C \quad CH_2$$

NH₂

H₂C   CHCH₂OH

N
H
(9-18)

A similar cyclization involving an ω-aminoalcohol has been reported in the LAH reduction of ethyl 2-decyl-2,4-dicyanobutyrate (XXXIII) (40).

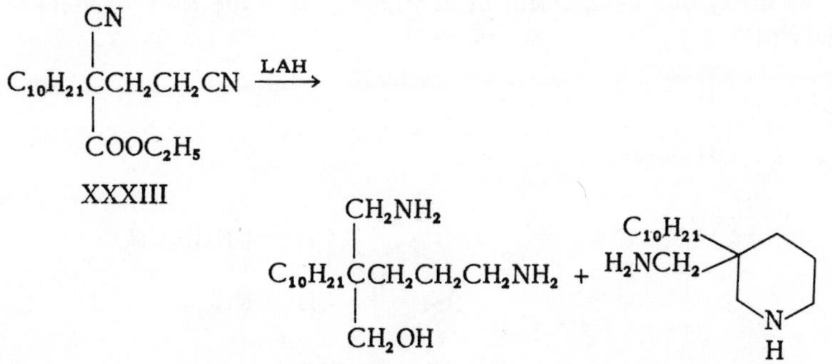

CN
|
$$C_{10}H_{21}CCH_2CH_2CN \xrightarrow{LAH}$$
|
COOC₂H₅

XXXIII

CH₂NH₂
|
$$C_{10}H_{21}CCH_2CH_2CH_2NH_2 + $$
|
CH₂OH

C₁₀H₂₁, H₂NCH₂

N
H
(9-19)

The LAH reduction of enolizable aliphatic esters is influenced by the degree of enolization. The attempted reduction of diethyl ethoxymethylenemalonate (XXXIV) yields 5% of diethyl methylenemalonate (41) while no reduction occurs in the case of the O-ethyl derivative of ethyl acetoacetate (XXXV) (41) and the dimethyl ester of α,α'-dihydroxymuconic acid (XXXVI) (42).

$$C_2H_5OCH = C \begin{matrix} COOC_2H_5 \\ COOC_2H_5 \end{matrix} \xrightarrow{LAH} CH_2 = C \begin{matrix} COOC_2H_5 \\ COOC_2H_5 \end{matrix} \qquad (9\text{-}20)$$

XXXIV

$$\underset{\text{XXXV}}{\overset{OC_2H_5}{CH_3C = CHCOOC_2H_5}} \qquad \underset{\text{XXXVI}}{\overset{O \quad OH}{CH_3OC - C = CH - CH = C - COCH_3}}$$

The yield of 2-substituted 1,3-butanediol obtained in the LAH reduction of substituted ethyl acetoacetate increases as the size of the substituent increases probably due to hindrance to enolization (43).

The reduction of α-aminocarboxylic acid esters has been utilized for the synthesis of aminoalcohols without attendant racemization (44). Bergmann, Bendas, and Taub (45) reported that the condensation of p-nitrobenzaldehyde with glycine ethyl ester gives the *threo* form of the β-p-nitrophenylserinate (XXXVII) which on reduction with LAH leads to the racemic form of *threo*-2-amino-1-p-nitrophenyl-1,3-propanediol (XXXVIII). Alberti et al. showed that the p-nitrophenylserine produced by the above condensation has the *erythro* or *allo* configuration (46). Holland and Nayler reported that the condensation does not give exclusively the *erythro* form, although this is the main product, since paper chromatography has revealed the presence of both forms. They have proposed that the LAH reduction reported by Bergman et al. was carried out on a crude reaction product containing both forms, and that the fortuitous isolation of the *threo* rather than the *erythro* form of the diol was responsible for the erroneous assignment of configuration to the main condensation product (47).

$$O_2N - \underset{\text{XXXVII}}{\underset{}{\overset{CH - CHCOOC_2H_5}{\underset{OH \quad NH_2}{|}}}} \xrightarrow{LAH}$$

$$O_2N - \underset{\text{XXXVIII}}{\underset{}{\overset{CH - CHCH_2OH}{\underset{OH \quad NH_2}{|}}}} \qquad (9\text{-}21)$$

The ready reduction of the ester group with LAH permits its selective reduction in the presence of other functional groups. Thus, ethyl p-nitrophenylacetate, ethyl 2,2-diethyl-3-oximinobutyrate and ethyl 2,2-dibenzyl-2-acetamidoacetate are reduced, by inverse addition, to the corresponding carbinols while the nitro, oximino and acetamido groups, respectively, are retained intact (48). Selective reduction involves the use of the calculated amount of LAH but may or may not require inverse addition. LAH has been used for the reduction of the terminal carboxyl groups (esterified or free) of a peptide to primary alcohols while retaining the amide linkages (49).

Carrara, Pace, and Cristiani (50) have found that the selective reduction of ethyl *erythro*-D,L and DL-β-p-nitrophenylserinate (XXXVII) to the corresponding 1,3-propanediols can be carried out in practically quantitative yield by the employment of somewhat less than the quantity of LAH calculated for the blocking of the amino and hydroxyl groups and the reduction of the ester group. They propose that the LAH reacts first with the oxygenated functions, i.e., hydroxyl and ester, and subsequently with the nitrogenated functional groups, i.e., amino and nitro groups. Attempts to apply a variety of reaction conditions for the selective reduction of ethyl *threo*-DL-β-p-nitrophenylserinate and its optical antipodes gave only red oils which gave reactions characteristic of azo compounds.

The use of low temperatures permits the reduction of a diester to a hydroxyester. Nystrom and Brown reported that the attempted selective reduction of sebacic acid and its half ethyl ester with the calculated amount of LAH in refluxing ether gives a mixture of diol and unchanged acid and suggested experimentation at lowered temperatures (51). Bachmann and Dreiding reported that while the reduction of methyl *cis*-(2-methyl-2-carbomethoxycyclohexyl)acetate (XXXIX) at room temperature gives an 80% yield of the diol (XL), reduction at −15° results in the selective reduction of the primary carbomethoxy group (52).

TABLE XXXVIII

$$\overset{\text{O}}{\overset{\|}{\text{LAH Reduction of R'C—OR} \rightarrow \text{R'CH}_2\text{OH (R = alkyl)}}}$$

	Ester	Product	% Yield	Ref.
C3H5O2R	Propionic-1-C13 ester	Propanol-1-C13	....	1
C4H5Cl3O2	Ethyl trichloroacetate	2,2,2-Trichloroethanol	65	2
C4H6Cl2O2	Ethyl dichloroacetate	2,2-Dichloroethanol	65	2
C4H7O2R	Butyric-1-C13 ester	Butanol-1-C13	....	1
C4H7ClO2	Ethyl chloroacetate	2-Chloroethanol	37	2
	Methyl 3-chloropropionate-1-C14	3-Chloropropanol-1-C14	78[3]	4
C4H7N2O2	Ethyl diazoacetate	Ethanolamine	72	5
C4H8O2	Ethyl acetate	Ethanol	....	6
	Acetic-1-C14 ester	Ethanol-1-C14	....	7
	Ethyl acetate-2-C14	Ethanol-2-C14	100[8]	9
	Ethyl acetate10	Ethanol-1-t	80	11
C4H9NO3	Methyl ester DL-serine	2-Amino-1,3-propanediol	33	12
C5H7NO2	Methyl 3-cyanopropionate	4-Amino-1-butanol	....	13
C5H8F2O3	Ethyl 2,2-difluoro-3-hydroxypropionate	2,2-Difluoro-1,3-propanediol	85	14
C5H11NO2	Ethyl ester DL-alanine	2-Amino-1-propanol	....	15,16
	Ethyl ester L(+)-alanine	L(+)-Alaninol	50	12
C5H11NO3	Ethyl ester serine	2-Amino-1,3-propanediol	....	16
C6H7Cl3O2	Ethyl 2,3,4-trichlorocrotonate17	2,3-Dichloro-2-buten-1-ol: cis trans	59} 10}	18
C6H9Cl3O2	Methyl tris-(chloromethyl)acetate	2,2,2-Tris-(chloromethyl) ethanol	76	19
C6H9F3O2	Butyl 2,2,2-trifluoroacetate	2,2,2-Trifluoroethanol	76	20
C6H10O2	Methyl pent-3-enoate	3-Penten-1-ol	75	21
C6H10O3	Ethyl acetoacetate	1,3-Butanediol	30	22
C6H10O4	Diethyl oxalate	Ethylene glycol	78[23]	24
C6H12O3	Ethyl ethoxyacetate	2-Ethoxyethanol	75	25

Formula	Ester	Reduction product	Yield	Ref.
$C_6H_{13}NO_2$	Methyl 3-methoxybutyrate	3-Methoxy-1-butanol	70	26
$C_6H_{13}NO_3$	Ethyl 2-dimethylaminoacetate-1-C^{14}	2-Dimethylaminoethanol-1-C^{14}	···[27]	28
$C_7H_{10}Cl_2O_4$	Ethyl ester threonine	2-Amino-1,3-butanediol	···	16
	Diethyl 2,2-dichloromalonate	2,2-Dichloro-1,3-propanediol	43	29
$C_7H_{11}BrO_4$	Diethyl 2-bromomalonate	1,3-Propanediol	5[30]	31
$C_7H_{12}O_2$	Ethyl pent-2-enoate	2-Penten-1-ol	62	32,33 / 34,35
	Methyl hex-2-enoate	trans-2-Hexen-1-ol	···	36
$C_7H_{12}O_3$	Ethyl 2-methylacetoacetate	2-Methyl-1,3-butanediol	60	22
	Methyl hexan-4-one-1-oate	1,4-Hexanediol	···	37
$C_7H_{12}O_5$	Dimethyl L-methoxysuccinate	L-2-Methoxy-1,4-butanediol	69,82[38]	39
$C_7H_{13}NO_4$	Methyl 4-methyl-4-nitropentanoate	4-Amino-4-methyl-1-pentanol	···	13
$C_7H_{14}O_2$	Methyl 4-methylpentanoate	4-Methyl-1-pentanol	90	40
$C_7H_{15}NO_2$	Ethyl ester valine	2-Amino-3-methyl-1-butanol	···	16
	Ethyl ester L-valine	L(+)-Valinol	···	41
	Ethyl 2-dimethylaminopropionate	2-Dimethylamino-1-propanol	···	42
$C_8H_7NO_4$	Methyl 2-oximinofuroylacetate	1-(2-Furyl)-2-amino-1,3-propanediol	"poor"	43
$C_8H_8O_2$	Phenyl acetate[44]	1,1-Dideuteroethanol	65[3]	45
$C_8H_{10}O_2$	Methyl hepta-2,4,6-trienoate	2,4,6-Heptatrien-1-ol	85.5	46 / 47
$C_8H_{10}F_4O_4$	Diethyl 2,2,3,3-tetrafluorosuccinate	2,2,3,3-Tetrafluoro-1,4-butanediol	90 / 86	14 / 48
$C_8H_{11}NO_2S$	Ethyl 4-methyl-5-thiazolylacetate	4-Methyl-5-(2-hydroxyethyl)thiazole	49–62	49
$C_8H_{13}NO_4$	Ethyl ester N,N-diacetylglycine	N,N-Diethylethanolamine	42.8	50
$C_8H_{13}N_3O_2$	Ethyl ester histidine	Histidinol	···	16
$C_8H_{14}O_2$	Ethyl 2,3-dimethylbut-2-enoate	2,3-Dimethyl-2-buten-1-ol	···	51
	Methyl heptan-4-one-1-oate	1,4-Heptanediol	···	37
$C_8H_{14}O_3$	Diethyl 2-methylmalonate	2-Methyl-1,3-propanediol	···	52
$C_8H_{14}O_4$	Diethyl succinate-2,3-C^{14}	1,4-Butanediol-2,3-C^{14}	···	53
	Diethyl ester aspartic acid	2-Amino-1,4-butanediol	···	12,16
$C_8H_{15}NO_4$	Diethyl ester L-aspartic acid	L(+)-2-Amino-1,4-butanediol	70	12

(Continued)

TABLE XXXVIII (*Continued*)

	Ester	Product	% Yield	Ref.
$C_8H_{16}O_2$	Methyl 5-methylhexanoate	5-Methyl-1-hexanol	100	40
	Ethyl hexanoate-1-C¹³	1-Hexanol-1-C¹³	...	54
	Ethyl 3-methylpentanoate	3-Methyl-1-pentanol	96	55
	Ethyl 2-methylpentanoate	2-Methyl-1-pentanol	91.5	56
$C_8H_{17}NO_2$	Ethyl ester leucine	2-Amino-4-methyl-1-pentanol	...	16
	Ethyl ester L-leucine	L(+)-Leucinol	80	12
	Ethyl ester isoleucine	2-Amino-3-methyl-1-pentanol	...	16
$C_8H_{17}NO_2S$	Ethyl ester L-S-propylcysteine	L-S-Propylcysteinol	60.5	57
$C_8H_{18}N_2O_2$	Ethyl ester lysine	2,6-Diamino-1-hexanol	...	16
$C_8H_{18}N_4O_2$	Ethyl ester arginine	Argininol	...	16,50
$C_9H_9NO_5$	Ethyl 2-oximinofuroylacetate	1-(2-Furyl)-2-amino-1,3-propanediol	2[59]	43
$C_9H_{10}NO_2$	Ethyl 2-(2-Pyridyl)acetate	2-(2-Pyridyl)ethanol	...	60
$C_9H_{10}F_6O_4$	Diethyl perfluoroglutarate	2,2,3,3,4,4-Hexafluoro-1,5-pentanediol	93	14
$C_9H_{12}O_4$	Methyl anhydromonocrotalate	2,3,4-Trimethylpent-3-ene-1,2,5-triol	87.2	48
$C_9H_{13}NO_4$	Ethyl furylserinate	1-(2-Furyl)-2-amino-1,3-propanediol	86	61
$C_9H_{14}O_4$	Methyl dihydroanhydromonocrotalate	2,3,4-Trimethyl-1,2,5-pentanetriol	50[59]	43
	Methyl monocrotalate	2,3,4-Trimethyl-1,2,3,5-pentanetetrol	93	61
$C_9H_{14}O_5$	Diethyl acetonedicarboxylate	1,3,5-Pentanetriol	92	61
$C_9H_{14}O_6$	Ethyl 2,3-diacetoxy-D,L-glycerate-1-C¹⁴	Glycerol-1-C¹⁴	40	62
	Diethyl 2-acetoxymalonate-1-C¹⁴	Glycerol-1-C¹⁴	...	63
	Diethyl 2-acetoxymalonate-2-C¹⁴	Glycerol-2-C¹⁴	85	64
$C_9H_{16}O_2$	Ethyl hept-2-enoate	2-Hepten-1-ol	85	64
$C_9H_{16}O_4$	Ethyl glutarate	1,5-Pentanediol	79	65
$C_9H_{16}O_5$	Ethyl 3-hydroxyglutarate	1,3,5-Pentanetriol	80	66
$C_9H_{17}NO_2$	Ethyl 2-(1-pyrrolidyl)propionate	2-(1-Pyrrolidyl)-1-propanol	61	67
			79	68
			82	69
	Methyl 2-methyl-3-(1-pyrrolidyl)propionate	2-Methyl-3-(1-pyrrolidyl)-1-propanol	89.7	68

Formula	Ester	Product	Yield	Ref.
C₉H₁₇NO₄	Diethyl L-glutamate	L-2-Amino-1,5-pentanediol	58 ⎫	70
		L-2-Hydroxymethylpyrrolidine	…[59] ⎭	16
	Diethyl glutamate	2-Amino-1,5-pentanediol	…	71
C₉H₁₈O₂	Methyl octanoate	1-Octanol	80–90	71
	Methyl octanoate[44]	1,1-Dideutero-1-octanol	…	72
	Methyl 2,2,2-triethylacetate	2,2,2-Triethylethanol	90	56
	Ethyl 2-methylcaproate	2-Methyl-1-hexanol	98.1	56
	Ethyl 5-methylcaproate	5-Methyl-1-hexanol	87.2	73
C₉H₁₈O₃	Methyl 3,4,4-trimethyl-1,3-hydroxyvalerate	3,4,4-Trimethyl-1,3-pentanediol	97	75
C₉H₁₈O₄	Ethyl 2,2-diethoxypropionate	2,2-Diethoxy-1-propanol	53[74]	76
	Methyl 6,6-dimethoxyhexanoate	6,6-Dimethoxy-1-hexanol	91	78
C₁₀H₈O₂	Methyl phenylpropiolate	3-Phenylprop-2-yn-1-ol	90[77]	78
		trans-Cinnamyl alcohol	75	14
C₁₀H₁₀F₈O₄	Diethyl perfluoroadipate	2,2,3,3,4,5,5-Octafluoro-1,6-hexanediol	88	79
C₁₀H₁₁ClO₂	Methyl DL-2-chloro-2-phenylpropionate	DL-2-Phenyl-1-propanol	61	79
		2-Phenylpropionaldehyde	11[80a,b]	79
		α-Methylstyrene	18[80a,c]	79
	Methyl (+)-2-chloro-2-phenylpropionate	(−)-2-Phenyl-1-propanol	62[81]	82
C₁₀H₁₁NO₄	Ethyl p-nitrophenylacetate	2-(p-Nitrophenyl)ethanol	54[3]	83
C₁₀H₁₃NO₂	Ethyl ester DL-phenylglycine	DL-2-Phenyl-2-aminoethanol	…	85
C₁₀H₁₃NO₃	Methyl ester DL-phenylserine	DL-threo-1-Phenyl-2-amino-1,3-propanediol	36[64]	86
	Methyl ester threo-phenylserine	threo-Phenylserinol	…	41
	Methyl ester L-tyrosine	L(−)-Tyrosinol	65	88
C₁₀H₁₄O₃	(C₇H₉O) COOC₂H₅[87]	compound C₈H₁₂O₂, m.p. 80°	56	32,33
C₁₀H₁₆O₂	Ethyl 3-methylhepta-2,6-dienoate	3-Methylhepta-2,6-dien-1-ol	…	88,89
C₁₀H₁₆O₃	Ethyl 2,3-epoxycyclohexylideneacetate	1-Hydroxyethyl-1-cyclohexanol	82, 60	90,91
C₁₀H₁₆O₄	Diethyl 2-allylmalonate	2-Hydroxymethyl-4-penten-1-ol	52	92
	Diethyl dihydromuconate	3-Hexen-1,6-diol	80	93

(Continued)

TABLE XXXVIII (Continued)

	Ester	Product	% Yield	Ref.
$C_{10}H_{16}O_5$	Diethyl ethoxymethylenemalonate	Diethyl methylenemalonate	5	94
$C_{10}H_{17}NO_3$	Ethyl N,N-pentamethylenemalonamate	3-Piperidino-1-propanol	...	95
$C_{10}H_{18}O_4$	Diethyl 2-methyl-2-ethylmalonate	2-Methyl-2-ethyl-1,3-propanediol	23.4	96
	Diethyl adipate	1,6-Hexanediol	...	97,98
			83	99
	Dimethyl 3,3-dimethyladipate	3,3-Dimethyl-1,6-hexanediol	85	100
			...	101
	Diethyl 2-ethylsuccinate	2-Ethyl-1,4-butanediol	...	37
	Dimethyl suberate	1,8-Octanediol	58.8	102
$C_{10}H_{19}NO_2$	Ethyl 2-methyl-3-(1-pyrrolidyl)-propionate	2-Methyl-3-(1-pyrrolidyl)-1-propanol	...	69
	Ethyl 3-(1-pyrrolidyl)butyrate	3-(1-Pyrrolidyl)-1-butanol	...	69
	cis-Ethyl 2-(2-aminocyclohexyl)acetate	cis-2-(2-Aminocyclohexyl)ethanol	86	103
$C_{10}H_{19}NO_3$	Ethyl N,N-diethylsuccinamate	4-Diethylamino-1-butanol	71	95
	Ethyl 2,2-diethyl-3-oximinobutyrate	2,2-Diethyl-3-oximino-1-butanol	61[3]	82
$C_{10}H_{19}N_3O_6$	Ethyl ester diglycylglycine acetate	N-Hydroxyethyldiethylenetriamine	42[30,104]	105
$C_{10}H_{20}O_2$	Ethyl 2-methylheptanoate	2-Methyl-1-heptanol	92.9	56
	Ethyl 4-methylheptanoate	4-Methyl-1-heptanol	94.7	56
	Ethyl 5-methylheptanoate	5-Methyl-1-heptanol	94.6	56
$C_{10}H_{20}O_4$	Ethyl 2-methyl-3,3-diethoxypropionate	2-Methyl-3,3-diethoxy-1-propanol	47.5[106]	75
$C_{11}H_9NO_2$	Methyl 2-cyanocinnamate	2-Benzyl-3-amino-1-propanol	30	107
$C_{11}H_{11}NO_4$	Ethyl 2-oximinobenzoylacetate	product not indicated	...	108
		2-Benzalamino-3-phenyl-3-hydroxypropionic acid or 2,5-diphenyl-4-carboxyoxazolidine	7[30]	109
		1-Phenyl-2-amino-1,3-propanediol	...	110
$C_{11}H_{12}O_3$	Ethyl o-hydroxycinnamate	3-(o-Hydroxyphenyl)-1-propanol	100	111
$C_{11}H_{12}O_4$	Dimethyl homophthalate	Homophthalyl alcohol	...	112
$C_{11}H_{12}Br_2O_2$	Ethyl 2,3-dibromo-3-phenylpropionate	Hydrocinnamyl alcohol	59[30]	31

C₁₁H₁₃Br₂NO₃	Ethyl ester L-3,5-dibromotyrosine	2-Amino-3-(3,5-dibromo-4-hydroxyphenyl)-1-propanol	66.3[113]	114
C₁₁H₁₄N₂O₄	Ethyl ester DL-p-nitrophenylalanine	2-Amino-3-(p-nitrophenyl)-1-propanol	67.5,60.7[113]	114
C₁₁H₁₄N₂O₅	Ethyl ester DL-erythro-3-p-nitrophenyl-serine	DL-erythro-1-p-Nitrophenyl-2-amino-1,3-propanediol	59–97	115
	Ethyl ester D-erythro-3-p-nitrophenyl-serine	D-erythro-1-p-Nitrophenyl-2-amino-1,3-propanediol	...	115
	Ethyl ester L-erythro-3-p-nitrophenyl-serine	L-erythro-1-p-Nitrophenyl-2-amino-1,3-propanediol	...	115
	Ethyl ester DL-, D-, and L-threo-3-p-nitrophenylserine	Red oils (azo compounds?)	...	115
	Ethyl ester p-nitrophenylserine	threo-1-p-Nitrophenyl-2-amino-1,3-propanediol	...	116
C₁₁H₁₅NO₂	Ethyl ester DL-phenylalanine	2-Amino-3-phenyl-1-propanol (phenylalaninol)	...	16,83,117, 118,119
			87	120
			81.4	114
	Ethyl ester L-phenylalanine	L-(-)-Phenylalaninol	75	12
C₁₁H₁₅NO₃	Ethyl ester DL-phenylserine	1-Phenyl-2-amino-1,3-propanediol (phenylserinol)	...	121,122
		threo-Phenylserinol	51	123
			57[38,124]	116
			30	125
	Ethyl ester threo-Phenylserine	threo-Phenylserinol	...	126,86
			75	127
	Ethyl ester DL-threo-phenylserine	DL-threo-Phenylserinol	47[59]	43
	Ethyl ester DL-allo-phenylserine	allo-Phenylserinol	...	122
	Ethyl ester tyrosine	2-Amino-3-(p-hydroxyphenyl)-1-propanol (tyrosinol)	45[28]	16, 129

(Continued)

TABLE XXXVIII (Continued)

	Ester	Product	% Yield	Ref.
$C_{11}H_{15}NO_3$ (contd.)	Ethyl ester L-tyrosine	L-Tyrosinol	...[84]	12
			...	114
$C_{11}H_{16}O_2$	Ethyl 3-methylocta-2,4,6-trienoate	3-Methylocta-2,4,6-trien-1-ol	60[30,130]	131
			25[113]	107
$C_{11}H_{17}NO_6$	Diethyl methylimino-di-α-formylacetate	N,N-Di-(1,3-propanediol-2-yl)-methylamine	87	132
			...	133
$C_{11}H_{18}O_2$	Ethyl 2-(2-methylcyclohex-1-enyl)-acetate	2-(2-Methylcyclohex-1-enyl)-ethanol (75)	87	134
	Ethyl 2-(6-methylcyclohex-1-enyl)-acetate	2-(6-Methylcyclohex-1-enyl)-ethanol (25)		
	Methyl 5-(cyclopent-1-enyl)valerate	5-(Cyclopent-1-enyl)-1-pentanol	90	135
	Methyl geranate	Geraniol / Nerol	...	136
$C_{11}H_{18}O_6$	Ethylene ketal of diethyl acetonedicarboxylate	Ethylene ketal of pentan-3-one-1,5-diol	53	62
$C_{11}H_{19}NO_2$	Ethyl ester meroquinene	2-(3-Vinylpiperidyl)ethanol	95.3	137
$C_{11}H_{20}O_2$	Ethyl non-2-enoate	2-Nonen-1-ol	97.7	65
$C_{11}H_{20}O_3$	Methyl 2-(2,2,6-trimethyltetrahydropyran-6-yl)acetate	2-(2,2,6-Trimethyltetrahydropyran-6-yl)-ethanol	95	138
$C_{11}H_{20}O_4$	Diethyl 2-n-butylmalonate	2-Butyl-1,3-propanediol	...	98
	Diethyl 2,2-diethylmalonate	2,2-Diethyl-1,3-propanediol	94	139
			95	140
			50	96
	Diethyl 2-methyl-2-n-propylmalonate	2-Methyl-2-n-propyl-1,3-propanediol	44.2	96
	Diethyl 2-methyl-2-isopropylmalonate	2-Methyl-2-isopropyl-1,3-propanediol	31.8	96
	Diethyl 2-isopropylsuccinate	2-Isopropyl-1,4-butanediol	96	141
	Diethyl 2-n-propylsuccinate	2-n-Propyl-1,4-butanediol	...	37
	Diethyl pimelate	1,7-Heptanediol	...	37
			60.1	102

Formula				Ref.
C₁₁H₂₀O₅	Diethyl 3,3-dimethylglutarate	3,3-Dimethyl-1,5-pentanediol	…	52
	Diethyl 2-ethyl-2-ethoxymalonate	2-Ethyl-2-ethoxy-1,3-propanediol	20.2	96
C₁₁H₂₀N₂O₅	Ethyl ester ethylglutamyl-γ-glycine	N-(2-Hydroxyethyl)-4-amino-5-hydroxy-valeramide	31[142]	143
C₁₁H₂₁NO₃	Ethyl N,N-diethylglutaramate	5-Diethylamino-1-pentanol	…	95
C₁₁H₂₂O₂	Ethyl 2-methyloctanoate	2-Methyl-1-octanol	87.7	56
	Ethyl 4-methyloctanoate	4-Methyl-1-octanol	92.7	56
	Ethyl 7-methyloctanoate	7-Methyl-1-octanol	89.8	56
C₁₁H₂₂O₄	Ethyl 4,4-diethoxypentanoate	4,4-Diethoxy-1-pentanol	56[144]	75
	Ethyl 2-ethyl-3,3-diethoxypropionate	2-Ethyl-3,3-diethoxy-1-propanol	46[145]	75
	Methyl 8,8-dimethoxyoctanoate	8,8-Dimethoxy-1-octanol	76	76
C₁₂H₉NO₄	Methyl 2-cyano-3-(3,4-methylene-dioxyphenyl)acrylate	3-Amino-2-(3,4-methylenedioxybenzyl)-1-propanol	33	107
C₁₂H₁₁NO₃	Methyl 2-cyano-3-(4-methoxyphenyl)-acrylate	3-Amino-2-(4-methoxybenzyl)-1-propanol	33	107
C₁₂H₁₂O₄	Ethyl 3,4-methylenedioxycinnamate	3,4-Methylenedioxycinnamyl alcohol	…	146
	Methyl 4-acetoxycinnamate	4-Hydroxycinnamyl alcohol	84	147
C₁₂H₁₄O₄	Methyl 3,4-dimethoxycinnamate	3,4-Dimethoxycinnamyl alcohol	…	146
	Ethyl 3-methoxy-4-hydroxycinnamate (ethyl ferulate)	3-Methoxy-4-hydroxycinnamyl alcohol (coniferyl alcohol)	80–83	148
C₁₂H₁₄N₂O₂	Methyl ester L-tryptophan	L-Tryptophanol	90	149
C₁₂H₁₅NO₄	Ethyl ester carbobenzoxyglycine	N-Methylethanolamine	… ⎫ 30	105
		Benzyl alcohol	… ⎭	
C₁₂H₁₆O₃	Ethyl DL-2-ethoxy-2-phenylacetate	DL-2-Ethoxy-2-phenylethanol	…	150
	Ethyl (−)-2-ethoxy-2-phenylacetate	(−)-2-Ethoxy-2-phenylethanol	24.2 ⎫	150
		Phenylethylene glycol	… ⎭	
	Ethyl (+)-2-ethoxy-2-phenylacetate	(+)-2-Ethoxy-2-phenylethanol	54	150
C₁₂H₁₇NO₂	Ethyl ester DL-N-methylphenylalanine	N-Methyl-DL-phenylalaninol	84	119
	Ethyl 2-benzylaminopropionate,	2-Benzylamino-1-propanol	87	151
			45	152
C₁₂H₁₈O₄	Ethyl 8-methylnon-7-ene-2,4-dione-1-oate	8-Methylnona-4,7-diene-1,2-diol	68	153
C₁₂H₂₀O₂	Ethyl 4,7-dimethylocta-3,7-dienoate	4,7-Dimethylocta-3,7-dien-1-ol	83	154

(Continued)

TABLE XXXVIII (*Continued*)

	Ester	Product	% Yield	Ref.
$C_{12}H_{20}O_2$ (*contd.*)	Ethyl 3,5,5-trimethylhepta-2,6-dienoate	3,5,5-Trimethylhepta-2,6-dien-1-ol	94	155
	2,6-Dimethyl-3-carbethoxyhepta-1,5-diene	2,6-Dimethyl-3-hydroxymethylhepta-1,5-diene	91	155
	Ethyl geranate	Geraniol	... }	136
		Nerol	... }	
$C_{12}H_{20}O_4$	Methyl *cis*-(2-methyl-2-carbomethoxy-cyclohexyl)acetate	*cis*-(2-Methyl-2-carbomethoxycyclohexyl)-ethanol	53[156]	157
		cis-(2-Methyl-2-hydroxymethylcyclohexyl)-ethanol	80[158]	157
$C_{12}H_{21}NO_3$	Ethyl N,N-pentamethyleneglutaramate	5-Piperidino-1-pentanol	75	95
$C_{12}H_{22}O_4$	Ethyl hydrogen sebacate	1,10-Decanediol	.....	98
			91	99
	Diethyl 2-methyl-2-*n*-butylmalonate	2-Methyl-2-*n*-butyl-1,3-propanediol	60.5	96
	Diethyl 2-ethyl-2-isopropylmalonate	2-Ethyl-2-isopropyl-1,3-propanediol	29.4	96
	Diethyl 2-*sec*-butylsuccinate	2-*sec*-Butyl-1,4-butanediol	96	141
	Diethyl 2-isobutylsuccinate	2-Isobutyl-1,4-butanediol	88	141
	Diethyl 3,3-dimethyladipate	3,3-Dimethyl-1,6-hexanediol	85	100
$C_{12}H_{22}O_6$	Di-*n*-butyl L-tartrate	L-Threitol	32[30,159]	160
			90[30,161]	160
$C_{12}H_{23}NO_2$	Butyl 3-(1-pyrrolidyl)butyrate	3-(1-Pyrrolidyl)-1-butanol	74.6	68
$C_{12}H_{24}O_2$	Ethyl 2-methylpelargonate	2-Methyl-1-nonanol	95.7	56
	Ethyl 4-methylpelargonate	4-Methyl-1-nonanol	90.2	56
	Ethyl 6-methylpelargonate	6-Methyl-1-nonanol	93	56
	Ethyl 7-methylpelargonate	7-Methyl-1-nonanol	96.3	56
$C_{13}H_{12}O_4$	Methyl 3-hydroxy-2-naphthylglycolate	3-Hydroxy-2-naphthylethylene glycol	100	162
$C_{13}H_{13}NO_2$	Ethyl 2-(2-quinolyl)acetate	2-(2-Quinolyl)ethanol	87	163
	Ethyl 2-(4-quinolyl)acetate	2-(4-Quinolyl)ethanol	94	164
$C_{13}H_{14}O_4$	Ethyl 4-acetoxycinnamate	4-Hydroxycinnamyl alcohol	84	147
$C_{13}H_{15}NO_2$	Ethyl 2-(1-methyl-3-indolyl)acetate	2-(1-Methyl-3-indolyl)ethanol	72	142

Formula	Ester	Alcohol	Yield	Ref.
$C_{13}H_{15}NO_4$	Ethyl 2-acetamidobenzoylacetate	DL-*erythro*-1-Phenyl-2-acetamido-1,3-propanediol	...[38]	165
$C_{13}H_{16}O_3$	Ethyl 2-benzylacetoacetate	2-Benzyl-1,3-butanediol	70	22
$C_{13}H_{16}O_4$	Ethyl homophthalate	2-Hydroxyethylbenzyl alcohol	91	166
$C_{13}H_{16}O_5$	Diethyl 2-phenoxymalonate	2-Phenoxy-1,3-propanediol	95	167
$C_{13}H_{22}O_2$	Ethyl 3,6,7-trimethylocta-2,6-dienoate	3,6,7-Trimethylocta-2,6-dien-1-ol (6-methylgeraniol)	...	168
$C_{13}H_{22}O_4$	3-Carbethoxy-4,4-dimethylhex-5-en-2-one-2-ethylene ketal	3-Hydroxymethyl-4,4-dimethylhex-5-en-2-one-2-ethylene ketal	82[124]	169
$C_{13}H_{22}O_6$	Triethyl methanetriacetate	3-Hydroxyethyl-1,5-pentanediol	70	170
$C_{13}H_{33}NO_2$	Ethyl 2-(1-quinolizidyl)acetate	2-(1-Quinolizidyl)ethanol	97	171
$C_{13}H_{33}NO_3$	Ethyl N,N-pentamethyleneadipamate	6-Piperidino-1-hexanol	...	95
$C_{13}H_{23}Cl_3O_2$	Methyl 12,12,12-trichlorododecanoate	12,12,12-Trichloro-1-dodecanol	97	172
$C_{13}H_{24}O_2$	Ethyl undec-10-enoate	10-Undecan-1-ol	75	102
$C_{13}H_{24}O_4$	Ethyl azelate	1,9-Nonanediol	40.5	102
	Diethyl 2,2-di-*n*-propylmalonate	2,2-Di-*n*-propyl-1,3-propanediol	96	96
	Diethyl 2-[2-(3-methylbutyl)]succinate	2-[2-(3-Methylbutyl)]-1,4-butanediol	85	141
$C_{13}H_{24}N_2O_4$	Ethyl 2,3-dimorpholinopropionate	2,3-Dimorpholino-1-propanol	...	173
$C_{13}H_{26}O_2$	Methyl dodecanoate	1-Dodecanol	94	98
	Ethyl 2-methyldecanoate	2-Methyl-1-decanol	98.1	99
	Ethyl 4-methyldecanoate	4-Methyl-1-decanol	91.2	56
	Ethyl 6-methyldecanoate	6-Methyl-1-decanol	91	56
	Ethyl 9-methyldecanoate	9-Methyl-1-decanol	90	56
$C_{13}H_{26}O_3$	Methyl 11-methoxyundecanoate	11-Methoxy-1-undecanol	...	174
$C_{13}H_{28}N_2O_2$	Ethyl 2,3-di-(diethylamino)propionate	2,3-Di-(diethylamino)-1-propanol	...	173
$C_{14}H_{14}O_6$	Methyl 3,4-diacetoxycinnamate	3,4-Dihydroxycinnamyl alcohol	...[23]	146
$C_{14}H_{16}O_3$	Methyl 2-(6-methoxy-3,4-dihydro-1-naphthyl)acetate	2-(6-Methoxy-3,4-dihydro-1-naphthyl)-ethanol	90	175

(Continued)

TABLE XXXVIII (Continued)

	Ester	Product	% Yield	Ref.
$C_{14}H_{16}O_5$	Ethyl 3-methoxy-4-acetoxycinnamate (ethyl acetoferulate)	Coniferyl alcohol	$73.7, 51^{23}$ / $....^{176}$ / $42.6, 67.3^{23}$	146 / 146 / 177
$C_{14}H_{16}ClNO_2$	Ethyl 3-acetoxy-4-methoxycinnamate	3-Hydroxy-4-methoxycinnamyl alcohol	....	146
	Ethyl 2-phenyl-2-cyano-5-chlorovalerate	2-Phenyl-2-cyano-5-chloro-1-pentanol	100	178
$C_{14}H_{18}O_5$	Ethyl 2-acetoxy-3-benzyloxypropionate-1-C^{14}	1-Benzyloxy-2,3-propanediol-3-C^{14}	....	179
	Ethyl o-toloxymalonate	2-o-Toloxy-1,3-propanediol	60	180
	Ethyl m-toloxymalonate	2-m-Toloxy-1,3-propanediol	92	180
	Ethyl p-toloxymalonate	2-p-Toloxy-1,3-propanediol	68	180
$C_{14}H_{19}NO_4$	Diethyl 2-(2'-pyridyl)ethylmalonate	2-Hydroxymethyl-4-(2'-pyridyl)-1-butanol	24 / 53	181 / 182
$C_{14}H_{20}O_2$	Ethyl 2-(1-methyl-4-isopropylphenyl)-acetate	2-(1-Methyl-4-isopropylphenyl)ethanol	$66, 80^{124}$ / 0^{184}	183 / 183
$C_{14}H_{22}O_4$	1,3-Dimethyldicarbethoxycyclohexene	1,3-Dimethyl-di-(hydroxymethyl)cyclohexene	48.3	96
$C_{14}H_{24}O_4$	Diethyl 2-cyclohexylsuccinate	2-Cyclohexyl-1,4-butanediol	90	141
$C_{14}H_{24}O_6$	Triethyl ethane-1,1,1-triacetate	1,1,1-Tris-(2-hydroxyethyl)ethane	62^{185}	186
		1,1,1-Tris-(2-hydroxyethyl)ethane	$12]^{187}$	186
		4-Methyl-4-(2-hydroxyethyl)tetrahydropyran	$49]$	
$C_{14}H_{25}NO_2$	Ethyl 3-(1-quinolizidyl)propionate	3-(1-Quinolizidyl)-1-propanol	93	171
$C_{14}H_{25}N_3O_6S$	Diethyl glutathione	Tripeptide diol	$30^{30}, 44^{142}$	143
$C_{14}H_{26}O_4$	Diethyl 2-ethyl-2-(1-methylbutyl)malonate	2-Ethyl-2-(1-methylbutyl)-1,3-propanediol	62	96
	Diethyl sebacate	1,10-Decanediol	93 / 80^{30}	102 / 188
$C_{14}H_{26}O_6$	Dimethyl 3,3,6,6-tetramethylsuberate	3,3,6,6-Tetramethyl-1,8-octanediol	74.5	189
	Di-n-amyl L-tartrate	L-Threitol	$....^{30}$	160
	Diethyl 2-(3,3-diethoxy-1-propyl)malonate	2-(3,3-Diethoxy-1-propyl)-1,3-propanediol	33.2	190

Formula	Ester	Alcohol		Ref
C$_{14}$H$_{28}$O$_2$	Ethyl 2-methylundecanoate	2-Methyl-1-undecanol	97.3	56
C$_{15}$H$_{16}$O$_2$	Ethyl 2-(5-methyl-1-naphthyl)acetate	2-(5-Methyl-1-naphthyl)ethanol	92.8	191
	Methyl 2-(2,5-dimethyl-1-naphthyl)acetate	2-(2,5-Dimethyl-1-naphthyl)ethanol	86	192
C$_{15}$H$_{16}$Cl$_2$N$_2$O$_7$	Ethyl 2-dichloroacetamido-3-acetoxy-3-p-nitrophenylpropionate	2-Dichloroacetamido-3-p-nitrophenyl-1,3-propanediol (chloramphenicol)	....	85
C$_{15}$H$_{17}$NO$_3$	Ethyl 1-benzyl-5-oxo-2-pyrroline-2-acetate	1-Benzylpyrrolidine-2-ethanol	47[193]	194
C$_{15}$H$_{17}$NO$_4$	Ethyl indole-2-carbethoxy-3-acetate	2-Hydroxymethyl-3-(2-hydroxyethyl)indole	90	195
C$_{15}$H$_{18}$O$_5$	Ethyl 3-ethoxy-4-acetoxycinnamate	3-Ethoxy-4-hydroxycinnamyl alcohol	....	146
C$_{15}$H$_{18}$O$_6$	Ethyl 3,5-dimethoxy-4-acetoxycinnamate (ethyl acetylsinapate)	3,5-Dimethoxy-4-hydroxycinnamyl alcohol (sinapyl alcohol)	40–47 55–58	196 197 198
C$_{15}$H$_{19}$NO$_5$	Ethyl 2-acetamido-3-acetoxy-3-phenylpropionate	2-Acetamido-1-phenyl-1,3-propanediol	....[199]	126
	Ethyl threo-2-acetamido-3-acetoxy-3-phenylpropionate	threo-1-Phenyl-1-acetoxy-2-acetamido-1,3-propanediol	58	127
C$_{15}$H$_{20}$O$_2$	Methyl 2-(2,5-dimethyl-1,2,3,4-tetrahydro-1-naphthyl)acetate	2-(2,5-Dimethyl-1,2,3,4-tetrahydro-1-naphthyl)ethanol	92	192
	Ethyl 5-benzosuberylacetate	2-(5-Benzosuberyl)ethanol	95[193]	200
C$_{15}$H$_{20}$O$_4$	Diethyl 2-ethyl-2-phenylmalonate	2-Ethyl-2-phenyl-1,3-propanediol	45	96
C$_{15}$H$_{20}$O$_4$S	Diethyl 2-ethyl-2-phenylmercaptomalonate	2-Ethyl-2-phenylmercapto-1,3-propanediol	40	96
C$_{15}$H$_{20}$O$_5$	Diethyl 2-ethyl-2-phenoxymalonate	2-Ethyl-2-phenoxy-1,3-propanediol	27.6	96
C$_{15}$H$_{21}$NO$_4$	Ethyl 2-hydroxy-3-morpholino-3-phenyl-propionate	3-Phenyl-3-morpholino-1,2-propanediol	53	201
C$_{15}$H$_{22}$O$_3$	Ethyl 2,2-diethyl-3-hydroxy-3-phenyl-propionate	2,2-Diethyl-1-phenyl-1,3-propanediol	80	96
C$_{15}$H$_{27}$NO$_2$	Ethyl 2-decyl-2-cyanoacetate	2-Decyl-3-amino-1-propanol	....	202,203
C$_{15}$H$_{28}$O$_4$	Diethyl 2,2-di-n-butylmalonate	2,2-Di-n-butyl-1,3-propanediol	48	96
	Diethyl 2-octylmalonate	2-Octyl-1,3-propanediol	....	203
	Diethyl 2-n-heptylsuccinate	2-n-Heptyl-1,4-butanediol	93.3	141

(Continued)

TABLE XXXVIII (*Continued*)

	Ester	Product	% Yield	Ref.
$C_{15}H_{28}N_2O_2$	Ethyl 2,3-dipiperidinopropionate	2,3-Dipiperidino-1-propanol	....	173
$C_{15}H_{30}O_2$	Ethyl 5-methyldodecanoate	5-Methyl-1-dodecanol	90.8	56
	Ethyl 6-methyldodecanoate	6-Methyl-1-dodecanol	88.6	56
	Ethyl 7-methyldodecanoate	7-Methyl-1-dodecanol	89.4	56
	Ethyl 8-methyldodecanoate	8-Methyl-1-dodecanol	91.6	56
	Ethyl 9-methyldodecanoate	9-Methyl-1-dodecanol	92.4	56
	Ethyl 10-methyldodecanoate	10-Methyl-1-dodecanol	92.1	56
	Ethyl 11-methyldodecanoate	11-Methyl-1-dodecanol	94	56
$C_{16}H_{16}O_2$	Ethyl diphenylacetate	2,2-Diphenylethanol	82	204
			98	205,206
$C_{16}H_{16}O_3$	Ethyl benzilate	1,1-Diphenylethylene glycol	86.4	205
	Ethyl 2-phenoxy-2-phenylacetate	2-Phenoxy-2-phenylethanol	84	207
$C_{16}H_{19}NO_3$	Ethyl 1-benzyl-3-methyl-5-oxo-2-pyrroline-2-acetate	1-Benzyl-3-methylpyrrolidine-2-ethanol	59	194
$C_{16}H_{20}O_8$	Methyl 2,3-diacetoxy-3-(3,4-dimethoxyphenyl)propionate	1-(3,4-Dimethoxyphenyl)-1,2,3-propanetriol	70	208
$C_{16}H_{23}NO_3$	Ethyl 2-hydroxy-3-piperidino-3-phenylpropionate	3-Piperidino-3-phenyl-1,2-propanediol	60	201
$C_{16}H_{24}O_2$	Methyl β-ionylideneacetate	2-(β-Ionylidene)ethanol	....	209
$C_{16}H_{26}O_2$	Methyl ester allobicyclofarnesylic acid	Allobicyclofarnesol, allophanate m.p. 187-190°	....	210
	Methyl ester allobicyclofarnesylic acid	Allobicyclofarnesol, allophanate m.p. 177-178°	....	210
	Methyl ester allobicyclofarnesylic acid	Allobicyclofarnesol, allophanate m.p. 141-145°	....	210
$C_{16}H_{28}O_3$	1,3,7-Tetramethyl-3-carbomethoxymethyl-2-oxabicyclo[4.4.0]decane	1,3,7,7-Tetramethyl-3-(hydroxyethyl)-2-oxabicyclo[4.4.0]decane	98	138
$C_{16}H_{30}O_4$	Diethyl dodecan-1,12-dioate	1,12-Dodecanediol	98	211
$C_{17}H_{16}O_3$	Ethyl 3-phenoxycinnamate[17]	3-Phenoxycinnamyl alcohol[17]	90	212

Formula	Ester	Alcohol		
$C_{17}H_{16}N_2O_3$	Ethyl 2-phenylhydrazinobenzoyl acetate	Benzaldehyde phenylhydrazone	45	110
$C_{17}H_{18}O_2$	Ethyl 3,3-diphenylpropionate	3,3-Diphenyl-1-propanol	83.8	205
$C_{17}H_{19}NO_2$	Ethyl 2-benzylamino-2-phenylacetate	2-Benzylamino-2-phenylethanol	60	213
$C_{17}H_{21}NO_4$	Ethyl 1-benzyl-3-methoxymethyl-5-oxo-2-pyrroline-2-acetate	1-Benzyl-3-methoxymethylpyrrolidine-2-ethanol	41	194
	Ethyl 1-benzyl-4-methoxymethyl-5-oxo-2-pyrroline-2-acetate	1-Benzyl-4-methoxymethylpyrrolidine-2-ethanol	73	194
$C_{17}H_{21}BrO_6$	Methyl 5-bromo-7,8-dimethoxy-2-tetralone-1-acetate 2-ethylene ketal	1-(2-Hydroxyethyl)-5-bromo-7,8-dimethoxy-2-tetralone 2-ethylene ketal	86	214
$C_{17}H_{24}N_2O_5$	Methyl ester carbobenzoxyglycyl-L-leucine	N-(2-Methylaminoethyl)-L-leucinol	...⎫[30]	105
		Benzyl alcohol	...⎭	
$C_{17}H_{25}NO_3$	ω-Carbomethoxypelargonanilide	10-Anilino-1-decanol	63^{215}	216
$C_{17}H_{26}O_2$	Methyl 6-(2',6',6'-trimethyl-1'-cyclo-hexenyl)-4-methylhexa-2,4-dien-1-oate	6-(2',6',6'-Trimethyl-1'-cyclohexenyl)-4-methylhexa-2,4-dien-1-ol	...	217
	Ethyl β-ionylidene acetate	2-(β-Ionylidene)ethanol[218]	75	219
			85	220
			83	221,222
				32,33,
				223,224
			100	225
	Ethyl β-ionylidene acetate ⎫[17]	2-(β-Ionylidene)ethanol ⎫[17,218]	...	
	Isomeric ester	Isomeric carbinol	100	32
	Ethyl retroionylidene acetate	2-(Retroionylidene)ethanol	91	226
	Ethyl α-ionylidene acetate	2-(α-Ionylidene)ethanol	94	227
$C_{17}H_{28}O_2$	Ethyl 3,8,11-trimethyldodeca-2,7,11-trienoate	3,8,11-Trimethyldodeca-2,7,11-trien-1-ol	79	154
	Ethyl 3,7,11-trimethyldodeca-2,6,10-trienoate	3,7,11-Trimethyldodeca-2,6,10-trien-1-ol (farnesol)	...	210
	Ethyl 3-methyl-5-(2',6',6'-trimethyl-1'-cyclohexenyl)pent-2-en-1-oate	3-Methyl-5-(2',6',6'-trimethyl-1'-cyclohexenyl)-pent-2-en-1-ol	...	210

(Continued)

TABLE XXXVIII (Continued)

Ester	Product	% Yield	Ref.
C₁₇H₂₈O₃			
Ethyl 3-methyl-5-(2',6',6'-trimethylcyclo-hex-2-en-1-yl)pent-4-en-3-ol-1-oate	3-Methyl-5-(2',6',6'-trimethylcyclohex-2-en-1-yl)pent-4-en-1,3-diol	…	210
Ethyl β-ionolacetate	2-(β-Ionol)ethanol	100	32
		89	226
C₁₇H₃₁NO₂			
Ethyl 2-dodecyl-2-cyanoacetate	2-Dodecyl-3-amino-1-propanol	…	203
C₁₇H₃₂O₂			
Ethyl 3,7,11-trimethyldodeca-2-enoate	3,7,11-Trimethyldodeca-2-en-1-ol	…	32
C₁₇H₃₂O₄			
Diethyl 2-decylmalonate	2-Decyl-1,3-propanediol	…	203
C₁₇H₃₄O₂			
Ethyl 5-methylmyristate	5-Methyl-1-tetradecanol	91.5	56
Ethyl 6-methylmyristate	6-Methyl-1-tetradecanol	94.5	56
Ethyl 7-methylmyristate	7-Methyl-1-tetradecanol	93.4	56
Ethyl 8-methylmyristate	8-Methyl-1-tetradecanol	85.5	56
Ethyl 9-methylmyristate	9-Methyl-1-tetradecanol	84	56
Ethyl 10-methylmyristate	10-Methyl-1-tetradecanol	93.4	56
Ethyl 11-methylmyristate	11-Methyl-1-tetradecanol	93.2	56
Ethyl 12-methylmyristate	12-Methyl-1-tetradecanol	84.1	56
Ethyl 13-methylmyristate	13-Methyl-1-tetradecanol	90	56
C₁₈H₂₂O₂			
Methyl 3,7-dimethyl-9-(1'-cyclohexenyl)-nona-2,4,6-trien-8-yn-1-oate (isomer A)	3,7-Dimethyl-9-(1'-cyclohexenyl)nona-2,4,6-trien-8-yn-1-ol (isomer A)	50	228
Methyl 3,7-dimethyl-9-(1'-cyclohexenyl)-nona-2,4,6-trien-8-yn-1-oate (isomer B)	3,7-Dimethyl-9-(1'-cyclohexenyl)nona-2,4,6-trien-8-yn-1-ol (isomer B)	94	228
Methyl 5-methyl-7-(2',6',6'-trimethyl-cyclohexa-1,3-dien-1-yl)hepta-2,4,6-trien-1-oate	5-Methyl-7-(2',6',6'-trimethylcyclohexa-1,3-dien-1-yl)hepta-2,4,6-trien-1-ol	50	229
C₁₈H₂₅NO₅			
Methyl tetrahydromorphilactonate	Tetrahydromorphitetrol	70[30]	230
Methyl tetrahydro-α-isomorphilactonate	Tetrahydro-α-isomorphitetrol	70[30]	230
C₁₈H₂₆O₂			
Methyl 5-methyl-7-(2',6',6'-trimethyl-1'-cyclohexenyl)hepta-2,4,6-trien-1-oate	5-Methyl-7-(2',6',6'-trimethyl-1'-cyclo-hexenyl)hepta-2,4,6-trien-1-ol	76	222
		75	229

Formula	Ester	Alcohol / amine	M.p.	Ref.
C$_{18}$H$_{27}$NO$_2$	Ethyl 3-(3-phenyl-1-ethyl-3-piperidyl)-propionate	3-(3-Phenyl-1-ethyl-3-piperidyl)-1-propanol	82	231
C$_{18}$H$_{30}$O$_2$	4,6,10-Tetramethyl-5-(2-carbomethoxyethyl)bicyclo[4.4.0]-3-decene	4,6,10-Tetramethyl-5-(3-hydroxypropyl)-bicyclo[4.4.0]-3-decene	70	232
C$_{18}$H$_{30}$N$_2$O$_2$	Ethyl 2-dodecyl-2,4-dicyanobutyrate	2-Dodecyl-2-aminomethyl-5-amino-1-pentanol	...	203
C$_{18}$H$_{30}$O$_4$	Dimethyl 3,3,6,6-di-(tetramethylene)octan-1,8-dioate	3,3,6,6-Di-(tetramethylene)-1,8-octanediol	87	189
C$_{18}$H$_{34}$O$_4$	Diethyl 2-n-decylsuccinate	2-n-Decyl-1,4-butanediol	94	141
C$_{18}$H$_{36}$O$_2$	Ethyl palmitate	1-Hexadecanol	...	98
			98	99
C$_{19}$H$_{20}$O$_4$	Diethyl 2,2-diphenylmalonate	2,2-Diphenyl-1,3-propanediol	97	233
C$_{19}$H$_{22}$O$_2$	Ethyl 3,7-dimethyl-9-phenylnona-2,4,6,8-tetraen-1-oate	3,7-Dimethyl-9-phenylnona-2,4,6,8-tetraen-1-ol	40	132
C$_{19}$H$_{24}$O$_2$	Ethyl 3,7-dimethyl-9-(1'-cyclohexenyl)nona-2,4,6-trien-8-yn-1-oate[17]	3,7-Dimethyl-9-(1'-cyclohexenyl)nona-2,4,6-trien-8-yn-1-ol[17]	96	228
C$_{19}$H$_{24}$O$_3$	Ethyl 2,2-dimethyl-3-(2-naphthyl)valerate	2,2-Dimethyl-3-(2-naphthyl)-1-pentanol	...	234
	Methyl 2,2-dimethyl-3-(6-methoxy-2-naphthyl)valerate	2,2-Dimethyl-3-(6-methoxy-2-naphthyl)-1-pentanol	...	234,235
C$_{19}$H$_{32}$O$_2$	Methyl linolenate	Linolenyl alcohol	93.5	236
C$_{19}$H$_{34}$O$_2$	Methyl linoleate	Linoleyl alcohol	93	236
C$_{19}$H$_{35}$NO$_2$	Ethyl 2-tetradecyl-2-cyanoacetate	2-Tetradecyl-3-amino-1-propanol	...	203
C$_{19}$H$_{35}$NO$_4$	Methyl 2-oximino-3-ketooctadecanoate	2-Amino-1,3-octadecanediol	...[237]	238
		"Mixture of long chain amines"	...	239
C$_{19}$H$_{36}$O$_2$	Methyl oleate	Oleyl alcohol	...	98
			86	99
	Methyl petroselinate	Octadec-6-en-1-ol	67	240
C$_{19}$H$_{36}$O$_4$	Diethyl 2-dodecylmalonate	2-Dodecyl-1,3-propanediol	...	203
			89	241
C$_{19}$H$_{39}$NO$_4$	Methyl 2-aminooctadecan-3-ol-1-oate	2-Amino-1,3-octadecanediol	45[215]	239
C$_{20}$H$_{23}$NO$_3$	Ethyl 2-acetamido-2-benzyl-3-phenyl-propionate	2-Acetamido-2-benzyl-3-phenyl-1-propanol	95[3]	82

(Continued)

TABLE XXXVIII (Continued)

Formula	Ester	Product	% Yield	Ref.
$C_{20}H_{25}N_3O_3$	Methyl ester dihydrolysergyl-L-alanine	L-N-(6-Methyl-ergolinyl-(8)-methyl)alaninol	...[142]	242
$C_{20}H_{34}O_4$	Dimethyl 3,3,6,6-di-(pentamethylene)octane-1,8-dioate	3,3,6,6-Di-(pentamethylene)-1,8-octanediol	94.5	189
$C_{20}H_{38}O_4$	Diethyl 2-n-dodecylsuccinate	2-n-Dodecyl-1,4-butanediol	95	141
$C_{21}H_{19}N_3O_4$	Methyl ester dibenzoyl-L-histidine	Monobenzoyl-L-histidinol	44	243
$C_{21}H_{24}O_4$	1,3-Bis-(4-carbomethoxymethylphenyl)-propane	1,3-Bis-[4-(2-hydroxyethyl)phenyl]propane	96	244
$C_{21}H_{28}O_2$	Methyl 3,7-dimethyl-9-(2',6',6'-trimethyl-cyclohexa-1',3'-dien-1'-yl)nona-2,4,6,8-tetraen-1-oate (methyl ester vitamin A₂ acid)	3,7-Dimethyl-9-(2',6',6'-trimethylcyclohexa-1',3'-dien-1'-yl)nona-2,4,6,8-tetraen-1-ol (vitamin A₂)	...	245
	crystalline Methyl ester vitamin A₂ acid	Vitamin A₂	...	246
	non-crystalline Methyl ester vitamin A₂ acid	Vitamin A₂	...	246
$C_{21}H_{30}O_2$	Methyl 3,7-dimethyl-9-(2',6',6'-trimethyl-1'-cyclohexenyl)nona-2,4,6,8-tetraen-1-oate (methyl ester vitamin A acid)	Vitamin A[215]	...	209
			95	247
			66	248
$C_{21}H_{34}O_2$	Methyl ester allotricyclo-ω-geranylgeranium acid	Allotricyclo-ω-geranylgeranium alcohol	...	249
$C_{22}H_{40}O_4$	Diethyl 2-tetradecylmalonate	2-Tetradecyl-1,3-propanediol	...	203
$C_{22}H_{26}O_4$	Diethyl 2-(2,2'-dimethylbenzhydryl)malonate	2-(2,2'-Dimethylbenzhydryl)-1,3-propanediol	95.5	250
$C_{22}H_{26}O_6$	Methyl β-(2-methoxy-4-propylphenoxy)-3,4-dimethoxycinnamate	β-(2-Methoxy-4-propylphenoxy)-3,4-dimethoxycinnamyl alcohol	81 ⎫	212
		3,4-Dimethoxycinnamyl alcohol	8.3 ⎬	
		2-Methoxy-4-propylphenol	9.7 ⎭	
$C_{22}H_{27}NO_3$	Ethyl 2,2-diphenyl-4-(N-morpholino)butyrate	2,2-Diphenyl-4-(N-morpholino)-1-butanol	85	251
$C_{22}H_{28}N_4O_4$	Ethyl ester dibenzoylarginine	Dibenzoylargininol	...[30]	58

Formula	Ester	Product	Yield	Ref.
$C_{22}H_{29}N_3O_3$	Methyl ester dihydrolysergyl-L-valine	L-N-(6-Methyl-ergolinyl-(8)-methyl)valinol	...	242
	Methyl ester dihydrolysergyl-D-valine	D-N-(6-Methyl-ergolinyl-(8)-methyl)valinol	...	242
$C_{22}H_{30}O_2$	Ethyl 3,7-dimethyl-9-(2',6',6'-trimethyl-1'-cyclohexenyl)nona-2,4,6-trien-8-yn-1-oate	3,7-Dimethyl-9-(2',6',6'-trimethyl-1'-cyclo-hexenyl)nona-2,4,6-trien-8-yn-1-ol (8,9-dehydrovitamin A)	24	252
$C_{22}H_{32}O_2$	Ethyl 3,7-dimethyl-9-(2',6',6'-trimethyl-1'-cyclohexenyl)nona-2,4,6,8-tetraen-1-oate (ethyl ester vitamin A acid)	Vitamin A[218]	99 / ... / 98 / 100 / ...	32 / 33,224 / 223 / 247 / 253
	Ethyl 3-methylene-7-methyl-9-(2',6',6'-trimethyl-1'-cyclohexenyl)nona-4,6,8-trien-1-oate (ethyl ester vitamin A₃ acid)	Vitamin A₃[218]	...	32,254
$C_{22}H_{39}NO_4$	Diethyl 2-n-dodecyl-2-(2-cyanoethyl)-malonate	4,4-Di-(hydroxymethyl)hexadecylamine	...	203
$C_{22}H_{42}O_2$	Ethyl 3,7,11,15-tetramethylhexadec-2-en-1-oate	3,7,11,15-Tetramethylhexadec-2-en-1-ol (phytol)	...	203
$C_{22}H_{42}O_4$	Dimethyl ester perhydrocrocetin	2,6,11,15-Tetramethyl-2,16-hexadecanediol (crocetane-1,16-diol)	96.6	255
	Diethyl octadecan-1,18-dioate	1,8-Octadecanediol	...	256
			88	257
			70	258
$C_{23}H_{26}N_2O_7$	α-Benzyl ester ethyl N-carbobenzoxy-β-DL-aspartylglycine	N-(2-Hydroxyethyl)-3-amino-4-hydroxy-butyramide	51[142]	259
$C_{23}H_{44}O_4$	Diethyl nonadecan-1,19-dioate	1,19-Nonadecanediol	90	260
$C_{24}H_{25}NO_7S_2$	Methyl ester N-(p-toluenesulfonyl)-L-tyrosine	N-(p-Toluenesulfonyl)-L-tyrosinol	81.5[30]	261
$C_{24}H_{28}N_2O_7$	α-Benzyl ester ethyl N-carbobenzoxy-glutamyl-α-glycine	N-(2-Hydroxyethyl)-4-amino-5-hydroxy-valeramide	11.2–40.3[142]	143

(Continued)

TABLE XXXVIII (*Continued*)

Ester	Product	% Yield	Ref.
Dimethyl 3,3,6,6,9,9,12,12-octamethyl-tetradecan-1,14-dioate	3,3,6,6,9,9,12,12-Octamethyl-1,14-tetradecanediol	98	189
Dimethyl ester perhydrobixin	4,8,13,17-Tetramethyl-1,20-eicosanediol (bixane-1,20-diol)	90	255
Diethyl *n*-hexacosan-1,26-dioate	1,26-*n*-Hexacosanediol	51	257
Methyl ester Pyrrochlorin	Pyrrochlorin propanol	...[263]	262
Methyl ester Pyrroporphyrin	Pyrroporphyrin propanol	...[263]	262
Dimethyl 3,3,6,6,9,9,12,12-tetra(tetramethylene)tetradecane-1,14-dioate	3,3,6,6,9,9,12,12-Tetra(tetramethylene)-1,14-tetradecanediol	97	189
Methyl ester phylloporphyrin	Phylloporphyrin propanol	...[263]	262
Methyl ester mesophyllochlorin	Mesophyllochlorin propanol	...	262
Dimethyl 3,3,6,6,9,9,12,12-tetra(pentamethylene)tetradecan-1,14-dioate	3,3,6,6,9,9,12,12-Tetra(pentamethylene)-1,14-tetradecanediol	100	189
Tripalmitin	Cetyl alcohol	96	264
Triolein	Oleyl alcohol	87	264
Lecithin	Fatty alcohols	...	265
	Glycerol	...	
	Choline	...	

Chemical formulas of esters (first column): $C_{24}H_{46}O_4$, $C_{26}H_{50}O_4$, $C_{30}H_{58}O_4$, $C_{32}H_{36}N_4O_2$, $C_{32}H_{54}O_4$, $C_{33}H_{38}N_4O_2$, $C_{33}H_{40}N_4O_2$, $C_{36}H_{62}O_4$, $C_{51}H_{98}O_6$, $C_{57}H_{104}O_6$, ...

References—Table XXXVIII

[1]C. D. Wagner, D. P. Stevenson, and J. W. Otvos, *J. Am. Chem. Soc.*, 72, 5786 (1950); Document 3028, American Documentation Institute.

[2]C. E. Sroog, Chen Ming Chih, F. A. Short, and H. M. Woodburn, *J. Am. Chem. Soc.*, 71, 1710 (1949).

[3]Inverse addition.

[4]H. Schmid and K. Schmid, *Helv. Chim. Acta*, 35, 1879 (1952).

[5]W. Ried and F. Müller, *Chem. Ber.*, 85, 470 (1952).

[6]H. Felkin, *Bull. soc. chim. France*, [5] 18, 347 (1951).

[7]V. Lorber, M. Cook, and J. Meyer, *J. Biol. Chem.*, 181, 475 (1949).

[8]Reduction carried out in diethyl carbitol, decomposition with the monophenyl ether of ethylene glycol.

[9]J. D. Cox and H. S. Turner, *J. Chem. Soc.*, 1950, 3176.

[10]Reduction carried out with lithium aluminum hydride-t (LiAlT$_4$).

[11]K. E. Wilzbach and L. Kaplan, *J. Am. Chem. Soc.*, 72, 5795 (1950).

[12]P. Karrer, P. Portmann, and M. Suter, *Helv. Chim. Acta*, 31, 1617 (1948).

[13]R. F. Brown and N. van Gulick, *Abstracts of Papers*, 122nd Meeting American Chemical Society, Atlantic City, N. J., September 1952, p. 7M.

[14]E. T. McBee, W. F. Marzluff, and O. R. Pierce, *J. Am. Chem. Soc.*, 74, 444 (1952).

[15]E. Chargoff, C. Levine, C. Green, and J. Kream, *Experientia*, 6, 229 (1950).

[16]C. Fromageot, M. Jutisz, D. Meyer, and L. Pénasse, *Biochim. et Biophys. Acta*, 6, 283 (1950).

[17]Mixture of isomers.

[18]L. F. Hatch and J. J. D'Amico, *J. Am. Chem. Soc.*, 73, 4393 (1951).

[19]W. H. Urry and J. R. Eiszner, *ibid.*, 74, 5822 (1952).

[20]K. N. Campbell, J. O. Knobloch, and B. K. Campbell, *ibid.*, 72, 4380 (1950).

[21]H. L. Goering, S. J. Cristol, and K. Dittmar, *ibid.*, 70, 3314 (1948).

[22]E. Buchta and H. Bayer, *Ann.*, 573, 227 (1951).

[23]Isolated as benzoate.

[24]R. Barré and L. Favreau, *Compt. rend.*, 235, 1404 (1952).

[25]E. Larsson, *Trans. Chalmers Univ. Technol.*, Gothenburg, 94, 15 (1950).

[26]W. von E. Doering and R. W. Young, *J. Am. Chem. Soc.*, 74, 2997 (1952).

[27]Reduction carried out in diethyl carbitol, decomposition with butyl carbitol.

[28]W. G. Dauben and M. Gee, *J. Am. Chem. Soc.*, 74, 1078 (1952).

[29]B. Berkoz and B. F. Daubert, *ibid.*, 73, 2968 (1951).

[30]Reduction carried out in tetrahydrofuran.

[31]L. W. Trevoy and W. G. Brown, *J. Am. Chem. Soc.*, 71, 1675 (1949).

[32]Distillation Products, Inc., Brit. Pat. 633,711 (December 19, 1949).

[33]J. D. Cawley, C. D. Robeson, E. M. Shantz, L. Weisler, and J. G. Baxter, U. S. Pat. 2,576,103 (November 27, 1951).

[34]F. K. Kawahara and H. J. Dutton, *J. Am. Oil Chemists' Soc.*, 29, 372 (1952).

[35]F. K. Kawahara, H. J. Dutton, and J. C. Cowan, *ibid.*, 29, 633 (1952).

[36]R. W. Freedman and E. I. Becker, *J. Am. Chem. Soc.*, 73, 2366 (1951).

[37]C. J. Morel and W. G. Stoll, *Helv. Chim. Acta*, 35, 2561 (1952).

[38]Isolated as diacetate.

[39]A. Lardon and T. Reichstein, *Helv. Chim. Acta*, 32, 2003 (1949).

[40]F. Šorm and J. Arient, *Collection Czech. Chem. Communs.*, 15, 175 (1950).

[41]P. Karrer, P. Portmann, and M. Suter, *Helv. Chim. Acta*, 32, 1156 (1949).

[42]K. Eiter and O. Svierak, *Monatsh.*, 83, 1453 (1952).

[43]K. Hayes and G. Gever, *J. Org. Chem.*, 16, 269 (1951).

[44]Reduction carried out with lithium aluminum deuteride (LiAlD$_4$).

[45]F. H. Westheimer, H. F. Fisher, E. E. Conn, and V. Vennesland, *J. Am. Chem. Soc.*, *73*, 2403 (1951).

[46]T. L. Cairns, V. A. Engelhardt, H. L. Jackson, G. H. Kalb, and J. C. Sauer, *ibid.*, *74*, 5636 (1952).

[47]A. D. Mebane, *ibid.*, *74*, 5227 (1952).

[48]A. L. Henne and S. B. Richter, *ibid.*, *74*, 5420 (1952).

[49]A. J. Eusebi, E. V. Brown, and L. R. Cerecedo, *ibid.*, *71*, 2931 (1949).

[50]R. H. Wiley, O. H. Borum, and L. L. Bennett, Jr., *ibid.*, *71*, 2899 (1949).

[51]L. F. Hatch and G. E. Journeay, *Abstracts of Papers*, 121st Meeting American Chemical Society, Buffalo, N. Y., March 1952, p. 34K.

[52]N. Rabjohn, T. R. Hopkins, and R. C. Nagler, *J. Am. Chem. Soc.*, *74*, 3215 (1952).

[53]K. M. Mann and R. F. Nystrom, *ibid.*, *73*, 5894 (1951).

[54]D. I. Crandall and S. Gurin, *J. Biol. Chem.*, *181*, 829 (1949).

[55]J. R. Nunn, *J. Chem. Soc.*, *1951*, 1740.

[56]G. Weitzel and J. Wojahn, *Z. Physiol. Chem.*, *287*, 65 (1951); through M. Ferles and J. Rudinger, *Chem. Listy*, *47*, 119–123 (1953).

[57]P. Karrer and G. Aman, *Helv. Chim. Acta*, *33*, 302 (1950).

[58]A. Rhein and M. Jutisz, *Biochim. et Biophys. Acta*, *9*, 645 (1952).

[59]Isolated as oxalate.

[60]G. R. Clemo, R. Raper, and W. S. Short, *J. Chem. Soc.*, *1949*, 663.

[61]R. Adams and T. R. Govindachari, *J. Am. Chem. Soc.*, *72*, 158 (1950).

[62]M. Viscontini and C. Ebnöther, *Helv. Chim. Acta*, *34*, 116 (1951).

[63]A. P. Doerschuk, *J. Am. Chem. Soc.*, *73*, 821 (1951); *74*, 4202 (1952).

[64]L. I. Gidez and M. L. Karnovsky, *ibid.*, *74*, 2413 (1952).

[65]C. J. Martin, A. I. Schepartz, and B. F. Daubert, *ibid.*, *70*, 2601 (1948).

[66]R. Lukeš and J. Hofman, unpublished work; through J. Rudinger, M. Ferles and M. Protiva, *Chem. Listy*, *45*, 352 (1951).

[67]R. Paul and S. Tchelitcheff, *Bull. soc. chim. France*, [5] *18*, 550 (1951).

[68]R. B. Moffett, *J. Org. Chem.*, *14*, 862 (1949).

[69]W. B. Reid, Jr., U. S. Pat. 2,605,266 (July 29, 1952).

[70]P. Karrer and P. Portmann, *Helv. Chim. Acta*, *31*, 2088 (1948).

[71]R. A. Max and F. E. Deatherage, *J. Am. Oil Chemists' Soc.*, *28*, 110 (1951).

[72]R. Lukeš and J. Langthaler, unpublished work, through J. Rudinger, M. Ferles, and M. Protiva, *Chem. Listy*, *45*, 352 (1951).

[73]R. Lukeš and J. Langthaler, unpublished work, through M. Ferles and J. Rudinger, *Chem. Listy*, *47*, 120 (1953).

[74]Acetol isolated, after acid hydrolysis, as osazone from 2,4-dinitrophenylhydrazine.

[75]W. Swoboda, *Monatsh.*, *82*, 388 (1951).

[76]C. D. Hurd and W. H. Saunders, Jr., *J. Am. Chem. Soc.*, *74*, 5324 (1952).

[77]Reduction carried out at −70°.

[78]E. R. H. Jones, M. C. Whiting, and E. B. Bates, unpublished work, private communication.

[79]E. L. Eliel and J. P. Freeman, *J. Am. Chem. Soc.*, *74*, 923 (1952).

[80](a) Reduction carried out with one-half mole LAH; (b) acid hydrolysis; (c) base hydrolysis.

[81]37% racemized.

[82]H. Felkin, *Compt. rend.*, *230*, 304 (1950).

[83]M. C. Rebstock, G. W. Moersch, A. C. Moore, and J. M. Vandenbelt, *J. Am. Chem. Soc.*, *73*, 3666 (1951).

[84]Reduction carried out in a dioxane-ether mixture.
[85]C. F. Huebner and C. R. Scholz, *J. Am. Chem. Soc.,* 73, 2089 (1951).
[86]H. E. Carter and E. H. Flynn, U. S. Pat. 2,556,868 (June 12, 1951).
[87]Product from catalytic hydrogenation of ethyl phenylglyoxalate with Adams' platinum catalyst in acetic acid.
[88]J. D. Billimoria and N. F. Maclagan, *J. Chem. Soc.,* 1951, 3067.
[89]J. D. Billimoria and N. F. Maclagan, *Nature,* 167, 81 (1951); product erroneously formulated as 1-cyclohexylethylene glycol.
[90]M. Mousseron and M. Canet, *Bull. soc. chim. France,* [5] 19, 247 (1952).
[91]M. Mousseron, R. Jacquier, M. Mousseron-Canet, and R. Zagdoun, *ibid.,* [5] 19, 1042 (1952).
[92]M. S. Kharasch and G. Büchi, *J. Org. Chem.,* 14, 84 (1949).
[93]R. Lukeš, unpublished work, through J. Rudinger, M. Ferles, and M. Protiva, *Chem. Listy,* 45, 353 (1951).
[94]R. L. Frank and H. K. Hall, Jr., *J. Am. Chem. Soc.,* 72, 1645 (1950).
[95]A. W. D. Avison, *J. Applied Chem. (London),* 1, 469 (1951).
[96]H. L. Yale, E. J. Pribyl, W. Braker, J. Bernstein, and W. A. Lott, *J. Am. Chem. Soc.,* 72, 3716 (1950).
[97]E. Wiberg and M. Schmidt, *Z. Naturforsch.,* 6b, 171 (1951).
[98]H. I. Schlesinger and A. E. Finholt, U. S. Pat. 2,576,311 (November 27, 1951).
[99]R. F. Nystrom and W. G. Brown, *J. Am. Chem. Soc.,* 69, 1197 (1947).
[100]F. Šorm and M. Streibl, unpublished work, through M. Ferles and J. Rudinger, *Chem. Listy,* 47, 120 (1953).
[101]R. W. Fawcett and J. O. Harris, *Chemistry and Industry,* 1953, 18.
[102]W. F. Huber, *J. Am. Chem. Soc.,* 73, 2730 (1951).
[103]E. D. Clair, F. H. Clarke, W. A. Edminston, and K. Wiesner, *Can. J. Research,* 28B, 745 (1950).
[104]Isolated as tripicrate.
[105]P. Karrer and B. J. R. Nicolaus, *Helv. Chim. Acta,* 35, 1581 (1952).
[106]2-Methyl-3-hydroxypropionaldehyde isolated, after acid hydrolysis, as 2,4-dinitrophenylhydrazone.
[107]A. Dornow, G. Messwarb, and H. H. Frey, *Chem. Ber.,* 83, 445 (1950).
[108]I. Elphimoff-Felkin, H. Felkin, B. Tchoubar, and Z. Welvart, *Bull. soc. chim. France,* [5] 19, 252 (1952).
[109]M. Viscontini and K. Adank, *Helv. Chim. Acta,* 35, 1342 (1952).
[110]M. Viscontini, *ibid.,* 35, 1803 (1952).
[111]P. Karrer and P. Banerjea, *ibid.,* 32, 1692 (1949).
[112]S. Siegel and S. Coburn, *J. Am. Chem. Soc.,* 73, 5494 (1951).
[113]Reduction carried out in a tetrahydrofuran-ether mixture.
[114]A. Dornow and G. Winter, *Chem. Ber.,* 84, 307 (1951).
[115]G. Carrara, E. Pace, and G. Cristiani, *J. Am. Chem. Soc.,* 74, 4949 (1952).
[116]E. D. Bergmann, H. Bendas, and W. Taub, *J. Chem. Soc.,* 1951, 2673.
[117]D. W. Woolley, *J. Biol. Chem.,* 185, 293 (1950).
[118]W. J. Gensler and J. C. Rockett, *J. Am. Chem. Soc.,* 74, 4451 (1952).
[119]F. Wessely and W. Swoboda, *Monatsh.,* 82, 621 (1951).
[120]G. Carrara, F. M. Chiancone, V. D'Amato, E. Ginouhliac, C. Martinuzzi, and G. Weitnauer, *Gazz. chim. ital.,* 80, 709 (1950).
[121]J. Buchi, S. Contini, and R. Lieberherr, *Helv. Chim. Acta,* 34, 274 (1951).
[122]K. N. F. Shaw and S. W. Fox, *Abstracts of Papers,* 118th Meeting American Chemical Society, Chicago, Ill., September 1950, p. 28N.
[123]C. G. Alberti, B. Asero, B. Camerino, R. Sannicolo, and A. Vercellone, *La Chimica e l'Industria,* 10, 357 (1949).

[124]Reduction carried out in dioxane.
[125]H. Bendas and E. D. Bergmann, *Bull. Res. Council Israel,* 1, No. 1/2, 131 (1951).
[126]G. Carrara and G. Weitnauer, *Gazz. chim. ital.,* 79, 856 (1949).
[127]Lepetit, S. A., Brit. Pat. 679,028 (September 10, 1952).
[128]Isolated as sulfate.
[129]M. Viscontini and K. Adank, *Helv. Chim. Acta,* 33, 2251 (1950).
[130]Isolated as triacetyl derivative.
[131]F. A. Hochstein, *J. Am. Chem. Soc.,* 71, 305 (1949).
[132]B. C. L. Weedon and R. J. Woods, *J. Chem. Soc.,* 1951, 2687.
[133]M. Viscontini, J. Bally, and J. Meier, *Helv. Chim. Acta,* 35, 451 (1952).
[134]N. C. Deno and J. D. Johnston, *J. Org. Chem.,* 17, 1466 (1952).
[135]R. Lukeš and J. Hofman, unpublished work, through M. Ferles and J. Rudinger, *Chem. Listy,* 47, 121 (1953).
[136]G. I. Samokhvalov, M. A. Miropol'skaya, L. A. Vakulova, and N. A. Preobrazhenskii, *Doklady Akad. Nauk S.S.S.R.,* 84, 1179 (1952), through *Chem. Abstracts,* 47, 3277 (1953).
[137]R. Lukeš and V. Galík, *Chem. Listy,* in press, through M. Ferles and J. Rudinger, *Chem. Listy,* 47, 121 (1953).
[138]A. Caliezi, E. Lederer, and H. Schinz, *Helv. Chim. Acta,* 34, 879 (1951).
[139]R. E. Nystrom, unpublished work, through W. G. Brown, in *Organic Reactions,* vol. VI, p. 499.
[140]D. M. Hall, S. Mahboob, and E. E. Turner, *J. Chem. Soc.,* 1952, 149.
[141]C. G. Overberger and C. W. Roberts, *J. Am. Chem. Soc.,* 71, 3618 (1949).
[142]Reduction carried out in N-ethylmorpholine.
[143]P. Jollès and C. Fromageot, *Biochim. et. Biophys. Acta,* 9, 287 (1952).
[144]Pentan-4-one-1-ol isolated, after acid hydrolysis, as 2,4-dinitrophenylhydrazone.
[145]2-Hydroxymethylbutyraldehyde isolated, after acid hydrolysis, as 2,4-dinitrophenylhydrazone.
[146]C. F. H. Allen and J. R. Byers, Jr., U. S. Pat. 2,545,439 (March 20, 1951).
[147]K. Freudenberg and G. Gehrke, *Chem. Ber.,* 84, 443 (1951).
[148]K. Freudenberg and H. H. Hubner, *ibid.,* 85, 1181 (1952).
[149]P. Karrer and P. Portmann, *Helv. Chim. Acta,* 32, 1034 (1949).
[150]K. Mislow, *J. Am. Chem. Soc.,* 73, 3954 (1951).
[151]A. M. Akkerman, D. K. de Jongh, and H. Veldstra, *Rec. trav. chim.,* 70, 899 (1951).
[152]J. F. Kerwin, G. C. Hall, F. J. Milnes, I. H. Witt, R. A. McLean, E. Macko, E. J. Fellows, and G. E. Ullyot, *J. Am. Chem. Soc.,* 73, 4162 (1951).
[153]R. Helg and H. Schinz, *Helv. Chim. Acta,* 35, 2406 (1952).
[154]G. R. Clemo and B. K. Davison, *J. Chem. Soc.,* 1951, 447.
[155]K. Brack and H. Schinz, *Helv. Chim. Acta,* 34, 2009 (1951).
[156]Reduction carried out at −60 to −15°.
[157]W. E. Bachmann and A. S. Dreiding, *J. Am. Chem. Soc.,* 71, 3222 (1949).
[158]Reduction carried out at room temperature.
[159]Isolated as dibenzylidene derivative.
[160]H. Klosterman and F. Smith, *J. Am. Chem. Soc.,* 74, 5336 (1952).
[161]Isolated as tetraacetate.
[162]M. D. Soffer, R. A. Stewart, and G. L. Smith, *J. Am. Chem. Soc.,* 74, 1556 (1952).
[163]K. Eiter and E. Mrazak, *Monatsh.,* 83, 926 (1952).
[164]K. Eiter and E. Mrazak, *ibid.,* 83, 915 (1952).

[165]G. Carrara, V. D'Amato, and M. Bellenghi, *Gazz. chim. ital.*, 80, 822 (1950).

[166]E. L. Anderson and F. G. Holliman, *J. Chem. Soc.*, 1950, 1037.

[167]S. W. Chaikin, *J. Am. Chem. Soc.*, 70, 3522 (1948).

[168]H. Favre and H. Schinz, *Helv. Chim. Acta*, 35, 1627 (1952).

[169]K. Brack and H. Schinz, *ibid.*, 34, 1523 (1951).

[170]R. Paul and S. Tchelitcheff, *Compt. rend.*, 232, 1939 (1951).

[171]G. R. Clemo and J. Rudinger, *J. Chem. Soc.*, 1951, 2714.

[172]G. Dupont, R. Dulon, and P. Quantin, *Bull. soc. chim. France*, [5] 18, 59 (1951).

[173]H. S. Mosher, D. P. Spalding, G. W. Moersch, R. B. Taylor, and F. C. Whitmore, *Abstracts of Papers*, 114th Meeting American Chemical Society, St. Louis, Mo., September 1948, p. 23L.

[174]G. I. Samokhvalov, V. E. Sibertseva, E. I. Genkin, and N. A. Preobrazhenskiĭ, *Doklady Akad. Nauk S.S.S.R.*, 84, 729 (1952); through *Chem. Abstracts*, 47, 3230 (1953).

[175]E. Buchta, M. Klisch, S. Maier, and H. Bayer, *Ann.*, 576, 7 (1952).

[176]Isolated as acetate and phenylacetate by treatment of reduction product with acetic anhydride and phenylacetic anhydride, respectively.

[177]C. F. H. Allen and J. R. Byers, Jr., *Science*, 107, 269 (1948); *J. Am. Chem. Soc.*, 71, 2683 (1949).

[178]A. W. D. Avison and A. L. Morrison, *J. Chem. Soc.*, 1950, 1474.

[179]*Chem. Eng. News*, 30, 1872 (1952).

[180]W. A. West and B. J. Ludwig, *J. Am. Chem. Soc.*, 74, 4466 (1952).

[181]V. Boekelheide and S. Rothchild, *ibid.*, 71, 879 (1949).

[182]K. Winterfeld and C. Heinen, *Ann.*, 573, 85 (1951).

[183]F. Šorm and K. Vereš, unpublished work; through J. Rudinger, M. Ferles and M. Protiva, *Chem. Listy*, 45, 355 (1951).

[184]Reduction carried out in ether.

[185]Reduction carried out at 18°, 2½ hours.

[186]R. Lukeš and M. Ferles, unpublished work; through J. Rudinger, M. Ferles, and M. Protiva, *Chem. Listy*, 45, 355 (1951).

[187]Reduction carried out at 35°, 1-3/4 hours.

[188]F. W. Schueler and C. Hanna, *J. Am. Chem. Soc.*, 74, 2112 (1952).

[189]S. F. Birch, V. E. Gripp, D. T. McAllan, and W. S. Nathan, *J. Chem. Soc.*, 1952, 1363.

[190]C. S. Marvel and H. W. Hill, Jr., *J. Am. Chem. Soc.*, 73, 481 (1951).

[191]M. S. Newman and W. K. Cline, *J. Org. Chem.*, 16, 934 (1951).

[192]M. Zimmermann, V. Prelog, and L. Ruzicka, *Helv. Chim. Acta*, 34, 1975 (1951).

[193]Reduction carried out in benzene-ether mixture.

[194]B. R. Baker, R. E. Schaub, and J. H. Williams, *J. Org. Chem.*, 17, 116 (1952).

[195]W. I. Taylor, *Helv. Chim. Acta*, 33, 164 (1950).

[196]K. Freudenberg and R. Dillenburg, *Chem. Ber.*, 84, 67 (1951).

[197]K. Freudenberg, R. Kraft, and W. Heimberger, *ibid.*, 84, 472 (1951).

[198]K. Freudenberg and H. H. Hübner, *ibid.*, 85, 1181 (1952).

[199]Reduction carried out in ether-chloroform mixture.

[200]R. C. Gilmore, Jr., and W. J. Horton, *J. Am. Chem. Soc.*, 73, 1411 (1951).

[201]Kwan-Chung Tsou and N. H. Cromwell, *J. Org. Chem.*, 15, 1293 (1950).

[202]V. C. Barry and D. Twomey, *Abstracts of Papers*, XIIth International Congress of Pure and Applied Chemistry, New York, N. Y., September 1951, p. 308.

[203]V. C. Barry, J. G. Belton, R. M. Kelly, and D. Twomey, *Nature*, 166, 303 (1950).

[204]D. O. Dean, W. B. Dickinson, O. R. Quayle, and C. T. Lester, *J. Am. Chem. Soc.*, 72, 1740 (1950).

[205]M. Protiva, *Chem. Listy*, 45, 20 (1951).

[206]M. Protiva and J. O. Jílek, *Coll. Czech. Chem. Communs.*, 16, 151 (1951).

[207]C. O. Guss, *J. Am. Chem. Soc.*, 71, 3460 (1949).

[208]E. Adler and K. J. Björkqvist, *Acta Chem. Scand.*, 5, 241 (1951).

[209]S. H. Harper and J. F. Oughton, *Chemistry and Industry*, 1950, 574.

[210]A. Caliezi and H. Schinz, *Helv. Chim. Acta*, 35, 1637 (1952).

[211]D. Jerchel and G. Jung, *Chem. Ber.*, 85, 1130 (1952).

[212]K. Freudenberg and G. Wilke, *ibid.*, 85, 78 (1952).

[213]C. L. Browne and R. E. Lutz, *J. Org. Chem.*, 17, 1187 (1952).

[214]G. Stork and H. Conroy, *J. Am. Chem. Soc.*, 73, 4743 (1951).

[215]Isolated as hydrochloride.

[216]R. E. Holman and D. D. Carroll, *J. Am. Chem. Soc.*, 73, 1859 (1951).

[217]C. Collin-Asselineau and E. Lederer, *Compt. rend.*, 234, 341 (1952).

[218]See text.

[219]N. A. Milas and T. M. Harrington, *J. Am. Chem. Soc.*, 69, 2247 (1947).

[220]N. L. Wendler, H. L. Slates, and M. Tishler, *ibid.*, 71, 3267 (1949).

[221]N. L. Wendler, H. L. Slates, N. R. Trenner, and M. Tishler, *ibid.*, 73, 719 (1951).

[222]H. H. Inhoffen, F. Bohlmann, and M. Bohlmann, *Ann.*, 565, 35 (1949).

[223]Distillation Products, Inc., Brit. Pat. 650,302 (February 21, 1951).

[224]C. D. Robeson, Ger. Pat. 855,992 (November 17, 1952).

[225]L. Weisler, U. S. Pat. 2,583,194 (January 22, 1952).

[226]H. O. Huisman, A. Smit, S. Vromen, and L. G. M. Fisscher, *Rec. trav. chim.*, 71, 899 (1952).

[227]P. Karrer, K. P. Karanth, and J. Benz, *Helv. Chim. Acta*, 32, 436 (1949).

[228]H. Bader, B. C. L. Weedon, and R. J. Woods, *J. Chem. Soc.*, 1951, 3099.

[229]K. R. Farrar, J. C. Hamlet, H. B. Henbest, and E. R. H. Jones, *ibid.*, 1952, 2657.

[230]H. Rapoport and G. B. Payne, *J. Org. Chem.*, 15, 1093 (1950).

[231]G. M. Badger, J. W. Cook and T. Walker, *J. Chem. Soc.*, 1949, 1141.

[232]O. Dürst, O. Jeger, and L. Ruzicka, *Helv. Chim. Acta*, 32, 46 (1949).

[233]F. F. Blicke and H. Raffelson, *J. Am. Chem. Soc.*, 74, 1730 (1952).

[234]Ciba Ltd., Brit. Pat. 666,051 (February 6, 1952).

[235]P. Wieland and K. Miescher, *Helv. Chim. Acta*, 31, 1844 (1948).

[236]S. P. Ligthelm, E. von Rudloff, and D. A. Sutton, *J. Chem. Soc.*, 1950, 3187.

[237]Isolated as tribenzoyl derivatives.

[238]N. Fisher, *Chemistry and Industry*, 1952, 130.

[239]G. I. Gregory and T. Malkin, *J. Chem. Soc.*, 1951, 2453.

[240]G. R. Clemo and R. Stevens, *ibid.*, 1952, 4684.

[241]D. E. Ames and R. E. Bowman, *ibid.*, 1952, 1057.

[242]A. Stoll, A. Hofmann, and T. Petrzilka, *Helv. Chim. Acta*, 34, 1544 (1951).

[243]P. Karrer, M. Suter, and P. Waser, *ibid.*, 32, 1936 (1949).

[244]D. J. Cram and H. Steinberg, *J. Am. Chem. Soc.*, 73, 5691 (1951).

[245]K. R. Farrar, J. C. Hamlet, H. B. Henbest, and E. R. H. Jones, *Chemistry and Industry*, 1951, 49.

[246]K. R. Farrar, J. C. Hamlet, H. B. Henbest, and E. R. H. Jones, *J. Chem. Soc.*, 1952, 2657.

[247]O. Schwarzkopf, H. J. Cahnmann, A. D. Lewis, J. Swidinsky, and H. M. Wüest, *Helv. Chim. Acta*, 32, 443 (1949).

[248]O. Schwarzkopf and H. J. Cahnmann, Brit. Pat. 660,368 (November 7, 1951); Ger. Pat. 828,543 (January 17, 1952).

[249] A. Caliezi and H. Schinz, *Helv. Chim. Acta, 35,* 1649 (1952).

[250] M. S. Newman and M. Wolf, *J. Am. Chem. Soc., 74,* 3225 (1952).

[251] M. E. Speeter, W. M. Byrd, L. C. Cheney, and S. B. Binkley, *ibid., 71,* 57 (1949).

[252] J. Attenburrow, A. F. B. Cameron, J. H. Chapman, R. M. Evans, B. A. Hems, A. B. A. Jansen, and T. Walker, *J. Chem. Soc., 1952,* 1094.

[253] H. O. Huisman, *Rec. trav. chim., 69,* 851 (1950).

[254] O. Schwarzkopf, H. J. Cahnmann, A. D. Lewis, J. Swidinsky, and H. M. Wüest, *Abstracts of Papers,* 115th Meeting American Chemical Society, San Francisco, Calif., March 1949, p. 11C.

[255] P. Karrer and W. Forter, *Helv. Chim. Acta, 35,* 1494 (1952).

[256] O. C. Musgrave, J. Stark, and F. S. Spring, *Nature, 168,* 298 (1951).

[257] O. C. Musgrave, J. Stark, and F. S. Spring, *J. Chem. Soc., 1952,* 4393.

[258] R. Lukeš and M. Soukupová, unpublished work; through M. Ferles and J. Rudinger, *Chem. Listy, 47,* 125 (1953).

[259] P. Jollès and C. Fromageot, *Bull. soc. chim. France,* [5] *18,* 862 (1951).

[260] R. Lukeš and V. Dudek, unpublished work, through M. Ferles and J. Rudinger, *Chem. Listy, 47,* 126 (1953).

[261] P. Karrer and K. Ehrhardt, *Helv. Chim. Acta, 34,* 2202 (1951).

[262] A. Kalojanoff, *Ann., 577,* 147 (1952).

[263] Reduction carried out in a pyridine-ether mixture.

[264] V. M. Mićović and M. L. Mihailović, Glasnik Chemiskog druztva (Beograd) (*Bull. soc. chim. Belgrade*) *14,* 256 (1949), through J. Rudinger, M. Ferles and M. Protiva, *Chem. Listy, 45,* 359 (1951).

[265] P. Karrer and E. Jucker, *Helv. Chim. Acta, 35,* 1586 (1952).

The influence of temperature is illustrated in the reduction of ethyl 2-(1-methyl-4-isopropylphenyl)acetate (XLII) to the corresponding ethanol (53).

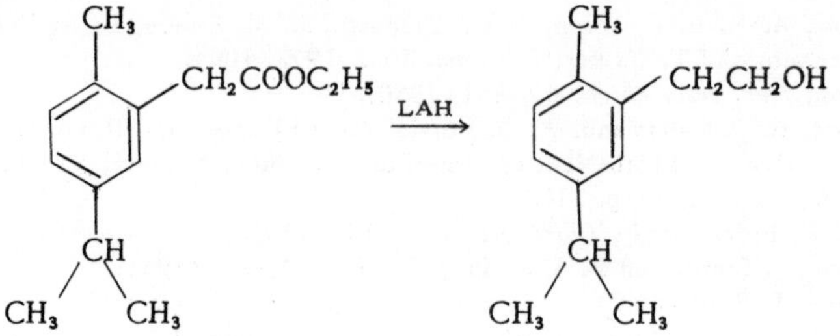

$$(9\text{-}24)$$

XLII

No reduction occurs in ether after 3 hours at 35° and 18 hours at 20°. After 3 hours at 100° and 64 hours at 18° in dioxane a 66% yield is obtained while 8 hours at 100° in dioxane increases the yield to 80%.

The following isotopically labeled esters of fatty acids have been reduced with LAH to the corresponding labeled carbinols:

Ester	Ref.
Ethyl acetate-1-C^{14}	54
Ethyl acetate-2-C^{14}	55
Ethyl 2-dimethylaminoacetate-1-C^{14}	56
Propionate-1-C^{13}	57
Methyl 3-chloropropionate-1-C^{14}	58
Butyrate-1-C^{13}	57
Ethyl 2,3-diacetoxy-DL-glycerate-1-C^{14}	59
Diethyl 2-acetoxymalonate-1-C^{14}	60
Diethyl 2-acetoxymalonate-2-C^{14}	60
Diethyl succinate-2,3-C^{14}	61
Ethyl hexanoate-1-C^{13}	62

The poor results obtained in the LAH reduction of α-oximino-β-keto-esters have been discussed in Section 7.2.1.g.

The LAH reduction of various aliphatic carboxylates is summarized in Table XXXVIII.

2. α,β-*Unsaturated aliphatic carboxylates.* The LAH reduction of α,β-unsaturated fatty acid esters generally leads to the corresponding α,β-unsaturated carbinol. However, where the carbon-carbon double bond is conjugated with a phenyl group as in ethyl o-hydroxycinnamate (XLIII) the saturated carbinol is obtained (63).

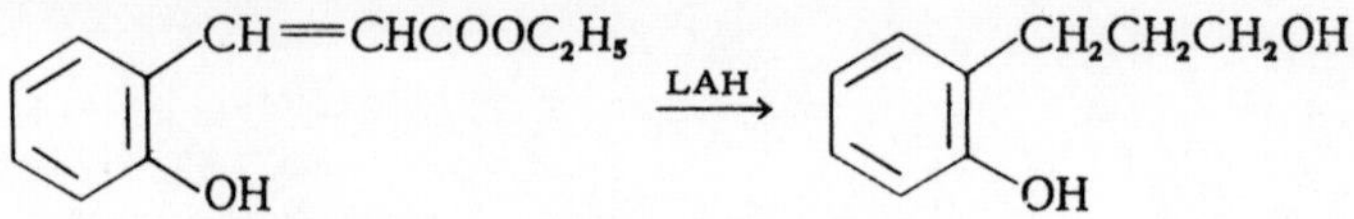

$$(9\text{-}25)$$

XLIII

Reduction in the quantity of LAH used in the reaction results in the recovery of unchanged XLIII rather than the formation of unsaturated carbinol. The reduction of the methyl or ethyl ester of p-acetoxycinnamate at low temperatures yields p-hydroxycinnamyl alcohol (64). The LAH reduction of ethyl β-phenoxycinnamate (XLIV) at low temperatures is reported to yield the substituted cinnamyl alcohol (65).

$$C_6H_5C\!=\!CHCOOC_2H_5 \xrightarrow{\text{LAH}} C_6H_5C\!=\!CHCH_2OH \qquad (9\text{-}26)$$
$$\underset{OC_6H_5}{|} \qquad\qquad\qquad\qquad \underset{OC_6H_5}{|}$$
$$\text{XLIV}$$

The low temperature reduction of the phenyl analogue of vitamin A acid (XLV) yields the phenyl analogue of vitamin A (66).

$$\overset{\overset{\textstyle CH_3}{|}}{C_6H_5(CH\!=\!CHC\!=\!CH)_2COOC_2H_5} \xrightarrow{\text{LAH}} \overset{\overset{\textstyle CH_3}{|}}{C_6H_5(CH\!=\!CHC\!=\!CH)_2CH_2OH}$$
$$\text{XLV} \qquad\qquad\qquad\qquad\qquad\qquad\qquad\qquad (9\text{-}27)$$

The LAH reduction of nuclear-substituted cinnamic esters (XLVI) containing two or more substituents from among the group hydroxy, methoxy, ethoxy, acetoxy, or methylenedioxy results in the formation of the corresponding substituted cinnamyl alcohol (65,67–72).

$$\text{XLVI} \qquad\qquad\qquad\qquad \text{XLVII} \qquad (9\text{-}28)$$

Allen and Byers reported that the reduction of XLVI gives a complex alcoholate of lithium and aluminum which is referred to as lithium salt A. Treatment of the latter with an aqueous solution of boric acid, disodium phosphate or ammonium chloride, sulfate or carbonate gives the substituted cinnamyl alcohol (XLVII). Treatment of lithium salt A with water gives a precipitate of a complex alcoholate of lithium referred to as lithium salt B. When an aqueous suspension of salt B is treated with carbon dioxide XLVII is formed. Treatment of dry lithium salt B on a steam bath with benzoic anhydride or acetic anhydride gives the benzoate and acetate, respectively, of the cinnamyl alcohol (67–69).

The presence of an α-cyano group results in the reduction of an α,β-unsaturated ester to the saturated amino alcohol. Thus, methyl α-cyanocinnamate (XLVIII: $R_1 = R_2 = H$), methyl β-(4-methoxyphenyl)-α-cyanoacrylate (XLVIII: $R_1 = OCH_3$, $R_2 = H$) and methyl β-(3,4-methylenedioxyphenyl)-α-cyanoacrylate (XLVIII: $R_1R_2 = OCH_2O$) are reduced to the substituted 2-benzyl-3-amino-1-propanol (73).

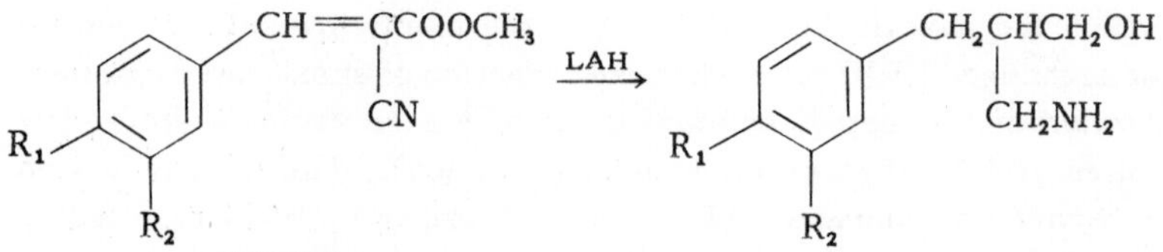

XLVIII   (9-29)

The LAH reduction of α,β-unsaturated esters has been widely used in the synthesis of vitamin A and its precursors. The Reformatsky reaction with β-ionone yields the β-ionol system (XLIX). Dehydration of the latter has been reported to yield ethyl β-ionylidene acetate (L). Reduction of the conjugated ester with LAH to yield β-ionylideneethanol (Table XXXVIII) has been used in the course of the synthesis of the ethyl ester of vitamin A acid (LI). The reduction of LI or the acid with LAH yields vitamin A (LII).

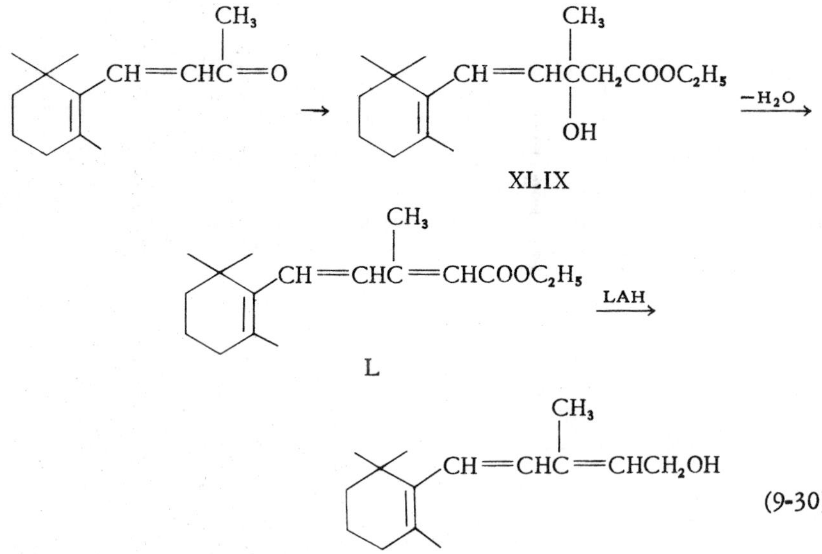

XLIX

L

(9-30)

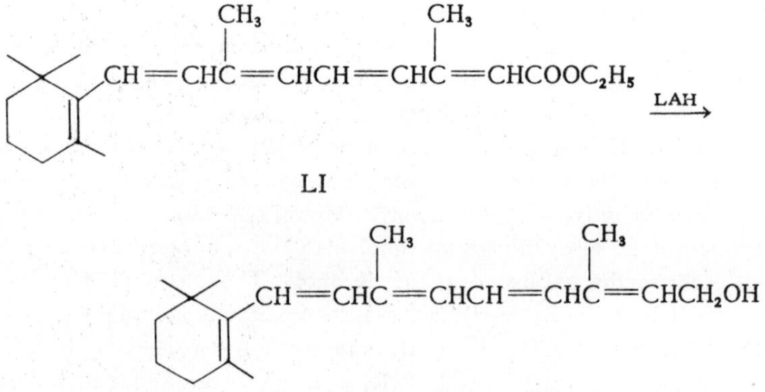

LI

(9-31)

LII

Oroshnik (74) and Huisman (75) and their co-workers have recently shown that the dehydration of a β-ionol or a vinylog thereof can take two competitive courses: (*a*) the formation of the β-ionylidene system (LIII) and (*b*) allylic rearrangement into the ring to form the retroionylidene system (LIV). The latter reaction always predominates.

$$\xrightarrow{-\text{H}_2\text{O}} \quad \text{CH}=\text{CHC}=\text{CHCOOR}$$

with CH_3 substituent

LIII   (9-32)

$$\text{CH}=\text{CHCCH}_2\text{COOR}$$
with CH_3 and OH substituents

$$\left[\text{CHCH}=\text{CCH}_2\text{COOR} \right]$$
with CH_3 and OH substituents

$$\downarrow -\text{H}_2\text{O}$$

$$\text{CHCH}=\text{CCH}_2\text{COOR}$$
with CH_3 substituent

LIV   (9-33)

Therefore all previous reports in which it was presumed that LIII was formed and used for further reactions, e.g., LAH reduction to β-ionylidene-ethanol, synthesis of vitamin A acid ester and LAH reduction to vitamin A, actually involved a mixture of LIII and LIV and the reduction products were mixtures of alcohols (74-76).

A British patent reports that the dehydration of XLIX may yield a mixture of isomeric esters formulated as ethyl β-ionylidene acetate and the isomer with an exocyclic double bond (LV). The LAH reduction of the mixture yields a mixture of carbinols (77).

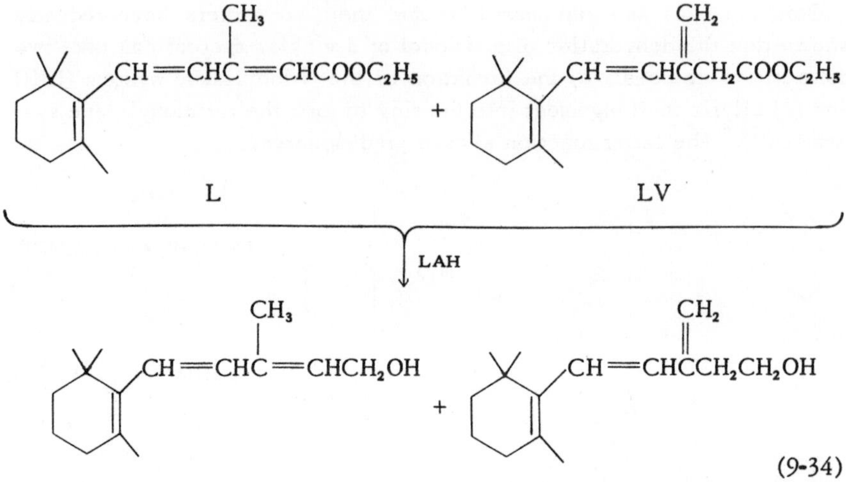

(9-34)

In view of the findings of Oroshnik and Huisman, it is more likely that the isomeric ester has the retroionylidene structure.

Schwarzkopf et al. (78) dehydrated LVI and obtained a compound clearly different from vitamin A acid ester. A β-methylene structure was postulated and a new alcohol (LVII), prepared by LAH reduction, has been named vitamin A₃. A similar reduction has been reported in the previously mentioned British patent (77). A more likely structure for the new alcohol involves the allylic rearrangement product (LVIII).

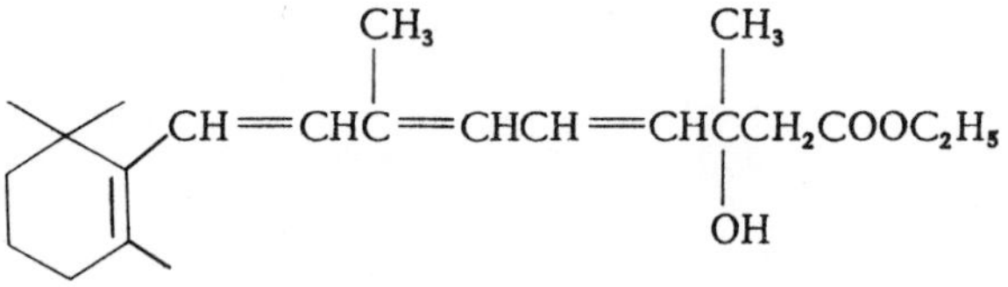

LVI

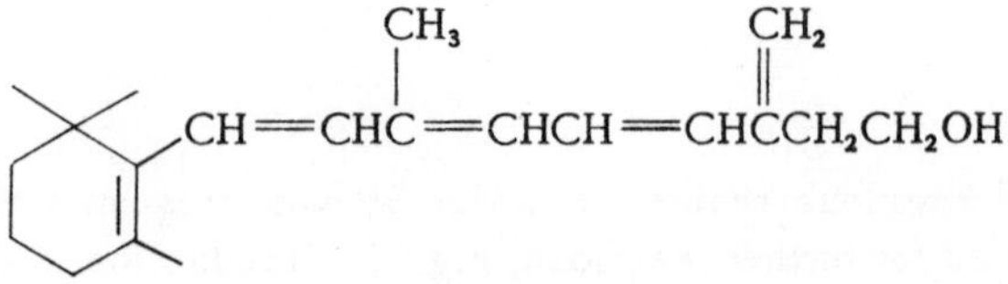

LVII

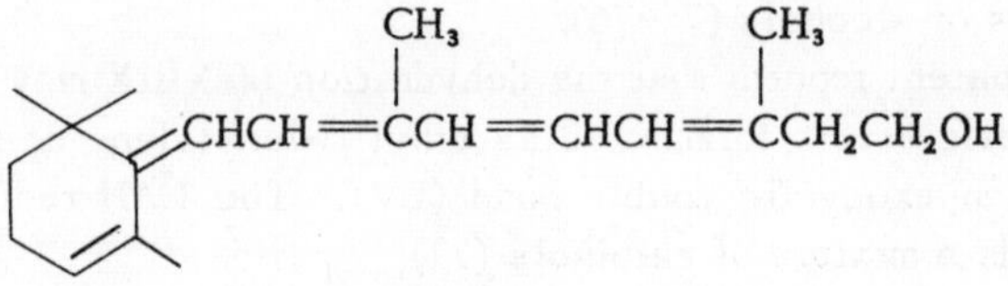

LVIII

The reduction of methyl phenylpropiolate (LIX) with one-half mole of LAH at $-70°$ yields 90% of 3-phenylprop-2-yn-1-ol (LX) while reduction with one mole of LAH at 20° yields 75% of *trans*-cinnamyl alcohol (LXI) (79).

$$C_6H_5C \equiv CCH_2OH \qquad (9\text{-}35)$$
$$LX$$

$$C_6H_5C \equiv CCOOCH_3 \xrightarrow[20°]{-70°}$$
$$LIX$$

$$C_6H_5CH = CHCH_2OH \qquad (9\text{-}36)$$
$$LXI$$

The LAH reduction of α,β-unsaturated aliphatic carboxylates is summarized in Table XXXVIII.

3. *Alicyclic carboxylates.* The LAH reduction of alicyclic esters proceeds in the normal manner, as summarized in Table XXXIX. However, the reduction of enolizable alicyclic β-ketoesters is attended by decreased yields. 3,5-Dicarbethoxy-4-methylcyclopentane-1,2-dione (LXII) reacts with LAH in the dienol form (80). Buchta and Bayer (43) reported that the reduction of 2-carbethoxycyclopentanone (LXIII: R = H) gives a 22% yield of diol while the 2-methyl compound (LXIII: R = CH₃) gives the diol in 66% yield. Similarly, 2-carbethoxycyclohexanone (LXIV: R = H) gives a 17% yield and 2-methyl-2-carbethoxycyclohexanone (LXIV: R = CH₃) an 87% yield of the corresponding diol.

LXII   LXIII   LXIV

Dreiding and Hartman (81) have shown that the LAH reduction of 2-carbomethoxycyclopentanone (LXV) actually yields only 25% of 2-hydroxymethylcyclopentanol (LXVI) accompanied by a 42% yield of 2-methylenecyclopentanol (LXVII) and 8% of 1-hydroxymethyl-1-cyclopentene (LXVIII).

LXV   LXVI

$$(9\text{-}37)$$

LXVII   LXVIII

TABLE XXXIX

LAH Reduction of Alicyclic Esters

Ester	Product	% Yield	Ref.
C$_6$H$_{10}$O$_2$ Carbethoxycyclopropane	1-Hydroxymethylcyclopropane	58	1
1-Methyl-1-carbomethoxycyclopropane	1-Methyl-1-hydroxymethylcyclopropane	54	2
C$_7$H$_9$O$_3$Na Sodium enolate of 2-carbomethoxycyclopentanone	2-Methylene-1-cyclopentanol	56	3
	1-Hydroxymethyl-1-cyclopentene	50	4
C$_7$H$_{10}$O$_3$ 2-Carbomethoxycyclopentanone	2-Methylene-1-cyclopentanol	42	
	2-Hydroxymethyl-1-cyclopentanol	25	4
	1-Hydroxymethyl-1-cyclopentene	8	
C$_8$H$_{10}$O$_4$R$_2$ Cyclohexane-1,2-dicarboxylate	1,2-Di-(hydroxymethyl)cyclohexane	....	5
Cyclohexane-1,3-dicarboxylate	1,3-Di-(hydroxymethyl)cyclohexane	....	5
Cyclohexane-1,4-dicarboxylate	1,4-Di-(hydroxymethyl)cyclohexane	....	5
C$_9$H$_{12}$O$_3$ 2-Carbethoxycyclopentanone	2-Hydroxymethyl-1-cyclopentanol	22	6
C$_8$H$_{14}$O$_2$ Carbethoxycyclopentane	1-Hydroxymethylcyclopentane	60	7
C$_8$H$_{14}$O$_3$ trans-3-Carbomethoxy-1-cyclohexanol	trans-3-Hydroxymethyl-1-cyclohexanol	64	8
C$_9$H$_{14}$O$_2$ 1-Carbethoxy-1-cyclohexene	1-Hydroxymethyl-1-cyclohexene	70	9
C$_9$H$_{14}$O$_3$ 2-Carbethoxycyclohexanone	2-Methylene-1-cyclohexanol	52	
	1-Hydroxymethyl-1-cyclohexene	21	4
	2-Hydroxymethyl-1-cyclohexanol	11	
	2-Hydroxymethyl-1-cyclohexanol	17	6
C$_9$H$_{16}$O$_3$ 2-Methyl-2-carbethoxycyclopentanone	2-Methyl-2-hydroxymethyl-1-cyclopentanol[10]	66	6
3-Carbethoxy-1-cyclohexanol	3-Hydroxymethyl-1-cyclohexanol	52	11
C$_{10}$H$_{16}$O$_3$ 2-Methyl-2-carbethoxycyclohexanone	2-Methyl-2-hydroxymethyl-1-cyclohexanol[10]	87	6
C$_{11}$H$_{16}$O$_2$ 1-Carbomethoxy-2-methylene-6,6-dimethyl-3-cyclohexene (methyl dehydro-γ-cyclogeranate)	Dehydro-γ-cyclogeraniol	....	12
C$_{11}$H$_{18}$O$_2$ 1-Carbethoxy-6,6-dimethyl-1- (and 2-)cyclohexene (ethyl apocyclogeranate)	Apocyclogeraniol	98	13
C$_{11}$H$_{18}$O$_3$ 8-Carbomethoxy-cis-hydrindane	8-Hydroxymethyl-cis-hydrindane	96	14
2-Carbethoxy-3,3-dimethylcyclohexanone	2-Hydroxymethyl-3,3-dimethyl-1-cyclohexanol	76	13

Formula	Ester	Product	Yield, %	Ref.
C₁₁H₁₈O₄	2-Methyl-2-carbethoxycyclopentanone ethylene ketal	2-Methyl-2-hydroxymethyl-1-cyclopentanone ethylene ketal	90	15
C₁₁H₂₀O₂	cis-1-Carbomethoxy-2,6,6-trimethylcyclohexane (methyl cis-dihydrocyclogeranate)	cis-Dihydrocyclogeraniol	53	16
	trans-1-Carbomethoxy-2,6,6-trimethylcyclohexane (methyl trans-dihydrocyclogeranate)	trans-Dihydrocyclogeraniol	76	16
C₁₂H₂₀O₄	1,2-Dicarbethoxycyclohexane	1,2-Di-(hydroxymethyl)cyclohexane	…	17
	Methyl cis-(2-methyl-2-carbomethoxycyclohexyl)-acetate	cis-(2-Methyl-2-carbomethoxycyclohexyl)ethanol	53[18]	19
		cis-(2-Methyl-2-hydroxymethylcyclohexyl)ethanol	80	19
C₁₃H₂₂O₂	1-Carbethoxy-2,5,6,6-tetramethyl-2-cyclohexene (ethyl 6-methyl-α-cyclogeranate)	6-Methyl-α-cyclogeraniol	94	20
C₁₄H₁₈O₅	Butadiene adduct of dimethyl 3,6-epoxy-3,4,5,6-tetrahydrophthalate, m.p. 78.5–79°	Glycol, C₁₂H₁₈O₃, m.p. 154–154.5°	…	21
C₁₆H₂₆O₂	Methyl ester α-bicyclofarnesylic acid (derived from liquid acid)	α-Bicyclofarnesol (liquid), allophanate, m.p. 193–194.5°	100	22
	Methyl ester α-bicyclofarnesylic acid (derived from solid acid)	α-Bicyclofarnesol, m.p. 64–65°	…	23
	Methyl ester β-bicyclofarnesylic acid	β-Bicyclofarnesol	100	24
C₁₇H₂₈O₂	Ethyl ester β-bicyclofarnesylic acid	β-Bicyclofarnesol (liquid), allophanate, m.p. 193.5–194.5°	…	23
	Ethyl ester α-bicyclofarnesylic acid		…	23
C₁₈H₂₄O₃	Methyl podocarpate	Podocarpinol	…	25
C₁₉H₂₆O₃	Methyl O-methylpodocarpate	O-Methylpodocarpinol	93	25,26
C₂₁H₃₀O₂	Methyl dehydroabietate	Dehydroabietinol	98[27]	28
C₂₂H₃₂O₃	Methyl O-methyl-7-isopropylpodocarpate	O-Methyl-7-isopropylpodocarpinol	93	29

References—Table XXXIX

[1]L. I. Smith and S. McKenzie, Jr., *J. Org. Chem.*, *15*, 74 (1950); L. I. Smith and E. R. Rogier, *J. Am. Chem. Soc.*, *73*, 4047 (1951).

[2]J. D. Roberts and R. H. Mazur, *ibid.*, *73*, 2509 (1951).

[3]S. Siegel and C. G. Bergstrom, *ibid.*, *72*, 3815 (1950).

[4]A. S. Dreiding and J. A. Hartman, *ibid.*, *75*, 939 (1953).

[5]G. A. Haggis and L. N. Owen, *Chemistry and Industry*, *1953*, 38.

[6]E. Buchta and H. Bayer, *Ann.*, *573*, 227 (1951).

[7]V. N. Ipatieff, W. W. Thompson, and H. Pines, *J. Am. Chem. Soc.*, *73*, 553 (1951).

[8]H. L. Goering and C. Serres, Jr., *ibid.*, *74*, 5908 (1952).

[9]R. Jacquier and R. Zagdoun, *Bull. soc. chim. France*, [5] *19*, 698 (1952); M. Mousseron, R. Jacquier, M. Mousseron-Canet, and R. Zagdoun, *ibid.*, [5] *19*, 1042 (1952).

[10]Mixture of stereoisomers.

[11]M. F. Clarke and L. N. Owen, *J. Chem. Soc.*, *1950*, 2108.

[12]K. Seitz, G. Büchi, and O. Jeger, *Helv. Chim. Acta*, *33*, 1746 (1950).

[13]R. Helg and H. Schinz, *ibid.*, *35*, 2406 (1952).

[14]R. L. Kronenthal and E. I. Becker, unpublished work, private communication.

[15]A. Eschenmoser and A. Frey, *Helv. Chim. Acta*, *35*, 1660 (1952).

[16]P. Bächli and H. Schinz, *ibid.*, *34*, 1160 (1951).

[17]W. J. Bailey and H. R. Golden, *Abstracts of Papers*, 117th Meeting American Chemical Society, Philadelphia, Pa., April 1950, p. 16L.

[18]Reduction carried out at −60 to −15°.

[19]W. E. Bachmann and A. S. Dreiding, *J. Am. Chem. Soc.*, *71*, 3222 (1949).

[20]H. Favre and H. Schinz, *Helv. Chim. Acta*, *35*, 1627 (1952).

[21]G. Stork, E. E. van Tamelen, L. J. Friedman, and A. W. Burgstahler, *J. Am. Chem. Soc.*, *73*, 4501 (1951).

[22]A. Caliezi and H. Schinz, *Helv. Chim. Acta*, *33*, 1129 (1950).

[23]A. Caliezi and H. Schinz, *ibid.*, *35*, 1637 (1952).

[24]A. Caliezi and H. Schinz, *ibid.*, *32*, 2556 (1949).

[25]H. H. Zeiss and C. E. Slimowicz, Fr. Pat. 979,346 (April 25, 1951).

[26]H. H. Zeiss, C. E. Slimowicz, and V. Z. Pasternak, *J. Am. Chem. Soc.*, *70*, 1981 (1948).

[27]Reduction carried out in 1:1 ether-dioxane.

[28]A. Brossi, H. Gutmann, and O. Jeger, *Helv. Chim. Acta*, *33*, 1730 (1950).

[29]M. M. Baizer, M. Karnowsky, and W. G. Bywater, *J. Am. Chem. Soc.*, *72*, 3800 (1950).

The reduction of the sodium enolate of LXV gives a mixture of LXVII and LXVIII in a combined yield of 50%. The reduction of 2-carbethoxy-cyclohexanone (LXIV: R = H) yields 11% of 2-hydroxymethylcyclohex-anol, 52% of 2-methylenecyclohexanol and 21% of 1-hydroxymethyl-1-cyclohexene. A more detailed discussion is given in Section 7.2.1.g.9.

Attempted cyclization of 2-carbethoxy-2-(2-ketocyclohexyl)cyclohex-anone (LXIX) with acetic anhydride and sulfuric acid is reported to yield a product, m.p. 158–159°, which may be the cyclization product LXX or LXXI.

LXIX

(9-38)

LXX   LXXI

The LAH reduction of the cyclization product yields an impure product, m.p. 180–200°, which has not been identified (82).

4. *Sugar carboxylates.* The alicyclic esters represented by the urono-sides are readily reduced at normal temperatures to the corresponding glycosides (83,84). The LAH reduction of various mono- and oligosaccharides is summarized in Table XL. The LAH reduction is much superior to catalytic hydrogenation under pressure because the yields are higher, reaction times are shorter and hydrogenolysis is usually avoided.

5. *Steroidal carboxylates.* The LAH reduction of various steroidal esters in which the carboalkoxy group is located at C_{21}, C_{22} and C_{24} is summarized in Table XLI. The reactions proceed in the expected manner to yield the corresponding carbinols in very good yields. The reduction of 3-carboalkoxycholest-5-ene and cholesta-5,7-diene to the 3β-hydroxy-methyl derivatives is included in Table XLI.

6. *Triterpene carboxylates.* Triterpene esters are usually reduced to the carbinols without undue difficulty, as summarized in Table XLII. The LAH reduction of methyl morolate acetate oxide (LXXII), followed

TABLE XL

LAH Reduction of Carbohydrate Esters

Ester	Source	Product	% Yield	Ref.
A. Monosaccharides				
C$_9$H$_{16}$O$_7$ Methyl ester 4-methyl-methyl-D-glucuronoside	....	4-Methyl-methyl-D-glucoside	....	1
	Gum myrrh	4-Methyl-methyl-D-glucoside	70[2]	3
Methyl ester 4-methyl-methyl-α-D-glucuronoside	Mesquite gum	4-Methyl-methyl-α-D-glucoside	90[2]	4
C$_{10}$H$_{18}$O$_7$ Methyl ester 3,4-dimethyl-methyl-D-glucuronoside	Glycyrrhinic acid	3,4-Dimethyl-methyl-D-glucoside	....	5
C$_{11}$H$_{18}$O$_6$ Methyl ester 3,4-isopropylidene-α-methyl-2-deoxy-D-galacturonoside	....	3,4-Isopropylidene-α-methyl-2-deoxy-D-galactoside	23	6
C$_{11}$H$_{20}$O$_7$ Methyl ester 2,3,4-trimethyl-methyl-D-galacturonoside	....	2,3,4-Trimethyl-methyl-D-galactoside	....	1
Methyl ester 2,3,4-trimethyl-α-methyl-D-glucuronoside	....	2,3,4-Trimethyl-α-methyl-D-glucoside	....	1
Methyl ester methyl-hexuronoside-trimethyl ether	Glycyrrhinic acid	Methyl-hexoside-trimethyl ether	....	5
B. Oligosaccharides				
C$_{20}$H$_{36}$O$_{12}$ Methyl ester 6β-(2,3,4-trimethyl-D-glucuronosyl)-2,3,4-trimethyl-α-methyl-D-galactoside	Mesquite gum	6β-(2,3,4-Trimethyl-D-glucosyl)-2,3,4-trimethyl-α-methyl-D-galactoside	....	7
Methyl ester 6β-(2,3,4-trimethyl-D-glucuronosyl)-2,3,4-trimethyl-β-methyl-D-galactoside	Mesquite gum	6β-(2,3,4-Trimethyl-D-glucosyl)-2,3,4-trimethyl-β-methyl-D-galactoside	....	1,7
.... Methylated pectic acid	Pectic acid	Methylated galactosan	....	1
.... Methylated pectic acid	Pectic acid	2,3-Dimethyl-D-glucose[8]	....	9
.... Methylated degraded arabic acid	Arabic acid	Methylated polysaccharide containing methylated galactose and glucose residues	....	1

Methyl esters of methylated mannuronic acids	Alginic acid	2,3-Dimethylmannose	88 [8]
		2,3,4-Trimethylmannose	1
		Monomethylmannose	4.5
		Dimethylglucose	6
			10
Methyl ester of methylated 2α-(4-methyl-D-glucuronosyl)-D-xylose	Aspen wood	3,4-Dimethyl-2-(2,3,4,6-tetramethyl-D-glucosyl)methyl-D-xyloside[11]	12
Methyl ester of methylated 2α-(4-methyl-D-glucuronosyl)-D-xylose [13]		3,4-Dimethyl-2-(2,3,4,6-tetramethyl-D-glucosyl)methyl-D-xyloside	12
Methyl ester of methylated D-galacturonic acid	Aspen wood	Tetramethyl methyl-D-galactoside [11]	12

[1] M. Abdel-Akher and F. Smith, *Nature*, 166, 1037 (1950).
[2] Reduction carried out in tetrahydrofuran.
[3] L. Hough, J. K. N. Jones, and W. H. Wadman, *J. Chem. Soc.*, 1952, 796.
[4] F. Smith, *ibid.*, 1951, 2646.
[5] B. Lythgoe and S. Trippett, *ibid.*, 1950, 1983.
[6] W. G. Overend, F. Shafizadeh, and M. Stacey, *ibid.*, 1951, 1487.
[7] M. Abdel-Akher, F. Smith, and D. Spriestersbach, *ibid.*, 1952, 3637.
[8] Isolated on hydrolysis of reduction products.
[9] E. L. Hurst and J. K. N. Jones, *Research*, 4, 411 (1951).
[10] S. K. Chanda, E. L. Hirst, E. G. V. Percival, and A. G. Ross, *J. Chem. Soc.*, 1952, 1833.
[11] Isolated on methylation of reduction product.
[12] J. K. N. Jones and L. E. Wise, *J. Chem. Soc.*, 1952, 3389.
[13] Indicated mixture reduced with LAH.

TABLE XLI

LAH Reduction of Steroidal Esters

A. $RCH_2COOR' \rightarrow RCH_2CH_2OH$

	Ester	No.	Product	% Yield	Ref.
$C_{21}H_{28}O_5$	Dimethyl Δ^5-3β-hydroxyetiobilienate	I	$\Delta^{9(14)}$-2,13-Dimethyl-7β-hydroxy-2-hydroxymethyl-1-hydroxyethyl-dodecahydrophenanthrene	84	1
$C_{22}H_{32}O_3$	Methyl pregna-5,17-diene-3β-ol-21-oate	II	Pregna-5,17-diene-3β,21-diol	85	2
$C_{22}H_{33}BrO_3$	Methyl 20-bromo-17-pregnene-3β-ol-21-oate	III	20-Bromo-17-pregnene-3β,21-diol	82	2-4
$C_{22}H_{34}O_2$	Methyl 17-allopregnene-21-oate	IV	17-Allopregnene-21-ol	83[5]	2
$C_{22}H_{34}O_3$	Methyl 17-pregnene-3β-ol-21-oate	V	17-Pregnene-3β,21-diol	65	2,3
$C_{22}H_{36}O_2$	Methyl allopregnane-21-oate	VI	Allopregnane-21-ol	95	6
	Methyl 17-isoallopregnane-21-oate	VII	17-Isoallopregnane-21-ol	86	6
$C_{23}H_{34}O_3$	Ethyl pregna-5,17-diene-3β-ol-21-oate	II	Pregna-5,17-diene-3β,21-diol	100	7
$C_{23}H_{36}O_3$	Methyl 3β-hydroxy-bisnor-5-cholenate	VIII	Bisnor-5-cholen-3β,22-diol	...	8
$C_{24}H_{34}O_3$	Methyl 3-ethoxypregna-3,5,17-triene-21-oate	IX	3-Ethoxypregna-3,5,17-triene-21-ol	...[9]	10
$C_{24}H_{34}O_4$	Methyl 3β-acetoxypregna-5,17-diene-21-oate	II	Pregna-5,17-diene-3β,21-diol	91	11
$C_{24}H_{36}O_4$	Methyl 3-ethoxypregna-3,5-diene-17β-ol-21-oate	X	3-Ethoxypregna-3,5-diene-17β,21-diol	...	10
$C_{25}H_{36}O_3$	Ethyl 3β-ethoxypregna-3,5,17-triene-21-oate	IX	3β-Ethoxypregna-3,5,17-triene-21-ol	91	12
$C_{25}H_{36}O_4$	Ethyl 3β-acetoxypregna-5,17-diene-21-oate	II	Pregna-5,17-diene-3β,21-diol	93	11
$C_{25}H_{38}O_3$	Methyl 3-ethoxy-bisnorchola-3,5-diene-22-oate	XI	3-Ethoxy-bisnorchola-3,5-diene-22-ol	63[13]	14
	Methyl 3-keto-9(11)-cholenate[15]	XII	9(11)-Lithocholenyl alcohol	86	16,17
$C_{25}H_{38}O_4$	Methyl 3-keto-9α,11α-oxidocholanate	XIII	9α,11α-Oxidocholane-3α,24-diol	80	16
	Methyl 11-keto-3α,9α-oxidocholanate	XIV	3α,9α-Oxidocholane-11β,24-diol	73	16
$C_{25}H_{38}O_5$	Ethyl 3β-acetoxy-17-isopregn-5-ene-17β-ol-21-oate	XV	17-Isopregn-5-ene-3β,17β,21-triol	82	11
$C_{25}H_{40}O_2$	Methyl 9(11)-cholenate	XVI	9(11)-Cholene-24-ol	"nearly quant."	18

$C_{25}H_{40}O_3$	Methyl 9(11)-lithocholenate	XVII	9(11)-Lithocholenyl alcohol	77	16
$C_{25}H_{40}O_4$	Methyl 3β-hydroxy-5-cholenate	XVIII	5-Cholene-3β,24-diol	91	19
$C_{26}H_{42}O_3$	Methyl 9α,11α-oxidolithocholanate	XIX	9α,11α-Oxidocholane-3α,24-diol	86	16
$C_{26}H_{44}O_2$	Methyl 3β-methoxy-9(11)-cholenate[20]	XVII	3β-Methoxy-9(11)-cholenyl alcohol	86	16,17
$C_{27}H_{42}O_4$	Methyl 3β-methoxycholanate[21]	XX	3β-Methoxycholanyl alcohol	...	16,17
$C_{27}H_{42}O_5$	Methyl 3α-acetoxy-11-cholenate	XXI	11-Cholene-3α,24-diol	100	19
	Methyl 3α-acetoxy-11,12α-oxidocholanate[22]	XXII	3α,11α,24-Cholanetriol	...	23,24
	Methyl 3α-acetoxy-11,12β-oxidocholanate[25]	XXII	3α,11β,24-Cholanetriol	...	23,24
$C_{27}H_{44}O_5$	Methyl 3α-acetoxy-11β-hydroxycholanate	XXIII	3α,11β,24-Cholanetriol	...	23,24
$C_{28}H_{44}O_5$	Ethyl 3α-acetoxy-11,12α-oxidocholanate	XXII	3α,11α,24-Cholanetriol	...	24
$C_{29}H_{46}O_5$	Propyl 3α-acetoxy-11,12α-oxidocholanate	XXII	3α,11α,24-Cholanetriol	...	24
$C_{29}H_{46}O_6$	Methyl 3α,11α-diacetoxycholanate	XXIV	3α,11α,24-Cholanetriol	...	23,24
$C_{30}H_{48}O_5$	Butyl 3α-acetoxy-11,12α-oxidocholanate	XXII	3α,11α,24-Cholanetriol	...	24

B. RCOOR′ → RCH_2OH

$C_{21}H_{28}O_5$	Dimethyl Δ⁵-3β-hydroxyetiobilienate	I	$Δ^{9(14)}$-2,13-Dimethyl-7β-hydroxy-2-hydroxy-methyl-1-hydroxyethyl-dodecahydro-phenanthrene	84	1
$C_{29}H_{46}O_2$	3-Carbomethoxycholesta-5,7-diene	XXV	3β-Hydroxymethylcholesta-5,7-diene (3-homoprovitamin D_3)	94	26
$C_{29}H_{48}O_2$	3-Carbomethoxycholest-5-ene	XXVI	3β-Hydroxymethylcholest-5-ene (3-homocholesterol)	99	26

CHART TO TABLE XLI

VII

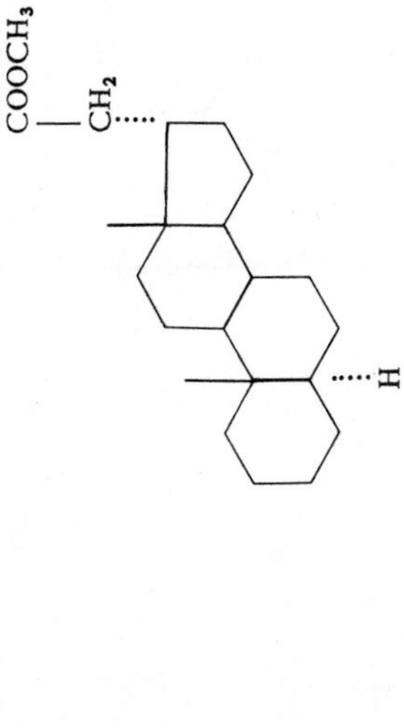

VIII

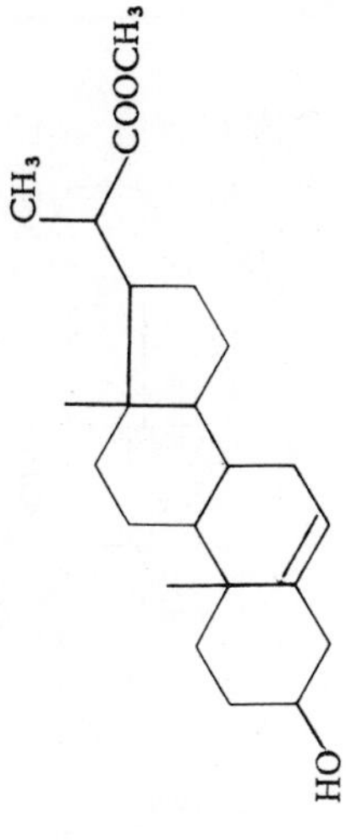

IX

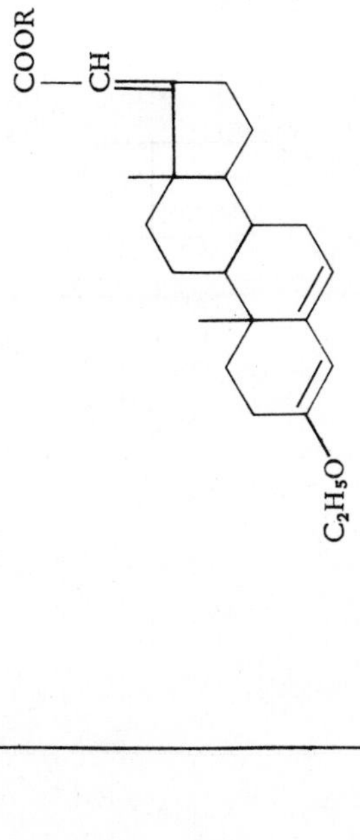

X

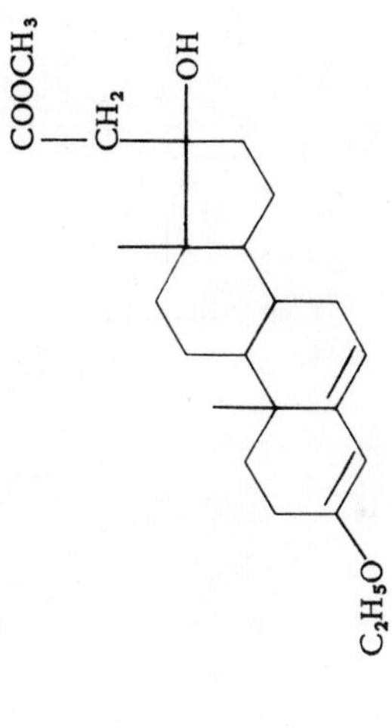

(continued)

CHART TO TABLE XLI (*continued*)

XI

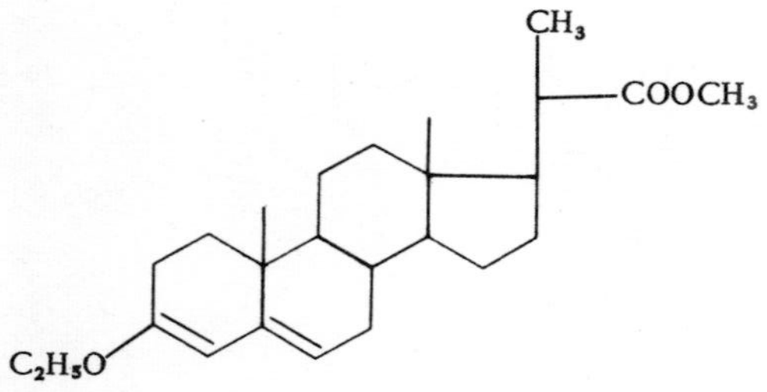

XII

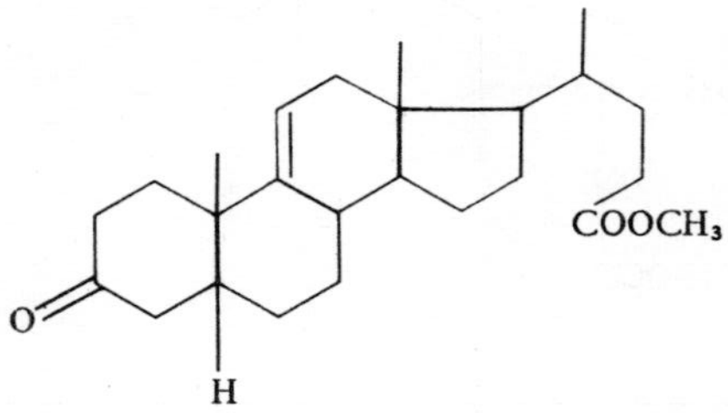

XIII

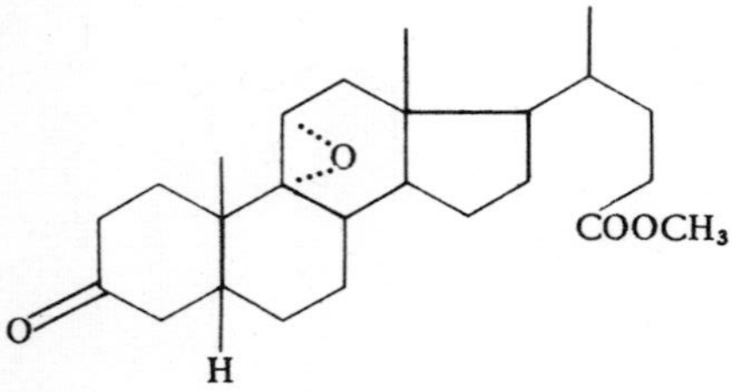

XIV

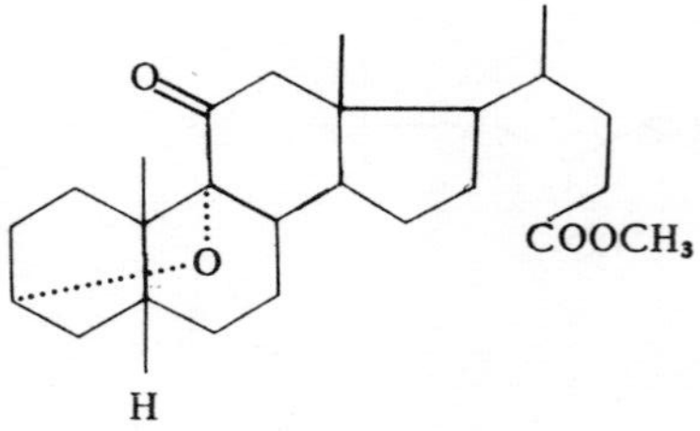

(continued)

CHART TO TABLE XLI (continued)

XXVI

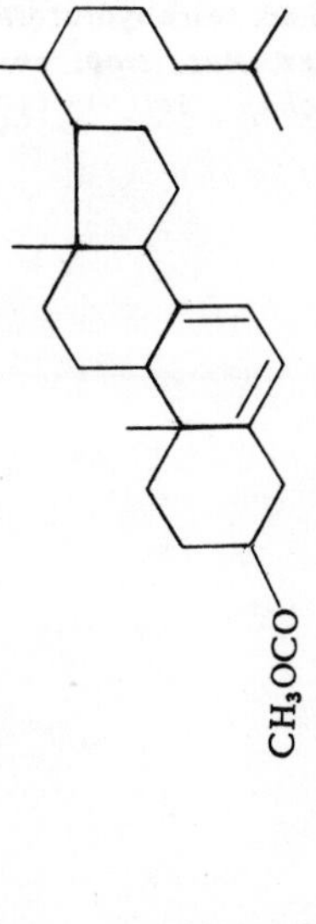

CH₃OCO

XXV

CH₃OCO

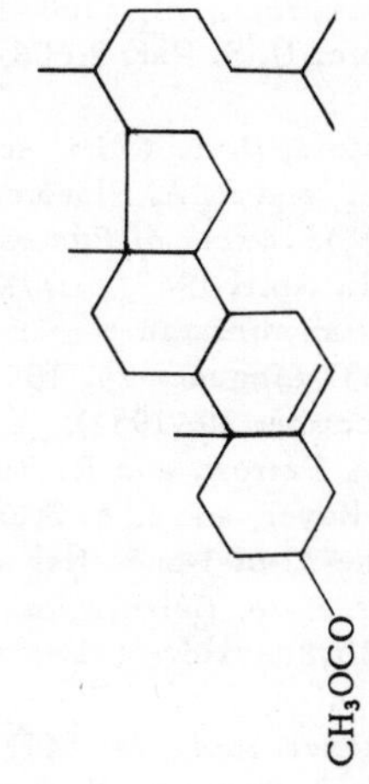

References—Table XLI

[1]G. Papineau-Couture, E. M. Richardson, and G. A. Grant, *Can. J. Research*, *27B*, 902 (1949).
[2]R. B. Wagner and J. A. Moore, *J. Am. Chem. Soc.*, *72*, 5301 (1950).
[3]R. B. Wagner and J. A. Moore, *ibid.*, *71*, 4160 (1949).
[4]R. B. Wagner and J. A. Moore, U. S. Pat. 2,606,198 (August 5, 1952).
[5]Isolated as acetate.
[6]R. Casanova and T. Reichstein, *Helv. Chim. Acta*, *32*, 647 (1949).
[7]H. Heusser, K. Eichenberger, and P. A. Plattner, *ibid.*, *33*, 1088 (1950).
[8]A. C. Ott and M. F. Murray, *Abstracts of Papers*, 113th Meeting American Chemical Society, Chicago, Ill., April 1948, p. 17K.
[9]Reduction carried out in tetrahydrofuran.
[10]Ciba Ltd., Brit. Pat. 665,337 (January 23, 1952); K. Miescher and C. Meystre, U. S. Pat. 2,623,885 (December 30, 1952).
[11]D. Magrath, D. S. Morris, V. Petrow, and R. Royer, *J. Chem. Soc.*, *1950*, 2393.
[12]D. K. Patel, V. Petrow, R. Royer, and I. A. Stuart-Webb, *ibid.*, *1952*, 161.
[13]Isolated as Δ⁴-bisnorcholene-22-ol-3-one after acid hydrolysis.
[14]C. Meystre and K. Miescher, *Helv. Chim. Acta*, *32*, 1758 (1949).
[15]Erroneously called methyl 3α,8α-oxido-9(11)-cholenate in ref. 16.
[16]L. F. Fieser and S. Rajagopalan, *J. Am. Chem. Soc.*, *73*, 118 (1951).
[17]J. C. Babcock and L. F. Fieser, *ibid.*, *74*, 5472 (1952).
[18]P. Bladon, J. M. Fabian, H. B. Henbest, H. P. Koch, and G. W. Wood, *J. Chem. Soc.*, *1951*, 2402.
[19]P. Bladon, H. B. Henbest, and G. W. Wood, *ibid.*, *1952*, 2737.
[20]Erroneously called methyl 3α,8α-oxidocholanate in ref. 16.
[21]Erroneously called methyl 8(?)-hydroxycholanate in ref. 16.
[22]Reduction carried out in ether or tetrahydrofuran.
[23]Ciba Ltd., Brit. Pat. 665,254 (January 16, 1952); Ciba S. A., Fr. Pat. 994,615 (August 8, 1951); P. Plattner, Ger. Pat. 834,848 (May 15, 1952).
[24]P. Plattner, U. S. Pat. 2,599,481 (June 3, 1952).
[25]Reduction carried out in ether, tetrahydrofuran or dioxane.
[26]J. Strating and H. J. Backer, *Rec. trav. chim.*, *70*, 389 (1951); *Proc. Koninkl. Nederland. Acad. Wetenschap.*, *54B*, 13 (1951).

by acetylation, is reported to yield the expected moradiol diacetate oxide (LXXIII) accompanied by 2-acetoxynorolean-16,18-diene (LXXIV) (16,85). The formation of LXXIV can be formulated as in the reduction of moradiol diacetate oxide (equation (9-5)):

(9-39)

7. *Alkaloid carboxylates.* The LAH reduction of various alkaloid esters, including the isomeric lysergic esters, readily yields the corresponding primary alcohols (Table XLIII). The alkaloid corynantheine, originally postulated as possessing structure (LXXV), has been reported to yield desmethylcorynantheine alcohol and desmethoxycorynantheine alcohol (86). The alkaloid has been shown to actually possess an ester-

TABLE XLII

LAH Reduction of Triterpene Esters

	Ester	No.	Product	% Yield	Ref.
$C_{31}H_{48}O_3$	Methyl elemadienonate		Epielemadienediol, $C_{30}H_{50}O_2$	78	1
$C_{31}H_{50}O_2$	Methyl trametenoate		Trametenol, $C_{30}H_{50}O$	99	2
$C_{31}H_{50}O_3$	Methyl trametenolate		Trametenediol, $C_{30}H_{50}O_2$	86	2
	Methyl eburicoate		Eburicodiol, $C_{30}H_{50}O_2$	......	3
	Methyl morolate	I	Moradiol	60–70	4
	Methyl olean-12(13)-en-2-ol-24-oate	II	Olean-12(13)-ene-2,24-diol	...[5]	6
	Methyl ursolate		Ursolic diol (uvaol)	86[7]	8
$C_{31}H_{50}O_5$	Methyl asiatate	III	Asiaticol	......	9
$C_{31}H_{52}O_2$	Methyl eburicenate		Eburicenol, $C_{30}H_{52}O$	98	10
$C_{33}H_{50}O_4$	Methyl dehydrooleanolate acetate	IV	Olean-11,13(18)-dien-2,28-diol	...[11]	12
$C_{33}H_{50}O_5$	Methyl 11-ketooleanolate acetate	V	Olean-11,13(18)-dien-2,28-diol	...[11]	12
$C_{33}H_{52}O_4$	Methyl acetylelemadienolate		Elemadienediol, $C_{30}H_{50}O_2$	100	1
	Methyl acetyleburicoate		Eburicodiol	......	3
	Methyl morolate acetate	I	Moradiol	60–70	4
	Methyl olean-13(18)-enolate acetate	VI	Olean-13(18)-ene-2,28-diol	......	13
	Methyl olean-10-enolate acetate	VII	Olean-10-ene-2,28-diol	...[11]	4
$C_{33}H_{52}O_5$	Methyl morolate acetate oxide	VIII	Norolean-16,18-dienol acetate	...[14]	12
			Norolean-16,18-dienol acetate	36 }[14]	13
			Moradiol diacetate oxide	......	4
$C_{33}H_{54}O_5$	Methyl 11-ketooleanolate acetate	IX	Oleanane-2,11,28-triol	...[11]	12
	Methyl 19-keto-18-isooleanolate acetate	X	18-Isooleanane-2,19,28-triol	...[11]	12,15
	Methyl dihydrosiaresinolate 2-acetate	XI	Oleanane-2,19,28-triol	...[11]	12

CHART TO TABLE XLII

I

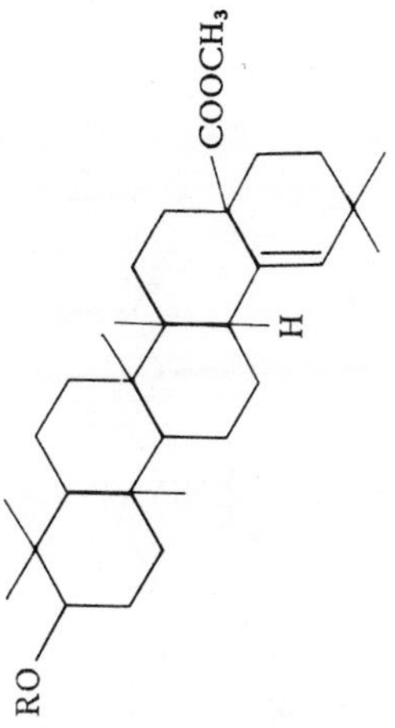

II

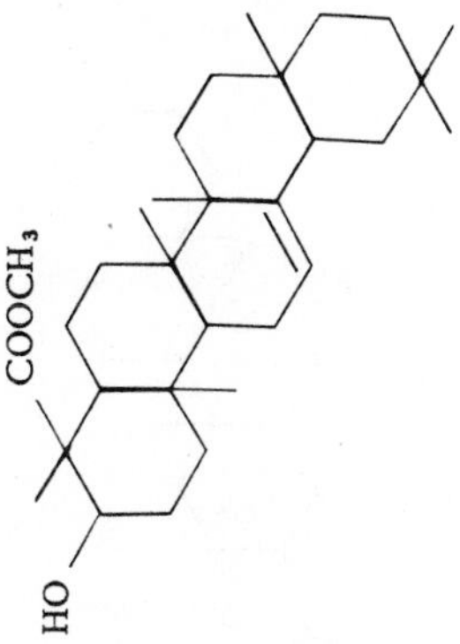

III

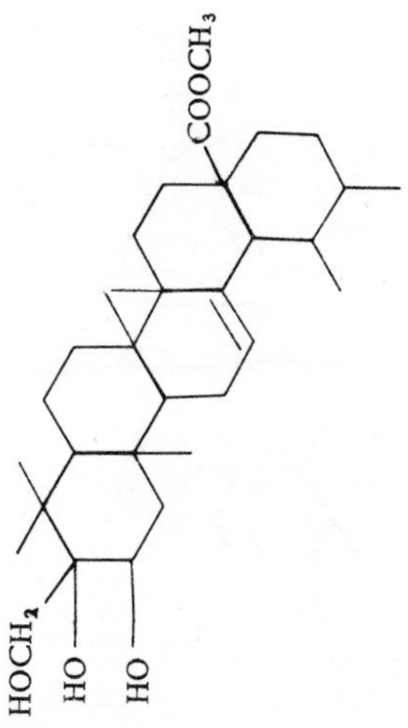

IV

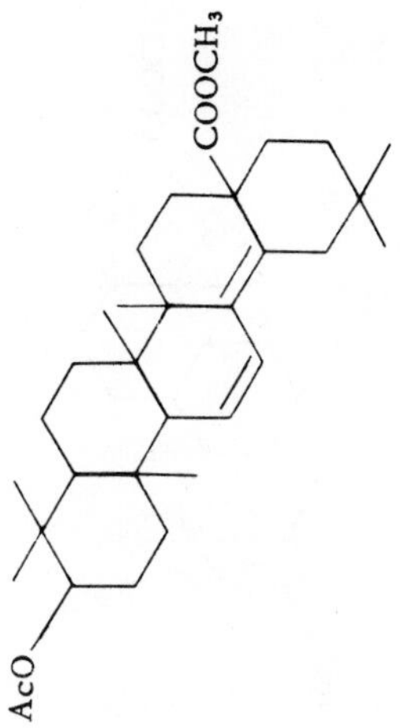

(continued)

CHART TO TABLE XLII (*continued*)

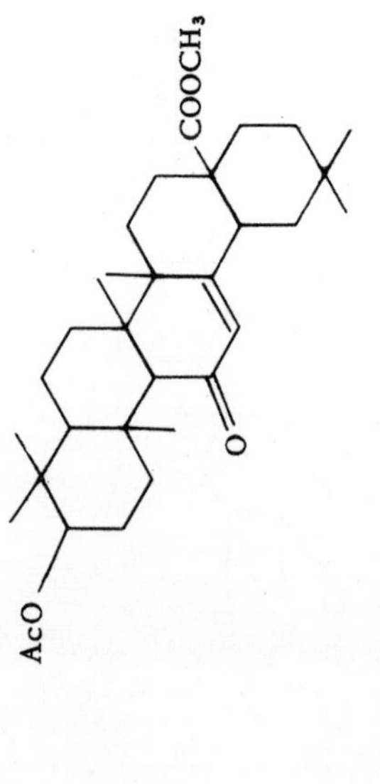

VI

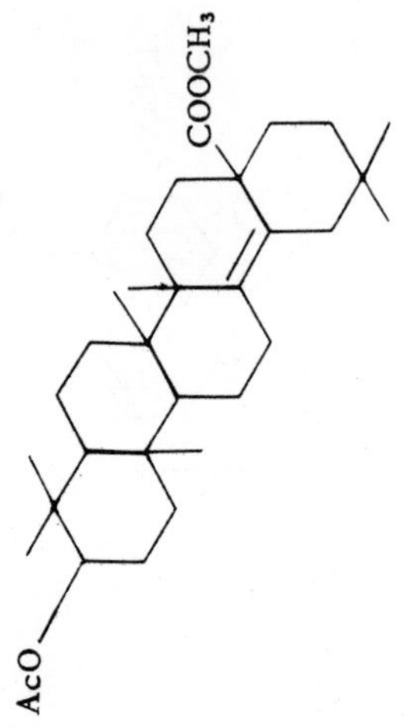

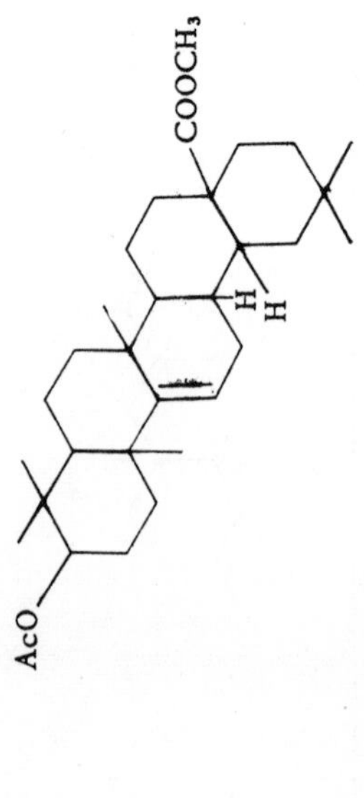

VIII

V

VII

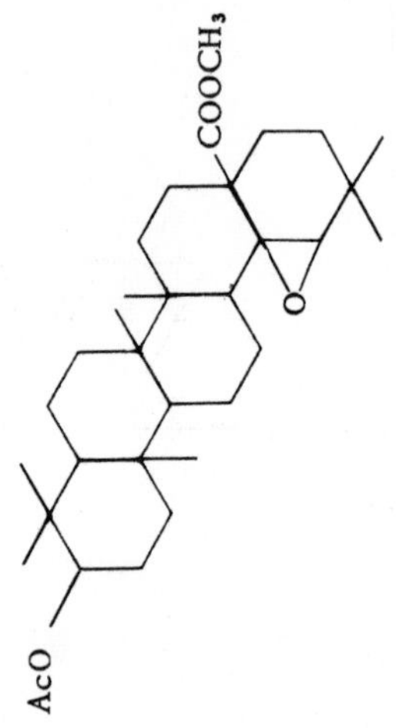

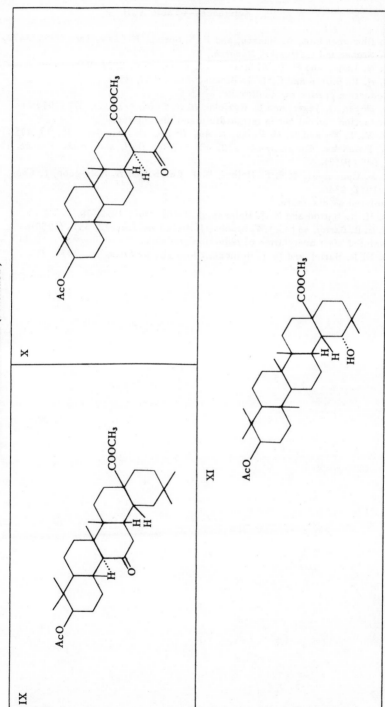

CHART TO TABLE XLII (*continued*)

References—Table XLII

[1]R. Bhuvanendram, W. Manson, and F. S. Spring, *J. Chem. Soc.*, *1950*, 3472.
[2]W. Gruber and G. Proske, *Monatsh.*, *81*, 1024 (1950).
[3]F. N. Lahey and P. H. A. Strasser, *J. Chem. Soc.*, *1951*, 873.
[4]D. H. R. Barton and C. J. W. Brooks, *ibid.*, *1951*, 257.
[5]Reduction carried out in dioxane.
[6]A. Meyer, O. Jeger, and L. Ruzicka, *Helv. Chim. Acta*, *33*, 672 (1950).
[7]Reduction carried out in tetrahydrofuran-ether mixture.
[8]B. Y. T. Wu and L. M. Parks, *J. Am. Pharm. Assoc., Sci. Ed.*, *39*, 475 (1950).
[9]J. Polonsky, *Compt. rend.*, *230*, 485 (1950); *Bull. soc. chim. France*, [5] *19*, 649 (1952).
[10]R. M. Gascoigne, J. S. E. Holker, B. J. Ralph, and A. Robertson, *J. Chem. Soc.*, *1951*, 2346.
[11]Isolated as diacetate.
[12]D. H. R. Barton and N. J. Holness, *J. Chem. Soc.*, *1952*, 78.
[13]D. H. R. Barton and C. J. W. Brooks, *J. Am. Chem. Soc.*, *72*, 3314 (1950).
[14]Isolated after acetylation of reduction products.
[15]D. H. R. Barton and N. J. Holness, *Chemistry and Industry*, *1951*, 233.

enol ether structure (LXXVI) (87) so that the reduction products may be formulated as follows:

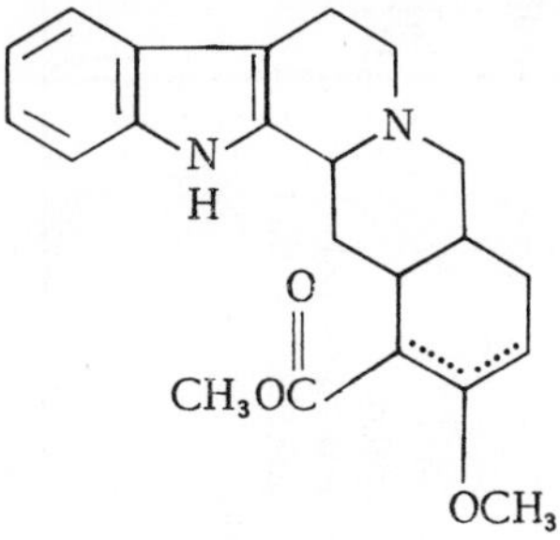

LXXV

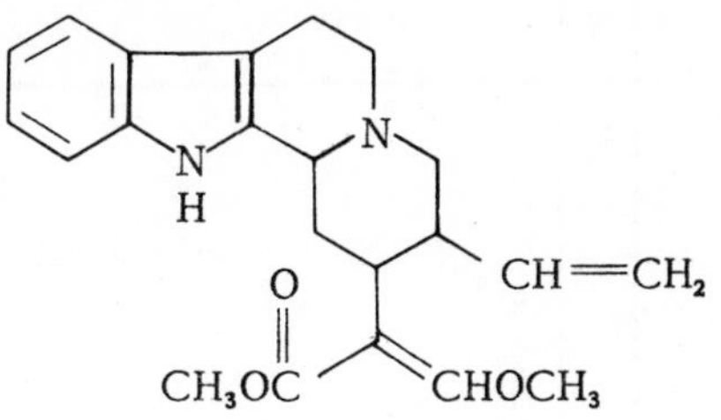

LXXVI

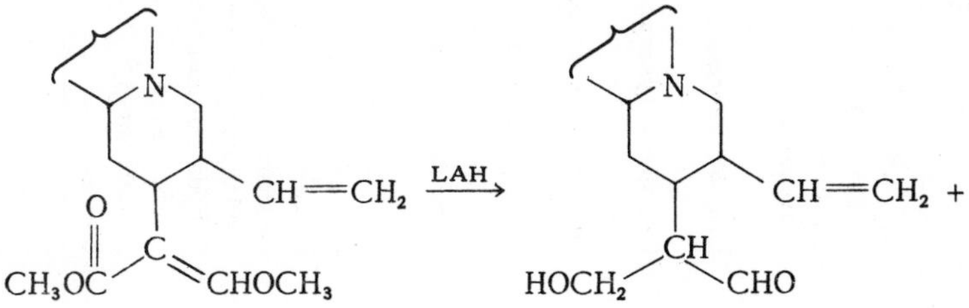

$$\text{LXXVI} \xrightarrow{\text{LAH}}$$

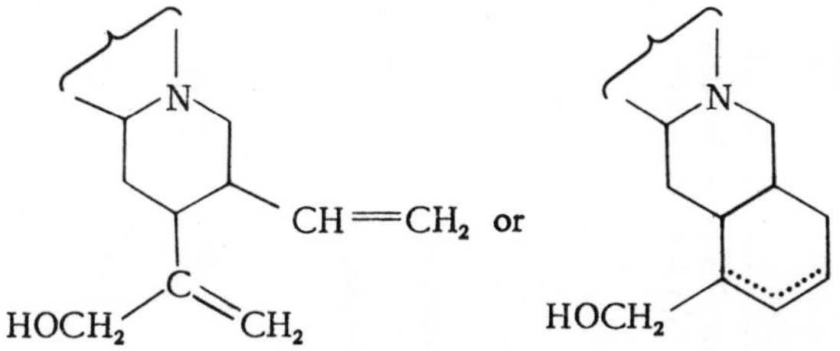

CH=CH₂ or (9-40)

A more detailed discussion of this reduction as well as that of dihydro-corynantheine is given in Section 11.5.2.

8. *Aromatic carboxylates.* The LAH reduction of the esters of aromatic carboxylic acids yields the corresponding hydroxymethyl derivatives. This reduction procedure has been applied in the benzene, naphthalene, phenanthrene, fluorene, benzofluorene and fluoranthrene series.

The following aromatic carboxylates-C[14] have been reduced to the methanol-C[14] derivatives: methyl benzoate-1-C[14] (88), methyl fluorene-9-(carboxylate-C[14]) (89), methyl 11H-benzo[b]fluorene-11-(carboxylate-C[14]) (90).

TABLE XLIII

LAH Reduction of Alkaloid Esters

Ester	No.	Product	% Yield	Ref.
$C_{17}H_{16}N_2O_3$ 4,5,7,8,9,10-Hexahydro-7-methyl-9-carbomethoxy-5-oxoindolo[4,3-fg]quinoline	I	4,5,7,8,9,10-Hexahydro-7-methylindolo[4,3-fg]quinoline-9-methanol	...[1]	2
$C_{17}H_{18}N_2O_2$ Methyl lysergate	II	Lysergol	90	3,4
Methyl isolysergate	III	Isolysergol	91	3
			...	4
$C_{17}H_{20}N_2O_2$ Methyl dihydrolysergate	IV	Dihydrolysergol	74	3
			...	4
Methyl dihydroisolysergate I	IV	Dihydroisolysergol I	75	3
			...	4
Methyl dihydroisolysergate II	IV	Dihydroisolysergol II	80	4
$C_{21}H_{24}N_2O_2$ Apoyohimbine	V	Apoyohimbyl alcohol	...[5]	6
$C_{21}H_{24}N_2O_3$ Tetrahydroalstonine	VI'	Tetrahydroalstonol	70[5]	8
$C_{21}H_{26}N_2O_3$ Yohimbine	VII	Yohimbyl alcohol	100[9]	6
			85–90[5]	8
			...[9]	10
$C_{22}H_{26}N_2O_3$ Corynantheine	VIII'	Desmethylcorynantheine alcohol	28,.... } [11]	6
		Desmethoxycorynantheine alcohol	....,34 }	
$C_{22}H_{28}N_2O_3$ Dihydrocorynantheine	IX	Desmethoxydihydrocorynantheine alcohol	5	13
		Isodesmethoxydihydrocorynantheine alcohol	11 [11,12]	
		Dihydrocorynantheine alcohol	13	
$C_{26}H_{37-39}NO_9$ Methyl lycoctonamate	....	Lycoctonine	55[14]	15
$C_{28}H_{43}NO_3$ 13-Carbomethoxysolanidane-3-one	X	Solanidane-3β,18-diol epimer	28	16
			...	

CHART TO TABLE XLIII

References—Table XLIII

[1]Reduction carried out in N-ethylmorpholine.
[2]A. Stoll, T. Petrzilka, and J. Rutschmann, *Helv. Chim. Acta,* 33, 2254 (1950).
[3]A. Stoll, A. Hofmann, and W. Schlientz, *ibid.,* 32, 1947 (1949); Sandoz Ltd., Brit. Pat. 674,061 (June 18, 1952).
[4]Sandoz A. G., Swiss Pat. 276,415 (October 16, 1951).
[5]Reduction carried out in tetrahydrofuran-ether mixture.
[6]A. Chatterjee and P. Karrer, *Helv. Chim. Acta,* 33, 802 (1950).
[7]M. M. Janot and R. Goutarel, *Bull. soc. chim. France,* [5] 18, 588 (1951).
[8]R. C. Elderfield and A. P. Gray, *J. Org. Chem.,* 16, 506 (1951).
[9]Reduction carried out in tetrahydrofuran.
[10]P. Karrer and R. Saemann, *Helv. Chim. Acta,* 35, 1932 (1952).
[11]See text.
[12]Reduction carried out in benzene-ether mixture.
[13]P. Karrer, R. Schwyzer, and A. Flam, *Helv. Chim. Acta,* 35, 851 (1952).
[14]Reduction carried out in dioxane-ether mixture.
[15]O. E. Edwards and L. Marion, *Can. J. Chem.,* 30, 627 (1952).
[16]Y. Sato and W. A. Jacobs, *J. Biol. Chem.,* 191, 63 (1951).

The ester group in aromatic compounds has been selectively reduced in the presence of other functional groups such as the aryl nitro (48), alkyl (91) and aryl (92) halides and carboxylic acids (92). The reduction of monomethyl phthalate (LXXVII) with three-quarters of a mole of LAH is reported to yield phthalide (LXXVIII) (20).

$$\text{(9-41)}$$

LXXVII   LXXVIII

The reduction of 3-chlorophthalic acid (LXXIX) and of 1-methyl-2-hydrogen-3-chlorophthalate (LXXX) with the calculated amount of LAH yields 7-chlorophthalide (LXXXI) while the reduction of methyl 3-chlorophthalate (LXXXII) and of 2-methyl-1-hydrogen-3-chlorophthalate (LXXXIII) yields 3-chloro-o-xylylene glycol (LXXXIV) (92).

$$\text{(9-42)}$$

LXXIX   LXXXI   LXXX

LXXXII   LXXXIV   LXXXIII (9-43)

As discussed earlier in Section 7.1.1.b, treatment of 4-formylphenanthrene-5-carboxylic acid with methanol and hydrochloric acid yields a pseudo methyl ester (LXXXV) which does not form carbonyl derivatives. Treatment of the aldehydo acid with diazomethane yields the normal methyl ester (LXXXVI). Reduction of the pseudo and normal esters yields 4,5-di-(hydroxymethyl)phenanthrene (93).

LXXXV   LXXXVI   (9-44)

The pseudo ethyl ester similarly yields the di-(hydroxymethyl) compound (94).

Conover and Tarbell (95) reported that while the reduction of methyl anthranilate (LXXXVII) with a large excess of LAH at 65° for 5 minutes gives 50% of o-aminobenzyl alcohol and 5% of o-toluidine, when the reduction is carried out for 15 hours a 39% yield of o-toluidine is obtained.

Attempts to extend the hydrogenolysis reaction to the hydroxy compounds, methyl salicylate and ethyl p-hydroxybenzoate, have been unsuccessful due to the precipitation which occurs on mixing the esters with a large excess of LAH (95). With the usual amount of LAH these reductions proceed readily to the substituted benzyl alcohol. Hydrogenolysis reactions are discussed in Section 16.1.

Wiberg and Schmidt have reported that no reduction occurs on treatment of the β-naphthol ester of benzoic acid with LAH (96).

The LAH reduction of various aromatic carboxylates is summarized in Table XLIV.

9. *Heterocyclic carboxylates.* The LAH reduction of the esters of heterocyclic carboxylic acids generally yields the corresponding hydroxymethyl compounds. Thus, pyrrolidine, piperidine and tetrahydropyridine carboxylates are readily reduced to carbinols. Imidazole (LXXXVIII)

(97) and isoindazole (LXXXIX) (98) carboxylates are reduced without decomposition of the heterocyclic nucleus.

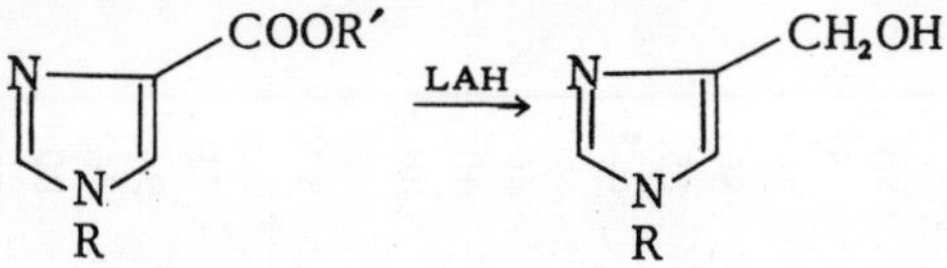

$$(9\text{-}47)$$

LXXXVIII

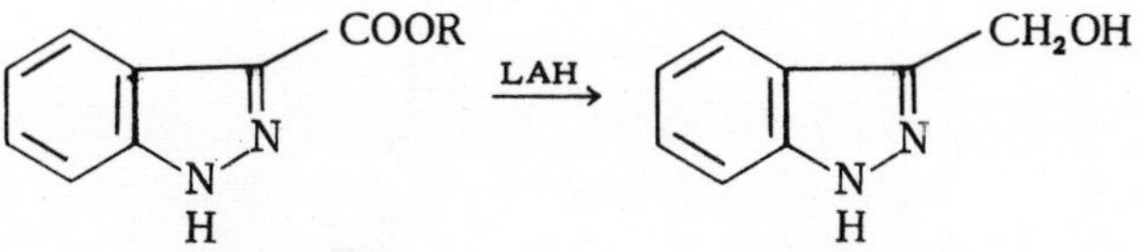

$$(9\text{-}48)$$

LXXXIX

Similarly, the esters of indole (XC) and pyrazole (XCI) carboxylic acids are converted to the appropriate carbinols (99).

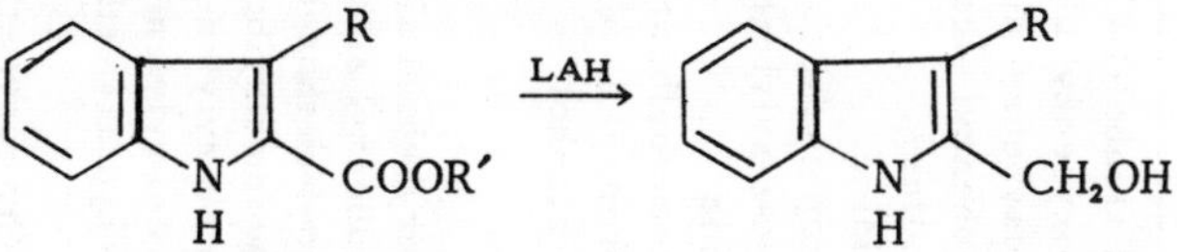

$$(9\text{-}49)$$

XC

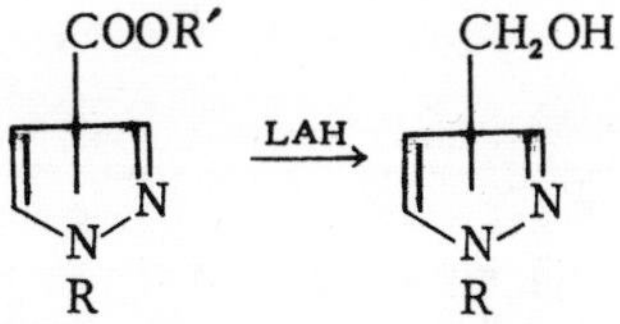

$$(9\text{-}50)$$

XCI

Although the LAH reduction of pyridine carboxylates (XCII) in refluxing or cold ether yields the pyridine carbinols in satisfactory yield, higher temperatures and slowly conducted reactions cause the formation of small amounts of piperidyl carbinols and methylpyridines (100).

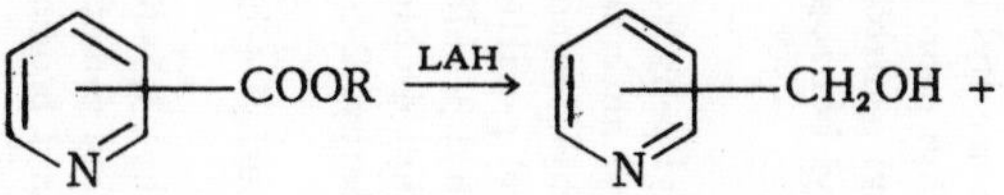

XCII

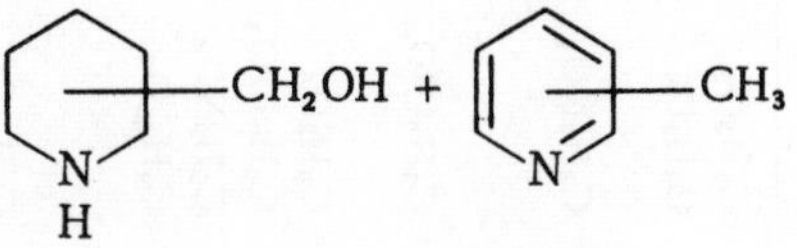

$$(9\text{-}51)$$

TABLE XLIV

LAH Reduction of Aryl Esters

	Ester	Product	% Yield	Ref.
$C_8H_8O_2$	Methyl benzoate-1-C^{14}	Benzyl alcohol-1-C^{14}	85.5	1
$C_8H_8O_3$	Methyl salicylate	o-Hydroxybenzyl alcohol	....	2
	Methyl p-hydroxybenzoate	p-Hydroxybenzyl alcohol	....	2
$C_8H_9NO_2$	Methyl anthranilate	o-Aminobenzyl alcohol	50[3]	4
		o-Toluidine	5[3]	
		o-Toluidine	39[3]	4
$C_9H_7ClO_4$	1-Methyl-2-hydrogen-3-chlorophthalate	7-Chlorophthalide	80	5
	2-Methyl-1-hydrogen-3-chlorophthalate	3-Chloro-o-xylylene glycol	85	5
$C_9H_8O_4$	Monomethyl phthalate	Phthalide	....[6]	7
$C_9H_9BrO_2$	Methyl p-bromomethylbenzoate	p-Bromomethylbenzyl alcohol	....	8
$C_9H_9NO_4$	Ethyl p-nitrobenzoate	p-Nitrobenzyl alcohol	40	9
$C_9H_{10}O_2$	Ethyl benzoate	Benzyl alcohol	90	10
			88	11
			....	4
$C_9H_{10}O_3$	Ethyl p-hydroxybenzoate	p-Hydroxybenzyl alcohol	57	12
$C_9H_{11}NO_2$	Ethyl anthranilate	o-Aminobenzyl alcohol	....	13
$C_9H_{11}NO_3$	Methyl 3-amino-4-methoxybenzoate	3-Amino-4-methoxybenzyl alcohol	71	14
$C_{10}H_9F_3O_2$	Ethyl p-trifluoromethylbenzoate	p-Trifluoromethylbenzyl alcohol	94	15
$C_{10}H_9ClO_4$	Methyl 3-chlorophthalate	3-Chloro-o-xylylene glycol	76	5
	Methyl 4-chlorophthalate	4-Chloro-o-xylylene glycol	80	5
$C_{10}H_{10}O_5$	Dimethyl 2-hydroxyisophthalate	2,6-Di-(hydroxymethyl)phenol	trace	16
				2
	Dimethyl 4-hydroxyisophthalate	2,4-Di-(hydroxymethyl)phenol	trace	16
				2
$C_{10}H_{12}O_4$	Methyl 3,5-dimethoxybenzoate	3,5-Dimethoxybenzyl alcohol	....	17
$C_{11}H_{12}O_4$	Methyl 6-methoxy-2-acetylbenzoate	2-(1-Hydroxyethyl)-6-methoxybenzyl alcohol	97	18
	Methyl bromophthalate	Bromophthalyl alcohol	....	19

Formula	Ester	Product	Yield	Ref
$C_{11}H_{14}O_5$	Methyl 3,4,5-trimethoxybenzoate	3,4,5-Trimethoxybenzyl alcohol	73	20
			77	21
$C_{11}H_{15}NO_2$	Methyl p-dimethylaminomethylbenzoate	p-Dimethylaminomethylbenzyl alcohol	....	8
$C_{12}H_{12}O_6$	Dimethyl 2-acetoxyisophthalate	2,6-Di-(hydroxymethyl)phenol	70	16
	Dimethyl 4-acetoxyisophthalate	2,4-Di-(hydroxymethyl)phenol	79	16
$C_{12}H_{12}O_7$	Trimethyl hydroxytrimesate	2,4,6-Tri-(hydroxymethyl)phenol	....	2
$C_{12}H_{14}O_2$	Methyl 1,2,3,4-tetrahydro-5-naphthoate	5-Hydroxymethyl-1,2,3,4-tetrahydronaphthalene	97.7	22
	Methyl 1,2,3,4-tetrahydro-6-naphthoate	6-Hydroxymethyl-1,2,3,4-tetrahydronaphthalene	70	22
$C_{12}H_{14}O_4$	Diethyl phthalate	Phthalyl alcohol	....	23
$C_{13}H_{12}O_3$	Methyl 3-methoxy-2-naphthoate	2-Hydroxymethyl-3-methoxynaphthalene	90-	24
$C_{13}H_{16}O_2$	Ethyl 1,2,3,4-tetrahydro-2-naphthoate	2-Hydroxymethyl-1,2,3,4-tetrahydronaphthalene	95.5	25
$C_{13}H_{16}O_4$	Ethyl homophthalate	Homophthalyl alcohol	91	26
$C_{14}H_{12}O_4$	Methyl naphthalate	1,8-Di-(hydroxymethyl)naphthalene	72	27
$C_{15}H_{12}O_2$	Methyl fluorene-9-(carboxylate-C^{14})	Fluorene-9-(methanol-C^{14})	87	28
$C_{15}H_{18}O_7$	Triethyl hydroxytrimesate	2,4,6-Tri-(hydroxymethyl)phenol	18.5[29]	30
			trace	16
$C_{15}H_{22}O_4$	p-Carbethoxyacetophenone diethyl ketal	p-Hydroxymethylacetophenone diethyl ketal	93	31
$C_{16}H_{14}O_4$	Dimethyl diphenate	2,2'-Di-(hydroxymethyl)diphenyl	100	32
			91	33
$C_{17}H_{12}O_3$	Methyl 4-formylphenanthrene-5-carboxylate	4,5-Di-(hydroxymethyl)phenanthrene	100	34
	ψ-Methyl 4-formylphenanthrene-5-carboxylate	4,5-Di-(hydroxymethyl)phenanthrene	"excellent"	34
$C_{17}H_{20}O_8$	Triethyl acetoxytrimesate	2,4,6-Tri-(hydroxymethyl)phenol	27	16
$C_{18}H_{12}O_2$	Methyl fluoranthene-8-carboxylate	Fluoranthene-8-methanol	84	35
$C_{18}H_{14}O_3$	ψ-Ethyl 4-formylphenanthrene-5-carboxylate	4,5-Di-(hydroxymethyl)phenanthrene	90	36
$C_{18}H_{18}O_4$	Ethyl diphenate	2,2'-Di-(hydroxymethyl)diphenyl	91	33
	4,4'-Dicarbomethoxydibenzyl	4,4'-Di-(hydroxymethyl)dibenzyl	51	37
$C_{18}H_{18}O_6$	Dimethyl 6,6'-dimethoxydiphenate	2,2'-Di-(hydroxymethyl)-6,6'-dimethoxydiphenyl	90	38
$C_{19}H_{14}O_2$	Methyl 11H-benzo[b]fluorene-11-(carboxylate-C^{14})	11H-Benzo[b]fluorene-11-(methanol-C^{14})	80	39
$C_{19}H_{20}O_4$	1,3-Bis-(4-carbomethoxyphenyl)propane	1,3-Bis-(4-hydroxymethylphenyl)propane	94	37

(Continued)

TABLE XLIV (Continued)

	Ester	Product	% Yield	Ref.
$C_{20}H_{20}O_2$	Methyl retene-2-carboxylate	2-Hydroxymethylretene	86	40
$C_{20}H_{20}N_2O_3$	3-(β-o-Carbomethoxyphenylacetamidoethyl)-indole	3-(β-o-Hydroxymethylphenylacetamidoethyl)indole	76[41]	42
$C_{20}H_{22}O_6$	Methyl 9,10-dihydro-2,3,4,7-tetramethoxy-9-phenanthroate	9,10-Dihydro-9-hydroxymethyl-2,3,4,7-tetra-methoxyphenanthrene	....	43
$C_{21}H_{16}O_2$	9-Carbomethoxy-9-phenylfluorene	9-Hydroxymethyl-9-phenylfluorene	93	44
$C_{24}H_{18}O_4$	Dimethyl 1,1'-dinaphthyl-2,2-dicarboxylate	2,2'-Di-(hydroxymethyl)-1,1'-dinaphthyl	100	45

References—Table XLIV

[1] W. G. Dauben and P. Coad, *J. Am. Chem. Soc.*, *71*, 2928 (1949).

[2] J. Reese, *Angew. Chem.*, *64*, 399 (1952).

[3] Reduction carried out in a diethyl ether–di-*n*-butyl ether mixture at 65° with 5 equivalents excess LAH; see text.

[4] L. H. Conover and D. S. Tarbell, *J. Am. Chem. Soc.*, *72*, 3586 (1950).

[5] R. F. Bird and E. E. Turner, *J. Chem. Soc.*, *1952*, 5050.

[6] Reduction carried out with three-quarters of a mole of LAH.

[7] G. Papineau-Couture, E. M. Richardson and G. A. Grant, *Can. J. Research*, *27b*, 902 (1949).

[8] M. Charpentier-Morize and B. Tchoubar, *Compt. rend.*, *233*, 1621 (1951).

[9] H. Felkin, *ibid.*, *230*, 304 (1950).

[10] R. F. Nystrom and W. G. Brown, *J. Am. Chem. Soc.*, *69*, 1197 (1947).

[11] H. I. Schlesinger and A. E. Finholt, U. S. Pat. 2,576,311 (November 27, 1951).

[12] E. Larsson, *Trans. Chalmers. Univ. Technol.*, Gothenburg, *94*, 15 (1950).

[13] B. Witkop, J. B. Patrick, and H. M. Kissman, *Chem. Ber.*, *85*, 949 (1952).

[14] R. Lukeš and E. Bochníčková, unpublished work, through M. Ferles and J. Rudinger, *Chem. Listy*, *47*, 120 (1953).

[15] H. B. Hass and M. L. Bender, *J. Am. Chem. Soc.*, *71*, 1767 (1949).

[16] J. H. Freeman, *ibid.*, *74*, 6257 (1952).

[17] E. R. Shepard, H. D. Porter, J. F. Noth, and C. K. Simmans, *J. Org. Chem.*, *17*, 568 (1952).

[18] R. Kuhn and K. Dury, *Chem. Ber.*, *84*, 848 (1951).

[19] S. Siegel and S. Coburn, *J. Am. Chem. Soc.*, *73*, 5494 (1951).

[20] M. U. Tsau, *ibid.*, *73*, 5495 (1951).

[21] A. Dornow and G. Petsch, *Arch. pharm.*, *285*, 323 (1952).

[22] M. S. Newman and T. S. Bye, *J. Am. Chem. Soc.*, *74*, 905 (1952).

[23] R. G. Jones, *ibid.*, *74*, 1489 (1952).

[24] A. Ebnöther, T. M. Meijer, and H. Schmid, *Helv. Chim. Acta*, *35*, 910 (1952).

[25] M. S. Newman and J. R. Mangham, *J. Am. Chem. Soc.*, *71*, 3342 (1949).

[26] E. L. Anderson and F. G. Holliman, *J. Chem. Soc.*, *1950*, 1037.

[27] M. H. Beeby, G. H. Cookson, and F. G. Mann, *ibid.*, *1950*, 1917.

[28] C. J. Collins, *J. Am. Chem. Soc.*, *70*, 2418 (1948).

[29] Reduction carried out in dioxane.

[30] A. T. Carpenter and R. F. Hunter, *J. Applied Chem. (London)*, *1*, 217 (1951).

[31] L. Schmid, W. Swoboda, and M. Wichtl, *Monatsh.*, *83*, 185 (1952).

[32] D. M. Hall and E. E. Turner, *Nature*, *163*, 537 (1949).

[33] D. M. Hall, M. S. Lesslie, and E. E. Turner, *J. Chem. Soc.*, *1950*, 711.

[34] G. M. Badger, J. E. Campbell, J. W. Cook, R. A. Raphael, and A. I. Scott, *ibid.*, *1950*, 2326.

[35] M. C. Kloetzel and H. E. Mertel, *J. Am. Chem. Soc.*, *72*, 4786 (1950).

[36] M. S. Newman and H. S. Whitehouse, *ibid.*, *71*, 3664 (1949).

[37] D. J. Cram and H. Steinberg, *ibid.*, *73*, 5691 (1951).

[38] D. M. Hall and E. E. Turner, *J. Chem. Soc.*, *1951*, 3072.

[39] C. J. Collins, J. G. Burr, Jr., and D. N. Hess, *J. Am. Chem. Soc.*, *73*, 5176 (1951).

[40] K. J. Karrman, *Acta Chem. Scand.*, *5*, 901 (1951).

[41] Reduction carried out in a benzene–ether mixture.

[42] G. A. Swan, *J. Chem. Soc.*, *1949*, 1720.

[43] J. W. Cook, J. Jack, and J. D. Loudon, *ibid.*, *1952*, 607

[44] van Dyken, unpublished work, through W. G. Brown, in *Organic Reactions*, Vol. VI, p. 502.

[45] E. D. Bergmann and J. Szmuszkovicz, *J. Am. Chem. Soc.*, *73*, 5153 (1951).

Although the LAH reduction of ethyl picolinate (XCIII) at $-7°$ to $0°$ is reported to yield 70% 2-hydroxymethylpyridine (100), at normal temperatures the yield is decreased to 25% and, in one case, an equal amount of a high boiling material was also obtained (101).

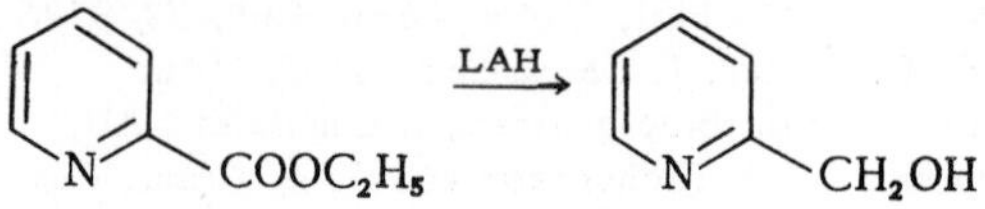

(9-52)

XCIII

A hydrogenolysis reaction has been reported in the reduction of 2,6-dimethyl-3,4-dicarbethoxypyridine (XCIV) (102). The reduction of 0.5 mole of XCIV with 0.7 mole of LAH in ether gives a 50% yield of 2,6-dimethyl-3,4-di-(hydroxymethyl)pyridine (XCV). When XCIV is reduced using four moles of LAH for each mole of ester during a 24-hour reflux period, a trimethylhydroxymethylpyridine is obtained in 20% yield. The latter has been formulated as 2,4,6-trimethyl-3-hydroxymethylpyridine (XCVI) by analogy with desoxypyridoxin which is formed by catalytic hydrogenolysis of vitamin B_6.

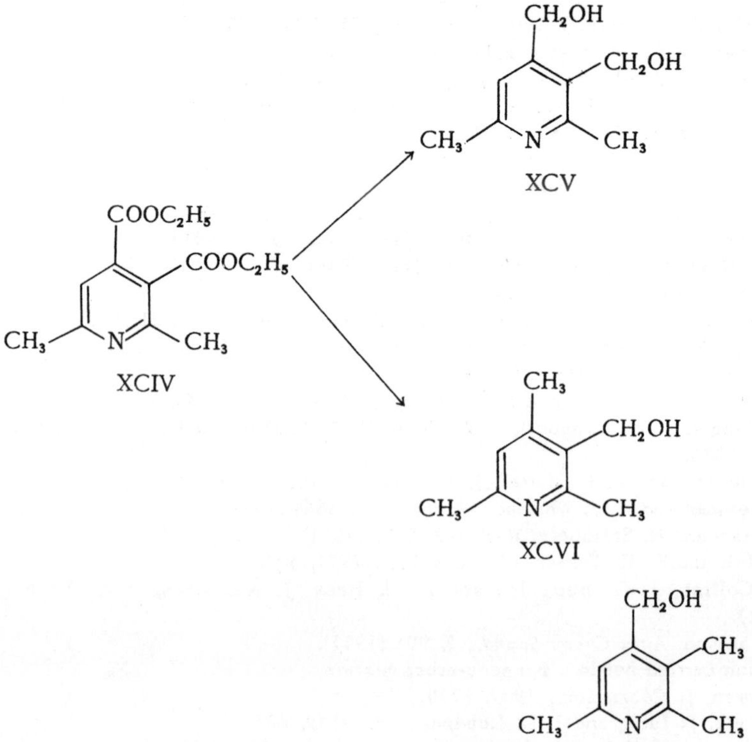

(9-53)

However, as discussed in Section 16.1, XCVII is the more probable structure based on the principle that hydrogenolysis in this case is due to the reduction of the vinylog of an amide (103).*

The reduction of pyridine carboxylates has found widespread application in the synthesis of vitamin B_6 and its analogs. Thus, reduction of 2-methyl-3-hydroxy-4,5-dicarbalkoxypyridine (XCVIII) or the 3-acetoxy compound yields vitamin B_6 (XCIX) (102,104–106).

$$(9\text{-}54)$$

XCVIII   XCIX

As an alternate route to XCIX, 2-methyl-3-amino-4-carbethoxy-5-aminomethylpyridine (C) or 2-methyl-3-amino-4-carbethoxy-5-cyano-6-chloropyridine (CI) is reduced with LAH to 2-methyl-3-amino-4-hydroxymethyl-5-aminomethylpyridine (CII). Treatment of CII with nitrous acid followed by hydrolysis yields pyridoxin (XCIX) (107).

$$(9\text{-}55)$$

*Note added in proof: E. C. Kornfeld has experimentally verified that XCVII is the correct structure for the product originally postulated as XCVI (*J. Am. Chem. Soc.*, in press).

Mariella and Belcher reported that the LAH reduction of 2-hydroxy-3-carbethoxy-4,6-dimethylpyridine (CIII) in ether gives 60% of the expected 3-hydroxymethyl compound (108). However, attempted reduction of 2-hydroxy-3-carbomethoxy-6-methylpyridine (CIV) with LAH in either diethyl or di-*n*-butyl ether failed to yield any carbinol (109).

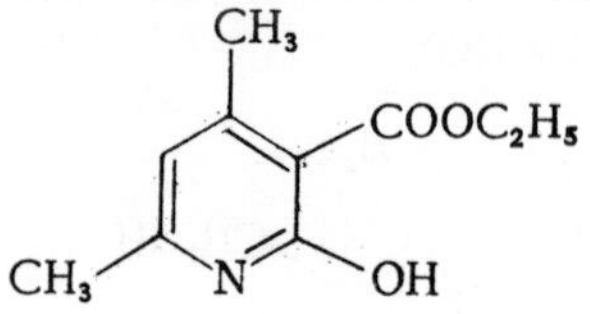

CIII 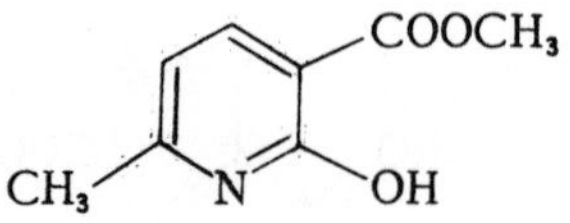   CIV

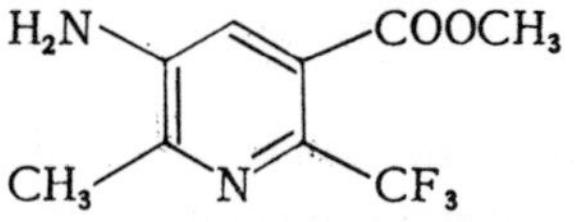

CV

The attempted preparation of 2-trifluoromethyl-3-hydroxymethyl-5-amino-6-methylpyridine by the LAH reduction of the 3-carbomethoxy compound (CV) has been reported to give an unstable compound which decomposes during attempts at purification (110).

Rosenmund and Zymalkowski (111) reported that the LAH reduction of 2- and 4-carbalkoxyquinolines (CVI) at $-12°$ gives good yields of the hydroxymethyl quinolines. When the reductions are carried out in refluxing ether the products are glossy materials which become viscous liquids on warming.

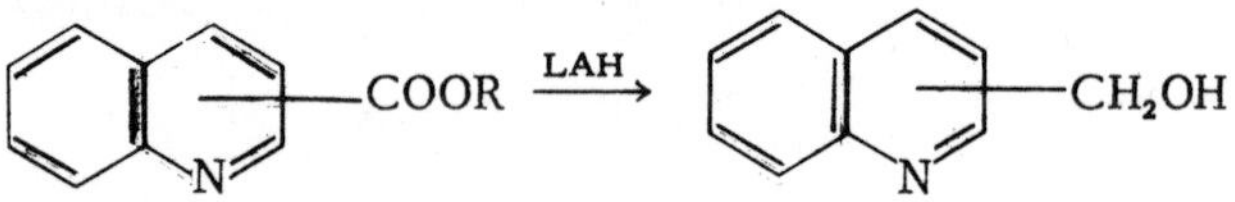

CVI   (9-56)

The reduction of 1-carbomethoxyphenazine (CVII) yields the corresponding carbinol (112). Birkofer and Birkofer postulate that the 5,10-dihydro compound is an intermediate in the reduction. A temporary red color which develops is possibly the N-monohydrophenazyl radical.

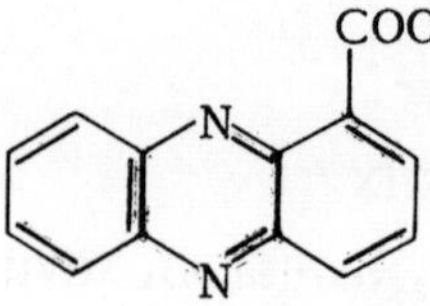

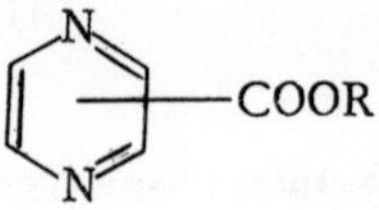

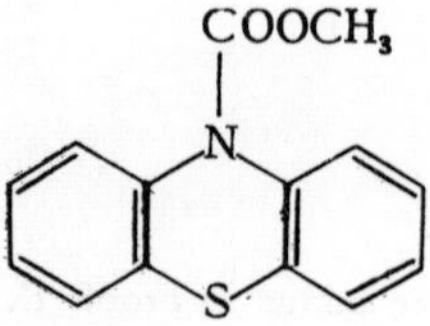

CVII   CVIII   CIX

The reduction of pyrazine carboxylates (CVIII) results in decomposition of the heterocyclic nucleus (102). The LAH reduction of 10-carbomethoxy-phenothiazine (CIX) is reported to yield phenothiazine as the only identi-fiable product (113). The latter is also formed by the LAH reduction of 10-aminoacylphenothiazine (114). The cleavage of amides in which the nitrogen is part of a heterocyclic system is discussed in Section 10.1.1.d.2.

The ester grouping in 1-carbomethoxyquinolizidine (CX) is readily re-duced to yield 1-hydroxymethylquinolizidine (115).

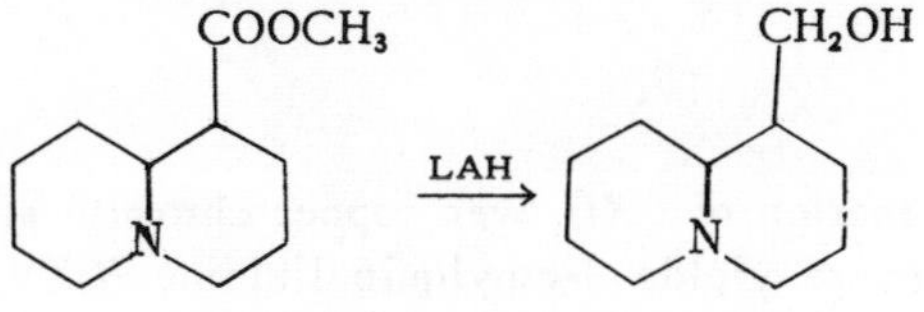

CX

(9-57)

The 1-carbethoxyquinolizidine fragment in the ethyl ester of aphyllinic acid behaves in a similar manner (116). The 2-carbomethoxyquinolizidine (CXI) structure is also reduced to the carbinol (117) as is the 3-carbethoxy group in 3-carbethoxy-4-methylquinolizidine (CXII) (37).

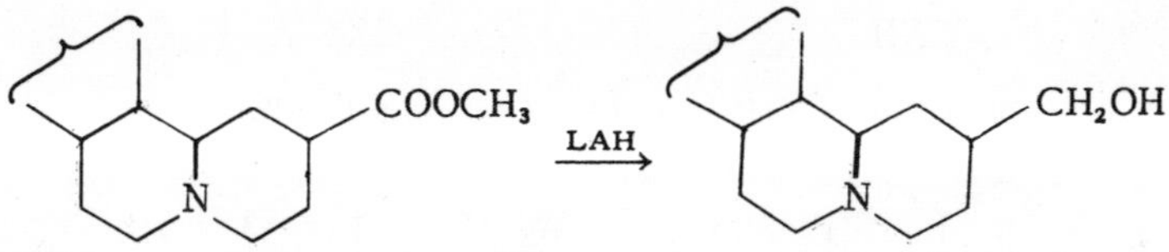

CXI

(9-58)

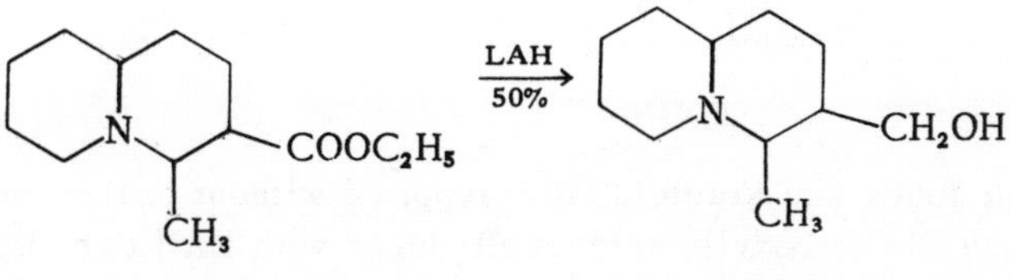

CXII

(9-59)

On the other hand, LAH reduction of 3-carbethoxy-4-ketoquinolizidine (CXIII) results in cleavage of the carbethoxy group to yield 4-ketoquino-lizidine (37).

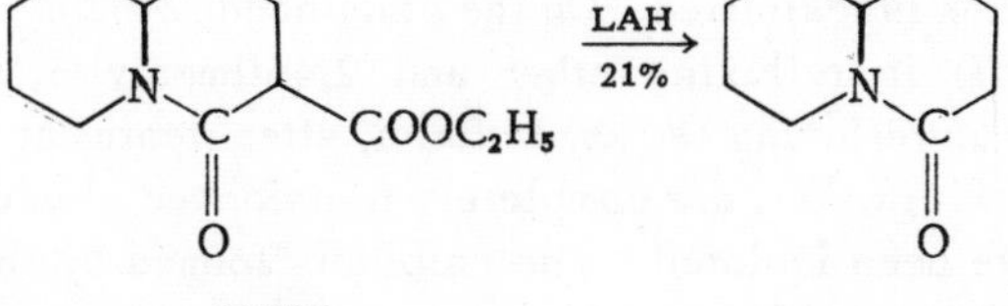

CXIII

(9-60)

However, 1,3-dicarbethoxy-4-ketoquinolizidine (CXIV) is reduced in the normal manner (118).

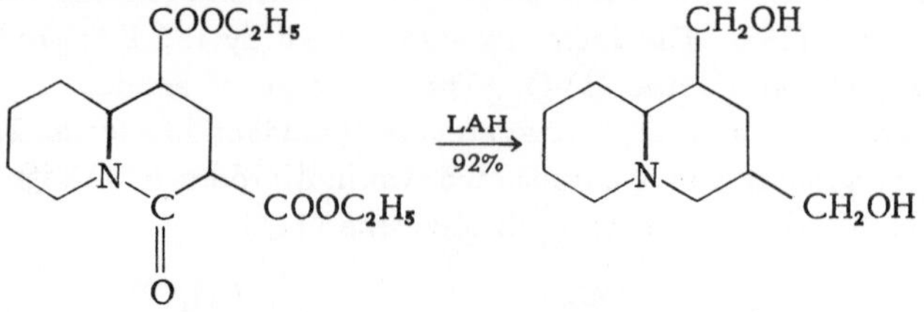

$$\tag{9-61}$$

CXIV

Catalytic hydrogenation of CXII over copper chromite at 250° under 200 atmospheres pressure yields 3-ethylquinolizidine (CXV) as a result of rearrangement after a reductive cleavage (37).

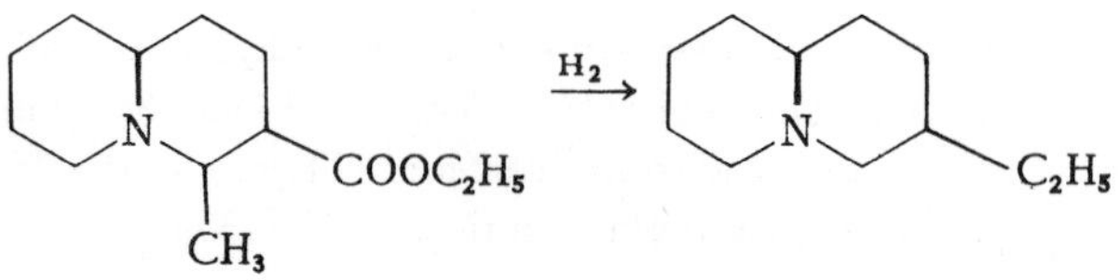

$$\tag{9-62}$$

CXII   CXV

Under the same conditions CXIII is reduced to quinolizidine (37).

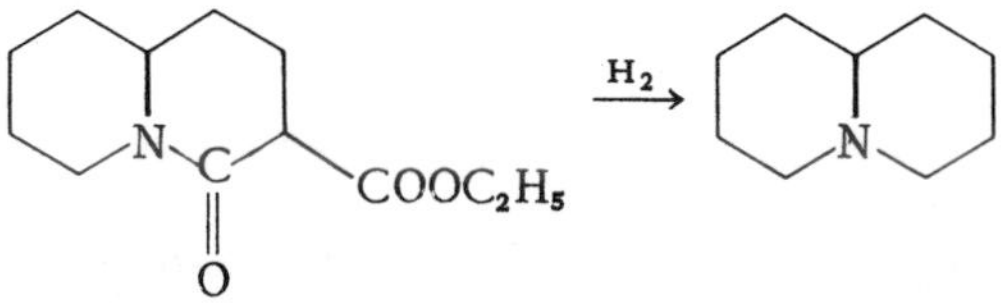

$$\tag{9-63}$$

CXIII

Although Jones and Kornfeld (102) reported without further details that esters of pyrrole carboxylic acids are reduced with LAH to hydroxymethyl compounds, Treibs and Scherer (119) were unable to successfully carry out such reductions. Thus, 2,4-dimethyl-5-carbethoxypyrrole (CXVI) is quantitatively recovered after treatment with large excesses of LAH in boiling ether or tetrahydrofuran. Similarly, after refluxing for 12 hours with LAH in tetrahydrofuran, a major portion of the starting 2,4-dimethyl-5-carbethoxypyrrole-3-carboxaldehyde (CXVII) is recovered unchanged although a portion is resinified. On the other hand, 2-methyl-3-carbethoxy-pyrrole (CXVIII) in refluxing ether and 2,4-dimethyl-3,5-dicarbethoxy-pyrrole (CXIX) in refluxing tetrahydrofuran, after treatment with LAH and decomposition with water, are completely transformed although no definite compounds have been isolated. The carbinols formed by the reduction of CXVIII and CXIX probably react by condensation to high molecular weight compounds such as those obtained in the reduction of 2,4-dimethyl-3-acetylpyrrole (Section 7.2.1.e.).

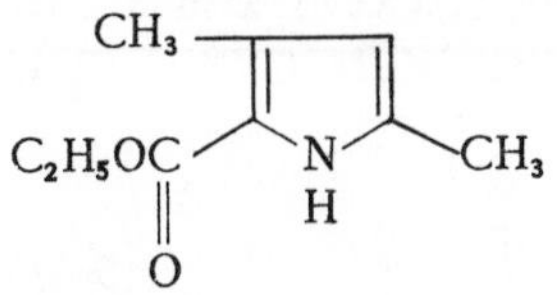

CXVI

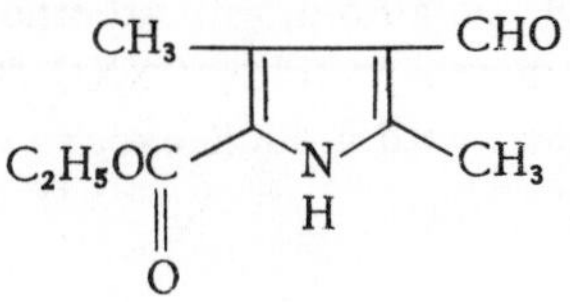

CXVII

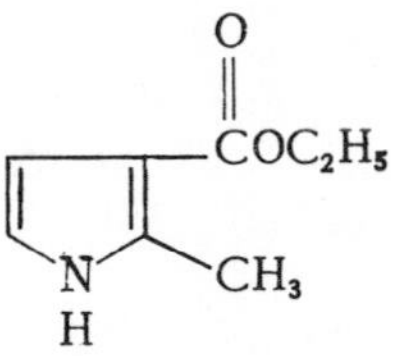

CXVIII

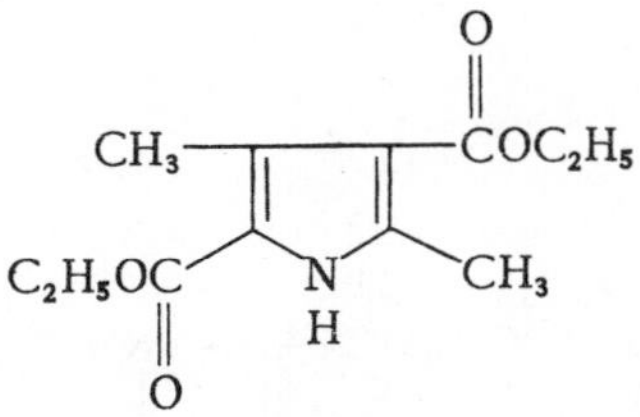

CXIX

The transformation occurring in the reduction of CXVIII and CXIX may proceed through an intermediate hydrogenolysis reaction as discussed in Section 16.1 (103).

Hydrogenolysis reactions have been reported by Conover and Tarbell in the LAH reduction of various thiazole carboxylates (120). While 2-methyl-4,5-dicarbethoxythiazole (CXX) and 2-amino-4-carbethoxythiazole (CXXI) are reduced with excess LAH in a mixture of benzene and ether to the corresponding carbinols similar treatment of 2-amino-4-hydroxy-methyl-5-carbethoxythiazole (CXXII: R = CH_2OH) and 2-amino-4-methyl-5-carbethoxythiazole (CXXII: R = CH_3) yields the 5-methyl derivatives.

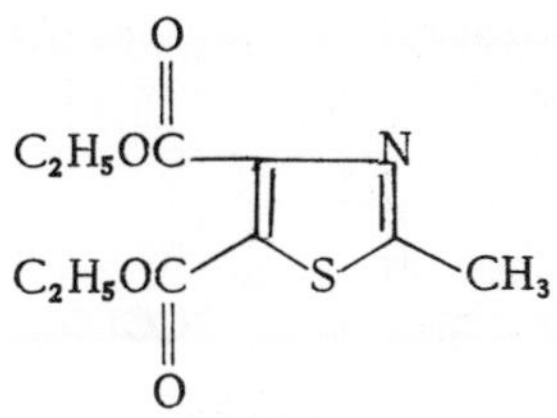

CXX

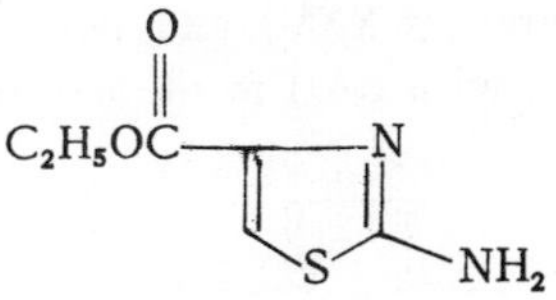

CXXI

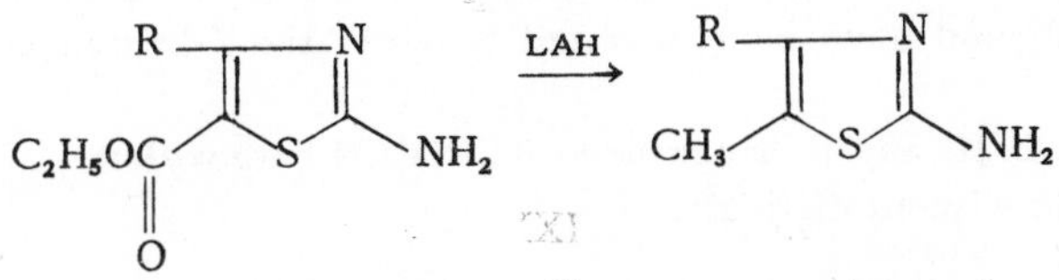

(9-64)

CXXII

CXXIII

The 5-carbethoxy group in CXXII is particularly resistant to reduction. Treatment of CXXII (R = CH_3) with a small excess of LAH at room tem-

perature or at 88° yields only starting material. The reaction of CXXII
(R = CH₂OH) with LAH in ether similarly yields only starting material.
The reduction of 2-amino-4,5-dicarbethoxythiazole (CXXIV) with a 25%
excess of LAH in ether yields CXXII (R = CH₂OH) while CXXIII (R =
CH₂OH) is obtained with a 400% excess of LAH.

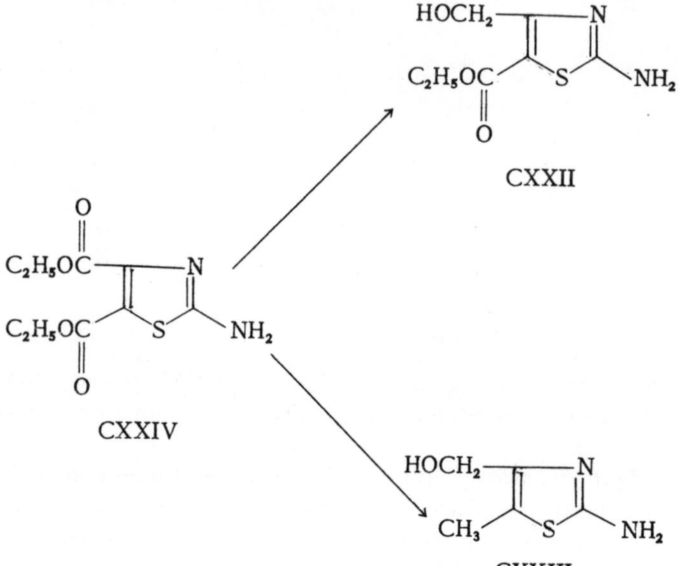

(9-65)

CXXII

CXXIV

(9-66)

CXXIII

In contrast to the resistance of the 5-carbethoxy group in CXXII and
CXXIV, the same group in CXX and in 5-carbethoxythiazole is readily
reduced (121).

Furan (CXXV) and benzofuran (CXXVI) carboxylates are readily reduced with LAH to the heterocyclic carbinols.

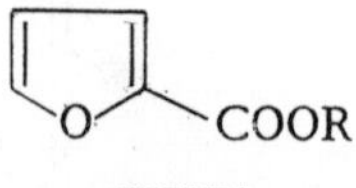

CXXV 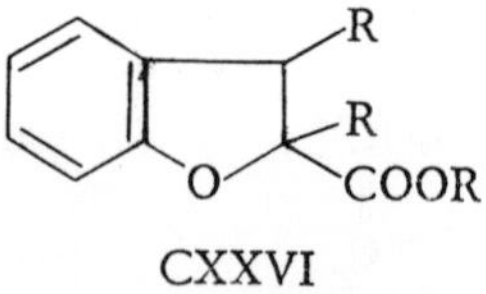   CXXVI

Attempts to reduce 2-methyl-3-sulfonamido-5-carbomethoxyfuran to the
2,5-dimethyl compound have been reported to yield the 5-hydroxymethyl
derivative (122).

Thiophene (CXXVII) and thianaphthene (CXXVIII) carboxylates are reduced to carbinols without difficulty.

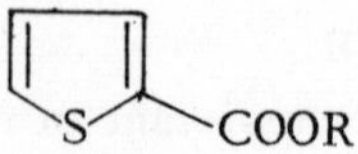

CXXVII 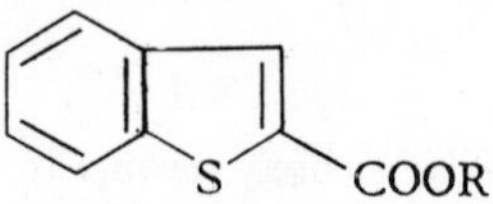   CXXVIII

Jones and Kornfeld (102) have reported without further details, that the esters of oxazole carboxylic acid (CXXIX) are reduced with LAH with concurrent cleavage of the heterocyclic nucleus. The reduction of 2,5-disubstituted 4-carbethoxyoxazolines (CXXX) with LAH in ether at low temperatures yields the corresponding 4-hydroxymethyloxazolines.

CXXIX   CXXX

The LAH reduction of various heterocyclic carboxylates is summarized in Table XLV.

9.1.2   Reductions with Aluminum Hydride

Patents involving the reduction of esters with LAH generally state that the reductions can equally well be carried out with aluminum hydride, although no specific examples are given (123). Wiberg and Jahn (124) investigated the mechanism of the reduction of ethyl acetate to ethanol. An ethereal ethyl acetate solution was added to an ethereal aluminum hydride solution (ester: $AlH_3 = 3 : 2.2$) and the white precipitate which separated as well as the residue left after distillation of the ether was found to be aluminum ethylate.

$$3 \ CH_3COOC_2H_5 + 2 \ AlH_3 \rightarrow 2 \ Al(OC_2H_5)_3 \qquad (9\text{-}67)$$

The reaction is postulated as involving the addition of the hydride to the carbonyl double bond.

$$CH_3CH\!=\!\!O \xrightarrow{+\,alH} CH_3CH_2Oal \qquad (9\text{-}68)$$

al = 1 equivalent Al

The addition compound ($AlH_2Cl + AlHCl_2$), obtained by the interaction of aluminum hydride and aluminum chloride, reduces esters in a manner similar to that indicated in equation (9-68). Thus, methyl salicylate yields 50% of o-hydroxybenzyl alcohol while ethyl benzoate yields 80% of benzyl alcohol (125).

TABLE XLV

LAH Reduction of Heterocyclic Esters

	Ester	Product	% Yield	Ref.
$C_6H_7NO_2S$	5-Carbethoxythiazole	5-Hydroxymethylthiazole	88.5	1
$C_6H_8N_2O_2$	5-Carbethoxyimidazole	5-Hydroxymethylimidazole	92	2
	1-Methyl-5-carbomethoxyimidazole	1-Methyl-5-hydroxymethylimidazole	88	2
	3-Carbethoxypyrazole	3-Hydroxymethylpyrazole	84	3
	4-Carbethoxypyrazole	4-Hydroxymethylpyrazole	86	3
$C_6H_8N_2O_2S$	2-Amino-4-carbethoxythiazole	2-Amino-4-hydroxymethylthiazole	21[4,5]	6
$C_7H_7ClO_3$	2-Carbethoxy-5-chlorofuran	2-Hydroxymethyl-5-chlorofuran	97	7
$C_7H_9NO_5$	2-Methyl-3-sulfonamido-5-carbomethoxyfuran	2-Methyl-3-sulfonamido-5-hydroxymethylfuran	....	8
$C_7H_{10}N_2O_2S$	2-Amino-4-methyl-5-carbethoxythiazole	2-Amino-4,5-dimethylthiazole	54[4,5]	6
$C_7H_{10}N_2O_3S$	2-Amino-4-hydroxymethyl-5-carbethoxythiazole	2-Amino-4-hydroxymethyl-5-methylthiazole	8[4]	6
$C_7H_{11}NO_3$	L-2-Carbethoxy-5-pyrrolidone	L-2-Hydroxymethylpyrrolidine	31	9
$C_7H_{13}NO_2$	2-Carbethoxypyrrolidine (ethyl ester proline)	2-Hydroxymethylpyrrolidine (prolinol)	....	10
	Ethyl ester L-proline	L-(+)-Prolinol	73	11
$C_8H_9NO_2$	2-Carbethoxypyridine (ethyl picolinate)	2-Hydroxymethylpyridine	26	12
			22	13
			70.2	14
	3-Carbethoxypyridine (ethyl nicotinate)	3-Hydroxymethylpyridine	62	15
			82	16
			64[5]	12
			49	13
			75.7	14
			22	17
	4-Carbethoxypyridine (ethyl isonicotinate)	4-Hydroxymethylpyridine	53	18
			75	12
			53.2	13
			73.4	14
$C_8H_{12}N_2O_2$	3,5-Dimethyl-4-carbethoxypyrazole	3,5-Dimethyl-4-hydroxymethylpyrazole	64	19

$C_8H_{13}NO_2$	1-Methyl-3-carbomethoxy-1,2,5,6-tetrahydropyridine (arecoline)	1-Methyl-3-hydroxymethyl-1,2,5,6-tetrahydropyridine	80	9
	3-Carbethoxy-1,2,5,6-tetrahydropyridine (ethyl ester guvacine)	3-Hydroxymethyl-1,2,5,6-tetrahydropyridine	60	9
$C_8H_{15}NO_2$	2-Carbethoxypiperidine (ethyl pipecolinate)	2-Hydroxymethylpiperidine[20]	71	21
	1-Methyl-2-carbethoxypyrrolidine (ethyl hygrinate)	1-Methyl-2-hydroxymethylpyrrolidine	82	22
$C_9H_8N_2O_2$	3-Carbomethoxyisoindazole	3-Hydroxymethylisoindazole	72[23]	24
$C_9H_9F_3N_2O_2$	2-Trifluoromethyl-3-carbomethoxy-5-amino-6-methylpyridine	unstable product	...	25
$C_9H_{12}N_2O_4S$	2-Amino-4,5-dicarbethoxythiazole	2-Amino-4-hydroxymethyl-5-carbethoxythiazole	30[26]	6
		2-Amino-4-hydroxymethyl-5-methylthiazole	34[27]	6
$C_{10}H_{10}ClN_3O_2$	2-Methyl-3-amino-4-carbethoxy-5-cyano-6-chloropyridine	2-Methyl-3-amino-4-hydroxymethyl-5-aminomethylpyridine	...	28
$C_{10}H_{11}NO_5$	2-Methyl-3-hydroxy-4,5-dicarbomethoxypyridine	2-Methyl-3-hydroxy-4,5-di-(hydroxymethyl)pyridine (vitamin B₆)	77[5]	16
$C_{10}H_{11}N_3O_2$	2-Methyl-3-amino-4-carbethoxy-5-cyanopyridine	2-Methyl-3-amino-4-hydroxymethyl-5-aminomethylpyridine	...	29
$C_{10}H_{12}N_2O_4$	2-Methyl-3-amino-4,5-dicarbomethoxypyridine	2-Methyl-3-amino-4,5-di-(hydroxymethyl)pyridine	89	16
	4-Amino-6-methyl-2,5-dicarbomethoxypyridine	4-Amino-6-methyl-2,5-di-(hydroxymethyl)pyridine	83	25
	5-Amino-6-methyl-2,3-dicarbomethoxypyridine	5-Amino-6-methyl-2,3-di-(hydroxymethyl)pyridine	70–80	25
$C_{10}H_{13}NO_3$	2-Hydroxy-3-carbethoxy-4,6-dimethylpyridine	2-Hydroxy-3-hydroxymethyl-4,6-dimethylpyridine	60	30
$C_{10}H_{13}NO_4S$	2-Methyl-4,5-dicarbethoxythiazole	2-Methyl-4,5-di-(hydroxymethyl)thiazole	38[4]	6
$C_{10}H_{15}N_3O_2$	2-Methyl-3-amino-4-carbethoxy-5-aminomethylpyridine	2-Methyl-3-amino-4-hydroxymethyl-5-aminomethylpyridine	...	28
$C_{10}H_{16}O_4S$	2,5-Dicarbethoxythiophene	2,5-Di-(hydroxymethyl)thiophene	100	31
$C_{11}H_{10}N_2O_2$	1-Phenyl-5-carbomethoxyimidazole	1-Phenyl-5-hydroxymethylimidazole	84	2

(Continued)

TABLE XLV (*Continued*)

	Ester	Product	% Yield	Ref.
$C_{11}H_{11}NO_2$	2-Carbethoxyindole	2-Hydroxymethylindole	68	32
			....	33
$C_{11}H_{13}NO_4$	3,4-Dicarbethoxypyridine (ethyl cinchomeronate)	3,4-Di-(hydroxymethyl)pyridine	22.5	12
$C_{11}H_{17}NO_2$	Ethyl ester of ecgonidine (I)	2-Hydroxymethyl-2,3-dihydrotropane (2,3-dehydrohomotropene)	100	18
$C_{11}H_{19}NO_2$	1-Carbomethoxyquinolizidine	1-Hydroxymethylquinolizidine (*dl*-lupinine)	47	34
$C_{11}H_{19}NO_3$	Ethyl ester of ecgonine (II)	2-Hydroxymethyltropine	100	18
$C_{12}H_{11}NO_2$	2-Carbethoxyquinoline	2-Hydroxymethylquinoline	83	18
	4-Carbethoxyquinoline	4-Hydroxymethylquinoline	77[35]	18
$C_{12}H_{12}N_2O_2$	1-Benzyl-5-carbomethoxyimidazole	1-Benzyl-5-hydroxymethylimidazole	82	2
$C_{12}H_{12}O_2S$	2-Carbethoxy-3-methylthianaphthene	2-Hydroxymethyl-3-methylthianaphthene	....	36
$C_{12}H_{13}NO_2$	2-Carbethoxy-3-methylindole	2-Hydroxymethyl-3-methylindole	....	33
$C_{12}H_{13}NO_6$	2-Methyl-3-acetoxy-4,5-dicarbomethoxypyridine	2-Methyl-3-hydroxy-4,5-di-(hydroxymethyl)-pyridine	84[5]	16
$C_{12}H_{14}N_2O_6$	2,3,4-Tricarbomethoxy-5-amino-6-methylpyridine	2,3,4-Tri-(hydroxymethyl)-5-amino-6-methyl-pyridine	61	25
$C_{12}H_{15}NO_4$	2-Methyl-4,5-dicarbethoxypyridine	2-Methyl-4,5-di-(hydroxymethyl)pyridine	60	16
$C_{12}H_{15}NO_5$	2-Methyl-3-hydroxy-4,5-dicarbethoxypyridine	2-Methyl-3-hydroxy-4,5-di-(hydroxymethyl)-pyridine	....	37
$C_{12}H_{16}N_2O_4$	2,3-Dicarbethoxy-5-amino-6-methylpyridine	2,3-Di-(hydroxymethyl)-5-amino-6-methylpyridine	70–80	25
$C_{12}H_{19}NO_3$	3-Carbethoxy-4-ketoquinolizidine	4-Ketoquinolizidine	21	38
$C_{13}H_{12}Cl_2N_2O_5$	trans-2-Dichloromethyl-4-carbethoxy-5-p-nitrophenyloxazoline	trans-2-Dichloromethyl-4-hydroxymethyl-5-p-nitrophenyloxazoline	....	39
$C_{13}H_{13}Cl_2NO_3$	L-*threo*-2-Dichloromethyl-4-carbethoxy-5-phenyloxazoline	D-*threo*-2-Dichloromethyl-4-hydroxymethyl-5-phenyloxazoline	90	40
	l-*trans*-2-Dichloromethyl-4-carbethoxy-5-phenyloxazoline	l-*trans*-2-Dichloromethyl-4-hydroxymethyl-5-phenyloxazoline	....	41
$C_{13}H_{14}N_2O_2$	1-Benzyl-4-carbethoxypyrazole	1-Benzyl-4-hydroxymethylpyrazole	92–96	3

	Ester	Product		
C13H14N2O5	trans-2-Methyl-4-carbethoxy-5-p-nitro-phenyloxazoline	trans-2-Methyl-4-hydroxymethyl-5-p-nitro-phenyloxazoline	....	39
C13H15NO3	DL-threo-2-Methyl-4-carbethoxy-5-phenyl-oxazoline	DL-threo-2-Methyl-4-hydroxymethyl-5-phenyl-oxazoline	65	42
C1₃H16O3	2-Carbethoxy-2,3-dimethyl-2,3-dihydrobenzo-furan	2-Hydroxymethyl-2,3-dimethyl-2,3-dihydrobenzo-furan	82	43
C13H16N2O6	2,3-Dicarbethoxy-4-carboxy-5-amino-6-methyl-pyridine	2,3,4-Tri-(hydroxymethyl)-5-amino-6-methyl-pyridine	47	25
C13H17NO4	2,6-Dimethyl-3,4-dicarbethoxypyridine	2,6-Dimethyl-3,4-di-(hydroxymethyl)pyridine	50	16
		2,4,6-Trimethyl-3-hydroxymethylpyridine[44]	20	16
C13H17NO5	2-Methyl-3-methoxy-4,5-dicarbethoxypyridine	2-Methyl-3-methoxy-4,5-di-(hydroxymethyl)-pyridine	....	37
C13H23NO2	3-Carbethoxy-4-methylquinolizidine	3-Hydroxymethyl-4-methylquinolizidine	50	38
C14H10N2O2	1-Carbomethoxyphenazine	1-Hydroxymethylphenazine	30	45
C14H11NO2S	10-Carbomethoxyphenothiazine	Phenothiazine	....	46
C14H19NO4	2,4,6-Trimethyl-3,5-dicarbethoxypyridine (3,5-dicarbethoxycollidine)	2,4,6-Trimethyl-3,5-di-(hydroxymethyl)pyridine	77	47
C15H17NO4	Ethyl 2-carbethoxyindole-3-acetate	2-Hydroxymethyl-3-(2-hydroxymethyl)indole	90	33
C15H23NO5	1,3-Dicarbethoxy-4-ketoquinolizidine	1,3-Di-(hydroxymethyl)quinolizidine	92	48
C16H24N2O4	2-Methyl-3-amino-4,5-dicarbobutoxypyridine	2-Methyl-3-amino-4,5-di-(hydroxymethyl)-pyridine	56	16
C17H13NO2	2-Phenyl-4-carbomethoxyquinoline	2-Phenyl-4-hydroxymethylquinoline	88[35]	18
C17H15NO5	2-Methyl-3-hydroxy-4,5-dicarbethoxypyridine	2-Methyl-3-hydroxy-4,5-di-(hydroxymethyl)-pyridine	35[5]	17
C17H23NO4	2-Carbomethoxy-10,11-dimethoxy-1,2,3,4,6,7-hexahydrobenzquinolizine	2-Hydroxymethyl-10,11-dimethoxy-1,2,3,4,6,7-hexahydrobenzquinolizine	....	49
C17H30N2O2	Ethyl ester aphyllinic acid (IV)	1-Hydroxymethyl-3-(2-piperidyl)quinolizidine	76	50
C18H16N2O5	trans-2-Phenyl-4-carbethoxy-5-p-nitrophenyl-oxazoline	trans-2-Phenyl-4-hydroxymethyl-5-p-nitrophenyl-oxazoline	....	39
C18H17NO3	dl-trans-2,5-Diphenyl-4-carbethoxyoxazoline	dl-trans-2,5-Diphenyl-4-hydroxymethyloxazoline	....	41
	trans-2,5-Diphenyl-4-carbethoxyoxazoline	trans-2,5-Diphenyl-4-hydroxymethyloxazoline	80[51]	52

(Continued)

TABLE XLV (*Continued*)

	Ester	Product	% Yield	Ref.
$C_{18}H_{17}NO_5$	2-Methyl-3-methoxy-4,5-dicarbethoxypyridine	2-Methyl-3-methoxy-4,5-di-(hydroxymethyl)-pyridine	....	17
$C_{19}H_{21}NO_5$	2-Methyl-3-benzyloxy-4,5-dicarbethoxypyridine	2-Methyl-3-benzyloxy-4,5-di-(hydroxymethyl)-pyridine	85[5]	17
			....	37
$C_{20}H_{16}N_2O_2$	1-(2'-Carbomethoxyskatyl)isoquinoline (V)	1-(2'-Hydroxymethylskatyl)isoquinoline	74[4]	53
$C_{20}H_{37}NO_3$	2-Keto-3-dodecyl-3-carbethoxypiperidine	3-Dodecyl-3-hydroxymethylpiperidine	55	54
$C_{21}H_{22}N_2O_2$	1-(2'-Carbethoxyskatyl)-1,2,3,4-tetrahydroisoquinoline (VI)	1-(2'-Hydroxymethylskatyl)-1,2,3,4-tetrahydroisoquinoline	54	55
			....	53
$C_{22}H_{20}N_2O_4$	2-Methyl-3-amino-4,5-dicarbobenzyloxypyridine	2-Methyl-3-amino-4,5-di-(hydroxymethyl)-pyridine	35	16
$C_{23}H_{21}NO_5$	2-Benzyl-3-benzyloxy-4,5-dicarbethoxypyridine	2-Benzyl-3-benzyloxy-4,5-di-(hydroxymethyl)-pyridine	88.5[5]	56

CHART TO TABLE XLV

I

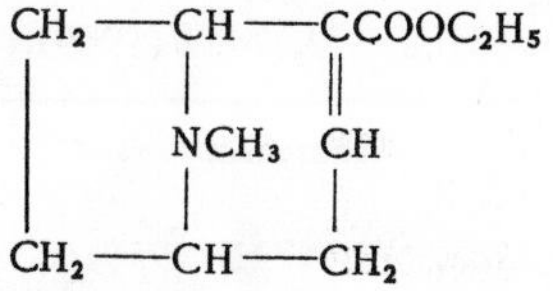

$$CH_2 - CH - CCOOC_2H_5$$
$$| \quad \quad ||$$
$$NCH_3 \quad CH$$
$$| \quad \quad |$$
$$CH_2 - CH - CH_2$$

II

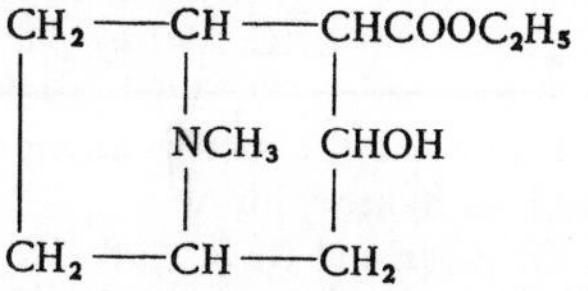

$$CH_2 - CH - CHCOOC_2H_5$$
$$| \quad \quad |$$
$$NCH_3 \quad CHOH$$
$$| \quad \quad |$$
$$CH_2 - CH - CH_2$$

III

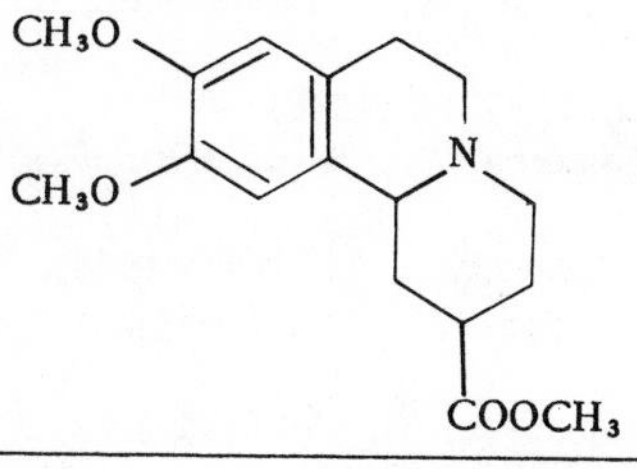

CH_3O, CH_3O ... N ... $COOCH_3$

IV

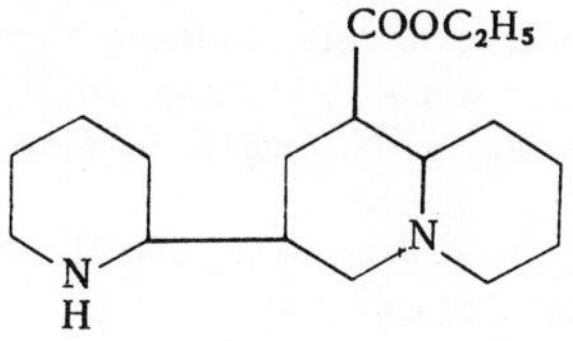

$COOC_2H_5$ ... N, H

V

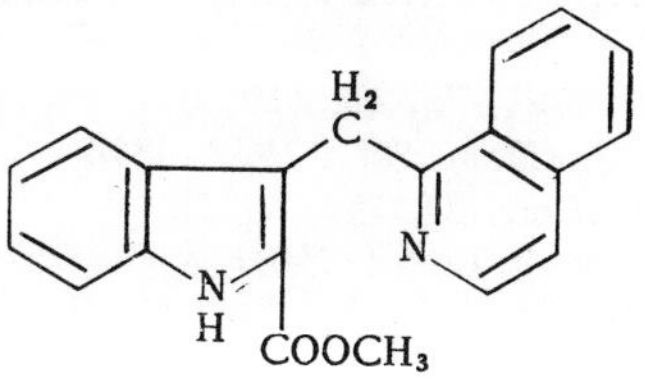

H_2C ... N, H ... N ... $COOCH_3$

VI

H_2C ... N, H ... HN ... $COOC_2H_5$

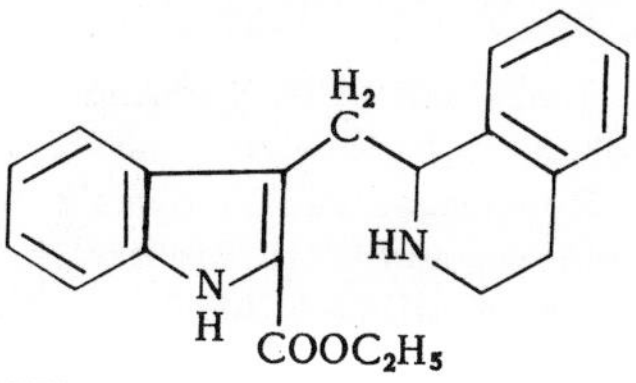

References—Table XLV

[1]S. Fallab, *Helv. Chim. Acta,* 35, 215 (1952).

[2]R. G. Jones and K. C. McLaughlin, *J. Am. Chem. Soc.,* 71, 2444 (1949).

[3]R. G. Jones, *ibid.,* 71, 3994 (1949).

[4]Reduction carried out with excess LAH in a benzene-ether mixture.

[5]Isolated as hydrochloride.

[6]L. H. Conover and D. S. Tarbell, *J. Am. Chem. Soc.,* 72, 5221 (1950).

[7]K. Hayes, G. Gever, and J. Orcutt, *ibid.,* 72, 1205 (1950).

[8]J. F. Scully and E. V. Brown, *Abstracts of Papers,* 121st Meeting American Chemical Society, Buffalo, New York, March 1952, p. 44K.

[9]P. Karrer and P. Portmann, *Helv. Chim. Acta,* 31, 2088 (1948).

[10]C. Fromageot, M. Jutisz, D. Meyer and L. Penasse, *Biochem. et Biophys. Acta,* 6, 283 (1950).

[11]P. Karrer, P. Portmann, and M. Suter, *Helv. Chim. Acta,* 31, 1617 (1948).

[12]H. S. Mosher and J. E. Tessieri, *J. Am. Chem. Soc.,* 73, 4925 (1951).

[13]M. Protiva, *Chem. Listy,* 45, 20 (1951).

[14]V. M. Mićović and M. L. Mihailović, *Rec. trav. chim.,* 71, 970 (1952).

[15]Roche Products Ltd. and A. Cohen, Brit. Pat. 631,078 (October 26, 1949); Fr. Pat. 971,445 (January 17, 1951); A. Cohen, U. S. Pat. 2,520,037 (August 22, 1950).

[16]R. G. Jones and E. C. Kornfeld, *J. Am. Chem. Soc.,* 73, 107 (1951).

[17]A. Cohen, J. W. Haworth, and E. G. Hughes, *J. Chem. Soc.,* 1952, 4374.

[18]K. W. Rosenmund and F. Zymalkowski, *Chem. Ber.,* 85, 152 (1952).

[19]I. Dvoretzky and G. H. Richter, *J. Org. Chem.,* 15, 1285 (1950).

[20]Erroneously called 2-β-hydroxyethylpiperidine.

[21]R. Lukeš and J. Plešek, unpublished work; through M. Ferles and J. Rudinger, *Chem. Listy,* 47, 119 (1953).

[22]R. Lukeš and O. Červinka, unpublished work; through J. Rudinger, M. Ferles, and M. Protiva, *Chem. Listy,* 45, 352 (1951).

[23]Reduction carried out in tetrahydrofuran.

[24]H. R. Snyder, C. B. Thompson, and R. L. Hinman, *J. Am. Chem. Soc.,* 74, 2009 (1952).

[25]R. G. Jones, *ibid.,* 74, 1489 (1952).

[26]Reduction carried out at $-10°$ to room temperature.

[27]Reduction carried out with a large excess of LAH at room temperature for 24 hours.

[28]K. J. Verrill and A. M. Schneider, Brit. Pat. 686,012 (January 14, 1953).

[29]T. Matsukawa and K. Sirakawa, *J. Pharm. Soc., Japan,* 71, 1498 (1952).

[30]R. P. Mariella and E. P. Belcher, *J. Am. Chem. Soc.,* 73, 2616 (1951).

[31]V. Horák and J. Černý, unpublished work; through M. Ferles and J. Rudinger, *Chem. Listy,* 47, 120 (1953).

[32]W. J. Brehm, *J. Am. Chem. Soc.,* 71, 3541 (1949).

[33]W. I. Taylor, *Helv. Chim. Acta,* 33, 164 (1950).

[34]V. Boekelheide and J. P. Lodge, Jr., *J. Am. Chem. Soc.,* 73, 3681 (1951).

[35]Isolated as hydrobromide.

[36]R. Gaertner, *J. Am. Chem. Soc.,* 74, 2991 (1952).

[37]A. Cohen, U. S. Pat. 2,590,841 (April 1, 1952).

[38]V. Boekelheide and S. Rothchild, *J. Am. Chem. Soc.,* 71, 879 (1949).

[39]I. Elphimoff-Felkin, H. Felkin, and Z. Welvart, *Compt. rend.,* 235, 1789 (1952).

[40]F. Hoffmann-La Roche and Co., Akt., Swiss Pat. 275,968 (October 1, 1951).

[41]G. W. Moersch and A. C. Moore, U. S. Pat. 2,562,114 (July 24, 1951).

[42]F. Hoffmann-La Roche and Co., Akt., Brit. Pat. 681,130 (October 15, 1952).

[43]R. Gaertner, *J. Am. Chem. Soc.*, 74, 5319 (1952).

[44]See text.

[45]L. Birkofer and A. Birkofer, *Chem. Ber.*, 85, 286 (1952).

[46]R. Dahlbom, *Acta Chem. Scand.*, 6, 310 (1952).

[47]P. Karrer and S. Mainoni, *Helv. Chim. Acta*, 34, 2151 (1951).

[48]F. Galinovsky, O. Vogl and W. Moroz, *Monatsh.*, 83, 242 (1952).

[49]M. Pailer, K. Schneglberger, and W. Reifschneider, *ibid.*, 83, 513 (1952).

[50]F. Galinovsky and E. Jarisch, *ibid.*, 84, 199 (1953).

[51]Isolated as N-benzoyl-*threo*-phenylserinol after treatment of reduction product with acetic acid.

[52]I. Elphimoff-Felkin, H. Felkin, B. Tchoubar, and Z. Welvart, *Bull. soc. chim. France*, [5] 19, 252 (1952).

[53]V. Boekelheide and Chu-Tsin Liu, *J. Am. Chem. Soc.*, 74, 4920 (1952).

[54]D. E. Ames and R. E. Bowman, *J. Chem. Soc.*, 1952, 1057.

[55]V. Boekelheide and C. Ainsworth, *J. Am. Chem. Soc.*, 72, 2134 (1950).

[56]A. Cohen and J. A. Silk, *J. Chem. Soc.*, 1952, 4386.

Aluminum hydride in the medium aluminum chloride-tetrahydrofuran has been used for the reduction of peptide esters to β-hydroxyalkylamides at $-40°$. The latter is rearranged in the presence of phosphorus oxychloride to a β-aminoester which on further treatment with the aluminum hydride yields the free amino alcohol and the residual peptide (126).

$$\underset{\text{RCNHCHCNHCHCOOC}_2\text{H}_5}{\overset{\text{O R' O R''}}{\overset{\| \ | \ \| \ |}{}}} \xrightarrow[85\%]{\text{AlH}_3} \underset{\text{RCNHCHCNHCHCH}_2\text{OH}}{\overset{\text{O R' O R''}}{\overset{\| \ | \ \| \ |}{}}} \xrightarrow{\text{POCl}_3}$$

$$\underset{\text{RCNHCHCOCH}_2\text{CHNH}_2 \cdot \text{HCl}}{\overset{\text{O R' O   R''}}{\overset{\| \ | \ \| \quad \ |}{}}} \xrightarrow[90\%]{\text{AlH}_3}$$

$$\underset{\text{RCNHCHCH}_2\text{OH}}{\overset{\text{O R'}}{\overset{\| \ |}{}}} + \underset{\text{HOCH}_2\text{CHNH}_2}{\overset{\text{R''}}{\overset{|}{}}} \qquad (9\text{-}69)$$

The milder reducing action of aluminum hydride is advantageous here where LAH might normally reduce the amide function.

9.1.3   Reductions with Magnesium Aluminum Hydride

Magnesium aluminum hydride resembles LAH in its ability to reduce esters. Methyl benzoate has been reduced to benzyl alcohol in 32% yield the reaction being postulated as proceeding through an acetal intermediate (127).

9.1.4   Reductions with Sodium Borohydride

Esters are generally resistant to reduction with sodium borohydride. The reduction of other functional groups with the borohydride in aqueous, methanol, ethanol, or dioxane solution results in retention of the ester group or its recovery as the acid as a result of hydrolysis. The formation of a hydroxyl group by the reduction of a carbonyl group or an acid chloride may result in the formation of a lactone when the hydroxyl and carboxyl groups are appropriately located (128).

9.1.4.a   *Reduction of carbinol esters to the parent carbinols.* Carbinol acetates, propionates, etc., including steroid derivatives, have been subjected to reduction with sodium borohydride. Under mild conditions, no reduction occurs (Table XLVI). However, with longer reaction times and higher temperature, reduction to the parent carbinol occurs (Table XLVII).

Biel (22) reported that reduction of estrone esters (CXXXI) where the acid moiety does not contain a highly branched side chain such as the acetate, propionate, butyrate and benzoate yields β-estradiol.

TABLE LXVI

Non-Reduction of Carbinol Esters with Sodium Borohydride

	Ester	Medium[1]	Product	% Yield	Ref.
$C_{21}H_{32}O_3$	17β-Acetoxyetiocholan-3-one	W-M	17β-Acetoxyetiocholan-3-ol[2]	95	3
$C_{22}H_{32}O_3$	3β-Acetoxy-D-homoandrost-5-ene-17a-one	W-D	3β-Acetoxy-17aβ-benzoxy-D-androst-5-ene[4]	85	5
$C_{23}H_{30}O_3$	Estrone trimethylacetate	M	β-Estradiol 3-trimethylacetate	89	6
$C_{23}H_{32}O_4$	3β-Acetoxy-14,15β-oxido-20-keto-5-allo-16-pregnene	M-W-D-C	compound, $C_{23}H_{34}O_4$, m.p. 149–150°[7]	....	8
$C_{24}H_{32}O_3$	Estrone t-butylacetate	M	β-Estradiol 3-t-butylacetate	70	6
$C_{27}H_{40}O_5$	Methyl 3α-acetoxy-7-keto-9(11)-cholenate	....	Methyl 3α-acetoxy-7-hydroxy-9(11)-cholenate	....	9
$C_{27}H_{42}O_6$	Methyl 3β-acetoxy-9α-hydroxy-11-ketocholanate	M	Methyl 3β-acetoxy-9α,11β-dihydroxy-cholanate	98	10

[1]Medium: W = water; M = methanol; D = dioxane; C = chloroform.

[2]Mixture of epimers.

[3]E. Elisberg, H. Vanderhaeghe, and T. F. Gallagher, J. Am. Chem. Soc., 74, 2814 (1952).

[4]Isolated after treatment of reduction product with benzoyl chloride.

[5]H. Heusser, P. T. Herzig, A. Fürst, and P. A. Plattner, Helv. Chim. Acta, 33, 1093 (1950).

[6]J. H. Biel, J. Am. Chem. Soc., 73, 847 (1951).

[7]Isolated after treatment of reduction product with chromic oxide in glacial acetic acid.

[8]Ciba Ltd., Brit. Pat. 665,254 (January 16, 1952); Ciba S. A., Fr. Pat. 994,615 (August 8, 1951); P. Plattner, Ger. Pat. 834,848 (May 15, 1952); U. S. Pat. 2,599,481 (June 3, 1952).

[9]L. F. Fieser, J. C. Babcock, J. E. Herz, Wei-Yuan Huang, and W. P. Schneider, J. Am. Chem. Soc., 73, 4053 (1951).

[10]H. Heymann and L. F. Fieser, ibid, 73, 5252 (1951).

TABLE XLVII

Reduction of Carbinol Esters to the Parent Carbinols with Sodium Borohydride

Ester		Medium[1]	Product	% Yield	Ref.
$C_{13}H_{10}Cl_4NO_6$	α-Dichloroacetamido-β-dichloroacetoxy-p-nitropropiophenone	E	dl-erythro-1-p-Nitrophenyl-2-dichloroacetamido-1,3-propanediol	....	2
$C_{13}H_{12}Cl_2NO_6$	α-Dichloroacetamido-β-acetoxy-p-nitropropiophenone	E	dl-erythro-1-p-Nitrophenyl-2-dichloroacetamido-1,3-propanediol	40–45	2
$C_{13}H_{14}NO_6$	α-Acetamido-β-acetoxy-p-nitrophenyl-propiophenone	E	dl-erythro-1-p-Nitrophenyl-2-acetamido-1,3-propanediol	47.6	2
$C_{20}H_{24}O_3$	Estrone acetate	M	β-Estradiol	....	3
$C_{21}H_{26}O_3$	Estrone propionate	M	β-Estradiol	....	3
$C_{21}H_{28}O_3$	3β-Acetoxyandrosta-5,14-dien-17-one	M	Androsta-5,14-diene-3β,17β-diol	68	4
$C_{21}H_{30}O_3$	3β-Acetoxy-14-androsten-17-one	M	14-Androstene-3β,17β-diol	57	4
$C_{21}H_{30}O_4$	3β-Acetoxy-14ξ-hydroxy-5-androsten-17-one	M	3β,17β-Diacetoxy-5-androstene-14ξ-ol[5]	....	4
$C_{21}H_{32}O_3$	3β-Acetoxy-14-isoandrostane-17-one	M	14-Isoandrostane-3β,17α-diol	....	4
$C_{21}H_{32}O_4$	3β-Acetoxy-14ξ-hydroxyandrostane-17-one	M	3β,17β-Diacetoxyandrostane-14ξ-ol[5]	44	4
$C_{22}H_{28}O_3$	Estrone buryrate	M	β-Estradiol	....	3
$C_{25}H_{26}O_3$	Estrone benzoate	M	β-Estradiol	....	3
$C_{29}H_{42}O_6$	3β-Acetoxy-9α,11α-oxido-22-isoallospirostan-7-one	M	9α,11α-Oxido-22-isoallospirostan-3β,7(β?)-diol	....	6

[1]Medium: E = ethanol; M = methanol.

[2]Parke Davis and Co., Australian Pat. Appln. 13,395/52 (October 15, 1952).

[3]J. H. Biel, J. Am. Chem. Soc., 73, 847 (1951).

[4]A. F. St. André, H. B. MacPhillamy, J. A. Nelson, A. C. Shabica, and C. R. Scholz, ibid., 74, 5506 (1952).

[5]Isolated after acetylation of reduction product.

[6]C. Djerassi, E. Batres, M. Velasco, and G. Rosenkranz, J. Am. Chem. Soc., 74, 1712 (1952).

CXXXI   (9-70)

However, highly branched aliphatic esters such as estrone trimethylacetate and estrone *t*-butylacetate yield β-estradiol-3-trimethylacetate
and 3-*t*-butylacetate, respectively, in excellent yield and high purity. In
contrast, estrone trimethylacetate is reduced with LAH to β-estradiol
while calcium hydride yields estrone.

A recent patent application (129) presents an interesting picture of the
reduction of an acetoxy group. Treatment of α-acetamido-β-acetoxy-*p*-
nitropropiophenone (CXXXII) with sodium borohydride in ethanol yields
47.6% of *dl-erythro*-1-*p*-nitrophenyl-2-acetamido-1,3-propanediol (CXXXIII).
Under the same conditions α-acetamido-β-hydroxy-*p*-nitropropiophenone
(CXXXIV) yields 47% of the *erythro* form and 25% of the *threo* form of
CXXXIII.

CXXXII: R′ = COCH₃   CXXXIII   (9-71)
CXXXIV: R′ = H

Similarly, reduction of α-dichloroacetamido-β-acetoxy-*p*-nitropropiophe-
none yields 40–45% of *dl-erythro*-1-*p*-nitrophenyl-2-dichloroacetamido-1,3-
propanediol while the β-hydroxy compound yields 27% of the *erythro* and
39% of the *threo*-propanediol. α-Dichloroacetamido-β-dichloroacetoxy-*p*-
nitropropiophenone also gives the *erythro* product. The exact mechanism
by which the acyloxy group is removed is considered to be an ester inter-
change with the solvent rather than a reductive removal since the β-acyl-
oxy ketones favor the *erythro* form of the diol to the exclusion of the
threo while the β-hydroxy ketones yield more or less equal amounts of
the two diastereoisomeric forms.

9.1.4.b *Reduction of esters to alcohols.* Aliphatic carboxylates including steroid derivatives are generally not attacked by sodium borohydride (Table XLVIII). However, reduction has been reported in the
case of two steroidal esters. Thus, the carbomethoxy groups in methyl

3α-hydroxy-12-keto-9(11)-cholenate (CXXXV) (130) and in methyl 3-keto-bisnor-4-cholenate 3-ethylene ketal (CXXXVI) (131) are reduced with sodium borohydride to the corresponding carbinols.

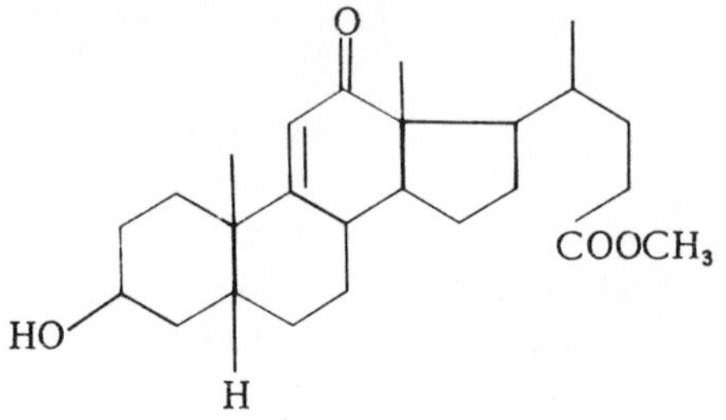

CXXXV

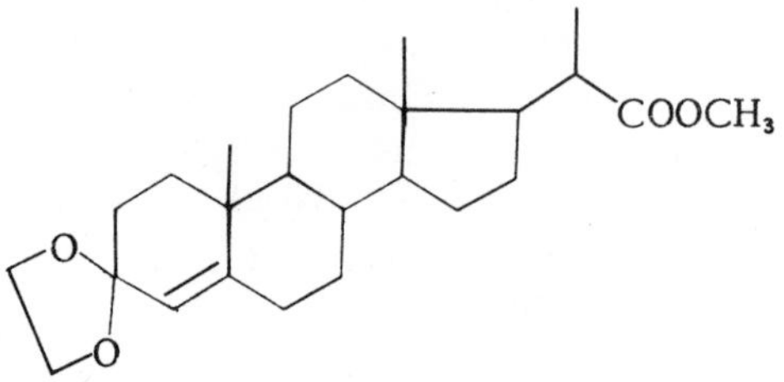

CXXXVI

Heymann and Fieser (130) reported that methyl 3β-hydroxy-3α,9α-oxido-11-ketocholanate is reduced with sodium borohydride under mild conditions without reduction of the ester group but variable results and incomplete reduction prompted saponification of the ester group to avoid attack at this point and adoption of more drastic reaction conditions.

Wolfrom and Anno (132) have utilized sodium borohydride in the reduction of various sugar carboxylates. Methyl ester glycosides of uronic acids have been reduced in an aqueous system to glycosides of the corresponding hexoses. The following uronates have been reduced in this manner:

methyl (methyl α-D-galactopyranosid)uronate monohydrate
→ methyl α-D-galactopyranoside monohydrate   (61%)

methyl (methyl β-D-galactopyranosid)uronate
→ methyl β-D-galactopyranoside   (64%)

methyl (methyl α-D-glucopyranosid)uronate
→ methyl α-D-glucopyranoside   (37%)

Sodium borohydride has been used in combination with lithium chloride as a replacement for lithium borohydride in the reduction of esters to alcohols (see Section 9.1.6).

TABLE XLVIII

Carboxylates Not Attacked by Sodium Borohydride

	Ester	Medium[1]	Product	% Yield	Ref.
$C_6H_9ClO_3$	3-Carbethoxypropionyl chloride	D	Butyrolactone	40	2
$C_6H_{12}O_2$	Ethyl butyrate	D	No reduction		2
$C_{10}H_{12}O_2$	Ethyl phenylacetate	D	No reduction		2
$C_{12}H_{20}O_4S$	Ethyl 6-keto-8-thioacetoxyoctanoate	M	DL-8-Thiol-6-hydroxyoctanoic acid[3]	....	4
$C_{17}H_{32}O_3$	Methyl 2-n-hexyl-3-ketodecanoate	D-M	2-n-Hexyl-3-hydroxydecanoic acid[3]	36	5
$C_{21}H_{26}O_3$	Methyl dl-3-ketoetiochola-4,9(11),16-trienate	E	Methyl dl-3-hydroxy-etiochola-4,9(11),16-trienate[6]	100	7,8
	Methyl d-3-ketoetiochola-4,9(11),16-trienate	E	Methyl d-3-hydroxy-etiochola-4,9(11),16-trienate[6]	100	8
$C_{21}H_{30}O_3$	Methyl 3-ketoetio-9(11)-cholenate } Methyl 3-ketoetioallo-9(11)-cholenate }[9]	E	Methyl 3α-hydroxyetio-9(11)-cholenate } Methyl 3β-hydroxyetioallo-9(11)-cholenate }	.... } .... }	8,10
$C_{21}H_{30}O_4$	Methyl 3,11-diketoetiocholanate	E	Methyl 3α-acetoxy-11β-hydroxyetiocholanate[11] } Methyl 3α-acetoxy-11-ketoetiocholanate[11] }	61	8,10
$C_{21}H_{32}O_3$	Methyl 3-ketoetioallocholanate	E	Methyl 3β-hydroxyetioallocholanate	....	12
	Methyl 3-ketoetiocholanate } Methyl 3-ketoetioallocholanate }[14]	E	Methyl 3β-hydroxyetioallocholanate Methyl 3α-hydroxyetiocholanate Methyl 3β-hydroxyetioallocholanate 3-desoxy compound	65[13] } 40 } 14 } 30	8
$C_{22}H_{32}O_4$	Ethyl 3-keto-19-hydroxyetio-4-cholenate	E-W	Ethyl 3β,19-dihydroxyetio-4-cholenate	31	15
$C_{27}H_{40}O_5$	Methyl 3α-acetoxy-7-keto-9(11)-cholenate	....	Methyl 3α-acetoxy-7-hydroxy-9(11)-cholenate	....	16
$C_{27}H_{42}O_6$	Methyl 3β-acetoxy-9α-hydroxy-11-keto-cholanate	M	Methyl 3β-acetoxy-9α,11α-dihydroxycholanate	98	17
$C_{37}H_{72}O_3$	Methyl 2-n-hexadecyl-3-eicosanoate	D-M	2-n-Hexadecyl-3-hydroxyeicosanoic acid	78.5	5

References—Table XLVIII

[1]Medium: D = dioxane; M = methanol; E = ethanol; W = water.
[2]S. W. Chaikin and W. G. Brown, *J. Am. Chem. Soc.*, 71, 122 (1949).
[3]Isolated after hydrolysis of the reduction product.
[4]M. W. Bullock, J. A. Brockman, Jr., E. L. Patterson, J. V. Pierce and E. L. R. Stokstad, *J. Am. Chem. Soc.*, 74, 3455 (1952).
[5]E. Lederer, V. Portelance, and K. Serck-Hanssen, *Bull. soc. chim. France,* [5] 19, 413 (1952).
[6]Mixture of epimers.
[7]R. B. Woodward, F. Sondheimer, and D. Taub, *J. Am. Chem. Soc.*, 73, 3547 (1951).
[8]R. B. Woodward, F. Sondheimer, D. Taub, K. Heusler, and W. M. McLamore, *ibid.*, 74, 4223 (1952).
[9]Mixture containing equal parts of esters.
[10]R. B. Woodward, F. Sondheimer, and D. Taub, *J. Am. Chem. Soc.*, 73, 4057 (1951).
[11]Isolated after acetylation of the reduction products.
[12]R. B. Woodward, F. Sondheimer, and D. Taub, *J. Am. Chem. Soc.*, 73, 3548 (1951).
[13]Small amounts of 3α-epimer also formed.
[14]Mixture obtained after catalytic hydrogenation followed by chromic acid oxidation of methyl d-3-ketoetiochola-4,9(11),16-trienate.
[15]P. T. Herzig and M. Ehrenstein, *J. Org. Chem.*, 17, 713 (1952).
[16]L. F. Fieser, J. C. Babcock, J. E. Herz, Wei-Yuan Huang, and W. P. Schneider, *J. Am. Chem. Soc.*, 73, 4053 (1951).
[17]H. Heymann and L. F. Fieser, *ibid.*, 73, 5252 (1951).

9.1.5 Reductions with Potassium Borohydride

A solution of potassium borohydride in aqueous sodium hydroxide has been utilized in the reduction of various quaternary pyridinium salts. Ester groups present in these compounds have not been attacked and have been retained in the reduction products. Thus, N-tetraacetylglucosidyl-pyridinium bromide (CXXXVII) and N-tetraacetylglucosidylnicotinamide bromide (CXXXVIII) have been reduced to the corresponding o-dihydro-pyridine derivatives (133). Similarly, methyl nicotinate methiodide (CXXXIX) has been reduced to 1-methyl-3-carbomethoxy-1,2,5,6-tetra-hydropyridine (134).

CXXXVII: R = H
CXXXVIII: R = CONH₂

Potassium borohydride has been used in combination with lithium chloride in the reduction of esters to alcohols (see Section 9.1.6).

9.1.6 Reductions with Lithium Borohydride

Esters react slowly with lithium borohydride in ether or tetrahydrofuran solution to yield the corresponding primary alcohols. The following esters have been reduced in this manner:

	Ester	Medium	Product	% Yield	Ref.
$C_9H_{10}O_2$	Ethyl benzoate	THF	Benzyl alcohol	62	135
$C_{14}H_{26}O_4$	Diethyl sebacate	THF	1,10-Decanediol	60	135
$C_{16}H_{14}O_4$	Dimethyl diphenate	Ether	2,2′-Bis-(hydroxymethyl)-diphenyl	93	136
$C_{20}H_{40}O_2$	n-Butyl palmitate	THF	n-Hexadecanol	95	135

Patents relating to the reduction of ethyl β-ionylideneacetate (123) and methyl 3-ethoxypregna-3,5,17-trien-21-oate (131) have indicated that lithium borohydride may be substituted for LAH in the reduction of these esters to the carbinols.

The reduction of cortisone acetate 3-monosemicarbazone (CXL) with lithium borohydride in tetrahydrofuran and subsequent acetylation and removal of the semicarbazone grouping has yielded Reichstein's Substance E 21-acetate (CXLI), Substance E 20,21-diacetate (CXLII) and Substance U 20,21 diacetate (CXLIII) (137,138).

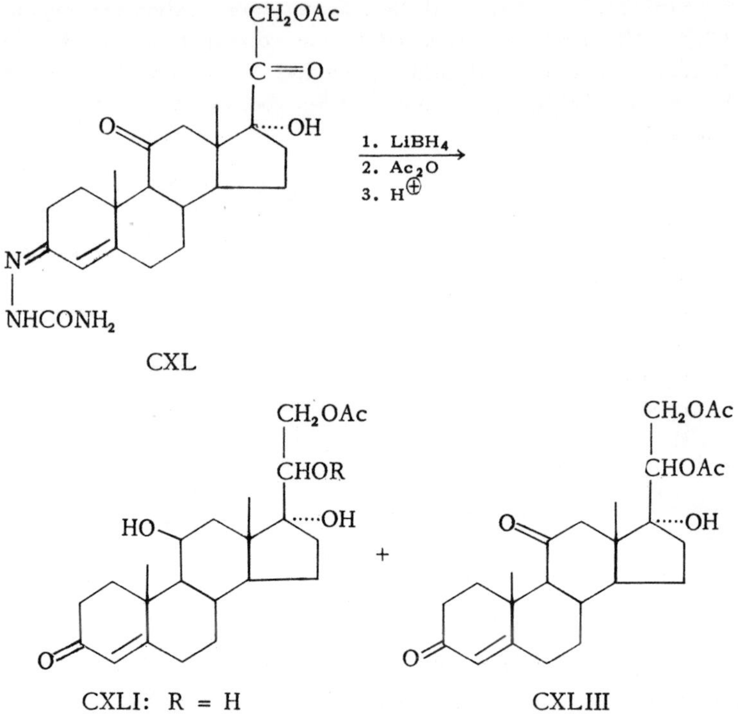

CXL

$$1.\ LiBH_4$$
$$2.\ Ac_2O$$
$$3.\ H^{\oplus}$$

CXLI: R = H
CXLII: R = COCH₃

CXLIII

(9-72)

It has been demonstrated that the 21-acetate group is removed during the reduction and then replaced by acetylation by omitting the acetylation step to yield the free tetrol as the major product.

Lithium borohydride has been used in investigations on the structure of insulin (139,140). The latter is esterified with diazomethane and the ester is reduced by refluxing with excess borohydride in tetrahydrofuran. The esterification process converts the γ-carboxyls of glutamyl residues, the β-carboxyls of aspartyl residues and the α-carboxyls of terminal residues to carbomethoxy groups which are subsequently reduced to hydroxyl groups. Acid hydrolysis of the reduced insulin yields amino acids and alcohols. The results indicate that the untreated insulin molecule must have contained 8 glutaminyl, 6 glutamyl, 4 asparaginyl and 2 aspartyl residues. When oxidized insulin is treated in a similar way corresponding results are obtained.

Owing to the slowness of ester reduction selective reductions have been carried out with lithium borohydride utilizing low temperatures. Thus, ethyl levulinate has been reduced to γ-valerolactone in 44% yield. The attempted selective reduction of ethyl acetoacetate yields a borat complex from which the reduction product can not be isolated (135).

Paul and Joseph (141) have reported that an equimolecular mixture of potassium borohydride and lithium chloride can be utilized in place of lithium borohydride in the reduction of esters in refluxing tetrahydrofuran. By this method the following esters have been reduced to alcohols:

Ester	Product	% Yield
Butyl stearate	1-Octadecanol	91⎫
	1-Butanol	86⎭
Ethyl benzoate	Benzyl alcohol	88
Ethyl cinnamate	Cinnamyl alcohol	10⎫
	3-Phenyl-1-propanol	66⎭
Ethyl phenylacetate	2-Phenylethanol	85
Ethyl 3-(2-tetrahydrofuryl)propionate	3-(2-Tetrahydrofuryl)-1-propanol	75
Ethyl undecylinate	10-Undecen-1-ol	82

The reduction of ethyl p-nitrobenzoate at 25° gives 86% of p-nitrobenzyl alcohol. The reduction of ethyl cinnamate under the same conditions results in a decreased conversion of ester but the yields of cinnamyl and hydrocinnamyl alcohols are the same as in the case where the reduction is carried out with heating. Dioxane, glycol formal, and tetrahydrofuran are good solvents for the reaction while diethyl and dibutyl ethers are ineffective. Although the reaction proceeds in ethanol, the yield is poor because of the decomposition of the potassium borohydride.

The replacement of potassium borohydride by sodium borohydride results in decreased yields. Although potassium borohydride and lithium chloride reduce ethyl benzoate to 88% benzyl alcohol, the sodium borohydride system gives only 13% benzyl alcohol. The lithium chloride in the potassium borohydride system has been found to be replaceable by lithium nitrate or lithium iodide without decreasing the yields but the rate of the reaction is reduced. In addition, the mixture of potassium borohydride and lithium nitrate tends to ignite under the influence of heat. With lithium bromide and lithium sulfate reduction occurs but with greatly diminished yields. No reaction is observed by replacement of lithium chloride by lithium hydroxide, carbonate, or fluoride.

9.1.7 Reductions with Lithium Gallium Hydride

Lithium gallium hydride has been utilized in the attempted reduction of two esters. Both diethyl adipate and β-naphthyl benzoate have been treated with the hydride with negative results (96).

9.2 LACTONES

9.2.1 Reductions with Lithium Aluminum Hydride

The reduction of lactones is analogous to that of esters, consuming one-half mole of LAH per mole of lactone to yield the corresponding diol. The reaction can be represented stoichiometrically as follows:

$$2 \; \underset{\displaystyle \underset{O}{\rule{0pt}{0pt}}}{RCHCH_2CH_2C} = O \; + \; LiAlH_4 \; \rightarrow \; \left[\begin{array}{c} RCHCH_2CH_2CH_2O \\ | \\ O \end{array} \right]_2 LiAl \qquad (9\text{-}73)$$

$$\downarrow 4\,H_2O$$

$$2 \; \underset{OH}{RCHCH_2CH_2CH_2OH} \qquad + \; LiOH \; + \; Al(OH)_3$$

The reductions generally proceed in good yield with a minimum of complications.

9.2.1.a *Acyclic lactones.* The LAH reduction of lactones derived from an acyclic backbone usually yields the expected diol.

While the reduction of γ-valerolactone yields 1,4-pentanediol (142) reduction of α-angelica lactone (CXLV) after 24 hours in ether at 35° yields pentan-4-one-1-ol (3).

$$\begin{array}{c} CH_2\!-\!CH_2 \\ | \qquad | \\ CH_3CH \quad C = O \\ \diagdown \! O \! \diagup \end{array} \xrightarrow[85\%]{LAH} \begin{array}{c} CH_2\!-\!CH_2 \\ | \qquad | \\ CH_3CHOH \quad CH_2OH \end{array} \qquad (9\text{-}74)$$

CXLIV

$$\begin{array}{c} CH\!-\!CH_2 \\ \| \qquad | \\ CH_3C \quad C = O \\ \diagdown \! O \! \diagup \end{array} \xrightarrow[65\%]{LAH} \begin{array}{c} CH_2\!-\!CH_2 \\ | \qquad | \\ CH_3C = O \quad CH_2OH \end{array} \qquad (9\text{-}75)$$

CXLV

The γ-lactone structure in CXLV is opened at the oxygen-carbonyl bond with subsequent reduction of the carbonyl group and isomerization of the enol. The reduction of ketene dimers existing in the β,γ-unsaturated β-lactone structure proceeds in an analogous manner. Reduction of ethylketene dimer (CXLVI) yields the β-ketoalcohol which can be reduced to the diol in a separate reaction (143).

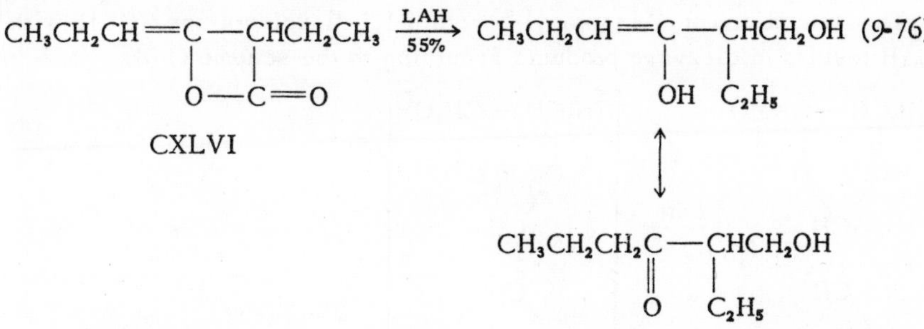

$$CH_3CH_2CH = C - CHCH_2CH_3 \xrightarrow[55\%]{LAH} CH_3CH_2CH = C - CHCH_2OH \quad (9\text{-}76)$$

$$\underset{\underset{\textstyle CXLVI}{O - C = O}}{\qquad\qquad} \qquad\qquad\qquad \underset{OH \quad C_2H_5}{}$$

$$CH_3CH_2CH_2C - CHCH_2OH$$
$$\underset{O \quad\quad C_2H_5}{\|}$$

Application of the reduction to (ω-cyclohexylalkyl)ketene dimers (CXLVII) also yields the ketoalcohol. However, the latter are not further reduced with LAH. While LAH reduction of CXLVII proceeds satisfactorily when n = 0, 1, 2 or 4, the reduction is unsuccessful when n = 3 (144). Catalytic hydrogenation of CXLVII yields the corresponding diols (145).

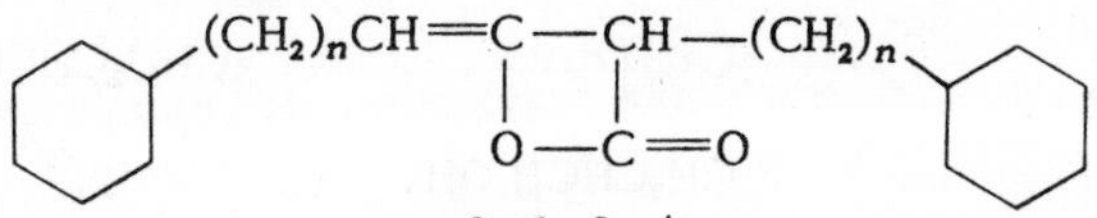

$$(CH_2)_n CH = C - CH - (CH_2)_n$$
$$O - C = O$$

$$n = 0, 1, 2, 4$$

CXLVII

The reduction of β-angelica lactone (CXLVIII) with LAH in tetrahydrofuran is reported to yield the saturated diol (3) while reduction of the analogous compound, methyl anhydromonocrotalate (CXLIX), yields the unsaturated triol (146).

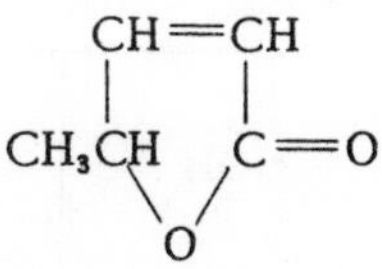

$$CH = CH$$
$$CH_3CH \quad C = O$$
$$O$$

$$CH_3C = CCH_3$$
$$CH_3C \quad C = O$$
$$O$$
$$COOCH_3$$

CXLVIII 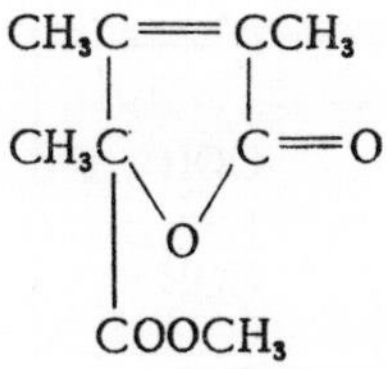   CXLIX

Attempts to reduce the dilactone (CL) have been reported as failing to yield crystalline products (147).

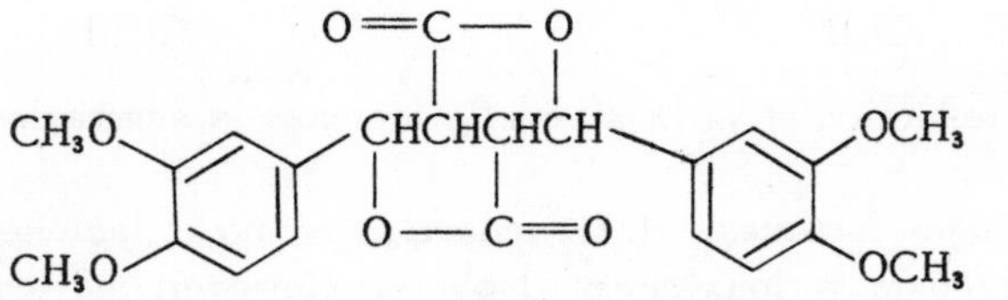

$$O = C - O$$
$$CH_3O \quad CHCHCHCH \quad OCH_3$$
$$O - C = O$$
$$CH_3O \quad\qquad\qquad\qquad OCH_3$$

CL

The reduction of 2-isopropyl-5-methyl-1,3-dioxolan-4-one (CLI) with LAH results in cleavage products according to the scheme (148):

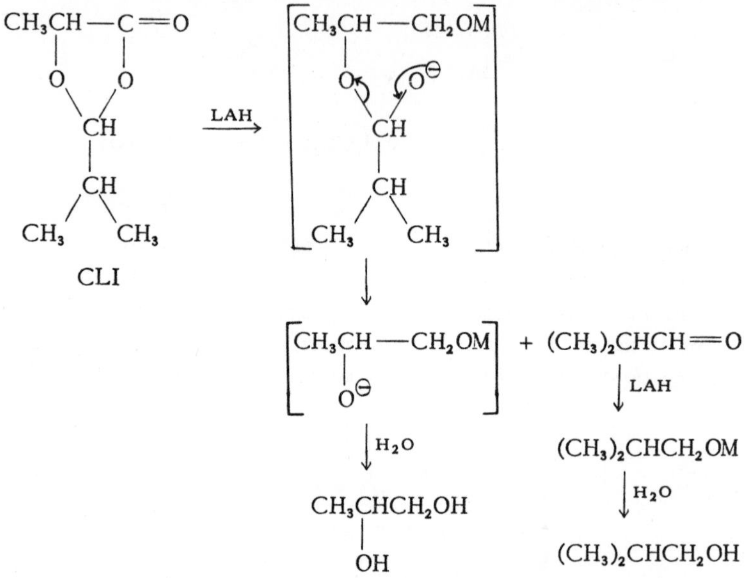

$$CH_3CH-C=O$$

CLI

$$\xrightarrow{LAH} \quad [CH_3CH-CH_2OM]$$

$$\downarrow$$

$$[CH_3CH-CH_2OM] + (CH_3)_2CHCH=O$$

$$\downarrow H_2O \qquad\qquad \downarrow LAH$$

$$CH_3CHCH_2OH \qquad (CH_3)_2CHCH_2OM$$
$$|$$
$$OH \qquad\qquad\qquad \downarrow H_2O$$

$$(CH_3)_2CHCH_2OH \qquad (9\text{-}77)$$

In Section 7.1.1.a it was shown that the mesomeric system in glucoreductone is not reduced with LAH. Similarly, *l*-ascorbic acid (CLII) and isoascorbic acid (CLIII) are recovered unchanged after refluxing for 15 hours with LAH in ether (42).

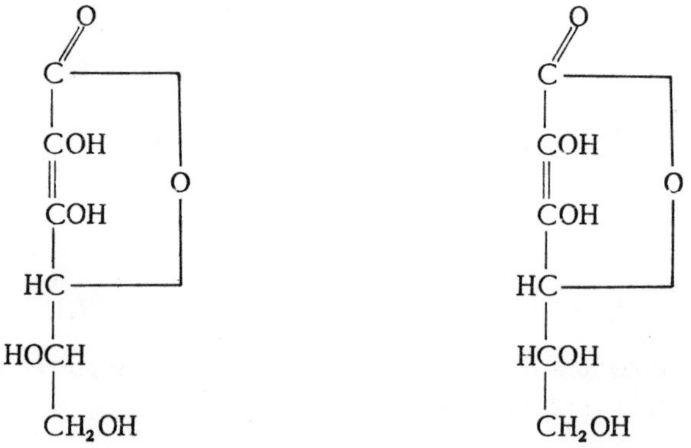

CLII

CLIII

The LAH reduction of various acyclic lactones is summarized in Table XLIX.

9.2.1.b *Sugar lactones.* LAH reduction of sugar lactones has been utilized to prepare various sugar alcohols. However, the low solubility of the sugar lactone in ethereal solvents necessitates conversion to a more soluble derivative. Reduction of 2,3,6-trimethyl-D-mannono-γ-lac-

TABLE XLIX

LAH Reduction of Acyclic Lactones

	Lactone	Product	% Yield	Ref.
$C_5H_6O_2$	α-Angelica lactone (I)	Pentan-4-on-1-ol	65	1
	β-Angelica lactone (II)	1,4-Pentanediol[2]	10[3]	1
$C_5H_8O_2$	γ-Valerolactone	1,4-Pentanediol	85	4
$C_8H_{12}O_2$	Ethylketene dimer (III: R = C_2H_5)	3-Hydroxymethyl-4-heptanone	55	5
$C_9H_{12}O_4$	Methyl anhydromonocrotalate (IV)	2,3,4-Trimethylpent-3-en-1,2,5-triol	86	6
$C_9H_{14}O_4$	Methyl dihydroanhydromonocrotalate (V)	2,3,4-Trimethyl-1,2,5-pentanetriol	93	6
$C_9H_{14}O_5$	Methyl monocrotalate (VI)	2,3,4-Trimethyl-1,2,3,5-pentanetetrol	92	6
$C_{12}H_{22}O_2$	2,4-Diethyl-3-n-propyl-δ-valerolactone	2,4-Diethyl-3-n-propyl-1,5-pentanediol	72[7]	8
$C_{16}H_{19}NO_3$	β-Erythroidine (VII)	Diol	....	9
$C_{16}H_{21}NO_3$	Dihydro-β-erythroidine	Dihydro-β-erythroidinol	74	10
$C_{16}H_{28}O_2$	Cyclohexylketene dimer (III: R = C_6H_{11})	2,4-Dicyclohexylbutan-3-on-1-ol	21	11
$C_{18}H_{32}O_2$	(ω-Cyclohexylmethyl)ketene dimer (III: R = $C_6H_{11}CH_2$)	1,5-Dicyclohexyl-2-hydroxymethyl-3-pentanone	62	11
$C_{20}H_{18}O_6$	(−)-Hinokinin (trans) (VIII)	(−)-1,4-Di-(3,4-methylenedioxyphenyl)-2,3-di-(hydroxymethyl)butane	92[12]	13
$C_{20}H_{26}O_6$	(−)-Matairesinol dimethyl ether (trans) (IX)	(−)-1,4-Di-(3,4-dimethoxyphenyl)-2,3-di-(hydroxymethyl)butane	87[12]	13
	(+)-Isomatairesinol dimethyl ether (cis)	meso-1,4-Di-(3,4-dimethoxyphenyl)-2,3-di-(hydroxymethyl)butane	78[12]	13
$C_{20}H_{36}O_2$	(ω-Cyclohexylethyl)ketene dimer (III: R = $C_6H_{11}CH_2CH_2$)	1,7-Dicyclohexyl-3-hydroxymethyl-4-heptanone	45	11
$C_{24}H_{44}O_2$	(ω-Cyclohexylbutyl)ketene dimer (III: R = $C_6H_{11}(CH_2)_4$)	1,11-Dicyclohexyl-5-hydroxymethyl-6-undecanone	71	11
$C_{26}H_{40}O_4$	3β-Acetoxy-20-hydroxyallocholanic acid lactone (X)	Allocholane-3β,20,24-triol	79[3]	14

I

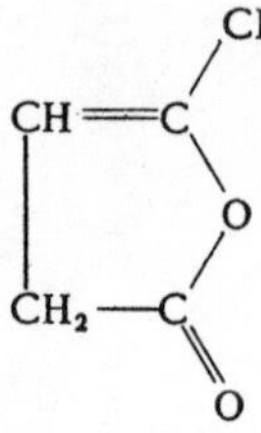

II

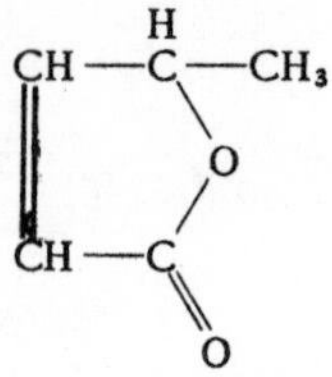

III

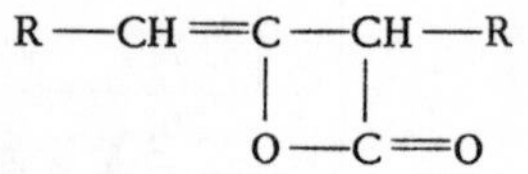

IV

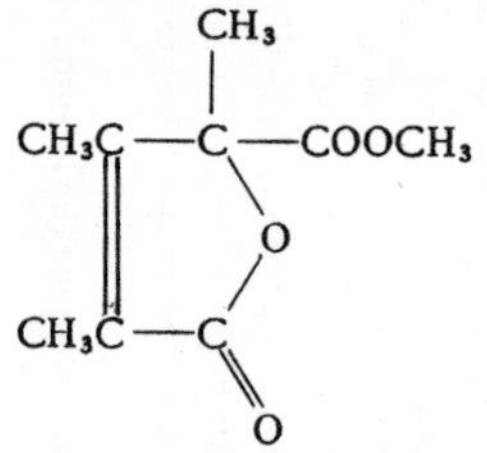

V

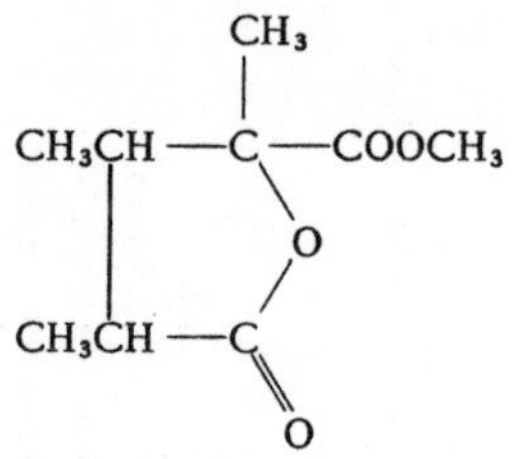

VI

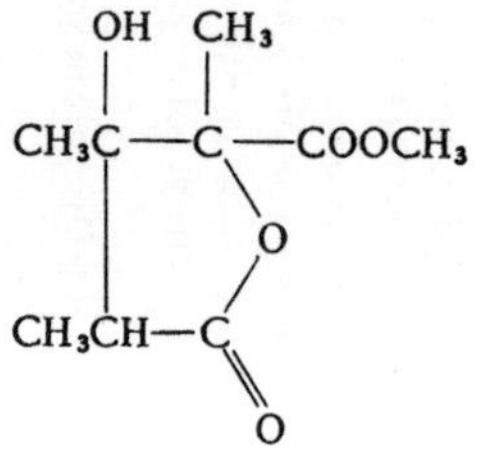

VII

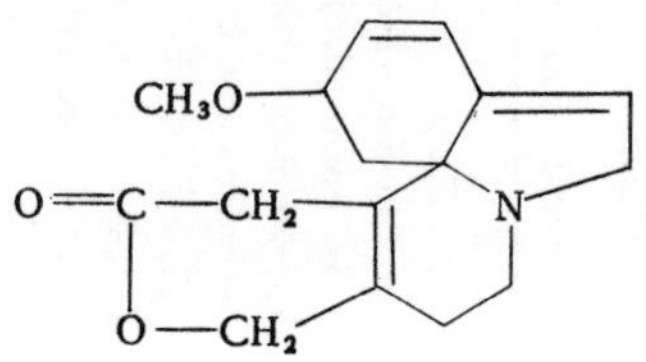

VIII

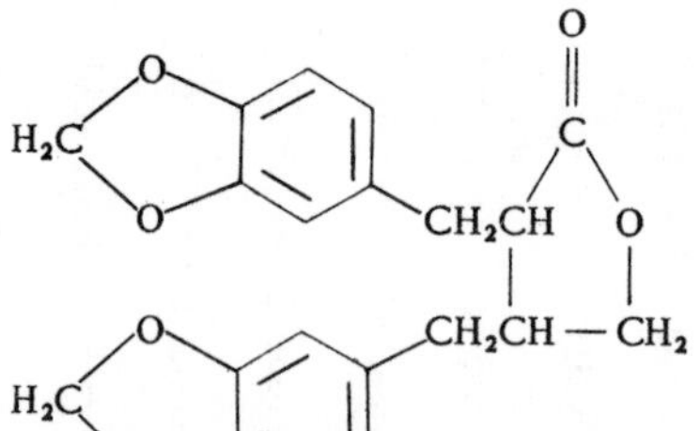

IX

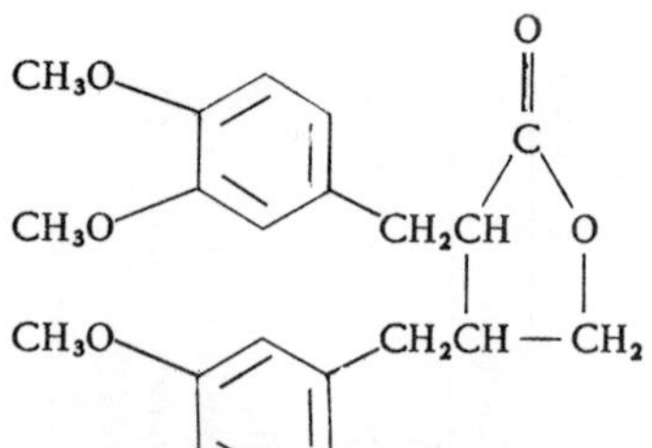

X

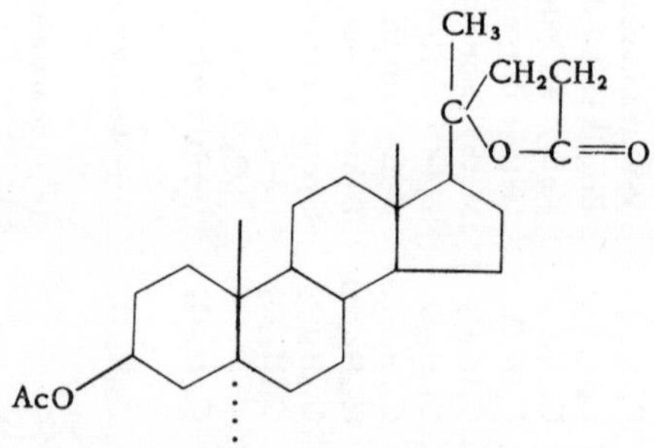

References—Table XLIX

[1]F. A. Hochstein, *J. Am. Chem. Soc.*, 71, 305 (1949).
[2]Reduction carried out in tetrahydrofuran.
[3]Isolated as diacetate.
[4]R. F. Nystrom and W. G. Brown, *J. Am. Chem. Soc.*, 70, 3738 (1948).
[5]R. L. Wear, *ibid.*, 73, 2390 (1951).
[6]R. Adams and T. R. Govindachari, *ibid.*, 72, 158 (1950).
[7]Isolated as cyclic ether (substituted tetrahydropyran) formed on distillation of 1,5-diol
[8]M. Häusermann, *Helv. Chim. Acta*, 34, 1482 (1951).
[9]V. Boekelheide and J. Weinstock, *Abstracts of Papers*, 122nd Meeting American Chemical Society, Atlantic City, N. J., September 1952, p. 12M.
[10]V. Boekelheide and E. Agnello, *J. Am. Chem. Soc.*, 73, 2286 (1951).
[11]A. S. Spriggs, C. M. Hill, and G. W. Senter, *ibid.*, 74, 1555 (1952).
[12]Reduction carried out in benzene-ether mixture.
[13]R. D. Haworth and L. Wilson, *J. Chem. Soc.*, 1950, 71.
[14]A. I. Ryer and W. H. Gebert, *J. Am. Chem. Soc.*, 74, 4336 (1952).

tone (CLIV) and tetraacetyl-D-gulono-γ-lactone (CLV) yields 2,3,6-tri-methyl-D-mannitol (83) and D-gulitol (149), respectively.

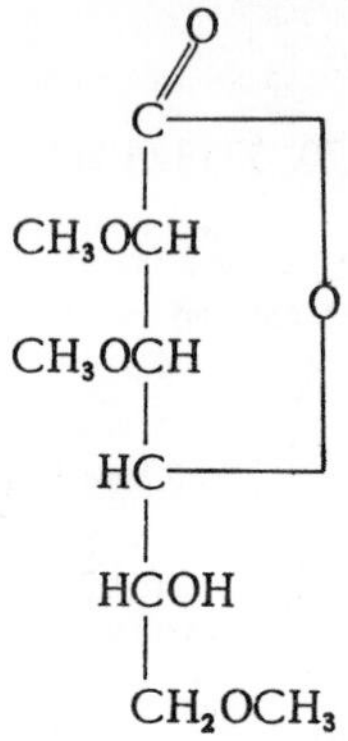

$$
\begin{array}{cc}
\text{CLIV} & \text{CLV} \\
\end{array}
$$

CLIV:
- C=O
- CH₃OCH
- CH₃OCH
- HC (O bridge to C and CH₃OCH)
- HCOH
- CH₂OCH₃

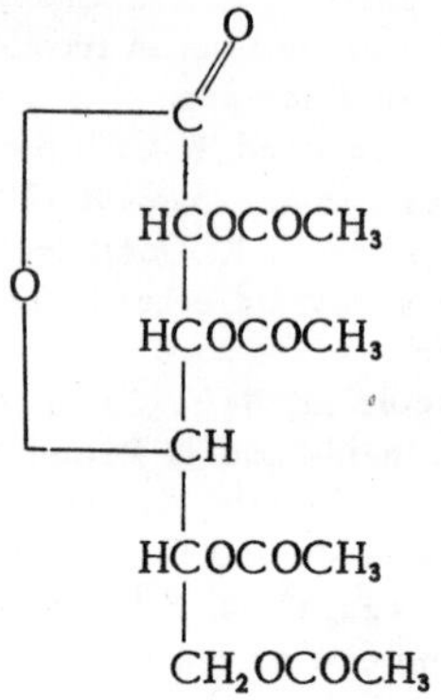

CLV:
- C=O
- HCOCOCH₃
- HCOCOCH₃
- CH
- HCOCOCH₃
- CH₂OCOCH₃

    Reduction of 6-C¹⁴-1,2-isopropylidene-D-glucuronolactone (CLVI) with LAH in ether permits the isolation of 6-C¹⁴-1,2-isopropylidene-D-glucose in good yield. Acid hydrolysis of the isopropylidene group yields 6-C¹⁴-D-glucose (CLVII) in an 80% yield based on the lactone (150).

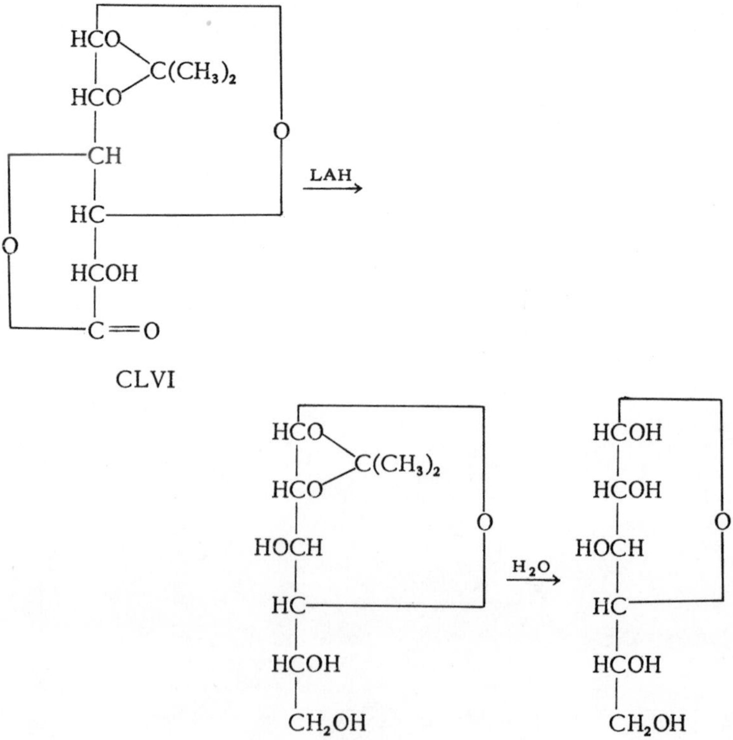

CLVI:
- HCO
- HCO ⟩ C(CH₃)₂
- CH
- HC
- HCOH
- C=O

  LAH →

(9-78)

Left structure:
- HCO
- HCO ⟩ C(CH₃)₂
- HOCH
- HC
- HCOH
- CH₂OH

  H₂O →

CLVII (right structure):
- HCOH
- HCOH
- HOCH
- HC
- HCOH
- CH₂OH

The reduction of CLVI with sodium borohydride in aqueous solution yields CLVII in 60% yield without permitting the isolation of the intermediate monoacetone compound (151). With both reducing agents ion-exchange resins are utilized for purification purposes, although with the borohydride some difficulty is experienced in complete removal of the borate ion.

9.2.1.c *Alicyclic lactones.* Reduction of lactones containing an alicyclic backbone proceeds in the same manner as with acyclic lactones. Reductions of γ- and δ-lactones with LAH have been carried out in ether, tetrahydrofuran, dioxane, and benzene-ether solutions.

Goering and Serres have converted *cis*-3-hydroxycyclohexanecarboxylic acid (CLVIII) to the lactone (CLIX) by heating at 170° for one-half hour followed by distillation. The lactone is reduced with LAH in ether solution to the *cis*-diol with retention of configuration of C_1 and C_3. The cyclic ether (CLX) is obtained instead of the *cis*-diol when the latter is distilled from a flask containing traces of acid causing acid-catalyzed intramolecular dehydration (152).

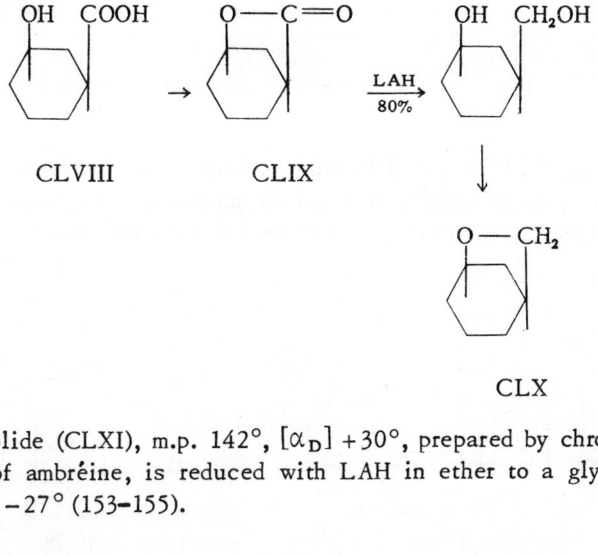

$$(9\text{-}79)$$

CLVIII   CLIX

CLX

Ambreinolide (CLXI), m.p. 142°, $[\alpha_D] +30°$, prepared by chromic acid oxidation of ambréine, is reduced with LAH in ether to a glycol, m.p. 133°, $[\alpha_D] -27°$ (153–155).

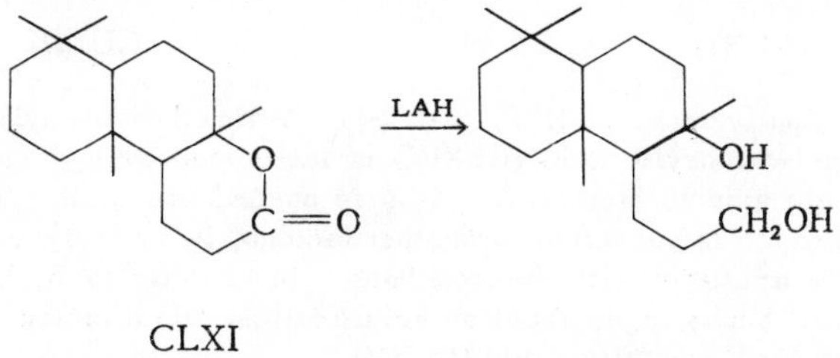

$$(9\text{-}80)$$

CLXI

Cyclization of farnesylacetic acid with formic acid gives a lactone, m.p. 136–138°, which is racemic ambreinolide. LAH reduction of racemic ambreinolide yields a racemic glycol, m.p. 128–129° (156).

On treating ambreinolide (CLXI) with 80% sulfuric acid at 20°, 60°, or 90°, three isomeric lactones are obtained, named by Collin-Asselineau, Lederer, Mercier, and Polonsky (153) as isoambreinolides. Reduction of the isoambreinolides with LAH in ether yields isomeric glycols. The properties of these isomeric compounds are summarized in Table L.

TABLE L (153)

$$\text{ambreinolide} \xrightarrow{\text{80\% } H_2SO_4} \text{isoambreinolide} \xrightarrow{\text{LAH}} \text{glycol}$$

$C_{17}H_{28}O_2$ m.p. 142°, $[\alpha_D]$ +30°	$C_{17}H_{28}O_2$	$C_{17}H_{32}O_2$
Isomerization Temp.	Isoambreinolide[a]	Glycol[a]
20°	m.p. 143°, $[\alpha_D]$ +20°	m.p. 93°, $[\alpha_D]$ +17° [b]
60°	m.p. 98°, $[\alpha_D]$ −13°	m.p. 89°, $[\alpha_D]$ +13.7°
90°	Liquid, b.p. 130–140° (0.2 mm.), $[\alpha_D]$ < ±1°	Liquid, $[\alpha_D]$ ± −1°

[a] $[\alpha_D]$ in chloroform.
[b] Product containing a substance $C_{34}H_{62}O_3$, m.p. 114–116°, whose analysis indicates elimination of one molecule of water between two molecules of glycol.

Marrubiin, $C_{20}H_{28}O_4$, a diterpene isolated from horehound (*Marrubium vulgare* L.), is reduced with LAH to marrubenol, $C_{20}H_{32}O_4$, m.p. 138°. The structure of marrubiin has been postulated as either CLXII or CLXIII (157).

CLXII   CLXIII

It was originally reported (158) that 2-(3,4,5-trimethoxyphenyl)-4,5-dimethyl-cyclohex-4-en-1-carboxylic acid (CLXIV) is lactonized by hydrogen fluoride or methanesulfonic acid to lactone A. This is opened irreversibly by alkali to a hydroxy acid which is converted to another lactone, B, by recrystallization from acetic acid or treatment with diazomethane. In contrast to A, lactone B dissolves in alkali but is regenerated on acidification. Both lactones are reduced by LAH to the same crystalline diol (CLXV).

$$(9\text{-}81)$$

These results are explicable by assuming that the two lactones are epimeric around the α-carbon. However, since the apparent inversion accompanying the reductions is contrary to the reported absence of inversion in LAH reductions the structures of the compounds need to be established conclusively (159).

As discussed in Section 9.1.1.b.3, the cyclization of 2-carbethoxy-2-(2-ketocyclohexyl)cyclohexane yields a product which may contain a lactone grouping (equation (9-38)). The LAH reduction of the cyclization product yields an unidentified product (82).

The LAH reduction of various alicyclic γ- and δ-lactones is summarized in Table LI.

9.2.1.d   *Aromatic lactones.* The reduction of aromatic lactones, such as the phthalides, with LAH has been carried out with considerable success. The reaction has been applied to phthalides and naphthalides including various alkaloids and other natural products.

Among the phthalides the reduction proceeds equally well whether the lactone is derived from a phenol or a benzoic acid derivative. Thus, phthalides such as CLXVI as well as phenolic derivatives such as CLXVII are reduced with LAH to the corresponding glycols.

CLXVI   CLXVII

TABLE LI

LAH Reduction of Alicyclic Lactones

Lactone	Product	% Yield	Ref.
A. γ-Lactones			
$C_7H_{10}O_2$ — cis-3-Hydroxycyclohexane carboxylic acid lactone	cis-3-Hydroxymethylcyclohexanol	80	1
	1,3-Endomethyleneoxycyclohexane	50	1
$C_8H_{12}O_2$ — Hexahydrophthalide	Hexahydrophthalyl alcohol	...	2
$C_{10}H_{14}O_5$ — Acetonequinide (I)	Acetone quinalcohol	44[3]	4
$C_{12}H_{16}O_6$ — Acetyl acetonequinide	Acetone quinalcohol	80	4
$C_{16}H_{26}O_2$ — 1,1,4a,6-Tetramethyl-6-hydroxydecahydro-5-naphthaleneacetic acid lactone (II)	1,1,4a,6-Tetramethyl-6-hydroxydecahydro-5-naphthaleneethanol	96	5
$C_{18}H_{25}NO_5$ — Methyl tetrahydromorphilactonate (III)	Tetrahydromorphitetrol (IV)	70[6]	7
	Methyl tetrahydro-α-isomorphilactonate	Tetrahydro-α-isomorphitetrol (V)	70[6]	7
$C_{20}H_{24}O_6$ — (−)-Conidandrin dimethyl ether (VI)	(+)-Isolariciresinol dimethyl ether	84[8]	9
$C_{22}H_{22}O_7$ — Desoxypicropodophyllin (VII)	Diol, glass	79	10
$C_{22}H_{22}O_8$ — Picropodophyllin (VIII)	Triol, m.p. 160.2–162.2°	53[3]	10
	Podophyllotoxin (IX)	Triol, m.p. 198.5–200.5°	75	10
$C_{30}H_{46}O_3$ — Betulonic acid lactone (X)	Triol, m.p. 296°	81[6]	11–13
$C_{32}H_{50}O_4$ — Betulinic acid "lactone A" acetate (XI)	Triol	...	14
B. δ-Lactones			
$C_{17}H_{24}O_3$ — Ketolactone, m.p. 187° (XII)	Triol, m.p. 116°	...	15
$C_{17}H_{28}O_2$ — Ambreinolide[16] m.p. 142°, $[\alpha_D]+30°$	Glycol, m.p. 133°, $[\alpha_D]-27°$	97	5
		...	17
Ambreinolide[16] m.p. 136–138°, racemic	Glycol, m.p. 128–129°, racemic	95	18
Isoambreinolide[20]		57	19
$C_{19}H_{24}O_3$	Glycol	...	18
Product from oxidation of estrone	Glycol, m.p. 128–129°	...	21

CHART TO TABLE LI

I

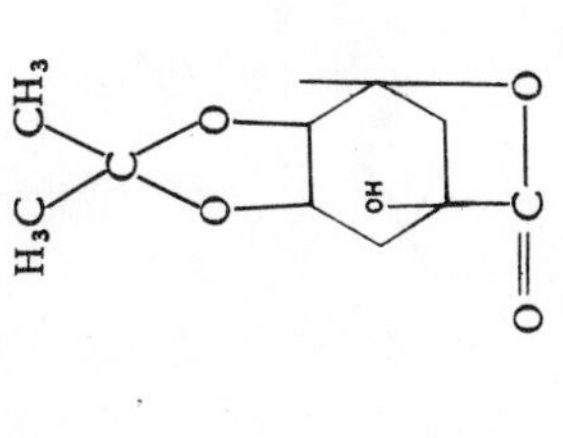

II

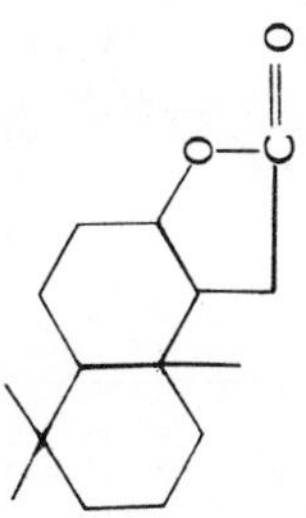

III

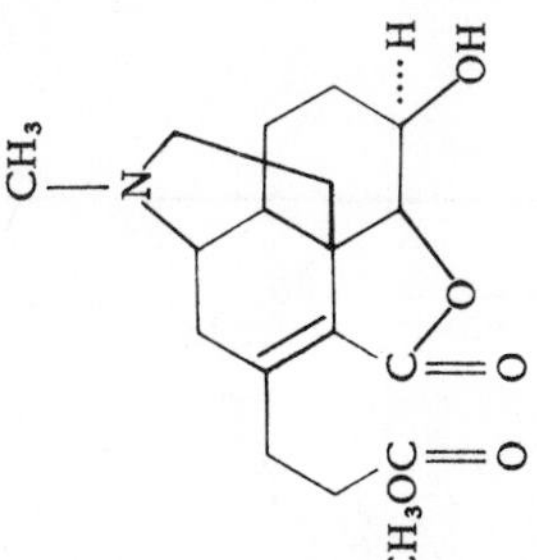

IV

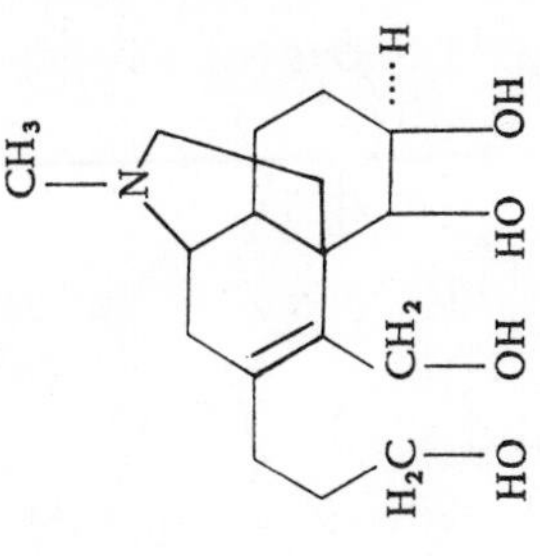

V

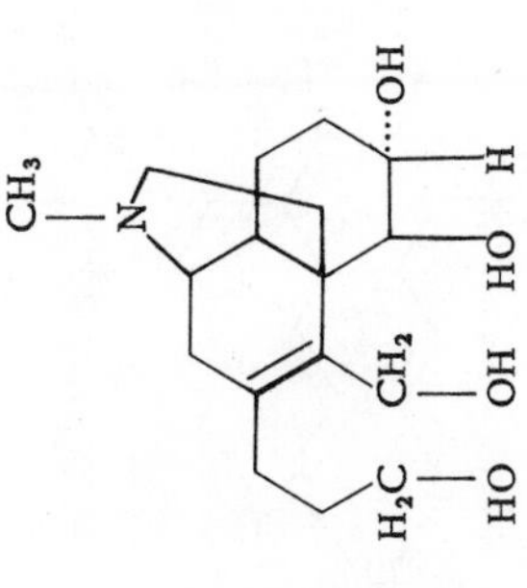

VI

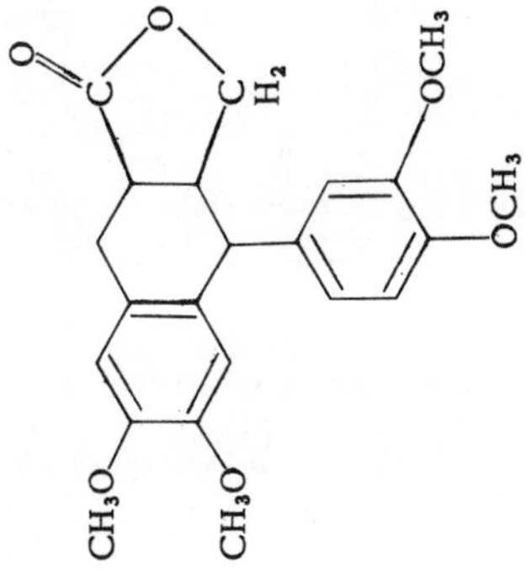

VII

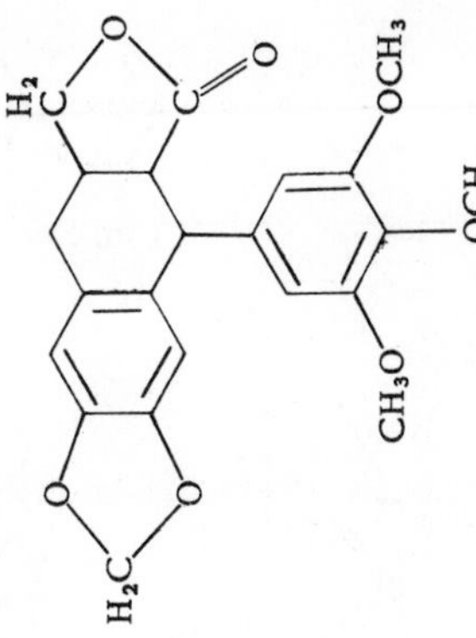

(continued)

CHART TO TABLE LI (*continued*)

References—Table LI

[1]H. L. Goering and C. Serres, Jr., *J. Am. Chem. Soc.*, 74, 5908 (1952).

[2]R. Ratouis and A. Willemart, *Compt. rend.*, 233, 1124 (1951).

[3]Reduction carried out in dioxane-ether mixture.

[4]R. Grewe and E. Nolte, *Ann.*, 575, 1 (1951).

[5]M. Hinder and M. Stoll, *Helv. Chim. Acta*, 33, 1308 (1950).

[6]Reduction carried out in tetrahydrofuran.

[7]H. Rapoport and G. B. Payne, *J. Org. Chem.*, 15, 1093 (1950).

[8]Reduction carried out in benzene-ether mixture.

[9]R. D. Haworth and L. Wilson, *J. Chem. Soc.*, 1950, 71.

[10]N. L. Drake and E. H. Price, *J. Am. Chem. Soc.*, 73, 201 (1951).

[11]G. S. Davy, T. G. Halsall and E. R. H. Jones, *Chemistry and Industry*, 1951, 233.

[12]G. S. Davy, T. G. Halsall, and E. R. H. Jones, *J. Chem. Soc.*, 1951, 2696.

[13]G. S. Davy, T. G. Halsall, E. R. H. Jones, and G. D. Meakins, *ibid.*, 1951, 2702.

[14]G. S. Davy, T. G. Halsall, and E. R. H. Jones, *Chemistry and Industry*, 1950, 732.

[15]C. Collin-Asselineau, *Compt. rend.*, 235, 634 (1952).

[16]See text.

[17]E. Lederer and M. Stoll, *Helv. Chim. Acta*, 33, 1345 (1950).

[18]C. Collin-Asselineau, E. Lederer, D. Mercier, and J. Polonsky, *Bull. soc. chim. France*, [5] 17, 720 (1950).

[19]P. Dietrich and E. Lederer, *Helv. Chim. Acta*, 35, 1148 (1952).

[20]See text and Table L.

[21]J. Jacques, A. Horeau, and R. Courrier, *Compt. rend.*, 229, 321 (1949).

Weygand (160) has utilized a phthalide (CLXVIII) in the synthesis of a dihydroxynaphthoquinone by the following scheme:

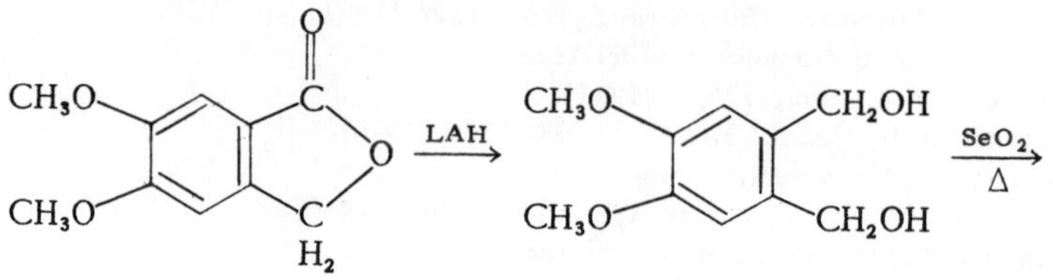

CLXVIII

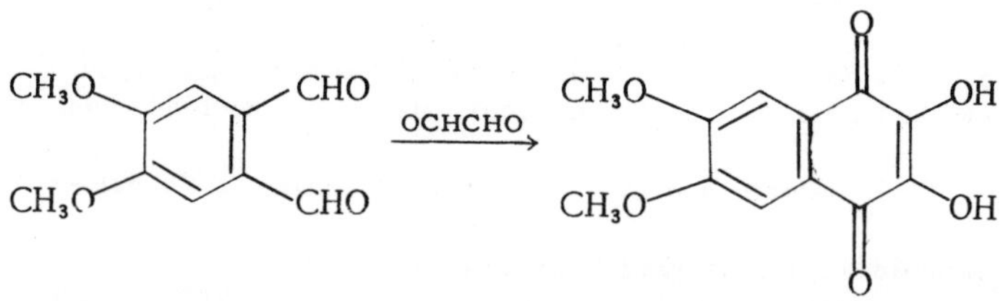

(9-82)

Treatment of terramycin with 20% sodium hydroxide in the presence of zinc yields, among other products, a phenolic lactone identified as 7-hydroxy-3-methylphthalide (CLXIX). Reduction with LAH yields the phenolic glycol which on methylation with diazomethane yields a methoxy-diol identical with the product obtained by the LAH reduction of the ketoester (CLXX) (161,162).

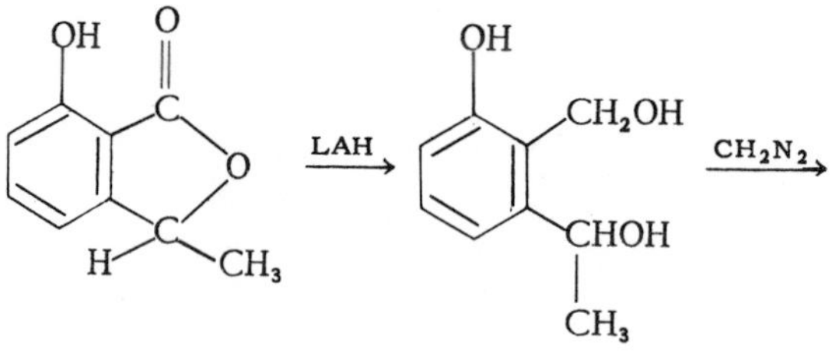

CLXIX

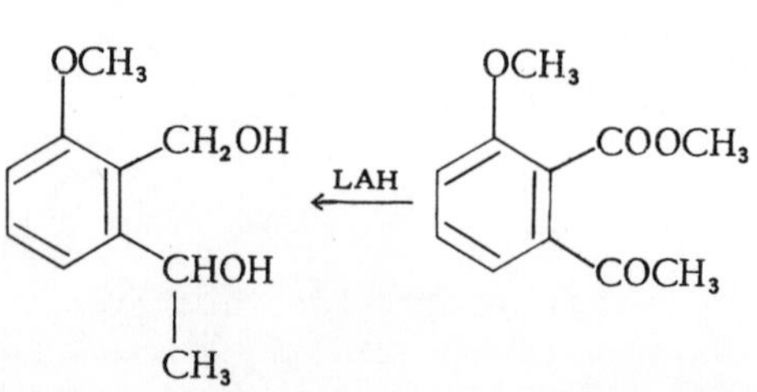

(9-83)

CLXX

The influence of steric effects is seen in the report that phthalide (CLXVI) is reduced to o-xylylene glycol with the calculated amount of

LAH while the reduction of 7-chlorophthalide (CLXXI) requires five moles of LAH (92).

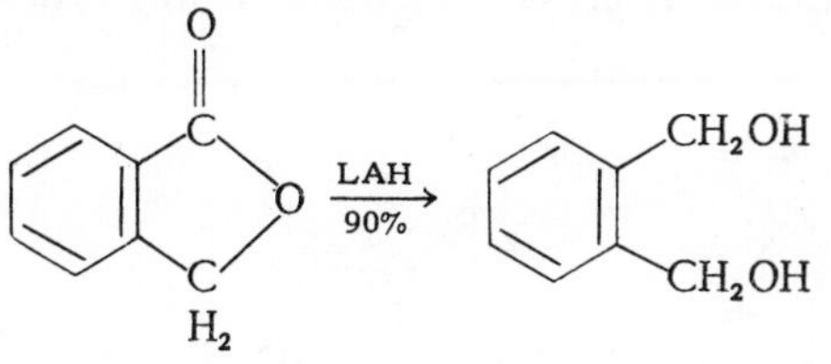

(9-84)

CLXVI

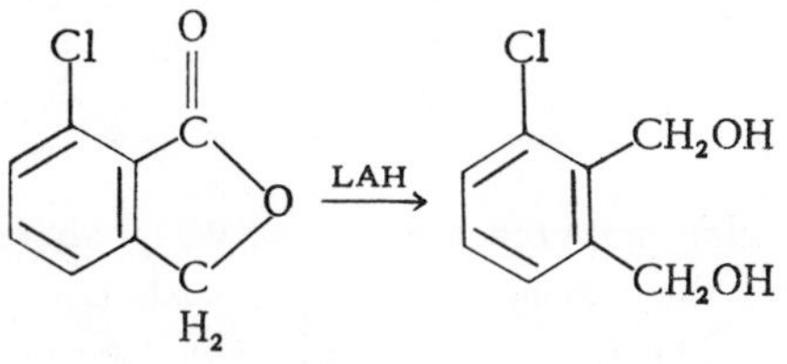

(9-85)

CLXXI

The reduction of naphthalides presents an interesting problem. Treatment of (+)-eleutherol methyl ether (CLXXII) with LAH yields the (+)-glycol after a 16-hour reflux in ethereal solution (163). LAH reduction of pentamethyldecarboxamidoterrinolide (CLXXIII), derived from an acid degradation product of terramycin, similarly yields the corresponding dialcohol (164).

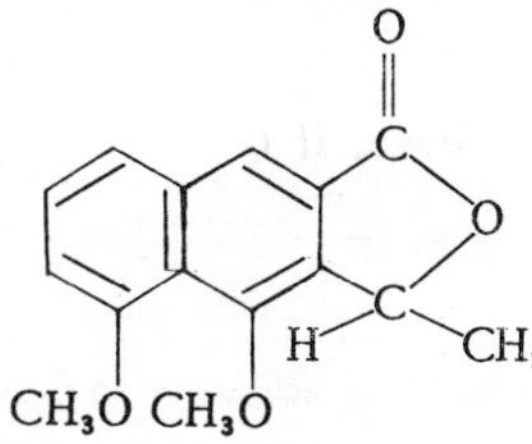

CLXXII 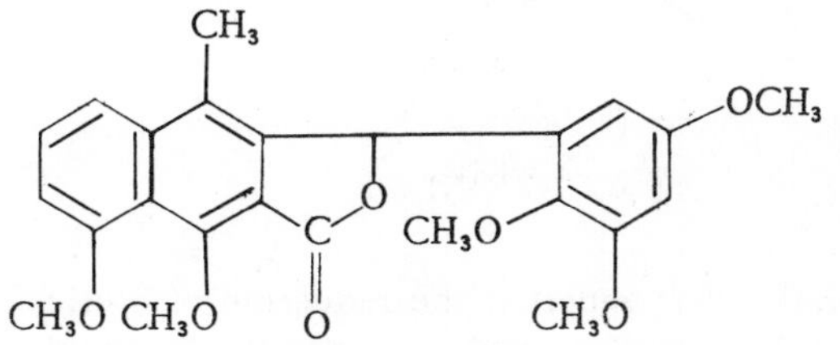   CLXXIII

Here the reduction of 2,3-naphthalides, in which the carbonyl group is attached to the aromatic nucleus, proceeds as expected. No examples of 2,3-naphthalides based on 2-naphthol have been reported.

LAH reduction of 1,2-naphthalides based on 1- or 2-naphthol proceeds, as expected even where steric influences might be anticipated. Thus, LAH reduction of the lactones of α-(1-hydroxy-2-naphthyl)phenylacetic acid (CLXXIV: R = C_6H_5; R_1 = H), α-(1-hydroxy-2-naphthyl)diphenylacetic acid (CLXXIV: R = R_1 = C_6H_5), α-(2-hydroxy-1-naphthyl)phenylacetic acid (CLXXV: R = C_6H_5; R_1 = H), α-(2-hydroxy-1-naphthyl)diphenylacetic acid (CLXXV: R = R_1 = C_6H_5) and 2-hydroxy-1-naphthalene-propionic acid (CLXXVI) gives the corresponding diol in excellent yield (165,166).

CLXXIV   CLXXV   CLXXVI

In contrast, refluxing naphthalide (CLXXVII), wherein the carbonyl group is attached to the aromatic nucleus, with LAH in diethyl ether causes no reduction. The reduction of the anhydride of naphthalene-1,2-dicarboxylic acid with LAH in diethyl ether yields CLXXVII, with no further reduction under the same conditions. However, if the anhydride is refluxed with LAH in di-n-butyl ether the final product is the diol (CLXXVIII) (167).

CLXXVII   CLXXVIII

Baker has reported the reduction of sterically hindered acids with LAH in boiling di-n-butyl ether (168). It would be of interest to examine the behavior of a naphthalide in which the carbonyl group is in the β-position on the naphthalene ring.

The failure of the LAH reduction of tetraphenylphthalic anhydride in diethyl ether to proceed beyond the phthalide stage, while a separate reduction of the phthalide with LAH in the same ether yields the glycol (169) is discussed in Section 8.2.1.b.

Hochstein (3) reported that the reduction of coumarin (CLXXIX) with LAH in refluxing ether for 24 hours gives 50% of 3-(o-hydroxyphenyl)-propanol (CLXXX), in which the double bond has been reduced, as well as 10% of o-hydroxycinnamyl alcohol (CLXXXI).

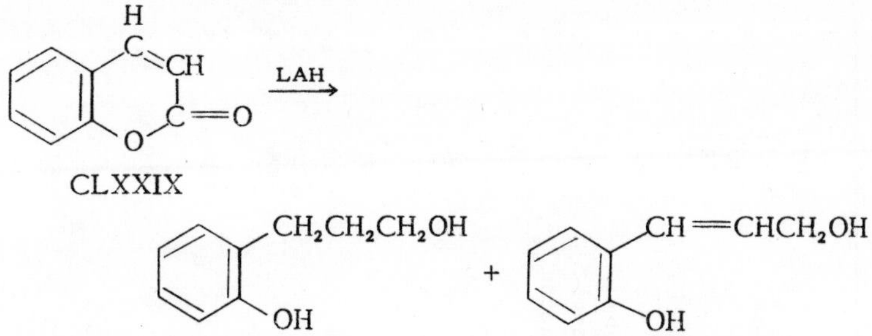

CLXXIX

CLXXX　　　　　　　CLXXXI

(9-86)

Karrer and Banerjea (63) reported that when the reduction is carried out in ethereal solution at room temperature by adding the lactone to LAH (2:1 mole ratio) over a 20-minute period, followed by an additional 30 minutes of stirring, the product obtained in 75% yield is the unsaturated alcohol CLXXXI. In contrast the ethyl ester of coumaric acid gives the saturated alcohol CLXXX.

Siegel and Coburn (170) reported that reduction of 3-phenylisocoumarin (CLXXXII) with LAH in the "usual way" gives a 59% yield of the saturated diol.

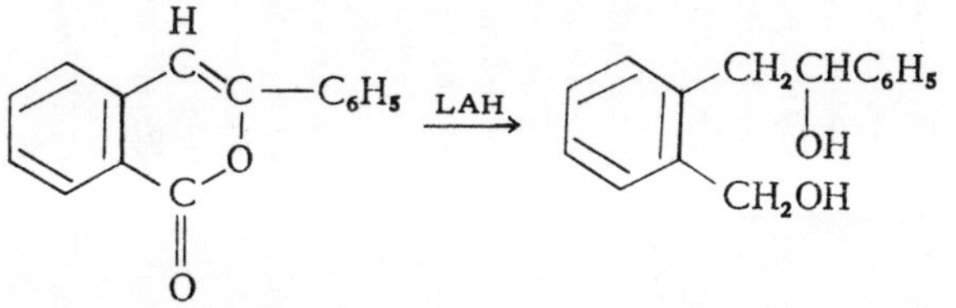

CLXXXII

(9-87)

The LAH reduction of benzoylanthranil (CLXXXIII) yields o-benzamino-benzyl alcohol (CLXXXIV). With one-quarter mole of LAH the reduction product retains the intact lactone grouping (CLXXXV) (171).

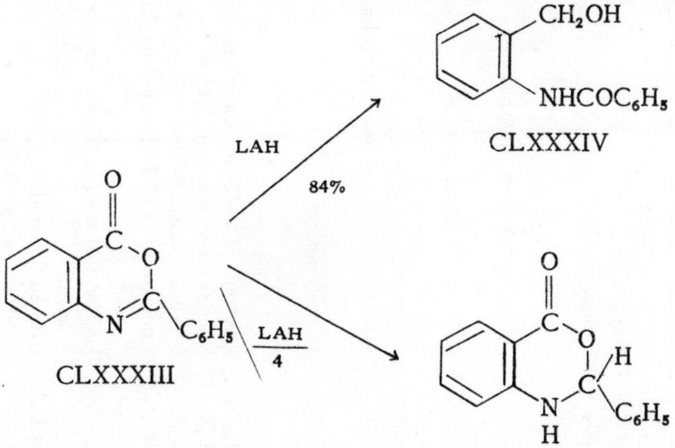

(9-88)

CLXXXIV

(9-89)

CLXXXV

TABLE LII

LAH Reduction of Aromatic Lactones

	Lactone	Product	% Yield	Ref.
$C_8H_5ClO_2$	7-Chlorophthalide	3-Chloro-o-xylylene glycol	....	1
$C_8H_6O_2$	Phthalide	o-Xylylene glycol	90	1
$C_9H_6O_2$	Coumarin (I)	3-(o-Hydroxyphenyl)propanol	50⎫	2
		o-Hydroxycinnamyl alcohol	10⎭	3
		cis-o-Hydroxycinnamyl alcohol	75	4
$C_9H_8O_3$	7-Hydroxy-3-methylphthalide	1-[2-(Hydroxymethyl)-3-hydroxyphenyl]ethanol	....	5
$C_{10}H_{10}O_2$	5,6-Dimethoxyphthalide	1,2-Di-(hydroxymethyl)-4,5-dimethoxybenzene	63	6
$C_{10}H_{10}O_3$	7-Methoxy-3-methylphthalide	1-[2-(Hydroxymethyl)-3-methoxyphenyl]ethanol	....	5
$C_{11}H_{12}O_2$	5,6,7-Trimethoxyphthalide	1,2-Di-(hydroxymethyl)-3,4,5-trimethoxybenzene	78	6
$C_{12}H_{14}O_2$	4,5,7-Trimethoxy-6-methylphthalide	1,2-Di-(hydroxymethyl)-3,5,6-trimethoxy-4-methylbenzene	37	7
$C_{14}H_9NO_2$	Benzoylanthranil (II)	o-Benzaminobenzyl alcohol[8]	84	9
		6-Keto-2-phenyl-4,5-benzo-2,3-dihydro-1,3-oxazine (III)[9,10]	....	9
$C_{14}H_{10}O_2$	Lactone of α-(2-hydroxyphenyl)phenylacetic acid	2-(2-Hydroxyphenyl)-2-phenylethanol	....	11
$C_{15}H_{10}O_2$	3-Phenylisocoumarin (IV)	1-Phenyl-2-(o-hydroxymethylphenyl)ethanol	93	12
$C_{15}H_{14}O_4$	(+)-Eleutherol methyl ether (V)	(+)-glycol	59	13
$C_{18}H_{12}O_2$	Lactone of α-(2-hydroxy-1-naphthyl)phenylacetic acid	2-(2-Hydroxy-1-naphthyl)-2-phenylethanol	....	14
	Lactone of α-(1-hydroxy-2-naphthyl)phenylacetic acid	2-(1-Hydroxy-2-naphthyl)-2-phenylethanol	95	15
$C_{20}H_{14}O_2$	Diphenylphthalide (VI)	1-(o-Hydroxymethyl)-1,1-diphenylmethanol	100	16
$C_{21}H_{21}NO_6$	l-β-Hydrastine (VII)	Glycol, m.p. 143°	94	17
$C_{22}H_{23}NO_7$	l-α-Narcotine (VIII)	Glycol, m.p. 134°	....	17
	l-β-Narcotine (VIII)	Glycol, m.p. 131–132°	81[18]	19
		Glycol, oil	....	17

Formula	Lactone	Product	Yield	Ref
$C_{24}H_{16}O_2$	Lactone of α-(2-hydroxy-1-naphthyl)diphenylacetic acid	2-(2-Hydroxy-1-naphthyl)-2,2-diphenylethanol	99	15
	Lactone of α-(1-hydroxy-2-naphthyl)diphenylacetic acid	2-(1-Hydroxy-2-naphthyl)-2,2-diphenylethanol	100[20]	15
$C_{24}H_{24}O_7$	Pentamethyldecarboxamidoterrinolide (IX)	Dialcohol	....	21
$C_{32}H_{22}O_2$	Tetraphenylphthalide	Tetraphenyl-o-xylylenediol	53	22

[1] R. F. Bird and E. E. Turner, J. Chem. Soc., 1952, 5050.
[2] F. A. Hochstein, J. Am. Chem. Soc., 71, 305 (1949).
[3] P. Karrer and P. Banerjea, Helv. Chim. Acta, 32, 1692 (1949).
[4] R. Kuhn and K. Dury, Chem. Ber., 84, 848 (1951).
[5] F. A. Hochstein and R. Pasternack, J. Am. Chem. Soc., 74, 3905 (1952).
[6] F. Weygand, Angew. Chem., 61, 441 (1949).
[7] F. Weygand, K. G. Kinkel, and D. Tietjen, Chem. Ber., 83, 394 (1950).
[8] Inverse addition.
[9] B. Witkop, J. B. Patrick, and H. M. Kissman, Chem. Ber., 85, 949 (1952).
[10] Reduction with one-quarter mole of LAH.
[11] C. O. Guss, H. R. Williams, and L. H. Jules, J. Am. Chem. Soc., 73, 1257 (1951).
[12] S. Siegel and S. Coburn, ibid., 73, 5494 (1951).
[13] H. Schmid and A. Ebnöther, Helv. Chim. Acta, 34, 1041 (1951).
[14] C. O. Guss and L. H. Jules, J. Am. Chem. Soc., 72, 3462 (1950).
[15] C. O. Guss, ibid., 73, 608 (1951).
[16] Van Dyken, unpublished work; through W. G. Brown, in Organic Reactions, Vol. VI, p. 501.
[17] R. Mirza and R. Robinson, Nature, 166, 271 (1950).
[18] Reduction carried out in benzene.
[19] M. Semonsky, Chem. Listy, 45, 392 (1951).
[20] Reduction carried out in dioxane.
[21] F. A. Hochstein, P. P. Regna, K. J. Brunings, and R. B. Woodward, J. Am. Chem. Soc., 74, 3706 (1952).
[22] E. F. Bonner, A. G. Finkensieper, and E. I. Becker, J. Org. Chem., 18, 426 (1953).

CHART TO TABLE LII

Calophyllide, $C_{25}H_{22}O_5$, m.p. 158–160°, an aromatic polycyclic compound isolated from the tropical tree "Calophyllum inophyllum," contains two double bonds and a lactone group. The reduction of calophyllide by LAH has been reported to give only amorphous products (172).

The reduction of the pseudo esters (CLXXXVI: R = CH_3 or C_2H_5) with LAH yields the diol (93,94), as discussed in Sections 7.1.1.b, 9.1.1.b.8 and 11.3.1.b.

$$\text{(9-90)}$$

CLXXXVI

The LAH reduction of various aromatic lactones is summarized in Table LII.

9.2.1.e *Heterocyclic lactones.* Mariella and Belcher reported (13) that the attempted reduction of the lactone of 3-carboxy-6-methyl-4-hydroxymethyl-2(1)-pryidone (CLXXXVII) with LAH in diethyl ether, diethyl ether-tetrahydrofuran (1:1), dioxane-diethyl ether (1:2), di-*n*-butyl ether, or di-*n*-butyl ether-dioxane (1:1), with variations in the time of refluxing (1 to 7 days), the method of adding reagents and the working up of the product fails to yield any bis-hydroxymethyl compound. The only product which can be isolated besides unreacted starting material is a light yellow oil, which is not basic and does not give a positive ferric chloride test. Catalytic hydrogenation with copper chromite at 170° and 190 atmospheres pressure for 6 hours also fails to reduce CLXXXVII. The attempted reductions of the lactones CLXXXVIII and CLXXXIX with LAH have also been unsuccessful.

CLXXXVII   CLXXXVIII   CLXXXIX

9.2.2 Reductions with Sodium Borohydride

The use of the borohydride in the reduction of 6-C^{14}-1,2-isopropylidene-D-glucuronolactone to 6-C^{14}-D-glucose (equation 9-78) has been discussed in Section 9.2.1.b.

Under controlled conditions the reduction of aldonic acid lactones with sodium borohydride can be utilized to obtain either the aldose or the glycitol. Thus, the addition of an aqueous solution of the borohydride to an aqueous solution of D-gluco-D-*gulo*-heptono-γ-lactone (CXC), while maintaining the temperature at 0–3° and the pH at 3–4, yields 66% of D-gluco-D-*gulo*-heptose (CXCI). Reductions carried out in 95% aqueous methanol give much lower yields while in absolute methanol the reaction is extremely slow or absent. By reversing the order of addition, i.e., addition of an aqueous solution of the lactone to an aqueous solution of sodium borohydride, at room temperature while maintaining the reaction temperature below 50° yields 67% of *meso*-gluco-*gulo*-heptitol (CXCII) (173,174).

Under similar reaction conditions D-lyxono-γ-lactone is reduced to D-lyxose or D-arabitol (132). Under the conditions described for reducing the lactone to the aldose, the following lactones give final reaction mixtures strongly reducing to Benedict solution (173): D-galactono-γ-lactone, D-ribono-γ-lactone, D-manno-D-*gala*-heptono-γ-lactone. Dulcitol has been isolated from the reaction mixture from D-galactono-γ-lactone.

The lactone groups present in gluconic acid oxycelluloses have been reduced by sodium borohydride in a low pH solution to aldehyde groups and in alkaline solution to alcohol groups (175).

The lactone group in various glycosides and aglycones has been reported to be resistant to the action of sodium borohydride in 80% dioxane solution. Thus, reduction of strophanthidin (CXCIII) results in reduction of the aldehyde group without attacking the lactone ring (176).

CXCIII

Other cardiac active glycosides and aglycones treated in a similar manner are: convallatoxin (176), desgluco-hellebrin (176), gofruside (177), corotoxigenin (177).

9.3 ENOL ESTERS

The reduction of steroidal enol esters with the complex metal hydrides yields mixtures of products which can be separated by chromatography on alumina or precipitation with digitonin. Since a major portion of the work in this field has been concerned with a comparison of the reducing action of LAH and sodium borohydride the material in this section is also presented in this manner.

Dauben, Micheli, and Eastham (178) have carried out the LAH reduction of the enol acetate of cholestanone, 3-acetoxy-2-cholestene (CXCIV) and coprostanone, 3-acetoxy-3-coprostene (CXCVIII), with both normal and inverse addition. The β-isomer, cholestanol (CXCVI), is the major product in the reduction of CXCIV while the α-isomer, epicoprostanol (CXCIX), is the major product in the reduction of CXCVIII. The free ketones, cholestanone (CXCVII) and coprostanone (CCI), respectively, are also found in the reduction mixtures.

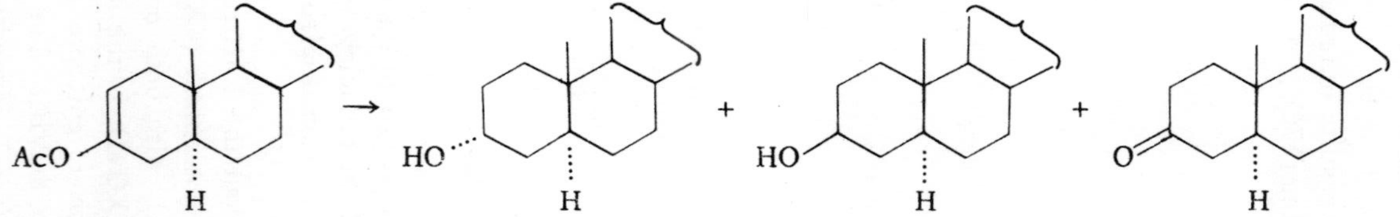

(9-93)

AcO — CXCIV → HO⋯ CXCV + HO CXCVI + O= CXCVII

	CXCV	CXCVI	CXCVII
LAH normal addition	17	58	21
LAH inverse addition	20	59	10
NaBH$_4$	13	84	0

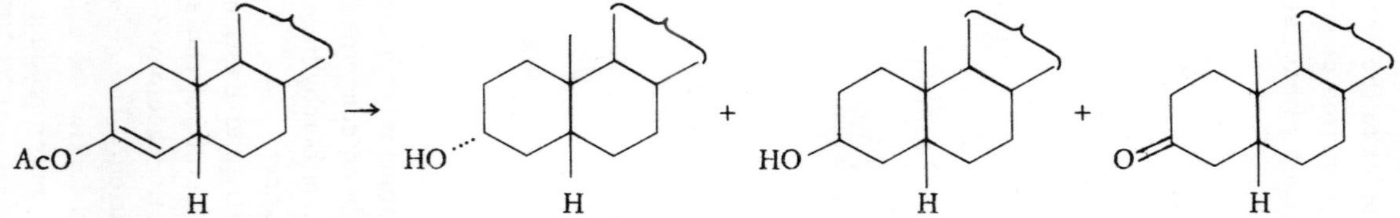

(9-94)

AcO — CXCVIII → HO⋯ CXCIX + HO CC + O= CCI

	CXCIX	CC	CCI
LAH normal addition	70	13	10
LAH inverse addition	63	20	8

Carbon-carbon double bond reduction is observed in all the products. Inverse addition appears to increase the yield of the less available isomer. In contrast, reduction of CXCIV with sodium borohydride in a methanol-ether mixture reduces the yield of this isomer and increases the yield of the β-isomer. In addition no ketone is recovered from the borohydride reduction, probably due to the initial solvolysis of the enol acetate to the ketone which in turn is reduced, as discussed later in this section.

These results can be compared with those obtained in the reduction of the parent ketones, cholestanone (CCII) and coprostanone (CCIII), (Section 7.2.1.1).

CCII   CCIII

Ketone	Reducing Agent	Mode of Addition	% Yield		Ref.
			α-ol	β-ol	
CCII	LAH	Normal	4	91	179
	LAH	Inverse	12	82	178
	NaBH$_4$		13	84	178
CCIII	LAH	Normal	94	4	179
	LAH	Inverse	87	7	178
	NaBH$_4$		76	16	178

The less available isomer is formed to a slightly greater amount when the borohydride is used. The ratio of isomers from the ketone (CCII) is similar to the ratio obtained from the enol acetate (CXCIV) with borohydride reduction, while LAH reduction gives a higher yield of the more available isomer and a smaller yield of the less available isomer from the ketones CCII and CCIII as compared with the enol acetates CXCIV and CXCVIII.

Dauben and Eastham have carried out the reduction of the enol acetate of 4-cholestene-3-one (CCIV) with both LAH (180,181) and sodium borohydride (182) under a variety of reaction conditions. Belleau and Gallagher have carried out the reduction with sodium borohydride (183). The reduction of CCIV with LAH yields a mixture consisting of 4-cholestene-3-one (CCV), epicholesterol (CCVI), cholesterol (CCVII), and 4-cholesten-3α- and 3β-ols (CCVIII). The Δ^4-stenols were not isolated directly but were detected by the isolation of cholesta-3,5-diene after a mild acid treatment. The reduction of CCIV with sodium borohydride yields a mixture of the four isomeric stenols but no free ketone (CCV) is obtained. The relative amounts of these products are summarized below:

CCIV   →   CCV   +

CCVI   +   CCVII   +   CCVIII   (9-95)

Temp., °C.	Solvent	Mode of Addition	% Yield				Ref.
			CCV	CCVI	CCVII	CCVIII	
		LAH					
−10	Et₂O	Normal	32	15	34	8	180,181
25	Et₂O	Inverse	34	16	34	0	181
65	THF	Normal	29	17	32	13	181
90	n-Bu₂O	Inverse	28	6	33	9	181
		NaBH₄					
2	MeOH-Et₂O	Inverse	0	13	75	7	182
55	MeOH-Et₂O	Inverse	0	13	69	8	182
55	MeOH-Et₂O	Normal	0	14	58	23	182
5	EtOH-H₂O	Normal	0	7.5	70	1-3	183

The reduction with LAH yields a ratio of cholestenone, cholesterol, and epicholesterol which is not significantly affected by the time, temperature, concentration of hydride or the mode of addition. Higher temperatures favor the formation of the 4-cholesten-3-ols while inverse addition at lower temperatures apparently prevents their formation. In a few runs, an unknown steroid, $C_{27}H_{46}O_2$, m.p. 168–169°, was isolated in 2-3% yield but not further characterized.

The reduction with sodium borohydride yields cholesterol as the predominant product. The quantity of the 3α-ol obtained in this case is similar to that obtained in the LAH reduction while the yield of the 3β-ol is essentially doubled. Since sodium borohydride does not normally reduce esters the mechanism of the borohydride reduction must differ from that of the LAH reduction. It has been proposed (182,183) that the initial step in the former reduction is the solvolysis of the enol acetate (CCIV) to yield the free ketone (CCIX) via the enol form. The 5-cholesten-3-one (CCIX) is almost completely reduced before it can rearrange to the more stable 4-cholesten-3-one (CCV). The reduction of the ketones CCIX and CCV yields the 5-stenols and 4-stenols, respectively.

$$(9\text{-}96)$$

The recovery of unchanged enol acetate after treatment with sodium borohydride in pyridine is considered evidence for the initial step of the reduction, i.e., solvolysis of the ester to the enol, since a carbonyl group is readily reduced by this method (183). Further, the reduction of 5-cholesten-3-one with the borohydride is reported to yield 72% of cholesterol and 23% of epicholesterol (178), a ratio similar to that obtained in the reduction of the enol acetate (CCIV).

Brown (184) has reported that the results obtained by Dauben and Eastham (181) in the LAH reduction of the enol acetate of 4-cholesten-3-one have been confirmed and that aluminum hydride yields the same results. However, the action of aluminum hydride in the presence of aluminum chloride causes the reaction to follow a different course, yielding 16% of 4-cholestene (CCX), 20% of 4-cholesten-3-one (CCV) and 49% of a molecular compound, $C_{27}H_{46}O_2$, m.p. 196–197°. The action of aluminum chloride on the enol acetate in ether quantitatively yields 4-cholesten-3-one.

$$+ \; C_{27}H_{46}O_2 \qquad (9\text{-}97)$$

Acetylation of the molecular compound yields two diacetates, m.p. 157–158° and 112–113°. These on hydrolysis give two diols, m.p. 177–178° and 179–180°, respectively. An equimolar mixture of the two diols, on recrystallization, yields the original molecular compound as does hydrolysis of an equimolar mixture of the two diacetates. A mixed melting point of the two diols has m.p. 70–193°. Brown suggests that the compound isolated by Dauben and Eastham (181) in 2–3% yield may be an impure specimen of the molecular compound or one of its component diols and further speculates that the diols are the trans-5-cholesten-3,4-diols.

4-Cholesten-3-one-4-C^{14} has been converted to cholesterol-C^{14} in 50% yield, based on recovered ketone, by LAH reduction of the enol acetate (181). The enol acetate of 4-cholesten-3-one-3-C^{14} has been reduced to cholesterol-3-C^{14} in 60% yield with sodium borohydride in ethanol (185).

Belleau and Gallagher have treated 4-cholesten-3-one with t-butylmagnesium chloride to obtain the enolate. Hydrolysis of the latter apparently regenerates the Δ^5-3-ketone since reduction with sodium borohydride in aqueous ethanol gives a 37% overall yield of cholesterol (183).

The reduction of 3-acetoxycholesta-3,5,7-triene (CCXI) with sodium borohydride in a methanol-ether mixture at room temperature yields a mixture of 3α- and 3β-hydroxycholesta-5,7-dienes containing 70% of the 3β-isomer, 7-dehydrocholesterol (186).

$$(9\text{-}98)$$

CCXI

The reduction of 3-acetoxy-22-isospirosta-3,5,7-triene (CCXII) with sodium borohydride in a dioxane-methanol-water mixture at 10° yields approximately 70% of 22-isospirosta-5,7-dien-3β-ol (CCXIII). When the reduction is carried out at 80° the crude 3β-ol (85% yield) is contaminated with some $\Delta^{4,6}$-dien-3-ol (187).

CCXII

$$(9\text{-}99)$$

CCXIII

In accordance with the mechanism outlined in equation (9-96), CCXIII results from the rapid reduction of the unconjugated ketone formed by hydrolysis of the enol acetate. Apparently, at the higher temperature some isomerization of the unconjugated ketone to the $\Delta^{4,6}$-dien-3-one occurs prior to the reduction. The reduction of 3-acetoxy-22-isospirosta-3,5,7, 9(11)-tetraene (CCXIV) with sodium borohydride yields essentially the same yield of 22-isospirosta-5,7,9(11)-trien-3β-ol whether the reduction is carried out at 10° (69% yield) or 80° (68% yield).

CCXIV   (9-100)

Owing to the longer conjugated triene system, the isomerization of the initially formed unconjugated ketone to the conjugated form is slow so that reduction of the unconjugated ketone predominates (187).

REFERENCES

1. Nystrom, R. F., and W. G. Brown, *J. Am. Chem. Soc.*, **69**, 1197 (1947).
2. Schlesinger, H. I., and A. E. Finholt, U. S. Pat. 2,567,972 (September 18, 1951); U. S. Pat. 2,576,311 (November 27, 1951).
3. Hochstein, F. A., *J. Am. Chem. Soc.*, **71**, 305 (1949).
4. Eliel, E. L., and J. P. Freeman, *J. Am. Chem. Soc.*, **72**, 923 (1952).
5. Freeman, J. H., *J. Am. Chem. Soc.*, **74**, 6257 (1952).
6. Carpenter, A. T., and R. F. Hunter, *J. Applied Chem. (London)*, **1**, 217 (1951).
7. Finn, S. R., and J. W. G. Musty, *Chemistry and Insustry*, **1950**, 677.
8. Finn, S. R., and J. W. G. Musty, *J. Applied Chem. (London)*, **1**, 182 (1951).
9. Pasternack, R., A. Bavley, R. L. Wagner, F. A. Hochstein, P. P. Regna, and K. J. Brunings, *J. Am. Chem. Soc.*, **74**, 1926 (1952).
10. Hochstein, F. A., C. R. Stephens, L. H. Conover, P. P. Regna, R. Pasternack, P. N. Gordon, F. J. Pilgrim, K. J. Brunings, and R. B. Woodward, *J. Am. Chem. Soc.*, **75**, 5455 (1953).
11. Cram, D. J., *J. Am. Chem. Soc.*, **71**, 3863 (1949); **74**, 2129, 2137, 2159 (1952).
12. Cram, D. J., and J. D. Knight, *J. Am. Chem. Soc.*, **74**, 5839 (1952).
13. Mariella, R. P., and E. P. Belcher, *J. Am. Chem. Soc.*, **74**, 4049 (1952).
14. Newman, M. S., and R. Gaertner, *J. Am. Chem. Soc.*, **72**, 264 (1950).
15. Burgstahler, A. W., *J. Am. Chem. Soc.*, **73**, 3021 (1951).
16. Barton, D. H. R., and C. J. W. Brooks, *J. Chem. Soc.*, **1951**, 257.
17. Carrara, G., and G. Weitnauer, *Gazz. chim. ital.*, **79**, 856 (1949).
18. Huebner, C. F., and C. R. Scholz, *J. Am. Chem. Soc.*, **73**, 2089 (1951).
19. Lepetit S. A., Brit. Pat. 679,028 (September 10, 1952).

20. Papineau-Couture, G., E. M. Richardson, and G. A. Grant, *Can. J. Research, 27B,* 902 (1949).
21. Šorm, F., and M. Vrany, unpublished work; through J. Rudinger, M. Ferles and M. Protiva, *Chem. Listy, 45,* 346 (1951).
22. Biel, J. H., *J. Am. Chem. Soc., 73,* 847 (1951).
23. Barton, D. H. R., and T. Bruun, *J. Chem. Soc., 1951,* 2728.
24. Macbeth, A. K., and J. S. Shannon, *J. Chem. Soc., 1952,* 4748.
25. Cram, D. J., and J. D. Knight, *J. Am. Chem. Soc., 74,* 5835 (1952).
26. Doering, W. von E., and H. H. Zeiss, *J. Am. Chem. Soc., 72,* 147 (1950).
27. Zeiss, H. H., *J. Am. Chem. Soc., 73,* 2391 (1951).
28. English, J., Jr., and V. Lamberti, *J. Am. Chem. Soc., 74,* 1909 (1952).
29. Soffer, L. M., E. W. Parrotta and J. Di Domenico, *J. Am. Chem. Soc., 74,* 5301 (1952).
30. Ansell, E. G., J. Honeyman, and G. H. Williams, *Chemistry and Industry, 1952,* 149.
31. Ansell, E. G., and J. Honeyman, *J. Chem. Soc., 1952,* 2778.
32. Karrer, P., and E. Jucker, *Helv. Chim. Acta, 35,* 1586 (1952).
33. Yale, H. L., E. J. Pribyl, W. Braker, J. Bernstein, and W. A. Lott, *J. Am. Chem. Soc., 72,* 3716 (1950).
34. Overberger, C. G., and C. W. Roberts, *J. Am. Chem. Soc., 71,* 3618 (1949).
35. Wojcik, B., and H. Adkins, *J. Am. Chem. Soc., 55,* 4939 (1933).
36. Marvel, C. S., R. L. Myers, and J. H. Saunders, *J. Am. Chem. Soc., 70,* 1694 (1948).
37. Boekelheide, V., and S. Rothchild, *J. Am. Chem. Soc., 71,* 879 (1949).
38. Lukeš, R., and M. Ferles, unpublished results; through J. Rudinger, M. Ferles, and M. Protiva, *Chem. Listy, 45,* 355 (1951).
39. Karrer, P., and P. Portmann, *Helv. Chim. Acta, 31,* 2088 (1948).
40. Barry, V. C., J. G. Belton, R. M. Kelly, and D. Twomey, *Nature, 166,* 303 (1950).
41. Frank, R. L., and H. K. Hall, Jr., *J. Am. Chem. Soc., 72,* 1645 (1950).
42. Petuely, F., and H. F. Bauer, *Monatsh., 83,* 758 (1952).
43. Buchta, E., and H. Bayer, *Ann., 573,* 227 (1951).
44. Karrer, P., P. Portmann, and M. Suter, *Helv. Chim. Acta, 31,* 1617 (1948).
45. Bergmann, E. D., H. Bendas, and W. Taub, *J. Chem. Soc., 1951,* 2673.
46. Alberti, C. G., B. Camerino, and A. Vercellone, *Experienta, 8,* 261 (1952).
47. Holland, D. O., and J. H. C. Nayler, *Chemistry and Industry, 1952,* 518.
48. Felkin, H., *Compt. rend., 230,* 304 (1950).
49. Fromageot, C., M. Jutisz, D. Meyer, and L. Pénasse, *Compt. rend., 230,* 1905 (1950).
50. Carrara, G., E. Pace, and G. Cristiani, *J. Am. Chem. Soc., 74,* 4949 (1952).
51. Nystrom, R. F., and W. G. Brown, *J. Am. Chem. Soc., 69,* 2548 (1947).
52. Bachmann, W. E., and A. S. Dreiding, *J. Am. Chem. Soc., 71,* 3222 (1949).
53. Šorm, F., K. Vereš, unpublished work; through J. Rudinger, M. Ferles, and M. Protiva, *Chem. Listy, 45,* 355 (1951).
54. Lorber, V., M. Cook, and J. Meyer, *J. Biol. Chem., 181,* 475 (1949).
55. Cox, J. D., and H. S. Turner, *J. Chem. Soc., 1950,* 3176.
56. Dauben, W. G., and M. Gee, *J. Am. Chem. Soc., 74,* 1078 (1952).
57. Wagner, C. D., D. P. Stevenson, and J. W. Otvos, *J. Am. Chem. Soc., 72,* 5786 (1950).
58. Schmid, H., and K. Schmid, *Helv. Chim. Acta, 35,* 1879 (1952).
59. Doerschuk, A. P., *J. Am. Chem. Soc., 73,* 821 (1951); 74, 4202 (1952).
60. Gidez, L. I., and M. L. Karnovsky, *J. Am. Chem. Soc., 74,* 2413 (1952).

61. Mann, K. M., and R. F. Nystrom, *J. Am. Chem. Soc.*, *73*, 5894 (1951).
62. Crandall, D. I., and S. Gurin, *J. Biol. Chem.*, *181*, 829 (1949).
63. Karrer, P., and P. Banerjea, *Helv. Chim. Acta*, *32*, 1692 (1949).
64. Freudenberg, K., and G. Gehrke, *Chem. Ber.*, *84*, 443 (1951).
65. Freudenberg, K., and G. Wilke, *Chem. Ber.*, *85*, 78 (1952).
66. Weedon, B. C. L., and R. J. Woods, *J. Chem. Soc.*, *1951*, 2687.
67. Allen, C. F. H., and J. R. Byers, Jr., *Science*, *107*, 269 (1948).
68. Allen, C. F. H., and J. R. Byers, Jr., *J. Am. Chem. Soc.*, *71*, 2683 (1949).
69. Allen, C. F. H., and J. R. Byers, Jr., U. S. Pat. 2,545,439 (March 20, 1951).
70. Freudenberg, K., and R. Dillenburg, *Chem. Ber.*, *84*, 67 (1951).
71. Freudenberg, K., R. Kraft, and W. Heimberger, *Chem. Ber.*, *84*, 472 (1951).
72. Freudenberg, K., and H. H. Hübner, *Chem. Ber.*, *85*, 1181 (1952).
73. Dornow, A., G. Messwarb, and H. H. Frey, *Chem. Ber.*, *83*, 445 (1950).
74. Oroshnik, W., G. Karmas, and A. D. Mebane, *J. Am. Chem. Soc.*, *74*, 3807 (1952).
75. Huisman, H. O., A. Smit, S. Vromen, and L. G. M. Fisscher, *Rec. trav. chim.*, *71*, 899 (1952).
76. Karrer, P., and J. Kebile, *Helv. Chim. Acta*, *35*, 2570 (1952).
77. Distillation Products, Inc., Brit. Pat. 633,711 (December 19, 1949).
78. Schwarzkopf, O., H. J. Cahnmann, A. D. Lewis, J. Swidinsky, and H. M. Wüest, *Helv. Chim. Acta*, *32*, 443 (1949); *Abstracts of Papers*, 115th Meeting American Chemical Society, San Francisco, Calif., March 1949, p. 11C.
79. Jones, E. R. H., M. C. Whiting, and E. B. Bates, unpublished work, private communication.
80. Petuely, F., and U. Künssberg, *Monatsh.*, *83*, 80 (1952).
81. Dreiding, A. S., and J. A. Hartman, *J. Am. Chem. Soc.*, *75*, 939 (1953).
82. Winternitz, F., and R. M. Thakkar, *Bull. soc. chim. France*, [5] *19*, 471 (1952).
83. Abdel-Akher, M., and F. Smith, *Nature*, *166*, 1037 (1950).
84. Hardegger, E., H. J. Leemann, and F. G. Robinet, *Helv. Chim. Acta*, *35*, 824 (1952).
85. Barton, D. H. R., and C. J. W. Brooks, *J. Am. Chem. Soc.*, *72*, 3314 (1950).
86. Chatterjee, A., and P. Karrer, *Helv. Chim. Acta*, *33*, 802 (1950).
87. Janot, M. M. and R. Goutarel, *Bull. soc. chim. France*, [5] *18*, 588 (1951).
88. Dauben, W. G., and P. Coad, *J. Am. Chem. Soc.*, *71*, 2928 (1949).
89. Collins, C. J., *J. Am. Chem. Soc.*, *70*, 2418 (1948).
90. Collins, C. J., J. G. Burr, Jr., and D. N. Hess, *J. Am. Chem. Soc.*, 5176 (1951).
91. Charpentier-Morize, M., and B. Tchoubar, *Compt. rend.*, *233*, 1621 (1951).
92. Bird, R. F., and E. E. Turner, *J. Chem. Soc.*, *1952*, 5050.
93. Badger, G. M., J. E. Campbell, J. W. Cook, R. A. Raphael, and A. I. Scott, *J. Chem. Soc.*, *1950*, 2326.
94. Newman, M. S., H. S. Whitehouse, *J. Am. Chem. Soc.*, *71*, 3664 (1949).
95. Conover, L. H., and D. S. Tarbell, *J. Am. Chem. Soc.*, *72*, 3586 (1950).
96. Wiberg, E., and M. Schmidt, *Z. Naturforsch.*, *6b*, 171 (1951).
97. Jones, R. G., and K. C. McLaughlin, *J. Am. Chem. Soc.*, *71*, 2444 (1949).
98. Snyder, H. R., C. B. Thompson, and R. L. Hinman, *J. Am. Chem. Soc.*, *74*, 2009 (1952).
99. Jones, R. G., *J. Am. Chem. Soc.*, *71*, 3994 (1949).
100. Mićović, V. M., and M. L. Mihailović, *Rec. trav. chim.*, *71*, 970 (1952).
101. Mosher, H. S., and J. E. Tessieri, *J. Am. Chem. Soc.*, *73*, 4925 (1951).

102. Jones, R. G., and E. C. Kornfeld, *J. Am. Chem. Soc.*, 73, 107 (1951).
103. Gaylord, N. G., *Experientia*, 10, 166 (1954).
104. *Chem. Inds.*, 68, 20 (1950).
105. Cohen, A., U. S. Pat. 2,590,841 (April 1, 1952).
106. Cohen, A., J. W. Haworth, and E. G. Hughes, *J. Chem. Soc.*, 1952, 4374.
107. Verrill, K. J., and A. M. Schneider, Brit. Pat. 686,012 (January 14, 1953).
108. Mariella, R. P., and E. P. Belcher, *J. Am. Chem. Soc.*, 73, 2616 (1951).
109. Mariella, R. P., and A. J. Havlik, *J. Am. Chem. Soc.*, 74, 1915 (1952).
110. Jones, R. G., *J. Am. Chem. Soc.*, 74, 1489 (1952).
111. Rosenmund, K. W., and F. Zymalkowski, *Chem. Ber.*, 85, 152 (1952).
112. Birkofer, L., and A. Birkofer, *Chem. Ber.*, 85, 286 (1952).
113. Dahlbom, R., *Acta Chem. Scand.*, 6, 310 (1952).
114. Dahlbom, R., and T. Ekstrand, *Acta Chem. Scand.*, 5, 102 (1951).
115. Boekelheide, V., and J. P. Lodge, Jr., *J. Am. Chem. Soc.*, 73, 3681 (1951).
116. Galinovsky, F., and E. Jarisch, *Monatsh.*, 84, 199 (1953).
117. Pailer, M., K. Schneglberger, and W. Reifschneider, *Monatsh.*, 83, 513 (1952).
118. Galinovsky, F., O. Vogl, and W. Moroz, *Monatsh.*, 83, 242 (1952).
119. Treibs, A., and H. Scherer, *Ann.*, 577, 139 (1952).
120. Conover, L. H., and D. S. Tarbell, *J. Am. Chem. Soc.*, 72, 5221 (1950).
121. Fallab, S., *Helv. Chim. Acta*, 35, 215 (1952).
122. Scully, J. F., and E. V. Brown, *Abstracts of Papers*, 121st Meeting American Chemical Society, Buffalo, New York, March 1952, p. 44K.
123. Robeson, C. D., Ger. Pat. 855,992 (November 17, 1952).
124. Wiberg, E., and A. Jahn, *Z. Naturforsch.*, 7b, 581 (1952).
125. Wiberg, E., and A. Jahn, *Z. Naturforsch.*, 7b, 580 (1952).
126. Bailey, J. L., *Biochem. J.*, 52, iv (1952).
127. Wiberg, E., and R. Bauer, *Z. Naturforsch.*, 7b, 131 (1952).
128. Chaikin, S. W., and W. G. Brown, *J. Am. Chem. Soc.*, 71, 122 (1949).
129. Parke Davis and Co., Australian Pat. Appln. 13,395/52 (October 15, 1952).
130. Heymann, H., and L. F. Fieser, *J. Am. Chem. Soc.*, 73, 5252 (1951).
131. Ciba Ltd., Brit. Pat. 665,337 (January 23, 1952).
132. Wolfrom, M. L., and K. Anno, *J. Am. Chem. Soc.*, 74, 5583 (1952).
133. Panouse, J. J., *Compt. rend.*, 233, 260 (1951).
134. Panouse, J. J., *Compt. rend.*, 233, 1200 (1951).
135. Nystrom, R. F., S. W. Chaikin, and W. G. Brown, *J. Am. Chem. Soc.* 71, 3245 (1949).
136. Wittig, G., P. Davis, and G. Koenig, *Chem. Ber.*, 84, 627 (1951).
137. Wendler, N. L., Huang-Minlon, and M. Tishler, *J. Am. Chem. Soc.*, 73, 3818 (1951).
138. Huang-Minlon and R. H. Pettebone, *J. Am. Chem. Soc.*, 74, 1562 (1952).
139. Chibnall, A. C., and M. W. Rees, *Biochem. J.*, 48, xlvii (1951).
140. Chibnall, A. C., and M. W. Rees, *Biochem. J.*, 52, iii (1952).
141. Paul, R., and N. Joseph, *Bull. soc. chim. France*, [5] 19, 550 (1952).
142. Nystrom, R. F., and W. G. Brown, *J. Am. Chem. Soc.*, 70, 3738 (1948).
143. Wear, R. L., *J. Am. Chem. Soc.*, 73, 2390 (1951).
144. Spriggs, A. S., C. M. Hill, and G. W. Senter, *J. Am. Chem. Soc.*, 74, 1555 (1952).
145. Hill, C. M., M. E. Hill, H. I. Schofield, and L. Haynes, *J. Am. Chem. Soc.*, 74, 166 (1952).
146. Adams, R., and T. R. Govindachari, *J. Am. Chem. Soc.*, 72, 158 (1950).
147. Haworth, R. D., and L. Wilson, *J. Chem. Soc.*, 1950, 71.

148. Gaylord, N. G., and J. R. Snyder, *Chemistry and Industry*, in press.
149. Ness, R. K., H. G. Fletcher, Jr., and C. S. Hudson, *J. Am. Chem. Soc.*, 73, 4759 (1951).
150. Roseman, S., *J. Am. Chem. Soc.*, 74, 4467 (1952).
151. Swoden, J. C., *J. Am. Chem. Soc.*, 74, 4377 (1952).
152. Goering, H. L., and C. Serres, Jr., *J. Am. Chem. Soc.*, 74, 5908 (1952).
153. Collin-Asselineau, C., E. Lederer, D. Mercier, and J. Polonsky, *Bull. soc. chim. France,* [5] 17, 720 (1950).
154. Hinder, M., and M. Stoll, *Helv. Chim. Acta*, 33, 1308 (1950).
155. Lederer, E., and M. Stoll, *Helv. Chim. Acta*, 33, 1345 (1950).
156. Dietrich, P., and E. Lederer, *Helv. Chim. Acta*, 35, 1148 (1952).
157. Cocker, W., B. E. Cross, S. R. Duff, and T. F. Holley, *Chemistry and Industry, 1952,* 827.
158. Zeftel, L., D. S. Tarbell, and R. G. Nelb, *Abstracts of Papers,* 119th Meeting American Chemical Society, Boston, Mass., April 1951, P. 19M.
159. Tarbell, D. S., private communication.
160. Weygand, F., *Angew. Chem.*, 61, 441 (1949).
161. Kuhn, R., and K. Dury, *Chem. Ber.*, 84, 848 (1951).
162. Hochstein, F. A., and R. Pasternack, *J. Am. Chem. Soc.*, 74, 3905 (1952).
163. Schmid, H., and A. Ebnöther, *Helv. Chim. Acta*, 34, 1041 (1951).
164. Hochstein, F. A., P. P. Regna, K. J. Brunings, and R. B. Woodward, *J. Am. Chem. Soc.*, 74, 3706 (1952).
165. Guss, C. O., *J. Am. Chem. Soc.*, 73, 608 (1951).
166. Guss, C. O., and L. H. Jules, *J. Am. Chem. Soc.*, 72, 3462 (1950).
167. Weygand, F., K. G. Kinkel, and D. Tietjen, *Chem. Ber.*, 83, 394 (1950).
168. Baker, R. H., *J. Am. Chem. Soc.*, 70, 3857 (1948).
169. Bonner, E. F., A. G. Finkensieper, and E. I. Becker, *J. Org. Chem.*, 18, 426 (1953).
170. Siegel, S., and S. Coburn, *J. Am. Chem. Soc.*, 73, 5494 (1951).
171. Witkop, B., J. B. Patrick, and H. M. Kissman, *Chem. Ber.*, 85, 949 (1952).
172. Ormancey-Potier, A., A. Buzas, and E. Lederer, *Bull. soc. chim. France,* [5] 18, 577 (1951).
173. Wolfrom, M. L., and H. B. Wood, *J. Am. Chem. Soc.*, 73, 2933 (1951).
174. Wolfrom, M. L., H. B. Wood, and K. Anno, *Abstracts of Papers,* 119th Meeting American Chemical Society, Boston, Mass., April 1951, p. 8Q.
175. Meller, A., *Tappi,* 36, 366 (1953).
176. Hunger, A., and T. Reichstein, *Chem. Ber.*, 85, 635 (1952).
177. Hunger, A., and T. Reichstein, *Helv. Chim. Acta*, 35, 1073 (1952).
178. Dauben, W. G., R. A. Micheli, and J. F. Eastham, *J. Am. Chem. Soc.*, 74, 3852 (1952).
179. Shoppee, C. W., and G. H. R. Summers, *J. Chem. Soc., 1950,* 687.
180. Dauben, W. G., and J. F. Eastham, *J. Am. Chem. Soc.*, 72, 2305 (1950).
181. Dauben, W. G., and J. F. Eastham, *J. Am. Chem. Soc.*, 73, 3260 (1951).
182. Dauben, W. G., and J. F. Eastham, *J. Am. Chem. Soc.*, 73, 4463 (1951).
183. Belleau, B., and T. F. Gallagher, *J. Am. Chem. Soc.*, 73, 4458 (1951).
184. Brown, B. R., *J. Chem. Soc., 1952,* 2756.
185. Schwenk, E., M. Gut, and J. Belisle, *Arch. Biochem. et Biophys.*, 31, 456 (1951).
186. Dauben, W. G., J. F. Eastham, and R. A. Micheli, *J. Am. Chem. Soc.*, 73, 4496 (1951).
187. Ringold, H. J., G. Rosenkranz, and C. Djerassi, *J. Am. Chem. Soc.*, 74, 3441 (1952).

CHAPTER 10

Reduction of
OXYGEN-CONTAINING ORGANIC COMPOUNDS
IV. Carboxylic Acid Derivatives
(Amides, Lactams, Imides, Carbamates)

10.1 AMIDES

10.1.1 Reductions with Lithium Aluminum Hydride

The reduction of an amide with LAH generally proceeds to yield the amine with the same number of carbon atoms (1,2). However, various N-acylated heterocyclic compounds with aromatic character as well as amides containing large bulky groups can undergo reductive decomposition to aldehydes or alcohols and the amine component. The reaction is carried out without difficulty although yields of products are often somewhat lower than those obtained in the LAH reduction of various other functional groups. The reduction of amides by other means requires the use of vigorous conditions. Thus, catalytic hydrogenation is carried out under 200–300 atmospheres of hydrogen at 250–265° in the presence of at least 15% copper chromite. In the hydrogenation of unsubstituted amides by this method the product consists of a mixture of primary and secondary amines in which the latter frequently predominates (3). Other methods utilized have been electrolytic reduction, reduction with sodium in boiling alcohol and replacement of the amide oxygen with sulfur followed by electrolytic reduction or catalytic hydrogenation over Raney nickel (2).

10.1.1.a *Mechanisms of reduction.* The reduction of amides consumes one-half mole of LAH per mole of amide according to the equation:

$$2\ RCNR'_2 + LiAlH_4 \rightarrow 2\ RCH_2NR'_2 + LiAlO_2 \qquad (10\text{-}1)$$

with O double-bonded above the first carbon.

Unsubstituted or monosubstituted amides require an additional one-quarter mole of LAH for each active hydrogen atom present.

The reduction of the amide to an amine has been explained on the basis of the attack of a positive $AlH_2^{\oplus}$ ion on two molecules of amide, yielding a complex aluminum ion (I) which upon hydrolysis is cleaved to form the corresponding amine. The formation of aldehydes is postulated as proceeding through the complex (II) formed by the attack of the aluminohydride ion $AlH_4^{\ominus}$. Upon hydrolysis, this complex yields an unstable amino alcohol, which would decompose, by intramolecular displacement, to the aldehyde and the starting amine (4,5).

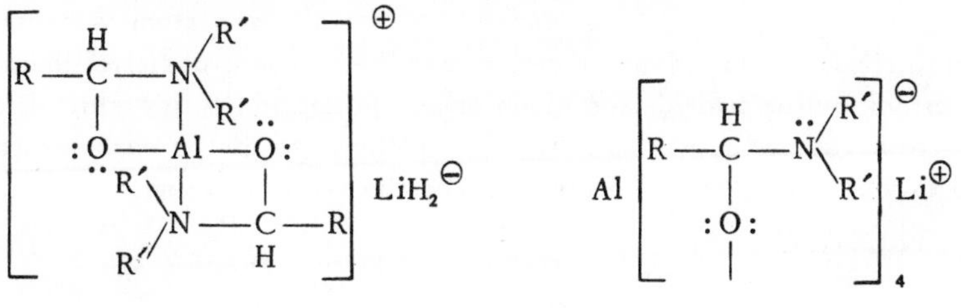

I   II

Steric hindrance on the nitrogen atom, preventing formation of an aluminum-nitrogen bond, and stabilization of the resonance structure (III) by suitable substituents on the nitrogen atom, favor formation of aldehydes (4,6).

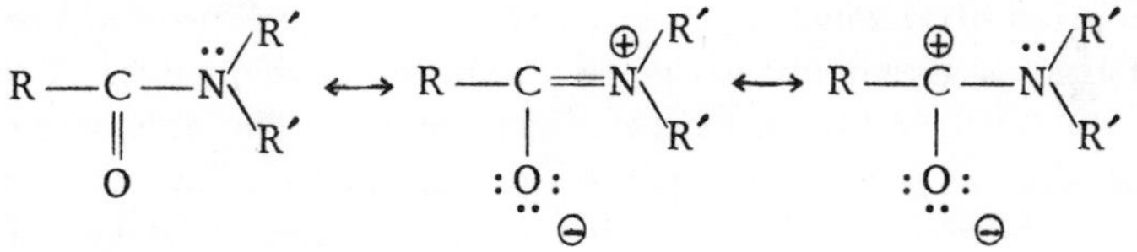

(10-2)

III

The formation of alcohols is also favored by steric hindrance and the stability of resonance structure (III) but has been attributed to the decomposition or hydrolysis of the amide molecule at the moment of reaction with the hydride with simultaneous reduction to the alkoxide anion (4).

The postulation of a simple single common intermediate appears to be more probable and logical than three distinct mechanisms involving different reactive species. The following mechanism can be postulated (7,8) for the reduction of amides and vinylogs of amides to yield the corresponding oxygen-free compounds:

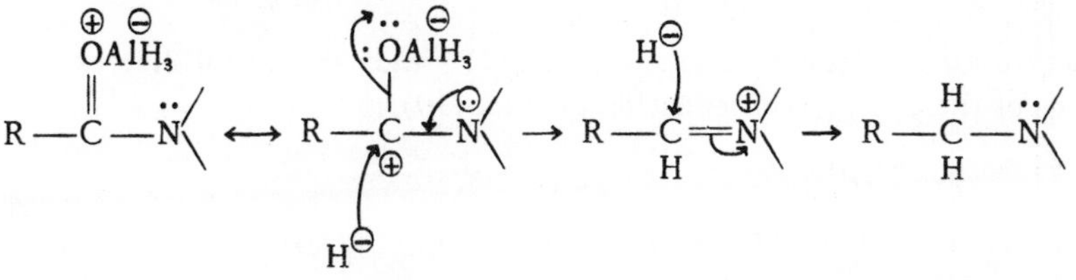

IV   (10-3)

The reactive species here is the aluminohydride ion $AlH_4^{\ominus}$ which, according to Paddock (9), exists in ether solution in equilibrium with aluminum hydride and the hydride ion. The attack of the hydride ion and the tendency of the nitrogen atom to donate its electron pair to the electron deficient carbon results in a cleavage of the carbon-oxygen bond to yield the amine, with a total consumption of one-half mole of lithium aluminum hydride.

When the electron-donating tendency of the nitrogen atom is decreased by stabilization, the adjacent carbon assumes a more positive character. The attack by the hydride ion alone or in conjunction with a shift of electrons from the oxygen atom results in a cleavage of the carbon-nitrogen bond to yield the carbonyl derivative and the starting amine.

$$R-\underset{\oplus}{\overset{:\overset{\ominus}{OAlH_3}}{C}}-\overset{..}{N}\Big<\;\longleftrightarrow\;R-\underset{\oplus}{\overset{\overset{:\overset{\ominus}{OAlH_3}}{|}}{C}}\overset{\delta^-}{\underset{|}{N}}=\;\longrightarrow\;R-\overset{\overset{O}{||}}{\underset{H}{C}}+\left[\overset{..}{\underset{|}{N}}=\right]^{\ominus} \qquad (10\text{-}4)$$

IV

The isolation of aldehydes generally requires the addition of one-quarter mole of lithium aluminum hydride to a solution of the amide. These conditions are fulfilled by the indicated mechanism. The aldehyde therefore does not arise as a result of hydrolysis of an intermediate complex but is present in the reaction mixture prior to hydrolysis. The use of excess complex hydride causes a reduction of the aldehyde to the corresponding alcohol.

10.1.1.b   *Unsubstituted amides.*   The LAH reduction of unsubstituted amides has been utilized in the synthesis of primary amines as summarized in Table LIII.

The reduction of half amide-half acids has been used to prepare aminoalcohols. Reduction of succinamic acid (V) yields the open-chain 4-amino-1-butanol (10).

$$\begin{array}{c}CH_2COOH\\ |\\ CH_2CONH_2\\ V\end{array}\quad\xrightarrow{\;LAH\;}\quad\begin{array}{c}CH_2CH_2OH\\ |\\ CH_2CH_2NH_2\end{array}\qquad(10\text{-}5)$$

Reduction of 2-dodecylsuccinamic acid (VI) yields the pyrrolidine by ring closure of the open-chain reduction product (10).

$$\begin{array}{c}C_{12}H_{25}CHCOOH\\ |\\ CH_2CONH_2\\ VI\end{array}\quad\xrightarrow{\;LAH\;}\quad\begin{array}{c}C_{12}H_{25}CH-CH_2\\ |\qquad\qquad|\\ H_2C\qquad CH_2\\ \diagdown\diagup\\ N\\ H\end{array}\qquad(10\text{-}6)$$

Reduction of 2-dodecyl-3-methylsuccinamic acid is reported to yield a mixture of the open-chain aminoalcohol and the pyrrolidine (11).

The attempted reduction of pivalamide (VII) has been reported as unsuccessful (12). Attempts to reduce 4,5-dihydroglyoxaline-2-acetamide (VIII) with LAH in boiling dioxane or catalytically over platinum oxide have been unsuccessful (13). The failure of the LAH reduction is attributed to the insolubility of VIII.

$$CH_3$$
$$|$$
$$CH_3CCONH_2$$
$$|$$
$$CH_3$$

VII

$$H_2C——CH_2$$
$$|\qquad\qquad|$$
$$HN\qquad N$$
$$\diagdown\ \diagup$$
$$C$$
$$|$$
$$CH_2CONH_2$$

VIII

The amide derivatives of lysergic acid, isolysergic acid and dihydro-lysergic acid have been reduced with LAH to the corresponding amines (14). Polymethylol compounds isolated or postulated in phenol-formaldehyde condensations have been synthesized by LAH reduction of phenol carboxylic acids. By reduction of the amides of these acids the amines can be prepared (15).

Reid and Smith (16) reported that the attempted hydrolysis of the reaction mixture from the reduction of $\alpha,\alpha,\beta,\beta$-tetrafluorosuccinamide with LAH in ether resulted in a violent explosion and ether fire upon addition of a few drops of water. The explosion has been explained by the reaction of the diamide and LAH to give an unstable complex. The solid complex isolated by the evaporation of the ether from the reaction mixture detonates at room temperature with great violence. Small scale reductions of the succinamide can be successfully carried out to yield the diamine. The complexes from LAH and perfluorobutyramide and perfluoroadipamide require heating on a hot plate to cause decomposition. However, the production of free carbon indicates the deep-seated nature of the decomposition.

Husted and Ahlbrecht have reported that the reduction of perfluorobutyramide (IX) with excess LAH in ether yields 1,1-dihydroperfluorobutylamine and perfluorobutyraldehydrol (X). The latter, arising by the reaction of the aldehyde and the aqueous hydrolysis medium, is dehydrated to the aldehyde with concentrated sulfuric acid (17).

$$CF_3CF_2CF_2CONH_2 \xrightarrow{\text{LAH}} CF_3CF_2CF_2CH_2NH_2 + CF_3CF_2CF_2CH(OH)_2$$
$$\text{IX} \qquad\qquad\qquad\qquad\qquad\qquad \text{X} \qquad\qquad (10\text{-}7)$$

The reduction of α-hydroxyvaleramide (XI) with LAH in ether followed by acetylation of the reduction products has been reported to yield the expected 1-amino-2-pentanol accompanied by 1,2-pentanediol, isolated as the diacetyl derivatives (18).

$$CH_3CH_2CH_2CHCONH_2 \xrightarrow{\text{LAH}} CH_3CH_2CH_2CHCH_2NH_2 +$$
$$\qquad\qquad | \qquad\qquad\qquad\qquad\qquad\qquad\qquad | $$
$$\qquad\qquad OH \qquad\qquad\qquad\qquad\qquad\qquad\quad OH$$
$$\qquad\quad \text{XI} \qquad\qquad\qquad\qquad\qquad CH_3CH_2CH_2CHCH_2OH \quad (10\text{-}8)$$
$$\qquad\qquad\qquad\qquad\qquad\qquad\qquad\qquad\qquad\qquad | $$
$$\qquad\qquad\qquad\qquad\qquad\qquad\qquad\qquad\qquad\quad OH$$

TABLE LIII

LAH Reduction of Unsubstituted Amides

	Amide	Product	% Yield	Ref.
$C_2H_2F_3NO$	Trifluoroacetamide	Trifluoroethylamine	80[1]	2
$C_3H_7NO_2$	Dg-Lactamide	Dg-1-Amino-2-propanol	…	3
$C_4H_2NOF_7$	Perfluorobutyramide	1,1-Dihydroperfluorobutylamine[4]	} 10–15	5
		Perfluorobutyraldehydrol		
$C_4H_4F_4N_2O_2$	α,α,β,β-Tetrafluorosuccinamide	2,2,3,3-Tetrafluoro-1,4-diaminobutane	…	6
C_4H_7NO	Cyclopropylcarboxamide-1-C^{14}	Cyclopropylmethylamine-1-C^{14}	…	7
$C_4H_7NO_3$	Succinamic Acid	4-Amino-1-butanol	…	8
$C_5H_{11}NO_2$	α-Methoxyisobutyramide	2-Methoxyisobutylamine	42	9
	L-α-Hydroxyvaleramide	L-1-Amino-2-pentanol[10]	} 29	12
		1,2-Pentanediol[11]		12
	DL-α-Hydroxyvaleramide	DL-1-Amino-2-pentanol[10]	} …	12
		1,2-Pentanediol[11]		12
$C_6H_8N_2O$	1-Pyrrylacetamide	2-(1-Pyrryl)ethylamine	88.3	13
	2-Pyrrylacetamide	2-(2-Pyrryl)ethylamine	…	14
		2-(2-Pyrryl)ethylamine	52	15
$C_6H_{11}NO$	2-Ethylcrotonamide	2-Ethylbutylamine	…	16–18
$C_6H_{14}N_2O_3$	Ammonium 2,2-dimethylsuccinamate } [19]	4-Bromo-2,2-dimethylbutylamine[20,21]	…	22
	Ammonium 3,3-dimethylsuccinamate }			
C_7H_7NO	Benzamide	Benzylamine	85	23
$C_7H_{11}NO$	1-Cyclohexenylcarboxamide	1-Aminomethylcyclohexane	50	24,25
$C_7H_{15}NO_2$	2-Hydroxy-2-methylisocaproamide	1-Amino-2,4-dimethyl-2-pentanol	32	26
$C_8H_7NO_2$	Phenylglyoxylamide	2-Amino-1-phenylethanol	34[1]	27
C_8H_9NO	Phenylacetamide	2-Phenylethylamine	…	16–18,28
$C_8H_9NO_2$	Phenoxyacetamide	2-Phenoxyethylamine	80	16–18,28
$C_8H_{13}NO$	1-Cyclohexenylacetamide	2-(1-Cyclohexenyl)ethylamine	66[29]	30
$C_8H_{17}N_3O_2$	Glycyl-L-leucinamide	L-N-2-(1-Amino-4-methylpentyl)-ethylenediamine	…	31

Formula	Amide	Product	Yield	Ref.
C_9H_7NOS	Thianaphthene-2-carboxamide	2-Aminomethylthianaphthene	58	32
$C_{10}H_{10}N_2O$	3-Indolylacetamide	Tryptamine	26[1,33]	34
$C_{10}H_{13}NO_3$	(2,3-Dimethoxyphenyl)acetamide	2-(2,3-Dimethoxyphenyl)ethylamine	46	35
$C_{11}H_{10}N_2O$	2-Quinolylacetamide	β-(2-Quinolyl)ethylamine	10	36
$C_{11}H_{15}NO_4$	3,4,5-Trimethoxyphenylacetamide	3,4,5-Trimethoxyphenylethylamine	40[37]	38
$C_{13}H_{13}NO_2$	7-Methoxy-α-naphthylacetamide	2-(7-Methoxy-α-naphthyl)ethylamine	35[1]	39
$C_{14}Y_{12}NO$	α-(1-Phenylcyclohexyl)acetamide	2-(1-Phenylcyclohexyl)ethylamine	...[1]	40
	4-Phenylcyclohexylacetamide	2-(4-Phenylcyclohexyl)ethylamine	52[1]	40
$C_{15}H_{12}NO$	9-Phenanthrylcarboxamide	9-Aminomethylphenanthrene	...	17,18,28
$C_{16}H_{23}N_3O_4$	Carbobenzoxyglycyl-L-leucinamide	L-N-Methyl-N′-2-(1-amino-4-methylpentyl)-ethylenediamine; Benzyl alcohol	... ...	31
$C_{16}H_{31}NO_3$	2-Dodecylsuccinamic acid	3-Dodecylpyrrolidine	83[1]	8
$C_{16}H_{33}NO$	Palmitamide	Cetylamine	...	41
$C_{17}H_{16}N_2O_2$	5-Benzyloxyindole-3-acetamide	5-Benzyloxytryptamine	...[1]	42
$C_{17}H_{33}NO_3$	2-Dodecyl-3-methylsuccinamic acid	2-Dodecyl-3-methyl-4-amino-1-butanol; 3-Methyl-4-dodecylpyrrolidine	... ...[1]	43
$C_{18}H_{35}NO$	Petroselinamide	Octadec-6-enylamine	53[20]	44
$C_{18}H_{37}NO$	Stearamide	Octadecylamine	88[1]	41
$C_{24}H_{41}NO$	Cholanic acid amide	24-Aminocholane	67[1]	45
$C_{24}H_{41}NO_2$	Lithocholic acid amide	24-Aminocholan-3-ol	75[1]	45
$C_{24}H_{41}NO_3$	Desoxycholic acid amide	24-Aminocholan-3,12-diol	63[1]	45
$C_{24}H_{41}NO_4$	Cholic acid amide	24-Aminocholan-3,17,12-triol	49[1]	45

References—Table LIII

[1]Isolated as hydrochloride.
[2]E. J. Bourne, S. H. Henry, C. E. M. Tatlow, and J. C. Tatlow, *J. Chem. Soc.*, *1952*, 4014.
[3]D. E. Wolf, W. H. Jones, J. Valiant, and K. Folkers, *J. Am. Chem. Soc.*, *72*, 2820 (1950).
[4]Isolated as sulfate.
[5]D. R. Husted and A. H. Ahlbrecht, *J. Am. Chem. Soc.*, *74*, 5422 (1952).
[6]T. S. Reid and G. H. Smith, through *Chem. Eng. News*, *29*, 3042 (1951).
[7]J. D. Roberts and R. H. Mazur, *J. Am. Chem. Soc.*, *73*, 3542 (1951).
[8]V. C. Barry and D. Twomey, *Abstracts of Papers*, XIIth International Congress of Pure and Applied Chemistry, New York, September, 1951, p. 308.
[9]D. S. Tarbell and P. Noble, Jr., *J. Am. Chem. Soc.*, *72*, 2657 (1950).
[10]Isolated as N,O-diacetyl derivative.
[11]Isolated as diacetate.
[12]R. U. Lemieux and J. Giguere, *Can. J. Chem.*, *29*, 678 (1951).
[13]O. Klamerth and W. Kutscher, *Chem. Ber.*, *85*, 444 (1952).
[14]W. Kutscher and O. Klamerth, *Z. physiol. Chem.*, through ref. 13.
[15]K. Eiter, *Monatsh.*, *83*, 252 (1952).
[16]A. Uffer and E. Schlittler, *Helv. Chim. Acta*, *31*, 1397 (1948).
[17]Ciba, S. A., Fr. Pat. 987,158 (August 9, 1951).
[18]E. Schlittler and A. Uffer, Ger. Pat. 824,491 (December 13, 1951).
[19]Mixture from ammonolysis of 2,2-dimethylsuccinic anhydride.
[20]Reduction carried out in tetrahydrofuran.
[21]Isolated in 27% yield after treatment of reduction product (16% yield) with hydrobromic acid.
[22]Brown, R. F., and N. van Gulick, *Abstracts of Papers*, 122nd Meeting American Chemical Society, Atlantic City, N. J., September 1952, p. 7M; R. F. Brown, private communication.
[23]Matlow, unpublished work, through W. G. Brown, in *Organic Reactions*, Vol. VI, p. 505.
[24]R. Jacquier and R. Zagdoun, *Bull. soc. chim. France*, [5] *19*, 699 (1952).
[25]M. Mousseron, R. Jacquier, M. Mousseron-Canet, and R. Zagdoun, *ibid.*, *19*, 1042 (1952).
[26]W. J. Close, *J. Am. Chem. Soc.*, *73*, 95 (1951).
[27]A. W. D. Avison, *J. Applied Chem. (London)*, *1*, 469 (1951).
[28]Ciba Akt., Swiss Pat. 273,953 (June 1, 1951).
[29]Inverse addition.
[30]O. Schnider and J. Hellerbach, *Helv. Chim. Acta*, *33*, 1437 (1950).
[31]P. Karrer and B. J. R. Nicolaus, *ibid.*, *35*, 1581 (1952).
[32]D. A. Shirley and M. D. Cameron, *J. Am. Chem. Soc.*, *74*, 664 (1952).
[33]Reaction carried out in tetrahydrofuran-ether mixture.
[34]L. H. Groves and G. A. Swan, *J. Chem. Soc.*, *1952*, 650.
[35]A. Lindenmann, *Helv. Chim. Acta*, *32*, 69 (1949).
[36]K. Eiter and E. Mrazek, *Monatsh.*, *83*, 926 (1952).
[37]Isolated as picrate.
[38]K. Banholzer, T. W. Campbell, and H. Schmid, *Helv. Chim. Acta*, *35*, 1577 (1952).
[39]C. Mentzer and C. Beaudet, *Compt. rend.*, *234*, 1692 (1952).
[40]E. B. Carton, H. F. Lederle, L. H. Schwartzman, and G. F. Woods, *J. Am. Chem. Soc.*, *74*, 5126 (1952).

[41]F. Wessely and W. Swoboda, *Monatsh.*, *82*, 621 (1951).
[42]K. E. Hamlin and F. E. Fischer, *J. Am. Chem. Soc.*, *73*, 5007 (1951).
[43]V. C. Barry, J. G. Belton, R. M. Kelly, and D. Twomey, *Nature*, *166*, 303 (1950).
[44]G. R. Clemo and R. Stevens, *J. Chem. Soc.*, *1952*, 4684.
[45]F. Wessely and W. Swoboda, *Monatsh.*, *82*, 437 (1951).

The LAH reduction of amides to aldehydes and alcohols is discussed in Section 10.1.1.d.2.

10.1.1.c *Monosubstituted amides.* The LAH reduction of monosubstituted amides generally yields the corresponding secondary amine. The yield of amine may depend upon the concentration of LAH, the reaction conditions and the method of isolation of reduction products.

1. *N-Formyl amines.* The formylation of a primary amine yields an N-formyl derivative which is reduced with LAH to the N-methyl compound (19).

$$RNH_2 \rightarrow RNHCHO \xrightarrow{\text{LAH}} RNHCH_3 \qquad (10\text{-}9)$$

The reduction of N-formylamines is summarized in Table LIV.

Eiter and Svierak have carried out an investigation of the constitution of folicanthine, an alkaloid from the leaves of *Calycanthus floridus* L. Distillation of folicanthine with zinc dust (20) or hydrolysis with concentrated hydrochloric acid (21) gives an oily base, $C_{12}N_{16}N_2$, containing one N-methyl group. This base with ethyl or methyl formate gives a monoformyl derivative which is reduced with LAH in ether or tetrahydrofuran to yield an N-methyl compound (20,21). The non-identity of 7,ω-N-dimethyltryptamine (20,21), ω-N-ethyltryptamine (21) and ω-N-methylhomotryptamine (21), obtained by LAH reduction of the corresponding amides, with the product derived from folicanthine has resulted in the postulation that the base $C_{12}H_{16}N_2$ has structure XII. However, various schemes to synthesize this compound have been unsuccessful at intermediate stages. The structure XIII has been proposed for folicanthine.

XII   XIII

Eiter and Mrazak (22) have reported that reduction of ω-N-formyl-β-[4-(1,2,3,4-tetrahydroquinolyl)]ethylamine (XIV) with LAH in tetrahydro-

TABLE LIV

LAH Reduction of N-Formylamines

	Amide	Product	% Yield	Ref.
$C_4H_8N_2O_2$	N,N'-Diformylethylenediamine	N,N'-Dimethylethylenediamine	60[1]	2
$C_5H_{11}NO$	N-Formylbutylamine	N-Methylbutylamine	87	2
$C_5H_{12}N_2O$	N,N-Dimethyl-N'-formylethylenediamine	N,N,N'-Trimethylethylenediamine	72.4[3]	4
C_7H_7NO	N-Formylaniline	N-Methylaniline	85	5
$C_7H_7NO_2$	p-Hydroxy-N-formylaniline	p-Hydroxy-N-methylaniline	92[6,7]	8
$C_7H_{13}NO$	N-Formylcyclohexylamine	N-Methylcyclohexylamine	80	2
			67.5	9
C_8H_9NO	N-Formylbenzylamine	N-Methylbenzylamine	85	2
$C_9H_9NO_3$	N-Formyl-2-amino-2-phenylacetic acid	2-Methylamino-2-phenylethanol	42[8]	10
$C_9H_{11}NO$	N-Formyl-2-phenylethylamine	N-Methyl-2-phenylethylamine	84	2
$C_9H_{13}NO$	N-Formyl-2-(1-cyclohexenyl)ethylamine	N-Methyl-2-(1-cyclohexenyl)ethylamine	64	11
$C_{10}H_{11}NO_3$	N-Formyl-DL-β-phenylalanine	N-Methyl-DL-β-phenylalaninol	73	5
$C_{11}H_9NO$	N-Formyl-β-naphthylamine	N-Methyl-β-naphthylamine	82	5
$C_{11}H_{11}N_2O$	ω-N-Formyltryptamine	ω-N-Methyltryptamine	86	12
$C_{12}H_{12}N_2O$	β-(2-Quinolyl)-N-formylethylamine	β-(2-Quinolyl)-N-methylethylamine	67[9]	13
	β-(4-Quinolyl)-N-formylethylamine	β-(4-Quinolyl)-N-methylethylamine	68[9]	14
$C_{12}H_{14}N_2O$	ω-N-Formylhomotryptamine	ω-N-Methylhomotryptamine	73	15
	ω-N-Formyl-7-methyltryptamine[16]	7,ω-Dimethyltryptamine	...[17]	15
$C_{12}H_{15}NO_3$	N-Formyl-1,1-dimethyl-2-(3,4-methylenedioxyphenyl)ethylamine	N-Methyl-1,1-dimethyl-2-(2,4-methylenedioxyphenyl)ethylamine	...[17]	18
$C_{12}H_{16}N_2O$	ω-N-Formyl-2-[4-(1,2,3,4-tetrahydroquinolyl)]-ethylamine	N-Methyl-2-[4-(1,2,3,4-tetrahydroquinolyl)]-ethylamine	81[6]	14
		N-Methyl-2-[4-(1,2,3,4-tetrahydroquinolyl)]-ethylamine	54 }[6,19,20]	14
		Cyclized product, $C_{12}H_{16}N_2$, m.p. 148°	36 }	14
	ω-N-Formyl-2-[2-(1,2,3,4-tetrahydroquinolyl)]-ethylamine	N-Methyl-2-[2-(1,2,3,4-tetrahydroquinolyl)]-ethylamine	67[6,19,20]	14

	Amide	Amine	Yield	Ref.
$C_{12}H_{17}NO_2$	N-Formyl-1,1-dimethyl-2-p-methoxyphenyl-ethylamine	N-Methyl-1,1-dimethyl-2-p-methoxyphenyl-ethylamine	....	18
$C_{13}H_{14}N_2O_2$	1,ω-N-Diformyl-7-methyltryptamine	7,ω-N-Dimethyltryptamine	....[6]	15,21
$C_{15}H_{16}N_2O$	$(C_{12}H_{14}N)NHCHO$[20]	$(C_{12}H_{14}N)NHCH_3$	....[6]	15,21
$C_{14}H_{11}NO$	N-Formyl-9-aminofluorene	N-Methylfluorenylamine	20	22
			70[1]	22
$C_{21}H_{24}N_2O_2$	N(a)-Formyl-dihydrodesoxogelsamine	N(a)-Methyl-dihydrodesoxogelsamine	....	23

[1] Reaction carried out in an ether-dioxane mixture.

[2] F. F. Blicke and Chi-Jung Lu, J. Am. Chem. Soc., 74, 3933 (1952).

[3] Isolated as 2,4-dinitrophenolate.

[4] O. Hromatka and C. Skopalik, Monatsh., 83, 38 (1952).

[5] F. Wessely and W. Swoboda, ibid., 82, 621 (1951).

[6] Reaction carried out in tetrahydrofuran.

[7] Isolated as nitrosamine.

[8] J. Ehrlich, J. Am. Chem. Soc., 70, 2286 (1948).

[9] M. Mousseron, R. Jacquier, and R. Zagdoun, Bull. soc. chim. France [5] 19, 197 (1952).

[10] A. Dornow, G. Messwarb, and H. H. Frey, Chem. Ber., 83, 445 (1950).

[11] O. Schnider and J. Hellerbach, Helv. Chim. Acta, 34, 2218 (1951).

[12] P. E. Norris and F. F. Blicke, J. Am. Pharm. Assoc., Sci. Ed., 41, 637 (1952).

[13] K. Eiter and E. Mrazak, Monatsh., 83, 926 (1952).

[14] K. Eiter and E. Mrazak, ibid., 83, 915 (1952).

[15] K. Eiter and O. Svierak, ibid., 83, 1453 (1952).

[16] Mixture of mono- and diformyl compounds obtained by formylation of 7-methyltryptamine.

[17] Reaction carried out in di-n-butyl ether.

[18] W. F. Bruce, U. S. Pat. 2,597,446 (May 20, 1952).

[19] Reduction carried out with practical grade LAH.

[20] See text.

[21] K. Eiter and O. Svierak, Monatsh., 82, 186 (1951).

[22] H. Dahn and U. Solms, Helv. Chim. Acta, 34, 907 (1951).

[23] T. Habgood, L. Marion, and H. Schwarz, ibid., 35, 638 (1952).

furan gives β-[4-(1,2,3,4-tetrahydroquinolyl)]-N-methylethylamine (XV) in 81% yield.

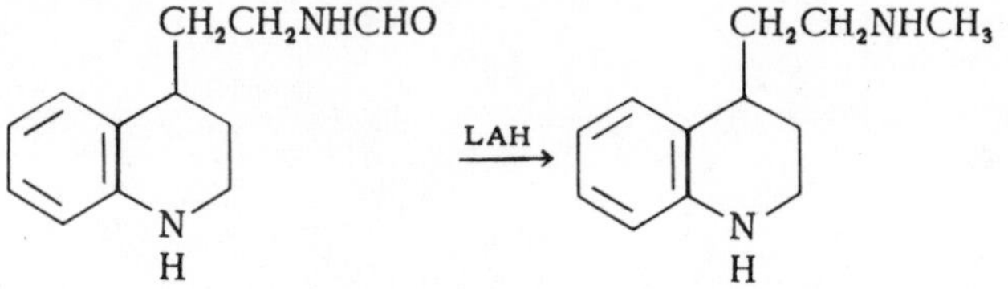

(10-10)

When the reduction of XIV is carried out with a "practical" grade of LAH, in addition to a 54% yield of XV, a compound, m.p. 148°, with the empirical formula $C_{12}H_{16}N_2$, is obtained in 36% yield. This compound contains one N-methyl group and one active hydrogen. Two possible structures, XVI and XVII, have been postulated, with preference given to XVI due to the similarity in the ultra-violet spectra between the unknown compound and 3-N-methyl-4-pyrroquinoline.

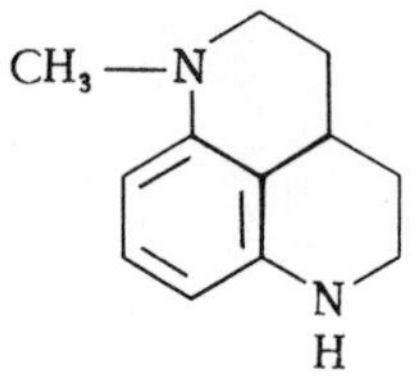

Analysis of the LAH utilized in this study indicates that the only difference between the pure and practical grades of LAH is the higher LAH content in the pure grade. The reduction of ω-N-formyl-β-[2-(1,2,3,4-tetrahydroquinolyl)]ethylamine (XVIII) with the practical grade of LAH gives a 67% yield of β-[2-(1,2,3,4-tetrahydroquinolyl)]-N-methylethylamine (XIX). No product arising from a cyclization reaction is isolated.

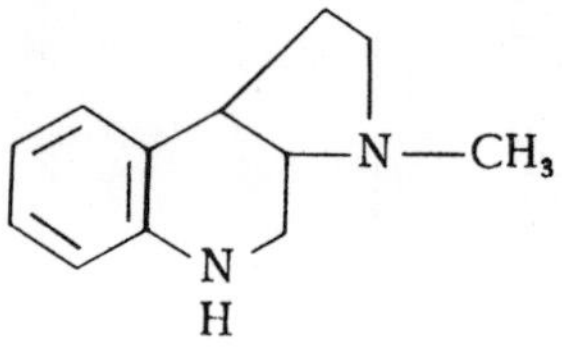

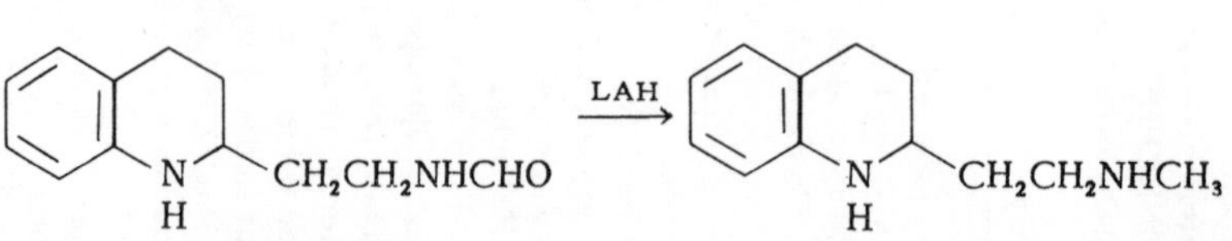

(10-11)

2. *Other monosubstituted amides.* Although the LAH reduction of monosubstituted amides to the corresponding amines can be carried out without difficulty, in some cases extended heating is necessary for maximum yields. Thus, acetanilide, after one hour of heating with a 200% excess of LAH, gives 72%, and after five hours 93% N-ethylaniline. Butyr-anilide is reduced to N-butylaniline in 77% yield after one hour and in 92% yield after seven hours of heating. N-Cyclohexylacetamide after one

hour of heating gives 39%, after 24 hours 82% and after 36 hours 88% of the corresponding amine. The reduction of N-cyclohexylbenzamide requires 34 hours of heating to yield 89% of N-cyclohexylbenzylamine (4).

Although the reduction of pivalamide has been reported as unsuccessful (12) the reduction of (+)-N-trimethylacetyl-α-phenylethylamine (XX) gives the neopentylamine in 97% yield (23).

$$(CH_3)_3CCONHCHC_6H_5 \xrightarrow{\text{LAH}} (CH_3)_3CCH_2NHCHC_6H_5$$

$$\underset{CH_3}{|} \qquad\qquad \underset{CH_3}{|} \qquad (10\text{-}12)$$

XX

The LAH reduction of monosubstituted amides containing the quinoline nucleus presents an interesting picture. While reduction of β-(2-quinolyl)-ω-N-formylethylamine (XXI) and β-(4-quinolyl)-ω-N-formylethylamine (XXII) yields the corresponding N-methylethylamine in 67 and 68% yields, respectively, the attempted reduction of 2-quinolyl-N-methylacetamide (XXIII) and 4-quinolyl-N-methylacetamide (XXIV) yields only traces of the same products (22,24).

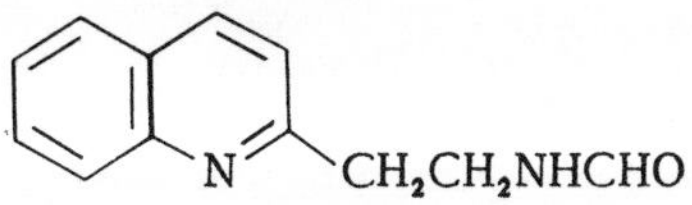

XXI

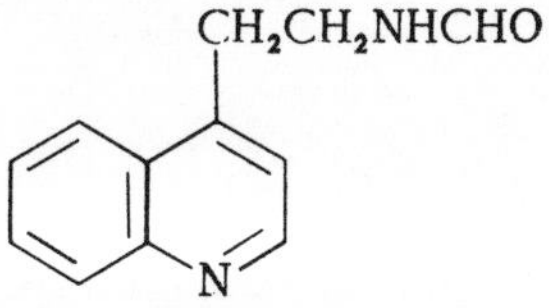

XXII

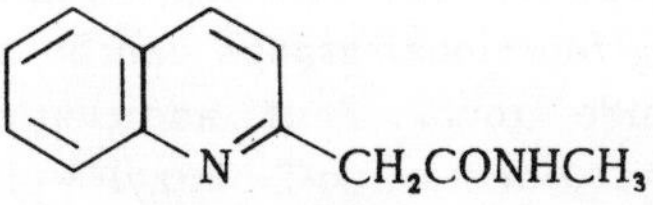

XXIII

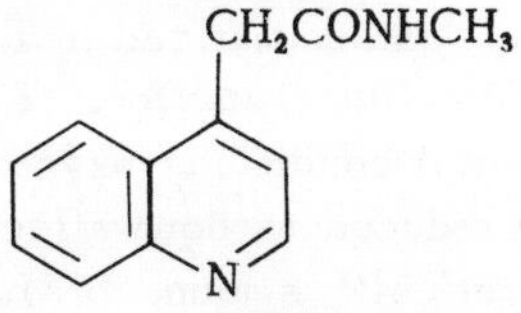

XXIV

Thus, the removal of the amide grouping from the terminal position to an internal position closer to the heterocyclic nucleus and where the relative positions of the amine and carbonyl groups are reversed appears to have resulted in a much decreased reducibility.

The reduction of N-benzoyl-O-acetyl-o-aminophenol (XXV) with LAH in tetrahydrofuran yields the expected o-benzylaminophenol (XXVI) and an oil of which the infrared constants and the analytical data of the product with phenyl isocyanate, m.p. 192–195°, indicate an isomer of XXVI.

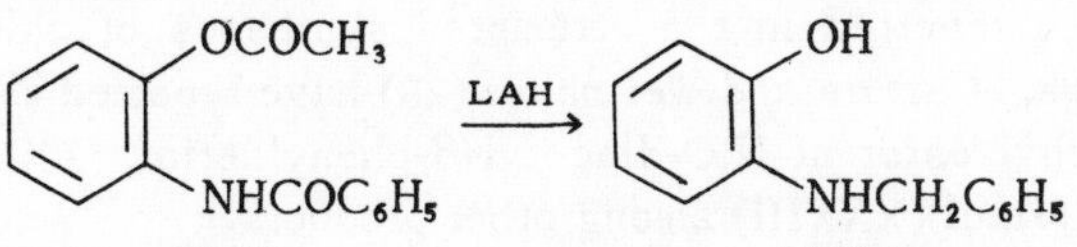

XXV

XXVI

$$(10\text{-}13)$$

A similar oily by-product is obtained in the LAH reduction of N,N,O-triacetyl-o-aminophenol (XXVII) while reduction of N,N-diacetyl-o-anisidine (XXVIII) yields only the expected product (25).

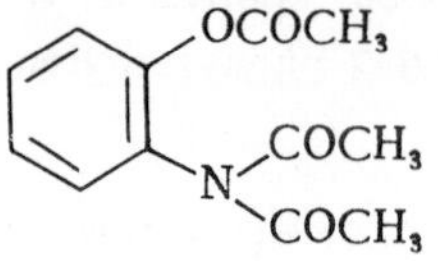

XXVII 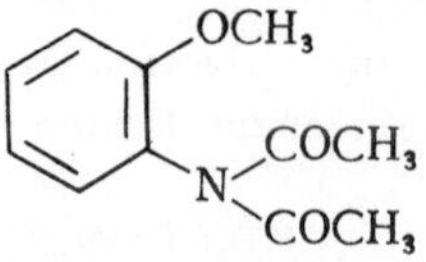   XXVIII

The phenolic hydroxyl, already present or formed by reduction of the ester, therefore seems essential for the formation of the oily by-products.

Stork and Conroy reported that the reduction of the N-methylacetamide (XXIX) with LAH is extremely slow and leads to considerable removal of aromatically bound halogen. No definite products have been isolated (26).

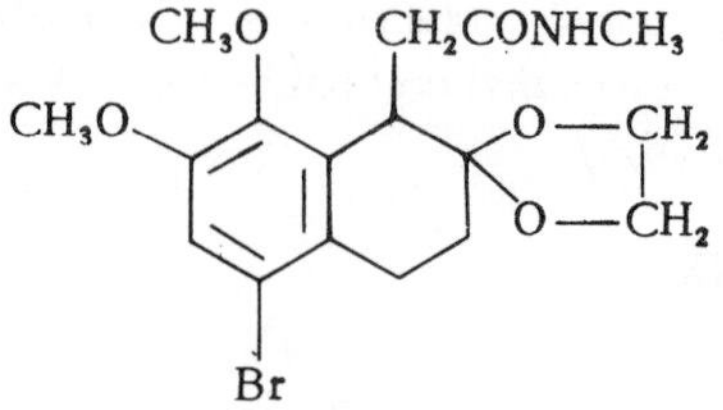

XXIX

The LAH reduction of monosubstituted amides other than N-formyl derivatives is summarized in Table LV.

3. *Selective reduction.* Felkin (27) reported that under appropriate experimental conditions oxygen containing functional groups can be selectively reduced without affecting the amide group. Thus, addition of the "theoretical" amount of LAH to ethyl 2-acetamido-2-benzyl-3-phenyl-propionate (XXX) gives 2-acetamido-2-benzyl-3-phenyl-1-propanol (XXXI).

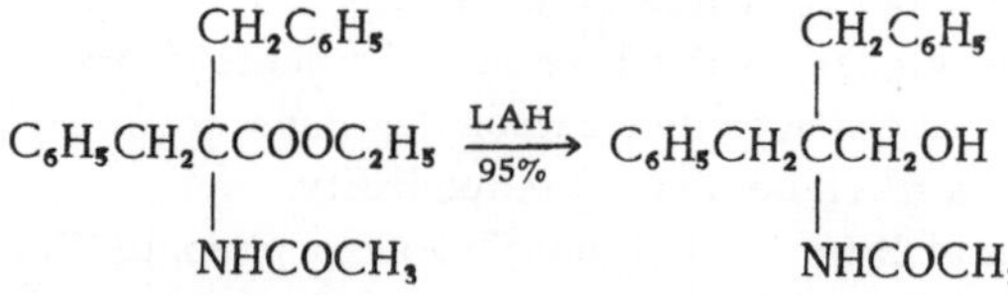

(10-14)

XXX   XXXI

Various reductions in which the amide grouping has been retained intact have been reported in the attempted syntheses of chloramphenicol and its analogs. Carrara and Weitnauer (28) have reported that the reduction of the ethyl ester of N,O-diacetyl-β-phenylserine (XXXII) gives N-acetylphenylserinol (XXXIII) among other products.

$$C_6H_5CH-\!\!\!\!\!\!-\!\!-CHCOOC_2H_5 \xrightarrow{\text{LAH}} C_6H_5CH-\!\!-CHCH_2OH$$

$$\underset{\text{XXXII}}{\underset{\overset{|}{OCOCH_3}\quad \overset{|}{NHCOCH_3}}{}} \qquad \underset{\text{XXXIII}}{\underset{\overset{|}{OH}\quad \overset{|}{NHCOCH_3}}{}} \quad (10\text{-}15)$$

A recent British patent (29) reports that the LAH reduction of XXXII utilizing 3.1 moles of LAH per mole of XXXII yields N,O-diacetylphenylserinol wherein both the acetoxy and acetamido groups are retained. Reduction of ethyl 2-acetamidobenzoylacetate (XXXIV) utilizing 3.0 moles of LAH per mole of XXXIV yields 1-phenyl-2-acetamido-1,3-propanediol, isolated as the N,O,O-triacetyl compound (30).

$$C_6H_5C-\!\!-CHCOOC_2H_5 \xrightarrow{\text{LAH}} C_6H_5CH-\!\!-CHCH_2OH$$

$$\underset{\text{XXXIV}}{\underset{\overset{\|}{O}\quad \overset{|}{NHCOCH_3}}{}} \qquad \underset{\text{XXXIII}}{\underset{\overset{|}{OH}\quad \overset{|}{NHCOCH_3}}{}} \quad (10\text{-}16)$$

The biphenylyl analogue of XXXIII is reportedly prepared by the LAH reduction of 1-p-biphenylyl-2-acetamidopropan-3-ol-1-one (31). Reduction of the ethyl ester of N-dichloroacetyl-O-acetyl-p-nitrophenylserine (XXXV) utilizing 1.35 moles of LAH per mole of XXXV is reported to yield a noncrystalline syrup containing DL-chloroamphenicol (XXXVI) (32).

$$\text{XXXV} \xrightarrow{\text{LAH}} \text{XXXVI} \qquad (10\text{-}17)$$

Reduction of α-acetamido-p-nitrocinnamaldehyde (XXXVII) with the calculated amount of LAH in tetrahydrofuran yields p-nitrophenylacetol (XXXIX) wherein the intermediate (XXXVIII) retains the acetamido group (33).

$$(10\text{-}18)$$

TABLE LV

LAH Reduction of Monosubstituted Amides

	Amide	Product	% Yield	Ref.
$C_5H_6N_2OS$	2-Acetamidothiazole	2-Ethylaminothiazole	77	1
$C_5H_{11}NO$	N-Ethylpropionamide	Ethylpropylamine	53	2-5
C_8H_9NO	Acetanilide	N-Ethylaniline	60	6
			92.9	7
$C_8H_{17}N_3O_2$	Glycyl-L-leucinamide (I)	L-N-2-(1-Amino-4-methylpentyl)ethylenediamine	...[8]	9
$C_{10}H_7ClN_2OS$	2-(p-Chlorobenzamido)thiazole	2-(p-Chlorobenzylamino)thiazole	90	10
$C_{10}H_8N_2OS$	2-Benzamidothiazole	2-Benzylaminothiazole	85	1
$C_{10}H_{11}NO_3$	Succinanilic acid (II)	N-Hydroxybutylaniline	42	11
$C_{10}H_{13}NO$	Butyranilide	N-Butylaniline	92.1	7
$C_{10}H_{15}NO$	N-Cyclohexylacetamide	N-Ethylcyclohexylamine	88	7
$C_{10}H_{19}N_3O_6$	Ethyl ester diglycyl glycine (III)[12]	N-(β-Aminoethyl)-N'-(β-hydroxyethyl)ethylene-diamine	42[8,13]	9
$C_{11}H_{10}N_2O_2S$	2-(p-Methoxybenzamido)thiazole	2-(p-Methoxybenzylamino)thiazole	82	10
$C_{12}H_8N_2OS_2$	N-(2'-Thiazolyl)thianaphthene-2-carboxamide	N-(2'-Thiazolyl)-2-aminomethylthianaphthene	38[8]	14
$C_{12}H_{12}N_2O$	2-Quinolyl-N-methylacetamide	β-(2-Quinolyl)-N-methylethylamine	3	15
	4-Quinolyl-N-methylacetamide	β-(4-Quinolyl)-N-methylethylamine	...[16]	17
$C_{12}H_{14}N_2O$	ω-N-Acetyltryptamine (IV)	ω-N-Ethyltryptamine	23[18]	19
$C_{12}H_{17}NO_4$	3,4,5-Trimethoxy-N-methylphenylacetamide	N-Methylmescaline	16[20]	21
$C_{13}H_{11}NO_2$	o-Hydroxybenzanilide	o-Benzylaminophenol	58	22
$C_{13}H_{17}NO$	N-Cyclohexylbenzamide	N-Cyclohexylbenzylamine	89.5	7
$C_{13}H_{20}NO$	(+)-N-Trimethylacetyl-α-phenylethylamine	L-(+)-N-Neopentyl-α-phenylethylamine	97	23
$C_{13}H_{20}N_2O$	N-Benzylamino-N',N'-diethylglycinamide	N-Benzyl-N',N'-diethylethylenediamine	...[24]	25
$C_{14}H_{10}N_2OS$	N-(2'-Pyridyl)thianaphthene-2-carboxamide	N-(2'-Pyridyl)-2-aminomethylthianaphthene	35[8]	14
$C_{14}H_{22}N_2O$	N-β-Phenylethyl-N',N'-diethylglycinamide	N-β-Phenylethyl-N,N'-diethylethylenediamine	...[24]	25
$C_{15}H_{11}NOS$	N-Phenylthianaphthene-2-carboxamide	N-Phenyl-2-aminomethylthianaphthene	42[8]	14
$C_{15}H_{13}NO_2$	o-Acetylbenzanilide	1-(o-Benzylaminophenyl)ethanol	...	26

Formula	Amide	Product	Yield	Ref.
$C_{15}H_{13}NO_3$	o-Acetoxybenzanilide	o-Benzylaminophenol	...[8]	22
		Isomer	...[24]	25
$C_{15}H_{14}N_2O$	N-β-Phenylethyl-N,N′-diethylalaninamide	N-β-Phenylethyl-N,N′-diethylpropylenediamine		14
$C_{16}H_{13}NOS$	N-o-Tolylthianaphthene-2-carboxamide	N-o-Tolyl-2-aminomethylthianaphthene	26[8]	27
$C_{16}H_{15}NO_2$	cis-1-Benzamidoindanol-2	cis-1-Benzylaminoindanol-2	68	27
	trans-1-Benzamidoindanol-2	trans-1-Benzylaminoindanol-2		28
$C_{16}H_{18}N_2OS$	o-(Dimethylaminoacetamido)diphenylsulfide (V)	o-(Dimethylaminoethylamino)diphenylsulfide		9
$C_{16}H_{23}N_3O_4$	Carbobenzoxyglycyl-L-leucinamide	(L-N-Methyl-N′-2-(1-amino-4-methylpentyl)ethyl-enediamine	...[8]	28
		Benzyl alcohol		
$C_{17}H_{20}N_2OS$	o-(3-Dimethylaminopropionamido)diphenylsulfide (V)	o-(3-Dimethylaminopropylamino)diphenylsulfide		28
	o-(2-Dimethylaminopropionamido)diphenylsulfide (V)	o-(2-Dimethylaminopropylamino)diphenylsulfide		28
$C_{17}H_{24}N_2O$	N-[2-(1,2,3,4-Tetrahydronaphthyl)]piperidino-acetamide	N-[2-(1,2,3,4-Tetrahydronaphthyl)]-2′-piperidino-ethylamine	...[24]	**29**
$C_{17}H_{24}N_2O_5$	Methyl ester carbobenzoxyglycyl-L-leucine	N-(β-N′-Methylaminoethyl)-L-leucinol	...[6]	9
$C_{17}H_{25}NO_3$	ω-Carbomethoxypelagonanilide	N-Hydroxydecylaniline	63[30]	11
$C_{18}H_{22}N_2OS$	o-(Diethylaminoacetamido)diphenylsulfide (V)	o-(Diethylaminoethylamino)diphenylsulfide	80[24]	28
$C_{18}H_{23}N_3O_3S$	p-Dimethylamino-p′-(dimethylaminoacetamido)di-phenylsulfone (VI)	p-Dimethylamino-p′-dimethylaminoethylaminodi-phenylsulfone		31
$C_{18}H_{26}N_2O$	N-Acetyl-spiro(cyclohexane-1,1′,x′-amino-3′-di-methylaminoindane) (VII)	Spiro(cyclohexane-1,1′,3′-dimethylamino-x′-ethylaminoindane)	91[24]	32
$C_{19}H_{24}N_2OS$	o-(3-Diethylaminopropionamido)diphenylsulfide (V)	o-(3-Diethylaminopropylamino)diphenylsulfide		28
	o-(2-Diethylaminopropionamido)diphenylsulfide (V)	o-(2-Diethylaminopropylamino)diphenylsulfide		28
$C_{19}H_{28}N_3O_2$	Dihydrolysergyl-L-isopropanolamide (VIII)	L-N-(6-Methyl-ergolinyl-(8)-methyl)alaninol	...[33]	34
	Dihydrolysergyl-D-isopropanolamide (VIII)	D-N-(6-Methyl-ergolinyl-(8)-methyl)alaninol	...[33]	34
$C_{20}H_{25}N_3O_3$	Methyl ester dihydrolysergyl-L-alanine (IX)	L-N-(6-Methyl-ergolinyl-(8)-methyl)alaninol	...[33]	34
$C_{20}H_{27}N_3O_3S$	p-Dimethylamino-p′-(diethylaminoacetamido)di-phenylsulfone (VI)	p-Dimethylamino-p′-diethylaminoethylaminodi-phenylsulfone	72[24]	31

(Continued)

TABLE LV (Continued)

	Amide	Product	% Yield	Ref.
C$_{22}$H$_{29}$N$_3$O$_3$	Methyl ester dihydrolysergyl-L-valine (X)	L-N-(6-Methyl-ergolinyl-(8)-methyl)valinol	...[33]	34
	Methyl ester dihydrolysergyl-D-valine (X)	D-N-(6-Methyl-ergolinyl-(8)-methyl)valinol	...[33]	34
C$_{22}$H$_{31}$N$_3$O$_3$S	p-Dimethylamino-p'-(di-n-propylaminoacetamido)-diphenylsulfone (VI)	p-Dimethylamino-p'-di-n-propylaminoethylamino-diphenylsulfone	86[24]	31
	p-Diethylamino-p'-(diethylaminoacetamido)di-phenylsulfone (VI)	p-Diethylamino-p'-diethylaminoethylaminodi-phenylsulfone	85[24]	31
C$_{24}$H$_{35}$N$_3$O$_3$S	p-Dimethylamino-p'-(di-n-butylaminoacetamido)di-phenylsulfone (VI)	p-Dimethylamino-p'-di-n-butylaminoethylaminodi-phenylsulfone	70[24]	31
C$_{29}$H$_{37}$NO$_2$	3-Hydroxy-2-(4'-dodecyl)naphthanilide	3-p-Dodecylanilinomethyl-2-naphthol	...	35
C$_{30}$H$_{59}$N$_5$O$_5$	Dihydroergosine (XI)	Polyamine, C$_{30}$H$_{47}$N$_5$, m.p. 192° (XII) Polyamine, C$_{30}$H$_{47}$N$_5$, m.p. 152° (XII) D,L-N-(6-Methylergolinyl-(8)-methyl)alaninol (XIII)	28[33] 2[33] ...	34
C$_{30}$H$_{43}$N$_5$O$_2$	Dihydrolysergyl-L-alanyl-L,L-1,2-trimethylene-5-isobutylpiperazide (XIV)	Polyamine, C$_{30}$H$_{47}$N$_5$, m.p. 156° (XII)	74[33]	34
	Dihydroysergyl-D-alanyl-L,L-1,2-trimethylene-5-isobutylpiperazide	Polyamine, C$_{30}$H$_{47}$N$_5$, m.p. 192° (XII)	57[33]	34
	Dihydrolysergyl-L-alanyl-L,D-1,2-trimethylene-5-isobutylpiperazide (XIV)	Polyamine, C$_{30}$H$_{47}$N$_5$, m.p. 204° (XII)	25[33]	34
	Dihydrolysergyl-D-alanyl-L,D-1,2-trimethylene-5-isobutylpiperazide (XIV)	Polyamine, C$_{30}$H$_{47}$N$_5$, m.p. 205° (XII)	24[33]	34
C$_{31}$H$_{41}$N$_5$O$_5$	Dihydroergocornine (XV)	Polyamine, C$_{31}$H$_{49}$N$_5$, m.p. 145° (XVI)	9[33]	34
C$_{32}$H$_{43}$N$_5$O$_5$	Dihydroergocryptine (XVII)	Polyamine, C$_{32}$H$_{51}$N$_5$, m.p. 153° (XVIII) L,L-1,2-Trimethylene-5-isobutylpiperazine (XIX)	12[33] ...	34
C$_{32}$H$_{47}$N$_5$O$_2$	Dihydrolysergyl-L-valyl-L,L-1,2-trimethylene-5-isobutylpiperazide (XX)	Polyamine, C$_{32}$H$_{51}$N$_5$, m.p. 154° (XVIII)	25[33]	34
	Dihydrolysergyl-D-valyl-L,L-1,2-trimethylene-5-isobutylpiperazide (XX)	Polyamine, C$_{32}$H$_{51}$N$_5$, m.p. 151° (XVIII)	9[33]	34
C$_{35}$H$_{41}$N$_5$O$_5$	Dihydroergocristine (XXI)	Polyamine, C$_{35}$H$_{49}$N$_5$, m.p. 144° (XXIII) 1,2-Trimethylene-5-benzylpiperazine D,L-N-(6-Methylergolinyl-(8)-methyl)valinol	29[33] 12[33] ...	34

CHART TO TABLE LV

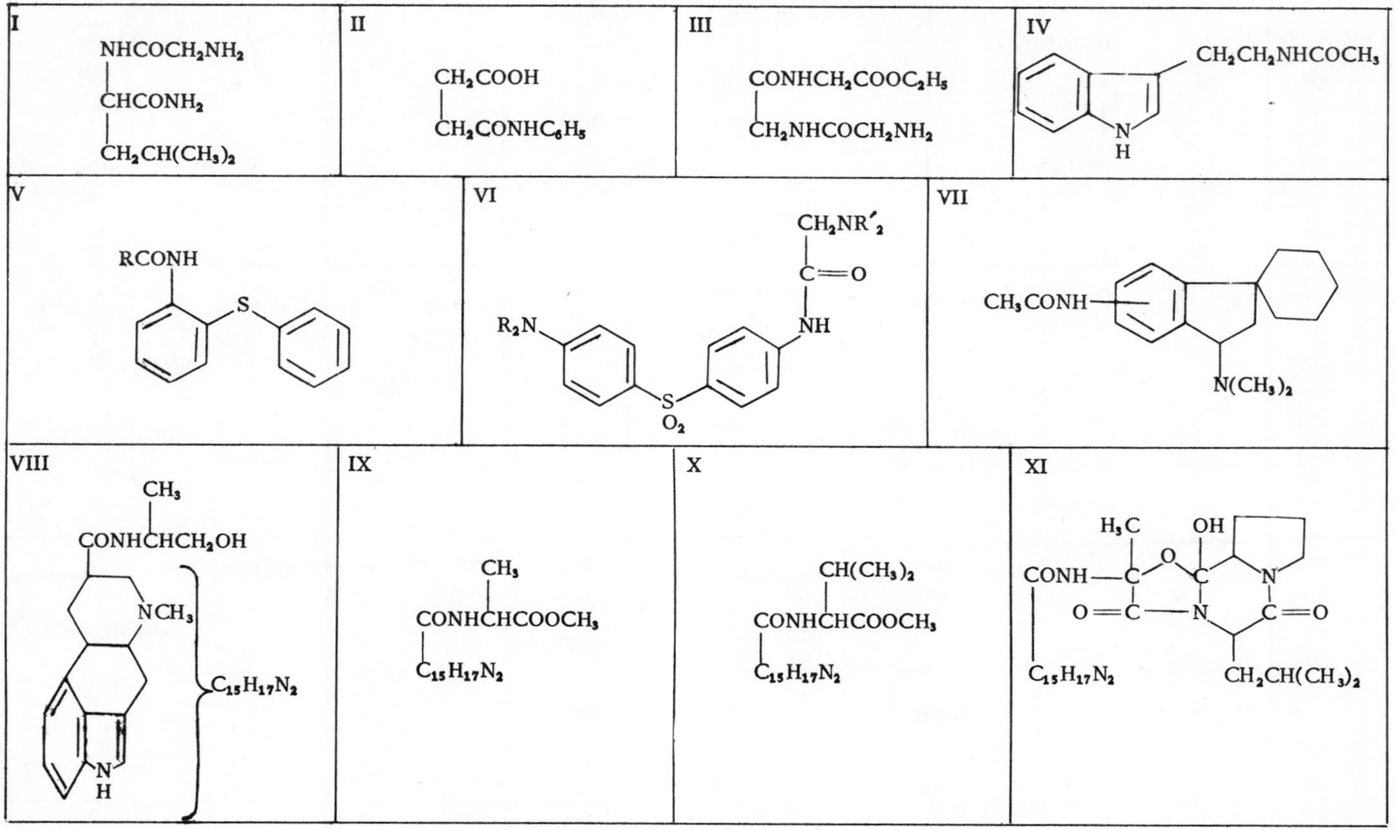

I

$NHCOCH_2NH_2$

$CHCONH_2$

$CH_2CH(CH_3)_2$

II

CH_2COOH

$CH_2CONHC_6H_5$

III

$CONHCH_2COOC_2H_5$

$CH_2NHCOCH_2NH_2$

IV

$CH_2CH_2NHCOCH_3$

(indole, N–H)

V

$RCONH$ (phenyl–S–phenyl)

VI

$CH_2NR'_2$

$C=O$

NH

R_2N (with SO_2 bridge)

VII

CH_3CONH

$N(CH_3)_2$

VIII

CH_3

$CONHCHCH_2OH$

NCH_3

$C_{15}H_{17}N_2$

(N–H indole)

IX

CH_3

$CONHCHCOOCH_3$

$C_{15}H_{17}N_2$

X

$CH(CH_3)_2$

$CONHCHCOOCH_3$

$C_{15}H_{17}N_2$

XI

H_3C

OH

$O=C$

$C=O$

$CONH$

$CH_2CH(CH_3)_2$

$C_{15}H_{17}N_2$

(continued)

CHART TO TABLE LV (*continued*)

XII, XIII, XIV, XV, XVI, XVII, XVIII, XIX, XX, XXI, XXII

References—Table LV

[1] I. A. Kaye and C. L. Parris, *J. Org. Chem.*, 17, 737 (1952).

[2] A. Uffer and E. Schlittler, *Helv. Chim. Acta*, 31, 1397 (1948).

[3] Ciba Akt., Swiss Pat. 273,953 (June 1, 1951).

[4] Ciba, S. A., Fr. Pat. 987,158 (August 1, 1951).

[5] E. Schlittler and A. Uffer, Ger. Pat. 824,491 (December 13, 1951).

[6] R. F. Nystrom and W. G. Brown, *J. Am. Chem. Soc.*, 70, 3738 (1948).

[7] V. M. Mićović and M. Mihailović, *J. Org. Chem.*, 18, 1190 (1953).

[8] Reduction carried out in tetrahydrofuran.

[9] P. Karrer and B. J. R. Nicolaus, *Helv. Chim. Acta*, 35, 1581 (1952).

[10] I. A. Kaye and C. L. Parris, *J. Org. Chem.*, 16, 1761 (1951).

[11] R. E. Holman and D. D. Carroll, *J. Am. Chem. Soc.*, 73, 1859 (1951).

[12] Reacted in form of acetic acid salt.

[13] Isolated as tripicrate.

[14] D. A. Shirley and M. D. Cameron, *J. Am. Chem. Soc.*, 74, 664 (1952).

[15] K. Eiter and E. Mrazak, *Monatsh.*, 83, 926 (1952).

[16] Only traces of product obtained when reduction carried out in ether or tetrahydrofuran.

[17] K. Eiter and E. Mrazak, *Monatsh.*, 83, 915 (1952).

[18] 60% amide recovered.

[19] K. Eiter and O. Svierak, *Monatsh.*, 83, 1453 (1952).

[20] Isolated as picrate.

[21] K. Banholzer, T. W. Campbell, and H. Schmid, *Helv. Chim. Acta*, 35, 1577 (1952).

[22] B. Witkop and J. B. Patrick, *J. Am. Chem. Soc.*, 74, 3861 (1952).

[23] D. J. Cram and F. A. Abd Elhafez, *ibid.*, 74, 5851 (1952).

[24] Reduction carried out in ether-benzene mixture.

[25] S. Chiavarelli and G. B. Marini-Bettolo, *Gazz. chim. ital.*, 81, 89 (1951).

[26] B. Witkop and J. B. Patrick, *J. Am. Chem. Soc.*, 74, 3855 (1952).

[27] R. E. Lutz and R. L. Wayland, Jr., *ibid.*, 73, 1639 (1951).

[28] E. Knüsli, *Experientia*, 8, 262 (1952).

[29] G. B. Marini-Bettolo and S. Chiavarelli, *Gazz. chim. ital.*, 81, 98 (1951).

[30] Combined yield as hydrochloride and free base.

[31] E. Knüsli, *Gazz. chim. ital.*, 80, 522 (1950).

[32] L. H. Schwartzman and G. F. Woods, *J. Org. Chem.*, 17, 492 (1952).

[33] Reduction carried out in ethylmorpholine.

[34] A. Stoll, A. Hofmann, and T. Petrzilka, *Helv. Chim. Acta*, 34, 1544 (1951).

[35] C. H. Giles and E. L. Neustädter, *J. Chem. Soc.*, 1952, 3806.

Reduction of 3-(2'-o-carbomethoxyphenylacetamidoethyl)indole (XL) with 2.6 moles of LAH per mole of XL in a benzene-ether mixture yields the hydroxymethyl compound retaining the amide group (34).

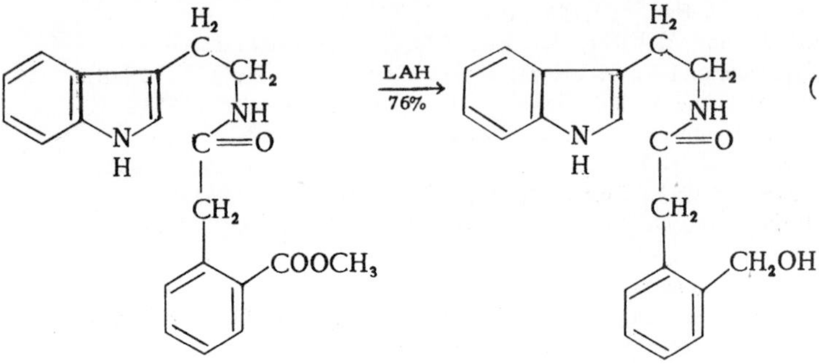

(10-19)

XL

Reduction of the methyl ester of dibenzoyl-L-histidine (XLI) with an ethereal LAH solution, utilizing 4.5 moles of LAH per mole of XLI results in the isolation of the monobenzoyl-L-histidinol (XLII) (35).

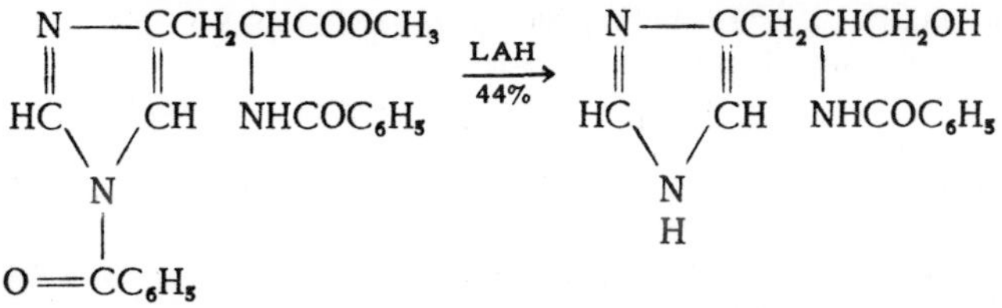

(10-20)

XLI

The inverse addition of the calculated amount of LAH at $-15°$ to N-methylcyclohexanecarboxamide (5,36) and other monosubstituted amides (4) has been reported to result in the complete recovery of the amide. Treatment of cis-2-benzamido-3-acetoxy-1-methanesulfonyloxy-1-phenyl-propane (XLII) in a benzene-ether mixture with 0.87 mole of LAH per mole of XLII has been reported to yield an uncrystallizable gum whose constitution was not determined (37).

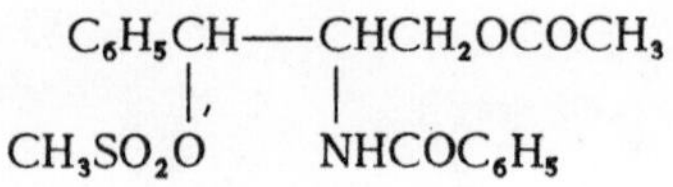

$$C_6H_5CH—CHCH_2OCOCH_3$$
$$CH_3SO_2O \quad NHCOC_6H_5$$

XLII

Benzoylation of arginine followed by esterification yields the ethyl ester of dibenzoylarginine, probably XLIII. Reduction with LAH in tetrahydrofuran yields dibenzoylargininol which is hydrolyzed to argininol with 20% sulfuric acid (38).

$$
\begin{array}{ccc}
\underset{\substack{|}}{CH_2CH_2NHC}\overset{NH}{\overset{\big\|}{-}}NHCOC_6H_5 & & \underset{\substack{|}}{CH_2CH_2NHC}\overset{NH}{\overset{\big\|}{-}}NHCOC_6H_5 \\
\underset{\substack{|}}{CH_2CHCOOC_2H_5} & \xrightarrow{\;LAH\;} & \underset{\substack{|}}{CH_2CHCH_2OH} \\
NHCOC_6H_5 & & NHCOC_6H_5
\end{array}
\qquad (10\text{-}21)
$$

XLIII

Karrer and Nicolaus (39) have reduced a number of peptides to the corresponding amines with excess LAH in tetrahydrofuran. The following peptides have been successfully reduced by this treatment: glycyl-L-leucinamide hydrochloride, carbobenzoxyglycyl-L-leucinamide, carbobenzoxyglycyl-L-leucine methyl ester, diglycylglycine ethyl ester acetate.

Jolles and Fromageot (40,41) have reported the reduction of peptide esters and acids with LAH in N-ethylmorpholine. Although ester, acid and carbamate groups are reduced by the reagent the amide is reported as being retained in the product peptide alcohol. Thus, reduction of the following peptides gives the corresponding peptide diol with the indicated yield:

Peptide	% Peptide Diol
Benzyl ester of carbobenzoxy-DL-aspartylglycine ethyl ester	51
Benzyl ester of carbobenzoxyglutamylglycine ethyl ester	11.2-40.3
Glutamylglycine	5
Glutamylglycine diethyl ester	31
Glutathione diethyl ester	30-44

Fromageot *et al.* (42,43) have described a method for the characterization of terminal carboxylic groups in proteins involving reduction with LAH in N-ethylmorpholine. The reduction product, a peptide alcohol containing an intact amide group, is hydrolyzed and the hydrolysate consisting of aminoacids and aminoalcohols is separated and characterized by paper chromatography. This method has been applied to a characterization of insulin. Bailey (44) has reported that LAH is not satisfactory for the determination of the amino acid sequence in peptides since evidence of amide reduction has been observed.

Avison and Morrison attempted the selective reduction of the N-methyl-amide group in XLIV with LAH but obtained only a mixture of basic products from which a pure compound was not isolated (45).

$$\text{ClCH}_2\text{CH}_2\text{CH}_2\overset{\overset{\displaystyle C_6H_5}{|}}{\underset{\underset{\displaystyle CN}{|}}{C}}\text{CONHCH}_3$$

XLIV

10.1.1.d   *Disubstituted amides.*   The LAH reduction of N,N-disubstituted amides under normal conditions, e.g., with a slight excess of hydride, generally yields the tertiary amine. However, in some cases alcohols or aldehydes may be obtained as a result of the reaction conditions or the structure of the amide.

1. *Reduction of amides to amines.* The LAH reduction of disubstituted amides requires one-half mole of hydride according to the equation

$$2 \text{ RCONR}'_2 + \text{LiAlH}_4 \rightarrow 2 \text{ RCH}_2\text{NR}'_2 + \text{LiAlO}_2 \qquad (10\text{-}22)$$

Although in most cases a large excess of LAH has been used, Mićović and Mihailović (4) have reported quantitative reductions with a 25-30% excess of LAH and have stated that a larger amount of hydride does not increase the yield of amine. It is of interest to note that the reaction of a disubstituted amide with the Grignard reagent also yields a tertiary amine (46).

$$\begin{array}{c}(CH_3)_2CH\\ \diagdown\\ \diagup\\ (CH_3)_2CH\end{array}NCHO + RMgX \rightarrow \begin{array}{c}(CH_3)_2CH\\ \diagdown\\ \diagup\\ (CH_3)_2CH\end{array}NCHR_2 \qquad (10\text{-}23)$$

XLV

Although reductions according to equation (10-22) generally proceed without difficulty an interesting rearrangement has been observed. Dahn and Solms (47) have reported that the reduction of N-methyl-N-α-naphthoyl-9-fluorenylamine (XLVI) with LAH in refluxing ether gives a 73% yield of the expected N-methyl-N-α-naphthylmethyl-9-fluorenylamine (XLVII). When the reduction of XLVI is carried out in refluxing tetrahydrofuran, instead of the tertiary amine, the product in 56% yield is the secondary amine N-methyl-9-α-naphthylmethyl-9-fluorenylamine (XLVIII). That the reduction proceeds through XLVII is proved by the conversion of the tertiary amine to the secondary amine by the action of LAH in tetrahydrofuran.

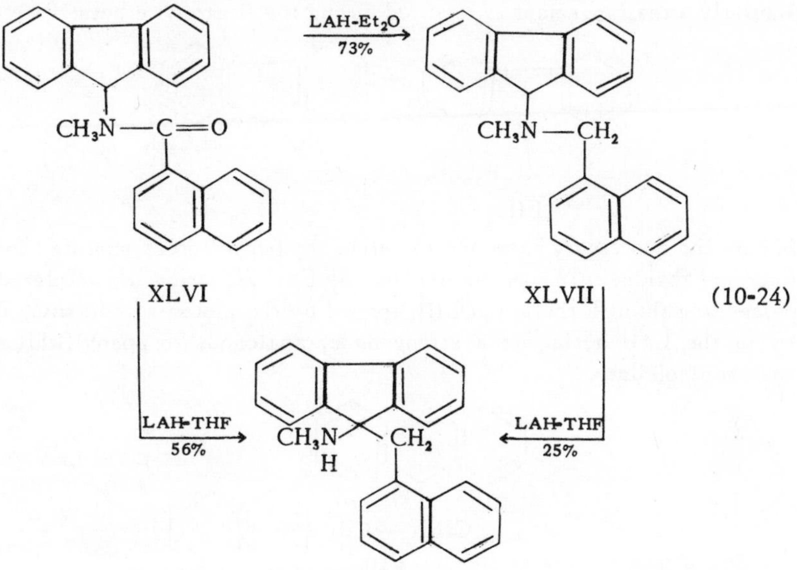

$$(10\text{-}24)$$

XLVI   XLVII

XLVIII

The same reaction is observed in the reduction of N-methyl-N-β-naphthoyl-9-fluorenylamine (XLIX) with LAH in tetrahydrofuran to N-methyl-9-β-naphthylmethyl-9-fluorenylamine (L).

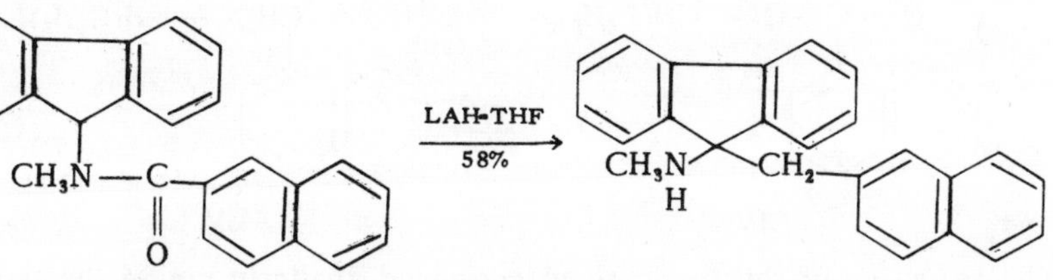

XLIX   L $(10\text{-}25)$

A rearrangement which corresponds to the above has been observed in the action of alkali on a quaternary base:

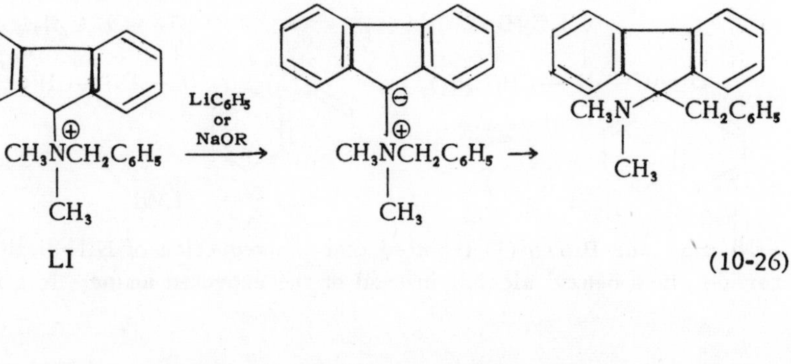

LI $(10\text{-}26)$

Similarly a rearrangement is reported among the fluorenyl ethers:

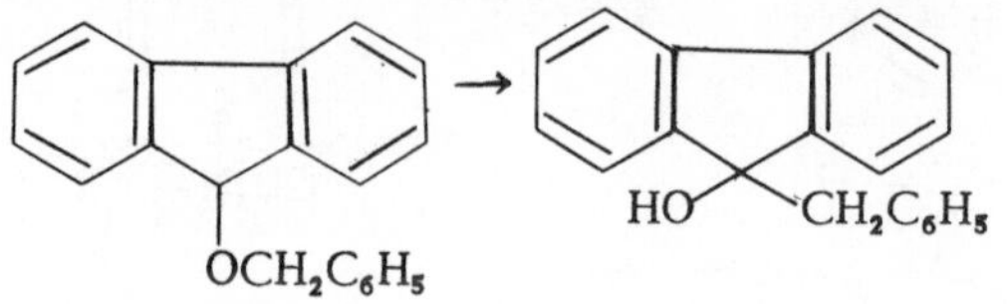

$$(10\text{-}27)$$

LII

In both the quaternary base and the ether the benzyl group migrates to the fluorenyl residue. The mechanism for the LAH reduction is postulated as proceeding through the anion LIII, formed by the proton-withdrawing ability of the LAH acting as a strong base, analogous to phenyllithium or sodium alcoholate.

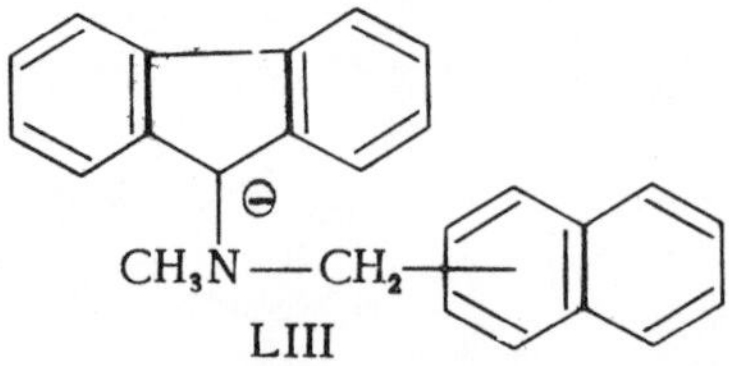

LIII

The non-occurrence of the rearrangement under mild conditions is shown in the reduction of N-methyl-N-α-naphthoylbenzhydrylamine (LIV) with LAH in ether to the α-naphthylmethyl tertiary amine LV (48).

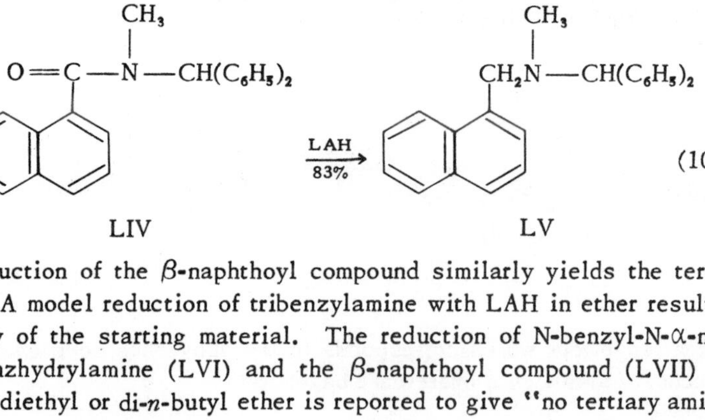

$$(10\text{-}28)$$

LIV   LV

The reduction of the β-naphthoyl compound similarly yields the tertiary amine. A model reduction of tribenzylamine with LAH in ether results in recovery of the starting material. The reduction of N-benzyl-N-α-naphthoylbenzhydrylamine (LVI) and the β-naphthoyl compound (LVII) with LAH in diethyl or di-n-butyl ether is reported to give "no tertiary amine."

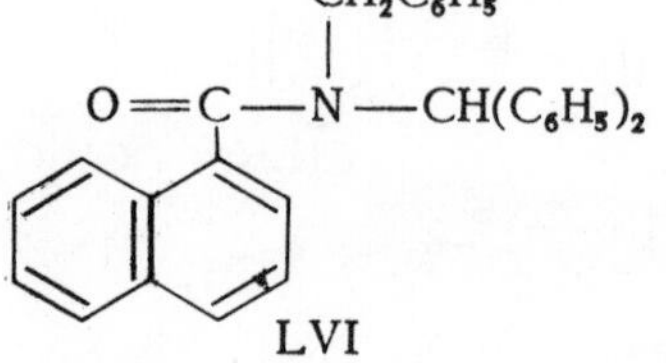

LVI 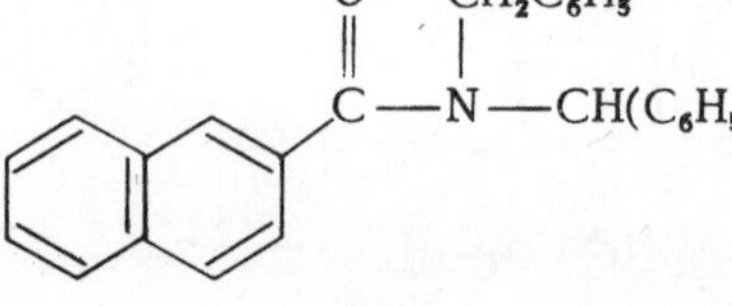   LVII

Nyström and Brown (1) reported that the reduction of N,N-diethylbenzamide gives benzyl alcohol instead of the expected amine. In a recent review, however, it has been pointed out that this reduction was carried out in the hope of obtaining benzaldehyde as an intermediate product and not under conditions favoring reduction to the amine (49). Mousseron and his coworkers (5,36) have reported that the reduction of N,N-diethylbenzamide with an equimolar quantity of LAH at ambient temperature gives a 90% yield of N,N-diethylbenzylamine without any trace of benzyl alcohol. Mićović and Mihailović (4) have also obtained the corresponding amine in over 90% yield under normal conditions. As discussed in Section 10.1.1.d.2, benzyl alcohol and/or benzaldehyde are obtained by carrying out the reduction with decreased quantities of LAH at low temperatures.

The LAH reduction of various disubstituted amides, in which the amido nitrogen is not part of a heterocyclic ring, to the corresponding amines is summarized in Table LVI.

The LAH reduction of amides in which the amide nitrogen is part of a heterocyclic ring yields the corresponding tertiary amines. Thus, reduction of 1-acyl-2-piperidinomethylpiperidines (LVIII) yields the 1-alkyl-2-piperidinomethylpiperidine (50).

(10-29)

LVIII

R = H, alkyl, arylalkyl, phenyl, substituted phenyl

The alkaloid veatchine, $C_{22}H_{33}NO_2$, has been assigned the partial structure LIX (51). Selenium dehydrogenation followed by LAH reduction yields a tetrahydro base, $C_{20}H_{33}NO$, which contains a secondary alcohol and a secondary amino group. Formation of the O,N-diacetate derivative followed by LAH reduction yields an oily base, $C_{22}H_{37}NO$, in which the N-acetyl group has been converted to the N-ethyl group.

LIX

(10-30)

Morrison, Long, and Königstein (52) have reported that reduction of the piperidide LX with one mole of LAH yields 30% of the piperidine (LXI)

TABLE LVI

LAH Reduction of N,N-Disubstituted Amides to Amines

	Amide	Product	% Yield	Ref.
$C_5H_{11}NO$	N,N-Diethylformamide	Methyldiethylamine	64	1
$C_6H_{11}NO_3$	N,N-Dimethylsuccinamic acid	4-Dimethylamino-1-butanol	60	2
$C_6H_{13}NO$	N,N-Diethylacetamide	Triethylamine	50	3–6
$C_9H_{11}NO$	N-Methylacetanilide	N-Ethyl-N-methylaniline	91	7
$C_9H_{15}NO$	N,N-Dimethyl-1-cyclohexene-1-carboxamide	1-(N,N-Dimethylaminomethyl)cyclohexene	70–75	8,9
$C_{10}H_{11}N_3O$	N,N-Dimethyl-3-indazolecarboxamide (I)	3-Dimethylaminomethylindazole	80[10]	11
$C_{10}H_{13}NO$	N-Formyl-N-methyl-β-phenylethylamine	N,N-Dimethyl-β-phenylethylamine	83	1
$C_{10}H_{14}N_2O$	N,N-Diethylnicotinamide (coramine)	3-(Diethylaminomethyl)pyridine	55	3
			84.1	12
$C_{10}H_{19}NO_3$	Ethyl N,N-diethylsuccinamate	4-Diethylamino-1-butanol	71	2
$C_{10}H_{20}N_2O$	N,N-Dimethyl-β-(2-piperidyl)propionamide	N,N-Dimethyl-γ-(2-piperidyl)propylamine[13]	20	14
$C_{11}H_{12}N_2O$	N,N-Dimethylindole-2-carboxamide	2-Dimethylaminomethylindole	71	15
$C_{11}H_{15}NO$	N,N-Diethylbenzamide	N,N-Diethylbenzylamine	90	9,16
			91.9	12
$C_{11}H_{21}NO_3$	Ethyl N,N-diethylglutaramate	5-Diethylamino-1-pentanol	....	2
$C_{12}H_{15}NO_2$	N,N-Diethylphenylglyoxylamide (II)	2-Diethylamino-1-phenylethanol	33	2
$C_{12}H_{17}NO_4$	N,N-Dimethyl-3,4,5-trimethoxybenzamide	N,N-Dimethyl-3,4,5-trimethoxybenzylamine	54	3–6
$C_{13}H_{19}NO_4$	N,N-Dimethyl-3,4,5-trimethoxyphenylacetamide	N,N-Dimethyl-β-(3,4,5-trimethoxyphenyl)ethylamine	59[17]	18
$C_{14}H_{13}NO$	N-Phenylacetanilide	N-Ethyldiphenylamine	....[19]	18
		Diphenylamine	....	18
$C_{14}H_{27}N_3O_3$	Ethanetriacetic acid tris-dimethylamide (III)	3-Methyl-3-(2'-dimethylaminoethyl)-1,4-bis-dimethylaminopentane	69	20,21
$C_{15}H_{15}NO$	N-Ethylbenzanilide	N-Ethyl-N-phenylbenzylamine	45	22
		N-Ethylaniline	41	22
		Benzyl alcohol	....	
$C_{16}H_{17}NO_2$	N-(α-Methoxybenzyl)acetanilide	N-Ethyl-N-phenylbenzylamine	83	22

Formula	Amide	Product	Yield	Ref.
$C_{17}H_{14}N_2OS$	2-Benzoylimino-3-benzylthiazoline (IV)	2-Benzylimino-3-benzylthiazoline	81	23
$C_{17}H_{17}NO_3$	N-(α-Acetoxybenzyl)acetanilide	N-Ethyl-N-phenylbenzylamine	8.5 $\Big\}$[19]	22
		N-Ethylaniline	79	
		Benzyl alcohol	....	
$C_{17}H_{19}NO_2$	N-(α-Ethoxybenzyl)acetanilide	N-Ethyl-N-phenylbenzylamine	88	22
	N,N-Dimethyldiphenylmethoxyacetamide	β-Dimethylaminoethylbenzhydryl ether	....	4-6
$C_{17}H_{26}N_2O$	N,N-Diethyl-N'-(1,2,3,4-tetrahydro-2-naphthyl)-N'-methylglycinamide	N,N-Diethyl-N'-(1,2,3,4-tetrahydro-2-naphthyl)-N'-methylethylenediamine	80[19]	24
$C_{18}H_{24}NO_5Br$	Ethylene glycol ketal of 5-bromo-7,8-dimethoxy-2-tetralone-1-(N,N-dimethylacetamide) (V)	Ethylene glycol ketal of 5-bromo-7,8-dimethoxy-1-dimethylaminoethyl-2-tetralone	....[25]	26
$C_{19}H_{21}NO_5$	N-(3-Methoxybenzyl)-N-(3-methoxy-4,5-methyl-enedioxyphenylethyl)formamide	N-(3-Methoxybenzyl)-N-(3-methoxy-4,5-methyl-enedioxyphenylethyl)methylamine	87[27]	28
$C_{19}H_{23}NO$	N,N-Dimethyl-β-benzyl-β-phenylbutyramide	N,N-Dimethyl-3-benzyl-3-phenyl-n-butylamine	....	29
$C_{20}H_{25}N_3O$	Lysergic acid diethylamide	6-Methyl-8-diethylaminoethylergolene	92	30
$C_{21}H_{41}NO_3$	N,N-Dimethyl-α-dodecyl-β-methylsuccinamic acid	2-Dodecyl-3-methyl-4-diethylamino-1-butanol	....	31,32
$C_{22}H_{44}N_2O_2$	N,N,N',N'-Tetramethylhexadecane-1,16-dicarboxamide	1,18-Bis-dimethylaminooctadecane	75[27]	33
$C_{24}H_{39}NO_3$	N-Methyl-N-phenyl-α-dodecyl-β-methyl-succinamic acid	2-Dodecyl-3-methyl-4-(N-phenyl)methylamino-1-butanol	....	31
$C_{25}H_{19}NO$	N-Methyl-N-α-naphthoyl-9-fluorenylamine[34]	N-Methyl-N-α-naphthylmethyl-9-fluorenylamine	73	35
	N-Methyl-N-β-naphthoyl-9-fluorenylamine	N-Methyl-9-α-naphthylmethyl-9-fluorenylamine	50[10,27]	35
		N-Methyl-9-β-naphthylmethyl-9-fluorenylamine	58[10]	35
$C_{25}H_{21}NO$	N-Methyl-N-α-naphthoylbenzhydrylamine[34]	N-Methyl-N-α-naphthylmethylbenzhydrylamine	83[27]	36
	N-Methyl-N-β-naphthoylbenzhydrylamine	N-Methyl-N-β-naphthylmethylbenzhydrylamine	91[27]	36
$C_{25}H_{27}N_3O_2$	N,N'-Benzyl-N,N'-ethylquinolinamide (VI)	2,3-Bis-(N-benzyl-N-ethylaminomethyl)pyridine	....	4-6
$C_{26}H_{45}NO_4$	Cholic acid dimethylamide (VII)	24-Dimethylaminocholane-3,7,12-triol	86[27]	37

CHART TO TABLE LVI

References—Table LVI

[1] F. F. Blicke and Chi-Jung Lu, *J. Am. Chem. Soc.*, 74, 3933 (1952).

[2] A. W. D. Avison, *J. Applied Chem. (London)*, 1, 469 (1951).

[3] A. Uffer and E. Schlittler, *Helv. Chim. Acta*, 31, 1397 (1948).

[4] Ciba Akt, Swiss Pat. 273,953 (June 1, 1951).

[5] Ciba S. A., Fr. Pat. 987,158 (August 9, 1951).

[6] E. Schlittler and A. Uffer, Ger. Pat. 824,491 (December 13, 1951).

[7] R. F. Nystrom and W. G. Brown, *J. Am. Chem. Soc.*, 70, 3738 (1948).

[8] R. Jacquier and R. Zagdoun, *Bull. soc. chim. France*, [5] 19, 698 (1952).

[9] M. Mousseron, R. Jacquier, M. Mousseron-Canet, and R. Zagdoun, *ibid.*, [5] 19, 1042 (1952).

[10] Reaction carried out in tetrahydrofuran.

[11] H. R. Snyder, C. B. Thompson, and R. L. Hinman, *J. Am. Chem. Soc.*, 74, 2009 (1952).

[12] V. M. Mićović and M. L. Mihailović, *J. Org. Chem.*, 18, 1190 (1953).

[13] Inverse addition.

[14] J. A. King, V. Hofmann, and F. H. McMillan, *J. Org. Chem.*, 16, 1100 (1951).

[15] E. C. Kornfeld, *ibid.*, 16, 806 (1951).

[16] M. Mousseron, R. Jacquier, M. Mousseron-Canet, and R. Zagdoun, *Compt. rend.*, 235, 177 (1952).

[17] Isolated as picrate.

[18] K. Banholzer, T. W. Campbell, and H. Schmid, *Helv. Chim. Acta*, 35, 1577 (1952).

[19] Reaction carried out in benzene-ether mixture.

[20] R. Lukeš and M. Ferles, *Chem. Listy*, in press, through J. Rudinger, M. Ferles, and M. Protiva, *Chem. Listy*, 45, 361 (1951).

[21] R. Lukeš and M. Ferles, *Coll. Czech. Chem. Communs.*, 16, 420 (1951).

[22] A. W. Burgstahler, *J. Am. Chem. Soc.*, 73, 3021 (1951).

[23] I. A. Kaye and C. L. Parris, *J. Org. Chem.*, 17, 737 (1952).

[24] G. B. Marini-Bettolo, S. Chiavarelli, and D. Bovet, *Gazz. chim. ital.*, 80, 281 (1950).

[25] Isolated as perchlorate.

[26] G. Stork and H. Conroy, *J. Am. Chem. Soc.*, 73, 4743 (1951).

[27] Isolated as hydrochloride.

[28] K. E. Hamlin and A. W. Weston, *J. Am. Chem. Soc.*, 71, 2210 (1949).

[29] R. C. Fuson, H. L. Jackson, and E. W. Grieshaber, *J. Org. Chem.*, 16, 1529 (1951).

[30] Sandoz Ltd., Brit. Pat. 674,061 (June 18, 1952).

[31] V. C. Barry, J. G. Belton, R. M. Kelly, and D. Twomey, *Nature*, 166, 303 (1950).

[32] V. C. Barry and D. Twomey, *Abstracts of Papers*, XIIth International Congress of Pure and Applied Chemistry, New York, September 1951, p. 308.

[33] D. E. Ames and R. E. Bowman, *J. Chem. Soc.*, 1952, 1057.

[34] See text.

[35] H. Dahn and U. Solms, *Helv. Chim. Acta*, 34, 907 (1951).

[36] H. Dahn, U. Solms, and P. Zoller, *ibid.*, 35, 2117 (1952).

[37] F. Wessely and W. Swoboda, *Monatsh.*, 82, 437 (1951).

and 32% of the propanol derivative (LXII) as well as piperidine, identified as the reineckate.

$$\text{LX}$$

$$\text{LXI} \qquad (10\text{-}31)$$

$$(C_6H_5)_2CCH_2CH_2N(CH_3)_2 \; + \; \text{(piperidine)}$$

with OH group below, labeled

$$\text{LXII}$$

The propanol (LXII) is also obtained by heating (2-dimethylaminoethoxy)diphenylmethane (LXIII) in benzene with powdered sodium. The reaction with sodium is formulated as follows:

$$(C_6H_5)_2CHOCH_2CH_2N(CH_3)_2 \xrightarrow{\text{Na}} (C_6H_5)_2\overset{\ominus}{C}-OCH_2CH_2N(CH_3)_2 \; Na^{\oplus}$$

$$\text{LXIII}$$

$$(10\text{-}32)$$

$$(C_6H_5)_2CCH_2CH_2N(CH_3)_2 \longleftarrow (C_6H_5)_2CCH_2CH_2N(CH_3)_2$$
$$\underset{OH}{|} \qquad\qquad \underset{O^{\ominus}\,Na^{\oplus}}{|}$$

$$\text{LXII}$$

The LAH reduction of LX is postulated analogously:

$$\text{LX}$$

$$\xrightarrow{\text{LAH}}$$

$$(10\text{-}33)$$

While the reductions of N-acetyl-1,2,3,4-tetrahydroquinoline (LXIV) (4) and 7-amino-2-benzoyl-1,2,3,4-tetrahydroisoquinoline (LXV) (53) yield the expected amines,

LXIV   LXV

the reduction of N-benzoyl-1,2,3,4-tetrahydroquinoline (LXVI) yields, besides the corresponding amine, benzyl alcohol and 1,2,3,4-tetrahydroquinoline. The ratio of products does not depend upon the amount of LAH nor upon the time of heating but is affected by the temperature of the reduction (4).

LXVI   (10-34)

The LAH reduction of amides, in which the amido nitrogen is part of a heterocyclic ring, to amines is summarized in Table LVII.

2. *Reductive decomposition.* By appropriate modification of the experimental conditions the LAH reduction of amides can be directed to yield, by reductive decomposition, aldehydes or alcohols. N-Acylated heterocyclic compounds with aromatic character are reduced even under normal conditions to alcohols and the heterocyclic amines. By applying special conditions these compounds give aldehydes and the heterocyclic amines.

Friedman reported that the inverse addition of one-quarter mole of LAH in ether or tetrahydrofuran per mole of disubstituted amide, at temperatures maintained from $-70°$ to $0°$, depending upon the compound under investigation, results in the formation of the corresponding aldehyde (54).

$$RCON\begin{smallmatrix}R'\\ \\R''\end{smallmatrix} \xrightarrow{\text{LAH/4}} RCHO \qquad (10\text{-}35)$$

This technique and modifications thereof have been applied to the synthesis of various aldehydes. The amides utilized have included N,N-dimethyl-, N,N-diethyl-, N,N-dibutyl-, N-methyl-N-phenyl-, N,N-pentamethylene-, and aromatic heterocyclic derivatives. Attempts to synthesize aldehydes from N-methylcyclohexanecarboxamide (LXVII) (5,36),

TABLE LVII

LAH Reduction of Amides Containing Heterocyclic Amido Groups to Amines

	Amide	Product	% Yield	Ref.
C_5H_9NO	N-Formylpyrrolidine	1-Methylpyrrolidine	60	1
$C_5H_9NO_2$	N-Formylmorpholine	1-Methylmorpholine	61	1
$C_6H_{11}NO$	N-Formyl-3-methylpyrrolidine	1,3-Dimethylpyrrolidine	50	1
	N-Formylpiperidine	1-Methylpiperidine	90	1
$C_7H_{13}NO$	N-Acetylpiperidine	1-Ethylpiperidine	92.3	2
$C_{10}H_{13}NOS$	N-(2-Thenoyl)piperidine	1-(2-Thenyl)piperidine	77[3-5]	6
$C_{10}H_{17}NO_2$	N-Acetylisopelletierine (I)	1-(α-N-Ethylpiperidyl)-2-propanol	99	7
$C_{10}H_{17}NO_3$	Ethyl N,N-pentamethylenemalonamate	3-Piperidino-1-propanol	...	8
$C_{11}H_{13}NO$	N-Acetyl-1,2,3,4-tetrahydroquinoline	N-Ethyl-1,2,3,4-tetrahydroquinoline	90.6	2
$C_{11}H_{14}N_2O$	N-(2'-Picolinoyl)piperidine	2-(Piperidinomethylpyridine)	55	9,10
$C_{11}H_{19}NO$	N-Acetyldecahydroisoquinoline	N-Ethyldecahydroisoquinoline	84	11-14
$C_{12}H_{15}NO$	N-Benzoylpiperidine	1-Benzylpiperidine	85	15,16
			93.3	2
$C_{12}H_{19}NO$	N,N-Pentamethylene-1-cyclohexenecarboxamide	1-Piperidinomethyl-1-cyclohexene	70-75	15-17
$C_{12}H_{21}NO$	N,N-Pentamethylenecyclohexanecarboxamide	1-Hexahydrobenzylpiperidine	75	15,16
$C_{12}H_{21}NO_3$	Ethyl N,N-pentamethyleneglutaramate	5-Piperidino-1-pentanol	75	8
$RC_{12}H_{21}N_2O$	N-Acyl-2-piperidinomethylpiperidine[18]	N-Substituted-2-piperidinomethylpiperidine	...	9
$C_{13}H_{15}N_3O$	N,N-Pentamethylene-3-indazolecarboxamide[18]	3-Piperidinomethylindazole	75[19]	20
$C_{13}H_{23}NO_3$	Ethyl N,N-pentamethyleneadipamate	6-Piperidino-1-hexanol	...	8
$RC_{13}H_{23}N_2O$	N-Acyl-2-piperidinoethylpiperidine[18]	N-Substituted-2-piperidinoethylpiperidine	...	9
$C_{14}H_{19}NO_2$	N-(3-Methoxybenzoyl)-2-methylpiperidine	1-(3-Methoxybenzyl)-2-methylpiperidine	...[21]	22
$C_{14}H_{19}NO_3$	N-(3,5-Dimethoxybenzoyl)piperidine	1-(3,5-Dimethoxybenzyl)piperidine	92	23
$C_{15}H_{21}NO_2$	N-(3-Methoxybenzoyl)-2,6-dimethylpiperidine	1-(3-Methoxybenzyl)-2,6-dimethylpiperidine	...[21]	22
$C_{15}H_{21}NO_3$	N-(3,4-Dimethoxybenzoyl)-2-methylpiperidine	1-(3,4-Dimethoxybenzyl)-2-methylpiperidine	...[21]	22
$C_{16}H_{15}NO$	N-Benzoyl-1,2,3,4-tetrahydroquinoline	N-Benzyl-1,2,3,4-tetrahydroquinoline	37-39	2
		1,2,3,4-Tetrahydroquinoline	44-47	
		Benzyl alcohol	49-53	

Formula	Amide	Product(s)	Yield	Ref.
$C_{16}H_{16}N_2O$	N-Benzoyl-1,2,3,4-tetrahydroquinoline	N-Benzoyl-1,2,3,4-tetrahydroquinoline	21 ⎫	2
		1,2,3,4-Tetrahydroquinoline	72 ⎬[24]	
		Benzyl alcohol	74 ⎭	
	7-Amino-2-benzoyl-1,2,3,4-tetrahydroisoquinoline	7-Amino-2-benzoyl-1,2,3,4-tetrahydroisoquinoline	95	25
$C_{16}H_{23}NO_2$	N-(2-Methoxy-5-methylbenzoyl)-2,6-dimethyl-piperidine	1-(2-Methoxy-5-methylbenzyl)-2,6-dimethyl-piperidine	…[21]	22
$C_{16}H_{23}NO_4$	N-(3,4,5-Trimethoxybenzoyl)-2-methylpiperidine	1-(3,4,5-Trimethoxybenzyl)-2-methylpiperidine	…[21]	22
$C_{19}H_{21}NO$	Diphenylacetopiperidide	1,1-Diphenyl-2-piperidinoethane	65[26]	27
$C_{19}H_{21}NO_2$	α-Hydroxy-α,α-diphenylacetopiperidide	1,1-Diphenyl-2-piperidinoethanol	54.5[28]	27
$C_{21}H_{24}N_2O_2$	N(a)-Formyldihydrodesoxogelsemine (III)	N(a)-Methyl-dihydrodesoxogelsemine (III)	…	29
$C_{23}H_{30}N_2O_2$	α-(2-Dimethylaminoethoxy)-α,α-diphenylaceto-piperidide	2-(2-Dimethylaminoethoxy)-2,2-diphenyl-1-piperidinoethane	30[23] ⎫	27
		3-Dimethylamino-1,1-diphenyl-1-propanol Piperidine[30]	32 ⎬	
			… ⎭	
$C_{24}H_{23}NO_2$	Triphenylacetomorpholide	N-(2,2,2-Triphenylethyl)morpholine	…	31
$C_{24}H_{27}NO$	1,2,3,10b-Tetrahydrofluoranthene-10b-[3-(propiopiperidide)] (IV)	10b-Piperidinopropyl-1,2,3,10b-tetrahydrofluor-anthene	80	32
$C_{27}H_{41}NO_4$	N-Acetyloxazolidine (V)	N-Ethyl-N-isopropylaminomethyl-5-androsten-3β,17β-diol (VI)	85	33
$C_{30}H_{43}N_5O_2$	Dihydrolysergyl-L-alanyl-L,L-1,2-trimethylene-5-isobutylpiperazide (VII: R = CH₃)	Polyamine, $C_{30}H_{47}N_5$, m.p. 158° (VIII: R = CH₃)	74[34]	35
	Dihydrolysergyl-D-alanyl-L,L-1,2-trimethylene-5-isobutylpiperazide	Polyamine, $C_{30}H_{47}N_5$, m.p. 193°	57[34]	35
	Dihydrolysergyl-L-alanyl-L,D-1,2-trimethylene-5-isobutylpiperazide	Polyamine, $C_{30}H_{47}N_5$, m.p. 206°	25[34]	35
	Dihydrolysergyl-D-alanyl-L,D-1,2-trimethylene-5-isobutylpiperazide	Polyamine, $C_{30}H_{47}N_5$, m.p. 206°	24[34]	35
$C_{32}H_{47}N_5O_2$	Dihydrolysergyl-L-valyl-L,L-1,2-trimethylene-5-isobutylpiperazide (VII: R = CH(CH₃)₂)	Polyamine, $C_{32}H_{51}N_5$, m.p. 155° (VIII: R = CH(CH₃)₂)	25[34]	35
	Dihydrolysergyl-D-valyl-L,L-1,2-trimethylene-5-isobutylpiperazide	Polyamine, $C_{32}H_{51}N_5$, m.p. 153°	9[34]	35
$C_{33}H_{45}NO_6$	Triacetyl-5,6-oxidoveratramine (IX)	N-Ethyldihydroveratramine-3,5,23-triol	… ⎫[3,36]	37
		N-Ethyldihydroveratramine-3,5,6,23-tetrol	… ⎭	

CHART TO TABLE LVII

References—Table LVII

[1]F. F. Blicke and Chi-Jung Lu, *J. Am. Chem. Soc.*, 74, 3933 (1952).

[2]V. M. Mićović and M. L. Mihailović, *J. Org. Chem.*, 18, 1190 (1953).

[3]Reduction carried out in ether-benzene mixture.

[4]Isolated as picrate.

[5]Yield based on carboxylic acid from which amide derived.

[6]T. W. Campbell and W. W. Kaeding, *J. Am. Chem. Soc.*, 73, 4018 (1951).

[7]F. Galinovsky and O. Vogl, *Monatsh.*, 83, 1055 (1952).

[8]A. W. Avison, *J. Applied Chem. (London)*, 1, 469 (1951).

[9]A. H. Sommers, K. M. Beck, M. Freifelder, and A. W. Weston, *Abstracts of Papers*, 121st Meeting American Chemical Society, Milwaukee, Wis., March 1952, p. 4J.

[10]A. H. Sommers, M. Freifelder, H. B. Wright, and A. W. Weston, *J. Am. Chem. Soc.*, 75, 57 (1953).

[11]A. Uffer and E. Schlittler, *Helv. Chim. Acta*, 31, 1397 (1948).

[12]Ciba Akt., Swiss Pat. 273,953 (June 1, 1951).

[13]Ciba S. A., Fr. Pat. 987,158 (August 9, 1951).

[14]E. Schlittler and A. Uffer, Ger. Pat. 824,491 (December 13, 1951).

[15]M. Mousseron, R. Jacquier, M. Mousseron-Canet, and R. Zagdoun, *Compt. rend.*, 235, 177 (1952).

[16]M. Mousseron, R. Jacquier, M. Mousseron-Canet, and R. Zagdoun, *Bull. soc. chim. France*, [5] 19, 1042 (1952).

[17]R. Jacquier and R. Zagdoun, *ibid.*, [5] 19, 698 (1952).

[18]Acyl group is RCO- where R is hydrogen, alkyl, arylalkyl, phenyl or substituted phenyl.

[19]Reduction carried out in tetrahydrofuran.

[20]H. R. Snyder, C. B. Thompson, and R. L. Hinman, *J. Am. Chem. Soc.*, 74, 2009 (1952).

[21]Reduction carried out in benzene.

[22]A. Pohland, U. S. Pat. 2,589,205 (March 11, 1952).

[23]K. Hejno and Z. Arnold, *Chem. Listy*, in press, through M. Ferles and J. Rudinger, *Chem. Listy*, 47, 132 (1953).

[24]Reduction carried out at 0°.

[25]A. McCoubrey and D. W. Mathieson, *J. Chem. Soc.*, 1951, 2851.

[26]Isolated as hydrochloride.

[27]A. L. Morrison, R. F. Long, and M. Königstein, *J. Chem. Soc.*, 1951, 952.

[28]Isolated as hydrogen sulfate.

[29]T. Habgood, L. Marion, and H. Schwarz, *Helv. Chim. Acta*, 35, 638 (1952).

[30]Isolated as reineckate.

[31]F. G. Bordwell, B. M. Pitt, and M. Knell, *J. Am. Chem. Soc.*, 73, 5004 (1951).

[32]Ciba Ltd., Brit. Pat. 658,208 (October 3, 1951).

[33]H. Heusser, P. T. Herzig, A. Fürst, and P. A. Plattner, *Helv. Chim. Acta*, 33, 1093 (1950).

[34]Reduction carried out in N-ethylmorpholine.

[35]A. Stoll, A. Hofmann, and T. Petrzilka, *Helv. Chim. Acta*, 34, 1544 (1951).

[36]Isolated as 3,23-diacetate.

[37]W. A. Jacobs and Y. Sato, *J. Biol. Chem.*, 191, 71 (1951).

N,N'-dimethyl-o-phthalamide (LXVIII) (55) and various other monosubstituted amides (4) have been unsuccessful.

LXVII   LXVIII   LXIX

Although it has been reported (56) that LAH reduction of N,N-dimethylbenzamide (LXIX) at "low temperatures" gives a "good" yield of benzaldehyde, Mićović and Mihailović (4) have stated that LXIX does not react or gives only negligible quantities of aldehydes with the inverse addition of 0.25 mole of LAH at $-15°$ to $-10°$.

Weygand and Tietjen (55) have pointed out that a considerable steric hindrance appears necessary for the smooth course of the reduction unless special precautions are taken. Although N,N-dimethylcarboxamides of aromatic systems are reduced satisfactorily to aldehydes by the inverse addition technique, this technique applied to N,N-dimethylcyclohexanecarboxamide (LXX) yields only 5% of the aldehyde accompanied by 25% of dimethylaminomethylcyclohexane and 60% of the starting amide is recovered (5,36).

LXX

Weygand and Eberhardt (57) have prepared a series of aldehydes in 50-75% yields by the reduction of the N-methylanilides of the corresponding acids (LXXI) with 0.25 mole of LAH in tetrahydrofuran at $0°$.

$$RCON\overset{CH_3}{\underset{C_6H_5}{\diagup}}\ \xrightarrow[THF]{LAH/4}\ RCHO \qquad (10\text{-}37)$$

LXXI

As mentioned in Section 10.1.1.d.1, Nystrom and Brown (1,49) obtained benzyl alcohol in the attempted reduction of N,N-diethylbenzamide (LXXII) to benzaldehyde. Mićović and Mihailović (4) have obtained 37% of benzaldehyde, 12% of benzyl alcohol and 28% of unreacted amide by carrying out the reduction in ether with the inverse addition of 0.25 mole of LAH at $-15°$.

$$C_6H_5CON(C_2H_5)_2 \ \rightarrow\ C_6H_5CHO + C_6H_5CH_2OH \qquad (10\text{-}38)$$

LXXII

By carrying out the reduction with normal addition with 0.5 mole of LAH at $0°$ the expected N,N-diethylbenzylamine is accompanied by 13% of benzyl alcohol.

The inverse addition of 0.25 mole of LAH at $-15°$ to N,N-diethylnicotinamide (coramine) (LXXIII) yields 13% of nicotinaldehyde, 28% of 3-pyridinemethanol, 5% of 3-(diethylaminomethyl)pyridine and 25% of unreacted amide.

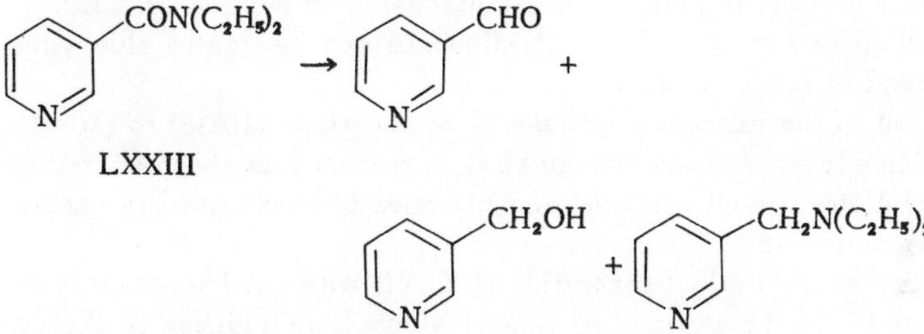

LXXIII

$$(10\text{-}39)$$

Reduction with the normal addition of 0.5 mole of LAH at $0°$ yields the expected amine as well as 18% of 3-pyridinemethanol (4).

The reduction of N-benzoylpiperidine (LXXIV) with inverse addition of 0.25 mole of LAH yields 47% of benzaldehyde, 18% of benzyl alcohol and 20.5% of unreacted amide.

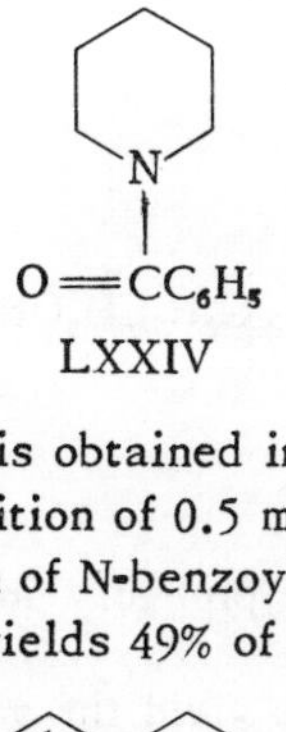

$$\rightarrow C_6H_5CHO + C_6H_5CH_2OH \qquad (10\text{-}40)$$

$$O = CC_6H_5$$

LXXIV

Benzyl alcohol is obtained in 10% yield when the reduction is carried out with normal addition of 0.5 mole of LAH at $0°$ (4).

The reduction of N-benzoyl-1,2,3,4-tetrahydroquinoline (LXXV) with inverse addition yields 49% of benzaldehyde and 14% of benzyl alcohol.

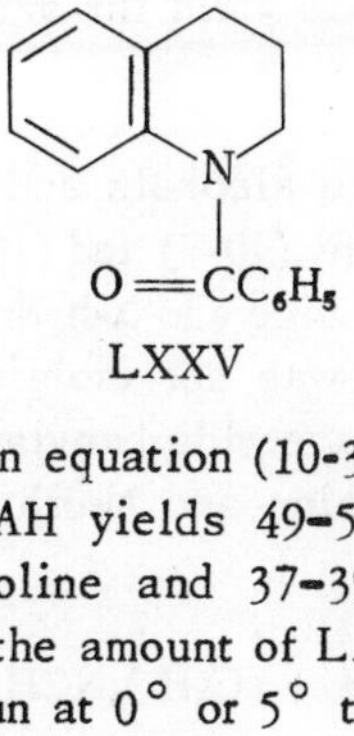

$$\rightarrow C_6H_5CHO + C_6H_5CH_2OH \qquad (10\text{-}41)$$

$$O = CC_6H_5$$

LXXV

As indicated in equation (10-34), the reduction of LXXV with the normal addition of LAH yields 49–53% of benzyl alcohol, 44–47% of 1,2,3,4-tetrahydroquinoline and 37–39% of N-benzyl-1,2,3,4-tetrahydroquinoline regardless of the amount of LAH or the time of heating. However, if the reduction is run at $0°$ or $5°$ the yields of benzyl alcohol and tetrahydroquinoline are increased to 74% and 72%, respectively, while the yield of N-alkylated tetrahydroquinoline is decreased to 21% (4).

King, Hofmann, and McMillan (58) attempted to synthesize the aldehyde pelletierine by the inverse addition of the calculated amount of LAH to N,N-dimethyl-β-(2-piperidyl)propionamide at $-60°$. A 20% yield of the tertiary amine was obtained instead of the desired aldehyde. Inverse addition of LAH to the lactam, 3-ketooctahydropyrrocoline, results in the isolation of a polymer of pelletierine as discussed in Section 10.2.1.c.

The LAH reduction of various N,N-disubstituted amides to aldehydes is summarized in Table LVIII.

In addition to the examples formulated in equations (10-38) to (10-41), wherein alcohols accompany the aldehydes produced in the LAH reduction of N,N-disubstituted amides, alcohols have been obtained in various other amide reductions.

The reduction of N-ethylbenzanilide (LXXVI) with LAH in ether is reported to yield N-ethylaniline and benzyl alcohol, in addition to the expected tertiary amine (59).

$$C_6H_5CONCH_2CH_3 \xrightarrow{\text{LAH}} C_6H_5CH_2NCH_2CH_3 + C_6H_5CH_2OH + NHCH_2CH_3$$
$$\underset{\underset{\text{LXXVI}}{C_6H_5}}{|} \qquad \underset{C_6H_5}{|} \qquad \underset{C_6H_5}{|}$$

$$(10\text{-}42)$$

The reduction of N-(α-acetoxybenzyl)acetanilide (LXXVII) unexpectedly yields the same cleavage products.

$$\overset{\overset{\displaystyle OCOCH_3}{|}}{C_6H_5CHNCOCH_3} \xrightarrow{\text{LAH}} C_6H_5CH_2NCH_2CH_3 + C_6H_5CH_2OH + NHCH_2CH_3$$
$$\underset{\underset{\text{LXXVII}}{C_6H_5}}{|} \qquad \underset{C_6H_5}{|} \qquad \underset{C_6H_5}{|}$$

$$(10\text{-}43)$$

The course of the reduction of LXXVII is probably influenced by the cleavage of the $-\overset{|}{N}-\overset{|}{C}-O-$ grouping to yield the same intermediate as in the reduction of LXXVI.

The reduction of unsubstituted amides to alcohols and aldehydes has been mentioned in Section 10.1.1.b, equations (10-7) and (10-8), with reference to the LAH reduction of perfluorobutyramide and α-hydroxyvaleramide.

Although the oxygen-containing product was not isolated, a cleavage reaction is apparent in the reduction of N-acetyldiphenylamine (LXXVIII) in an ether-benzene mixture to diphenylamine and N-ethyldiphenylamine (60).

$$(C_6H_5)_2NCOCH_3 \xrightarrow{\text{LAH}} (C_6H_5)_2NH + (C_6H_5)_2NCH_2CH_3 \qquad (10\text{-}44)$$
$$\text{LXXVIII}$$

Kaye and Parris (61) have attempted to determine whether acylated 2-benzylaminothiazoles have the 2-benzylimino-3-acylthiazoline (LXXX) rather than the N-benzyl-N-(2-thiazolyl)amide (LXXXI) structure. However, when the benzoyl and acetyl derivatives of 2-benzylaminothiazole (LXXIX) are treated with LAH to form either disubstituted 2-thiazolyl-amines or 2-iminothiazolines, the acyl compounds undergo acyl cleavage to yield only 2-benzylaminothiazole.

$$(10\text{-}45)$$

In addition, while 2-benzoylimino-3-benzylthiazoline (LXXXII) is reduced to 2-benzylimino-3-benzylthiazoline, reduction of 2-acetylimino-3-benzyl-thiazoline (LXXXIII) results in acyl cleavage to 2-imino-3-benzylthiazoline.

$$(10\text{-}46)$$

$$(10\text{-}47)$$

On the other hand, LAH reduction of 2-benzamidothiazole (LXXXIV: R = C_6H_5) and 2-acetamidothiazole (LXXXIV: R = CH_3) yields the corresponding aminothiazole.

$$(10\text{-}48)$$

The LAH reduction of N,N-diethyl- (4) and N,N-diphenylcinnamamide (6) (LXXXV) with excess hydride is reported to yield 30% and 37%, respectively, of cinnamyl alcohol.

TABLE LVIII

LAH Reduction of N,N-Disubstituted Amides to Aldehydes

Amide	Reaction Conditions				% Yield	Ref.
	Temp.	Time	Solvent	Product		
$C_9H_{11}NO$ N-Methylacetanilide	0°	3 hrs.	THF	Acetaldehyde	67	1
N,N-Dimethylbenzamide	"low"	....	....	Benzaldehyde	"good"	2
$C_9H_{15}NO$ N,N-Pentamethylenecyclopropanecarboxamide	-15°	30 min.	E	Cyclopropanecarboxaldehyde	0	3
	+25°	3-4 hrs.	E		20	4
$C_9H_{17}NO$ N,N-Dimethylcyclohexanecarboxamide	-15°	30 min.	E	Cyclohexanecarboxaldehyde	5[5]	6
	ambient	3 hrs.		Dimethylaminomethylcyclohexane	25	
$C_{10}H_{14}N_2O$ N,N-Diethylnicotinamide	-15°	30 min.	E	Nicotinaldehyde	12.9	4
	+25°	60 min.		3-(Diethylaminomethyl)pyridine	5.1[7]	
				3-Pyridinemethanol	28	
$C_{11}H_{15}NO$ N,N-Diethylbenzamide	-15°	30 min.	E	Benzaldehyde	36.6[8]	4
	+25°	60 min.		Benzyl alcohol	11.6	
$C_{12}H_{15}NO$ N-Benzoylpiperidine	-15°	30 min.	E	Benzaldehyde	30[9]	6,10
	ambient	30 min.		Piperidine	....	
	-15°	30 min.	E	Benzaldehyde	47.1[11]	4
	+25°	60 min.		Benzyl alcohol	17.9	
$C_{12}H_{16}N_2O_2$ N,N,N′,N′-Tetramethyl-o-phthalamide	20°	Overnight	THF-E	o-Phthalaldehyde[12]	70	13
$C_{12}H_{19}NO$ N,N-Pentamethylene-1-cyclohexenecarboxamide	-15°	....	E	1-Cyclohexenecarboxaldehyde	75	6,10,14
$C_{12}H_{21}NO$ N,N-Pentamethylenecyclohexanecarboxamide	-15°	30 min.	E	Cyclohexanecarboxaldehyde	87	6
	ambient	3 hrs.		Piperidine	76	
$C_{13}H_{12}N_2O$ N-Methyl-N-phenylnicotinamide	0°	10 hrs.	THF	Nicotinaldehyde	65	1
$C_{14}H_{13}NO$ N-Methylbenzanilide	0°	10 hrs.	THF	Benzaldehyde	68	1
$C_{14}H_{13}NO_2$ N-Methylsalicylanilide	0°	10 hrs.	THF	Salicylaldehyde	54	1

Formula	Amide	Temp.	Time	Solvent	Products	Yield	Ref.
$C_{14}H_{19}NO$	N-Methylcyclohexanecarboxanilide	$-15°$	...	E	Cyclohexanecarboxaldehyde N-Methylaniline	$40\text{--}45]_{15}$ ...	6,10
$C_{15}H_{13}N_3O$	N,N-Dimethylphenazine-1-carboxamide	$-40°$ to $-60°$	4 days	THF-E	Phenazine-1-carboxaldehyde	...	16
$C_{15}H_{19}NO$	N,N-Dibutylcyclohexanecarboxamide	$-15°$	...	E	Cyclohexanecarboxaldehyde Di-γ-butylamine	$40\text{--}45]_{15}$ ...	6,10
$C_{16}H_{15}NO$	N-Benzoyl-1,2,3,4-tetrahydroquinoline	$-15°$ $+25°$	30 min. 60 min.	E	Benzaldehyde Benzyl alcohol	49 13,7	4
$C_{18}H_{20}N_2O_2$	N,N'-Dimethylsuccinanilide	$0°$	12-15 hrs.	THF	Succinic dialdehyde	68	1
$C_{18}H_{20}N_2O_3$	N,N'-Dimethyl-N,N'-diphenyl-D,L-malic acid	$0°$	12-15 hrs.	THF	Malic dialdehyde	75	1
$C_{18}H_{24}N_2O_2$	N,N,N',N'-Dipentamethylene-o-phthalamide	$20°$	...	THF-E	o-Phthalaldehyde	20	13
$C_{22}H_{20}N_2O_2$	N,N'-Dimethyl-o-phthalanilide	$0°$	24 hrs.	THF	o-Phthalaldehyde	70	1
$C_{24}H_{24}N_2O_4$	N,N'-Dimethyl-4,5-dimethoxy-o-phthalanilide	$0°$	...	THF	4,5-Dimethoxy-o-phthalaldehyde	"good"	1

References—Table LVIII

[1]F. Weygand and G. Eberhardt, *Angew. Chem.*, 64, 458 (1952).
[2]A. Kjaer, through F. Weygand and D. Tietjen, *Chem. Ber.*, 84, 625 (1951).
[3]V. M. Mićović and M. L. Mihailović, *J. Org. Chem.*, 18, 1190 (1953).
[4]L. I. Smith and E. R. Rogier, *J. Am. Chem. Soc.*, 73, 4047 (1951).
[5]60% amide recovered.
[6]M. Mousseron, R. Jacquier, M. Mousseron-Canet, and R. Zagdoun, *Bull. soc. chim. France*, [5] 19, 1042 (1952).
[7]24.9% amide recovered.
[8]28.2% amide recovered.
[9]53% amide recovered.
[10]M. Mousseron, R. Jacquier, M. Mousseron-Canet, and R. Zagdoun, *Compt. rend.*, 235, 177 (1952).
[11]20.5% amide recovered.
[12]Isolated as isonaphthazarin by condensation with the bisulfite addition compound of glyoxal in the presence of sodium cyanide.
[13]F. Weygand and D. Tietjen, *Chem. Ber.*, 84, 625 (1951).
[14]R. Jacquier and R. Zagdoun, *Bull. soc. chim. France*, [5] 19, 698 (1952).
[15]Starting amide recovered.
[16]L. Birkofer and A. Birkofer, *Chem. Ber.*, 85, 286 (1952).

$$C_6H_5CH = CHCONR_2 \xrightarrow{LAH} C_6H_5CH = CHCH_2OH \qquad (10\text{-}49)$$

$$LXXXV$$

$$R = C_2H_5 \text{ or } C_6H_5$$

The reduction of α,β-unsaturated amides is considered more fully in Section 10.1.1.e.

The LAH reduction of N-acylated heterocyclic compounds with aromatic character results in reductive decomposition even under normal conditions, to yield alcohols and the heterocyclic amine. Thus, reduction of N-acetylpyrrole (LXXXVI: $R = CH_3$) and N-benzoylpyrrole (LXXXVI: $R = C_6H_5$) with excess LAH in refluxing ether yields pyrrole and ethyl and benzyl alcohol, respectively (4).

$$\xrightarrow{LAH} + RCH_2OH \qquad (10\text{-}50)$$

$$O = C - R$$

$$LXXXVI$$

R	% Pyrrole	% Alcohol
CH₃	82.9	....
C₆H₅	85.6	80

Similarly, N-acylated indole derivatives (LXXXVII) undergo reductive cleavage in refluxing ether.

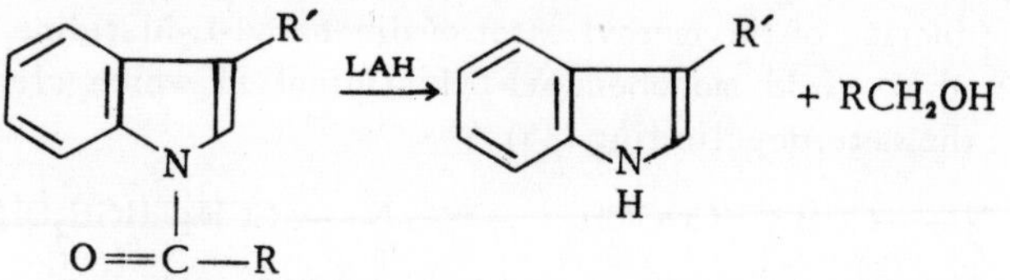

$$+ RCH_2OH \quad (10\text{-}51)$$

LXXXVII

R	R'	% Indole	% Alcohol	Ref.
CH₃	H	93.1	....	4
CH₃	CH₃	81	....	60
C₆H₅	H	89.5	92.5	4

Reductive cleavage of an acyl group is reported in the LAH reduction of 1,ω-diformyl-7-methyltryptamine (LXXXVIII) (20,21).

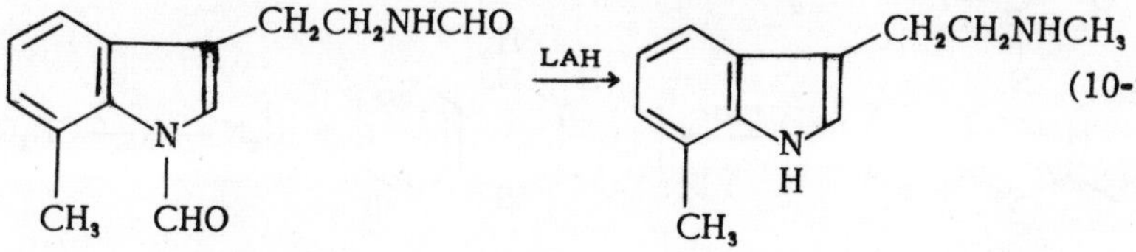

$$(10\text{-}52)$$

LXXXVIII

N-Acylated carbazoles (LXXXIX) also undergo a cleavage reaction with LAH.

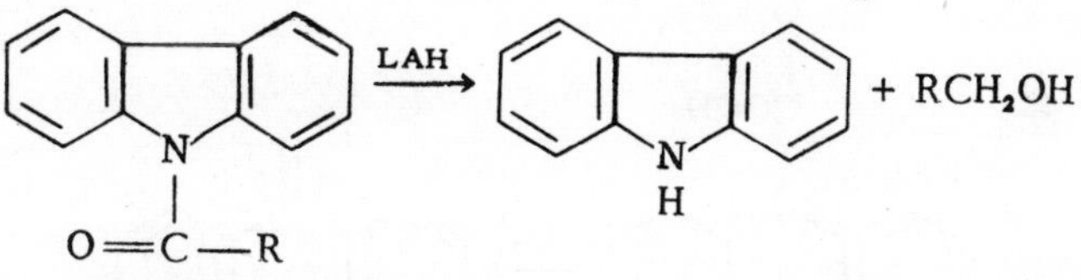

$$+ RCH_2OH \quad (10\text{-}53)$$

LXXXIX

R	% Carbazole	% Alcohol	Ref.
CH₃	98	....	60
C₆H₅	90	80.4	4

1-Benzoylbenzotriazole (XC) is cleaved with LAH in refluxing ether to yield 84% of benzotriazole and 59% of benzyl alcohol (62).

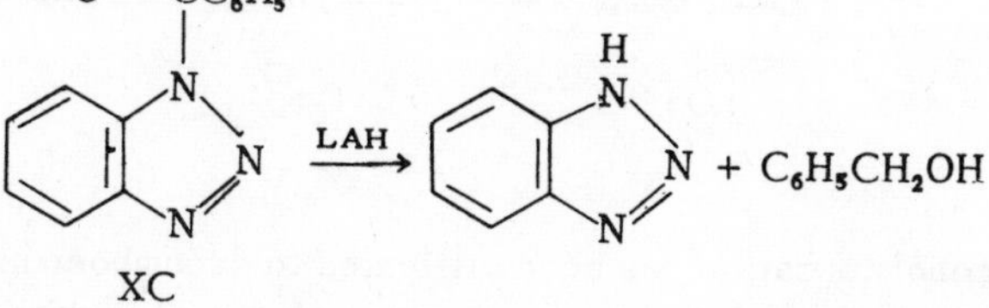

$$+ C_6H_5CH_2OH \quad (10\text{-}54)$$

XC

The LAH reduction of the methyl ester of dibenzoyl-L-histidine (XCI) has been reported to yield monobenzoyl-L-histidinol in which cleavage has occurred at the heterocyclic ring (35).

$$\text{XCI} \qquad\qquad (10\text{-}55)$$

Treatment of a 10-aminoacylphenothiazine (XCII) with LAH in ether at room temperature yields phenothiazine and an aminoalcohol (63).

$$\text{XCII} \qquad\qquad (10\text{-}56)$$

Reduction of 10-carbomethoxyphenothiazine (XCIII) similarly yields phenothiazine (64).

$$(10\text{-}57)$$

$$\text{XCIII}$$

As with non-heterocyclic amides the inverse addition of 0.25 mole of LAH at low temperatures results in the directed cleavage of N-acylated heterocyclics to aldehydes. As indicated in equation (10-2), steric hindrance on the nitrogen atom and stabilization of the resonance structure XCIV favor aldehyde formation.

$$(10\text{-}58)$$

$$\text{XCIV}$$

Although alcohol formation has been attributed to decomposition or hydrolysis of the amide molecule at the moment of reaction with LAH, with simultaneous reduction to the alkoxide anion (4), it has recently been shown that aldehyde formation precedes alcohol isolation. The infrared spectrum of a sample of the reaction mixture from the inverse addition of 0.25 mole of LAH in ether to 1-benzoylbenzotriazole (XC), withdrawn before hydrolysis, indicates the presence of benzaldehyde. The reduction products, after hydrolysis and the usual workup, are benzaldehyde and benzotriazole (8).

$$ \text{XC} \xrightarrow{\text{LAH}} \quad + \; C_6H_5CHO \qquad (10\text{-}59) $$

As shown in equation (10-54), reduction with excess LAH yields benzotriazole and benzyl alcohol.

Good yields of aldehydes have been obtained by the reduction of N-benzoylated pyrrole, indole, and carbazole (4).

Compound	Temp., °C.	% Benzaldehyde	% Amine
N-Benzoylpyrrole	−15	54.1	82.1
	0	51.7	74.5
N-Benzoylindole	−15	55.5	
	0	53.5	
N-Benzoylcarbazole	−15	60	83.3
	0	55	80

The LAH reduction of N-cinnamoylcarbazole (XCV) has been utilized in the synthesis of cinnamaldehyde.

$$ \xrightarrow{\text{LAH}} C_6H_5CH = CHCHO + $$

O =CCH =CHC₆H₅
XCV   (10-60)

Temp.	% Cinnamaldehyde	% Carbazole	Ref.
−10°	45.2	89.8	4
0°	45	89.8	4
	49	84	6

Small amounts of cinnamaldehyde are even obtained in the reduction of XCV under normal conditions (4). In a similar manner, cinnamalacetaldehyde (XCVI: n = 2), 9-phenylnonatetraenal (XCVI: n = 4) and 13-phenyltridecahexaenal (XCVI: n = 6) are obtained from the corresponding carbazole derivatives at low temperatures (6).

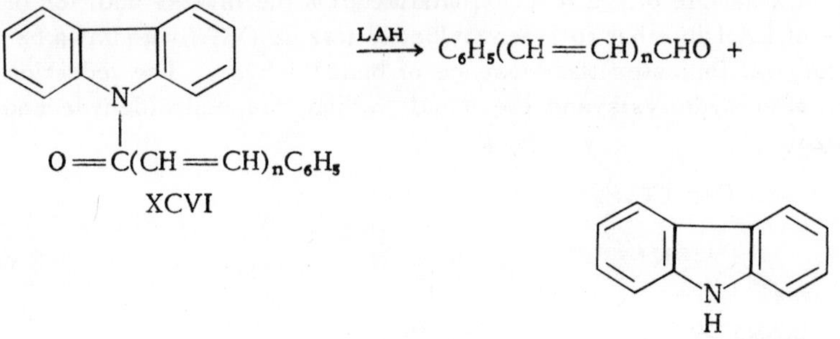

$$\xrightarrow{\text{LAH}} C_6H_5(CH=CH)_nCHO +$$

$$O=C(CH=CH)_nC_6H_5$$
XCVI

(10-61)

n	% Aldehyde	% Carbazole
2	73	....
4	81	85
6	60	91

The reduction of N-(9-phenylnonatetraenoyl)carbazole (XCVI: n = 4) has been utilized to compare the effectiveness of a number of complex hydrides. The results shown below indicate the increased yields obtained with LAH.

Agent	% Aldehyde	% Carbazole
LAH	81	85
LiBH₄	69	74
Li[BH(OC₄H₉)₃]	68	75–80
Li[ZnH(C₆H₅)₂]	45	
Li[BeH(C₆H₅)₂]	37	

A method of synthesizing unsaturated long chain aldehydes has been developed utilizing the carbazole intermediate (6):

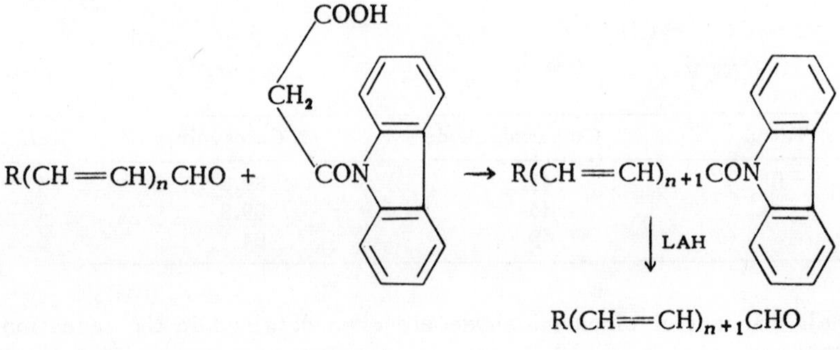

$$R(CH=CH)_nCHO +$$

$$\rightarrow R(CH=CH)_{n+1}CON$$

$$\downarrow \text{LAH}$$

$$R(CH=CH)_{n+1}CHO$$

(10-62)

10.1.1.e　α,β-*Unsaturated amides*.　The reduction of α,β-unsaturated amides presents a picture which is still somewhat uncertain.　Uffer and Schlittler reported that LAH reduction of α-ethylcrotonamide (XCVII) gives β-ethylbutylamine (erroneously reported as α-ethylbutylamine) in which the double bond has been reduced (2,65,66).

$$
\underset{\text{XCVII}}{CH_3CH = \underset{\overset{|}{\underset{C_2H_5}{}}}{C}CONH_2} \xrightarrow{\text{LAH}} CH_3CH_2\underset{\overset{|}{\underset{C_2H_5}{}}}{C}HCH_2NH_2 \qquad (10\text{-}63)
$$

On the other hand, Mousseron and his co-workers have reported that the double bond is not reduced in amides in which the α,β-double bond is part of a cyclohexene ring.　Thus, the following 1-cyclohexenecarboxamides have been reduced to the corresponding 1-aminomethylcyclohexenes: 1-cyclohexenecarboxamide (5,67), N,N-dimethyl-1-cyclohexenecarboxamide (5,68), N,N-pentamethylene-1-cyclohexenecarboxamide (5,36,68).

The attempted LAH reductions of the dimethylamide (XCVIII: R_1 = R_2 = CH_3) and the N-methylanilide (XCVIII: R_2 = CH_3, R_2 = C_6H_5) of cinnamic acid to cinnamaldehyde have been reported to yield an oil and a resin which were not further investigated (6).

$$
C_6H_5CH = CHCO\underset{\overset{|}{\underset{R_2}{}}}{\overset{\overset{R_1}{\overset{|}{}}}{N}} \qquad\qquad C_6H_5CH = CHCH = CHCO\underset{\overset{|}{\underset{R_2}{}}}{\overset{\overset{R_1}{\overset{|}{}}}{N}}
$$

XCVIII　　　　　　　　　　　　　　　　XCIX

The reaction of the diphenylamide of cinnamic acid (XCVIII: R_1 = R_2 = C_6H_5) m.p. 152-153°, with 0.25 mole of LAH in refluxing ether or tetrahydrofuran yields a compound, m.p. 191-192°, which is considered to be a stereoisomeric or polymorphic modification of the starting amide.　Treatment of the diphenylamide with 0.5 mole of LAH in refluxing ether yields 37% of cinnamyl alcohol (6).　The reaction of the diethylamide of cinnamic acid (XCVIII: R_1 = R_2 = C_2H_5) with an almost equimolar quantity of LAH in refluxing ether yields 30% of cinnamyl alcohol (4).

Treatment of the dimethylamide of cinnamalacetic acid (XCIX: R_1 = R_2 = CH_3), m.p. 109-110°, with 0.25 mole of LAH gives a *cis-trans* isomer of the starting amide, m.p. 70-72°, which after some time reverts to the higher melting form (6).　The diphenylamide of cinnamalacetic acid (XCIX: R_1 = R_2 = C_6H_5) is "resistant to reduction" with LAH (6).

As discussed in the preceding section and indicated in equations (10-60) and (10-61), aldehydes are obtained in the LAH reduction of N-

cinnamoylcarbazole, N-cinnamalacetylcarbazole, N-(9-phenylnonatetra-
enoyl)carbazole and N-(13-phenyltridecahexaenoyl)carbazole.

10.1.2   Reductions with Aluminum Hydride

An ethereal solution of aluminum hydride in the presence of aluminum
chloride is reported to reduce acetamide to ethylamine (69).

Aluminum hydride has been proposed as a selective reducing agent for
peptide esters.   Reductions are carried out at $-40°$ in an aluminum
chloride-tetrahydrofuran medium to yield an 85% conversion of peptide
ester to a β-hydroxyalkylamide.   Using the N-p-tosyl derivative of the
peptide, the β-hydroxyalkylamide is rearranged with phosphorous oxychloride to a β-amino ester which liberates an aminoalcohol and a β-
hydroxyalkylamide by reductive cleavage with aluminum hydride.   The
procedure can then be repeated with the residual peptide (44).

$$\underset{\quad\quad\underset{R'}{|}\quad\quad\underset{R''}{|}}{RCONHCHCONHCHCOOC_2H_5} \xrightarrow{AlH_3} \underset{\quad\quad\underset{R'}{|}\quad\quad\underset{R''}{|}}{RCONHCHCONHCHCH_2OH} \quad (10\text{-}64)$$

$$\downarrow POCl_3$$

$$\underset{\underset{R'}{|}}{RCONHCHCH_2OH} + \underset{\underset{R''}{|}}{HOCH_2CHNH_2} \xleftarrow{AlH_3} \underset{\quad\quad\underset{R'}{|}\quad\quad\underset{R''}{|}}{RCONHCHCOOCH_2CHNH_2 \cdot HCl} \quad (10\text{-}65)$$

10.1.3   Reductions with Magnesium Aluminum Hydride

An ethereal solution of magnesium aluminum hydride reduces acetamide
to ethylamine (70).

10.1.4   Reactions with Sodium Borohydride

Sodium borohydride has been utilized in the reduction of other functional groups in compounds containing amide groups.   Thus, the ketone
group in DL-N-[2-hydroxy-1-(2-thenoyl)ethyl]acetamide (C) and dichloro-
acetamide is reduced with sodium borohydride in methanol while the
amide group is retained (71).

$$\underset{C}{\underset{S}{\left[\,\right]}\underset{COCHNHCOR}{\overset{CH_2OH}{|}}} \xrightarrow{NaBH_4} \underset{S}{\left[\,\right]}\underset{CH}{\overset{OH}{|}}-\underset{}{\overset{CH_2OH}{|}}{CHNHCOR} \quad (10\text{-}66)$$

In a similar manner, α-acylamido-β-hydroxy-p-nitropropiophenones (CI)
have been reduced with sodium borohydride in ethanol to 1-p-nitrophenyl-
2-acylamido-1,3-propanediols (72).

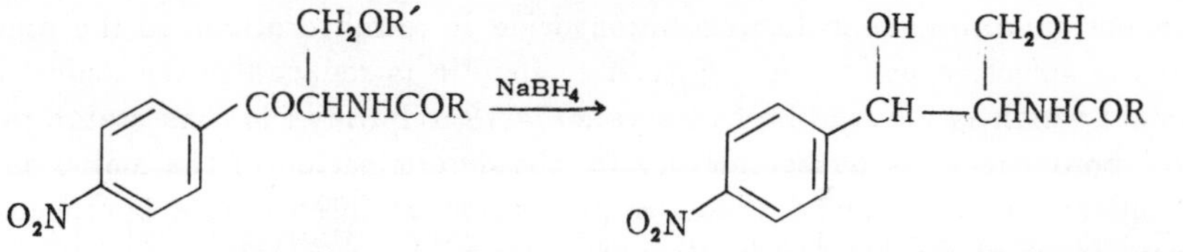

(10-67)

R = CH$_3$, Cl$_2$CH, C$_6$H$_5$, CH$_3$C$_6$H$_4$(p), CH$_3$OC$_6$H$_4$(m), BrC$_6$H$_4$(p),
CH$_3$OCH$_2$, C$_6$H$_5$CH$_2$
R' = H, CH$_3$CO, Cl$_2$CHCO

The amide group in peptide derivatives (CII) is unattacked while an acid chloride group is reduced to an alcohol with sodium borohydride (73,74).

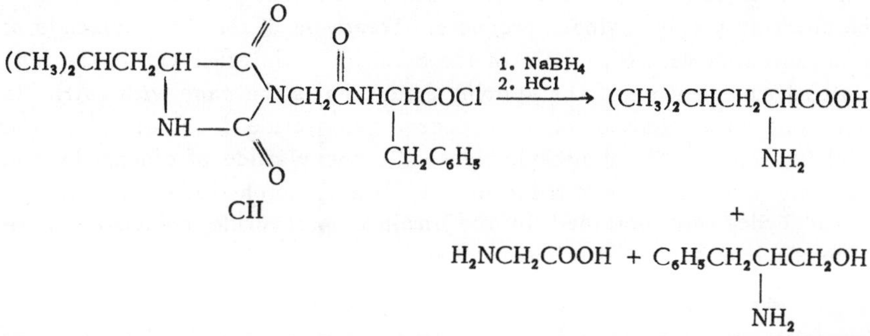

(10-68)

Treatment of 10-formylpteroylglutamic acid, which contains an N-formyl as well as a monosubstituted amide grouping, with sodium borohydride is reported to yield a "product with increased biological activity" although the nature of the product has not been determined (75).

10.1.5 Reactions with Potassium Borohydride

The amide group is resistant to attack by potassium borohydride. Reduction of the acylamido compound CI, where R = Cl$_2$CH and R' = H, with potassium borohydride in aqueous methanol proceeds as indicated in equation (10-67) (72). The reduction of several quaternary pyridinium salts based on nicotinamide with potassium borohydride results in the retention of the amide grouping (76).

10.1.6 Reductions with Lithium Borohydride

The non-reduction of amides with lithium borohydride has been utilized in the reduction of peptide esters. As discussed in Section 10.1.1.c.3, LAH has served in the characterization of various proteins, including insulin. Chibnall and Rees have applied an analogous technique involving reduction with excess lithium borohydride in tetrahydrofuran to the study of the structure of insulin. Esterified insulin is reduced to the amide alcohol which is cleaved by hydrolysis (77,78). Bailey (44) has stated that the borohydride is unsatisfactory for the determination of the amino acid sequence in peptides due to the production of intermediate boron compounds which are not easily cleaved under mild conditions.

Although lithium hydride used in conjunction with a little lithium borohydride as a carrier is an effective hydrogenolysis agent for tosylates and halides, N,N-dialkylamides are unaffected by the reagent in refluxing tetrahydrofuran (79).

Lithium borohydride has been examined as a potential reagent for the reduction of conjugated unsaturated amides to aldehydes (6). Analogous to the behavior of LAH, the attempted reduction of the dimethylamide and the N-methylanilide of cinnamic acid to cinnamaldehyde with lithium borohydride yields resinous products. Treatment of the diphenylamide of cinnamic acid with 0.25 mole of the borohydride in ether yields the high melting modification of the starting amide, as is the case with LAH. In contrast to the behavior of LAH, excess borohydride does not reduce the diphenylamide. The dimethylamide and diphenylamide of cinnamalacetic acid are also resistant to reduction with lithium borohydride.

Aldehydes are obtained in the lithium borohydride reduction of N-cinnamoylcarbazole, N-cinnamalacetylcarbazole and N-(9-phenylnonatetraenoyl)carbazole although the yields obtained with LAH are superior.

Carbazole derivative	% Aldehyde	
	With LiBH₄	With LiAlH₄
N-cinnamoyl-	13	49
N-cinnamalacetyl-	62	73
N-(9-phenylnonatetraenoyl)-	69	81

10.1.7   Reductions with Lithium Gallium Hydride

Reduction of acetamide with the complex gallium hydride in ether solution yields ethylamine (80).

10.2   LACTAMS

10.2.1   Reductions with Lithium Aluminum Hydride

The reduction of lactams with LAH is analogous to that of the open-chain amides, consuming one-half mole of hydride in the reduction of the carbonyl group to a methylene group.

10.2.1.a   *Monocyclic lactams.*   By the usual procedure pyrrolidones (CIII) and piperidones (CIV) have been converted to the corresponding pyrrolidines and piperidines, respectively.

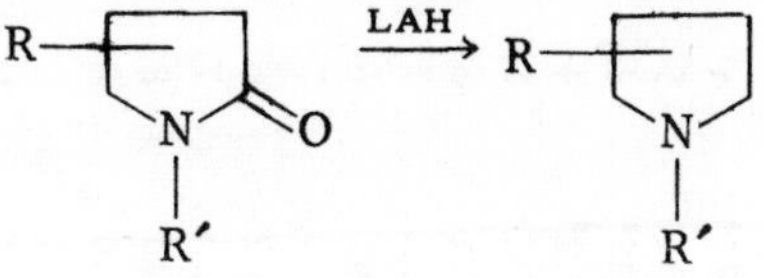

$$R \longrightarrow \boxed{} \xrightarrow{\text{LAH}} R \longrightarrow \boxed{} \qquad (10\text{-}69)$$

CIII

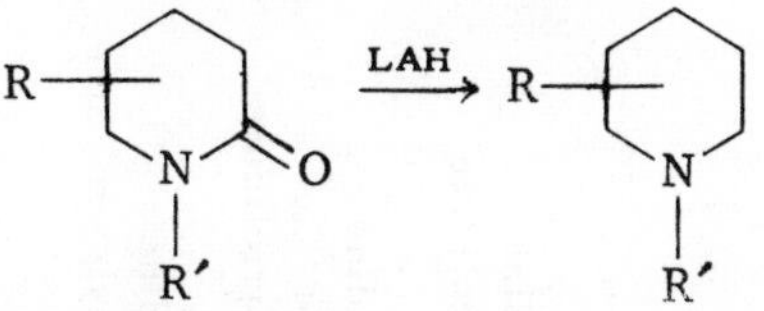

$$R \longrightarrow \boxed{} \xrightarrow{\text{LAH}} R \longrightarrow \boxed{} \qquad (10\text{-}70)$$

CIV

Karrer has reported the reduction of 5-carbethoxy- (81) and 5-methyl-pyrrolidone-2 (82) with LAH in ether. Moffett has shown that while N-β-hydroxyethylpyrrolidones are readily reduced with LAH in ether (83), in the case of 5-ethyl-, 5,5-dimethyl-, 3,5,5-trimethyl-, and 4,5,5-trimethyl-pyrrolidone-2 reduction fails under these conditions but proceeds smoothly when boiling tetrahydrofuran is used in place of ether (84).

Reduction of various pyrrolinones (CV) with LAH in ether results in attack at the pseudo imine double bond as well as the lactam and ester groups (85).

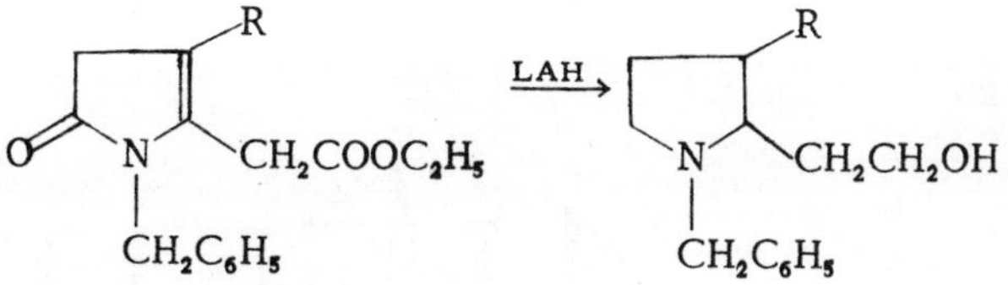

$$(10\text{-}71)$$

CV

The reduction of piperidone as well as various 3,3- and 5,5-disubstituted piperidones has been successfully carried out with LAH (86–88). The attempted selective reduction with LAH of the lactam group in 3-cyano-3-phenyl-1-methylpiperidone-2 (CVI) has given only mixtures of basic products (45).

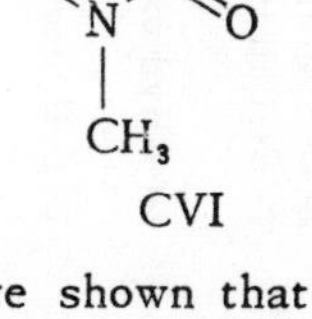

CVI

Galinovsky and Stern have shown that catalytic reduction of simple lactams such as 2-pyrrolidone and 2-piperidone is not feasible because of the slow rate of reaction even in the presence of a large quantity of catalyst (89).

TABLE LIX

LAH Reduction of Pyrrolidones and Piperidones

Lactam	Product	% Yield	Ref.
Pyrrolidones			
C_5H_9NO 5-Methylpyrrolidone-2	2-Methylpyrrolidine	45	1
$C_6H_{11}NO$ 5,5-Dimethylpyrrolidone-2	2,2-Dimethylpyrrolidine	...	2
		79[3]	4
5-Ethylpyrrolidone-2	2-Ethylpyrrolidine	87[3]	4
$C_7H_{11}NO_3$ L-5-Carbethoxypyrrolidone-2	L-2-Hydroxymethylpyrrolidine	31	5
$C_7H_{13}NO$ 3,5,5-Trimethylpyrrolidone-2	2,2,4-Trimethylpyrrolidine	85[3]	4
4,5,5-Trimethylpyrrolidone-2	2,2,3-Trimethylpyrrolidine	60.8[3]	4
$C_7H_{13}NO_2$ 1-(β-Hydroxyethyl)-5-methylpyrrolidone-2	1-(β-Hydroxyethyl)-2-methylpyrrolidine	76	6,7
$C_8H_{15}NO_2$ 1-(β-Hydroxyethyl)-4,5-dimethylpyrrolidone-3	1-(β-Hydroxyethyl)-2,3-dimethylpyrrolidine	89.4	6
		...	7
1-(3-Hydroxypropyl)-5-methylpyrrolidone-2	1-(3-Hydroxypropyl)-2-methylpyrrolidine	91	6
$C_9H_{17}NO_2$ 1-(β-Hydroxyethyl)-3,3,5-trimethylpyrrolidone-2	1-(β-Hydroxyethyl)-2,4,4-trimethylpyrrolidine	88.2	7
		...	6
$C_{15}H_{17}NO_3$ Ethyl 1-benzyl-5-oxo-2-pyrroline-2-acetate	1-Benzyl-2-(β-hydroxyethyl)pyrrolidine	47	8
$C_{16}H_{19}NO_3$ Ethyl 1-benzyl-3-methyl-5-oxo-2-pyrroline-2-acetate	1-Benzyl-2-(β-hydroxyethyl)-3-methylpyrrolidine	59	8
$C_{17}H_{17}NO$ 1-Methyl-3,3-diphenylpyrrolidone-2	1-Methyl-3,3-diphenylpyrrolidine	46	9
$C_{17}H_{21}NO_4$ Ethyl 1-benzyl-3-methoxymethyl-5-oxo-2-pyrroline-2-acetate	1-Benzyl-2-(β-hydroxyethyl)-3-methoxymethyl-pyrrolidine	41	8
Ethyl 1-benzyl-4-methoxymethyl-5-oxo-2-pyrroline-2-acetate	1-Benzyl-2-(β-hydroxyethyl)-4-methoxymethyl-pyrrolidine	73	8
Piperidones			
C_5H_9NO α-Piperidone	Piperidine	50 }	11
	Isopelletierine[10]	4 }	

$C_{11}H_{19}NO_2$	2-Methyl-9-oxy-2-azaspiro[5.5]hendecanone	2-Methyl-2-azaspiro[5.5]hendecan-9-ol	...	12
$C_{17}H_{26}N_2O$	5-Phenyl-5-(β-diethylaminoethyl)piperidone-2	3-Phenyl-3-(β-diethylaminoethyl)piperidine	...	13
$C_{20}H_{37}NO_3$	3-Dodecyl-3-carbethoxypiperidone-2	3-Dodecyl-3-hydroxymethylpiperidine	55	14

[1] P. Karrer and K. Ehrhardt, *Helv. Chim. Acta*, 34, 2202 (1951).

[2] R. B. Moffett and J. H. Hunter, *Abstracts of Papers*, XIIth International Congress of Pure and Applied Chemistry, September 1951, New York, p. 321.

[3] Reduction carried out in tetrahydrofuran.

[4] R. B. Moffett and J. L. White, *J. Org. Chem.*, 17, 407 (1952).

[5] P. Karrer and P. Portmann, *Helv. Chim. Acta*, 31, 2088 (1948).

[6] R. B. Moffett, *J. Org. Chem.*, 14, 862 (1949).

[7] W. B. Reid, Jr., U. S. Pat. 2,605,266 (July 29, 1952).

[8] B. R. Baker, R. E. Schaub, and J. H. Williams, *J. Org. Chem.*, 17, 116 (1952).

[9] A. L. Morrison, R. F. Long, and M. Königstein, *J. Chem. Soc.*, 1951, 952.

[10] One-half mole LAH per mole of α-piperidone; isopelletierine formed by reaction with acetone dicarboxylic acid.

[11] F. Galinovsky, A. Wagner, and R. Weiser, *Monatsh.*, 82, 55 (1951).

[12] N. F. Albertson, *J. Am. Chem. Soc.*, 74, 249 (1952).

[13] E. Tagmann, E. Sury, and K. Hoffmann, *Helv. Chim. Acta*, 35, 1235 (1952).

[14] D. E. Ames and R. E. Bowman, *J. Chem. Soc.*, 1952, 1057.

The reaction of 1-methylpiperidone-2 (CVII) with methylmagnesium bromide yields 1,2,2-trimethylpiperidine, analogous to the LAH reduction product, and 1,2-dimethyl-Δ^2-piperidine (90).

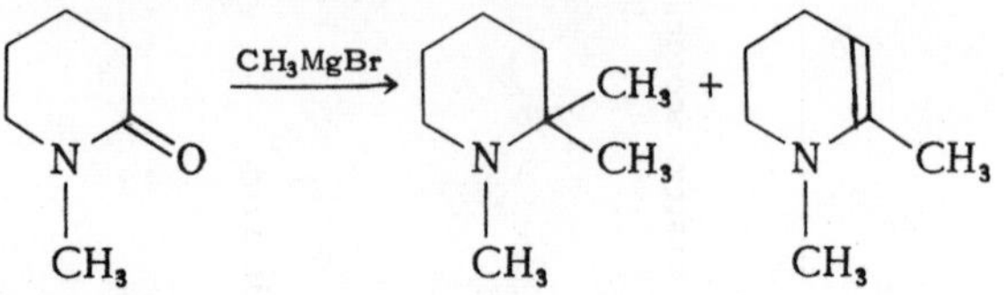

(10-72)

CVII

The LAH reduction of pyrrolidones, pyrrolines, and piperidones is summarized in Table LIX.

Lukeš, Málek, and Dobáš have compared the action of the Grignard reagent and that of LAH on various monocyclic lactams. 1-Methyl-1-azacycloheptan-2-one (CVIII) is reduced by LAH to 1-methylhexamethylenimine (90,91).

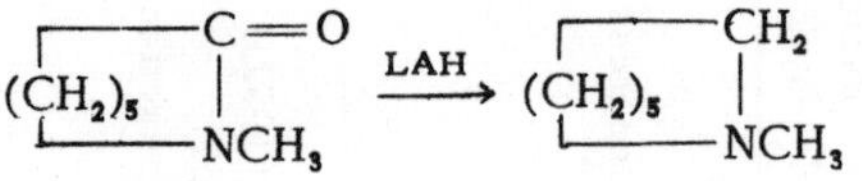

(10-73)

CVIII

The action of methylmagnesium bromide on CVIII yields the analogous 1,2,2-trimethylhexamethylenimine (CIX) and 1-methylamino-6-heptanone (92).

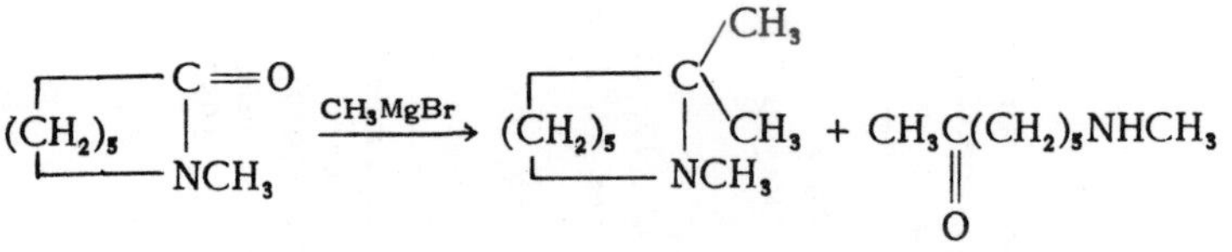

CVIII   CIX   (10-74)

Similarly the action of LAH on 1-methyl-1-azacyclooctan-2-one and 1-methyl-1-azacyclononan-2-one yields the corresponding polymethylenimine. Reaction with the methyl, ethyl, propyl and butyl Grignard reagents yields the tertiary amine and the open-chain ketone. Reaction with phenylmagnesium bromide yields only the open-chain ketone (90,91). The products from the Grignard reactions are accompanied by a long chain non-distillable material postulated as CX.

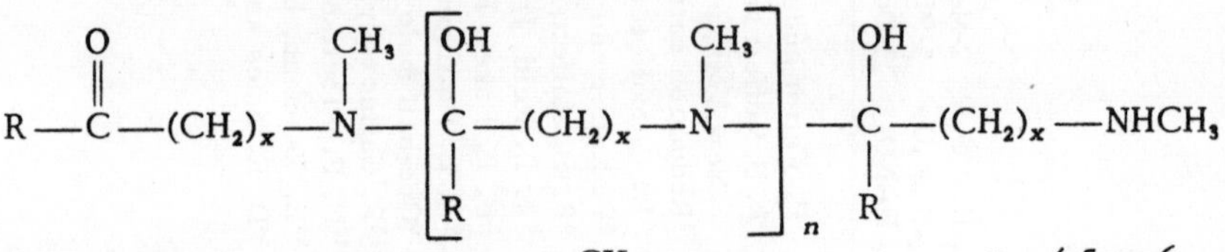

CX $x = 4, 5$ or 6

TABLE LX

LAH Reduction of Monocyclic Lactams to Polymethylenimines

	Lactam	Product	% Yield	Ref.
$C_6H_{11}NO$	1-Azacycloheptan-2-one	Hexamethylenimine	...[1]	2
$C_7H_{13}NO$	1-Methyl-1-azacycloheptan-2-one	1-Methylhexamethylenimine	82	3,4
	7-Methyl-1-azacycloheptan-2-one	2-Methylhexamethylenimine	44[5]	6
	1-Azacyclooctan-2-one	Heptamethylenimine	...[1]	2
$C_8H_{15}NO$	1-Methyl-1-azacyclooctan-2-one	1-Methylheptamethylenimine	88	3,4
	1-Azacyclononan-2-one	Octamethylenimine	...[1]	2
$C_9H_{17}NO$	1-Methyl-1-azacyclononan-2-one	1-Methyloctamethylenimine	89	3,4
	1-Azacyclodecan-2-one	Nonamethylenimine	...[1]	7
$C_{10}H_{19}NO$	1-Azacycloundecan-2-one	Decamethylenimine	...[1]	2
$C_{11}H_{21}NO$	1-Azacyclododecan-2-one	Undecamethylenimine	...[1]	2
$C_{12}H_{23}NO$	1-Azacyclotridecan-2-one	Dodecamethylenimine	...[1]	2
$C_{13}H_{25}NO$	1-Azacyclotetradecan-2-one	Tridecamethylenimine	...[1]	2
$C_{14}H_{27}NO$	1-Azacyclopentadecan-2-one	Tetradecamethylenimine	...[1]	2
$C_{15}H_{29}NO$	1-Azacyclohexadecan-2-one	Pentadecamethylenimine	...[1]	2
$C_{16}H_{31}NO$	1-Azacycloheptadecan-2-one	Hexadecamethylenimine	...[1]	2
$C_{17}H_{33}NO$	1-Azacyclooctadecan-2-one	Heptadecamethylenimine	...[1]	2
$C_{18}H_{35}NO$	1-Azacyclononadecan-2-one	Octadecamethylenimine	...[1]	2
$C_{19}H_{37}NO$	1-Azacycloeicosan-2-one	Nonadecamethylenimine	...[1]	2
$C_{20}H_{39}NO$	1-Azacycloheneicosan-2-one	Eicosamethylenimine	...[1]	2

[1] Reaction carried out in ether or tetrahydrofuran, 60–95% yield.
[2] L. Ruzicka, M. Kobelt, O. Häfliger, and V. Prelog, *Helv. Chim. Acta*, 32, 544 (1949).
[3] R. Lukeš and J. Málek, *Chem. Listy*, 45, 72 (1951).
[4] R. Lukeš and J. Málek, *Collection Czech. Chem. Commun.*, 16, 23 (1951).
[5] Isolated as hydrochloride.
[6] G. R. Clemo, R. Raper, and H. J. Vipond, *J. Chem. Soc.*, 1949, 2095.
[7] N. J. Leonard, S. Swann, Jr., and J. Figueras, Jr., *J. Am. Chem. Soc.*, 74, 4620 (1952).

The LAH reduction of various monocyclic lactams to polymethylenimines is summarized in Table LX.

Various monocyclic lactams containing more than one hetero atom have been subjected to treatment with LAH. Thus, the LAH reduction of 1,2-dimethyl-3-ketopiperazine(CXI) yields the expected 1,2-dimethylpiperazine (93).

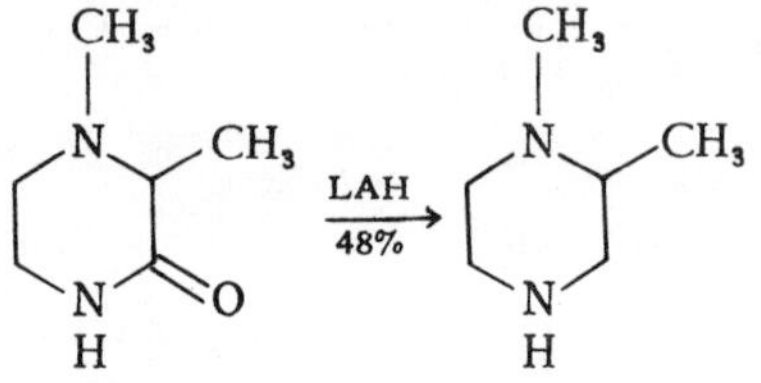

$$\text{(10-75)}$$

CXI

Karrer and Krishna (94) have reported that the LAH reduction of aneurinthiazolone (CXII) in a mixture of N-ethylmorpholine and tetrahydrofuran gives dihydroaneurin (CXIII).

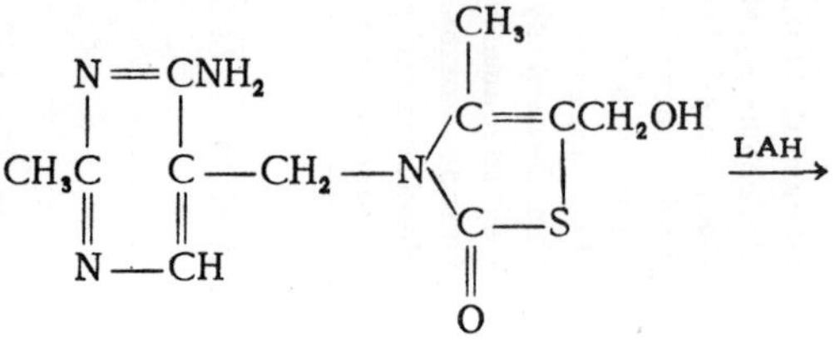

CXII

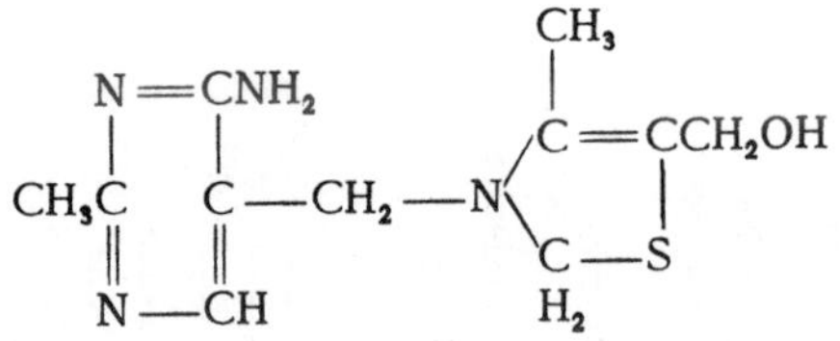

$$\text{(10-76)}$$

CXIII

The reduction of 3-keto-4-methyl-2,2-diphenylmorpholine (CXIV) with excess LAH in ether gives a mixture containing a 32% yield of the carbinol-amine (CXV) and 39% of 4-methyl-2,2-diphenylmorpholine (CXVI).

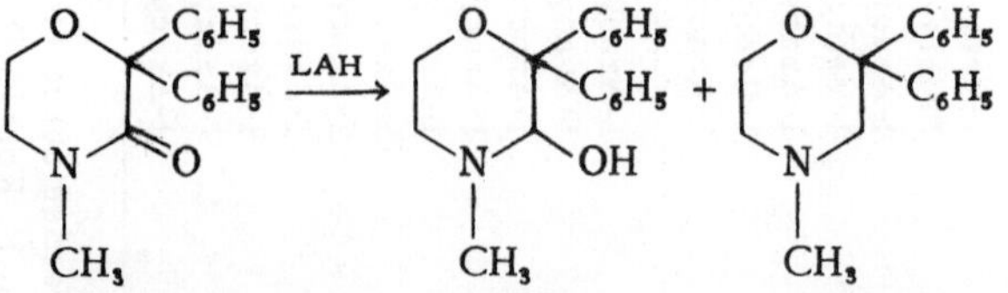

$$\text{(10-77)}$$

CXIV   CXV   CXVI

The further action of LAH on the carbinol-amine (CXV) yields 88% of CXVI (52). The carbinol-amine appears to be an intermediate in the reduction of an amide group to the oxygen-free compound.

Reduction of 1,3-diphenylazetidinone (CXVII) with LAH in tetrahydro-furan results in cleavage to yield 3-anilino-3-phenyl-1-propanol. The same amino alcohol is formed in ether solution (95).

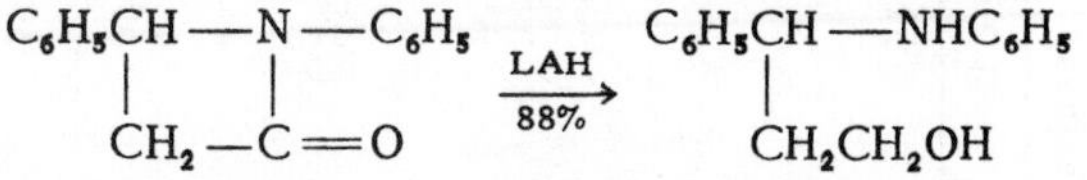

$$C_6H_5CH-N-C_6H_5 \quad \xrightarrow[88\%]{LAH} \quad C_6H_5CH-NHC_6H_5 \qquad (10\text{-}78)$$

with $CH_2-C=O$ below the left structure (CXVII) and CH_2CH_2OH below the right structure.

CXVII

This cleavage is analogous to the reductive decomposition discussed in Section 10.1.1.d.2.

10.2.1.b *Polycyclic lactams.* The LAH reduction of polycyclic lac-tams in which the lactamic nitrogen is not located at a bridgehead yields the corresponding cyclic amine without undue difficulty. Thus, deriva-tives of dihydrocarbostyril (CXVIII) yield the corresponding derivatives of tetrahydroquinoline while isodihydrocarbostyril (CXIX) is reduced to tetrahydroisoquinoline.

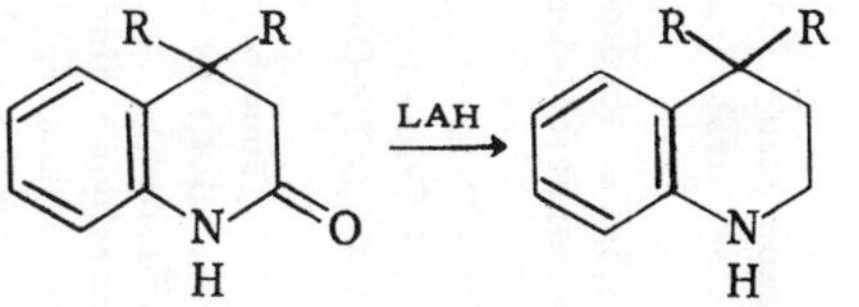

(10-79)

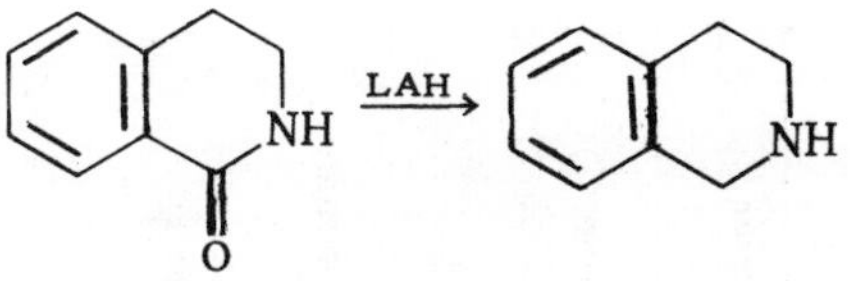

CXVIII

(10-80)

CXIX

The reduction of compounds in this category including diketopiperazines and those which lead to products related to yohimbine and morphine is summarized in Table LXI.

The product of the LAH reduction of oxindoles is dependent upon the substituents in the 1- and 3-positions. Julian and Printy reported that practically no reduction occurs with oxindole (CXX) even when the reac-tion is carried out at elevated temperatures in dibutyl ether, dioxane or tetrahydrofuran (96). However, Smith and Yu have successfully reduced oxindole to indoline (97).

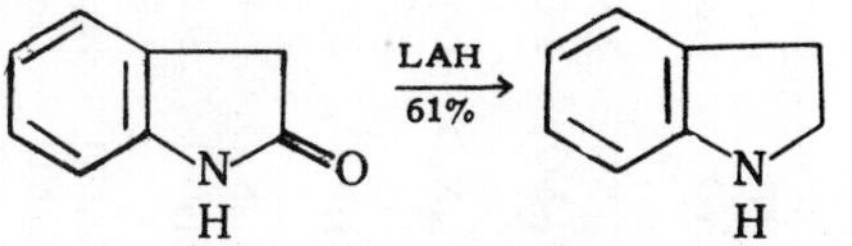

(10-81)

CXX

TABLE LXI

LAH Reduction of Polycyclic Lactams with Non-Bridgehead Lactamic Nitrogen (Except Oxindole Derivatives)

	Lactam	Product	% Yield	Ref.
C$_8$H$_{13}$NO	cis-(3-Aminocyclohexyl)acetic acid lactam	2-Azabicyclo[3.3.1]nonane	51	1
C$_9$H$_9$NO	Isodihydrocarbostyril	1,2,3,4-Tetrahydroisoquinoline	...	2-4
				5
C$_{10}$H$_{11}$NO	2,3,4,5-Tetrahydro-3,1H-benzazepin-2-one (I)	2,3,4,5-Tetrahydro-3,1H-benzazepine	...[6]	7
C$_{11}$H$_{17}$NO$_3$	1-Carboxymethyl-5-methyl-2-azabicyclo[3.3.1]nonan-3-one	1-Hydroxyethyl-5-methyl-2-azabicyclo[3.3.1]nonane	...	8
C$_{11}$H$_{18}$N$_2$O$_2$	L-Leucyl-L-proline lactam (II)	L,L-1,2-Trimethylene-5-isobutylpiperazine	...	9
	L-Leucyl-D-proline lactam	L,D-1,2-Trimethylene-5-isobutylpiperazine	...	9
C$_{12}$H$_{12}$N$_2$O$_2$	2,7-Dioxo-1,2,3,4,5,6,7,8-octahydro-p-phenanthroline (III)	1,2,3,4,5,6,7,8-Octahydro-p-phenanthroline	90	5
C$_{14}$H$_{16}$N$_2$O$_2$	L-Phenylalanyl-D-proline lactam	L,D-1,2-Trimethylene-5-benzylpiperazine	...	9
C$_{14}$H$_{17}$NO	Spiro(cyclohexane-1,4'-dihydrocarbostyril)	Spiro(cyclohexane-1,4'-1',2',3',4'-tetrahydroquinoline)	96[10]	11
C$_{16}$H$_{15}$NO	lactam, m.p. 202° (IV)	polymethylenimine, m.p. 148°	...	12
C$_{16}$H$_{19}$NO	lactam, m.p. 208-209° (V)	N-Methylisomorphinane	...	14
C$_{17}$H$_{17}$NO	4-Benzyl-4-methyldihydrocarbostyril	4-Benzyl-4-methyl-1,2,3,4-tetrahydroquinoline	65[10]	15
C$_{18}$H$_{23}$NO$_3$	lactam, m.p. 210-212.5° (VI)	dl-β-Δ^6-Dihydrodesoxycodeine methyl ether	...	16
C$_{20}$H$_{18}$N$_2$O$_2$	1-Methyl-3-[2-N-(1-oxo-1,2-dihydroisoquinolyl)-ethyl]oxindole (VII)	oxygen-free base, m.p. 132-135° (VIII)	30[17]	18

CHART TO TABLE LXI

604 REDUCTION OF CARBOXYLIC ACID DERIVATIVES 10.2

References—Table LXI

[1]D. Ginsburg, *J. Org. Chem.*, 15, 1003 (1950).
[2]Ciba S. A., Fr. Pat. 987,158 (August 9, 1951).
[3]Ciba Akt., Swiss Pat. 273,953 (June 1, 1951).
[4]E. Schlittler and A. Uffer, Ger. Pat. 824,491 (December 13, 1951).
[5]P. A. S. Smith and Tung-yin Yu, *J. Am. Chem. Soc.*, 74, 1096 (1952).
[6]Reduction carried out in dioxane.
[7]J. O. Halford and B. Weissmann, *J. Org. Chem.*, 17, 1646 (1952).
[8]M. W. Cronyn and G. H. Riesser, *Abstracts of Papers*, 121st Meeting American Chemical Society, Milwaukee, Wis., April 1952, p. 87K.
[9]A. Stoll, A. Hofmann and T. Petrzilka, *Helv. Chim. Acta*, 34, 1544 (1951).
[10]Reduction carried out in benzene-ether mixture.
[11]L. H. Schwartzman, *J. Org. Chem.*, 15, 517 (1950).
[12]A. J. Manson, Z. Valenta, and K. Wiesner, *Chemistry and Industry*, 1952, 805.
[13]Isolated after methylation of the oxygen-free base with formaldehyde and formic acid.
[14]M. Gates, R. B. Woodward, W. F. Newhall, and R. Künzli, *J. Am. Chem. Soc.*, 72, 1141 (1950).
[15]R. C. Fuson, H. L. Jackson, and E. W. Grieshaber, *J. Org. Chem.*, 16, 1529 (1951).
[16]M. Gates and G. Tschudi, *J. Am. Chem. Soc.*, 72, 4839 (1950).
[17]Reduction carried out in dioxane-ether mixture.
[18]P. L. Julian and A. Magnani, *J. Am. Chem. Soc.*, 71, 3207 (1949).

The LAH reduction of 1-methyloxindoles containing a hydrogen atom in the 3-position yields a mixture of the corresponding indole and indoline, even with reverse addition of LAH to excess oxindole. Thus, 1-methyloxindole (CXXI) is reduced to 1-methylindole (CXXII) and 1-methylindoline (96),

(10-82)

CXXI   CXXII

The formation of the indoline may proceed through the intermediate formation of the indole since 1-methylindole (CXXII) is reduced in 25–30% yield to 1-methylindoline.

(10-83)

CXXII

In contrast, indole itself is not reduced with LAH (96).

The reduction of 1,3-dimethyloxindole (CXXIII) yields 1,3-dimethyl-
indole (CXXIV) and 1,3-dimethylindoline.

CXXIII   CXXIV   (10-84)

Analogous to the reduction of CXXII, CXXIV is reduced by LAH to the
indoline (96). The intermediate formation of the indole is postulated in
the LAH reduction of 1-methyl-3-[2-N-(1,2-dihydroisoquinolyl)ethyl]oxin-
dole (CXXV) (98).

CXXV

CXXVI   (10-85)

The same product is formed in the LAH reduction of CXXVI.
  The reduction of dioxindole (CXXVII, R = H) and 1-methyldioxindole
(CXXVII, R = CH$_3$) yields a mixture of indole and oxindole. Indolines
have not been isolated (96).

CXXVII   (10-86)

The LAH reduction of 3,3-disubstituted oxindoles yields indolines. Thus, 3,3-dimethyloxindole (CXXVIII) is reduced to 3,3-dimethylindoline with LAH in dioxane (99,100).

$$\text{(10-87)}$$

CXXVIII

The LAH reduction of oxindoles has played a major part in the elucidation of the structure of the indole alkaloid gelsemine. LAH reduction of gelsemine in an ether-dioxane mixture results in the reduction of a carbonyl group to a methylene to yield dihydrodesoxogelsemine (99-102). Catalytic hydrogenation of gelsemine over palladium black or platinum yields dihydrogelsemine which is in turn reduced with LAH in dioxane to tetrahydrodesoxogelsemine (99-101).

$$\begin{array}{ccc} \text{gelsemine} & \xrightarrow{\text{LAH}} & \text{dihydrodesoxogelsemine} \\ C_{20}H_{22}N_2O_2 & & C_{20}H_{24}N_2O \end{array} \qquad \text{(10-88)}$$

$$\downarrow H_2\text{:Pd or Pt} \qquad\qquad \downarrow H_2\text{:Pd}$$

$$\begin{array}{ccc} \text{dihydrogelsemine} & \xrightarrow{\text{LAH}} & \text{tetrahydrodesoxogelsemine} \\ C_{20}H_{24}N_2O_2 & & C_{20}H_{26}N_2O \end{array} \qquad \text{(10-89)}$$

Since oxindoles containing a hydrogen atom in the 3-position are converted to indoles by the action of LAH, the reduction of the carbonyl group in gelsemine and dihydrogelsemine to a methylene group was considered by Kates and Marion as indicative of a 3,3-disubstituted oxindole structure, as in equation (10-87). Gibson and Robinson have proposed structure CXXIX for gelsemine (103). Based on further work Goutarel et al. have proposed structure CXXX (104).

CXXIX   CXXX

Goutarel, Janot, Prelog, and Sneeden (104) have carried out the Hofmann degradation of gelsemine methiodide with sodium hydroxide in a high vacuum to yield "des-N-methylgelsemine" formulated as CXXXI. Dihydrogelsemine methiodide similarly yields "des-N-methyldihydrogelsemine" (CXXXII). Reduction of CXXXI and CXXXII with LAH reduces the lactam oxygen to hydrogen to yield the corresponding desoxo-

dihydro derivatives. LAH reduction of the methiodides of the des-bases
CXXXI and CXXXII gives the same products as obtained from the des-bases.

CXXXI   (10-90)

CXXXII   (10-91)

Habgood, Marion, and Schwarz (102) and Prelog, Patrick, and Witkop
(105) have found that the products of the Hofmann degradation of gelsemine methiodide and dihydrogelsemine methiodide are N(a)-methylgelse-
mine derivatives and not des-N-methyl bases. Thus, the "des-N-methyl-
gelsemine" (CXXXI) obtained by the degradation, on LAH reduction gives
a product identical with the N(a)-methyl-desoxodihydrogelsemine (CXXXIV)
obtained on LAH reduction of N(a)-formyldesoxodihydrogelsemine (CXXXIII)
(102).

CXXXIII   CXXXIV   (10-92)

Prelog, Patrick, and Witkop (105) have postulated the following transformation in the course of the pyrolysis:

(10-93)

Therefore, Goutarel *et al.* (104) actually carried out the reduction of N(a)-methylgelsemine (CXXXV) and N(a)-methyldihydrogelsemine instead of the reported des-bases CXXXI and CXXXII. Similarly, the methiodides reduced are derived from CXXXV and the analogous dihydro compound instead of the reported des-bases.

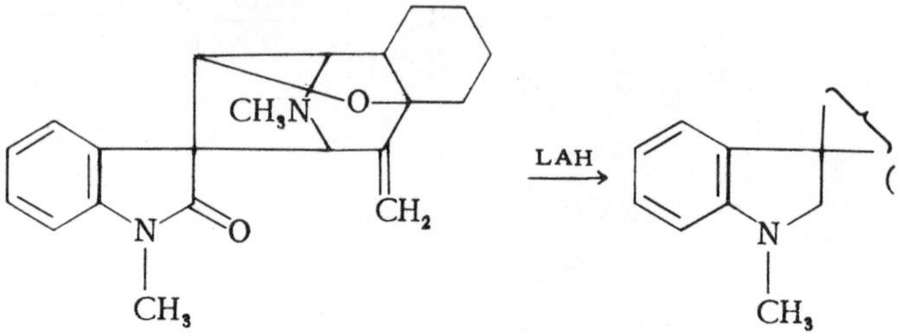

$$(10\text{-}94)$$

CXXXV

Reaction of gelsemine (CXXX) with bromine in a chloroform solution yields bromoallogelsemine hydrobromide (CXXXVI) (101).

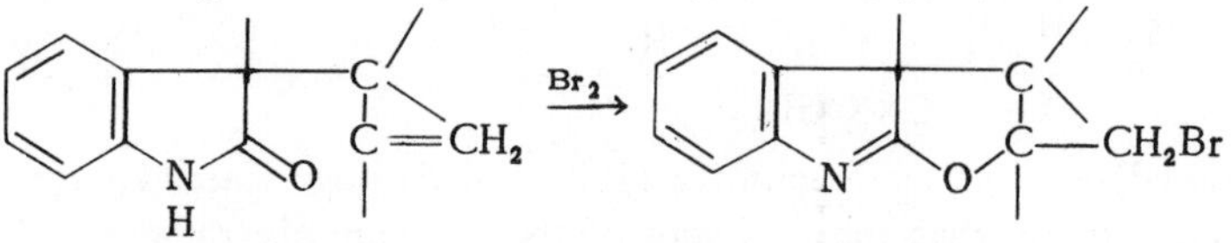

CXXX   CXXXVI   (10-95)

Treatment of CXXXVI with LAH in dioxane gives a compound, $C_{20}H_{26}O_2N_2$, for which the constitution of desoxohydroxytetrahydrogelsemine (CXXXVII) has been advanced. On warming CXXXVI with acid one mole of water is taken up and a compound is formed which is formulated as bromohydroxydihydrogelsemine hydrobromide (CXXXVIII). The reduction of CXXXVI to CXXXVII with LAH is postulated as proceeding through CXXXVIII.

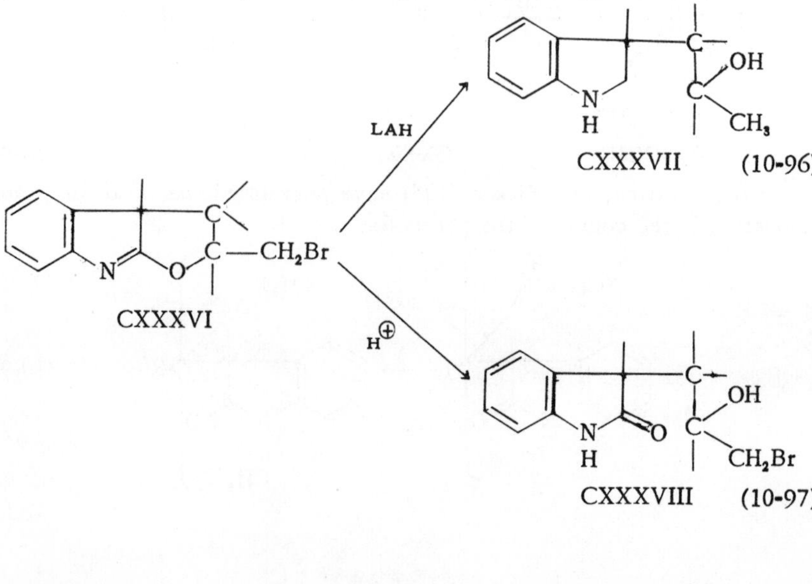

CXXXVII   (10-96)

CXXXVI

CXXXVIII   (10-97)

TABLE LXII

LAH Reduction of Oxindoles

Oxindole	Product	% Yield	Ref.
C$_8$H$_7$NO Oxindole	Indoline	61	1
C$_8$H$_7$NO$_2$ Dioxindole	Oxindole	0 }	2
	Indole	61.7 } 14 }	2
C$_8$H$_{13}$NO Hexahydrooxindole	cis-Octahydroindole	69	3
C$_9$H$_9$NO 1-Methyloxindole[4]	1-Methylindole	61.8 } 12 }	2
	1-Methylindoline		
C$_9$H$_9$NO$_2$ 1-Methyldioxindole	1-Methyloxindole	17 }	2
	1-Methylindole	46.7 }	
C$_{10}$H$_9$NO$_3$ 7-Methoxy-1-methylisatin	See text	....	5
C$_{10}$H$_{11}$NO 3,3-Dimethyloxindole[4]	3,3-Dimethylindoline	82[6]	7,8
1,3-Dimethyloxindole[4]	1,3-Dimethyloxindole	85.8 }	2
	1,3-Dimethylindoline	13 }	
C$_{10}$H$_{11}$NO$_2$ 4-Methoxy-1-methyloxindole[4]	4-Methoxy-1-methylindole	66 }	5
	4-Methoxy-1-methylindoline	16 }	
5-Methoxy-1-methyloxindole[4]	5-Methoxy-1-methylindole	40	9
	5-Methoxy-1-methylindoline	"small quantity"	
7-Methoxy-1-methyloxindole[4]	7-Methoxy-1-methylindole	... }	5
	7-Methoxy-1-methylindoline	... }	
C$_{11}$H$_{13}$NO$_2$ 5-Ethoxy-1-methyloxindole[4]	5-Ethoxy-1-methylindole	60 }	2
	5-Ethoxy-1-methylindoline	6 }	
C$_{14}$H$_{18}$N$_2$O$_2$ 3-Spiro(N-methylpiperidine-4)-1-methyloxindole	3-Spiro(N-methylpiperidine-4)-1-methylindoline	95[10]	11
C$_{16}$H$_{22}$N$_2$O$_2$ 5-Ethoxy-3-spiro-(N-methylpiperidine-4)-1-methyloxindole	5-Ethoxy-3-spiro(N-methylpiperidine-4)-1-methylindoline	76[10,12]	11
C$_{20}$H$_{18}$N$_2$O$_2$ 1-Methyl-3-[2-(1-oxo-1,2-dihydroisoquinolyl)ethyl]oxindole[4]	Oxygen-free base, m.p. 132–135° [13]	30[6]	14
C$_{20}$H$_{20}$N$_2$O 1-Methyl-3-[2-(1,2-dihydroisoquinolyl)ethyl]oxindole[4]	Oxygen-free base, m.p. 132–135° [13]	70[6]	14
Gelsemine and its degradation products	See text		

References—Table LXII

[1]P. A. S. Smith and Tung-yin Yu, *J. Am. Chem. Soc.,* 74, 1096 (1952).
[2]P. L. Julian and H. C. Printy, *ibid.,* 71, 3206 (1949).
[3]E. D. Clair, F. H. Clarke, W. A. Edmiston, and K. Wiesner, *Can. J. Research,* 28B, 745 (1950).
[4]Inverse addition.
[5]J. W. Cook, J. D. Loudon, and P. McCloskey, *J. Chem. Soc.,* 1952, 3904.
[6]Reduction carried out in dioxane-ether mixture.
[7]M. Kates and L. Marion, *J. Am. Chem. Soc.,* 72, 2308 (1950).
[8]M. Kates and L. Marion, *Can. J. Chem.,* 29, 37 (1951).
[9]J. W. Cook, J. D. Loudon, and P. McCloskey, *J. Chem. Soc.,* 1951, 1203.
[10]Reduction carried out in tetrahydrofuran-ether mixture.
[11]E. Kretz, J. M. Müller, and E. Schlittler, *Helv. Chim. Acta,* 35, 520 (1952).
[12]Isolated on dihydrochloride.
[13]See Table LXI.
[14]P. L. Julian and A. Magnani, *J. Am. Chem. Soc.,* 71, 3207 (1949).

The anhydrous medium utilized in LAH reductions should preclude CXXXVIII as an intermediate in the reduction. A more likely explanation involves the reduction of the —N=C—O— grouping to —NH—CH—O—, followed by cleavage of the latter under the influence of LAH, as discussed in Sections 12.16.1.e and 12.17.

The attempted reduction of 7-methoxy-1-methylisatin (CXXXIX) with LAH in ether gives only a small quantity of a steam-volatile indole and an unidentified, non-volatile material (106).

CXXXIX

The LAH reduction of various oxindoles is summarized in Table LXII.

The reduction of naphthostyrils (CXL), containing the oxindole structure, with LAH yields the corresponding benz[cd]indoline (CXLI) (107,108).

$$\text{(10-98)}$$

CXL   CXLI

Grob and Schmid (107) have reported that LAH reduction of 5-hydroxy-naphthostyril (CXLII) gives 5-hydroxybenz[cd]indoline (CXLIII) while reduction with sodium in liquid ammonia results in hydrogenolysis of the hydroxyl group to yield naphthostyril (CXLIV).

Reduction of 5-methoxynaphthostyril (CXLV) follows a similar pattern and in addition reduction with sodium in butanol gives a mixture of 1,3,4,5-tetrahydrobenz[cd]indole and 1-hydroxymethyl-8-amino-1,2,3,4-tetrahydronaphthalene.

Stoll, Petrzilka, and Rutschmann (108) have carried out the LAH reduction, in N-ethylmorpholine, of the naphthostyrils CXLVI and CXLVII in addition to naphthostyril and 4-(1-piperidyl)naphthostyril.

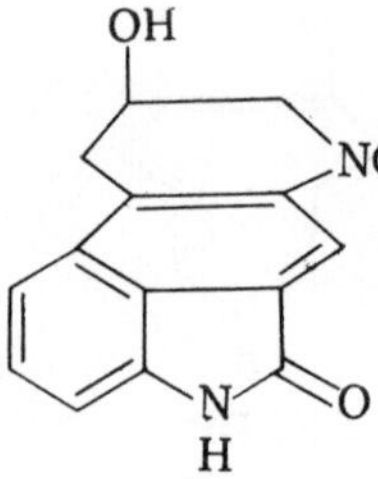

CXLVI 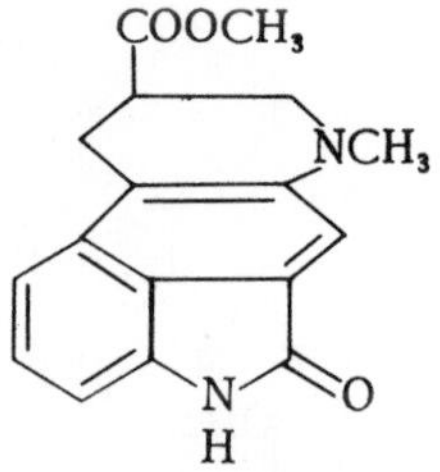   CXLVII

The product in all cases is the corresponding benz[cd]indoline.

de Mayo and Rigby (109) have reported that LAH reduction of phenanthridone (CXLVIII) and 4-methylphenanthridone gives the corresponding phenanthridine (CXLIX) instead of the expected amine.

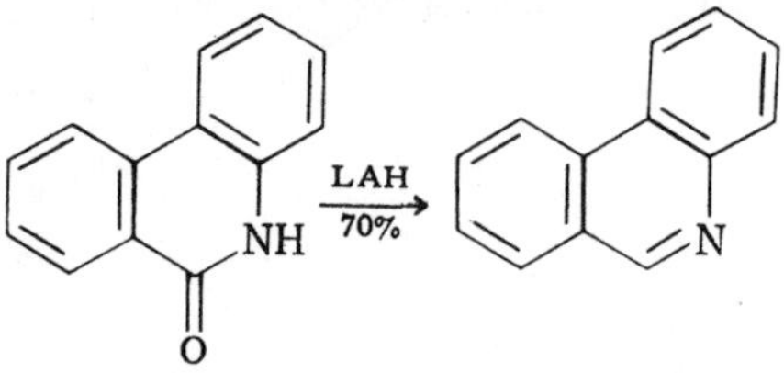

                                                              (10-104)

CXLVIII   CXLIX

Badger, Seidler, and Thomson (110) obtained 5,6-dihydrophenanthridine (CL) on reducing CXLVIII with excess LAH in dioxane.

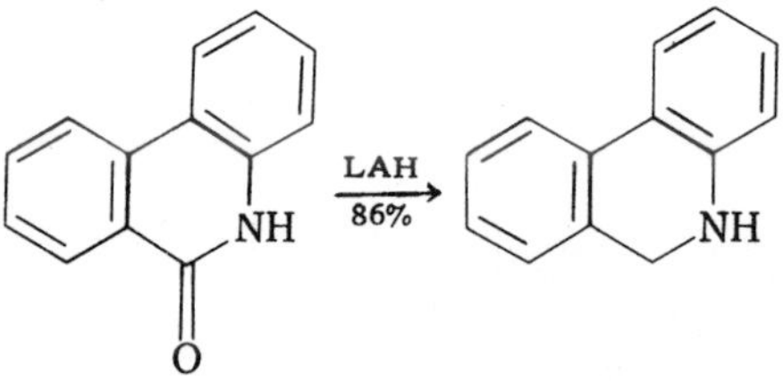

                                                              (10-105)

CXLVIII   CL

The isolation of CXLIX by de Mayo and Rigby is evidently due to the use of the theoretical quantity of LAH since Wooten and McKee (111) have found that CXLIX is reduced to CL with LAH in ether.

de Mayo and Rigby (109) reported that LAH reduction of N-methylphenanthridone (CLI) gives a 60% yield of phenanthridine methiodide (CLII).

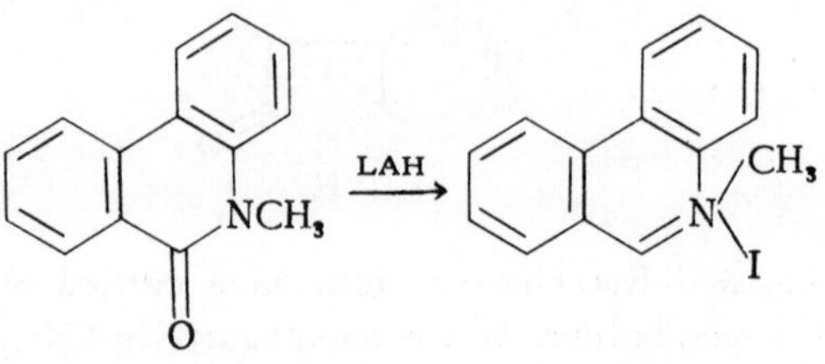

                                                              (10-106)

CLI   CLII

Similarly, N,2-dimethylphenanthridone, N-methylquinoline, and N-methyl-pyridone give the corresponding quaternary ammonium salt. Karrer *et al.* (112) reported that the LAH reduction of N-methylphenanthridone (CLI) or the methiodide (CLII) gives 5-methyl-5,6-dihydrophenanthridine.

Garryine, an alkaloid isolated from the bark of *Garrya veatchii* Kellogg, on oxidation with potassium permanganate gives oxygarryine, $C_{22}H_{33}NO_5$, for which the partial structure CLIII has been advanced (51). LAH reduction of CLIII yields dihydroveatchine, $C_{22}H_{35}NO_2$, associated with reduction of a lactam to a cyclic amine (113).

CH₂CH₂OH

CLIII

Pithecolobine, $C_{22}H_{46}N_4O_2$, an alkaloid from the bark of *Pithecolobium saman* Benth, contains a lactam group which is reduced to methylene to yield desoxypithecolobine, $C_{22}H_{48}N_4$. In the course of the LAH reduction a hydroxyl group which is present in pithecolobine is eliminated (114). In the absence of information relative to the structure of the alkaloid it is not possible to account for the latter reaction.

Lycoctonine, $C_{25}H_{39-41}NO_7$, an alkaloid of unknown structure, on oxidation with neutral potassium permanganate in acetone containing acetic acid yields two neutral products, lycoctonam, isolated as the monoacetate, $C_{27}H_{39-41}NO_9$, m.p. 189°, and des(oxymethylene)lycoctonam, $C_{24}H_{35-37}NO_7$, m.p. 188°, and an acid fraction lycoctonamic acid, $C_{25}H_{35-37}NO_9$, m.p. 204°. Although lycoctonine contains an amino group, all three oxidation products contain a lactam grouping. Oxidation of lycoctonam with permanganate yields lycoctonamic acid while the latter is decarboxylated on heating to 205° to yield des(oxymethylene)lycoctonam. Reduction of lycoctonam monoacetate with LAH in an ether-dioxane mixture yields 83% of lycoctonine while reduction of the methyl ester of lycoctonamic acid, $C_{26}H_{37-39}NO_9$, m.p. 167°, under the same conditions yields 55% of lycoctonine. Reduction of des(oxymethylene)lycoctonam with LAH in the ether-dioxane mixture gives 96% of des(oxymethylene)lycoctonine (115).

The LAH reduction of lactams with bridgehead lactamic nitrogen yields the expected cyclic amine. However, in most cases, the reaction proceeds with somewhat more difficulty than with compounds without bridgehead nitrogen. This type of reduction has been applied with considerable success in the synthesis and elucidation of alkaloid structures as summarized in Table LXIII.

Edwards and Marion (116) and Swan (117) have carried out the LAH reduction of 3,4-dihydro-6-keto-7,8-benzindolo(2′,3′,1,2)pyridocoline (CLIV) to yield the expected cyclic amine (CLV).

TABLE LXIII

LAH Reduction of Lactams with Bridgehead Lactamic Nitrogen

	Lactam	No.	Product	% Yield	Ref.
$C_8H_{13}NO$	3-Ketooctahydropyrrocoline	I	Octahydropyrrocoline	76	1
$C_{11}H_{18}N_2O_2$	L-Leucyl-L-proline lactam	II	L,L-1,2-Trimethylene-5-isobutylpiperazine	...	2
	L-Leucyl-D-proline lactam	II	L,D-1,2-Trimethylene-5-isobutylpiperazine	...	2
$C_{12}H_{13}NO$	3-Oxojulolidine	III	Julolidine	97	3
$C_{14}H_{16}N_2O_2$	L-Phenylalanyl-D-proline lactam	III	L,D-1,2-Trimethylene-5-benzylpiperazine	...	2
$C_{15}H_{22}N_2O_2$	Dilactam A, m.p. 262–263°	IV	ψ-Sparteine A	86[4]	5
	Dilactam B, m.p. 161–162°	IV	ψ-Sparteine B	98[4]	5
$C_{15}H_{23}NO_3$	1,3-Dicarbethoxy-4-quinolizidone	V	1,3-Di-(hydroxymethyl)quinolizine	92	6
$C_{15}H_{24}N_2O$	d-α-Isolupanine	VI	l-α-Isosparteine	14	7
	(−)-Oxysparteine	VII	(−)-Sparteine	37	8,9
$C_{19}H_{14}N_2O$	3,4-Dihydro-6-keto-7,8-benzindolo(2′,3′,1,2)-pyridocoline	VIII	3,4-Dihydro-7,8-benzindolo(2′,3′,1,2)-pyridocoline	89[4]	10
				88[11,12]	13
			Product not specified	...	14
$C_{21}H_{22}N_2O$	Strychnine	IX	Strychnidine	91	15
$C_{22}H_{24}N_2O_3$	α-Colubrine	X	α-Colubridine	90	16
	β-Colubrine	XI	β-Colubridine	80	16
$C_{22}H_{26}N_2O_6S$	Strychnine methosulfate		Strychnidine	62[17]	18
$C_{23}H_{32}N_2O_2$	Diketodibenzosparteine	XII	Dibenzo[c,k]sparteine	65	19
$C_{23}H_{26}N_2O_4$	Brucine	XIII	Dehydrobrucidine (XIV)	71	16
$C_{23}H_{28}N_2O_4$	Dihydrobrucine	XV	Dihydrobrucidine	47	16
$C_{30}H_{39}N_5O_5$	Dihydroergosine				2
$C_{31}H_{41}N_5O_5$	Dihydroergocornine		20		2
$C_{32}H_{43}N_5O_5$	Dihydroergocryptine		20		2
$C_{35}H_{41}N_5O_5$	Dihydroergocristine		20		2

CHART TO TABLE LXIII

I

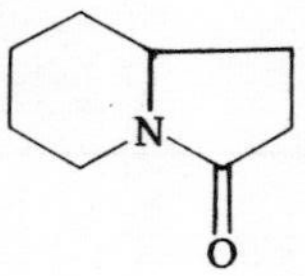

II

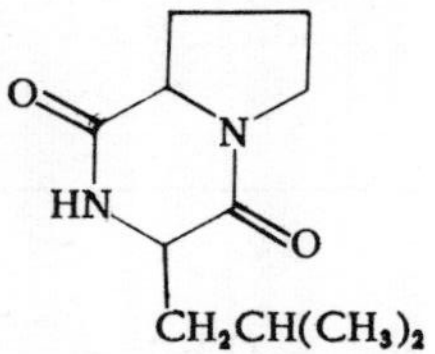

III

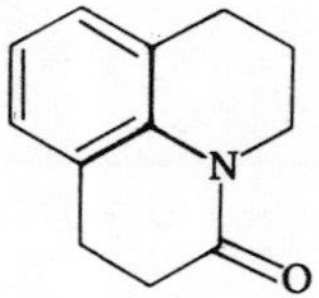

IV

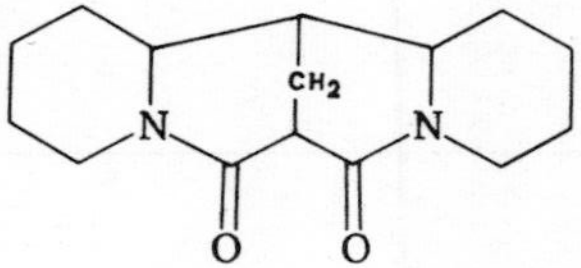

V

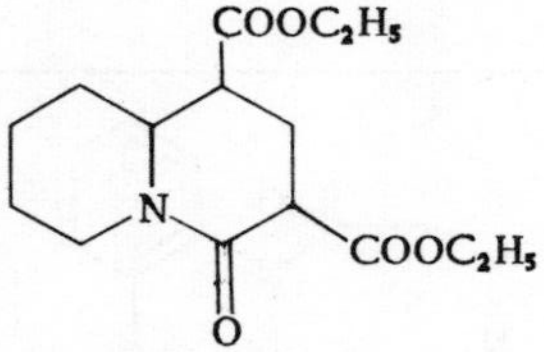

VI

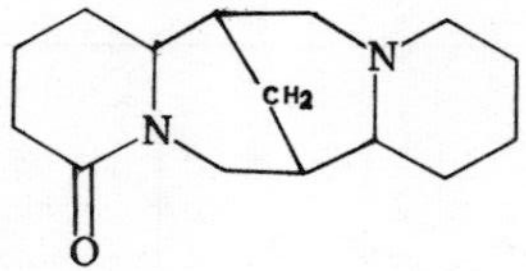

VII

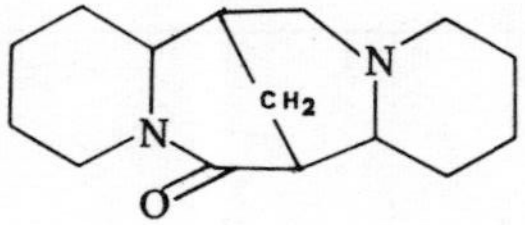

VIII

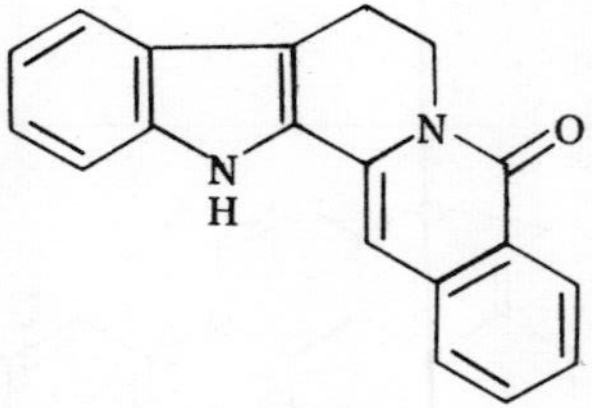

IX

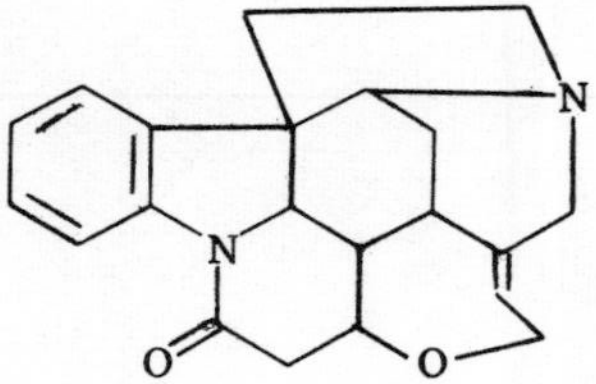

X

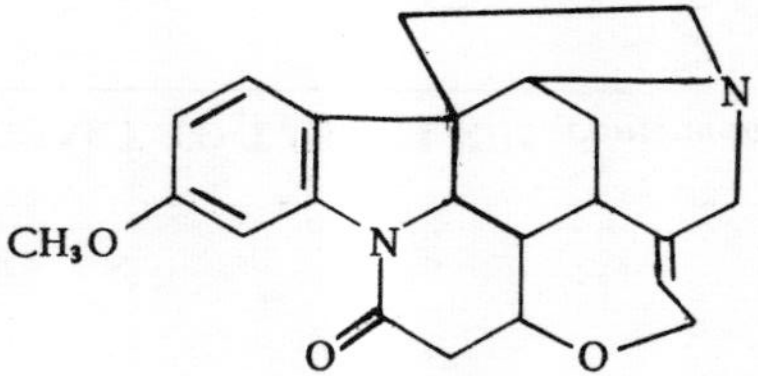

XI

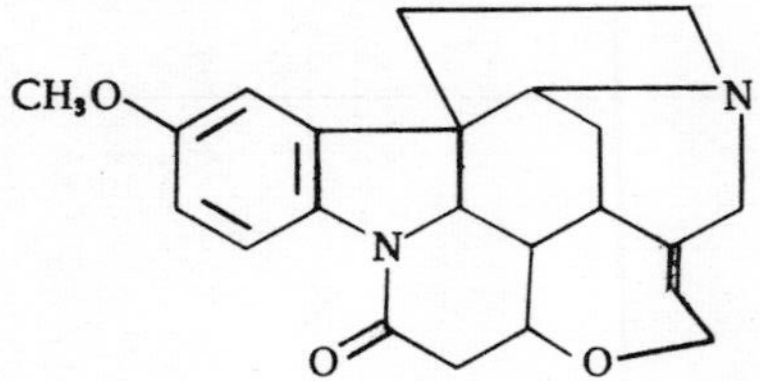

(*continued*)

CHART TO TABLE LXIII (*continued*)

References—Table LXIII

[1]F. Galinovsky, O. Vogl, and R. Wieser, *Monatsh.*, 83, 114 (1952).
[2]A. Stoll, A. Hofmann, and T. Petrzilka, *Helv. Chim. Acta*, 34, 1544 (1951).
[3]P. A. S. Smith and Tung-yin Yu, *J. Am. Chem. Soc.*, 74, 1096 (1952).
[4]Reduction carried out in dioxane-ether mixture.
[5]E. Leete and L. Marion, *Can. J. Chem.*, 30, 563 (1952).
[6]F. Galinovsky, O. Vogl, and W. Moroz, *Monatsh.*, 83, 242 (1952).
[7]L. Marion, F. Turcotte, and J. Ouellet, *Can. J. Chem.*, 29, 22 (1951).
[8]G. R. Clemo, R. Raper, and W. Short, *Nature*, 162, 296 (1948).
[9]G. R. Clemo, R. Raper, and W. S. Short, *J. Chem. Soc.*, 1949, 663.
[10]O. E. Edwards and L. Marion, *J. Am. Chem. Soc.*, 71, 1694 (1949).
[11]Reduction carried out in tetrahydrofuran-ether mixture.
[12]Isolated as hydrochloride.
[13]G. A. Swan, *J. Chem. Soc.*, 1949, 1720.
[14]J. Jost, *Helv. Chim. Acta*, 32, 1297 (1949).
[15]P. Karrer, C. H. Eugster, and P. Waser, *ibid.*, 32, 2381 (1949).
[16]S. P. Findlay, *J. Am. Chem. Soc.*, 73, 3008 (1951).
[17]Reduction carried out in tetrahydrofuran.
[18]G. W. Kenner and M. A. Murray, *J. Chem. Soc.*, 1950, 406.
[19]G. R. Clemo and B. Nath, *J. Chem. Soc.*, 1952, 2196.
[20]See text.

$$\text{CLIV} \quad \xrightarrow{\text{LAH}} \quad \text{CLV} \quad (10\text{-}107)$$

Jost (118) carried out the catalytic hydrogenation and the LAH reduction of CLIV in an effort to simultaneously reduce the 9,10-carbon-carbon double bond as well as the amide grouping. The desired product could not be obtained by these methods but was obtained by an electrolytic reduction.

The attempted LAH reduction of 1,2-benzo-7,8-(2′,3′-indolo)-3,4-dihydro-6-quinolizone (CLVI) has been reported to give back starting material (119).

CLVI   CLVII

Attempts to bring about the reaction between 4-quinolizone (CLVII) and LAH or *n*-butylmagnesium bromide have given orange colored complexes which on hydrolysis yield unchanged CLVII (120).

Rhombifoline, $C_{15}N_{20}N_2O$, an alkaloid isolated from *Thermopsis rhombifolia* (Nutt.) Richards, has been postulated as having structure CLVIII (121). Reduction of CLVIII to dihydrodesoxyrhombifoline with LAH in ether gives an oil which darkens in air and whose analysis for $C_{15}H_{22}N_2$ is unsatisfactory.

CLVIII

Boekelheide and Rothchild (122) have reported that LAH reduction of 3-carbethoxy-4-quinolizidone (CLIX) results in cleavage of the carbethoxy group while the amide grouping remains intact. Catalytic hydrogenation over copper chromite at 260°C. under 250 atmospheres pressure gives a 76% yield of quinolizidine (CLX).

Galinovsky, Vogl and Moroz (123) reported that the reduction of 1,3-dicarbethoxy-4-quinolizidone (CLXI) with LAH in ether gives a 92% crude yield of the expected 1,3-di-(hydroxymethyl)quinolizidine (CLXII).

CLXI   CLXII

LAH reduction of various alkaloids (CLXIII) containing the lactam grouping yields the expected amine.

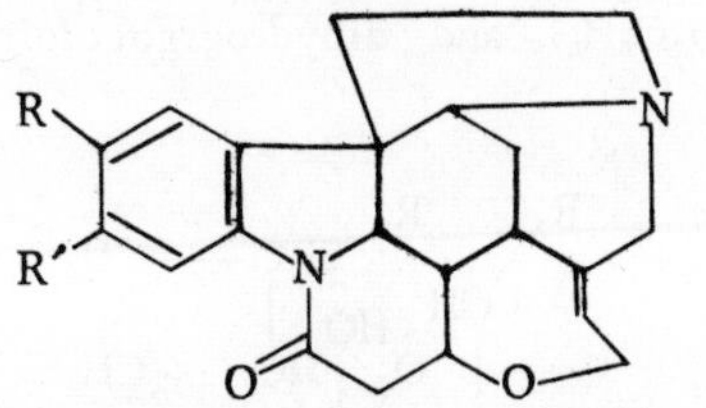

CLXIII

Thus, reduction of α-colubrine (R = H, R′ = OCH_3) (124), β-colubrine (R = OCH_3, R′ = H) (124), strychnine (R = R′ = H) (125) and strychnine methosulfate (126) proceeds as expected although a considerable reaction time is necessary. On the other hand reduction of brucine (R = R′ = OCH_3) proceeds only partially to yield dehydrobrucidine (CLXIV) which can be converted to dihydrobrucidine (CLXV) by catalytic hydrogenation (124).

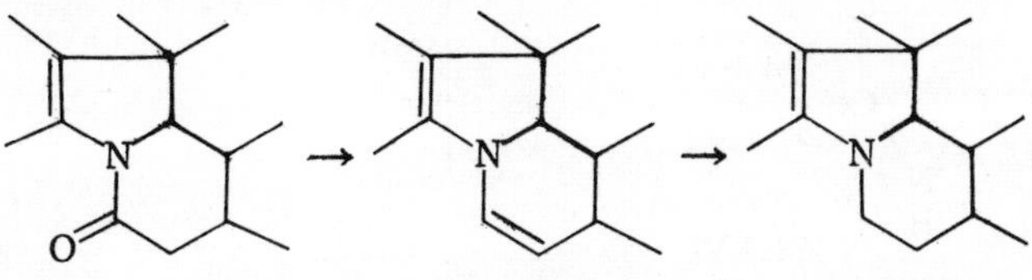

(10-111)

CLXIV CLXV

Dihydrobrucine yields the expected dihydrobrucidine on LAH reduction. The formation of CLXIV in the reduction of brucine is attributed to the fact that the intermediate complex undergoes an elimination reaction in preference to further reduction.

$$>N-\overset{O}{\overset{\|}{C}}-CH_2- \xrightarrow{LAH} >N-\underset{OLiAlH_3}{\underset{|}{\overset{H}{\overset{|}{C}}}}-CH_2- \xrightarrow{-LiAlH_3OH} >N-\overset{H}{\overset{|}{C}}=CH- \quad (10\text{-}112)$$

This is analogous to the formation of indoles in the LAH reduction of oxindoles.

10.2.1.c *Reductive cleavage.* Stoll, Hofmann, and Petrzilka (127) have carried out an extensive investigation of the structure of the ergot alkaloids of the ergotamine and ergotoxin types. Reduction with LAH gives three types of well-defined reduction products whose constitution and configuration have been determined by synthesis. The reduction products, as shown in equation (10-113), consist of a polyamine (CLXVII), an aminoalcohol (CLXVIII) and a piperazine derivative (CLXIX). Based upon the structures of these products and the products formed by thermal cleavage at 200–220° in high vacuo, structure CLXVI has been advanced for dihydroergosine (R_1 = H, R_2 = $CH_2CH(CH_3)_2$), dihydroergocryptine

(R_1 = CH_3, R_2 = $CH_2C_6H_5$) and dihydroergocornine (R_1 = CH_3, R_2 = $CH(CH_3)_2$).

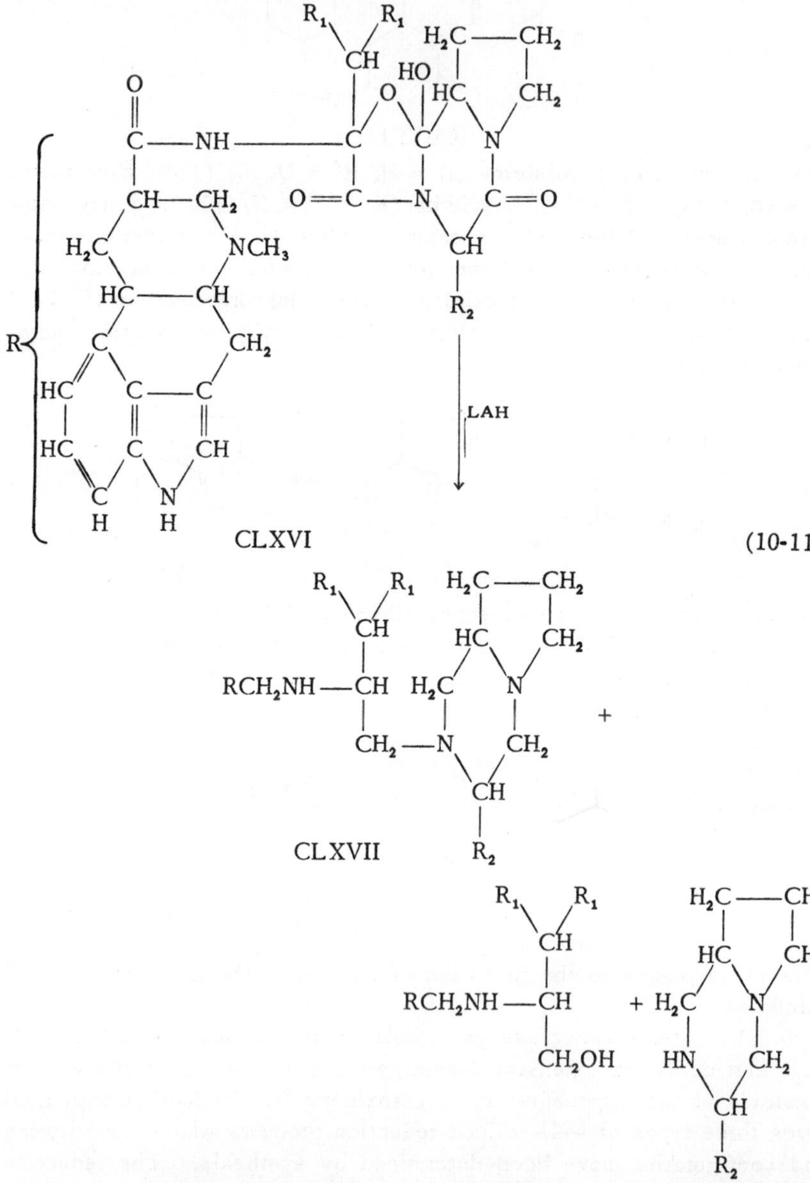

CLXVI   (10-113)

CLXVII

CLXVIII   CLXIX

The cleavage of the ether bridge in CLXVI is due to the presence of the —N—C—O— linkage as discussed in Section 12.17. While the formation of CLXVII involves the normal reduction of the lactam to a methyleneamine, the formation of CLXVIII and CLXIX is due to a cleavage of the lactam under the influence of LAH to form an aldehyde which is reduced to the alcohol by the excess reagent. This is analogous to the cleavage of the disubstituted amides discussed in Section 10.1.1.d.2, as well as the cleavage of 1,3-diphenylazetidinone formulated in equation (10-78).

Mustafa has reported that the LAH reduction of N,N'-diaryl-α-sulfonyl-dianthranilide (CLXX) yields o-arylsulfonamidobenzyl alcohol (CLXXI) (128).

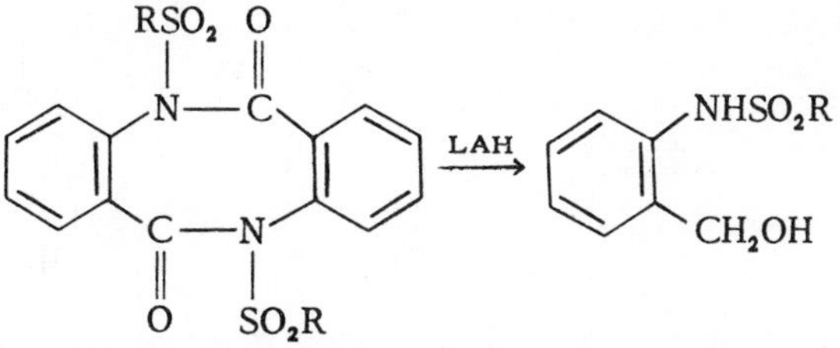

$$(10\text{-}114)$$

CLXX   CLXXI

R	% Yield
Phenyl	87
p-Tolyl	93
α-Naphthyl	91

The product arises by the cleavage of the lactam group in the tertiary amide. The reaction of CLXX with the Grignard reagent yields the analogous sulfonamidocarbinol (CLXXII) (129).

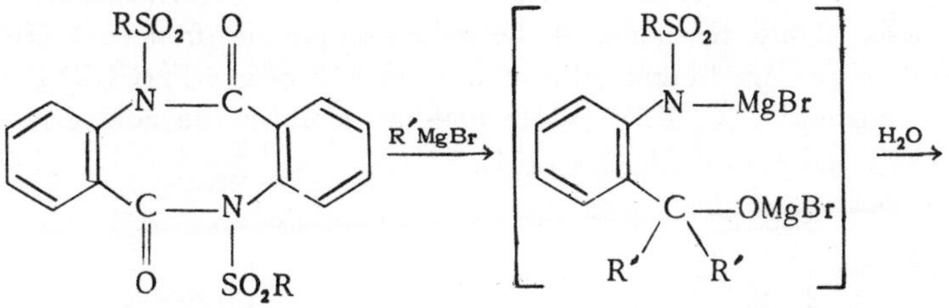

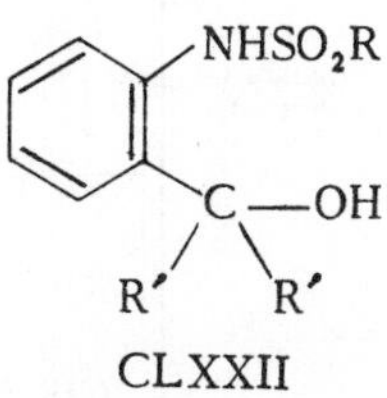

$$(10\text{-}115)$$

CLXXII

Galinovsky and Wieser (130) have reported that the reaction between a lactam and the calculated amount of LAH is stopped at an intermediate stage to conform to the following mechanism for the conversion of N-methyl-α-pyrrolidone (CLXXIII) to an ω-aminoaldehyde:

$$(10\text{-}116)$$

CLXXIII

The calculated amount of LAH is added to a solution of the lactam followed by a short reflux period and hydrolysis. Attempts to isolate the free aldehyde in the reduction of N-methyl-α-piperidone (CLXXVI) and 3-ketooctahydropyrrocoline (CLXXVIII) have not been successful, the product usually being isolated as a dimeric condensation product containing a double bond resulting from the splitting out of water. Similarly, unsuccessful attempts to prepare the acetal by the cautious reaction of alcoholic hydrogen chloride and the LAH reduction product have given the dimer or a higher condensation product (131,132). The identification of the reduction product as the ω-aminoaldehyde has been made on the basis of its strong reducing power, the tendency to form dimeric condensation products and unstable salts and its reaction with acetonedicarboxylic acid. Thus, treatment of the reduction product from CLXXIII with one mole of acetonedicarboxylic acid gives 47% of hygrin (CLXXIV) and 14% of cuskhygrin (CLXXV) while one-half mole of the acid gives 18% of CLXXIV and 39% of CLXXV (131).

$$(10\text{-}117)$$

Analogous products are obtained from N-methyl-α-piperidone (CLXXVI) (131), N-ethyl-α-piperidone (CLXXVII) (133) and 3-ketooctahydropyrrocoline (CLXXVIII) (132).

| CLXXVI | CLXXVII | CLXXVIII |

The reduction product from CLXXVIII has also been found to react with benzoylacetic acid to yield 64% ω-(3-octahydropyrrocolyl)acetophenone (132).

$$(10\text{-}118)$$

CLXXVIII

In addition to Galinovsky and Wieser (130,132), King, Hofmann, and McMillan (58) have carried out the controlled LAH reduction of CLXXVIII in ether solution under various conditions in an attempt to synthesize the ω-aminoaldehyde, pelletierine. The products in all cases consist of a mixture of unchanged lactam and octahydropyrrocoline or polymeric pelletierine. King and his coworkers have reported that in their work the reaction mixture prior to distillation has shown no reducing properties and the higher boiling material postulated as polymeric pelletierine is only obtained under drastic distillation conditions. They have postulated that the monomeric pelletierine formed in the reduction probably undergoes aldol condensation and on distillation the polymeric material is pyrolyzed to dimers and trimers which repolymerize slowly after distillation.

Reaction of α-piperidone (CLXXIX) with one-quarter mole of LAH results in replacement of the active hydrogen, and on hydrolysis the starting material is recovered. When the reduction is carried out with one-half mole of LAH, the amount calculated to replace the active hydrogen as well as to reduce the lactam to δ-aminovaleraldehyde, the reduction product on condensation with one mole of acetonedicarboxylic acid gives 4% of isopelletierine (CLXXX) and 50% of piperidine (131).

| CLXXIX | CLXXX | $(10\text{-}119)$ |

Here, in contrast to the reduction of the N-methyl compound (CLXXVI), the reaction proceeds primarily to the oxygen-free base.

Galinovsky and Vogl (133) have treated "Pelletierine hydrobromide Merck," obtained from *Punica granatum* L., with acetic anhydride. An ethereal solution of the acetylated base has been reduced with LAH and the reduction product oxidized with chromic oxide in acetic acid. The resultant product has been identified as N-ethylisopelletierine, identical with the LAH reduction product of N-acetylisopelletierine and the product obtained by the reaction of acetonedicarboxylic acid with the product of the controlled LAH reduction of N-ethyl-α-piperidone. It has therefore been concluded that the hydrobromide salt contains isopelletierine.

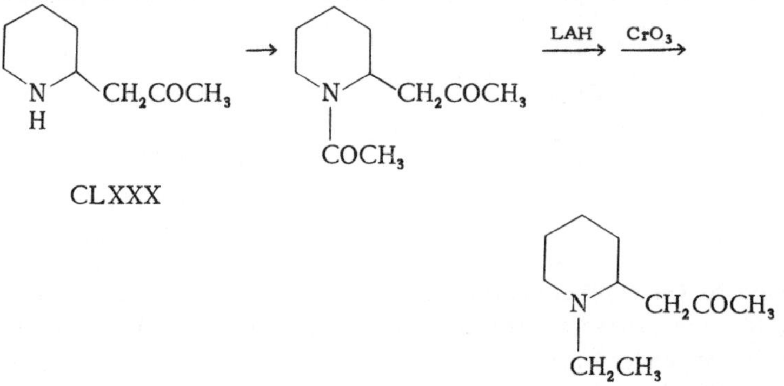

CLXXX

(10-120)

10.2.1.d   α-*Oxygenated pyridines, quinolines and quinoxalines.* de Mayo and Rigby (109) reported that the reduction of 2-hydroxyquinoline (CLXXXI) with LAH in refluxing dibutyl ether gives quinoline, isolated in 26% yield as the picrate, and tetrahydroquinoline, isolated in 5% yield as the benzoyl derivative.

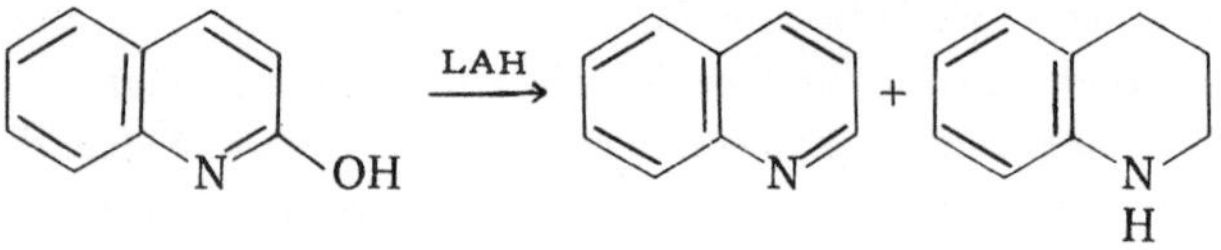

CLXXXI

(10-121)

Similarly, 2-hydroxypyridine (CLXXXII) under the same conditions gives pyridine and piperidine.

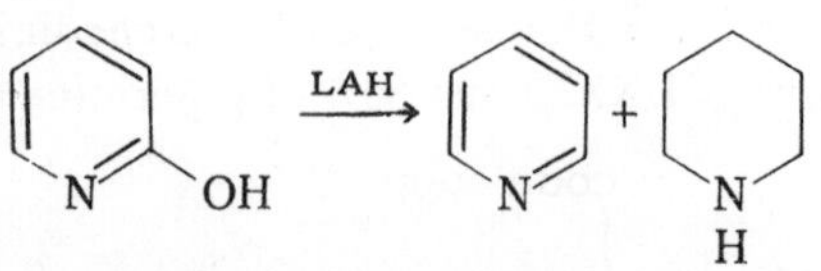

CLXXXII

(10-122)

Mariella and Belcher (134) reported that the attempted LAH reduction of the lactone of 3-carboxy-6-methyl-4-hydroxymethyl-2(1)-pyridone (CLXXXIII) in diethyl ether, diethyl ether-tetrahydrofuran (1:1), diethyl ether-dioxane (2:1), dibutyl ether or dibutyl ether-dioxane (1:1) with variations in the time of refluxing (one to seven days), variations in the method of adding reagents and variations in working up the reaction mixture fails to yield any of the expected diol (CLXXXIV). The only product which is isolated besides unreacted starting material is a light yellow oil which is not basic and does not give a positive ferric chloride test. The use of copper chromite at 170° and 190 atmospheres of hydrogen for six hours also fails to reduce CLXXXIII.

CLXXXIII   CLXXXIV

CLXXXV   CLXXXVI

The attempted LAH reductions of the lactone of 3-carboxy-1,6-dimethyl-4-hydroxymethyl-2(1)-pyridone (CLXXXV) and the lactone of 3-carboxy-4-hydroxymethyl-2-methoxy-6-methylpyridine (CLXXXVI) have also been unsuccessful (134). In contrast to the unsuccessful attempt to reduce CLXXXVI, it is of interest to note that 2-methoxy-3,4,5,6-tetrahydropyridine is readily reduced in ethereal solution to piperidine (135).

The attempted LAH reduction of 4-acetoxymethyl-3-carboxy-6-methyl-2-pyridol (CLXXXVII) has been reported as unsuccessful although the reaction conditions were not specified (134). While the LAH reduction of 3-carboxy-6-methyl-2(1)-pyridone (CLXXXVIII) in diethyl ether is unsuccessful, when the reduction is carried out in dibutyl ether the expected 2-hydroxymethyl-6-methyl-2-pyridol (CLXXXIX) is obtained in 17% yield (136).

CLXXXVII   CLXXXVIII   CLXXXIX

Although no carbinol has been isolated when 3-carbomethoxy-6-methyl-2-pyridol (CXC) is treated with LAH in diethyl or dibutyl ethers (136), the reduction of 3-carbethoxy-4,6-dimethyl-2-pyridol (CXCI) with LAH in diethyl ether by the Soxhlet extraction technique yields 60% of 3-hydroxymethyl-4,6-dimethyl-2-pyridol (CXCII) (137).

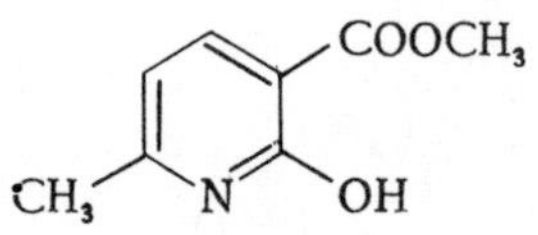

CXC 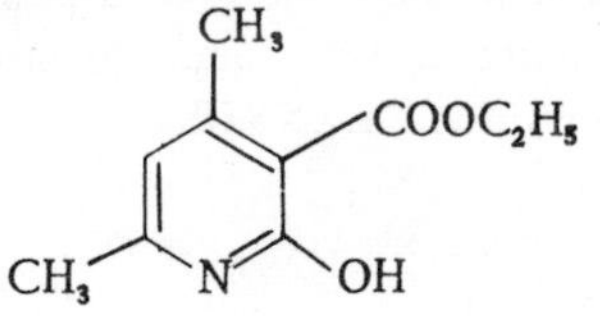   CXCI 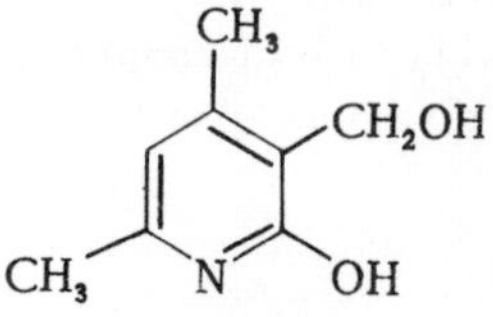   CXCII

Tetrahydroquinoxalines (CXCIV) are obtained from 2-oxo-1,2-dihydro-quinoxalines (CXCIII) by LAH reduction.

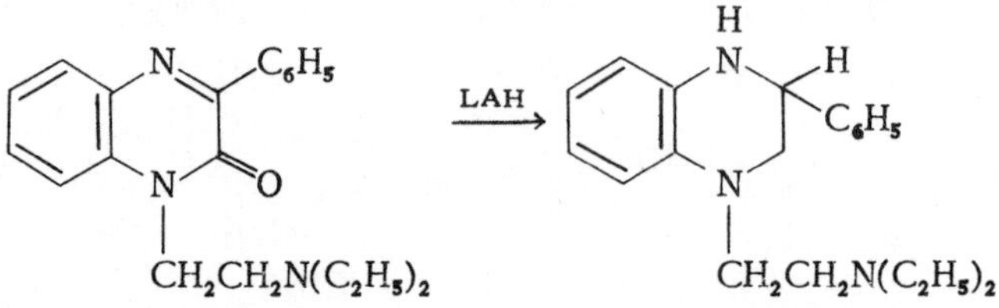

$$\text{CXCIII} \xrightarrow{\text{LAH}} \text{CXCIV} \qquad (10\text{-}123)$$

In the case of the 1-(β-hydroxyethyl) derivative (CXCV) the reduction yields an intermediate with an intact double bond which, although not isolated, can be converted to a quinoxalinium salt (CXCVI).

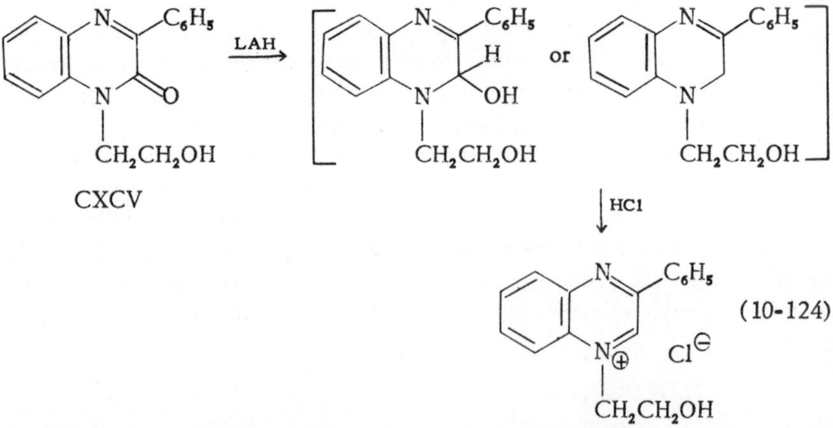

CXCV

$$\downarrow \text{HCl}$$

$$(10\text{-}124)$$

CXCVI

Treatment of a quinoxalinium salt (CXCVI) with alkali yields the pseudo base (CXCVII) which is reduced to the tetrahydroquinoxaline with LAH or by catalytic hydrogenation over platinum oxide (138).

CXCVI   CXCVII   (10-125)

10.3 IMIDES

10.3.1 Imides

10.3.1.a *Reductions with lithium aluminum hydride.* The reduction of imides is analogous to that of amides and lactams, consuming a total of one mole of LAH per mole of imide for the reduction of the two carbonyl groups to methylenes.

CXCVIII   (10-126)

The LAH reduction of substituted, including N-substituted, succinimides (CXCIX) yields pyrrolidine derivatives, while substituted glutarimides (CC) are converted to piperidine derivatives.

CXCIX   (10-127)

CC   (10-128)

Lukeš and Ferles (139) have reported that the reduction of the substituted N-methylglutarimide (CCI) yields the expected N-methylpiperidine (CCII).

$$\text{CCI} \xrightarrow{\text{LAH}} \text{CCII} \qquad (10\text{-}129)$$

However, reduction of the N-unsubstituted compound (CCIII) in an ether-dioxane mixture proceeds abnormally to the dihydropyridone derivative (CCIV).

$$\text{CCIII} \xrightarrow{\text{LAH}} \text{CCIV} \qquad (10\text{-}130)$$

The butyl ester (CCV) is reduced with LAH in dibutyl ether to the expected 4-(β-hydroxyethyl)-4-methylpiperidine (CCVI).

$$\text{CCV} \xrightarrow{\text{LAH}} \text{CCVI} \qquad (10\text{-}131)$$

The formation of CCIV is analogous to the previously indicated LAH reduction of oxindole derivatives to indole and indoline compounds (Section 10.2.1.b). Similarly, brucine is reduced to dehydrobrucidine (equation (10-111).

The reduction of o-phenylenediacetimide (CCVII) proceeds stepwise, the lactam (CCVIII) formed in the first stage being reduced in a further reaction (140).

$$\text{CCVII} \xrightarrow{\text{LAH}} \text{CCVIII} \xrightarrow{\text{LAH}} \qquad (10\text{-}132)$$

The LAH reduction of phthalimide yields isoindoline while naphthalimide derivatives are converted to derivatives of 2,3-dihydro-1-benz[de]isoquinoline. While LAH reduction of N-(β-acetoxyethyl)naphthalimide (CCIX) yields 2-β-hydroxyethyl-2,3-dihydro-1-benz[de]isoquinoline, the attempted reduction of N-(β-hydroxyethyl)naphthalimide (CCX) is reported to give negative results whether the LAH reduction is carried out in ether or tetrahydrofuran (141).

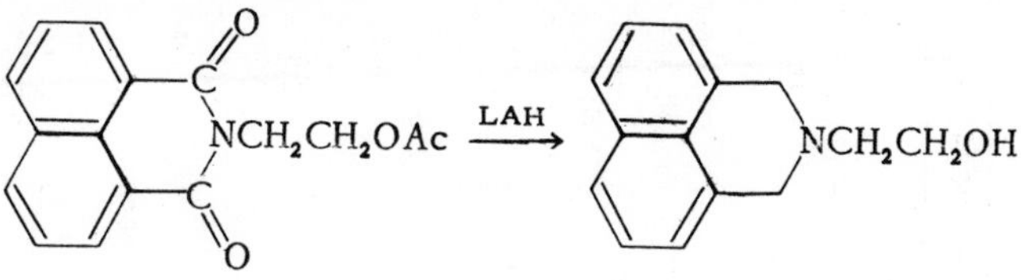

CCIX   (10-133)

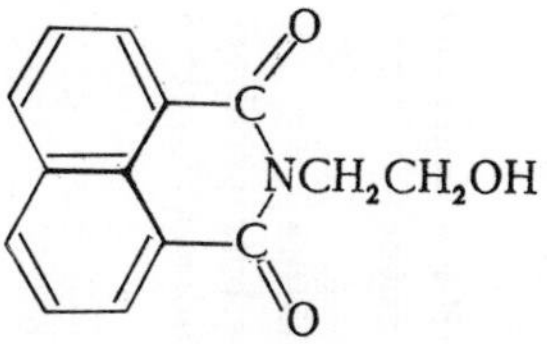

CCX 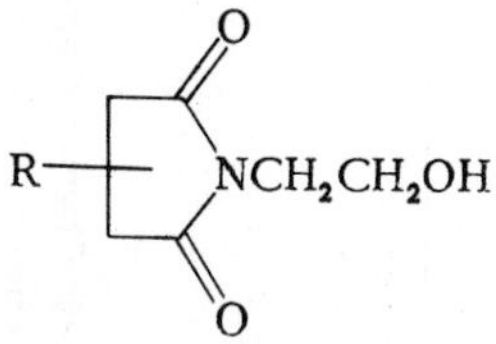   CCXI

On the other hand, substituted N-(β-hydroxyethyl)succinimides (CCXI) are readily reduced to the corresponding pyrrolidylethanols (142).

The dilactam of γ-aminopimelic acid (CCXII), which possesses the imide structure, is reduced with LAH in tetrahydrofuran to pyrrolizidine (143).

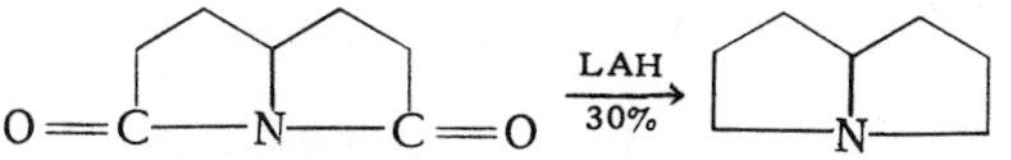

$$O = C - N - C = O \quad \xrightarrow[30\%]{LAH} \qquad \qquad (10\text{-}134)$$

CCXII

Weygand and Tietjan unsuccessfully attempted to prepare o-phthalalde-hyde by the reduction of phthalimide and N-methylphthalimide with the calculated amount of LAH (55).

The reduction of various imides with LAH is summarized in Table LXIV.

10.3.1.b   *Reactions with the borohydrides.*   The non-reduction of the imide group with sodium or potassium borohydride has been utilized in the following sequence (144,145):

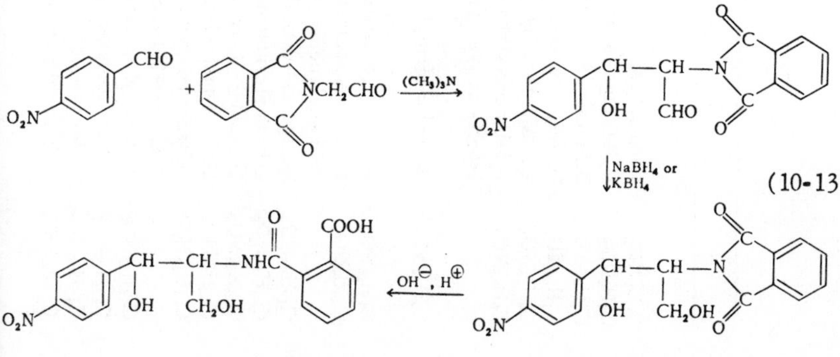

(10-135)

TABLE LXIV

LAH Reduction of Imides

	Imide	Product	% Yield	Ref.
A. Alicyclic				
C$_5$H$_7$NO$_2$	3-Methylsuccinimide	3-Methylpyrrolidine	67	1
C$_6$H$_9$NO$_2$	1-Methylglutarimide	1-Methylpiperidine	85	1
C$_7$H$_9$NO$_2$	Dilactam of γ-aminopimelic acid	Pyrrolizidine	30	3
C$_7$H$_{11}$NO$_3$	1-β-Hydroxyethyl-3-methylsuccinimide	1-β-Hydroxyethyl-3-methylpyrrolidine	68.1	4,5
C$_8$H$_{13}$NO$_2$	4-Ethyl-4-methylglutarimide	4-Ethyl-4-methylpiperidine	38.5	2
C$_8$H$_{13}$NO$_3$	1-β-Hydroxyethyl-3,3-dimethylsuccinimide	1-β-Hydroxyethyl-3,3-dimethylpyrrolidine	...	4,5
C$_8$H$_{13}$NO$_3$	1-β-Hydroxyethyl-3,4-dimethylsuccinimide	1-β-Hydroxyethyl-3,4-dimethylpyrrolidine	61.6	4
			...[6]	5
C$_9$H$_{13}$NO$_4$	Methyl 4-methyl-4-acetateglutarimide	4-β-Hydroxyethyl-4-methyl-4,5-dihydropyrid-6-one	...[6]	4
C$_9$H$_{15}$NO$_2$	4-Ethyl-1,4-dimethylglutarimide	4-Ethyl-1,4-dimethylpiperidine	50–60	7,8
C$_{10}$H$_9$NO$_2$	1-Phenylsuccinimide	1-Phenylpyrrolidine	69	9
C$_{10}$H$_9$NO$_2$	o-Phenylenediacetimide	2,3,4,5-Tetrahydro-3,1H-benzazepin-2-one	...[6]	10
C$_{10}$H$_{15}$NO$_4$	Methyl 1,4-dimethyl-4-acetateglutarimide	4-β-Hydroxyethyl-1,4-dimethylpiperidine	58	2
C$_{11}$H$_{11}$NO$_2$	1-Phenylglutarimide	1-Phenylpiperidine	52	11
C$_{12}$H$_{13}$NO$_2$	1-Ethyl-3-phenylsuccinimide	1-Ethyl-3-phenylpyrrolidine	71	12
C$_{12}$H$_{19}$NO$_4$	Butyl 4-methyl-4-acetateglutarimide	4-β-Hydroxyethyl-4-methylpiperidine	11[13]	2
C$_{15}$H$_{18}$N$_2$O$_2$	3-Benzyl-9-methyl-3,9-diazabicyclo[3.3.1]nonane-2,4-dione	3-Benzyl-9-methyl-3,9-diazabicyclo[3.3.1]nonane	...	14
C$_{16}$H$_{29}$NO$_2$	3-Dodecylsuccinimide	3-Dodecylpyrrolidine	50	15
C$_{17}$H$_{15}$NO$_2$	2,4-Diphenylglutarimide	3,5-Diphenylpiperidine	17.6[16]	17
C$_{17}$H$_{24}$N$_2$O$_2$	3-Phenyl-3-(β-diethylaminoethyl)glutarimide	3-Phenyl-3-(β-diethylaminoethyl)piperidine	...	18,19
C$_{17}$H$_{31}$NO$_2$	3-Dodecylglutarimide	3-Dodecylpiperidine	74	15

B. Aromatic

Formula	Phthalimide	Isoindoline		Ref.
$C_8H_5NO_2$	Phthalimide		...	20–23
		Tars[26]	5[24]	25
$C_{14}H_{11}NO_3$	N-(β-Hydroxyethyl)naphthalimide	2-β-Hydroxyethyl-2,3-dihydro-1-benz[de]-isoquinoline	...	27
$C_{16}H_{13}NO_4$	N-(β-Acetoxyethyl)naphthalimide		68.5[24]	27
$C_{24}H_{32}N_2O_2$	4-Amino-N-decylnaphthalimide	2-Decyl-6-amino-2,3-dihydro-1-benz[de]-isoquinoline	...	28

References—Table LXIV

[1]F. F. Blicke and Chi-Jung Lu, *J. Am. Chem. Soc.,* 74, 3933 (1952).
[2]R. Lukeš and M. Ferles, unpublished work, through J. Rudinger, M. Ferles and M. Protiva, *Chem. Listy,* 45, 317, 339 (1951).
[3]R. Lukeš and M. Ferles, unpublished work, through M. Ferles and J. Rudinger, *ibid.,* 47, 135 (1953).
[4]R. B. Moffett, *J. Org. Chem.,* 14, 862 (1949).
[5]W. B. Reid, Jr., U. S. Pat. 2,605,266 (July 29, 1952).
[6]Reduction carried out in ether-dioxane mixture.
[7]R. Lukeš and M. Ferles, *Collection Czech. Chem. Commun.,* 16, 252 (1951).
[8]R. Lukeš and M. Ferles, *Chem. Listy,* in press, through J. Rudinger, M. Ferles and M. Protiva, *Chem. Listy,* 45, 339 (1951).
[9]Spitzmueller, unpublished work, through W. G. Brown, in *Organic Reactions,* Vol. VI, p. 492, 505.
[10]J. O. Halford and B. Weissmann, *J. Org. Chem.,* 17, 1646 (1952).
[11]Spitzmueller, unpublished work, through W. G. Brown, in *Organic Reactions,* Vol. VI, p. 505.
[12]N. J. Leonard, A. B. Simon, and D. L. Felley, *J. Am. Chem. Soc.,* 73, 857 (1951).
[13]Reduction carried out in dibutyl ether.
[14]R. A. Barnes and H. M. Fales, *Abstracts of Papers,* 122nd Meeting American Chemical Society, Atlantic City, N. J., September 1952, p. 15M.
[15]D. E. Ames and R. E. Bowman, *J. Chem. Soc., 1952,* 1057.
[16]Reduction carried out in tetrahydrofuran.
[17]E. L. Eliel and R. T. McBride, unpublished work.
[18]K. Hoffmann, E. Tagmann, H. J. Bein, and J. Tripod, *Abstracts of Papers,* XIIth International Congress of Pure and Applied Chemistry, September 1951, New York, p. 324.
[19]E. Tagmann, E. Sury, and K. Hoffmann, *Helv. Chim. Acta,* 35, 1235 (1952).
[20]A. Uffer and E. Schlittler, *ibid.,* 31, 1397 (1948).
[21]Ciba Akt., Swiss Pat. 273,953 (June 1, 1951).
[22]Ciba S. A., Fr. Pat. 987,158 (August 9, 1951).
[23]E. Schlittler and A. Uffer, Ger. Pat. 824,491 (December 31, 1951).
[24]Isolated as hydrochloride.
[25]A. Dunet, J. Rollet, and A. Willemart, *Bull. soc. chim. France,* [5] 17, 877 (1950).
[26]No reduction in ether due to ether insolubility; in tetrahydrofuran tars obtained.
[27]W. L. Garbrecht, J. H. Hunter, and J. B. Wright, *J. Am. Chem. Soc.,* 72, 1359 (1950).
[28]L. M. Rice, M. Rubin, J. Scholler, and E. E. Reid, *J. Org. Chem.,* 16, 501 (1951).

10.3.2   Diacylamines

The diacylamine, N,N-diacetylglycine ethyl ester (CCXIII), which is the open chain analogue of an imide, is reduced with LAH, in the expected manner, to N,N-diethylethanolamine (146).

$$\begin{array}{c} CH_3CO \\ \diagdown \\ CH_3CO \diagup \end{array} NCH_2COOC_2H_5 \xrightarrow[42.8\%]{LAH} \begin{array}{c} CH_3CH_2 \\ \diagdown \\ CH_3CH_2 \diagup \end{array} NCH_2CH_2OH \quad (10\text{-}136)$$

CCXIII

Witkop and Patrick (25) have reported that LAH reduction of aromatic diacylamines yields alkylamines rather than dialkylamines. Thus, LAH reduction of N,N-diacetylaniline (CCXIV) and N,N-diacetyl-o-anisidine (CCXV) yields N-ethylaniline and o-N-ethylanisidine, respectively.

$$C_6H_5N \begin{array}{c} \diagup COCH_3 \\ \diagdown COCH_3 \end{array} \xrightarrow[92\%]{LAH} C_6H_5NHCH_2CH_3 \quad (10\text{-}137)$$

CCXIV

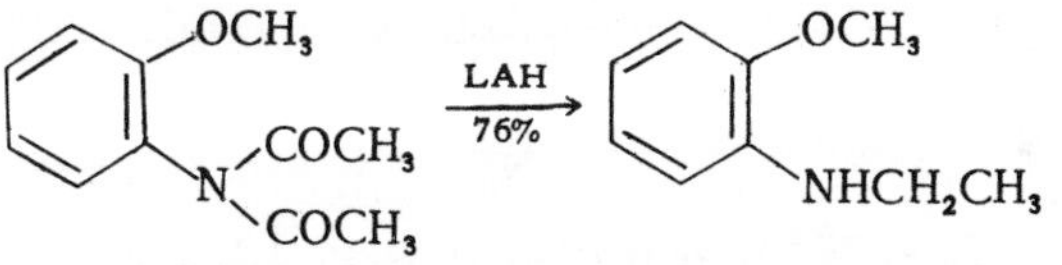

(10-138)

CCXV

Reduction of N,N,O-triacetyl-o-aminophenol (CCXVI) yields 57% o-ethyl-aminophenol and an oily by-product which forms a 3,5-dinitrobenzoate, m.p. 128.5–130°. A similar oily by-product is formed by the LAH reduction of N-benzoyl-O-acetyl-o-aminophenol (CCXVII) to o-benzylamino-phenol. The phenolic hydroxyl seems essential for the formation of these oily products since none of them are observed in the reduction of CCXIV or CCXV.

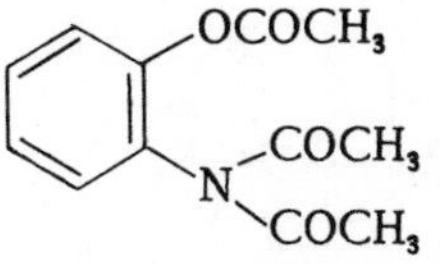

CCXVI 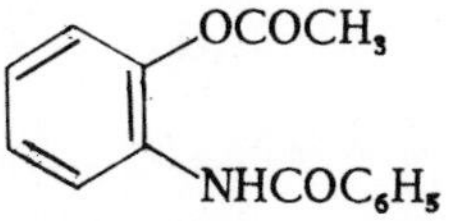   CCXVII

The formation of alkylamines by LAH reduction of diacylamines is formulated as follows:

$$R \longrightarrow N \underset{\text{COR}_2}{\overset{\text{COR}_1}{\diagup}} \longrightarrow R \longrightarrow N \begin{matrix} \overset{O^\ominus}{\overset{H}{\overset{|}{C}}} \longrightarrow R_1 \\ \\ \overset{|}{C} \longrightarrow R_2 \\ \overset{||}{\overset{+}{O}} \longrightarrow \overset{-}{A}lX_3 \\ \oplus \quad \ominus \end{matrix} \longrightarrow \begin{matrix} R_1CH = O \longrightarrow R_1CH_2OH \\ + \\ R \longrightarrow N = C \longrightarrow R_2 \longrightarrow RNHCH_2R_2 \\ \overset{|}{O}AlX_2 \end{matrix} \quad (10\text{-}139)$$

Witkop and Patrick, have indicated, without the publication of experimental results, that in mixed diacylamines hydrogenolysis by LAH removes acetyl rather than benzoyl.

10.3.3 Hydantoins

10.3.3.a *Reductions with lithium aluminum hydride.* Wilk and Close (147) have reported that the LAH reduction of the hydantoin nucleus can be directed to yield an imidazolone, imidazole or imidazolidine. Addition of an ethereal LAH solution to a suspension of 3-methyl-5-phenylhydantoin (CCXVIII) in ether, followed by room temperature stirring for 16 hours, yields 66% 1-methyl-4-phenyl-2(3H)-imidazolone (CCXIX). Further reduction of the 2-carbonyl group is only affected after prolonged refluxing of CCXIX with LAH, to yield 1-methyl-4-phenylimidazole (CCXX).

$$\begin{matrix} \overset{H}{\underset{H}{N}} \\ C_6H_5C \diagup \qquad \diagdown C = O \\ O = C \longrightarrow NCH_3 \\ \text{CCXVIII} \end{matrix} \xrightarrow{\text{LAH}} \begin{matrix} \overset{H}{N} \\ C_6H_5C \diagup \qquad \diagdown C = O \\ HC \longrightarrow NCH_3 \\ \text{CCXIX} \end{matrix} \xrightarrow{\text{LAH}} \begin{matrix} N \\ C_6H_5C \diagup \qquad \diagdown CH \\ HC \longrightarrow NCH_3 \\ \text{CCXX} \end{matrix}$$

(10-140)

Complete reduction of CCXVIII to 1-methyl-4-phenylimidazolidine (CCXXI) is carried out by treating the hydantoin with excess LAH under prolonged refluxing conditions.

$$\begin{matrix} \overset{H}{\underset{H}{N}} \\ C_6H_5C \diagup \qquad \diagdown C = O \\ O = C \longrightarrow NCH_3 \\ \text{CCXVIII} \end{matrix} \xrightarrow{\text{LAH}} \begin{matrix} \overset{H}{\underset{H}{N}} \\ C_6H_5C \diagup \qquad \diagdown CH_2 \\ H_2C \longrightarrow NCH_3 \\ \text{CCXXI} \end{matrix} \qquad (10\text{-}141)$$

5-Phenylhdydantoin has been converted to 4-phenyl-2(3H)-imidazolone in a manner similar to the conversion of CCXVIII to CCXIX.

10.3.3.b *Reactions with sodium borohydride.* Sodium borohydride does not attack the hydantoin nucleus and has consequently been utilized by Wessely, Schlögl, Korger, and Wawersich in a new method for the degradation of peptides. The procedure is outlined in Flow Sheet III (73,74).

Flow Sheet III

This technique has been applied to a series of tri- and tetrapeptides. A further application has been in differentiating between the isomeric hydantoins formed on treatment of the intermediate urea compound with 1:1 hydrochloric acid. The reduction product is hydrolyzed with concentrated hydrochloric acid followed by the addition of sodium hydroxide to pH 8. Ether extraction of the alkaline solution removes the aminoalcohol. The aqueous solution is evaporated and the residue taken up in ethanol. Paper chromatography permits the identification of the amino acids.

The following hydantoin acid chlorides have been reduced with sodium borohydride:

$$R_1CH - C \begin{smallmatrix} O \\ \diagup \\ \diagdown \\ NR_2 \end{smallmatrix}$$
$$HN - C \begin{smallmatrix} \diagup \\ \diagdown \\ O \end{smallmatrix}$$

CCXXII

R_1	R_2	Ref.
H	$CH(CH_2C_6H_5)COCl$	148
CH_3	$CH(CH_2CH(CH_3)_2)COCl$	149
$(CH_3)_2CHCH_2$	$CH(CH_3)COCl$	148
$(CH_3)_2CHCH_2$	$CH_2CONHCH(CH_2C_6H_5)COCl$	73,74
$C_6H_5CH_2$	CH_2COCl	73,150
$p\text{-}HOC_6H_4CH_2$	$CH(CH_3)COCl$	148

10.4 CARBAMATES

The reduction of carbamates with LAH yields N-methylamines and alcohols.

$$RNHCOOR' \xrightarrow{LAH} RNHCH_3 + R'OH \qquad (10\text{-}142)$$

The reduction of ethyl N-phenylcarbamate (CCXXIII) and ethyl N-benzylcarbamate (CCXXIV) is reported to yield N-methylaniline and N-methylbenzylamine, respectively:

$$C_6H_5NHCOOC_2H_5 \xrightarrow[88.5\%]{LAH} C_6H_5NHCH_3 \qquad (10\text{-}143)$$
$$\text{CCXXIII}$$

$$C_6H_5CH_2NHCOOC_2H_5 \xrightarrow[79\%]{LAH} C_6H_5CH_2NHCH_3 \qquad (10\text{-}144)$$
$$\text{CCXXIV}$$

The reduction of N-carbomethoxysarcosine (CCXXV) yields dimethylaminoethanol (151), while benzyl alcohol has been obtained in the reduc-

$$\begin{array}{c} CH_3NCH_2COOH \\ | \\ COOCH_3 \\ \text{CCXXV} \end{array} \xrightarrow[87\%]{LAH} \begin{array}{c} CH_3NCH_2CH_2OH \\ | \\ CH_3 \end{array} \qquad (10\text{-}145)$$

tion of benzyl carbamate (CCXXVI) (152).

$$C_6H_5CH_2OCONH_2 \xrightarrow{LAH} C_6H_5CH_2OH \qquad (10\text{-}146)$$
$$\text{CCXXVI}$$

Karrer and Nicolaus (39) reported that the carbobenzoxy group in various peptides is reduced with LAH in tetrahydrofuran to yield benzyl alcohol and the N-methylamino compound. Carbobenxozyglycine ester
(CCXXVII) is reduced to benzyl alcohol and N-methylethanolamine.

$$C_6H_5CH_2OCONHCH_2COOC_2H_5 \xrightarrow{LAH} C_6H_5CH_2OH + CH_3NHCH_2CH_2OH$$

$$\text{CCXXVII} \hspace{5cm} (10\text{-}147)$$

The reduction of carbobenzoxyglycyl-L-leucine ester and carbobenzoxyglycyl-L-leucinamide analogously yields the N-methylamine derivative.

Jolles and Fromageot (40) have reported that LAH reduction of the
α-benzyl ester of ethyl carbobenzoxy-DL-aspartyl-β-glycinate (CCXXVIII)
in N-ethylmorpholine yields 51% of the dipeptide diol (CCXXIX) accompanied by benzyl alcohol, ethanol, toluene and carbon dioxide.

$$C_6H_5CH_2OCOCHCH_2CONHCH_2COOC_2H_5 \xrightarrow{LAH}$$

$$| $$

$$NHCOOCH_2C_6H_5$$

$$\text{CCXXVIII}$$

$$HOCH_2CHCH_2CONHCH_2CH_2OH \quad (10\text{-}148)$$

$$|$$

$$NH_2$$

$$\text{CCXXIX}$$

These results are at variance with other carbamate reductions in yielding
the primary amine, toluene and carbon dioxide from the carbobenzoxy
group. The LAH reduction of the α-benzyl ester of ethyl carbobenzoxy-
glutamyl-γ-glycinate (CCXXX) is analogously reported to yield the dipeptide diol (CCXXXI) (41).

$$C_6H_5CH_2OCOCHCH_2CH_2CONHCH_2COOC_2H_5 \xrightarrow{LAH}$$

$$|$$

$$NHCOOCH_2C_6H_5$$

$$\text{CCXXX}$$

$$HOCH_2CHCH_2CH_2CONHCH_2CH_2OH \quad (10\text{-}149)$$

$$|$$

$$NH_2$$

$$\text{CCXXXI}$$

N-Carbobenzoxyglutathione has been reduced with LAH but the reduction
products have not been indicated.

The reduction of DL-phenylalanine-N-carboxyanhydride (CCXXXII)
yields phenylalaninol as the principal product indicating the cleavage of
the carboxyl group from nitrogen. The other products of the reduction are
N-formylphenylalanine and N-methylphenylalaninol (151).

$$C_6H_5CH_2CH-C\underset{HN-C}{\overset{O}{\diagdown}}O \xrightarrow{LAH} C_6H_5CH_2CHCH_2OH +$$

$$NH_2$$

CCXXXII

$$C_6H_5CH_2CHCOOH + C_6H_5CH_2CHCH_2OH \quad (10\text{-}150)$$
$$NHCHO \qquad\qquad NHCH_3$$

The N-formyl and N-methyl products are postulated as indicative of the reaction of the N-carboxyanhydride in the isomeric isocyanate form. However, they may also be considered as products of a carbamate reaction. Ferles and Rudinger (153) have postulated that these products as well as those in equations (10-148) and (10-149) arise through incomplete reduction to the hydroxymethyl derivative and hydrolysis of the latter during the work-up of the reaction mixture.

The reduction of 10-carbomethoxyphenothiazine (CCXXXIII) yields phenothiazine as the only identifiable product (64).

(10-151)

CCXXXIII

10-Aminoacylphenothiazines are similarly cleaved under the influence of LAH (63).

REFERENCES

1. Nystrom, R. F., and W. G. Brown, *J. Am. Chem. Soc.*, 70, 3738 (1948).
2. Uffer, A., and E. Schlittler, *Helv. Chim. Acta*, 31, 1397 (1948).
3. Grundmann, C., in *Newer Methods of Preparative Organic Chemistry*, Interscience Publishers, Inc., New York, 1948, pp. 118-20.
4. Mićović, V. M., and M. L. Mihailović, *J. Org. Chem.*, 18, 1190 (1953).
5. Mousseron, M., R. Jacquier, M. Mousseron-Canet, and R. Zagdoun, *Bull. soc. chim. France*, [5] 19, 1042 (1952).
6. Wittig, G., and P. Hornberger, *Ann.*, 577, 11 (1952).
7. Gaylord, N. G., *Experientia*, 10, 166 (1954).
8. Gaylord, N. G., *Experientia*, in press.
9. Paddock, N. L., *Nature*, 167, 1070 (1951).
10. Barry, V. C. and D. Twomey, *Abstracts of Papers*, XIIth International Congress of Pure and Applied Chemistry, New York, September 1951, p. 308.
11. Barry, V. C., J. G. Belton, R. M. Kelly, and D. Twomey, *Nature*, 166, 303 (1950).
12. Curtin, D. Y., and S. M. Gerber, *J. Am. Chem. Soc.*, 74, 4052 (1952).

13. Jílek, J. O., and M. Protiva, *Collection Czech. Chem. Communs.*, 15, 659 (1950).

14. Sandoz, A. G., Swiss Pat. 276,415 (October 16, 1951).

15. Reese, J., *Agnew. Chem.*, 64, 399 (1952).

16. Reid, T. S., and G. H. Smith, through *Chem. Eng. News*, 29, 3042 (1951).

17. Husted, D. R., and A. H. Ahlbrecht, *J. Am. Chem. Soc.*, 74, 5422 (1952).

18. Lemieux, R. U., and J. Giguere, *Can. J. Chem.*, 29, 678 (1951).

19. Blicke, F. F., and Chi-Jung Lu, *J. Am. Chem. Soc.*, 74, 3933 (1952).

20. Eiter, K., and O. Svierak, *Monatsh.*, 82, 186 (1951).

21. Eiter, K., and O. Svierak, *Monatsh.*, 83, 1453 (1952).

22. Eiter, K., and E. Mrazak, *Monatsh.*, 83, 915 (1952).

23. Cram, D. J., and F. A. Abd Elhafez, *J. Am. Chem. Soc.*, 74, 5851 (1952).

24. Eiter, K., and E. Mrazak, *Monatsh.*, 83, 926 (1952).

25. Witkop, B., and J. B. Patrick, *J. Am. Chem. Soc.*, 74, 3861 (1952).

26. Stork, G., and H. Conroy, *J. Am. Chem. Soc.*, 73, 4743 (1951).

27. Felkin, H., *Compt. rend.*, 230, 304 (1950).

28. Carrara, G., and G. Weitnauer, *Gazz. chim. ital.*, 79, 856 (1949).

29. Lepetit S. A., Brit. Pat. 679,028 (September 10, 1952).

30. Carrara, G., V. D'Ameto, and M. Bellenghi, *Gazz. chim. ital.*, 80, 822 (1950).

31. Colonna, M., and C. Runti, *Ann. chim. (Roma)*, 41, 740 (1951); through M. Ferles, and J. Rudinger, *Chem. Listy*, 47, 115 (1953).

32. Huebner, C. F., and C. R. Scholz, *J. Am. Chem. Soc.*, 73, 2089 (1951).

33. Eiter, K., and E. Sackl, *Monatsh.*, 83, 123 (1952).

34. Swan, G. A., *J. Chem. Soc.*, 1949, 1720.

35. Karrer, P., M. Suter, and P. Waser, *Helv. Chim. Acta*, 32, 1936 (1949).

36. Mousseron, M., R. Jacquier, M. Mousseron-Canet and R. Zagdoun, *Compt. rend.*, 235, 177 (1952).

37. Fodor, G., J. Kiss and I. Sallay, *J. Chem. Soc.*, 1951, 1858.

38. Rheim, A., and M. Jutisz, *Biochim. et Biophys. Acta*, 9, 645 (1952).

39. Karrer, P., and B. J. R. Nicolaus, *Helv. Chim. Acta*, 35, 1581 (1952).

40. Jolles, P., and C. Fromageot, *Bull. soc. chim. France*, [5] 18, 862 (1951).

41. Jolles, P., and C. Fromageot, *Biochim. et Biophys. Acta*, 9, 287 (1952).

42. Fromageot, C., M. Jutisz, D. Meyer, and L. Pénasse, *Compt. rend.*, 230, 1905 (1950).

43. Fromageot, C., M. Jutisz, D. Meyer, and L. Pénasse, *Biochim. et Biophys. Acta*, 6, 283 (1950).

44. Bailey, J. L., *Biochem. J.*, 52, iv (1952).

45. Avison, A. W. D., and A. L. Morrison, *J. Chem. Soc.*, 1950, 1474.

46. Kuffner, F., and E. Polke, *Monatsh.*, 82, 330 (1951).

47. Dahn, H., and U. Solms, *Helv. Chim. Acta*, 34, 907 (1951).

48. Dahn, H., U. Solms, and P. Zoller, *Helv. Chim. Acta*, 35, 2117 (1952).

49. Brown, W. G., in *Organic Reactions*, Vol. VI, p. 479.

50. Sommers, A. H., K. M. Beck, M. Freifelder, and A. W. Weston, *Abstracts of Papers*, 121st Meeting American Chemical Society, Milwaukee, Wisconsin, March 1952, p. 4J.

51. Bartlett, M. F., W. I. Taylor, and K. Wiesner, *Chemistry and Industry, 1953*, 173.

52. Morrison, A. L., R. F. Long, and M. Königstein, *J. Chem. Soc.*, 1951, 952.

53. McCoubrey, A., and D. W. Mathieson, *J. Chem. Soc.*, 1951, 2851.

54. Friedman, L., *Anstracts of Papers*, 116th Meeting American Chemical Society, Atlantic City, N. J., September 1949, p. 5M.

55. Weygand, F., and D. Tietjen, *Chem. Ber.*, 84, 625 (1951).
56. Kjaer, A., through ref. 55.
57. Weygand, F., and G. Eberhardt, *Angew. Chem.*, 64, 458 (1952).
58. King, J. A., V. Hofmann, and F. H. McMillan, *J. Org. Chem.*, 16, 1100 (1951).
59. Burgstahler, A. W., *J. Am. Chem. Soc.*, 73, 3021 (1951).
60. Banholzer, K., T. W. Campbell, and H. Schmid, *Helv. Chim. Acta*, 35, 1577 (1952).
61. Kaye, I. A., and C. L. Parris, *J. Org. Chem.*, 17, 737 (1952).
62. Gaylord, N. G., *J. Am. Chem. Soc.*, 76, 285 (1954).
63. Dahlbom, R. and T. Ekstrand, *Acta Chem. Scand.*, 5, 102 (1951).
64. Dahlbom, R., *Acta Chem. Scand.*, 6, 310 (1952).
65. Ciba S. A., Fr. Pat. 987,158 (August 9, 1951).
66. Schlittler, E., and A. Uffer, Ger. Pat. 824,491 (December 13, 1951).
67. Jacquier, R., and R. Zagdoun, *Bull. soc. chim. France*, [5] 19, 699 (1952).
68. Jacquier, R., and R. Zagdoun, *Bull. soc. chim. France*, [5] 19, 698 (1952).
69. Wiberg, E., and M. Schmidt, *Z. Naturforsch.*, 6b, 333 (1951).
70. Wiberg, E., and R. Bauer, *Z. Naturforsch.*, 7b, 131 (1952).
71. Hermann, E. C., and A. Kreuchunas, *J. Am. Chem. Soc.*, 74, 5168 (1952).
72. Parke, Davis and Co., Australian Pat. Appln. 13,395/52 (October 15, 1952).
73. Wessely, F., K. Schlögl, and G. Korger, *Monatsh.*, 83, 1156 (1952).
74. Wessely, F., K. Schlögl, and G. Korger, *Nature*, 169, 708 (1952).
75. Roth, B., M. E. Hultquist, M. J. Fahrenbach, D. B. Cosulich, H. P. Broquist, J. A. Brockman, Jr., J. M. Smith, Jr., R. P. Parker, E. L. R. Stokstad, and T. H. Jukes, *J. Am. Chem. Soc.*, 74, 3247 (1952).
76. Panouse, J. J., *Compt. rend.*, 233, 260 (1951).
77. Chibnall, A. C., and M. W. Rees, *Biochem. J.*, 48, xlvii (1951).
78. Chibnall, A. C., and M. W. Rees, *Biochem. J.*, 52, iii (1952).
79. Friedman, L., *Abstracts of Papers*, 122nd Meeting American Chemical Society, Atlantic City, N. J., September 1952, p. 46M.
80. Wiberg, E., and M. Schmidt, *Z. Naturforsch.*, 6b, 171 (1951).
81. Karrer, P., and P. Portmann, *Helv. Chim. Acta*, 31, 2088 (1948).
82. Karrer, P., and K. Ehrhardt, *Helv. Chim. Acta*, 34, 2202 (1951).
83. Moffett, R. B., *J. Org. Chem.*, 14, 862 (1949).
84. Moffett, R. B., and J. L. White, *J. Org. Chem.*, 17, 407 (1952).
85. Baker, B. R., R. E. Schaub, and J. H. Williams, *J. Org. Chem.*, 17, 116 (1952).
86. Hoffmann, K., E. Tagmann, H. J. Bein, and J. Tripod, *Abstracts of Papers*, XIIth International Congress of Pure and Applied Chemistry, September 1951, New York, p. 324.
87. Tagmann, E., E. Sury, and K. Hoffmann, *Helv. Chim. Acta*, 35, 1235 (1952).
88. Ames, D. E., and R. E. Bowman, *J. Chem. Soc.*, 1952, 1057.
89. Galinovsky, F., and E. Stern, *Ber.*, 77B, 132 (1944).
90. Lukeš, R., and J. Málek, *Chem. Listy*, 45, 72 (1951).
91. Lukeš, R., and J. Málek, *Collection Czech. Chem. Commun.*, 16, 23 (1951).
92. Lukeš, R., and J. Dobáš, *Collection Czech. Chem. Commun.*, 15, 303 (1950).
93. Beck, K. M., K. E. Hamlin, and A. W. Weston, *J. Am. Chem. Soc.*, 74, 605 (1952).
94. Karrer, P., and H. Krishna, *Helv. Chim. Acta*, 35, 459 (1952).
95. Speeter, M. E., and W. H. Maroney, unpublished work.
96. Julian, P. L., and H. C. Printy, *J. Am. Chem. Soc.*, 71, 3206 (1949).
97. Smith, P. A. S., and Tung-yin Yu, *J. Am. Chem. Soc.*, 74, 1096 (1952).

98. Julian, P. L., and A. Magnani, *J. Am. Chem. Soc.*, 71, 3207 (1949).
99. Kates, M., and L. Marion, *J. Am. Chem. Soc.*, 72, 2308 (1950).
100. Kates, M., and L. Marion, *Can: J. Chem.*, 29, 37 (1951).
101. Goutarel, R., M. M. Janot, V. Prelog, R. P. A. Sneeden, and W. I. Taylor, *Helv. Chim. Acta*, 34, 1139 (1951).
102. Habgood, T., L. Marion, and H. Schwarz, *Helv. Chim. Acta*, 35, 638 (1952).
103. Gibson, M. S., and R. Robinson, *Chemistry and Industry*, 1951, 93.
104. Goutarel, R., M. M. Janot, V. Prelog, and R. P. A. Sneeden, *Helv. Chim. Acta*, 34, 1962 (1951).
105. Prelog, V., J. B. Patrick, and B. Witkop, *Helv. Chim. Acta*, 35, 640 (1952).
106. Cook, J. W., J. D. Loudon, and P. McCloskey, *J. Chem. Soc.*, 1952, 3904.
107. Grob, C. A., and H. U. Schmid, *Helv. Chim. Acta*, 33, 1955 (1950).
108. Stoll, A., T. Petrzilka, and J. Rutschmann, *Helv. Chim. Acta*, 33, 2254 (1950).
109. de Mayo, P., and W. Rigby, *Nature*, 166, 1075 (1950).
110. Badger, G. M., J. H. Seidler, and B. Thomson, *J. Chem. Soc.*, 1951, 3207.
111. Wooten, W. C., and R. L. McKee, *J. Am. Chem. Soc.*, 71, 2946 (1949).
112. Karrer, P., L. Szabo, H. J. V. Krishna, and R. Schwyzer, *Helv. Chim. Acta*, 33, 294 (1950).
113. Wiesner, K., S. K. Figdor, M. F. Bartlett, and D. R. Henderson, *Can. J. Chem.*, 30, 608 (1952).
114. Wiesner, K., D. M. MacDonald, Z. Valenta, and R. Armstrong, *Can. J. Chem.*, 30, 761 (1952).
115. Edwards, O. E., and L. Marion, *Can. J. Chem.*, 30, 627 (1952).
116. Edwards, O. E., and L. Marion, *J. Am. Chem. Soc.*, 71, 1694 (1949).
117. Swan, G. A., *J. Chem. Soc.*, 1949, 1720.
118. Jost, J., *Helv. Chim. Acta*, 32, 1297 (1949).
119. Boekelheide, V., and C. Ainsworth, *J. Am. Chem. Soc.*, 72, 2134 (1950).
120. Boekelheide, V., and J. P. Lodge, Jr., *J. Am. Chem. Soc.*, 73, 3681 (1951).
121. Cockburn, W. F., and L. Marion, *Can. J. Chem.*, 30, 92 (1952).
122. Boekelheide, V., and S. Rothchild, *J. Am. Chem. Soc.*, 71, 879 (1949).
123. Galinovsky, F., O. Vogl, and W. Moroz, *Monatsh.*, 83, 242 (1952).
124. Findlay, S. P., *J. Am. Chem. Soc.*, 73, 3008 (1951).
125. Karrer, P., C. H. Eugster, and P. Waser, *Helv. Chim. Acta*, 32, 2381 (1949).
126. Kenner, G. W., and M. A. Murray, *J. Chem. Soc.*, 1950, 406.
127. Stoll, A., A. Hofmann, and T. Petrzilka, *Helv. Chim. Acta*, 34, 1544 (1951).
128. Mustafa, A., *J. Chem. Soc.*, 1952, 2435.
129. Mustafa, A., and A. M. Gad, *J. Chem. Soc.*, 1949, 384.
130. Galinovsky, F., and R. Weiser, *Experientia*, 6, 377 (1950).
131. Galinovsky, F., A. Wagner, and R. Weiser, *Monatsh.*, 82, 551 (1951).
132. Galinovsky, F., O. Vogl, and R. Weiser, *Monatsh.*, 83, 114 (1952).
133. Galinovsky, F., and O. Vogl, *Monatsh.*, 83, 1055 (1952).
134. Mariella, R. P., and E. P. Belcher, *J. Am. Chem. Soc.*, 74, 4049 (1952).
135. Lukeš, R., and O. Červinka, unpublished work, through M. Ferles and J. Rudinger, *Chem. Listy*, 47, 104,140 (1953).
136. Mariella, R. P., and A. J. Havlik, *J. Am. Chem. Soc.*, 74, 1915 (1952).
137. Mariella, R. P., and E. P. Belcher, *J. Am. Chem. Soc.*, 73, 2616 (1951).
138. Druey, J., and A, Hüni, *Helv. Chim. Acta*, 35, 2301 (1952).
139. Lukeš, R., and M. Ferles, unpublished work, through J. Rudinger, M. Ferles and M. Protiva, *Chem. Listy*, 45, 317 (1951).
140. Halford, J. O., and B. Weissmann, *J. Org. Chem.*, 17, 1646 (1952).

141. Garbrecht, W. L., J. H. Hunter, and J. B. Wright, *J. Am. Chem. Soc.*, 72, 1359 (1950).
142. Reid, W. B., Jr., U. S. Pat. 2,605,266 (July 29, 1952).
143. Lukeš, R., and M. Ferles, unpublished work, through M. Ferles and J. Rudinger, *Chem. Listy*, 47, 135 (1953).
144. Societe des Usines Chimiques Rhone Poulenc, Australian Pat. Appln. 955/51 (February 21, 1951).
145. Parke, Davis & Co., Australian Pat. Appln. 10,904/52 (June 24, 1952).
146. Wiley, R. H., O. H. Borum, and L. L. Bennett, Jr., *J. Am. Chem. Soc.*, 71, 2899 (1949).
147. Wilk, I. J., and W. J. Close, *J. Org. Chem.*, 15, 1020 (1950).
148. Wessely, F., K. Schlögl, and E. Wawersich, *Monatsh.*, 83, 1426 (1952).
149. Wessely, F., K. Schlögl, and E. Wawersich, *Monatsh.*, 83, 1439 (1952).
150. Schlögl, K., F. Wessely, and G. Korger, *Monatsh.*, 83, 493 (1952).
151. Wessely, F., and W. Swoboda, *Monatsh.*, 82, 621 (1951).
152. Gaylord, N. G., unpublished data.
153. Ferles, M., and J. Rudinger, *Chem. Listy*, 47, 99 (1953).

CHAPTER 11

Reduction of
OXYGEN-CONTAINING ORGANIC COMPOUNDS
V. Compounds Containing Ether Linkages

11.1 ETHERS

11.1.1 Reactions with Lithium Aluminum Hydride

Ethers are generally resistant to attack by LAH. Thus, the majority of LAH reductions are carried out in diethyl ether. Di-n-propyl and di-n-butyl ethers have also been widely used, as well as the cyclic ether tetrahydrofuran.

The synthesis of methanol by the LAH reduction of carbon dioxide proceeds with a satisfactory yield. However, the isolation of methanol from ether-water mixtures gives low yields. Nystrom, Yanko, and Brown (1) adopted the use of the diethyl ether of diethylene glycol (I) as a nonvolatile solvent replacing the diethyl ether, and the monobutyl ether of diethylene glycol (II) to decompose the excess LAH and to liberate methanol by alcoholysis of the intermediate complex.

$$\begin{array}{cc} C_2H_5OCH_2CH_2\diagdown \\ \qquad\qquad\qquad O \\ C_2H_5OCH_2CH_2\diagup \\ \qquad\quad I \end{array} \qquad\qquad \begin{array}{cc} C_4H_9OCH_2CH_2\diagdown \\ \qquad\qquad\qquad O \\ HOCH_2CH_2\diagup \\ \qquad\quad II \end{array}$$

Working with I and II, Nystrom, Skraba, and Mansfield reported that traces of diethyl ether are present in the methanol-C^{14} produced by this method (2). Cox, Turner, and Warne did not detect diethyl ether under these conditions but instead identified inactive ethanol, butanol and formaldehyde as impurities in the methanol (3,4). Using I as solvent for the LAH and benzyl alcohol or the monophenyl ether of ethylene glycol for the decomposition and alcoholysis gives ethanol and formaldehyde as impurities. The ethanol obtained in these reactions probably arises by the cleavage of the diethyl carbitol (I) by some lithium compound under the conditions of the reaction. Inactive ethanol has also been reported as an impurity in the labeled ethanol obtained by the LAH reduction of acetic-1-C^{14} and acetic-2-C^{14} acids, utilizing I and II as indicated above (5). In order to eliminate the ethanol produced in the reduction of carbon dioxide, Cox, Turner, and Warne have utilized solvents which cannot afford volatile by-products, i.e., tetrahydrofurfuryloxytetrahydropyran as solvent for LAH and tetrahydrofurfuryl alcohol for alcoholysis (3,4).

The non-reduction of i-steroid ethers by LAH has been utilized for the protection of the C_5 double bond system in a number of synthetic studies (6).

Karrer and Rüttner reported that the following ethers are not attacked by LAH at their boiling points (7): phenyl allyl ether, phenyl benzyl ether, phenyl trityl ether, α-naphthyl allyl ether, cinnamyl methyl ether, cinnamyl trityl ether. This is analogous to the behavior of Grignard reagents since ethers are stable at ordinary temperatures in the presence of organomagnesium compounds (7-9). However, ether cleavage does occur with the Grignard reagent in the presence of cobalt chloride (10). Treatment of phenyl allyl ether (III) with ethereal LAH in the presence of cobalt chloride under refluxing conditions gives 26% phenol (7-9).

$$C_6H_5OCH_2CH=CH_2 \xrightarrow{\text{LAH}-CoCl_2} C_6H_5OH \qquad (11\text{-}1)$$
$$\text{III}$$

Similar treatment of phenyl benzyl ether (IV) results in 10% cleavage into phenol and toluene.

$$C_6H_5OCH_2C_6H_5 \xrightarrow{\text{LAH}-CoCl_2} C_6H_5OH + C_6H_5CH_3 \qquad (11\text{-}2)$$
$$\text{IV}$$

Anisole is not attacked by ethereal LAH in the presence of cobalt chloride (7).

As discussed in Section 8.1.1.a, the reduction of cyclohexyloxyacetic acid (V) and trans-β-decahydronaphthyloxyacetic acid with LAH in ethereal solution yields 65% of the expected reduction product and 10% of the cleavage products cyclohexanol and β-decalol, respectively (11).

$$\text{V} \qquad (11\text{-}3)$$

Brown (12) has shown that the reduction of 2,2-disubstituted-4-phenoxybutyronitrile (VI) with an ethereal LAH solution yields the expected amine where R = methyl, ethyl, phenyl, or tolyl.

$$C_6H_5OCH_2CH_2\overset{R}{\underset{R}{C}}CN \xrightarrow[80-90\%]{\text{LAH}} C_6H_5OCH_2CH_2\overset{R}{\underset{R}{C}}CH_2NH_2 \qquad (11\text{-}4)$$
$$\text{VI}$$

When R = isopropyl, 85% of the starting material is recovered and 9% of a cyclization product is isolated as the hydrobromide.

$$C_6H_5OCH_2CH_2\underset{\underset{C_3H_7}{|}}{\overset{\overset{C_3H_7}{|}}{C}}CN \xrightarrow{\text{LAH}} C_3H_7-\underset{\underset{H_2C}{|}}{\overset{\overset{C_3H_7}{|}}{C}}-\underset{\underset{CH_2}{|}}{CH_2} \quad (11\text{-}5)$$

VII

The LAH reduction of 1-bromo-2-ethoxy-2-phenylethane (VIII) yields styrene as well as the expected 2-ethoxy-2-phenylethane (13).

$$\underset{\underset{OC_2H_5}{|}}{C_6H_5CHCH_2Br} \xrightarrow{\text{LAH}} \underset{\underset{OC_2H_5}{|}}{C_6H_5CHCH_3} + C_6H_5CH\!=\!CH_2 \quad (11\text{-}6)$$

VIII

A rearrangement has been reported (14) in the LAH reduction of α-(2-dimethylaminoethoxy)-α,α-diphenylacetopiperidide (IX) to yield 30% of the expected piperidinoethane and 32% of 3-dimethylamino-1,1-diphenyl-1-propanol.

$$\underset{\underset{C_6H_5}{|}}{\overset{\overset{O}{||}\quad\overset{C_6H_5}{|}}{N-C-C}}-OCH_2CH_2N(CH_3)_2$$

IX

$$\xrightarrow{\text{LAH}} \quad \underset{\underset{C_6H_5}{|}}{NCH_2\overset{\overset{C_6H_5}{|}}{C}}-OCH_2CH_2N(CH_3)_2$$

$$\underset{\underset{(C_6H_5)_2CCH_2CH_2N(CH_3)_2}{\overset{OH}{|}}}{} + \quad (11\text{-}7)$$

As discussed in Section 10.1.1.d.1, the reaction apparently involves a reductive cleavage of a carbon-carbon bond followed by a rearrangement as shown in equation (10-33).

The LAH reduction of the methyl esters of methylated mannuronic acids derived from alginic acid, followed by hydrolysis with dilute sulfuric acid, yields 2,3-dimethylmannose, dimethylglucose, 2,3,4-trimethylmannose, and monomethylmannose. Treatment of the methylmannoside derived from 2,3-dimethylmannose with LAH yields some monomethylmannose indicating that demethylation might account for much of the monomethylmannose found in the reduction products of the alginic acid derivative (15).

The apparent cleavage of the ether linkage in the LAH reduction of N-(α-ethoxybenzyl)acetanilide (X) and the analogous methoxy compound (16) occurs by virtue of the presence of the —NCO— grouping, as discussed in Section 12.17. Various other apparent ether cleavage reactions fall within this category. The reaction of LAH and 2-methoxy-3,4,5,6-tetrahydropyridine (XI) to yield piperidine (17) is also related to the presence of the —NCO— grouping.

OC₂H₅
|
C₆H₅CHNCOCH₃
|
C₆H₅
X

XI

11.1.2 Reactions with Other Complex Metal Hydrides

Aluminum hydride is reported to tenaciously retain ether and evidence has been obtained for a monoetherate stable below 0° (18).

Aluminum borohydride reacts with dimethyl ether to form an addition compound which decomposes at 40–60° to yield a mixture of products which are not the parent substances (19).

11.2 1,2-EPOXIDES

This section is primarily concerned with ethylene oxides (1,2-epoxides). Cyclic ethers containing more than two carbon atoms in the ring are considered in Section 11.9 as heterocyclic oxygen compounds.

11.2.1 Reductions with Lithium Aluminum Hydride

The reaction of LAH and 1,2-epoxides consumes one-quarter mole of the hydride per mole of epoxide, according to the equation:

$$4 R_1 - C(R_2) - C(R_3) - R_4 + LiAlH_4 \rightarrow \left[R_1 - C(R_2)(H) - C(R_3)(O) - R_4 \right]_4 LiAl \xrightarrow{4 H_2O}$$

$$4 R_1 - C(R_2)(H) - C(R_3)(OH) - R_4 \quad (11-8)$$

As discussed in Section 6.1.1, Trevoy and Brown (1) have proposed that the reduction of epoxides involves a bimolecular nucleophilic displacement proceeding by an S_N^2 mechanism. Inversion of configuration occurs on the carbon atom attacked in the LAH reduction. The reactive species is postulated as a series of complex aluminohydride ions, $AlH_{4-n}R_n^-$, which act as carriers for the hydride ion.

11.2.1.a *Acyclic Epoxides.* The opening of monosubstituted ethylene oxides usually proceeds with cleavage of the carbon-oxygen bond at the primary carbon to yield the secondary alcohol as the predominant product. Thus, epichlorohydrin is reduced to 2-propanol in 88% yield (20) while 1,2;5,6-diepoxyhexane is reduced to 2,5-hexanediol (21). The LAH reduction of 1,2-epoxydecane yields 90% of the secondary alcohol 2-decanol (22). In contrast, other methods of reduction yield mixtures of the primary and secondary alcohols as shown in Table LXV.

TABLE LXV

Reduction of 1,2-Epoxydecane (22)

Method	Product, %	
	1-Decanol	2-Decanol
Chemical Reduction		
LAH		90
Sodium amalgam-ethanol	5	35
Catalytic Reduction		
Raney nickel[a]	83–90	10
Raney nickel-NaOH[a]	5–7.5	85–95
Raney nickel-H₃PO₄[a]	50	50
Ni-on-kieselguhr[b]	85	10

[a]150°, 900 psi.
[b]200°, 1450 psi.

Styrene oxide is attacked by LAH at the terminal carbon to yield 1-phenylethanol (20,23). Catalytic hydrogenation with Raney nickel in the absence or presence of sodium hydroxide or phosphoric acid yields the primary alcohol 2-phenylethanol (22).

The reduction of 3,4-epoxy-1-butene (XII) with LAH yields a mixture of 3-buten-2-ol and 3-buten-1-ol in which the predominant product is the secondary alcohol (20).

$$CH_2{=}CHCH{-}CH_2 \xrightarrow{\text{LAH}}$$
$$\underset{O}{\diagdown\diagup}$$

XII

$$CH_2{=}CHCHCH_3 + CH_2{=}CHCH_2CH_2OH \quad (11\text{-}9)$$
$$\underset{OH}{\big|}$$

The yields and proportions of products are, however, dependent upon the concentration of LAH, as shown in Table LXVI (24).

TABLE LXVI

LAH Reduction of 3,4-Epoxy-1-butene (24)

LAH/Epoxide Mole Ratio	Total Alcohols, %	Relative %	
		3-Buten-2-ol	3-Buten-1-ol
2.1	100	70	30
2.1	76	72	28
0.68	90	78	22
0.26	72	83	17
0.67 (20)	71	82	18

The percentage of secondary attack to yield the primary alcohol increases with an increase in the LAH/epoxide ratio. Partial hydrolysis of the LAH with methyl isobutyl carbinol prior to its reaction with the epoxide (XII) results in a decrease in the percentage of secondary attack. These results are consistent with two postulations: (a) LAH reduction of epoxides is initiated by attack at the epoxide by a series of ions, AlH_4^-, AlH_3OR^-, $AlH_2(OR)_2^-$ and $AlH(OR)_3^-$, which although electronically similar increase in steric requirements in the indicated order, and (b) steric factors are important in determining position of attack and direction of ring opening.

Reduction of 1,1-disubstituted epoxides with LAH results in attack at the primary carbon atom to yield the tertiary alcohol as the major product. Reduction of α-methylstyrene oxide (XIII) yields 2-phenyl-2-propanol (25) while 1,1-dineopentylethylene oxide yields a mixture of the primary and tertiary alcohols with the latter as the more abundant product (26).

$$C_6H_5C\overset{\displaystyle CH_3}{\underset{\displaystyle \diagdown O \diagup}{|}}CH_2 \overset{LAH}{\longrightarrow} C_6H_5\overset{\displaystyle CH_3}{\underset{\displaystyle OH}{\overset{|}{\underset{|}{C}}}}CH_3 \qquad (11\text{-}10)$$

XIII

Reduction of 1,2-disubstituted epoxides yields secondary alcohols. While styrene oxide and α-methylstyrene oxide are attacked at the β-carbon, a substituent on the β-carbon, as in benzalacetophenone oxide (XIV), shifts the main attack to the α-position (20,27).

$$C_6H_5CH\underset{\diagdown O \diagup}{\overset{}{}}CH\overset{}{\underset{\parallel}{\overset{}{C}}}\overset{O}{\underset{}{}}C_6H_5 \overset{LAH}{\longrightarrow} C_6H_5CH_2CH\overset{|}{\underset{OH}{}}CHC_6H_5\overset{|}{\underset{OH}{}} \qquad (11\text{-}11)$$

XIV

Trevoy and Brown suggest that the reduction of the carbonyl group precedes the opening of the epoxide ring (20). Reaction with the Grignard reagent results in cleavage between the carbonyl and the epoxy groups (28).

Comparison of the reactions of 1,2-epoxides with Grignard reagents and those with LAH reveals several analogies (28). Monosubstituted epoxides react with the Grignard reagent to yield secondary alcohols, as with LAH. Grignard reactions with 1,1-disubstituted epoxides proceed through initial isomerization to an aldehyde followed by normal addition to the carbonyl group. The isomerization is attributed to the presence of the magnesium halide in the Grignard reagent equilibrium since reaction with the dialkylmagnesium gives the tertiary alcohol, as with LAH, by ring cleavage without isomerization. Reaction of an epoxide with a magnesium halide yields a halohydrin. LAH reduction of 4,5-isopropylidene-1,2;3,6-dianhydromannitol (XV) yields the secondary alcohol (XVI) while reaction of XV with the methyl Grignard reagent yields the halohydrin containing the secondary alcohol group (XVII) (29).

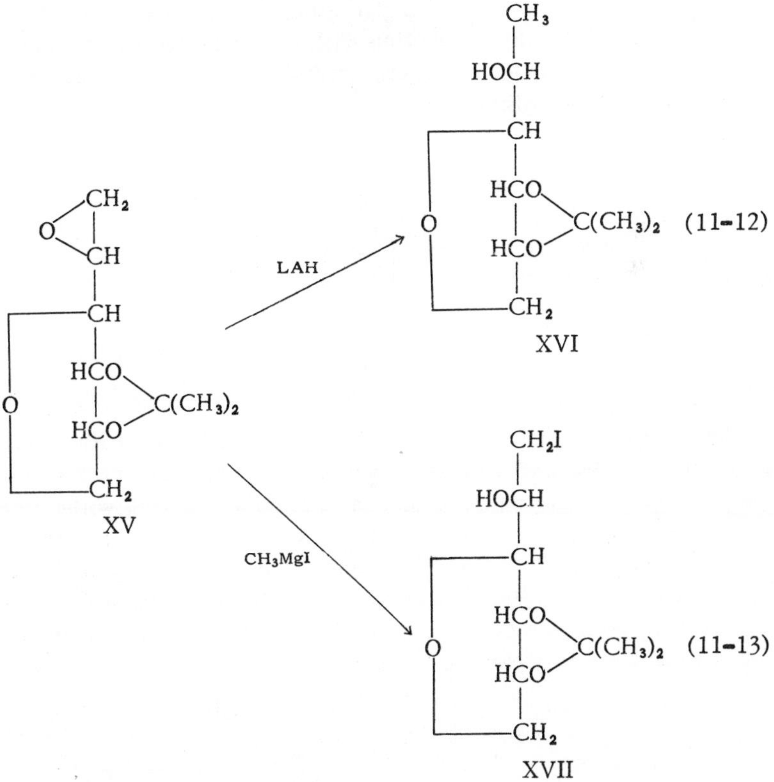

$$
\begin{array}{c}
CH_3 \\
| \\
HOCH \\
| \\
CH \\
\end{array}
$$

O—...—C(CH$_3$)$_2$ (11-12)

XVI (via LAH)

XV

CH$_3$MgI

CH$_2$I / HOCH ... C(CH$_3$)$_2$ (11-13)

XVII

Whereas styrene oxide reacts with LAH to yield the secondary alcohol, reaction with the Grignard reagent proceeds through isomerization to phenylacetaldehyde and reaction with a dialkyl magnesium yields a primary alcohol (28). The course of the reaction of 3,4-epoxy-1-butene with the Grignard reagent is governed by the size of the Grignard reagent, a factor which also appears to play a part in the reaction with LAH.

The reduction of *cis-* and *trans-*stilbene oxides (XVIII) with lithium aluminum deuteride yields 2-deutero-1,2-diphenylethanols (30).

$$C_6H_5CH\underset{O}{\diagdown\diagup}CHC_6H_5 \xrightarrow{\text{LiAlD}_4} \underset{OH \quad D}{C_6H_5CH-CHC_6H_5} \qquad (11\text{-}14)$$

XVIII

The reactions of LAH and various acyclic epoxides are summarized in Table LXVII.

Collin-Asselineau *et al.* (31) have reported the isolation of a hydroxy oxide, m.p. 143°, and a saturated, neutral trioxide, m.p. 178°, among the products from the chromic acid oxidation of ambréine. The hydroxy oxide, which has an empirical formula of $C_{30}H_{52}O_2$, and is postulated as XIX, is recovered unchanged after boiling in ether with LAH or refluxing for two hours at 140° in N-ethylmorpholine with ten times the theoretical amount of LAH. The trioxide, $C_{30}H_{52}O_3$, is resistant to the action of LAH in boiling N-ethylmorpholine.

XIX

The reaction between LAH and 1,1-di- and 1,1,2-trisubstituted epoxides in which the 1,1-substituent is a cyclohexane ring represents an interesting picture. Billimoria and Maclagan originally reported, without details, that the reaction of the glycidic ester (XX) and LAH yields 1-cyclohexylethylene glycol (32). In a subsequent account (33) they indicated that the reaction actually yields 1-hydroxyethyl-1-cyclohexanol (XXI), the alternative α,β-diol structure being unlikely as the product does not react with benzaldehyde or acetone.

$$\qquad (11\text{-}15)$$

XX   XXI

TABLE LXVII

LAH Reduction of Acyclic Epoxides

Epoxides	Product	% Yield	Ref.
C$_2$H$_4$O Ethylene oxide-1,2-C^{14}	Ethanol-1,2-C^{14}	93[1]	2
C$_3$H$_5$ClO Epichlorohydrin	2-Propanol	88[3]	4
C$_4$H$_8$O 3,4-Epoxy-1-butene	3-Buten-2-ol	58[5] }	4
	3-Buten-1-ol	13 }	
	3 Buten-2-ol	70→83 } 72-100[6]	7
	3-Buten-1-ol	17→30 }	
C$_4$H$_8$O D(+)-2,3-Epoxybutane	L(−)-2-Butanol	80	8
C$_6$H$_{10}$O$_2$ 1,2;5,6-Diepoxyhexane	2,5-Hexanediol	66	9
C$_8$H$_8$O Styrene oxide	α-Phenylethanol	94	10
C$_9$H$_{10}$O α-Methylstyrene oxide	2-Phenyl-2-propanol	75	4
C$_9$H$_{14}$O$_4$ 3,4-Isopropylidene-1,2,5,6-dianhydromannitol	3,4-Isopropylidene-1,2,5,6-desoxymannitol	75[11]	12
4,5-Isopropylidene-1,2,3,6-dianhydromannitol	4,5-Isopropylidene-3,6-anhydro-1-desoxymannitol	41	9
C$_{10}$H$_{29}$O 1,2-Epoxydecane	2-Decanol	68	13
C$_{12}$H$_{24}$O 1,1-Dineopentylethylene oxide	1,1-Dineopentylethanol	90	14
	2,2-Dineopentylethanol	⋯ }	15
C$_{14}$H$_{12}$O cis-Stilbene oxide[16]	threo-2-Deutero-1,2-diphenylethanol	⋯ }	17
trans-Stilbene oxide[16]	erythro-2-Deutero-1,2-diphenylethanol	⋯	17
		79	4
C$_{15}$H$_{12}$O$_2$ Benzalacetophenone oxide	1,3-Diphenyl-1,2-propanediol	62	18

References — Table LXVII

[1]Reduction carried out in tetrahydrofurfuryloxytetrahydropyran at $0°$; complex decomposed with tetrahydrofurfuryl alcohol.
[2]J. D. Cox and R. J. Warne, *J. Chem. Soc., 1951,* 1893.
[3]Reduction carried out in diethyl carbitol at $25°$.
[4]L. W. Trevoy and W. G. Brown, *J. Am. Chem. Soc.,* 71, 1675 (1949).
[5]Products with same composition when reduction carried out at $-40°$ or in refluxing ether.
[6]Percentage of primary and secondary alcohols in alcohol mixture varied with LAH-epoxide mole ratio as shown in Table LXVI.
[7]R. Fuchs and C. A. Vander Werf, *J. Am. Chem. Soc.,* 74, 5917 (1952).
[8]P. J. Leroux and H. J. Lucas, *ibid.,* 73, 41 (1951).
[9]L. F. Wiggins and D. J. C. Wood, *J. Chem. Soc., 1950,* 1566.
[10]R. F. Nystrom and W. G. Brown, *J. Am. Chem. Soc.,* 70, 3738 (1948).
[11]Reduction carried out in tetrahydrofuran.
[12]E. L. Eliel and J. P. Freeman, *J. Am. Chem. Soc.,* 74, 923 (1952).
[13]A. B. Foster and W. G. Overend, *J. Chem. Soc., 1951,* 1132.
[14]M. S. Newman, G. Underwood and M. Renoll, *J. Am. Chem. Soc.,* 71, 3362 (1949).
[15]W. J. Hickinbottom and D. G. M. Wood, *J. Chem. Soc., 1951,* 1600.
[16]Reduction carried out with lithium aluminum deuteride.
[17]D. B. Kellom and D. Y. Curtin, *Abstracts of Papers,* 122nd Meeting American Chemical Society, Atlantic City, N. J., September 1952, p. 23M.
[18]W. Herz, *J. Am. Chem. Soc.,* 74, 2928 (1952).

The same diol is obtained whether the ratio of oxide to LAH is 2:1 or vice versa.

Mousseron *et al.* (11,34) also concluded that the reduction of the glycidic ester (XX) gives XXI in 60% yield. On the other hand, ethylidenecyclohexane oxide (XXII) is cleaved with LAH to yield 1-cyclohexylethanol (11,34,35).

$$(11\text{-}16)$$

XXII

The reduction of the unsubstituted epoxymethylenecyclohexane (XXIII) yields 1-methylcyclohexanol (11,35).

$$(11\text{-}17)$$

XXIII

The reactions represented in equations (11–15) and (11–17) comply with the previously indicated generalization that the attack with LAH is upon

the least substituted carbon to yield the tertiary alcohol while equation
(11–16) indicates attack in the opposite direction. According to Mousseron
(11), the direction of ring opening in the reduction of XXIII is determined
by the resonance form XXIV.

XXIII   XXIV   (11–18)

The electron-donating effect of the methyl group determines the direction
of ring opening in the reduction of XXII, while the electron-attracting
substituent in XX reverses the direction.

XXII   XX

11.2.1.b *Alicyclic Epoxides.* LAH reduction of cyclohexene oxide
yields 91% cyclohexanol (20). Reaction of the oxide with the Grignard
reagent proceeds through initial contraction of the six- to a five-membered
ring to form cyclopentylformaldehyde which then reacts normally with
the reagent. Reaction of the oxide with a dialkylmagnesium proceeds
without rearrangement (28).

Mousseron, Jacquier, Mousseron-Canet, and Zagdoun (11,35–37) have
recently investigated the LAH reduction of a series of substituted cyclohexene oxides. The results of their studies are summarized in Table
LXVIII along with those of other investigators.

The LAH reduction of 3-ethoxy-1,2-epoxycyclohexane yields *trans*-2-
ethoxycyclohexanol while the 3-chloro compound yields *cis*-2-chloro-
cyclohexanol. If the direction of ring opening is the same in both cases
then the ethoxy compound has structure XXV whereas the chloro compound has structure XXVI.

XXV   XXVI

A small quantity of cyclohexanol is formed in the reduction of XXVI,
probably as the result of dehalogenation.

TABLE LXVIII

LAH Reduction of Alicyclic Epoxides

Epoxide	Product	% Yield	Ref.
Cyclohexene oxide	Cyclohexanol	91	1
3-Chloro-1,2-epoxycyclohexane	cis-2-Chloro-1-cyclohexanol Cyclohexanol	70 } 25 }	2–4
3-Ethoxy-1,2-epoxycyclohexane	trans-2-Ethoxy-1-cyclohexanol	74	2–4
1-Acetoxy-1,2-epoxycyclohexane	1,2-Cyclohexanediol (75% cis, 25% trans)	50	2–4
1-Chloro-1,2-epoxycyclohexane	Cyclohexanol cis-2-Chloro-1-cyclohexanol	75 } 10 }	2–4
1-Cyano-1,2-epoxycyclohexane	1-Aminomethyl-1-cyclohexanol	70	3–5
1-Dimethylamino-1,2-epoxycyclohexane	trans-2-Dimethylamino-1-cyclohexanol Cyclohexanol	49 } 3 }	3–5
1-Methyl-1,2-epoxycyclohexane	1-Methyl-1-cyclohexanol	88	3–5
1,2-Dimethyl-1,2-epoxycyclopentane	trans-1,2-Dimethyl-1-cyclopentanol	40	1
1,2-Dimethyl-1,2-epoxycyclohexane	trans-1,2-Dimethyl-1-cyclohexanol	73	1

[1]L. W. Trevoy and W. G. Brown, J. Am. Chem. Soc., 71, 1675 (1949).

[2]M. Mousseron, M. Canet, and R. Jacquier, Bull. soc. chim. France, [5] 19, 698 (1952).

[3]M. Mousseron, R. Jacquier, M. Mousseron-Canet, and R. Zagdoun, Compt. rend., 235, 177 (1952).

[4]M. Mousseron, R. Jacquier, M. Mousseron-Canet, and R. Zagdoun, Bull. soc. chim. France, [5] 19, 1042 (1952).

[5]M. Mousseron and M. Canet, ibid., [5] 18, 792 (1951).

The reduction of 1-methyl-, 1-chloro- and 1-cyano-1,2-epoxycyclo-
hexanes conforms to the expected behavior to yield the tertiary alcohols.
In the reduction of the 1-chloro derivative (XXVII) the predominant attack
is on the secondary carbon yielding the transitory *gem*-halohydrin. The
latter is converted to cyclohexanone which is in turn reduced to cyclohexanol. The normal inductive effect of the halogen provokes a rear
attack by the hydride ion on the tertiary carbon to give, with Walden inversion, *cis*-2-chlorocyclohexanol.

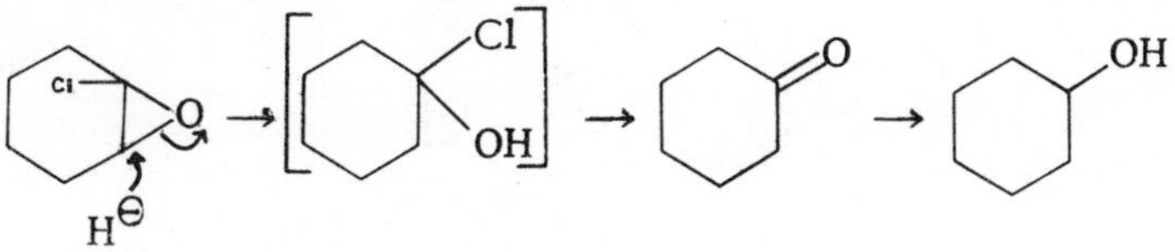

(11-19)

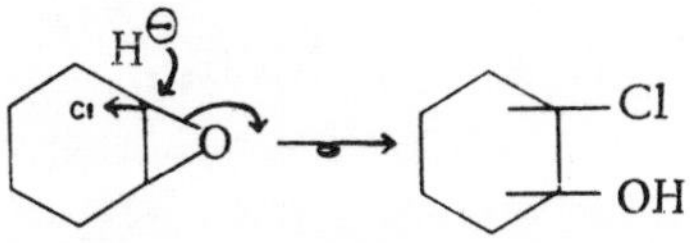

XXVII

(11-20)

XXVII

Mousseron (11) has postulated that in the reduction of 1-acetoxy-1,2-
epoxycyclohexane (XXVIII) an unexpected attack on the tertiary carbon
yields, with Walden inversion, *cis*-1,2-cyclohexanediol. The simultaneous
formation of the *trans*-diol is postulated as arising by a secondary reaction resulting in isomerization of the epoxide to 2-acetoxycyclohexanone.

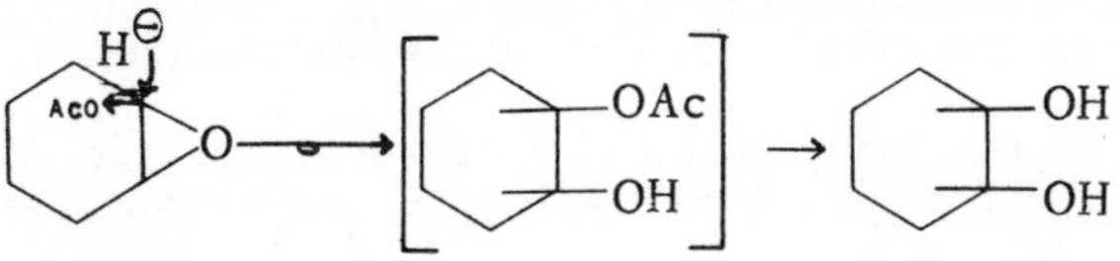

(11-21)

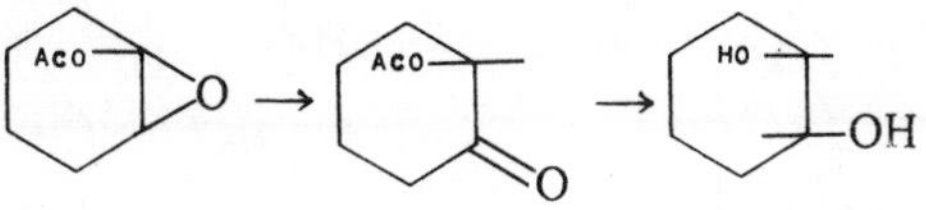

XXVIII

(11-22)

XXVIII

A more satisfactory mechanism involves the initial reduction of the ester
group.

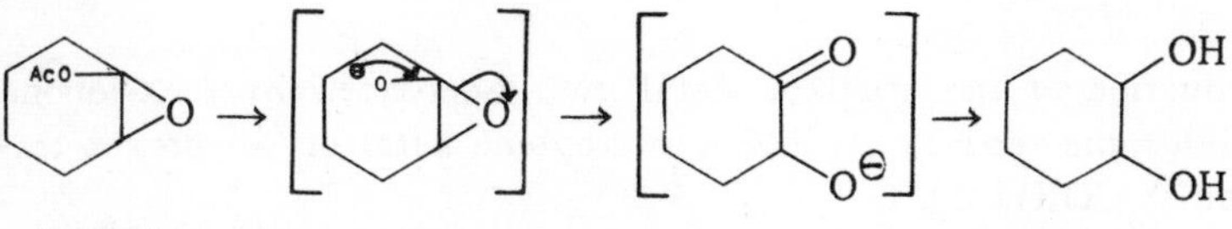

(11-23)

XXVIII

The reduction of 1-dimethylamino-1,2-epoxycyclohexane (XXIX) has also been postulated as involving a predominant, unexpected attack on the tertiary carbon, in this case without Walden inversion, to yield *trans*-2-dimethylamino-1-cyclohexanol. The isolation of the single diastereoisomer has also been observed in the reduction of 2-dimethylaminocyclohexanone. Attack on the secondary carbon of XXIX yields the intermediate *gem*-carbinol-amine which is converted to cyclohexanol.

$$(11\text{-}24)$$

$$(11\text{-}25)$$

The formation of the secondary alcohol instead of the expected tertiary alcohol is more satisfactorily explained by reference to the expected cleavage of the —NCO— grouping (Section 12.17).

Reduction of 1,2-dimethyl-1,2-epoxycyclopentane and cyclohexane is accompanied by inversion to yield the *trans* products (20).

Reduction of the cyclic acetal of epoxysuccinaldehyde, 3,4-epoxy-2,5-dimethoxytetrahydrofuran (XXX) with LAH yields the cyclic acetal of malic aldehyde (XXXI) (38).

$$(11\text{-}26)$$

LAH reduction of the ethylene ketal of 3,4-epoxytetrahydro-α-ionone (XXXII) yields the tertiary alcohol, the ethylene ketal of 3-hydroxytetrahydroionone (XXXIII) (39).

$$XXXII \qquad\qquad XXXIII \qquad\qquad (11\text{-}27)$$

Mallein has recently reported that reduction of the 5,6-epoxide of reti-
nene$_1$ (XXXIV) with LAH in ether solution yields Vitamin A$_1$ epoxide
(XXXV) wherein the 1,2-epoxide ring has not been attacked (40).

$$XXXIV \qquad\qquad\qquad XXXV \qquad (11\text{-}28)$$

Autooxidation of caryophyllene, a sesquiterpene hydrocarbon from oil
of cloves, yields caryophyllene oxide which on oxidation with potassium
permanganate is converted to an oxido-ketone, m.p. 62–63°. LAH reduction of the oxido-ketone in ether gives an oxido-alcohol, m.p. 140–141°.
That this compound is formed by reduction of the carbonyl group and that
the oxide ring is not attacked has been proved by chromic acid oxidation
which regenerates the original oxido-ketone (41). Three possible structures for the oxido-ketone were originally advanced since the structure
of caryophyllene had not been established at that time. Further work by
Barton and Lindsey has led to the postulation of the structure of the
sesquiterpene (42) and advancement of the structure of the oxido-ketone
as XXXVI (43).

$$XXXVI$$

11.2.1.c *Sugar Epoxides.* Application of LAH reduction of acyclic
epoxides in the sugar series has been shown in equation (11–12) and
Table LXVII. The same principles generally hold for alicyclic epoxides
in the sugar series.

Reduction of 2,3-anhydro derivatives is reported to yield the corresponding 2- or 3-desoxy compound. Thus, methyl 2,3-anhydro-4,6-ben-
zylidene-α-D-alloside (XXXVII) (44), methyl 2,3-anhydro-4,6-benzylidene-
α-D-guloside (XXXVIII) (45) and methyl 4,6-ditosyl-2,3-anhydro-α-D-

alloside (XXXIX) (46,47) are reduced with LAH to the 2-desoxy derivatives.

$$\text{XXXVII} \xrightarrow{\text{LAH}} \quad (11\text{-}29)$$

XXXVIII   XXXIX

Reduction of methyl 2,3-anhydro-4,6-benzylidene-α-D-mannoside (XL) (44) and methyl 2,3-anhydro-β-D-riboside (XLI) (48) yields the 3-desoxy derivatives.

XL   XLI

The reduction of XLI with LAH in ether yields 71% of a syrupy residue. On treatment with lead tetraacetate the presence of 14% of the 2-desoxy compound is detected, the remainder of the product being the 3-desoxy derivative (48).

The reduction of XXXVII with LAH yields 56% of the 2-desoxy compound, with preservation of the benzal residue. Catalytic hydrogenation over a nickel catalyst followed by treatment with benzaldehyde yields 58% of the 3-desoxy compound accompanied by only 3.5% of the 2-desoxy sugar (44).

Davoll, Lythgoe, and Trippett (49) have reported various attempts to prepare the 2'-desoxypentose from 2',3'-anhydro-7-α-D-lyxofuranosyl-theophylline (XLII). Opening of the ring with sodium thioethoxide gives 89% of the 3'-desoxy compound and only 0.8% of the 2'-desoxy compound. "Preliminary experiments in which the anhydro compound was treated with LAH indicate that the use of this reagent gives results no more favorable...." Therefore, the reduction in this case as well as the reduction of the analogous XL and XLI yields the 3-desoxy sugar.

$$C_7H_7O_2N_4$$

$$\begin{array}{c}
/ \\
HC \\
| \\
CH \\
O \diagup | \diagdown O \\
CH \\
| \\
HC \\
| \\
CH_2OH
\end{array}$$

XLII

11.2.1.d *Steroid Epoxides.* The course of the reduction of steroid epoxides is determined by the configuration of the oxirane ring. In addition, the direction of ring opening is dependent upon the degree of substitution of the carbon atoms comprising the ring.

Epoxides containing structure XLIII are reduced with LAH to the

$$\begin{array}{c}
\diagdown C \text{———} C \diagup \\
H \diagup \diagdown O \diagup \diagdown H
\end{array}$$

XLIII

polar hydroxy compound (50). 2α,3α-Oxidosteroids (XLIV) are converted to 3α-hydroxy derivatives and 2β,3β-oxidosteroids (XLV) yield the 2β-hydroxy compounds.

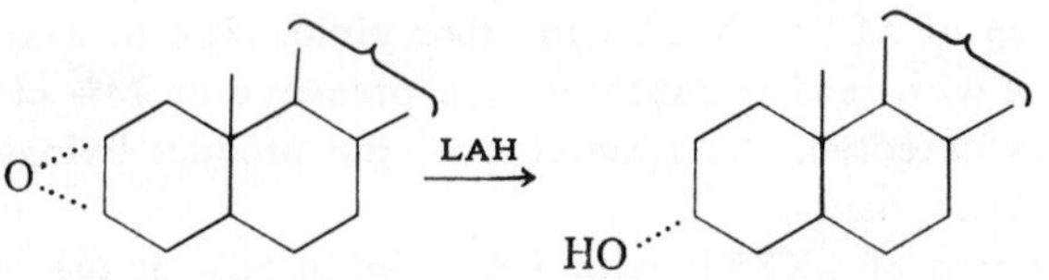

(11-30)

XLIV

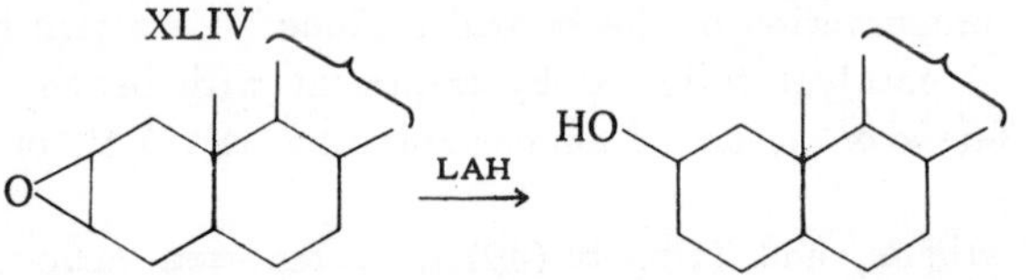

(11-31)

XLV

LAH reduction of 2α,3α-oxidocholestane (XLVI) yields epicholestanol (XLVII) (isolated as the monoacetate) as the major product (51-55). In addition cholestane-2,3-diol (isolated as the diacetate) and cholestane are produced in smaller amounts. The former is a by-product presumably produced by hydrolysis of unreacted epoxide.

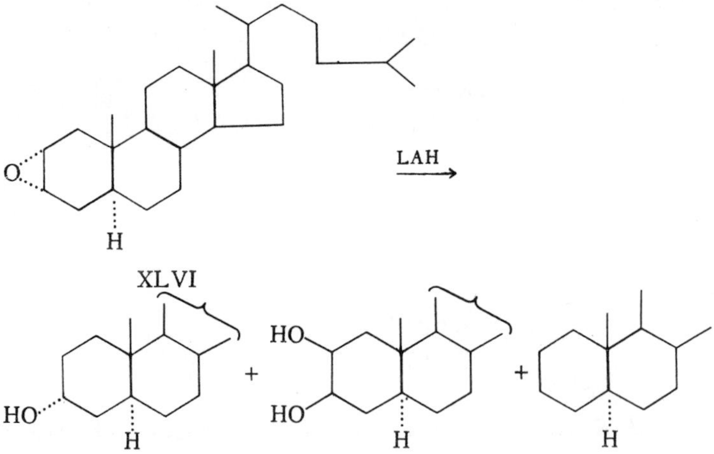

XLVI

XLVII

+   +   (11-32)

Catalytic hydrogenation of XLVI with Raney nickel in alcohol or dioxane or with platinum oxide in dioxane yields unchanged oxidocholestane. Reduction over a palladium-on-calcium carbonate catalyst yields chiefly unchanged epoxide with a small amount of cholestane-2,3-diol. Reduction with platinum oxide in ethanol yields the same products as with LAH while reduction with the platinum catalyst in acetic acid yields the same products, as the acetoxy derivatives (51). Fürst and Plattner (50) have pointed out that reduction of oxides such as XLIII with hydrogen over platinum in acetic acid and LAH normally leads to the same polar product.

The results of the reduction of various 2,3-epoxysteroids are summarized in Table LXIX.

TABLE LXIX

LAH Reduction of 2,3-Oxidosteroids

Epoxide		Product	% Yield	Ref.
$C_{27}H_{40}O_4$	$2\alpha,3\alpha$-Oxido-22-isoallospirostan-12-one	22-Isoallospirostane-$3\alpha,12$-diol	95	1
$C_{27}H_{42}O_3$	$2\alpha,3\alpha$-Oxido-22-isoallospirostane	22-Isoallospirostan-3α-ol (epitigogenin)	70	2
	$2\beta,3\beta$-Oxido-22-isoallospirostane	22-Isoallospirostan-2β-ol	76	2
$C_{27}H_{44}O_2$	$2\alpha,3\alpha$-Oxidocholestan-6-one	Cholestane-$3\alpha,6\beta$-diol	77[3]	4
$C_{27}H_{46}O$	$2\alpha,3\alpha$-Oxidocholestane	Cholestan-3α-ol	80 14	5
		Cholestane-$2,3$-diol		
		Cholestan-3α-ol	55[6] 16	7
		Cholestane-$2,3$-diol		
		Cholestane	3[3]	
	$2\beta,3\beta$-Oxidocholestane	Cholestan-2β-ol	83	5
			90	7

[1] N. L. Wendler, H. L. Slates, and M. Tishler, J. Am. Chem. Soc., 74, 4894 (1952).

[2] J. Pataki, G. Rosenkranz, and C. Djerassi, ibid., 73, 5375 (1951).

[3] Isolated as diacetate.

[4] C. W. Shoppee and G. H. R. Summers, J. Chem. Soc., 1952, 1790.

[5] Ciba, S. A., Fr. Pat. 994,615 (November 20,1951); Ciba Ltd., Brit. Pat. 665,254 (January 16, 1952); P. Plattner, Ger. Pat. 834,848 (May 15, 1952); P. Plattner, U. S. Pat. 2,599,481 (June 3, 1952).

[6] Isolated as acetate.

[7] A. Fürst and P. A. Plattner, Helv. Chim. Acta, 32, 275 (1949).

The reduction of 4,5-oxidosteroids with LAH yields 5-hydroxy compounds. Reduction of 3α-acetoxy- and 3β-acetoxy-4α,5-oxidocholestane (XLVIII) with LAH yields cholestane-3α,5-diol and cholestane-3β,5-diol, respectively (52–56).

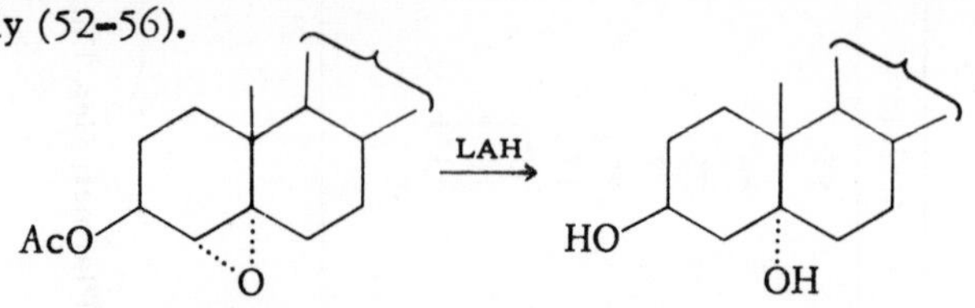

XLVIII

(11–33)

LAH reduction of the β-oxides of allocholesterol and epiallocholesterol e.g., 3β-acetoxy-4β,5-oxidocoprostane (XLIX) and 3α-acetoxy-4β-oxidocoprostane (L) yields the corresponding coprostane-3,5-diol (52–55, 57). Reduction of 3β-hydroxy-4β,5-oxidocoprostane (52–55) yields coprostane-3β,5-diol while the 3-keto derivative is converted to a mixture of the epimeric 3α,5- and 3β,5-diols (52–55,58). The 4β,5-oxide bridge is resistant to mild catalytic hydrogenation but on hydrogenation with Adams platinum oxide catalyst in glacial acetic acid the 4β-hydroxy derivative is formed (56,59).

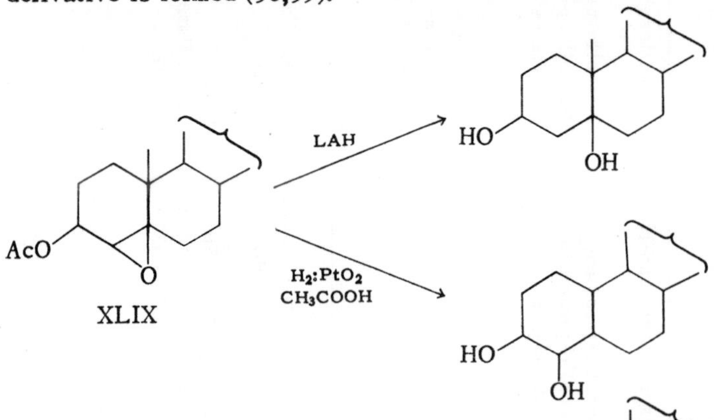

XLIX

(11–34)

H₂:PtO₂
CH₃COOH

(11–35)

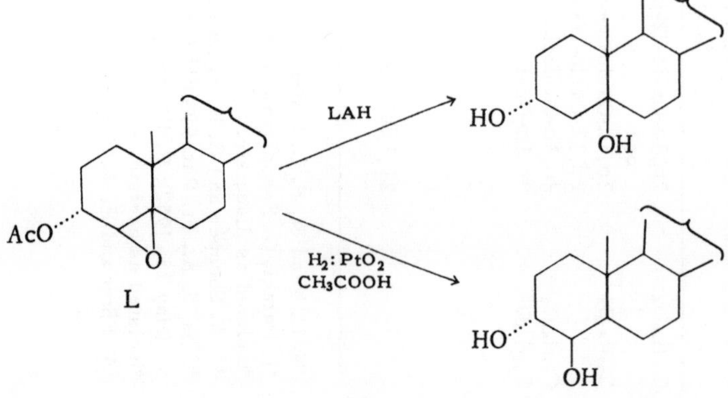

L

LAH

(11–36)

H₂: PtO₂
CH₃COOH

(11–37)

Therefore there is a difference in the steric course of the catalytic hydrogenation and the LAH reduction, the former yielding cholestane-3,4-diol
and the latter cholestane-3,5-diol. The 5-hydroxy compound formed with
LAH is a tertiary alcohol in accord with the previously indicated preferred direction of ring opening in secondary-tertiary epoxides.

The oxide ring in 3,5-oxido-3-methyl-A-norcholestene (LI) is very
stable. After refluxing for sixteen hours with excess LAH in tetrahydrofuran the epoxide is recovered unchanged (60).

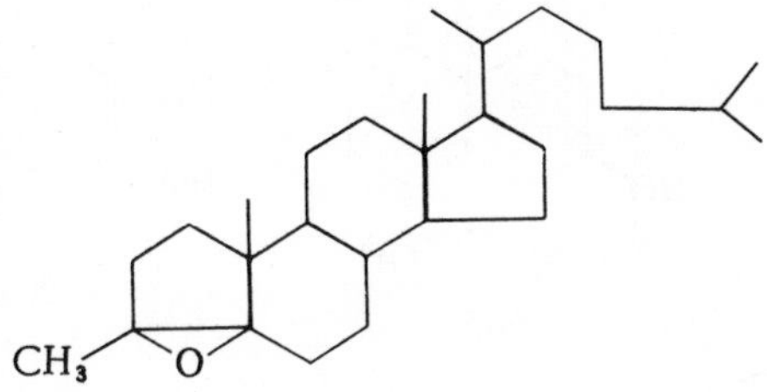

LI

The LAH reduction of 5,6-oxidosteroids is, analogous to the 2,3-oxides,
affected by the stereochemical configuration. Thus, reduction of 3β-
acetoxy-5,6α-oxido-17-ketoandrostane (LII) (61), 3α-hydroxy-5,6α-oxido-
cholestane (LIII) (52–55) and α-cholesterol oxide acetate (52–55,62) yields
the corresponding 3,5-diol, the secondary oxide linkage being attacked
in preference to the tertiary.

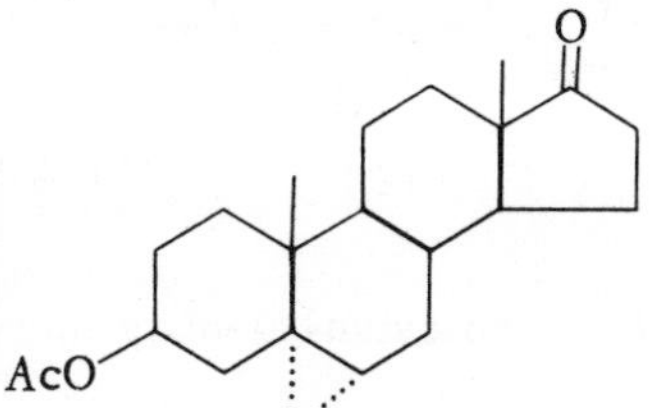

LII

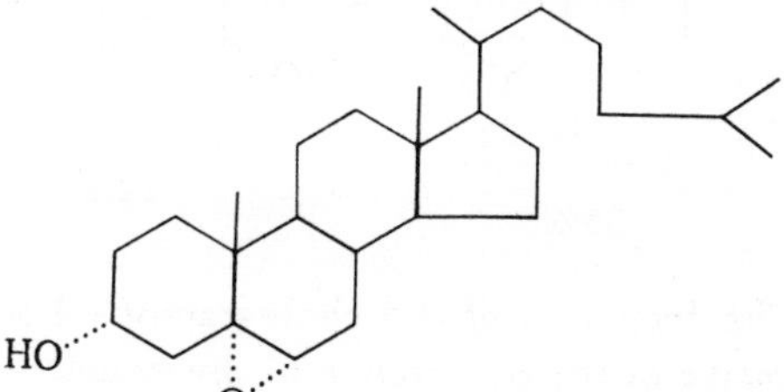

LIII

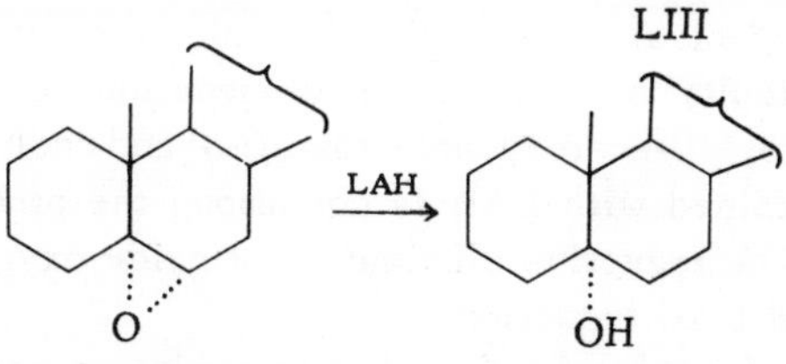

LIV

(11-38)

In contrast, LAH reduction of β-cholesterol oxide acetate (LV) yields
cholestane-3β,6β-diol as the main product (52–55,62) accompanied by
the expected coprostane-3β,5-diol (62). Similarly, LAH reduction of 3α-

hydroxy-5,6β-oxidocoprostane (LVI) yields cholestane-3α,6β-diol and coprostane-3α,5-diol as well as cholestan-3α-ol (52-55).

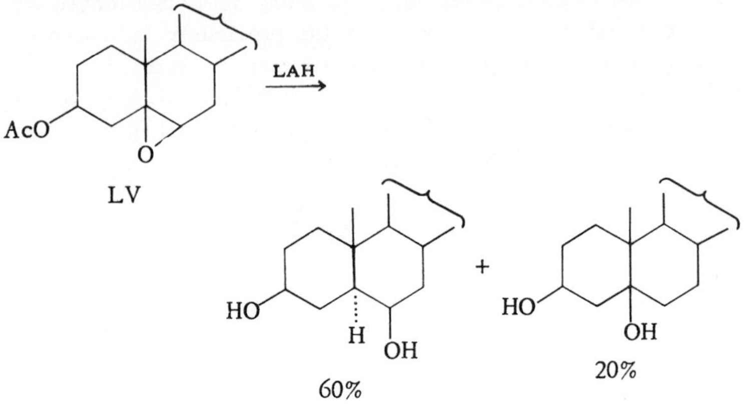

LV

+   (11-39)

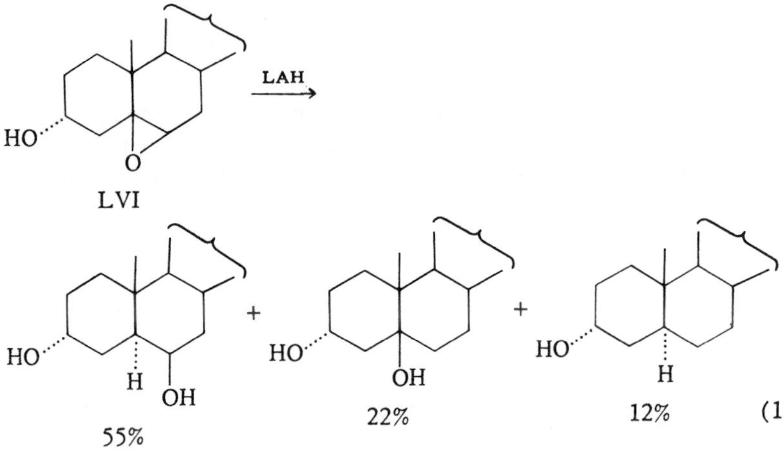

60%   20%

LVI

+   +

55%   22%   12%   (11-40)

The formation of the cholestan-6β-ol as well as cholestan-3α-ol is indicative of the occurrence of inversion.

The catalytic reduction of α-cholesterol oxide acetate yields 3β-acetoxycholestan-5-ol as with LAH. β-Cholesterol oxide acetate is reduced with difficulty by catalytic hydrogenation to a mixture of 3β-acetoxycholestane, 3β-acetoxycholestan-6β-ol and cholestane (63). Thus, the 3β,5-diol obtained with LAH is not among the products of catalytic hydrogenation. The reductive elimination of oxide oxygen is observed in both catalytic and LAH reduction.

The reduction of triacetyl-5,6-oxidoveratramine, a derivative of a steroidal alkaloid containing the partial structures shown above, with LAH yields the 5-hydroxy derivative as well as the 5,6-diol indicative of hydrolytic cleavage of the oxide ring (64).

The oxide bridge in 9,11-oxidosteroids (LVII) is resistant to attack with LAH in ether or tetrahydrofuran solution.

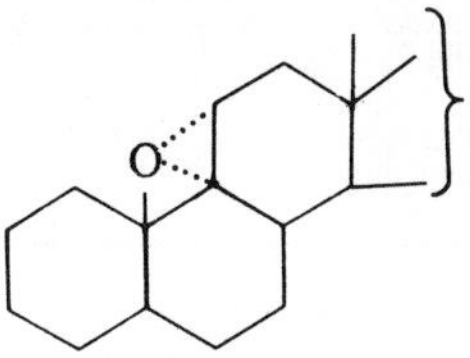

LVII

The 9α,11α-oxide grouping in the following compounds remains unchanged while other reactive groups are reduced by LAH: $C_{25}H_{38}O_4$, methyl 3-keto-9α,11α-oxidocholanate (65); $C_{25}H_{40}O_4$, methyl 9α,11α-oxidolithocholanate (65); $C_{27}H_{42}O_4$, 9α,11α-oxido-22-isoallospirostan-3β-ol (66); $C_{29}H_{42}O_6$, 3β-acetoxy-9α,11α-oxido-22-isoallospirostan-7-one (67). Sodium borohydride is similarly ineffective in reducing the 9α,11α-oxido ring in the 9α,11α-oxido-22-isoallospirostan-7-one (67).

Treatment of ergosteryl-D acetate (LVIII) with one mole of perbenzoic acid yields ergosteryl-D acetate epoxide, $C_{30}H_{46}O_3$. The latter has been postulated as being either the 9α,11α-epoxide (LIX) or the 7ξ,8ξ-epoxide (LX). The reaction of the epoxide with LAH in refluxing tetrahydrofuran reduces the ester group but leaves the oxide intact to yield ergosterol-D epoxide (68).

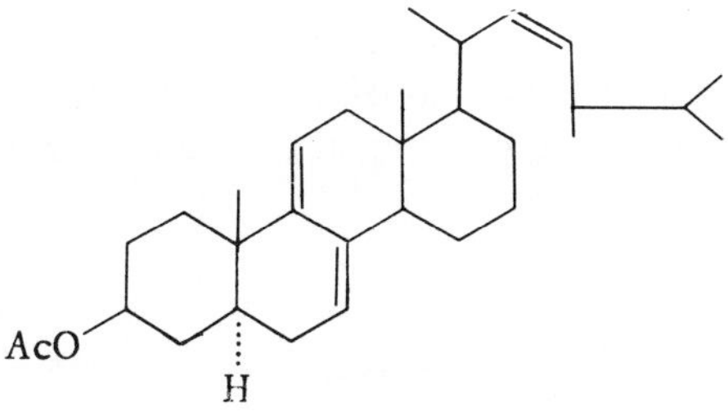

LVIII

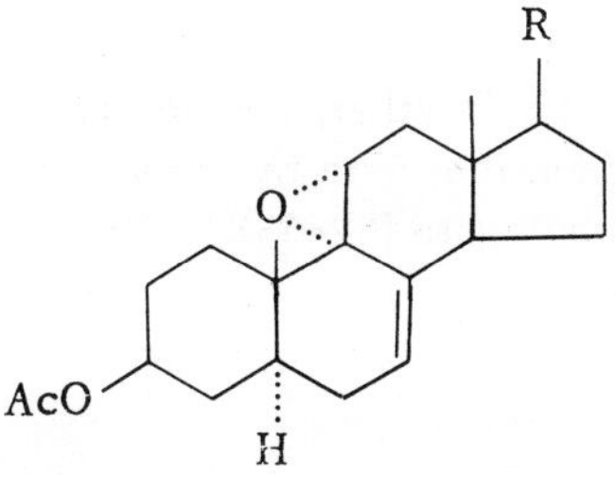

LIX

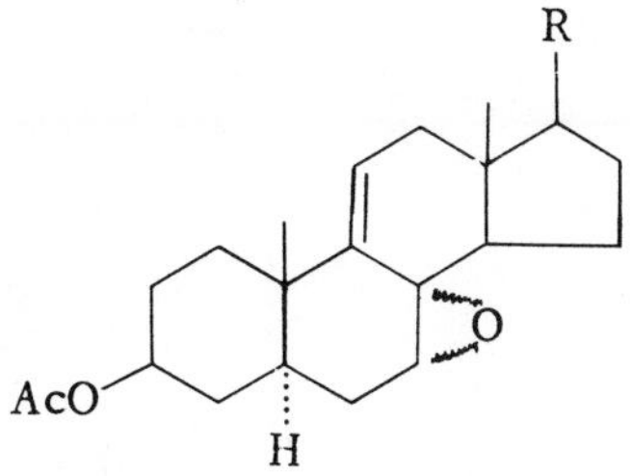

LX

The reaction of LAH with 11,12-oxidosteroids is reported to yield 11-hydroxysteroids with both α- and β-configurations of the oxide ring. Thus, the reduction of 3α-acetoxy-11,12α-oxidocholanic acid esters (LXI) with LAH in ether or tetrahydrofuran yields the triol (LXII), m.p. 183-

184°, identical with the product from the reduction of methyl 3α,11α-diacetoxycholanate.

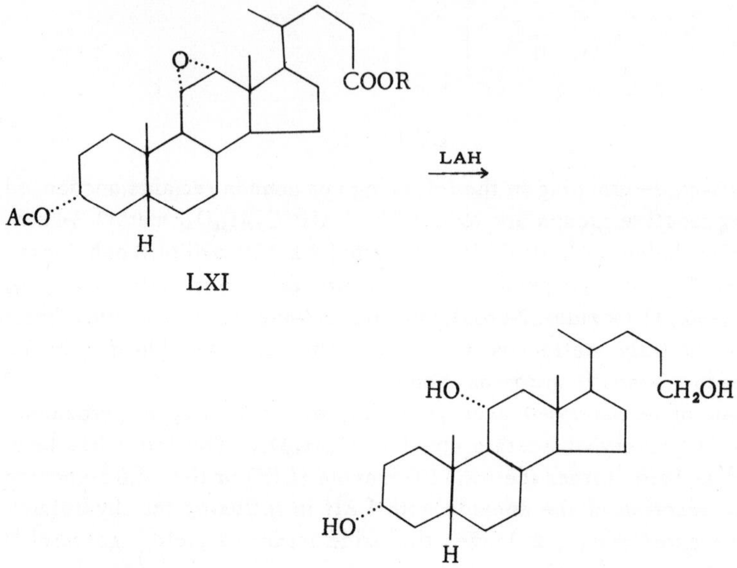

LXI

(11-41)

LXII

The reduction of methyl 3α-acetoxy-11,12β-oxidocholanate (LXIII) with LAH in ether, dioxane or tetrahydrofuran yields the triol, m.p. 186-188°, identical with the reduction product from methyl 3α-acetoxy-11β-hydroxy-cholanate (52-55).

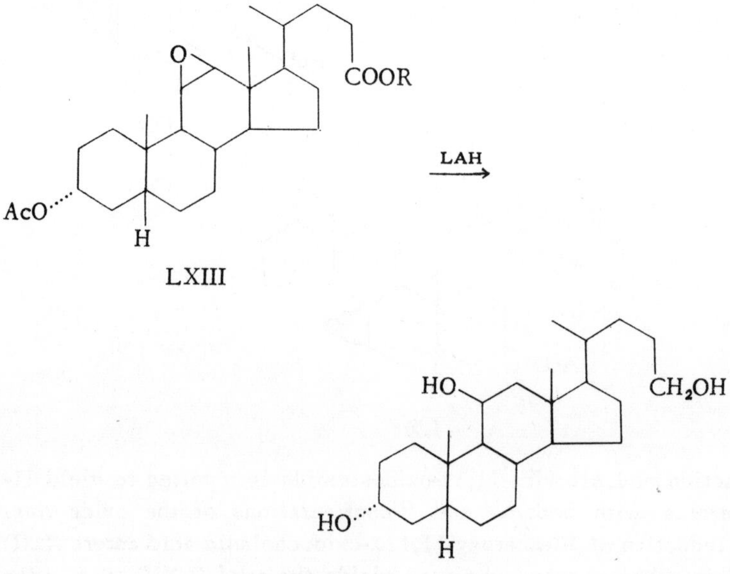

LXIII

(11-42)

Reduction   of, $\Delta^{16,17}$-3β-acetoxy-14,15β-oxido-20-keto-5-allopregnane (LXIV), $C_{23}H_{32}O_4$, with LAH in a mixture of ether and benzene is re-

LXIV

ported to yield a compound, $C_{21}H_{32}O_3$, m.p. 174°, and a compound $C_{21}H_{34}O_3$, m.p. 223–224°. The latter formula would correspond to the product arising by reduction of the ester and carbonyl groups to carbinols and opening of the oxide bridge. Based on other ring opening reductions the tertiary alcohol would be the expected product. When the reduction of LXIV in a mixture of methanol and chloroform is carried out with sodium borohydride in aqueous dioxane and the crude product is oxidized in the cold with chromic oxide in glacial acetic acid the reaction product has the formula $C_{23}H_{34}O_4$ and m.p. 149–150°. The nature of the product has not been further reported (52–55).

The reaction of peracids with the 16,17-double bond yields 16,17α-oxidosteroids.   LAH reduction of these 16,17α-oxides yields 17α-hydroxysteroids (69,70).

$$(11\text{-}43)$$

LXV

The oxide bridge is very stable to catalytic reduction while LAH reductions have been carried out in ether, tetrahydrofuran and ether-benzene mixtures.   The reduction of 3β-acetoxy-16α,17α-oxido-5-allopregnan-20-one (LXVI) with LAH in ether-benzene, followed by acetylation, is reported to yield Reichstein's substances J (20β) and O (20α) as diacetates, as well as an oxido diacetate (LXVII).   The latter by further reduction with LAH is transformed to Reichstein's substance J (71).   The isolation of LXVII indicates that the carbonyl group reacts more readily than the oxide bridge, as previously postulated in the reduction of benzal-acetophenone oxide (equation 11-11).

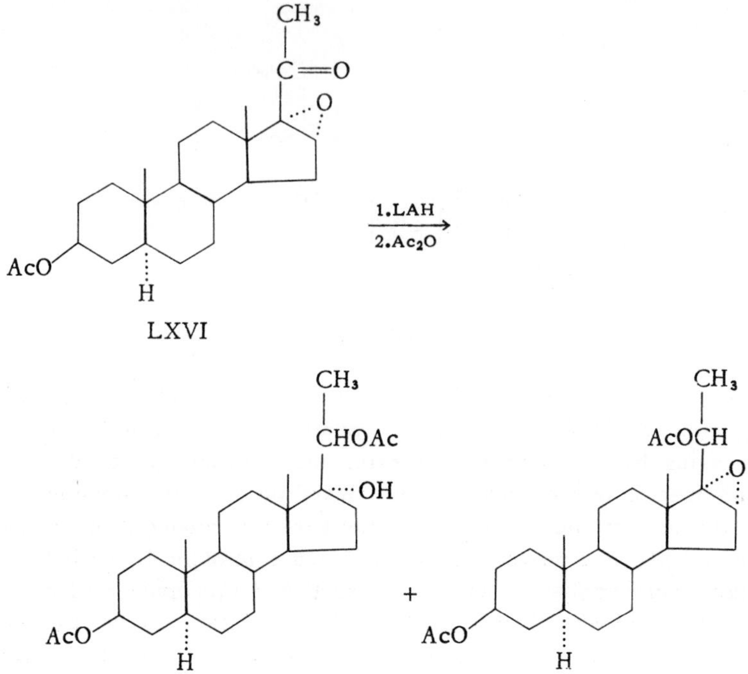

LXVI

+   (11-44)

LXVII

The results of the reduction of various 16,17α-oxidosteroids are summarized in Table LXX.

The reduction of Δ^4-17,17aα-oxido-17aβ-methyl-D-homoandrosten-3-one (LXVIII) with LAH in tetrahydrofuran yields the 17aα-hydroxy derivative (69,70).

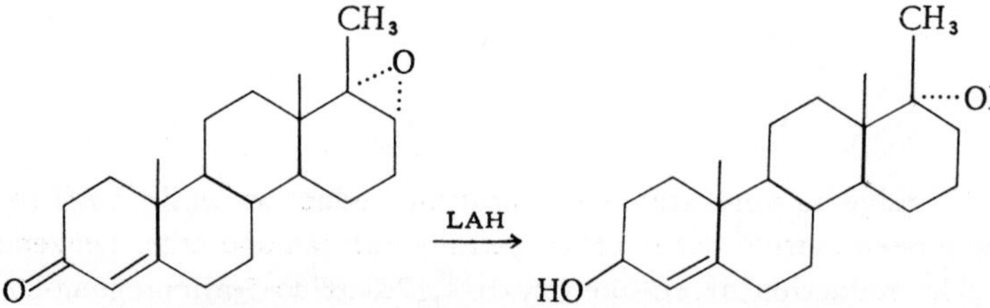

LXVIII

(11-45)

The LAH reduction of 17,20-oxido-4-pregnen-3-one (LXIX) is reported to yield a compound, m.p. 150°, which contains one double bond and two hydroxyl groups and yields a monoacetate (52-55).

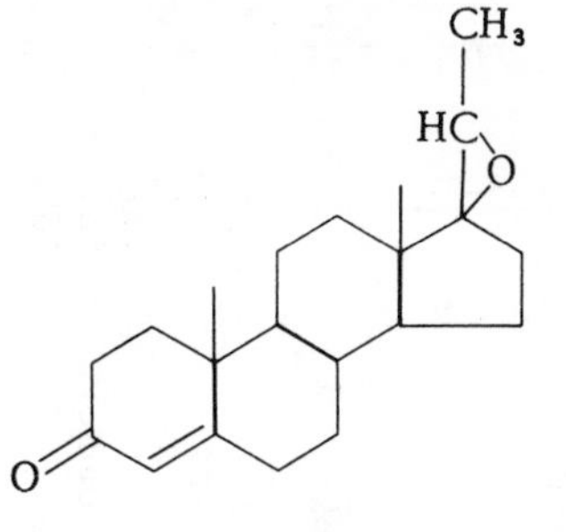

LXIX

Since LXIX contains a secondary-tertiary oxide the reduction product would be expected to be the tertiary alcohol, consistent with the formation of the monoacetate. In an analogous manner other 17,20-oxidopregnanes containing substituted or unsubstituted hydroxyl groups in the 3-, 11- or 12-position are reportedly reduced with LAH (55).

The reduction of 3-benzoxy-20α,21-oxido-17-isoallopregnan-3β,17β-diol (LXX) with LAH yields the 3β,17β,20α-triol, isolated in excellent yield as the 3,20-diacetate (72). The stereoisomeric 20β,21-oxide is reduced in "nearly quantitative yield" to the 20β-hydroxy compound. In these examples the secondary 20-ol is formed in both cases with the steric configuration dependent upon the oxide configuration.

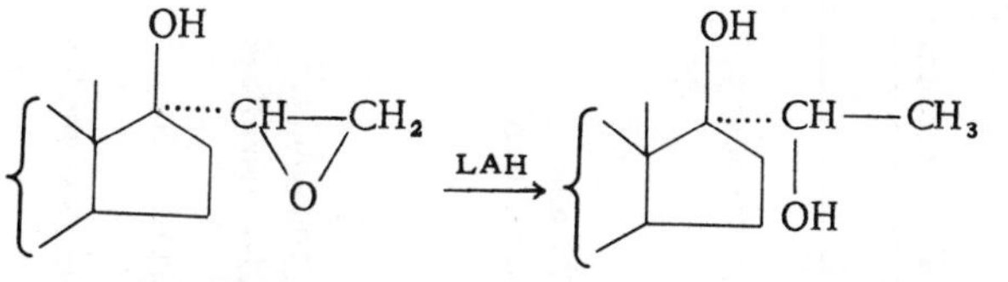

$$(11\text{-}46)$$

LXX

Hydrogenation of the 20α,21-oxide (LXX) with Raney nickel in methanol yields a mixture of the 3β,17β,20α-triol and 17-isoallopregnan-3β,17β, 21-triol, resulting from ring opening in the opposite direction. The reduction of the stereoisomeric 20β,21-oxide over Raney nickel yields an analogous mixture of the 3β,17β,20β-triol and the 3β,17β,21-triol (72).

The reduction of 3,8- and 3,9-oxidosteroids is discussed in Sections 11.9.1.b and c, under heterocyclic oxygen compounds.

11.2.1.e *Triterpene Epoxides.* Epoxide reduction with LAH has been employed in the triterpene series. The reduction of 2,3-oxidolupane containing the partial structure LXXXI yields epilupanol isolated as the acetate (52,53).

TABLE LXX

LAH Reduction of 16,17-Oxidosteroids

Epoxide	Product	% Yield	Ref.
$C_{19}H_{26}O_2$ 16,17α-Oxido-4-androsten-3-one	4-Androsten-3β,17α-diol	73	1
$C_{21}H_{32}O_3$ 3β-Hydroxy-16,17α-oxido-5-allopregnan-20-one	5-Allopregnan-3β,17α,20β-triol (Reichstein's substance J)	...	2
	5-Allopregnan-3β,17α,20α-triol (Reichstein's substance O)	...	
$C_{23}H_{32}O_4$ 3β-Acetoxy-16,17-oxido-5-pregnen-20-one	5-Pregnen-3β,17,20-triol[3]	...[5]	4
$C_{23}H_{34}O_4$ 3β-Acetoxy-16,17-oxido-5-allopregnan-20-one	5-Allopregnane-3β,17α,20-triol (Mixture of Reichstein's substances J and O)	...[5]	2,4
	5-Allopregnan-3β,17α,20β-triol	40[5]	6
	5-Allopregnan-3β,17α,20α-triol	20[5]	
	16,17α-Oxido-5-allopregnan-3β,20β-diol	25[5]	
$C_{25}H_{26}O_3$ 3-Benzoxy-16,17α-oxidoestra-1,3,5(10)-triene	Estra-1,3,5(10)-trien-3,17α-diol (17-epi-estradiol)	58	1
$C_{25}H_{34}O_5$ 3-Ethoxy-21-acetoxy-16,17-oxido-3,5-pregnadien-20-one	3-Ethoxy-3,5-pregnadien-17α,20α,21-triol	36[7]	8
	3-Ethoxy-3,5-pregnadien-17α,20β,21-triol	51[7]	
$C_{25}H_{36}O_5$ 3β-Acetoxy-16,17-oxido-5-pregnen-20-one 20-ethylene ketal	5-Pregnen-3β,17α-diol-20-one 20-ethylene ketal	80	4,9
$C_{25}H_{36}O_6$ 3β,21-Diacetoxy-16,17α-oxido-5-allopregnan-20-one	5-Allopregnan-3β,17α,20,21-tetrol (Reichstein's substance K)	...	2
$C_{25}H_{38}O_5$ 3β,20β-Diacetoxy-16,17α-oxido-5-allopregnane	5-Allopregnan-3β,17α,20β-triol	30	6

References — Table LXX

[1] H. Heusser, M. Feurer, K. Eichenberger, and V. Prelog, *Helv. Chim. Acta*, 33, 2243 (1950).
[2] Ciba, S. A., Fr. Pat. 994,615 (November 20, 1951); Ciba Limited, Brit. Pat. 665,254 (January 16, 1952); P. Plattner, Ger. Pat. 834,848 (May 15, 1952); P. Plattner, U. S. Pat. 2,599,481 (June 3, 1952).
[3] Mixture of epimers.
[4] P. L. Julian, E. W. Meyer, and I. Ryden, *J. Am. Chem. Soc.*, 71, 756 (1949).
[5] Isolated as diacetate.
[6] P. A. Plattner, H. Heusser, and M. Feurer, *Helv. Chim. Acta*, 31, 2210 (1948).
[7] Isolated after acid cleavage and acetylation as ketone diacetate.
[8] P. L. Julian, E. W. Meyer, W. J. Karpel, and W. Cole, *J. Am. Chem. Soc.*, 73, 1982 (1951).
[9] P. L. Julian, E. W. Meyer, and I. Ryden, *ibid.*, 72, 367 (1950).

$$(11\text{-}47)$$

LXXI

Morolic acid, a triterpenoid sapogenin, is postulated as olean-18-enolic acid (73,74). The methyl ester acetate of morolic acid is converted with perbenzoic acid to the corresponding oxide (LXXII). Reduction of LXXII with LAH in ether, followed by room temperature acetylation and chromatographic separation, gives an unsaturated acetate, $C_{31}H_{48}O_2$, m.p. 220–222° and moradiol diacetate oxide, $C_{34}H_{54}O_5$, m.p. 254–256° (LXXIII). The unsaturated acetate has been formulated as norolean-16,18-dienyl acetate (LXXIV), and its formation is interpreted by the mechanism shown in equation (9–5). Moradiol diacetate oxide (LXXIII) is reduced by LAH in ether and after acetylation, by heating with acetic anhydride and pyridine, and chromatography, furnishes two compounds. The major product is the dienyl acetate (LXXIV), while the second reduction product is obtained as the acetate $C_{32}H_{50}O_3$, m.p. 248–250°, which is unsaturated to tetranitromethane, gives no hydroxyl group in the infrared spectrum and shows an absorption band interpretive of ethereal oxygen and therefore is formulated as the 13(18)-ene-19,28-oxidoacetate (LXXV). The mechanism postulated for the formation of LXXIV and LXXV is shown in equation (9–5). This mechanism implies that an intermediate allylic alcohol is formed although the unstable nature of the intermediate has prevented its characterization (74).

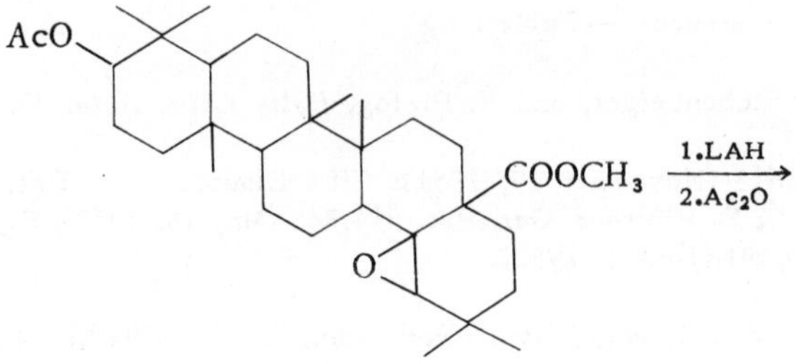

LXXII

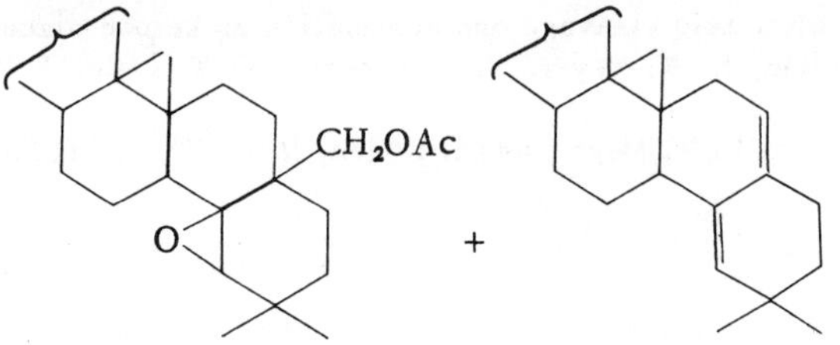

LXXIII   LXXIV   (11-48)

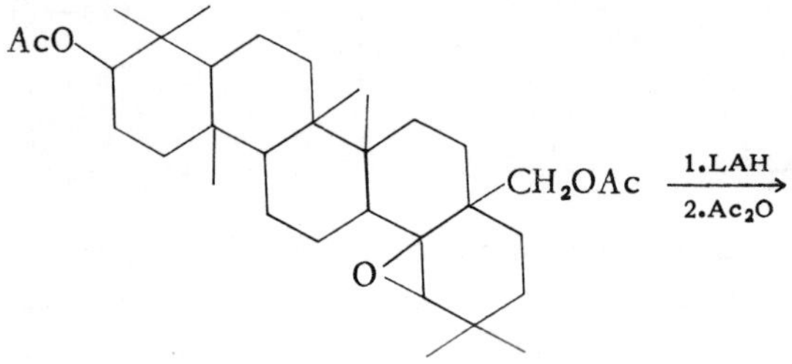

LXXIII

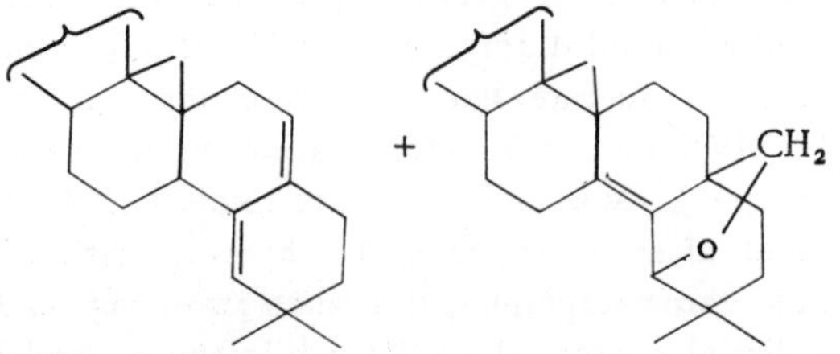

LXXIV   LXXV   (11-49)

11.2.1.f *Alkaloid Epoxides.* The LAH reduction of triacetyl-5,6-ox-idoveratramine, a steroidal alkaloid, yields the 5-hydroxy derivative, as mentioned in Section 11.2.1.d.

The cinchona alkaloid quinamine was postulated by Goutarel, Janot, Prelog, and Taylor (75) as having structure LXXVI containing an epoxide ring. On reduction with LAH quinamine is converted into cinchonamine (LXXVII), the reduction supposedly proceeding through ring opening to the alcohol which gives LXXVII by splitting out water. Witkop (76) has proposed structure LXXVIII for quinamine and has shown that the opening of the ring and loss of water is analogous to the similar conversion of 11-hydroxytetrahydrocarbazolenine. Since structure LXXVIII no longer contains the 1,2-epoxide ring, discussion of the reactions of this and related compounds is given in Section 11.9.1, under heterocyclic oxygen compounds.

LXXVI   LXXVII

LXXVIII

11.2.2 Reductions with Sodium Borohydride

A very limited number of epoxides have been subjected to treatment with sodium borohydride. As mentioned in Section 11.2.1.d, the $9\alpha,11\alpha$-oxide ring in the corresponding steroids is resistant to cleavage by the borohydride (67). The reduction of a $14,15\beta$-oxidosteroid, followed by chromic acid oxidation, has been reported to yield a product whose structure has not been elucidated (52–55).

11.3 ACETALS AND COMPOUNDS CONTAINING

THE —OCO— GROUPING

11.3.1 Reactions with Lithium Aluminum Hydride

11.3.1.a *Non-cleavage of the* —OCO— *Grouping.* The non-reduction of the acetal and ketal groups with LAH (44,77) has been utilized for the protection of carbonyl groups during LAH reductions. These acetals have included open structures, as in acetal (LXXIX), as well as cyclic structures, as in the dioxolanes (LXXX).

$$\begin{array}{c} R_1 \quad OR \\ \diagdown C \diagup \\ R_2 \quad OR \end{array}$$

LXXIX

R	R_1	R_2	Ref.
CH_3	H	$-(CH_2)_4COOCH_3$	78
CH_3	H	$-(CH_2)_6COOCH_3$	78
C_2H_5	H	CH_3-	77

C_2H_5	H	$-CHCOOC_2H_5$
		     |
		     CH_3
			79

C_2H_5	H	$-CHCOOC_2H_5$
		     |
		     C_2H_5
			79

C_2H_5	H	$-CH_2CH_2CH(COOC_2H_5)_2$	77
C_2H_5	CH_3	$-COOC_2H_5$	79
C_2H_5	CH_3	$-CH_2CH_2COOC_2H_5$	79
C_2H_5	CH_3	$-C_6H_4COOC_2H_5 (p)$	80
C_4H_9	H	$-COCH_3$	81

$$\begin{array}{c} R \quad\quad O-CH_2 \\ \diagdown C \diagup \quad\quad | \\ R_1 \quad\quad O-CH_2 \end{array}$$

LXXX

		Ref.
$C_{11}H_{18}O_4$	2-Methyl-2-carbethoxycyclopentanone ethylene ketal	82
$C_{11}H_{18}O_6$	Dicarbethoxyacetone ethylene ketal	83
$C_{13}H_{22}O_4$	α-(1,1-Dimethylpropen-2-yl)acetoacetic ester ethylene ketal	84
$C_{15}H_{26}O_2$	Dihydro-α-ionone ethylene ketal	39
$C_{15}H_{26}O_3$	3,4-Epoxytetrahydro-α-ionone	39
$C_{17}H_{21}BrO_6$	Methyl ester of 5-bromo-7,8-dimethoxy-2-tetralone-1-acetic acid ethylene ketal	85
$C_{17}H_{22}BrNO_5$	5-Bromo-7,8-dimethoxy-2-tetralone-1-(N-methylacetamide) ethylene ketal	85
$C_{18}H_{24}BrNO_5$	5-Bromo-7,8-dimethoxy-2-tetralone-1-(N,N-dimethylacetamide) ethylene ketal	85

An interesting application of this protective action has been reported in the case of α-(1,1-dimethylpropen-2-yl)acetoacetic ester (LXXXI) (84). The keto ester is converted to the ethylene ketal ester followed by reduction to the ketal alcohol and hydrolysis to the keto alcohol.

$$
\underset{\substack{| \\ R}}{\overset{\overset{\displaystyle O}{\|}}{CH_3CCHCOOC_2H_5}} \rightarrow \underset{\substack{| \\ R}}{CH_3—\overset{\overset{\displaystyle \underset{\displaystyle H_2C——CH_2}{\diagdown O \quad O \diagup}}{}}{C}—CHCOOC_2H_5} \xrightarrow[82\%]{LAH}
$$

LXXXI

$$
\underset{\substack{| \\ R}}{CH_3—\overset{\overset{\displaystyle \underset{\displaystyle H_2C——CH_2}{\diagdown O \quad O \diagup}}{}}{C}—CHCH_2OH} \rightarrow \underset{\substack{| \\ R}}{\overset{\overset{\displaystyle O}{\|}}{CH_3CCHCH_2OH}} \qquad (11\text{-}50)
$$

$$
R = \underset{\substack{| \\ CH_3}}{\overset{\overset{\displaystyle CH_3}{|}}{—CCH}}=CH_2
$$

The ketone group in various steroids has been protected by formation of the ethylene ketal prior to reduction with LAH. The following steroid ketals have been subjected to reduction with LAH with retention of the ketal grouping: allopregnan-3β-ol-11,20-dione 20-ethylene ketal 3-acetate (86),   pregnan-3α-ol-11,20-dione 20-ethylene ketal 3-acetate (87), 5-pregnene-17α,21-diol-3,11,20-trione 3,20-diethylene ketal (88), 16,17-oxido-5-pregnen-3β-ol-20-one 20-ethylene ketal 3-acetate (89).

Hemithioketals are also resistant to attack by LAH.

Benzylidene (LXXXII) and isopropylidene (LXXXIII) derivatives have been utilized for the blocking of 1,3- and 1,2-glycols, respectively, in LAH reductions.

$$
\begin{array}{cc}
\text{—C—O} & \\
\diagdown \quad \overset{\diagup}{C}HC_6H_5 & \\
\diagup \\
\text{—C—O} &
\end{array}
\qquad
\begin{array}{c}
\text{—C—O} \quad CH_3 \\
\diagdown C \diagup \\
\diagup \diagdown \\
\text{—C—O} \quad CH_3
\end{array}
$$

LXXXII   LXXXIII

The following compounds containing these and analogous groups have been subjected to LAH reduction:

		Ref.
$C_9H_{12}O_6$	1,2-Isopropylidene-D-glucuronolactone-6-C^{14}	90
$C_9H_{14}O_4$	3,4-Isopropylidene-1,2,5,6-dianhydromannitol	91
	4,5-Isopropylidene-1,2,3,6-dianhydromannitol	29
$C_{10}H_{14}N_2O_{10}$	4,6-Ethylidene-β-methyl-D-glucoside 2,3-dinitrate	92
$C_{10}H_{14}O_5$	Acetonequinide	93
$C_{10}H_{16}N_2O_{10}$	4,6-Propylidene-α-methyl-D-glucoside 2,3-dinitrate	92,94
$C_{11}H_{17}NO_4$	Acetone homoquinonitrile	93
$C_{11}H_{18}O_6$	3,4-Isopropylidene-α-methyl-2-deoxy-D-galacturonoside methyl ester	95
$C_{12}H_{16}O_6$	Acetyl acetonequinide	93
$C_{12}H_{20}O_6$	Diacetonemannose	96
$C_{14}H_{16}O_5$	4,6-Benzylidene-2,3-anhydro-α-methyl-D-allopyranoside	44
	4,6-Benzylidene-2,3-anhydro-α-methyl-D-mannopyranoside	44
	4,6-Benzylidene-2,3-anhydro-α-methyl-D-guloside <1,5>	45
$C_{19}H_{26}O_8S$	Diacetone-3-p-tosyl-D-glucoside <1,4>	97
	Diacetone-6-p-tosyl-D-galactose <1,5>	97
	Diacetone-1-p-tosyl-D-fructoside <2,6>	97
$C_{22}H_{26}O_8S$	4,6-Benzylidene-2-p-tosyl-α-methyl-D-altroside-3-methyl ether	98
$C_{24}H_{38}O_5$	Pregnane-3α,17α,20β,21-tetrol-11-one 20,21-acetonide	99

The reduction by LAH of pyranosides (LXXXIV) results in the retention of the —OĊO— grouping.

LXXXIV

		Ref.
$C_6H_{10}O_4$	2,3-Anhydro-β-methyl-D-riboside	48
$C_9H_{14}N_2O_{10}$	4,6-Ethylidene-β-methyl-D-glucoside 2,3-dinitrate	92
$C_9H_{16}O_7$	4-Methyl-α-methyl-D-glucuronoside methyl ester	96,100,101
$C_{10}H_{16}N_2O_{10}$	4,6-Propylidene-α-methyl-D-glucoside 2,3-dinitrate	92,94
$C_{10}H_{18}O_7$	3,4-Dimethyl-methyl-D-glucuronoside methyl ester	102
$C_{11}H_{18}O_6$	3,4-Isopropylidene-α-methyl-2-deoxy-D-galacturonoside methyl ester	95
$C_{11}H_{20}O_7$	2,3,4-Trimethyl-α-methyl-D-glucuronoside methyl ester	96,102
	2,3,4-Trimethyl-methyl-D-galacturonoside methyl ester	96
$C_{14}H_{16}O_5$	4,6-Benzylidene-2,3-anhydro-α-methyl-D-guloside <1,5>	45
	4,6-Benzylidene-2,3-anhydro-α-D-allopyranoside	44
	4,6-Benzylidene-2,3-anhydro-α-D-mannopyranoside	44

$C_{21}H_{24}O_9S_2$	2,3-Anhydro-4,6-ditosyl-α-methyl-D-alloside	46,47
$C_{22}H_{26}O_8S$	4,6-Benzylidene-2-tosyl-α-methyl-D-altroside-3-methyl ether	98
$C_{29}H_{34}O_{12}S_3$	2,4,6-Tritosyl-β-methyl-D-idoside-3-methyl ether	103

Pyranose and furanose derivatives containing the partial structure LXXXV are not attacked by LAH.

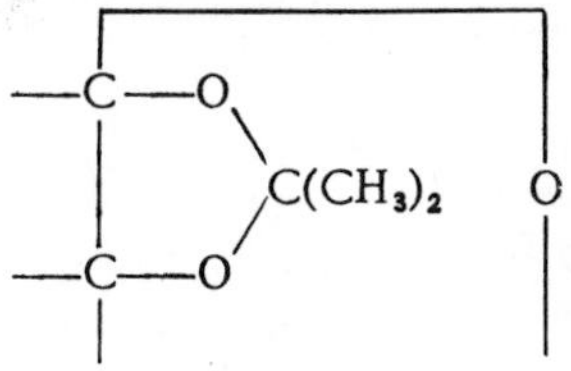

LXXXV

		Ref.
$C_9H_{12}O_6$	1,2-Isopropylidene-D-glucuronolactone-6-C^{14}	90
$C_{19}H_{26}O_8S$	Diacetone-3-p-tosyl-D-glucoside<1,4>	97
	Diacetone-6-p-tosyl-D-galactoside<1,5>	97

The —O—C—O—C—O— structure, as in LXXXV, has been subjected to LAH reduction in the form of 3,4-epoxy-2,5-dimethoxytetrahydrofuran, the cyclic acetal of epoxysuccinaldehyde (LXXXVI) (38).

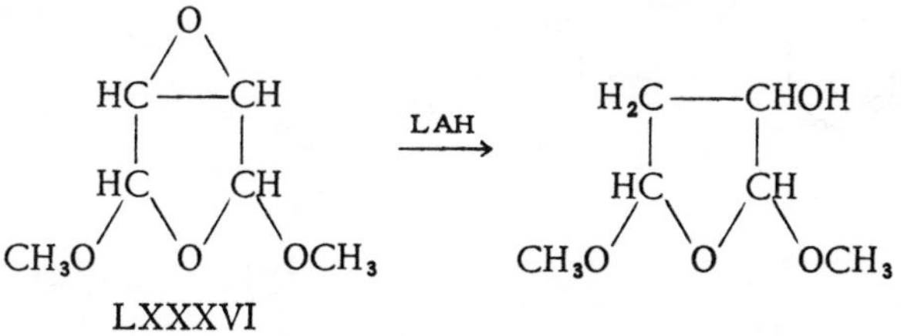

(11-51)

LXXXVI

The —OCO— grouping in various disaccharides including aldobiuronic acids is not attacked by LAH: 6β-(2,3,4-trimethyl-D-glucopyruronosyl)-2,3,4-trimethyl-α- and β-methyl-D-galactopyranoside methyl ester (96,104), 2-methyl-3-(2,3,4-trimethyl-α-D-glucuronoside-D-xylose (105), 3,4-dimethyl-2-(2,3,4,6-tetramethyl-D-glucosyl)methyl xyloside methyl ester (106).

Compounds containing the methylenedioxy group can be considered as cyclic acetals of formaldehyde and similarly are not attacked by LAH.

		Ref.
$C_8H_6O_3$	Piperonal	107
$C_9H_6BrNO_4$	3,4-Methylenedioxy-5-bromo-β-nitrostyrene	108
$C_9H_7NO_4$	3,4-Methylenedioxy-β-nitrostyrene	108,109

$C_{10}H_9NO_5$	3-Methoxy-4,5-methylenedioxy-β-nitrostyrene	110
$C_{12}H_9NO_4$	Methyl 2-cyano-3-(3,4-methylenedioxyphenyl)acrylate	111
$C_{12}H_{12}O_4$	Ethyl 3,4-methylenedioxycinnamate	112
$C_{12}H_{15}NO_3$	N-Formyl-ω-(3,4-methylenedioxyphenyl)-t-butylamine	113
$C_{19}H_{21}NO_5$	N-Formyl-N-(3-methoxybenzyl)-3-methoxy-4,5-methylenedioxyphenylethylamine	110
$C_{20}H_{18}O_6$	(–)-Hinokinin	114
$C_{20}H_{19}NO_8S$	Berberine sulfate	115
$C_{21}H_{21}NO_6$	l-β-Hydrastine	116
$C_{21}H_{23}NO_5$	Cryptopine	117
$C_{22}H_{22}O_7$	Desoxypicropodophyllin	118
$C_{22}H_{22}O_8$	Podophyllotoxin	118
	Picropodophyllin	118
$C_{22}H_{23}NO_7$	l-α-Narcotine	116,119
	l-β-Narcotine	116

The reaction of 2,3-dihydropyran with steroidal alcohols results in the formation of tetrahydropyranyl ethers such as LXXXVII. Reduction of LXXXVII with LAH leaves the —OCO— grouping intact and, on acid hydrolysis, the latter is cleaved to the alcohol (120,121).

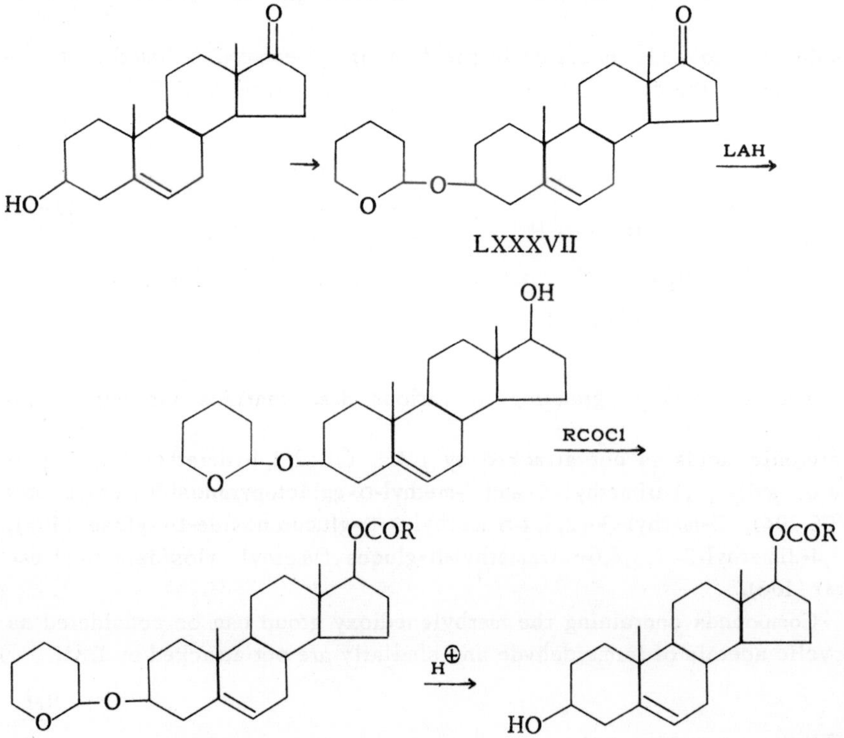

LXXXVII

(11-52)

An interesting application of the protective action of the tetrahydropyranyl ether has been reported by Goering and Serres (122). Reduction of the monotosylate of *cis*-3-hydroxymethylcyclohexanol (LXXXVIII) with LAH yields the endomethyleneoxy compound instead of the expected methylcyclohexanol. Conversion of the monotosylate to the tetrahydropyranyl ether (LXXXIX) followed by LAH reduction yields XC which is converted to the methylcyclohexanol by acid hydrolysis.

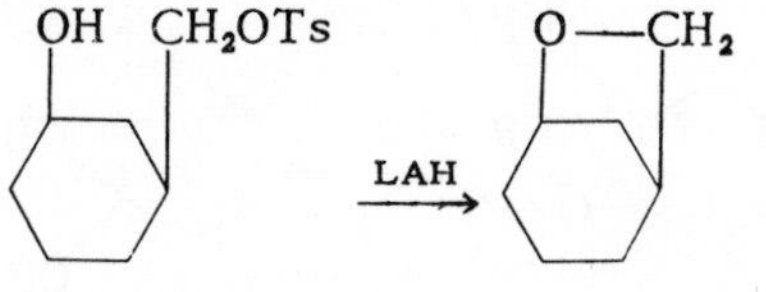

$$(11\text{-}53)$$

LXXXVIII

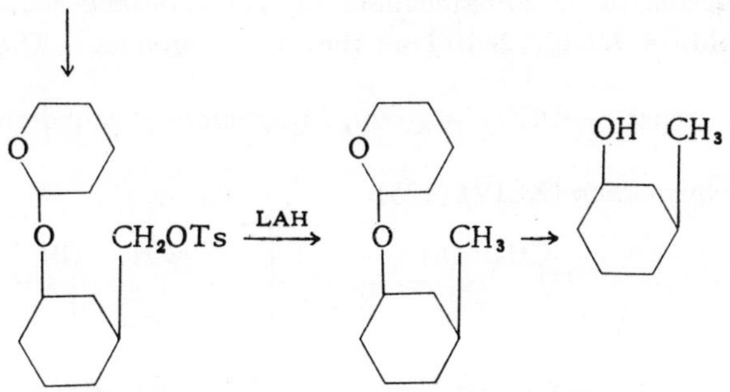

$$(11\text{-}54)$$

LXXXIX   XC

The *trans* isomer of LXXXIX has been similarly subjected to LAH reduction.

Reduction of 7,2′-tetrahydropyranyloxyoct-5-en-3-yn-2-ol (XCI) with LAH yields 7,2′-tetrahydropyranyloxyocta-3,5-dien-2-ol (123).

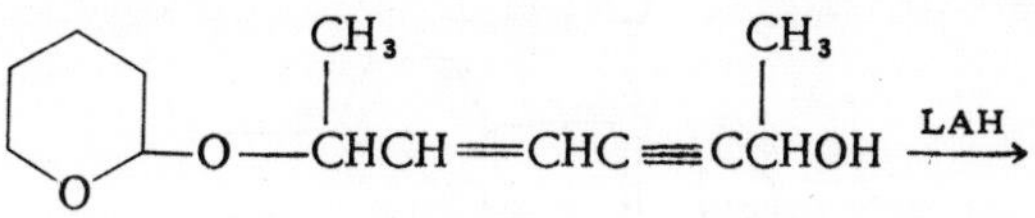

XCI

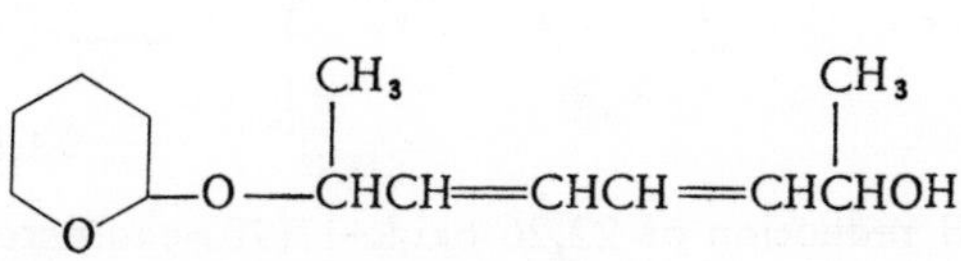

$$(11\text{-}55)$$

Cyclohexanone cyanohydrin has been converted to the tetrahydropyranyl ether which on treatment with the methyl, ethyl or phenyl Grignard reagents yields the corresponding ketimine (XCII). With excess LAH the latter is reduced to the corresponding amino ether which is hydrolyzed to the amino alcohol (124).

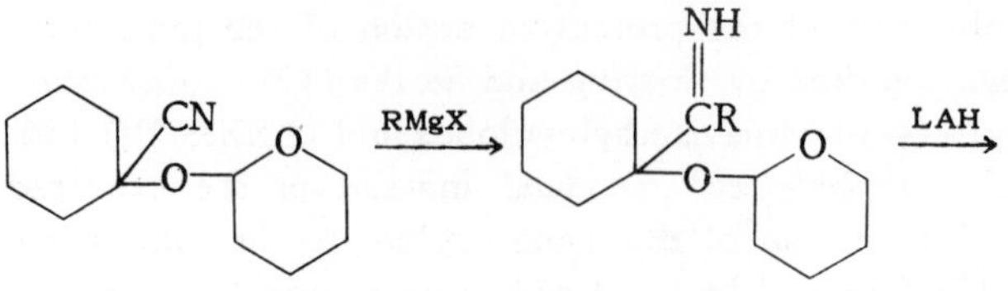

NH

CN   RMgX→   CR   LAH→

XCII

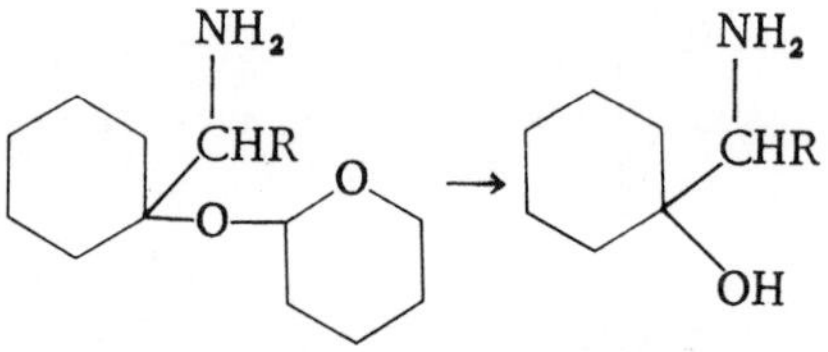

NH₂   NH₂

CHR   →   CHR   (11-56)

OH

The reduction of 22,26-oxidocholesta-5,17(20)-diene-3β,22-diol-16-one (XCIII) yields a 3β,16,22-triol as the initial product. The latter, containing the intact ——OCO—— group, is apparently dehydrated readily to form an isospirostane (XCIV) (125).

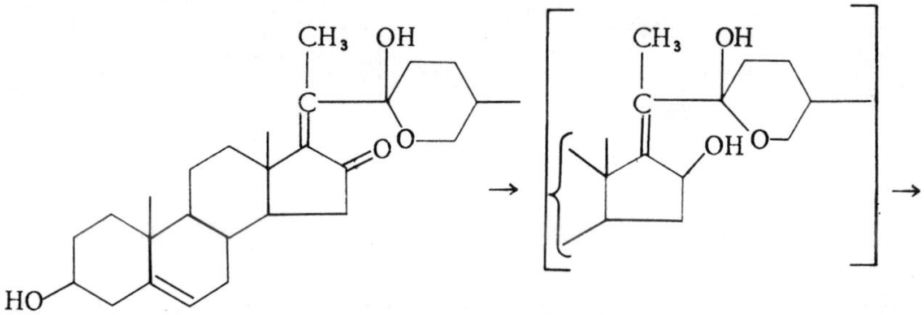

CH₃ OH   CH₃ OH

O   →   OH O   →

HO

XCIII

CH₃

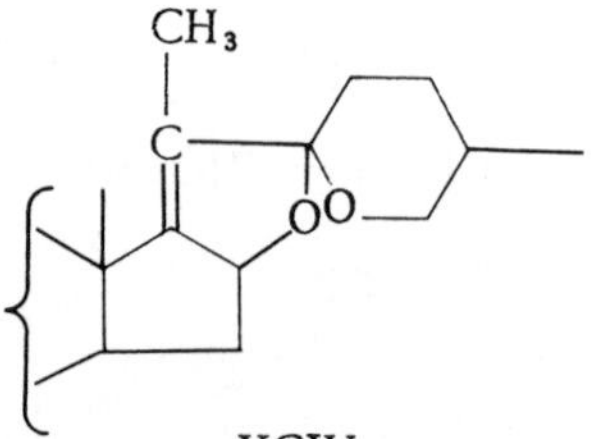

(11-57)

XCIV

The LAH reduction of 22,26 oxido-17(20)-cholestene-3β,22-diol-16-one analogously yields 22-isoallospirost-17(20)-en-3β-ol (126).

Various isospirostanes such as XCIV have been subjected to LAH reduction and in all cases no reaction with the ——OCO—— linkage has occurred.

Ref.

$C_{27}H_{38}O_3$	22-Isospirosta-4,6-dien-3-one	127
	22-Isospirosta-7,9(11)-dien-3-one	128
$C_{27}H_{40}O_3$	22-Isospirost-8(9)-en-3-one	129
$C_{27}H_{40}O_4$	22-Isoallospirostane-3,11-dione	67
	22-Isoallospirost-9(11)-en-3 β-ol-12-one	66
	2α,3α-Oxido-22-isospirostan-12-one	130
	22-Isoallospirostane-3,12-dione (hecogenone)	130
$C_{27}H_{42}O_3$	22-Isospirostan-3-one	129
	2α,3α-Oxido-22-isoallospirostane	131
	2β,3β-Oxido-22-isoallospirostane	131
$C_{27}H_{42}O_4$	9α,11α-Oxido-22-isoallospirostan-3β-ol	66
	22-Isoallospirostan-3β-ol-12-one (hecogenin)	132,133
$C_{27}H_{42}O_5$	22-Isoallospirostan-3β,12β-diol-11-one	66
$C_{29}H_{42}O_5$	22-Isospirost-5-en-3β-ol-7-one acetate	134
$C_{29}H_{42}O_6$	9α,11α-Oxido-22-isoallospirostan-3β-ol-7-one acetate	67

If the LAH reduction of the spirostane is carried out in the presence of anhydrous hydrogen chloride cleavage occurs at carbon 22 and opens the 22,26-oxido ring (135).

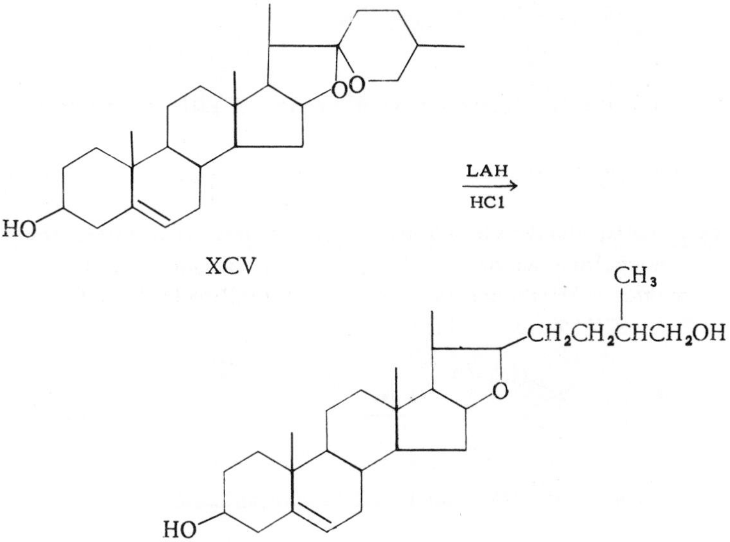

XCV

$$\xrightarrow[\text{HCl}]{\text{LAH}}$$

(11-58)

XCVI

Thus, reduction of 22-isospirost-5-en-3β-ol (diosgenin) (XCV) under these conditions yields 5-furostene-3β,26-diol (XCVI). Reduction of 22-isoallospirostan-3β-ol(tigogenin) and spirostan-3β-ol (sarsasapogenin) similarly results in cleavage of ring F in the presence of hydrogen chloride gas.

The cleavage of the —NCO— linkage in the presence of LAH is explained by the coordination of the available electron pair on nitrogen with aluminum hydride in the aluminum hydride etherate. The formation of a quasi ring is followed by a displacement by the hydride ion resulting in cleavage of the carbon-oxygen bond (Section 12.17) (136). In the case of the —OĊO— grouping there is no reason to believe that the electron pair on oxygen should displace the electron pair on oxygen in the weakly acidic aluminum hydride monoetherate. The fact that cleavage of the spirostanes can be induced by carrying out the LAH reduction in the presence of hydrogen chloride supports this view.

11.3.1.b *Cleavage of the* —OĊO— *Grouping.* The LAH reduction of secondary-tertiary epoxides generally yields the tertiary alcohol, as discussed in Section 11.2.1.b.

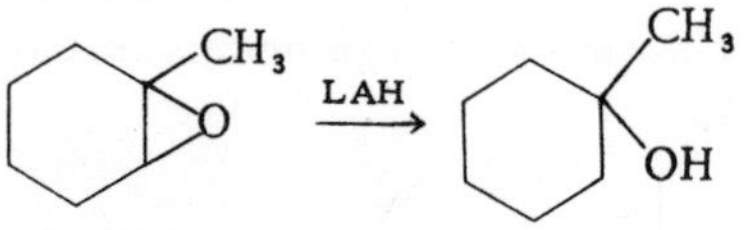

$$(11\text{-}59)$$

XCVII

The reduction of 1-acetoxy-1,2-epoxycyclohexane (XCVIII), based on this general behavior and on the non-reduction of the —OĊO— grouping in the presence of LAH, should yield 1,1-cyclohexanediol. The latter would be converted to cyclohexanone which, on LAH reduction, gives cyclohexanol. However, LAH reduction of XCVIII actually yields 1,2-cyclohexanediol (75% *cis*, 25% *trans*) (11,35,36).

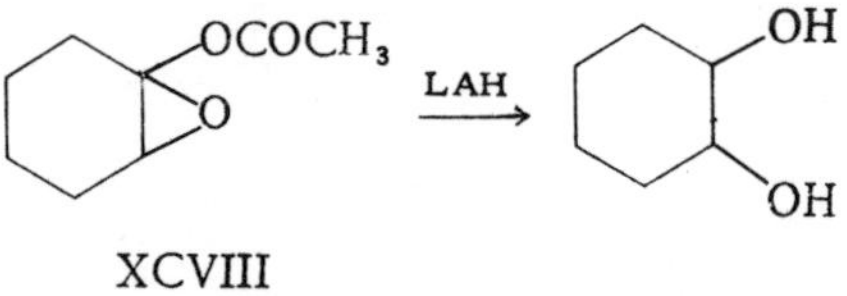

$$(11\text{-}60)$$

XCVIII

This apparent discrepancy with the non-cleavage of the —OĊO— grouping is due to the presence of the reducible ester group. Reduction of the ester group yields XCIX which would be cleaved as follows (136):

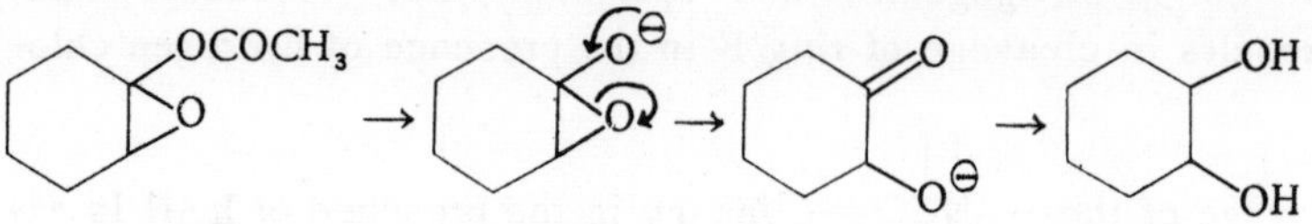

$$(11\text{-}61)$$

XCVIII   XCIX

The cleavage of the —OĊO— grouping in 2-isopropyl-5-methyl-1,3-dioxolan-4-one (C) is also attributable to the presence of a reducible group (137).

$$(11\text{-}62)$$

The LAH reduction of D-galactofuranose pentaacetate (CI) yields galactitol as a result of cleavage due to the presence of the contiguous ester group (138).

$$(11\text{-}63)$$

As mentioned in Sections 7.1.1.b (equation 7-5) and 9.1.1.b.8 (equation 9-44), the LAH reduction of 4-formylphenanthrene-5-carboxylic acid esters (CII) as well as the pseudo esters (CIII) yields the same diol (CIV) in excellent yield (139,140).

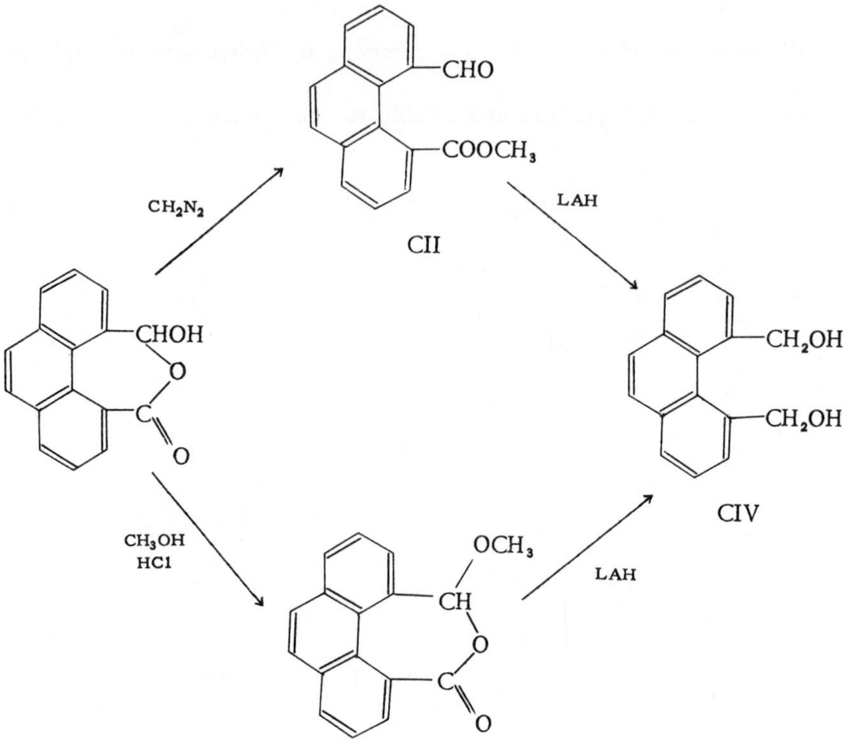

CHO

COOCH₃

CH₂N₂

LAH

CII

CHOH
O
C
O

-CH₂OH

-CH₂OH

CIV

CH₃OH
HCl

OCH₃
CH
O
C
O

LAH

CIII   (11-64)

The conversion of CIII to CIV appears to be another exception to the non-cleavage of the ──O$\overset{|}{\text{C}}$O── grouping. In this case it is possible that under the influence of LAH the pseudo ester is converted to the normal ester before reduction occurs. In this connection it is of interest that under the influence of aluminum isopropoxide, which might be expected in this respect to behave in a manner similar to that of LAH, the pseudo ester is converted to the lactone of 4-(hydroxymethyl)-5-phenanthrene-carboxylic acid (139). It has been shown that in the case of substituted 2-benzoylbenzoic acids, which also form pseudo as well as normal esters, a keto acid-hydroxylacetone equilibrium exists (141).

The reaction may be analogous to that indicated in the reduction of C. Reduction of the lactone grouping yields CV which would then undergo the indicated shifts to yield the carbonyl derivative. The latter would be converted to the diol with LAH.

$$(11\text{-}65)$$

The reaction of the trimer of phenylpropargyl aldehyde, 2,4,6-*tris*-(phenylethinyl)trioxane (CVI) with LAH, followed by decomposition of the intermediate complex with dilute sulfuric acid, yields a small quantity of cinnamyl alcohol, identified as the 3,5-dinitrobenzoate (142).

$$(11\text{-}66)$$

Cleavage of the trioxane nucleus with the acid used in the decomposition of the complex would yield the aldehyde. The isolation of some cinnamyl alcohol may be indicative of the action of LAH as an acid yielding the aldehyde in the course of the reaction, followed by normal reduction.

The reported LAH reductions of ozonides, as discussed in Section 11.8, introduce structural features which enable these reactions to fit within the scope of the generalization. Thus, the reduction of the ozonide (CVII) is reported to yield a mixture of products, according to equation (11–67) (143).

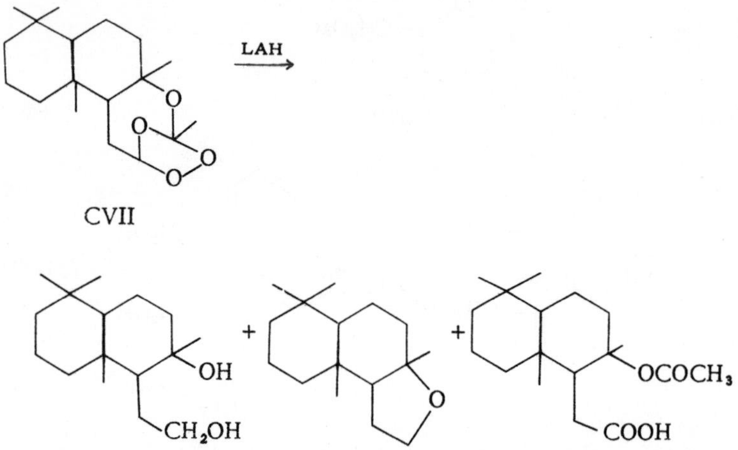

CVII

+   +   (11–67)

CH₂OH   COOH

CVIII

The initial reaction probably involves cleavage of the peroxide linkage. The isolation of CVIII among the reaction products indicates that the resultant orthoester structure would be cleaved at the oxygen bridge occupying the site of the original double bond. The cleavage of orthoesters to acetals is discussed in Section 11.4.1. The order of occurrence of these cleavages may be reversed without impairing the reasoning. The resultant derivatives of CVIII would react normally with LAH to yield the glycol.

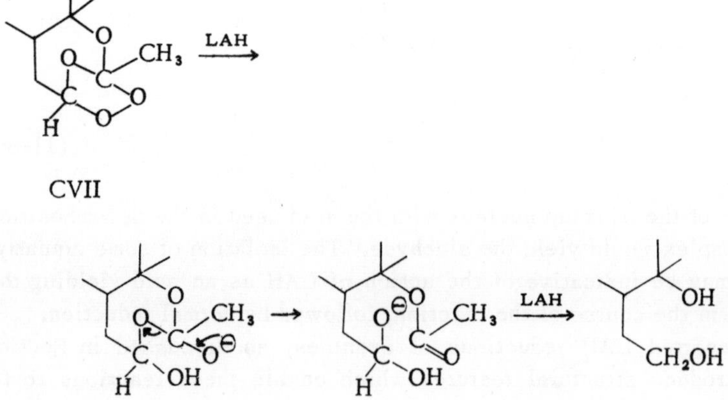

CVII

(11–68)

The LAH reduction of ozonide CIX followed by hydrolysis and chromic acid oxidation is reported to yield the diketone CX (144).

CIX   CX   (11-69)

The cleavage of the peroxide linkage would result in the formation of CXI which would be cleaved as shown.

CXI   (11-70)

The resultant carboxylic acid derivative would be reduced to the carbinol and chromic acid oxidation would yield the carbonyl function.

The reductive cleavage of the stable ozonide of 2-phenylskatole (CXII) is reported to yield o-benzylaminophenylmethylcarbinol (145).

CXII   (11-71)

The cleavage of the peroxide linkage and the cleavage of both —NCO—

linkages, as discussed in Section 12.17, result in the formation of a carboxylic acid derivative whose normal LAH reduction yields the in-dicated product.

The LAH reduction of the ergot alkaloids of the ergotamine and ergo-toxin types (CXIII) yields three kinds of reduction products (146).

The cleavage of the —OCO— linkage in CXIII is related to the cleavage of the —NCO— group in the partial structure CXIV (Section 12.17).

CXIV

11.3.2 Reactions with Sodium Borohydride

The —O$\overset{|}{\underset{|}{C}}$O— linkage is also resistant to attack by sodium boro-

hydride. The following compounds have been subjected to such attack
with retention of these structural features:

		Ref.
$C_8H_{14}O_7$	Methyl (methyl-α-D-glucopyranosid)uronate	147
	Methyl (methyl-α-D-galactopyranosid)uronate monohydrate	147
	Methyl (methyl-β-D-galactopyranosid)uronate	147
$C_9H_{12}O_6$	1,2-Isopropylidene-D-glucuronolactone-6-C^{14}	148
$C_{15}H_{26}O_{11}$	2-Methyl-3-(2,3,4-trimethyl-D-glucuronosido)-D-xylose	149
$C_{23}H_{30}O_5$	2β,4b-Dimethyl-2-methallyl-1-carboxymethylene-7-ethylenedioxy-1,2,3,4,4aα,4b,5,6,7,8,10,10aβ-dodecahydrophenanthren-4-one	150
$C_{24}H_{35}NO_4$	3,3-Dimethoxy-20-cyano-17-pregnen-21-ol-11-one	151
$C_{25}H_{38}O_4$	Ethylene acetal of methyl Δ^4-3-keto-bisnorcholenate	152
$C_{29}H_{38}O_4$	3-Acetoxy-22-isospirosta-3,5,7,9(11)-tetraene	153
$C_{29}H_{40}O_4$	3-Acetoxy-22-isospirosta-3,5,7-triene	153
$C_{29}H_{42}O_6$	9α,11α-Oxido-22-isoallospirostan-3β-ol-7-one acetate	67
$C_{29}H_{42}O_9$	Gofruside	154
$C_{29}H_{42}O_{10}$	Convallatoxin	155
$C_{30}H_{42}O_{10}$	Desgluco-hellebrin	155

11.3.3 Reactions with Potassium Borohydride

The —O$\overset{|}{\underset{|}{C}}$O— grouping in hecogenin, $C_{27}H_{42}O_4$, and manogenin,

$C_{27}H_{42}O_5$, is reportedly not attacked on treatment with potassium borohydride (156).

11.3.4 Reactions with Lithium Borohydride

The acetal grouping in 3,3-dimethoxy- (151) and 3,3-diethoxy-20-cyano-
17-pregnen-21-ol-11-one (157) is not attacked by the borohydride.

11.3.5 Reactions with Aluminum Borohydride

Treatment of methylal (CXV) with aluminum borohydride yields dimethyl
ether and diborane, contrary to the behavior with LAH and the other
borohydrides (158).

$$CH_2 \diagup^{OCH_3}_{\diagdown OCH_3} \xrightarrow{Al(BH_4)_3} CH_3OCH_3 + B_2H_6 \qquad (11\text{-}73)$$

CXV

11.4 ORTHOESTERS

11.4.1 Reductions with Lithium Aluminum Hydride

The reduction of orthoesters with LAH proceeds to yield the corresponding acetals in good yield (159). Thus, ethyl orthoformate (CXVI), orthoacetate and orthovalerate are reduced to the acetals by the addition of one-quarter molar equivalent of LAH to a refluxing solution of the orthoester in benzene.

$$HC(OC_2H_5)_3 \xrightarrow{LAH} H_2C(OC_2H_5)_2 \qquad (11\text{-}74)$$
$$CXVI$$

This reaction has been utilized in the conversion of nitriles to aldehydes. Thus, β-methylmercaptopropionitrile (CXVII) is converted through the intermediate imidoester to methyl or ethyl ortho β-methylmercaptopropionate. The ortho esters are reduced with LAH to the dimethyl and diethyl acetals, respectively, and the latter are readily hydrolyzed to β-methylmercaptopropionaldehyde (CXVIII).

$$CH_3SCH_2CH_2CN$$
$$CXVII$$

$$\begin{array}{cc}
OC_2H_5 & OCH_3 \\
| & | \\
CH_3SCH_2CH_2C=NH_2Cl & CH_3SCH_2CH_2C=NH_2Cl \\
\downarrow & \downarrow \\
CH_3SCH_2CH_2C(OC_2H_5)_3 & CH_3SCH_2CH_2C(OCH_3)_3 \\
\downarrow \text{ LAH} & \downarrow \text{ LAH} \\
CH_3SCH_2CH_2CH(OC_2H_5)_2 & CH_3SCH_2CH_2CH(OCH_3)_2
\end{array}$$

$$CH_3SCH_2CH_2CHO$$
$$CXVIII \qquad (11\text{-}75)$$

11.4.2 Reactions with Aluminum Borohydride

In contrast to the behavior of LAH, reduction of ethyl orthoformate (CXVI) with aluminum borohydride yields a mixture of ethyl methyl ether, diborane and compounds of the type $Al(OR)_x(BH_4)_{3-x}$ (158).

11.5 ENOLS AND ENOL ETHERS

11.5.1 Reactions of Enols with Lithium Aluminum Hydride

Enolates are generally resistant to attack by LAH. As discussed in Section 9.1.1.b.3, the reduction of enolizable compounds generally proceeds to give low yields of the reduction product due to the intermediate formation of a lithium aluminum enolate which, upon hydrolysis regenerates the original functional group. Buchta and Bayer (160) have observed that in the LAH reduction of various β-ketoesters possessing the partial structure CXIX, as the size of R increases the yield of reduction product increases.

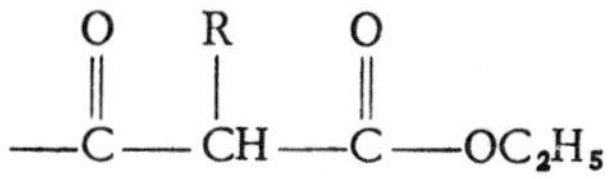

CXIX

This may be due to the hindrance to enolization with the increasing bulk of R.

Dreiding and Hartman reported that LAH treatment of the sodium enolate of 2-methylcyclohexanone results in an almost quantitative recovery of 2-methylcyclohexanone. However, the sodium enolate of 2-carbomethoxy-cyclopentanone (CXX) gives a 50% yield of a mixture of 1-cyclopentene-methanol and 2-methylenecyclopentanol (161).

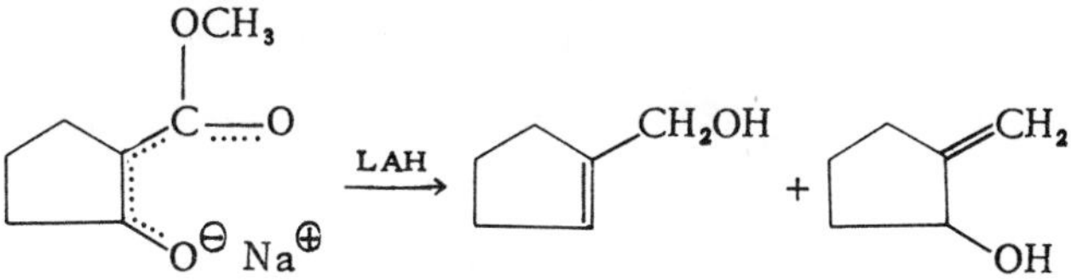

(11-76)

CXX

This demonstrates that enolates of some β-dicarbonyl compounds are attacked by LAH.

The reduction of 2-carbethoxycyclohexanone (CXXI) and 2-hydroxy-methylenecyclohexanone (CXXII), followed by hydrolysis with an aqueous solution of Rochelle salt, yields a mixture of 2-methylenecyclohexanol, 1-cyclohexenemethanol and 2-hydroxymethylcyclohexanol in a 5:2:1 ratio.

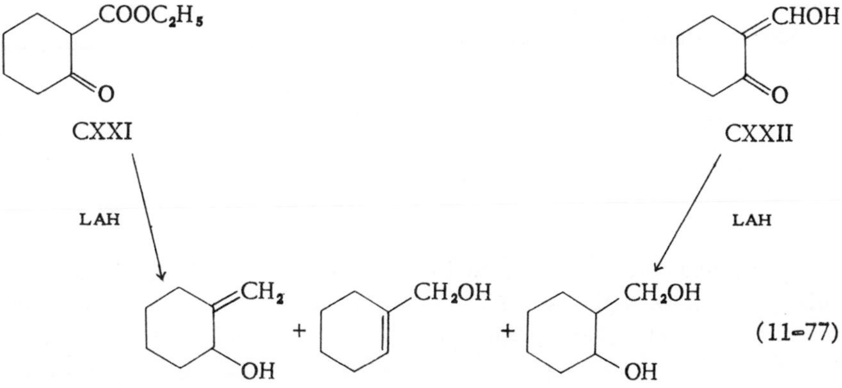

CXXI

CXXII

LAH

LAH

(11-77)

Analogously, the reduction of 2-carbomethoxycyclopentanone (CXXIII) and 2-hydroxymethylenecyclopentanone (CXXIV) yields 2-methylenecyclopentanol, 1-cyclopentenemethanol and 2-hydroxymethylcyclopentanol.

$$(11\text{-}78)$$

The postulated course of these reactions, as discussed in Section 7.2.1.g.9, equation (7-61), involves the reduction of enolate salts. The inverse addition of one-half mole of LAH to CXXII gives 1-cyclohexenecarboxaldehyde and a large quantity of viscous residue.

$$(11\text{-}79)$$

Vonderwahl and Schinz have reported that the LAH reduction of 1,1,5,5-tetramethyl-4-hydroxymethylcyclohexan-3-one ,(CXXV) gives a 49% yield of a mixture of 67% of 5,5-dimethyldihydroapocyclolavandulal (CXXVI) and 33% of α-5,5-dimethylapocyclolavandulal (CXXVII) accompanied by the glycol CXXVIII (162).

$$(11\text{-}80)$$

Petuely and Bauer reported that l-ascorbic acid (CXXIX), isoascorbic acid (CXXX), reductic acid (CXXXI), glucoreductone (CXXXII) and the dimethyl ester of α,α'-dihydroxymuconic acid (CXXXIII) are not reduced by LAH (163).

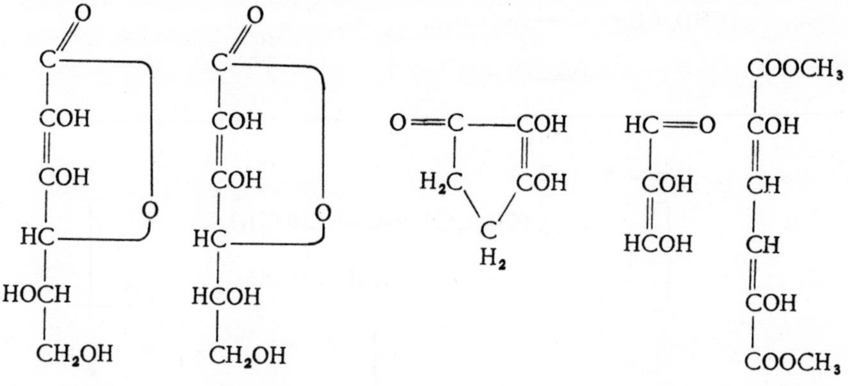

CXXIX   CXXX   CXXXI   CXXXII CXXXIII

Treatment of 3,7-diketocholestene (CXXXIV), which exists mainly in a monoenol form, with LAH in refluxing ether for three hours is reported to yield a non-ketonic gum, whereas treatment with LAH in tetrahydrofuran at 20 ° for four hours yields a ketonic gum (164).

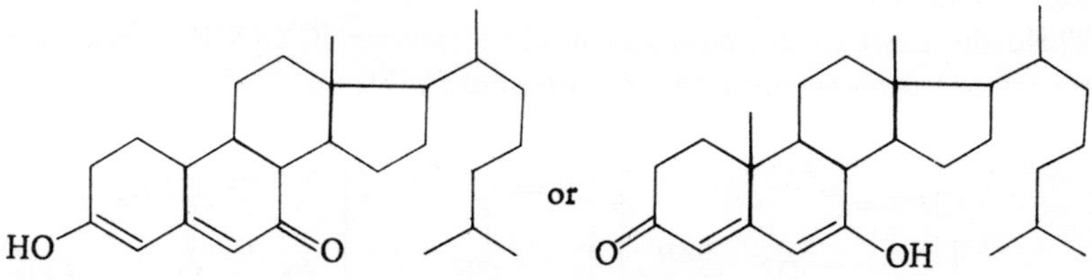

or

CXXXIV

The LAH reduction of ethylketene dimer (CXXXV) yields the β-keto-carbinol, CXXXVI, through the intermediate enol (165).

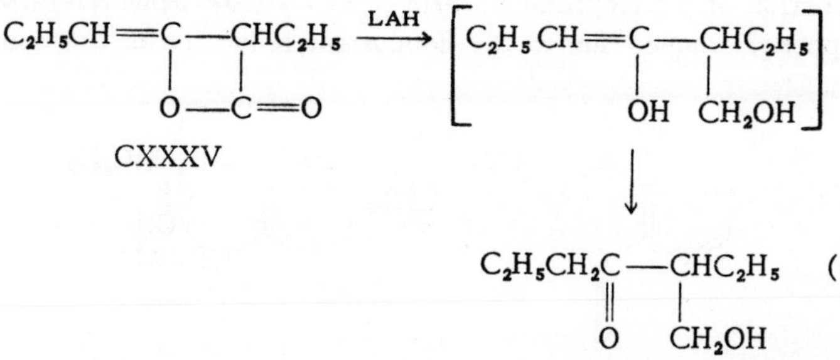

CXXXV

$$C_2H_5CH_2C\!\!-\!\!CHC_2H_5 \quad (11\text{-}81)$$

CXXXVI

Similarly, LAH reduction of (ω-cyclohexylalkyl)ketene dimers (CXXXVII) yields the β-ketocarbinols (CXXXVIII) (166).

$$\text{C}_6\text{H}_{11}\text{-}(\text{CH}_2)_n\,\text{CH}=\overset{\displaystyle |}{\text{C}}\text{-}\overset{\displaystyle |}{\text{C}}\text{H}(\text{CH}_2)_n\text{-}\text{C}_6\text{H}_{11} \quad \underset{\text{O}\text{-}\text{C}=\text{O}}{} \quad \xrightarrow{\text{LAH}}$$

CXXXVII

$n = 0, 1, 2, 4$

$$\left[\;\text{C}_6\text{H}_{11}\text{-}(\text{CH}_2)_n\,\text{CH}=\overset{\displaystyle |}{\text{C}}\text{-}\overset{\displaystyle |}{\text{C}}\text{H}(\text{CH}_2)_n\text{-}\text{C}_6\text{H}_{11}\;\right]$$

with OH and CH$_2$OH substituents

$$\downarrow$$

$$\text{C}_6\text{H}_{11}\text{-}(\text{CH}_2)_n\,\text{CH}_2\overset{\displaystyle \parallel}{\text{C}}\text{-}\overset{\displaystyle |}{\text{C}}\text{H}(\text{CH}_2)_n\text{-}\text{C}_6\text{H}_{11} \qquad (11\text{-}82)$$

with O and CH$_2$OH substituents

CXXXVIII

While CXXXVI is readily reduced to the 1,3-diol, CXXXVIII is not further reduced with LAH.

While the LAH reduction of α-angelica lactone (CXXXIX) yields the α-ketocarbinol through the intermediate enol (167),

$$\text{CXXXIX} \xrightarrow[65\%]{\text{LAH}} \left[\begin{array}{c}\text{CH}=\text{C}\text{-}\text{CH}_3\\ |\qquad\text{OH}\\ \text{CH}_2\text{CH}_2\text{OH}\end{array}\right] \rightarrow \begin{array}{c}\text{CH}_2\text{CCH}_3\\ |\;\;\overset{\parallel}{\text{O}}\\ \text{CH}_2\text{CH}_2\text{OH}\end{array} \qquad (11\text{-}83)$$

CXXXIX

the reduction of 3 phenylisocoumarin (CXL) yields 1-phenyl-2-(o-hydroxy-methylphenyl)ethanol due to the concurrent reduction of the double bond (168).

$$\text{CXL} \xrightarrow[59\%]{\text{LAH}} \begin{array}{c}\text{CH}_2\text{CHC}_6\text{H}_5\\ \text{OH}\\ \text{CH}_2\text{OH}\end{array} \qquad (11\text{-}84)$$

CXL

Reduction of tropolone (CXLI) with LAH in ether has been reported (169,170) to yield a primary product which rapidly resinifies when the reaction mixture is hydrolyzed. Distillation of the resulting tar gives a large amount of resin and a small yield of a liquid which readily yields a bis-2,4-dinitrophenylhydrazone. The reduction product is postulated as cyclohept-4-ene-1,2-dione (CXLII) produced by 1,4- or 1,6-addition of LAH to the dienone system of the initial lithium derivative. Hydrolysis of the resulting dienolate yields the dione by ketonization.

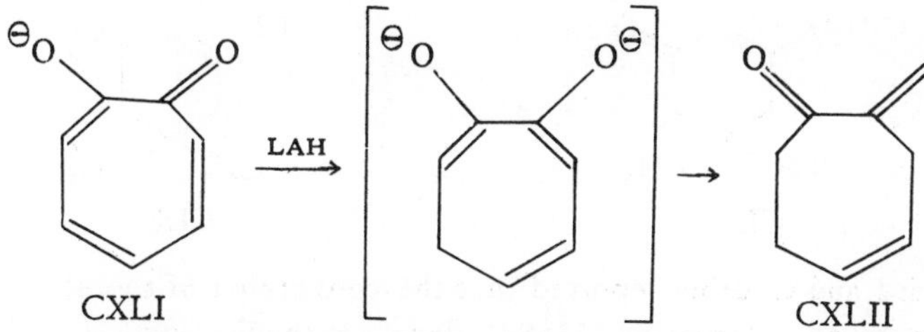

$$(11\text{-}85)$$

CXLI   CXLII

11.5.2 Reactions of Enol Ethers with Lithium Aluminum Hydride

Frank and Hall (171) have reported that the O-ethyl derivative of ethyl acetoacetate (CXLIII) and the O-methyl derivative of dibenzoylmethane (CXLIV) are resistant to attack with LAH.

$$\underset{CXLIII}{CH_3\overset{\overset{\displaystyle OC_2H_5}{|}}{C}=CHCOOC_2H_5} \qquad\qquad \underset{CXLIV}{C_6H_5\overset{\overset{\displaystyle OCH_3}{|}}{C}=CHCOC_6H_5}$$

Karrer and Rüttner reported that the LAH reduction of the O-methyl ether of the enol form of acetoacetic ester (CXLV) yields butan-3-on-1-ol (CXLVI) (7).

$$\underset{CXLV}{CH_3\overset{\overset{\displaystyle OCH_3}{|}}{C}=CHCOOC_2H_5} \xrightarrow{\text{LAH}} CH_3\overset{\overset{\displaystyle OH}{|}}{C}=CHCH_2OH \rightarrow \underset{CXLVI}{CH_3\overset{\overset{\displaystyle O}{||}}{C}CH_2CH_2OH} \quad (11\text{-}86)$$

The reduction of ethyl ethoxymethylenemalonate (CXLVII) is reported to yield 5% of ethyl methylenemalonate (171).

$$\underset{CXLVII}{C_2H_5OCH=C(COOC_2H_5)_2} \xrightarrow{\text{LAH}} CH_2=C(COOC_2H_5)_2 \quad (11\text{-}87)$$

Frank and Hall reported that the inverse addition of one-quarter mole of LAH to an ethereal solution of 3-ethoxy-5-isopropyl-2-cyclohexenone (CXLVIII), followed by acidification with dilute sulfuric acid, gives 5-isopropyl-2-cyclohexenone (CXLIX).

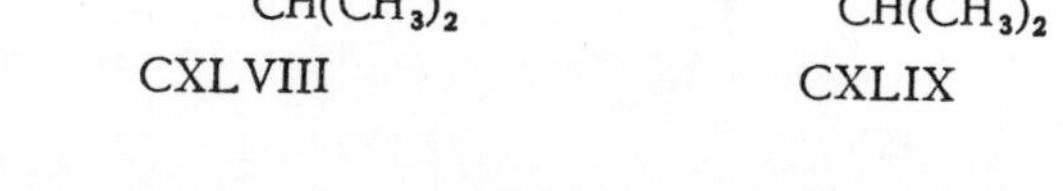

$$(11\text{-}88)$$

CXLVIII   CXLIX

By the same procedure 3-ethoxy-5,5-dimethyl-2-cyclohexenone (CL) is converted to 5,5-dimethyl-2-cyclohexenone in 48% yield. Treatment of 3-chloro-5,5-dimethyl-2-cyclohexenone (CLI) with LAH in ether results in recovery of the starting material (171).

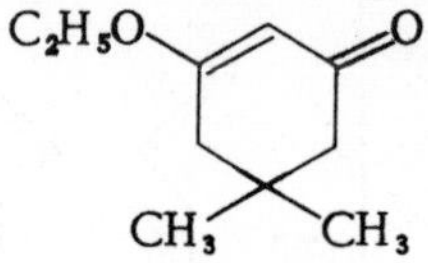

CL 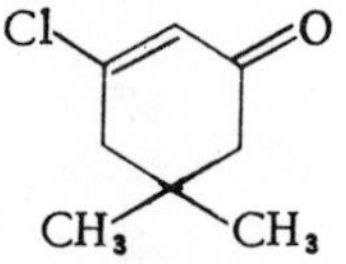   CLI

Blanchard and Goering reported that the conversion of the enol ether of a β-diketone, as in equation (11-88), does not require inverse addition or excess ketone (172). Reduction of the enol ether of 5-methyl-1,3-cyclo-hexanedione, 3-ethoxy-5-methyl-2-cyclohexenone (CLII), by the inverse technique gives 69% of 5-methyl-2-cyclohexenone (CLIII) and by the normal procedure gives 92% of CLIII. Decomposition of the metal al-coholate by alkali instead of acid gives 49% of CLIII. The reduction is postulated as proceeding through the intermediate hydroxy enol ether which is converted to the hydroxy ketone by hydrolysis followed by dehydration.

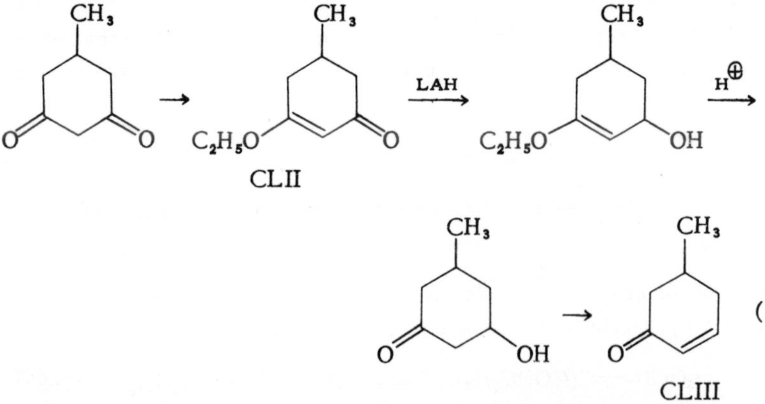

CLII

(11-89)

CLIII

The reduction of cis-5-ethoxy-8-methylhydrind-5-en-7-one (CLIV) is similarly postulated as proceeding through the hydroxy ketone to give the ene-one in 89% yield (173).

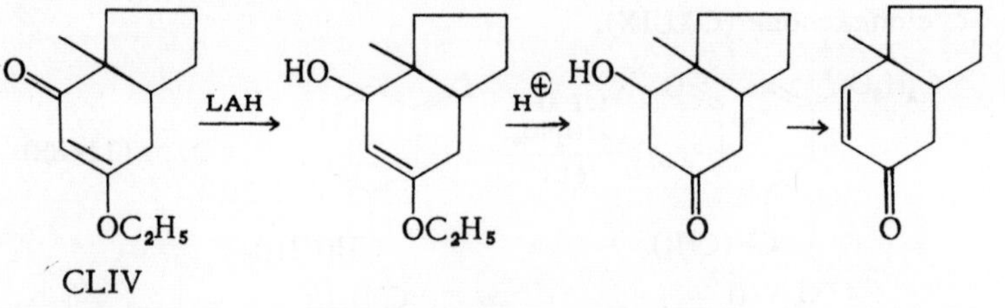

(11-90)

CLIV

The reduction of 3-methoxycholesta-3,5-dien-7-one (CLV) with LAH in tetrahydrofuran at 20°, followed by hydrolysis with an aqueous solution of tartaric acid, yields 60% of cholesta-4,6-dien-3-one (CLVI) (164). The first product of the reduction is presumed to be the 7-hydroxy compound which undergoes anionotropic rearrangement of the hydroxyl group to the 3-position under the influence of the tartaric acid. Loss of methanol then yields the dienone. When the decomposition of the reduction complex is carried out with water instead of tartaric acid the solution obtained exhibits an absorption maximum in agreement with the structure of the 7-hydroxy compound. Subsequent treatment with aqueous tartaric acid shifts the absorption maximum to that of the dienone.

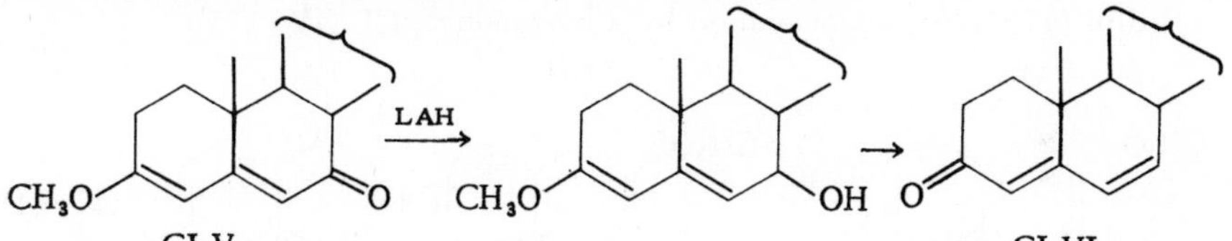

CLV CH₃O OH CLVI

(11-91)

The LAH reduction of 1,2,3,4,8,9-hexahydro-1-keto-6-methoxy-9-methyl-naphthalene (CLVII), followed by acid hydrolysis, yields 1,2,3,4,6,7,8,9-octahydro-1-hydroxy-6-keto-9-methylnaphthalene (CLIX). The reduction of 1,2,3,4,5,8-hexahydro-1-keto-6-methoxy-5-methylnaphthalene (CLVIII), present as an impurity in the reduction of CLVII, followed by acid hydrolysis, yields 2,3,4,6,7,8-hexahydro-2-keto-1-methylnaphthalene (CLX) (174).

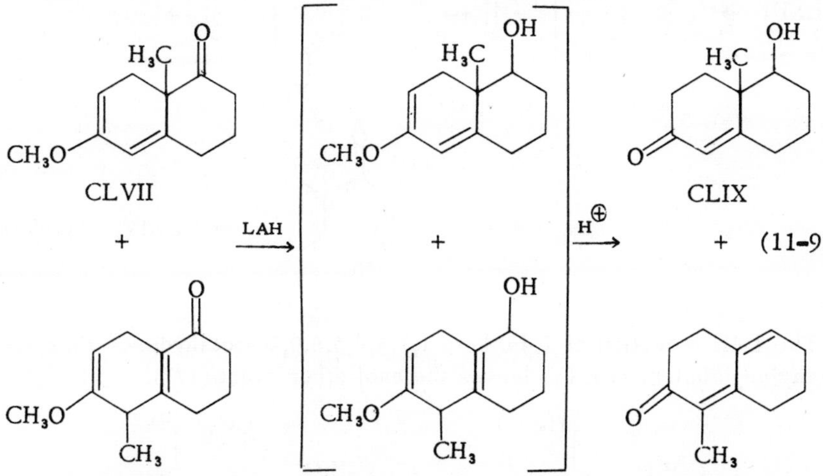

CLVII + CLVIII LAH → + H⊕ → CLIX + CLX (11-92)

The LAH reduction of trans-1,4-diketo-1,4,5,6,7,8,9,10-octahydro-2-methoxy-10-methylnaphthalene (CLXI) yields the corresponding 1,4-dihydroxy compound which, on treatment with sulfuric acid, is converted to CLXII (175).

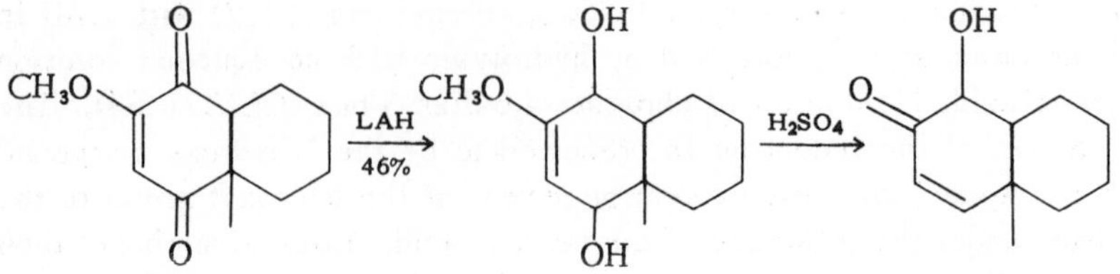

CLXI   CLXII   (11-93)

Reduction of *cis*-1,4-diketo-1,4,5,8,9,10-hexahydro-2-methoxy-10-methyl-naphthalene (CLXIII) similarly yields the 1,4-diol which is hydrolyzed to the *cis*-bicyclic ketol (175). The reduction of *trans*-CLXIII yields the 1,4-diol (175,176), accompanied by a by-product, CLXIV (175).

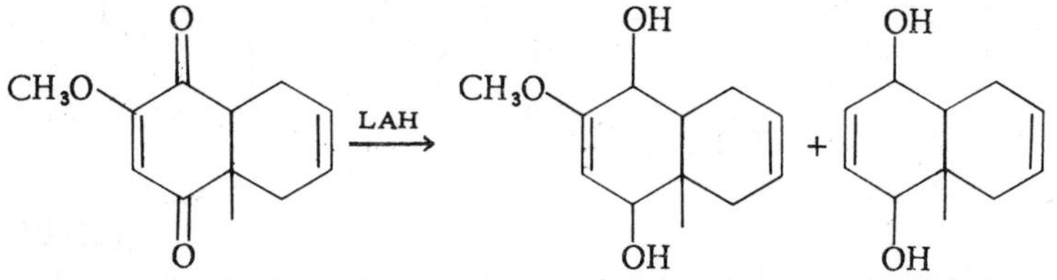

CLXIII   CLXIV   (11-94)

The by-product CLXIV is postulated as arising through successive 1,4-reduction, ketonization, elimination and reduction:

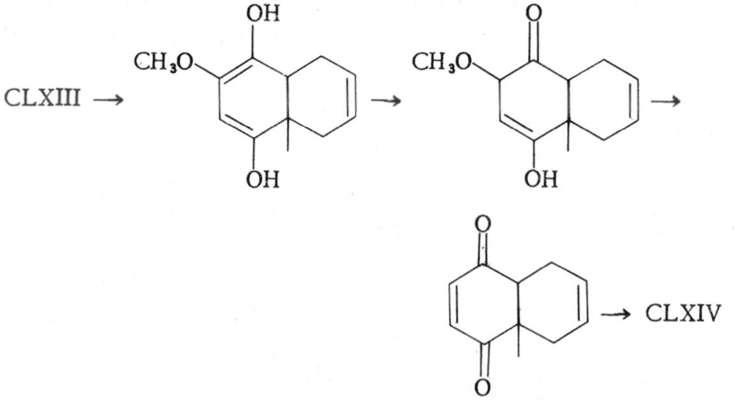

CLXIII →

→ CLXIV   (11-95)

The LAH reduction of 1,4-diketo-1,2,3,4,5,8,9,10-octahydro-6-ethoxy-5-methylnaphthalene (CLXV) leaves the enol ether intact (177).

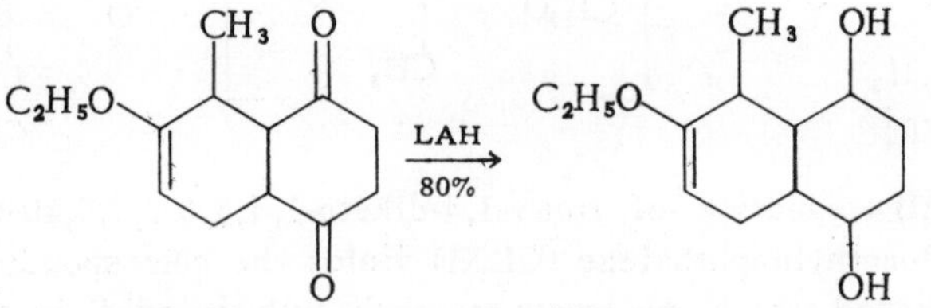

(11-96)

CLXV

Seifert and Schinz (178) reported that the LAH reduction of the isobutyl ether of 2-hydroxymethylenecyclohexanone (CLXVI) in refluxing ether, followed by the dropwise addition of concentrated sulfuric acid below 5°, gives 1-cyclohexenecarboxaldehyde (CLXVII).

$$\text{(11-97)}$$

CLXVI   CLXVII

The reduction and hydrolysis sequence applied to the following ethers of hydroxymethylenic ketones similarly yields the corresponding α,β-unsaturated aldehyde: isobutyl ether of 2-hydroxymethylenecyclopentanone, isobutyl ether of 3,3-dimethyl-6-hydroxymethylenecyclohexanone, isobutyl ether of 6-methyl-2-hydroxymethylenecyclohexanone, methyl ether of 6,6-dimethyl-2-hydroxymethylenecyclohexanone.

Vonderwahl and Schinz (162) found that the LAH reduction of the iso-butyl ether of 1,1,5,5-tetramethyl-4-hydroxymethylenecyclohexan-3-one (CLXVIII), under the conditions utilized by Seifert and Schinz, in refluxing ether, followed by a treatment with cold sulfuric acid gives a mixture of saturated and unsaturated aldehydes in which the saturated aldehyde (CLXIX) is the dominant product.

$$\text{(11-98)}$$

CLXVIII   CLXIX α β

The LAH reduction of the isobutyl ether of 1,1,5-trimethyl-4-hydroxy-methylenecyclohexan-3-one in refluxing ether, followed by hydrolysis, similarly gives the saturated aldehyde, 5-methyldihydroapocyclolavandulal, and the α-form of the unsaturated aldehyde. The reduction of CLXVIII with LAH at $-15°$, followed by a cold acid hydrolysis, gives a 52% yield of a mixture of aldehydes containing 20% of the saturated aldehyde CLXIX and 55% of the α-form and 25% of the β-form of the unsaturated aldehyde. Thus, the presence of one or more substituents on the carbon atom beta to the carbonyl group yields a mixture of saturated and unsaturated aldehydes whereas the β-unsubstituted ketone yields only the unsaturated aldehyde.

Whereas the LAH reduction of a mixture of the isomers of ethyl β-phenoxycinnamate yields β-phenoxycinnamyl alcohol, the LAH reduction of methyl β-(2-methoxy-4-propylphenoxy)-3,4-dimethoxycinnamate (CLXX) yields the corresponding alcohol accompanied by the cleavage products dimethoxycinnamyl alcohol and dihydroeugenol (179).

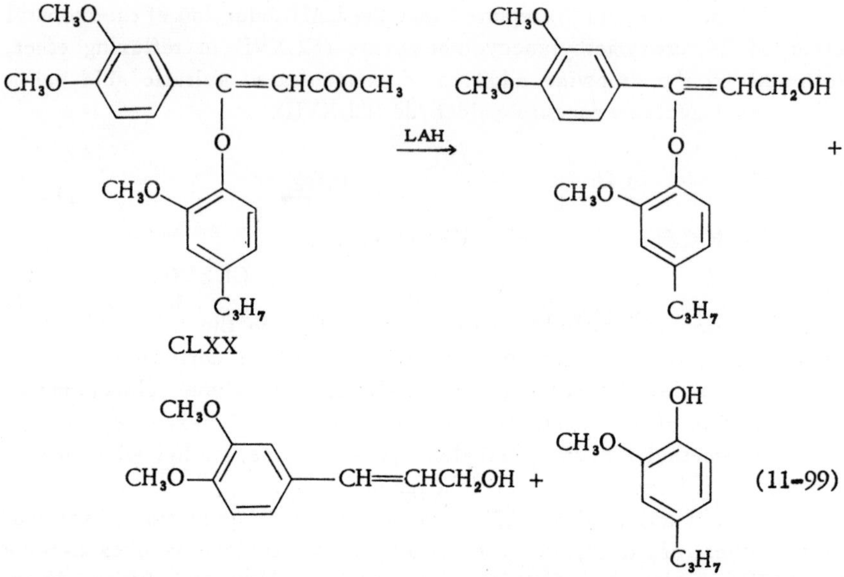

CLXX (11-99)

Although an ether saponification reaction may have occurred, in this case it seems more likely that the cleavage products arise as a result of a hydrogenolysis reaction due to the presence of the methoxy group in the ortho position on the benzene ring, as discussed in Section 16.1.

Methylation of α-cyanodesoxybenzoin (CLXXI) in alkaline medium yields a mixture of the *cis*- and *trans*-isomers of α,β-diphenyl-β-methoxyacrylonitrile (CLXXII), m.p. 106° and 84°. Reduction of CLXXII with one-half mole of LAH yields 1-cyano-1,2-diphenylethane (CLXXIII) (180).

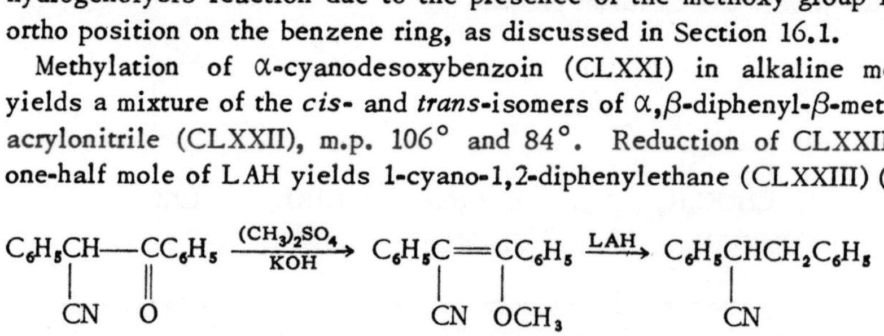

CLXXI CLXXII CLXXIII (11-100)

The formation of the enol ether of a Δ^4-3-ketosteroid has been utilized for the protection of the unsaturated carbonyl group in the course of LAH reductions of other functional groups. Thus, treatment of a Δ^4-3-ketosteroid with ethyl orthoformate in acidic ethanol yields the 3-ethoxy-3,5-diene (CLXXIV) which is resistant to attack by LAH. Hydrolysis with acidic methanol yields the Δ^4-3-ketosteroid.

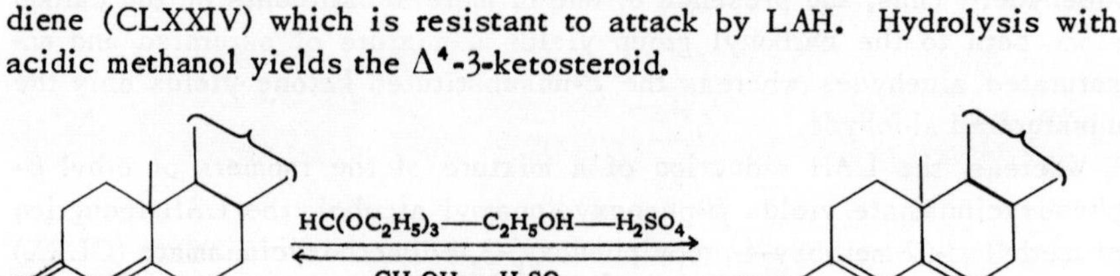

CLXXIV (11-101)

The following Δ^4-3-ketosteroids have been converted to the indicated 3-alkoxy-3,5-diene, treated with LAH and hydrolyzed to the Δ^4-3-ketosteroid:

Δ^4-3-Ketosteroid	3-Enol ether	Ref.
Androsta-4,11-dien-3,17-dione	$C_{21}H_{28}O_2$ ethyl	181
4-Androsten-3,17-dione	$C_{21}H_{30}O_2$ ethyl	152,182–185
Methyl pregna-4,17-dien-3-one-21-oate	$C_{24}H_{34}O_3$ ethyl	152,185
Methyl 4-pregnen-17β-ol-3-one-21-oate	$C_{24}H_{36}O_4$ ethyl	152,185
16,17-Oxido-4-pregnene-21-acetoxy-3,20-dione	$C_{25}H_{34}O_5$ ethyl	186
4-Pregnen-17α-ol-21-acetoxy-3,11,20-trione (cortisone acetate)	$C_{25}H_{34}O_6$ ethyl	99,186
4-Androsten-3,17-dione	$C_{25}H_{36}O_2$ cyclohexyl	182,184
Ethyl pregna-4,17-dien-3-one-21-oate	$C_{25}H_{36}O_3$ ethyl	187
4-Pregnen-17α-ol-21-acetoxy-3,20-dione	$C_{25}H_{36}O_5$ ethyl	186
Methyl Δ^4-3-keto-bisnor-cholenate	$C_{25}H_{38}O_3$ ethyl	152,185,188
4-Androsten-3,17-dione	$C_{26}H_{32}O_2$ benzyl	182,184

Treatment of 3α-acetoxypregnane-11,20-dione (CLXXV) with ethyl orthoformate in absolute alcohol in the presence of sulfuric acid is reported to yield an amorphous mixture of $\Delta^{17,20}$ and $\Delta^{20,21}$-enol-20-ethers (CLXXVI). Reduction of the enol ethers with LAH in ether followed by hydrolysis with alcohol and hydrochloric acid yields pregnane-3α,11β-diol-20-one (189).

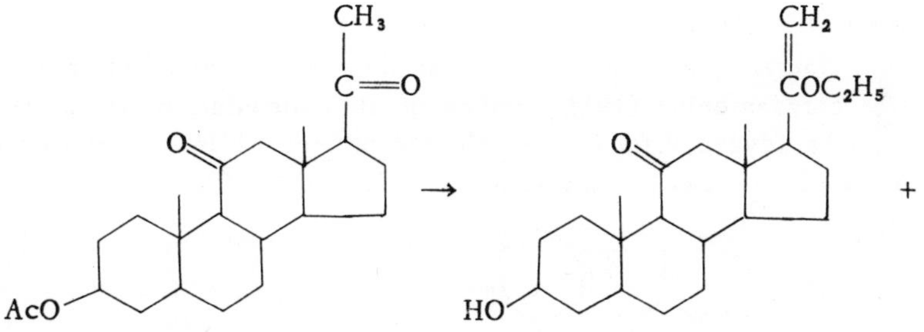

CLXXV

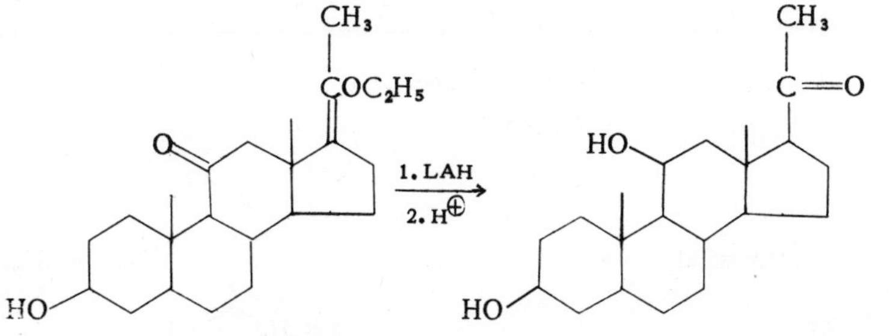

1. LAH
2. H$^{\oplus}$

(11-102)

CLXXVI

When the reduction product from CLXXVI, without hydrolysis, is treated with perbenzoic acid, the products are ethyl 3α,11β-dihydroxyetiocholanate and $3\alpha,11\beta$-dihydroxyetiocholan-17-one. This indicates that LAH reduction leaves the enol ether grouping intact.

As discussed in Section 7.2.1.m, the 3-enol thioethers have also been utilized for the protection of 3-keto group in Δ^4-3-ketosteroids.

Chatterjee and Karrer (190) reported that the LAH reduction of corynantheine, $C_{22}H_{26}N_2O_3$, gives a ketone alcohol named desmethylcorynantheine alcohol and, as a by-product, desmethoxycorynantheine alcohol. In the presence of excess LAH and a longer reaction time the desmethoxy alcohol becomes the main product of the reaction. Corynantheine was postulated as CLXXVII with the desmethyl and desmethoxy alcohols having structures CLXXVIII and CLXXIX, respectively.

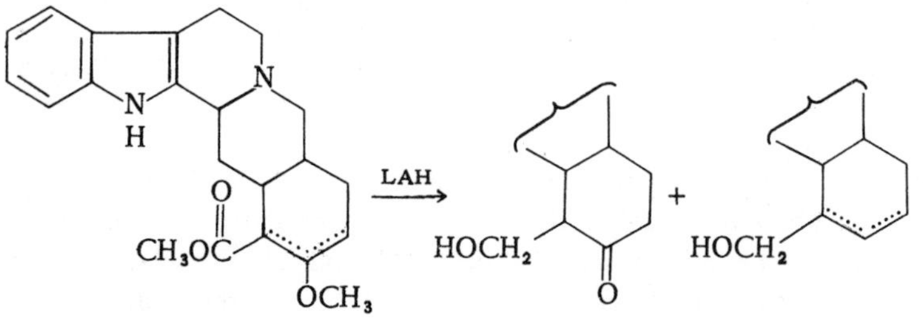

$$(11\text{-}103)$$

CLXXVII   CLXXVIII   CLXXIX

The position of the double bond in CLXXVII and CLXXIX was not established.

Janot and Goutarel, after a thorough examination, advanced structure CLXXX for corynantheine (191). Based on this formulation, structure CLXXXI can be advanced for desmethylcorynantheine while desmethoxycorynantheine alcohol can be represented by CLXXXII or CLXXIX.

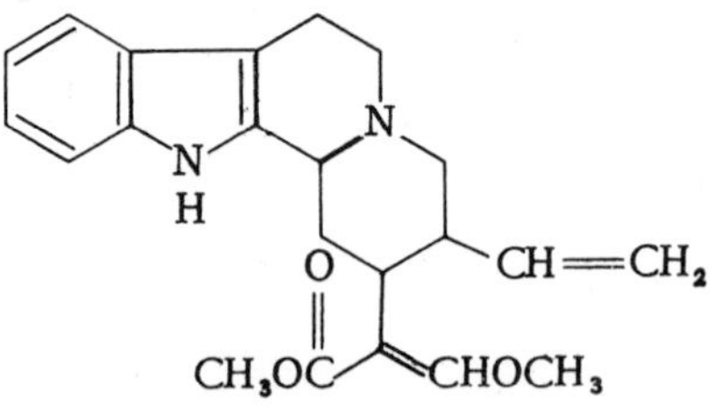

CLXXX

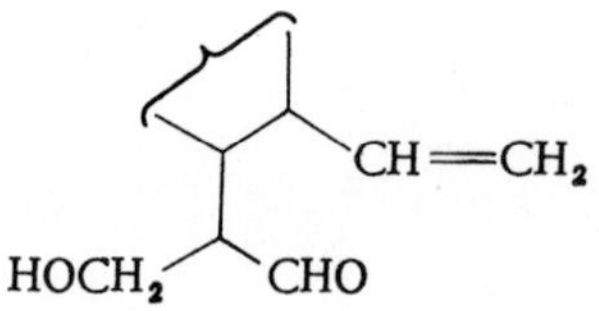

CLXXXI 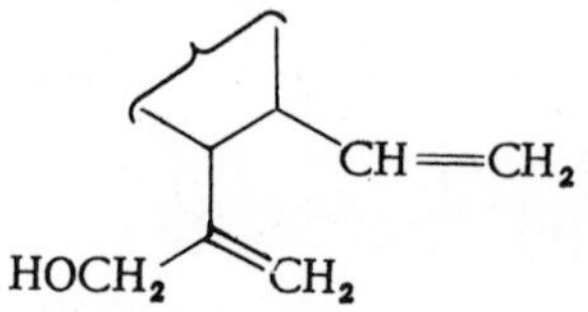   CLXXXII

Karrer, Schwyzer, and Flam (192) showed that all previously isolated and examined preparations of "corynantheine" are mixtures of two compounds, corynantheine (CLXXX), and dihydrocorynantheine (CLXXXIII). Various samples of "corynantheine" examined contained 40–45% CLXXX and 55–60% CLXXXIII. By chromatographic absorption the purest material obtained was 70% pure CLXXX. By catalytic reduction of the mixture of the bases, pure dihydrocorynantheine is obtained.

Reduction of CLXXXIII with LAH in a benzene-ether mixture gives two isomeric desmethoxydihydrocorynantheine alcohols, m.p. 214° and 204°. The first, m.p. 214°, is designated as the desmethoxydihydroalcohol (CLXXXIV) since it gives a positive Doeuvre reaction, while the latter, m.p. 204°, is designated as the iso-desmethoxydihydroalcohol (CLXXXV) and gives a negative reaction. By catalytic reduction over palladium-barium sulfate in ethanol both CLXXXIV and CLXXXV give the same tetrahydrodesmethoxycorynantheine alcohol (CLXXXVII), m.p. 211–213°. In addition to CLXXXIV and CLXXXV, the LAH reduction of CLXXXIII gives a third reduction product named dihydrocorynantheine alcohol (CLXXXVI), m.p. 136–137°.

CLXXXIII → [LAH] CLXXXIV + CLXXXV + CLXXXVI

CLXXXIV, CLXXXV, CLXXXVI → [H₂:Pd—BaSO₄] CLXXXVII

$$(11\text{--}104)$$

Elderfield and Gray have advanced structure CLXXXVIII for tetrahydroalstonine which yields tetrahydroalstanol on reduction with LAH in tetrahydrofuran (193).

CLXXXVIII → [LAH]

$$(11\text{--}105)$$

Janot and Goutarel (191) have proposed structure CLXXXIX with an ester-enol ether conjugation for tetrahydroalstonine. They suggest that

CLXXXIX is formed from the enol form of desmethylcorynantheine by ring closure.

$$(11\text{-}106)$$

CLXXXIX

Reduction of tropolone methyl ether (CXC) yields considerable benzaldehyde (170). It has been postulated that the primary reduction product undergoes anionotropy with a Wagner-Meerwein rearrangement of the resulting seven-membered carbonium ion to the more stable benzenoid carbonium ion.

$$(11\text{-}107)$$

Tarbell and Bill have reported that the LAH reduction of the oxime of 4,5-benztropolone methyl ether (CXCI) followed by acidification and acetylation gives a small amount of 5-acetaminobenzsuberone-4 (CXCII) (194).

CXCI   CXCII $(11\text{-}108)$

11.5.3 Reactions of Enol Ethers with Lithium Borohydride

Enol ethers are resistant to attack with lithium borohydride. 4-Androstene-3,17-dione (152,183) and methyl pregna-4,17-dien-3-one-21-oate (152) have been converted to the corresponding 3-enol ethers, treated with the borohydride and hydrolyzed to the Δ^4-3-ketosteroids, as has similarly been done with LAH.

11.6 HYDROPEROXIDES

The reduction of organic hydroperoxides with LAH proceeds smoothly to give the corresponding alcohol in good yield. Measurement of the volumes of hydrogen evolved indicate two moles of hydrogen per mole of hydroperoxide (195,196). It has therefore been postulated that the primary reaction with LAH involves fission between the oxygen atoms of the ——OOH group to give directly the lithium aluminum alkoxides (195).

$$4\ ROOH + LiAlH_4 \longrightarrow LiAl(OR)_4 + 4\ H_2O \qquad (11\text{--}109)$$

$$4\ H_2O + 2\ LiAlH_4 \longrightarrow 2\ LiAlO_2 + 8\ H_2 \qquad (11\text{--}110)$$

The reduction of α-tetralyl hydroperoxide (CXCIII) and cyclohex-2-en-1-yl hydroperoxide (CXCIV) with LAH in ether yields α-tetralol and cyclohex-2-en-1-ol, respectively (195).

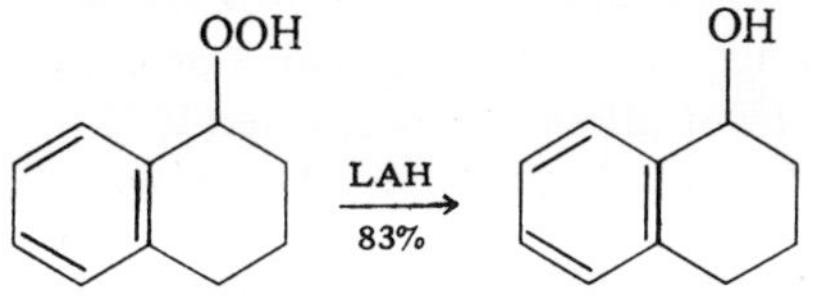

$$(11\text{--}111)$$

CXCIII

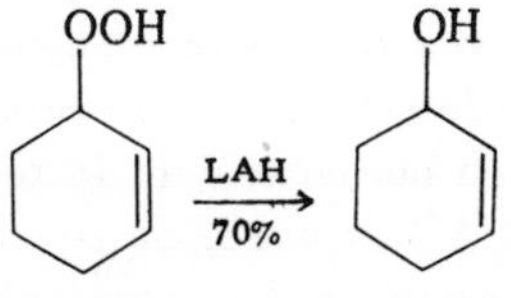

$$(11\text{--}112)$$

CXCIV

The action of LAH on triphenylmethyl hydroperoxide (CXCV) leads to the formation of triphenylmethanol in almost quantitative yield (197).

$$(C_6H_5)_3COOH \xrightarrow{\text{LAH}} (C_6H_5)_3COH \qquad (11\text{--}113)$$
CXCV

The autoxidation of 2-phenylskatole (CXCVI) in hydrocarbon solvents yields the hydroperoxide (CXCVII), 2-phenyl-3-methyl-3-hydroperoxyin-dolenine. By reduction with LAH, CXCVII is converted to CXCVI. Reduction of CXCVII with sodium borohydride in ethanol yields 2-phenyl-3-methyl-3-hydroxyindolenine (CXCVIII) and CXCVI (145).

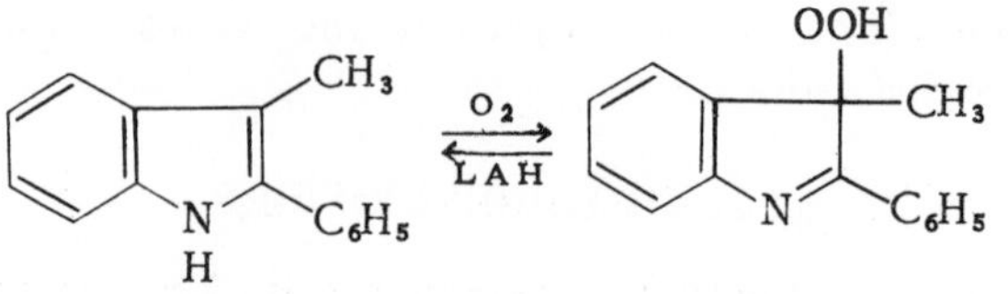

$$(11\text{-}114)$$

CXCVI   CXCVII

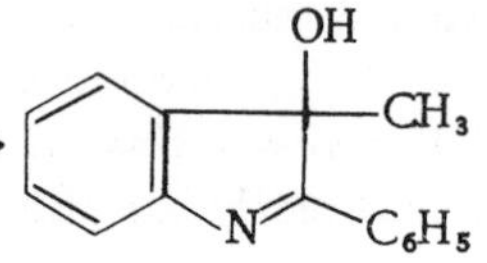

$$+ \text{CXCVI} \qquad (11\text{-}115)$$

CXCVIII

Catalytic hydrogenation of the hydroperoxide yields the indolenine, phenylskatole or unchanged starting material (145).

11.7 PEROXIDES

The reaction of dibenzoyl peroxide with LAH proceeds almost explosively to give 87.5% benzyl alcohol (196). Hochstein reported that the reaction consumes approximately 1.5 moles of LAH and evolves one mole of hydrogen per mole of dibenzoyl peroxide (167). Matic and Sutton (196) confirmed the evolution of one mole of hydrogen by the reaction of the peroxide with an excess of LAH in di-*n*-butyl ether and have postulated the stoichiometric relationship:

$$2\ (C_6H_5COO)_2 + 3\ \text{LiAlH}_4 \rightarrow \text{LiAl}(OCH_2C_6H_5)_4 + 2\ H_2 + 2\ \text{LiAlO}_2 \quad (11\text{-}16)$$

Ascaridole (CXCIX) gives one mole of hydrogen on reaction with excess LAH indicating conformation to the primary reaction of fission of the O—O bond. Although no ascaridole is recovered unchanged when a two-molar proportion of LAH is used, on reaction with a half-molar proportion of LAH about one-half of the ascaridole is recovered unchanged, the reaction product being *cis-p*-menthene-1,4-diol.

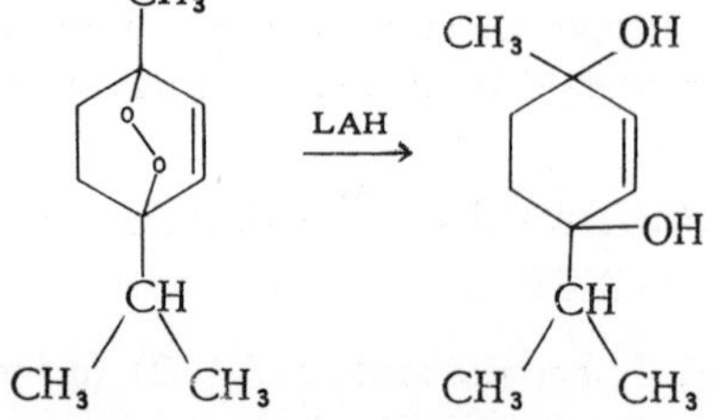

$$(11\text{-}117)$$

CXCIX

Ratio LAH/Peroxide	% Diol	% CXCIX
0.5	27	42
2	65	0

Matic and Sutton (196) postulated that only one-half of the hydrogen of LAH is available in the reduction of ascaridole. An excess of the peroxide is added at room temperature to a solution of LAH in di-n-butyl ether, the evolved hydrogen being measured. An excess of n-octyl alcohol is added and approximately twice the volume of hydrogen already evolved is collected. The following reaction scheme has been suggested:

$$RO-OR' + LiAlH_4 \rightarrow LiAl(OR)(OR')H_2 + H_2 \quad (11-118)$$

$$LiAl(OR)(OR')H_2 + 2 R''OH \rightarrow LiAl(OR)(OR')(OR'')_2 + 2 H_2 \quad (11-119)$$

Methyl α-tetralyl peroxide (CC) behaves similarly to ascaridole, one mole of hydrogen being evolved per mole of peroxide on reaction with excess LAH and only one-half of the total hydrogen of LAH being displaced on reaction with a deficiency of the hydride, the residual hydrogen being given off on treatment with n-octyl alcohol. Reduction with an equimolar proportion of LAH gives 52% methanol and 95% crude α-tetralol (196).

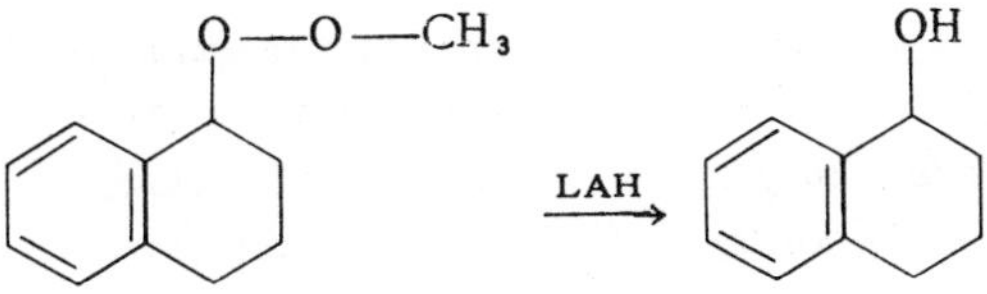

$$+ CH_3OH \quad (11-120)$$

CC

The reduction of di-$tert$-butyl peroxide in refluxing di-n-butyl ether at 135° gives a 67% yield of $tert$-butyl alcohol based on the total hydrogen content of LAH used (196).

Mustafa (197) has shown that the reduction of 9,10-diarylanthracene photoperoxides (CCI) with LAH yields 9,10-diaryl-9,10-dihydro-9,10-dihydroxyanthracenes (CCII).

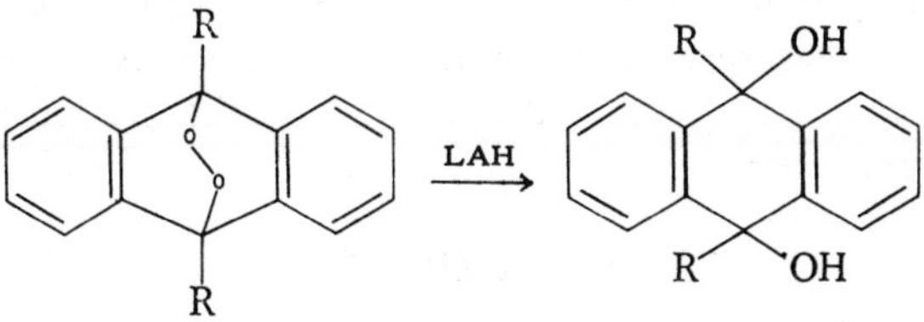

$$(11-121)$$

CCI   CCII

R	% Yield
phenyl	85
m-tolyl	83
p-tolyl	87

The analogy between the reactions of LAH and those of the Grignard reagent is sharply brought out here since treatment of CCI with phenylmagnesium bromide also yields CCII with biphenyl as the second reaction product (198).

The attempted dehydrogenation of acepleiadiene (CCIII) over palladium-on-charcoal yields a black, crystalline solid, $C_{32}H_{28}O_4$, m.p. about 325°. Catalytic hydrogenation of the solid, as well as treatment with LAH in a benzene-ether mixture, yields a product, $C_{16}H_{16}O_2$, m.p. 168-170°, indicative of the cleavage of a peroxide linkage (199).

CCIII

Campbell and Coppinger have reported that the reaction of 2,6-di-*tert*-butyl-*p*-cresol (CCIV) with *tert*-butyl hydroperoxide yields 1-methyl-1-*tert*-butylperoxy-3,5-di-*tert*-butylcyclohexadien-4-one (CCV). The peroxide is reduced to the phenol by LAH (200).

CCIV   CCV   (11-122)

The use of LAH to dry diethylene glycol dimethyl ether followed by distillation has been reported to result in a violent explosion. Analysis of various methyl ethers has indicated double the concentration of peroxides in normal ethers.

11.8 OZONIDES

The LAH reduction of ozonides appears to involve as a primary reaction the fission observed in the reduction of peroxides and hydroperoxides.

Hinder and Stoll (143) have reported that the reduction of the ozonide of 1,1,4a,6-tetramethyl-5-(2-butenyl)-6,5³-oxidecahydronaphthalene (CCVI) yields 75% of a glycol (CCVII), a small amount of the oxide arising from the dehydration of the glycol and a trace of the ester acid (CCVIII).

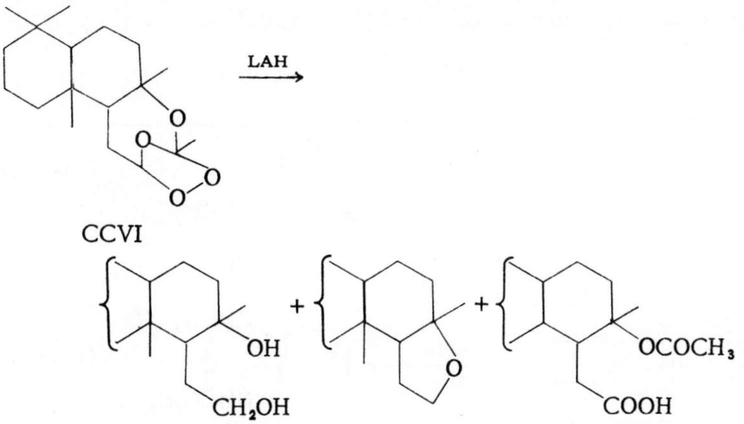

CCVI

OH

CH$_2$OH
CCVII

O

OCOCH$_3$

COOH
CCVIII

(11-123)

The probable course of this reaction has been discussed in Section 11.3.1.b, equation (11-68) (136).

Ozonization of the isopropylidene ketone CCIX and reductive cleavage of the ozonide with LAH, followed by hydrolysis and chromic acid oxidation is reported to yield the diketone CCX (144).

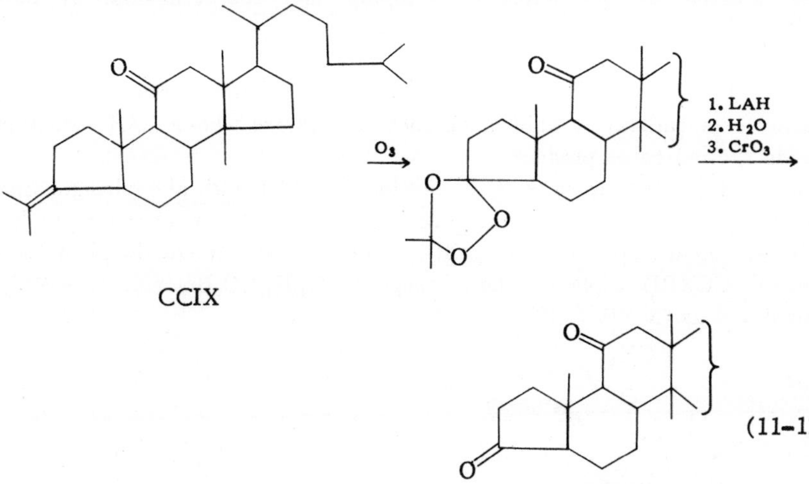

CCIX

1. LAH
2. H$_2$O
3. CrO$_3$

(11-124)

CCX

The probable course of this reaction involving the initial cleavage of the peroxide linkage has been discussed in Section 11.3.1.b, equation (11-70) (136).

The reaction of 2-phenylskatole with ozone yields a stable ozonide (CCXI). Reduction of CCXI with LAH yields o-benzylaminophenylmethylcarbinol while reduction with sodium borohydride yields o-benzaminophenylmethylcarbinol. Catalytic hydrogenation in the presence of palladium black yields o-benzaminophenylmethyl ketone. The LAH reduction product may be contaminated with o-ethylbenzylaniline formed by hydrogenolysis (145).

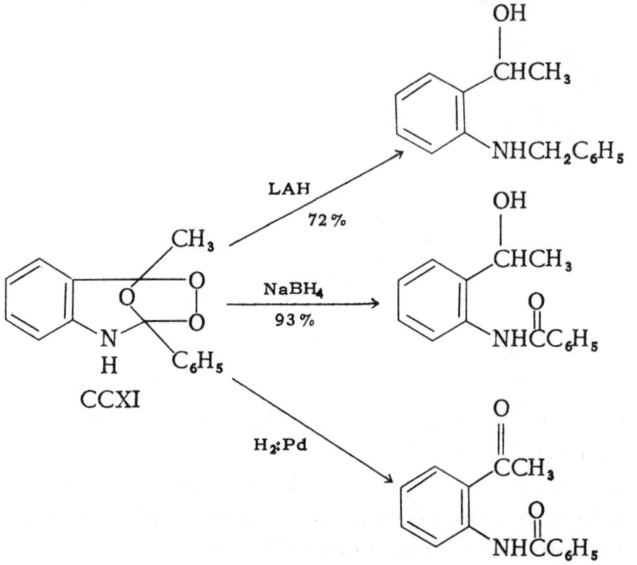

(11-125)

(11-126)

(11-127)

The fission of the peroxide grouping and the cleavage of both

$-N-C-O$ linkages as discussed in Section 12.17 results in the formation of a carboxylic acid or carbonyl derivative whose LAH reduction yields the indicated product.

It is of interest to note that reaction of CCXI with phenylmagnesium bromide yields four different products, separated by chromatography: o-benzaminoacetophenone (CCXII), 1-phenyl-1-(o-benzaminophenyl)-1-ethanol (CCXIII), diphenyl and a compound $C_{21}H_{18}NO_2Br$, m.p. 192–195°, formulated as CCXIV (145).

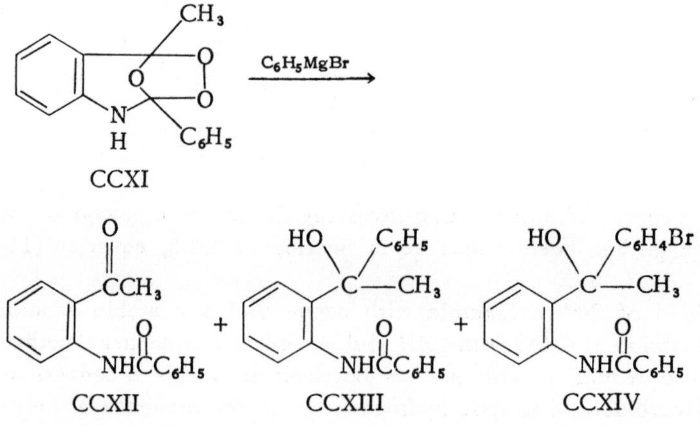

(11-128)

CCXII   CCXIII   CCXIV

The reaction of the ozonide with n-butylmagnesium bromide gives six different products: o-benzaminoacetophenone (CCXII) as the major product, benzoic acid, probably formed by cleavage of the amide by the action of the Grignard reagent, phenol, o-benzaminophenyl-n-butylmethylcarbinol, the normal Grignard addition product to CCXII, a compound $C_{15}H_{15}NO$, m.p. 154.5-156°, not further identified, and o-benzaminophenol (145).

11.9 HETEROCYCLIC OXYGEN COMPOUNDS

It has been shown that ether linkages are generally resistant to attack by LAH and other complex hydrides. When the oxygen atom is part of a cyclic compound cleavage is a function of ring and adjacent structure.

The cleavage of 1,2-epoxides with LAH has been discussed in Section 11.2.

11.9.1 Rings Containing One Hetero Atom

11.9.1.a *1,4-Epoxides.* Tetrahydrofuran (CCXV) is resistant to attack by LAH, as evidenced by its use as a solvent and reaction medium in LAH reductions. The 1,4-epoxy group in various compounds including 3,6-anhydro sugars (CCXVI) and sapogenins (CCXVII) is not attacked by LAH or sodium, potassium or lithium borohydrides.

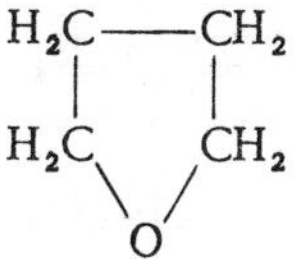

CCXV 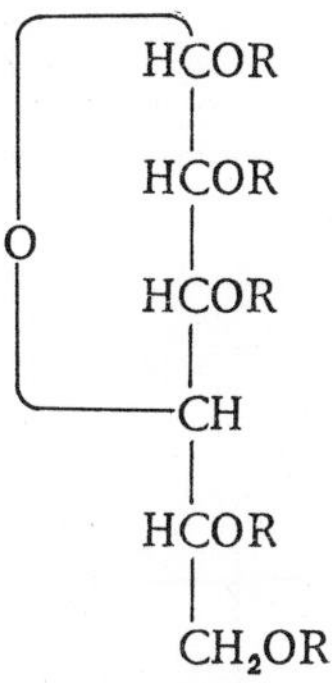   CCXVI 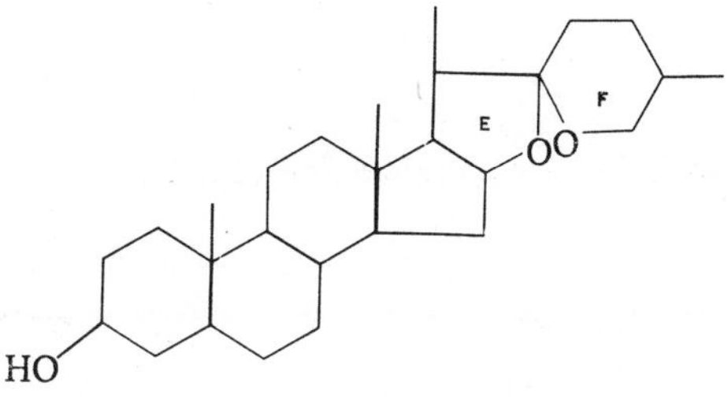   CCXVII

The replacement of the oxygen atom in ring F of CCXVII by nitrogen (CCXVIII) results in a cleavage of ring E with LAH, due to the presence of the —N̈CO— grouping.

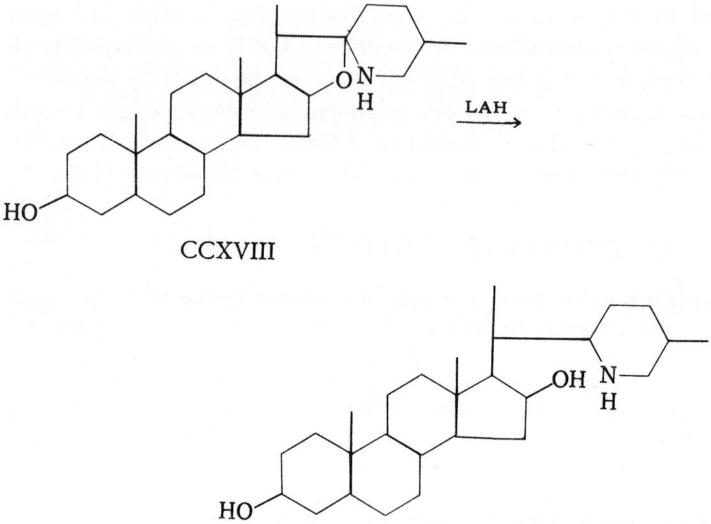

CCXVIII

(11-129)

The tetrahydrofuran ring in quinamine (CCXIX) is analogously cleaved,

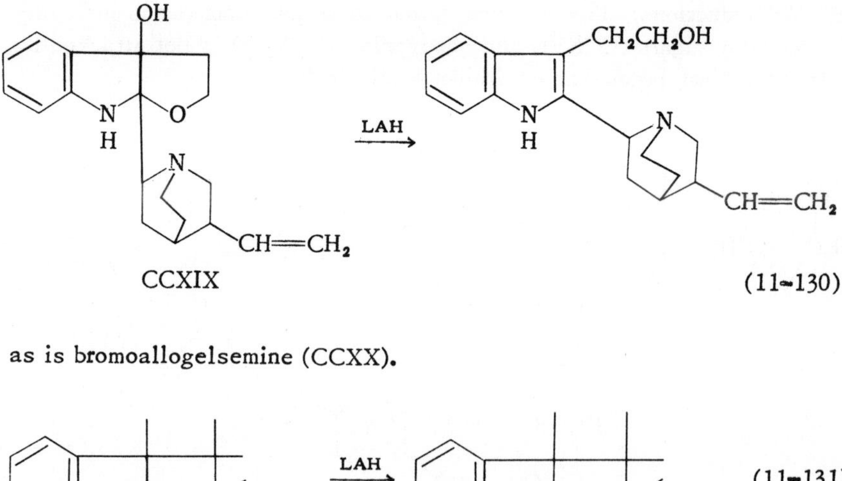

CCXIX

(11-130)

as is bromoallogelsemine (CCXX).

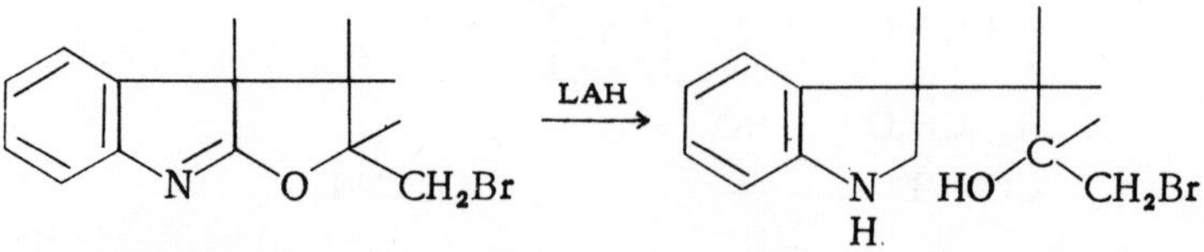

CCXX

(11-131)

The reduction of compounds containing the —N̈C̈O— grouping is discussed in Section 12.17.

The LAH reduction of furan (CCXXI) and benzofuran (CCXXII) derivatives results in retention of the heterocyclic nuclei.

CCXXI   CCXXII

The cyclic ether grouping in various opium alkaloids is not cleaved by LAH. Thus, the LAH reduction of the tosylates of codeine (CCXXIII) (202,203), morphine (CCXXIV) (202) and neopine (CCXXV) (203) as well as the reduction of 8-hydroxydihydrocodeinone (CCXXVI) (204) and 1-bromocodeinone (CCXXVII) (205) results in retention of the ether grouping.

CCXXIII   CCXXIV

CCXXV

CCXXVI   CCXXVII

Schmid and Karrer (206) reported that the reduction of thebaine (CCXXVIII) with LAH gives a phenolic dihydro compound which was represented as CCXXIX and called "β-dihydrothebaine." The reduction was postulated as proceeding by the path CCXXVIII → CCXXIX involving addition of a hydride ion to yield the unnatural configuration at C_{14}.

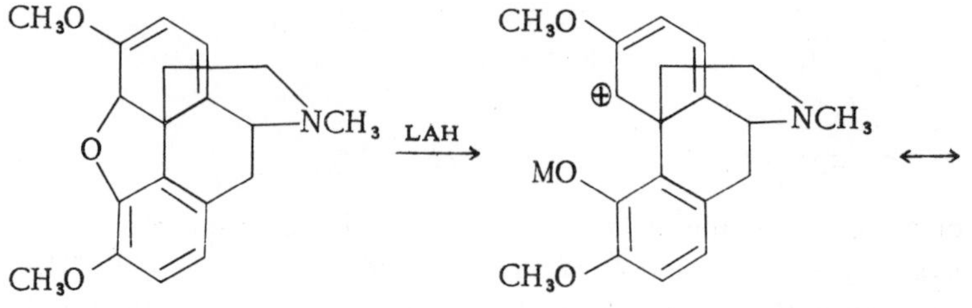

CCXXVIII

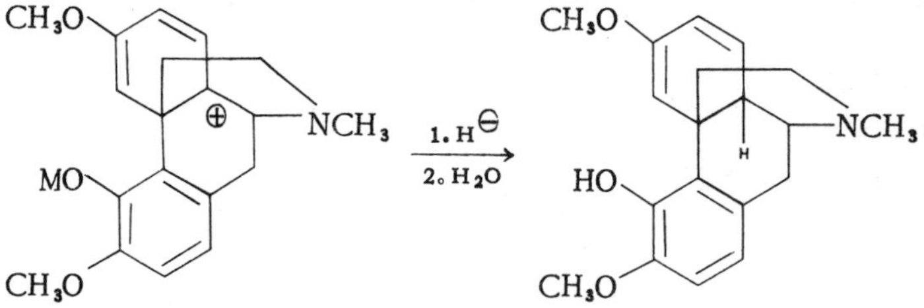

CCXXIX   (11-132)

Although the structure CCXXIX was accepted by Bentley and Robinson (207), Stork (208,209) has proposed that the reduction product which might be described as $\Delta^{6,8}$-phenolic dihydrothebaine has the structure CCXXX with the natural configuration at C_{14}.

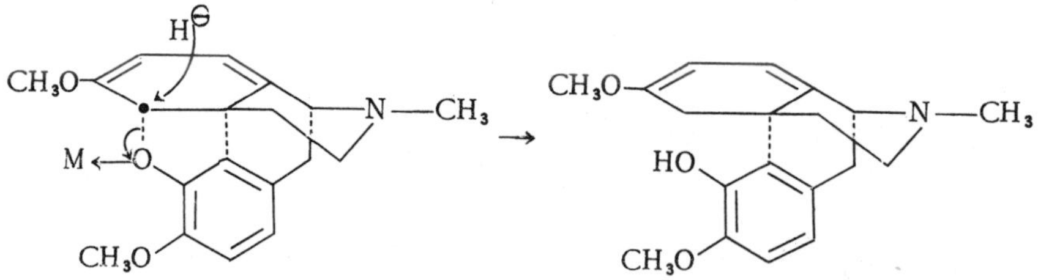

CCXXVIII   CCXXX   (11-133)

Stork has shown that the addition of a hydride ion at C_{14}, as proposed by Schmid and Karrer, would result in the attachment of hydrogen on the un-hindered side of the molecule, *trans* to the benzene ring, to yield a sub-stance whose formulation has been assigned to thebainone enol methyl ether.   Further, a substance with the unnatural configuration at C_{14} postulated for β-dihydrothebaine would not be expected to be catalytically reduced further to a product with the natural configuration at C_{14}, which is the structural configuration of the dihydrothebainol-6-methyl ether ob-tained by catalytic hydrogenation of the LAH reduction product (209). Schmid and Karrer (210) have accepted the structural proposals of Stork, while reporting that thebainone enol methyl ether, which is assumed to have the natural configuration at C_{14}, and β-dihydrothebaine on catalytic hydrogenation yield the same di- and tetrahydro products.

Schmid and Karrer (206) proposed that a similarity in the reactions of LAH and Grignard reagents was involved in the formation of phenyldihydrothebaine (CCXXXI) by the reaction between thebaine and phenylmagnesium bromide (211,212). While with LAH the C_{14} cation is stabilized by the addition of the hydride ion, the same reaction with the phenyl anion is sterically hindered and the cation rearranges as shown below to the C_9 cation which then adds the phenyl anion.

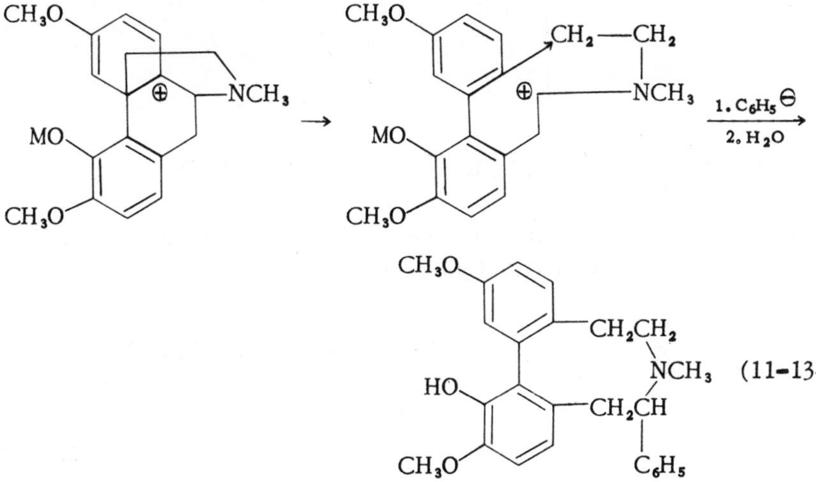

CCXXXI

Stork (209) has proposed that the reaction involves a simple Wagner-Meerwein rearrangement followed by establishment of the aromatic ring with transfer of the positive charge to the nitrogen atom.

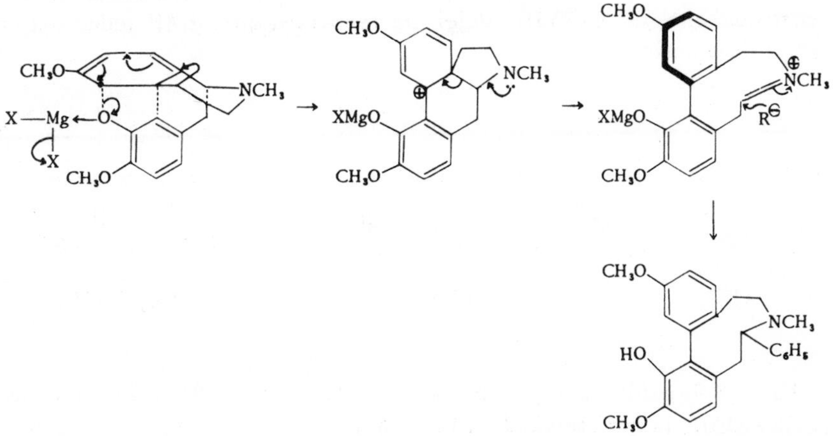

CCXXXI

(11-135)

The difference in the course of the reaction with the Grignard reagent and LAH emphasizes that the latter is a much weaker electron acceptor than magnesium bromide.

11.9.1.b *1,5-Epoxides.*   Tetrahydropyran (CCXXXII) and tetrahydropyranyl ethers are resistant to attack by the complex hydrides. The 1,5-epoxy ring in pyranosides (CCXXXIII) and sapogenins (CCXXXIV) are similarly not cleaved.

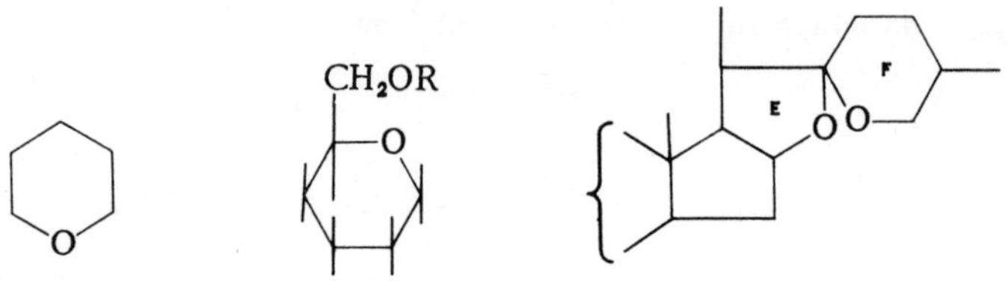

CCXXXII   CCXXXIII   CCXXXIV

In the presence of gaseous hydrogen chloride, ring F in CCXXXIV is cleaved by LAH (Section 11.3.1.a).

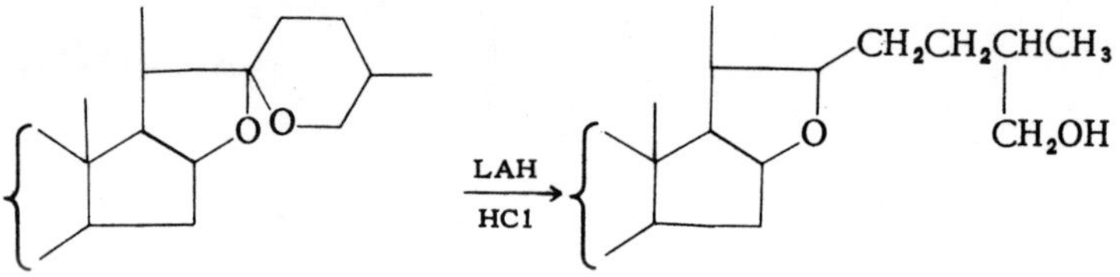

(11-136)

CCXXXIV

The benzopyran (CCXXXV) as well as the xanthene (CCXXXVI) and benzoxanthene (CCXXXVII) nuclei are recovered after LAH reduction of appropriate derivatives.

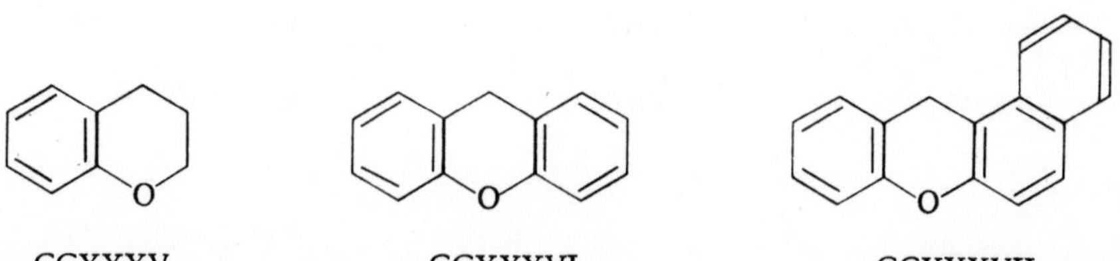

CCXXXV   CCXXXVI   CCXXXVII

The 3,9-oxido bridge in methyl 11-keto-3α,9α-oxidocholenate (CCXXXVIII) is not attacked by LAH (65).

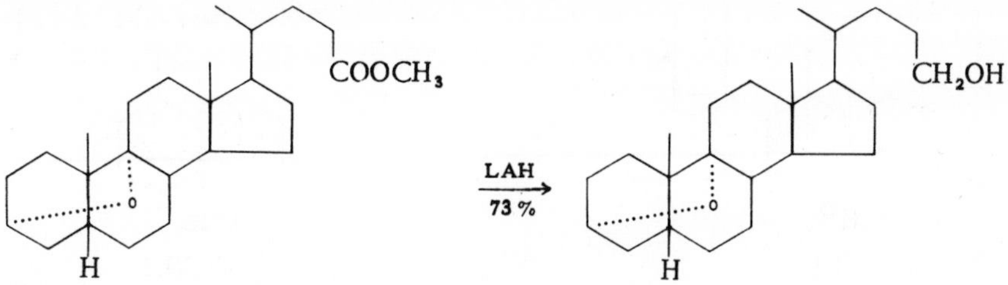

CCXXXVIII   (11-137)

The reduction of the sodium salt of 3β-methoxy-3α,9α-oxido-11-keto-cholanic acid (CCXXXIX) with sodium borohydride in aqueous ethanol yields 3β-methoxy-3α,9α-oxido-11β-hydroxycholanic acid (213).

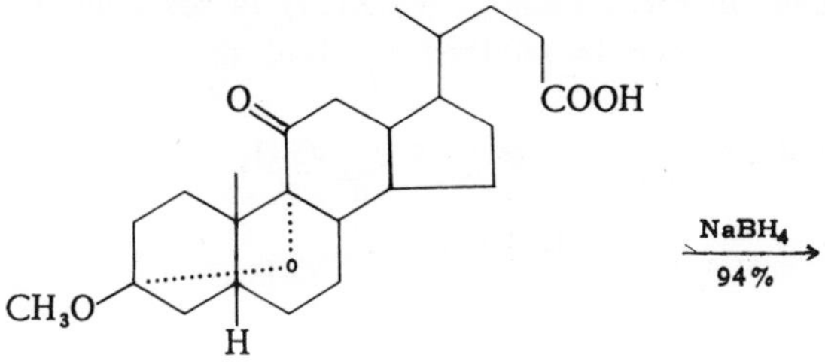

CCXXXIX

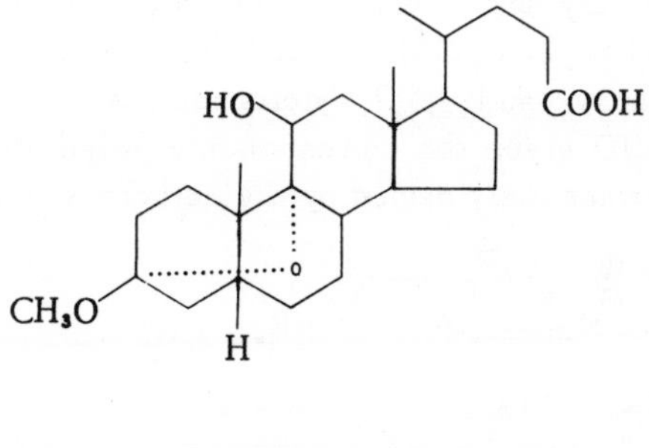

(11-138)

The reduction of 3β-hydroxy-3α,9α-oxido-11-ketocholanic acid (CCXL) and 3β,11β-dihydroxy-3α,9α-oxidocholanic acid (CCXLI) in boiling aqueous ethanol with sodium borohydride yields 3,9α,11β-trihydroxy-cholanic acid isolated as the methyl ester-3-acetate. In the reduction of CCXL, an 80% yield of the 3α-epimer is accompanied by a 9% yield of the 3β-epimer while in the reduction of CCXLI a 71% yield of the 3α-epimer is obtained while no 3β-epimer is detected (213).

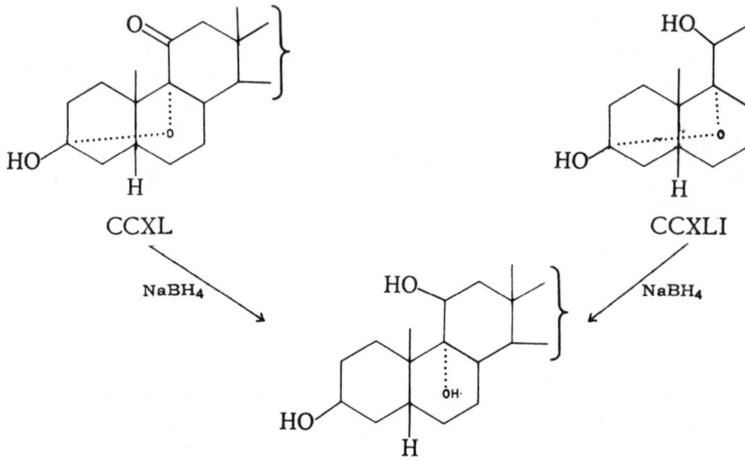

CCXL   CCXLI

(11-139)

NaBH₄   NaBH₄

The γ-pyrone ring present in the flavonols (CCXLII) is resistant to LAH attack while the ketone group is reduced to yield the γ-pyranol (214,215).

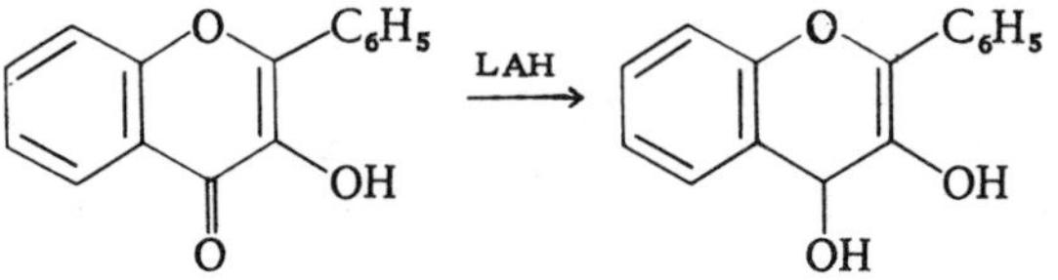

$\xrightarrow{\text{LAH}}$

(11-140)

CCXLII

The reduction of 2-phenylbenzopyrylium or flavylium salts with LAH yields the corresponding o-dihydro derivative analogous to the reduction of the quaternary ammonium salts of cyclic bases.

Karrer and Seyhan (216) reported that the reduction of 3,4'-dimethoxy-, 3,5,7-trimethoxy- and 3,5,7,4'-tetramethoxy-2-phenylbenzopyrylium chloride (CCXLIII) gives the corresponding polymethoxy-2-phenylbenzopyran (CCXLIV) erroneously named by the authors as a dihydrobenzopyran.

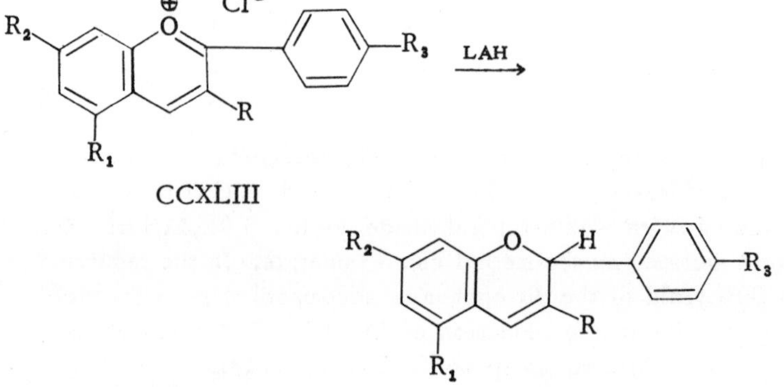

CCXLIII

$\xrightarrow{\text{LAH}}$

(11-141)

CCXLIV

R	R_1	R_2	R_3	% Yield
CH_3O	H	H	CH_3O	40
CH_3O	CH_3O	CH_3O	H	....
CH_3O	CH_3O	CH_3O	CH_3O	55

Elstow and Platt (217) reported that 6-ethyl-7-hydroxy-3',4'-dimethoxy-2-phenylbenzopyrylium chloride (CCXLV) is reduced in almost quantitative yield to the corresponding flavan by successive reduction with LAH and hydrogen over a Raney nickel catalyst. The reduction presumably proceeds via the benzopyran (flavene) formed as a result of the LAH reduction.

$$\text{CCXLV} \xrightarrow[\text{2. H}_2\text{: Raney Ni}]{\text{1. LAH}} \quad (11\text{--}142)$$

11.9.1.c *1,6-Epoxides.* The seven-membered oxide ring in strychnine (CCXLVI: $R_1 = R_2 = H$) (218,219) and analogous alkaloids such as brucine (CCXLVI: $R_1 = R_2 = OCH_3$) and colubrine (CCXLVI: $R_1 = H, R_2 = OCH_3$) (220) is resistant to cleavage by LAH.

CCXLVI

Fieser and Rajagopalan (65) reported that oxidation of methyl $\Delta^{9(11)}$-lithocholenate (CCXLVII) with chromate in aqueous acetic acid gives a product formulated as methyl $3\alpha,8\alpha$-oxido-$\Delta^{9(11)}$-cholenate (CCXLIX). Babcock and Fieser (221) have shown that the product actually is methyl 3-keto-$\Delta^{9(11)}$-cholenate (CCXLVIII).

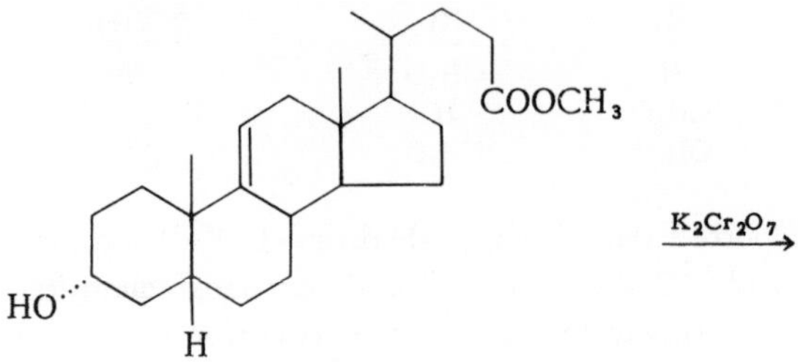

CCXLVII

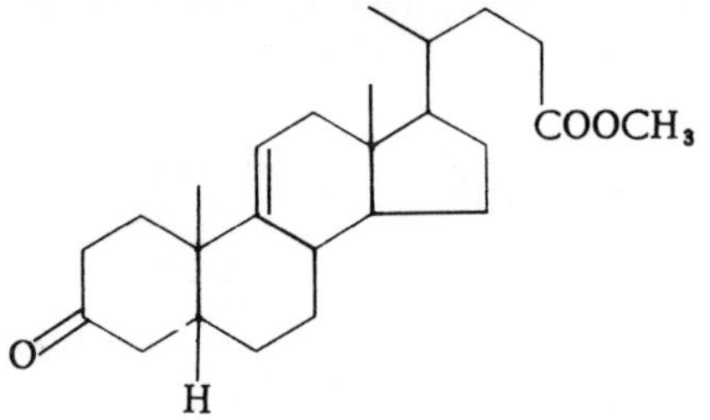

$$K_2Cr_2O_7$$

(11-143)

CCXLVIII

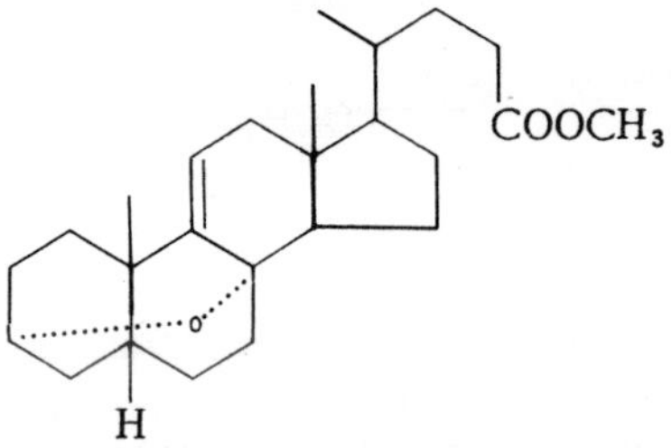

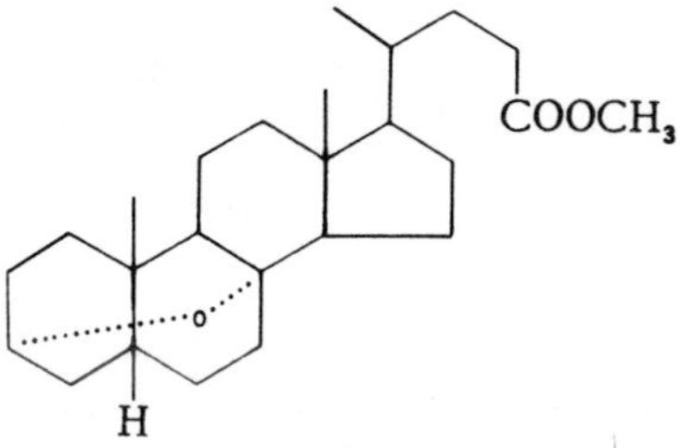

CCXLIX

CCL

Reduction of CCXLVIII, originally formulated as CCXLIX with LAH yields $\Delta^{9(11)}$-lithocholenyl alcohol. Catalytic hydrogenation of the oxidation product (CCXLVIII) with Adams' catalyst in methanol containing a few drops of hydrobromic acid yields methyl 3β-methoxy-$\Delta^{9(11)}$-cholenate (CCLI), originally formulated as methyl 3α,8α-oxidocholanate (CCL).

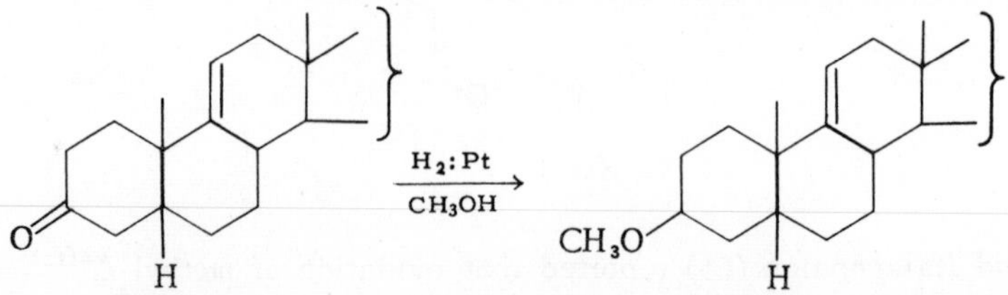

CCXLVIII

$$\xrightarrow[\text{CH}_3\text{OH}]{\text{H}_2: \text{Pt}}$$

CCLI

(11-144)

Reduction of CCLI with LAH yields 3β-methoxy-$\Delta^{9(11)}$-cholenyl alcohol, originally formulated as 8(?)-hydroxycholanyl alcohol-B. Catalytic hydrogenation of CCLI over platinum in acetic acid yields methyl 3β-methoxy-cholanate (CCLII), originally formulated as methyl 8(?)-hydroxycholanate (CCLIII).

$$\text{(11-145)}$$

Reduction of CCLII with LAH yields 3β-methoxycholanyl alcohol, orig-inally formulated as 8(?)-hydroxycholanyl alcohol-A.

11.9.2 Rings Containing Two or More Hetero Atoms

Cyclic ketals derived from the reaction of acetone and a 1,2-dihydroxy compound such as a sugar (CCLIV) as well as those derived from the reaction of ethylene glycol and a ketone (CCLV) are resistant to attack by complex hydrides as is generally true for compounds containing the

$$-\overset{|}{\underset{|}{O}}C O- \text{ grouping (Section 11.3).}$$

Cyclic acetals derived from the reaction of benzaldehyde and a sugar (CCLVI) contain the $-\overset{|}{\underset{|}{O}}CO-$ grouping and are not cleaved by the complex hydrides. Dioxane (CCLVII) is utilized as a solvent for LAH and other complex hydrides due to its resistance to attack.

CCLVI   CCLVII

Hemithioketals and thioxolanes (CCLVIII) are not attacked by LAH. Oxazolidines (CCLIX) are cleaved by LAH to the 2-aminoalcohols (Section 12.17).

CCLVIII   CCLIX

The LAH reduction of a dioxolanone (CCLX) results in cleavage, as discussed in Section 11.3.1.b., equation (11-62).

$$\xrightarrow{\text{LAH}} \quad \underset{\underset{\text{OH}}{|}}{CH_3CHCH_2OH} + R_2CHCH_2OH \quad (11\text{-}146)$$

CCLX

The trimer of phenylpropargyl aldehyde (CCLXI) is reduced with LAH to cinnamyl alcohol (142).

$$\xrightarrow{\text{LAH}} C_6H_5CH{=}CHCH_2OH$$

CCLXI   (11-147)

The reduction of various heterocyclic compounds such as benzoxazolone, containing both oxygen and nitrogen atoms in a reducible ring, is discussed under heterocyclic nitrogen compounds in Section 12.19.

REFERENCES

1. Nystrom, R. F., W. H. Yanko, and W. G. Brown, *J. Am. Chem. Soc.*, *70*, 441 (1948).
2. Nystrom, R. F., W. J. Skraba, and R. J. Mansfield, ORNL-395, U.S.A.E.C.
3. Cox, J. D., and R. J. Warne, *Nature*, *165*, 563 (1950).
4. Cox, J. D., H. S. Turner, and R. J. Warne, *J. Chem. Soc.*, *1950*, 3167.
5. Ostwald, R., P. T. Adams, and B. M. Tolbert, *J. Am. Chem. Soc.*, *74*, 2425 (1952).
6. King, L. C., *Abstracts of Papers*, 117th Meeting American Chemical Society, Philadelphia, Pa., April 1950, p. 45L.
7. Karrer, P., and O. Rüttner, *Helv. Chim. Acta*, *33*, 812 (1950).
8. Karrer, P., *Angew. Chem.*, *62*, 334 (1950).
9. Karrer, P., *Bull. soc. chim. France*, [5] *17*, 907 (1950).
10. Kharasch, M. S., and W. H. Urry, *J. Org. Chem.*, *13*, 101 (1948).
11. Mousseron, M., R. Jacquier, M. Mousseron-Canet, and R. Zagdoun, *Bull. soc. chim. France*, [5] *19*, 1042 (1952).
12. Brown, R. F., private communication.
13. Mislow, K., *J. Am. Chem. Soc.*, *73*, 3954 (1951).
14. Morrison, A. L., R. F. Long, and M. Königstein, *J. Chem. Soc.*, *1951*, 952.
15. Chanda, S. K., E. L. Hirst, E. G. V. Percival, and A. G. Ross, *J. Chem. Soc.*, *1952*, 1833.
16. Burgstahler, A. W., *J. Am. Chem. Soc.*, *73*, 3021 (1951).
17. Lukeš, R., and O. Červinka, unpublished work, through M. Ferles and J. Rudinger, *Chem. Listy*, *47*, 104, 140 (1953).
18. Paddock, N. L., *Nature*, *167*, 1070 (1951).
19. Schlesinger, H. I., R. T. Sanderson, and A. B. Burg, *J. Am. Chem. Soc.*, *62*, 3421 (1940).
20. Trevoy, L. W., and W. G. Brown, *J. Am. Chem. Soc.*, *71*, 1675 (1949).
21. Wiggins, L. F., and D. J. C. Wood, *J. Chem. Soc.*, *1950*, 1566.
22. Newman, M. S., G. Underwood, and M. Renoll, *J. Am. Chem. Soc.*, *71*, 3362 (1949).
23. Nystrom, R. F., and W. G. Brown, *J. Am. Chem. Soc.*, *70*, 3738 (1948).
24. Fuchs, R., and C. A. Vander Werf, *J. Am. Chem. Soc.*, *74*, 5917 (1952).
25. Eliel, E. L., and J. P. Freeman, *J. Am. Chem. Soc.*, *74*, 923 (1952).
26. Hickinbottom, W. J., and D. G. M. Wood, *J. Chem. Soc.*, *1951*, 1600.
27. Herz, W., *J. Am. Chem. Soc.*, *74*, 2928 (1952).
28. Gaylord, N. G., and E. I. Becker, *Chem. Revs.*, *49*, 413 (1951).
29. Foster, A. B., and W. G. Overend, *J. Chem. Soc.*, *1951*, 1132.
30. Kellom, D. B., and D. Y. Curtin, *Abstracts of Papers*, 122nd Meeting American Chemical Society, Atlantic City, N. J., September 1952, p. 23M.
31. Collin-Asselineau, C., E. Lederer, D. Mercier, and J. Polonsky, *Bull. soc. chim. France*, [5] *17*, 720 (1950).
32. Billimoria, J. D., and N. F. Maclagan, *Nature*, *167*, 81 (1951).
33. Billimoria, J. D., and N. F. Maclagan, *J. Chem. Soc.*, *1951*, 3067.
34. Mousseron, M., and M. Canet, *Bull. soc. chim. France*, [5] *19*, 247 (1952).
35. Mousseron, M., R. Jacquier, M. Mousseron-Canet, and R. Zagdoun, *Compt. rend.*, *235*, 177 (1952).
36. Mousseron, M., M. Canet, and R. Jacquier, *Bull. soc. chim. France*, [5] *19*, 698 (1952).
37. Mousseron, M., and M. Canet, *Bull. soc. chim. France*, [5] *18*, 792 (1951).
38. Sheehan, J. C., and B. M. Bloom, *J. Am. Chem. Soc.*, *74*, 3825 (1952).

39. Stoll, M., and M. Hinder, *Helv. Chim. Acta, 34,* 334 (1951).
40. Mallein, R., *Compt. rend., 234,* 143 (1952).
41. Barton, D. H. R., and A. S. Lindsey, *J. Chem. Soc., 1951,* 2988,
42. Barton, D. H. R., T. Bruun, and A. S. Lindsey, *Chemistry and Industry, 1952,* 691.
43. Barton, D. H. R., T. Bruun, and A. S. Lindsey, *J. Chem. Soc., 1952,* 2210.
44. Prins, D. A., *J. Am. Chem. Soc.,* 70, 3955 (1948).
45. Hauenstein, H., and T. Reichstein, *Helv. Chim. Acta, 32,* 22 (1959).
46. Bolliger, H. R., and R. Ulrich, *Helv. Chim. Acta, 35,* 93 (1952).
47. Bolliger, H. R., and M. Thürkauf, *Helv. Chim. Acta, 35,* 1426 (1952).
48. Allerton, R., and W. G. Overend, *J. Chem. Soc., 1951,* 1480.
49. Davoll, J., B. Lythgoe, and S. Trippett, *J. Chem. Soc., 1951,* 2230.
50. Fürst, A., and P. A. Plattner, *Abstracts of Papers,* XIIth International Congress of Pure and Applied Chemistry, September 1951, New York, New York, p. 409.
51. Fürst, A., and P. A. Plattner, *Helv. Chim. Acta, 32,* 275 (1949).
52. Ciba, S. A., Fr. Pat. 994,615 (November 20, 1951).
53. Ciba Ltd., Brit. Pat. 665,254 (January 16, 1952).
54. Plattner, P., Ger. Pat. 834,848 (May 15, 1952).
55. Plattner, P., U. S. Pat. 2,599,481 (June 3, 1952).
56. Plattner, P. A., H. Heusser, and A. B. Kulkarni, *Helv. Chim. Acta, 32,* 1070 (1949).
57. Plattner, P. A., H. Heusser, and A. B. Kulkarni, *Helv. Chim. Acta, 31,* 1885 (1948).
58. Plattner, P. A., H. Heusser, and A. B. Kulkarni, *Helv. Chim. Acta, 32,* 265 (1949).
59. Plattner, P. A., H. Heusser, and A. B. Kulkarni, *Helv. Chim. Acta, 31,* 1822 (1948).
60. Schmid, H., and K. Kägi, *Helv. Chim. Acta, 33,* 1582 (1950).
61. Julia, S. A., and P. A. Plattner, and H. Heusser, *Helv. Chim. Acta, 35,* 665 (1952).
62. Plattner, P. A., H. Heusser, and M. Feurer, *Helv. Chim. Acta, 32,* 587 (1949).
63. Plattner, P. A., T. Petrzilka, and W. Lang, *Helv. Chim. Acta, 27,* 513 (1944).
64. Jacobs, W. A., and Y. Sato, *J. Biol. Chem., 191,* 71 (1951).
65. Fieser, L. F., and S. Rajagopalan, *J. Am. Chem. Soc., 73,* 118 (1951).
66. Djerassi, C., H. Martinez, and G. Rosenkranz, *J. Org. Chem., 16,* 1278 (1951).
67. Djerassi, C., E. Batres, M. Velasco, and G. Rosenkranz, *J. Am. Chem. Soc., 74,* 1712 (1952).
68. Budziarek, R., G. T. Newbold, R. Stevenson, and F. S. Spring, *J. Chem. Soc., 1952,* 2892.
69. Heusser, H., N. Wahba, and T. Herzig, *Abstracts of Papers,* 120th Meeting American Chemical Society, September 1951, New York, New York, p. 9L.
70. Ruzicka, L., N. Wahba, P. T. Herzig, and H. Heusser, *Chem. Ber., 85,* 491 (1952).
71. Plattner, P. A., H. Heusser, and M. Feurer, *Helv. Chim. Acta, 31,* 2210 (1948).
72. Salamon, I., *Helv. Chim. Acta, 32,* 1306 (1949).
73. Barton, D. H. R., and C. J. W. Brooks, *J. Am. Chem. Soc., 72,* 3314 (1950).
74. Barton, D. H. R., and C. J. W. Brooks, *J. Chem. Soc., 1951,* 257.

75. Goutarel, R., M. M. Janot, V. Prelog, and W. I. Taylor, *Helv. Chim. Acta,* 33, 150 (1950).
76. Witkop, B., *J. Am. Chem. Soc.,* 72, 2311 (1950).
77. Marvel, C. S., and H. W. Hill, Jr., *J. Am. Chem. Soc.,* 73, 481 (1951).
78. Hurd, C. D., and W. H. Saunders, Jr., *J. Am. Chem. Soc.,* 74, 5324 (1952).
79. Swoboda, W., *Monatsh.,* 82, 388 (1951).
80. Schmid, L., W. Swoboda, and M. Wichtl, *Monatsh.,* 83, 185 (1952).
81. Hough, L., and J. K. N. Jones, *J. Chem. Soc.,* 1952, 4052.
82. Eschenmoser, A., and A. Frey, *Helv. Chim. Acta,* 35, 1660 (1952).
83. Viscontini, M., and C. Ebnöther, *Helv. Chim. Acta,* 34, 116 (1951).
84. Brack, K., and H. Schinz, *Helv. Chim. Acta,* 34, 1523 (1951).
85. Stork, G., and H. Conroy, *J. Am. Chem. Soc.,* 73, 4743 (1951).
86. Djerassi, C., E. Batres, J. Romo, and G. Rosenkranz, *J. Am. Chem. Soc.,* 74, 3634 (1952).
87. Rosenkranz, G., J. Pataki, and C. Djerassi, *J. Org. Chem.,* 17, 290 (1952).
88. Bernstein, S., R. M. Antonucci, and M. D. Heller, U. S. Pat. 2,622,081 (December 16, 1952).
89. Julian, P. L., E. W. Meyer, and I. Ryden, *J. Am. Chem. Soc.,* 71, 756 (1949); 72, 367 (1950).
90. Roseman, S., *J. Am. Chem. Soc.,* 74, 4467 (1952).
91. Wiggins, L. F., and D. J. C. Wood, *J. Chem. Soc.,* 1950, 1566.
92. Ansell, E. G., and J. Honeyman, *J. Chem. Soc.,* 1952, 2778.
93. Grewe, R., and E. Nolte, *Ann.,* 575, 1 (1951).
94. Ansell, E. G., J. Honeyman, and G. H. Williams, *Chemistry and Industry,* 1952, 149.
95. Overend, W. G., F. Shafizadeh, and M. Stacey, *J. Chem. Soc.,* 1951, 1487.
96. Abdel-Akher, M., and F. Smith, *Nature,* 166, 1037 (1950).
97. Schmid, H., and P. Karrer, *Helv. Chim. Acta,* 32, 1371 (1949).
98. Bolliger, H. R., and P. Ulrich, unpublished work, through H. R. Bolliger and P. Ulrich, *Helv. Chim. Acta,* 35, 93 (1952).
99. Sarett, L. H., M. Feurer, and K. Folkers, *J. Am. Chem. Soc.,* 73, 1777 (1951).
100. Smith, F., *J. Chem. Soc.,* 1951, 2646.
101. Hough, L., J. K. N. Jones, and W. H. Wadman, *J. Chem. Soc.,* 1952, 796.
102. Lythgoe, B., and S. Trippett, *J. Chem. Soc.,* 1950, 1983.
103. Fischer, R., and H. R. Bolliger, unpublished work; through H. R. Bolliger and P. Ulrich, *Helv. Chim. Acta,* 35, 93 (1952).
104. Abdel-Akher, M., F. Smith, and D. Spriestersbach, *J. Chem. Soc.,* 1952, 3637.
105. Chanda, S. K., E. L. Hirst, and E. G. V. Percival, *J. Chem. Soc.,* 1951, 1240.
106. Jones, J. K. N., and L. E. Wise, *J. Chem. Soc.,* 1952, 3389.
107. Larsson, E., *Trans. Chalmers Univ. Technol.,* Gothenburg, 94, 15 (1950); *Chem. Abstracts,* 45, 1494 (1951).
108. Erne, M., and F. Ramirez, *Helv. Chim. Acta,* 33, 912 (1950).
109. Gensler, W. J., and C. M. Samour, *J. Am. Chem. Soc.,* 72, 3318 (1950); 73, 5555 (1951).
110. Hamlin, K. E., and A. W. Weston, *J. Am. Chem. Soc.,* 71, 2210 (1949).
111. Dornow, A., G. Messwarb, and H. H. Frey, *Chem. Ber.,* 83, 445 (1950).
112. Allen, C. F. H., and J. R. Byers, Jr., U. S. Pat. 2,545,439 (March 20, 1951).
113. Bruce, W. F., U. S. Pat. 2,597,446 (May 20, 1952).

726   REDUCTION OF COMPOUNDS CONTAINING ETHER LINKAGES

114. Haworth, R. D., and L. Wilson, *J. Chem. Soc., 1950,* 71.
115. Schmid, H., and P. Karrer, *Helv. Chim. Acta, 32,* 960 (1949).
116. Mirza, R., and R. Robinson, *Nature, 166,* 271 (1950).
117. Mirza, R., *Experientia, 8,* 258 (1952).
118. Drake, N. L., and E. H. Price, *J. Am. Chem. Soc., 73,* 201 (1951).
119. Semonsky, M., *Chem. Listy, 45,* 392 (1951).
120. Ott, A. C., M. F. Murray, and R. L. Pederson, *J. Am. Chem. Soc., 74,* 1239 (1952).
121. Ott, A. C., and M. F. Murray, U. S. Pat. 2,625,556 (January 13, 1953).
122. Goering, H. L., and C. Serres, Jr., *J. Am. Chem. Soc., 74,* 5908 (1952).
123. Ahmad, R., F. Sondheimer, B. C. L. Weedon, and R. J. Woods, *J. Chem. Soc., 1952,* 4089.
124. Elphimoff-Felkin, I., *Compt. rend., 236,* 387 (1953).
125. Sandoval, A., J. Romo, G. Rosenkranz, S. Kaufmann, and C. Djerassi, *J. Am. Chem. Soc., 73,* 3820 (1951).
126. Nussbaum, A. L., A. Sandoval, G. Rosenkranz, and C. Djerassi, *J. Org. Chem., 17,* 426 (1952).
127. Romo, J., H. J. Ringold, G. Rosenkranz, and C. Djerassi, *J. Org. Chem., 16,* 1873 (1951).
128. Yashin, R., G. Rosenkranz, and C. Djerassi, *J. Am. Chem. Soc., 73,* 4654 (1951).
129. Djerassi, C., R. Yashin, and G. Rosenkranz, *J. Am. Chem. Soc., 74,* 422 (1952).
130. Wendler, N. L., H. L. Slates, and M. Tishler, *J. Am. Chem. Soc., 74,* 4894 (1952).
131. Pataki, J., G. Rosenkranz, and C. Djerassi, *J. Am. Chem. Soc., 73,* 5375 (1951).
132. Hirschmann, R., C. S. Snoddy, Jr., and N. L. Wendler, *J. Am. Chem. Soc., 74,* 2693 (1952).
133. Rothman, E. S., M. E. Wall, and C. R. Eddy, *J. Am. Chem. Soc., 74,* 4013 (1952).
134. Ringold, H. J., G. Rosenkranz, and C. Djerassi, *J. Am. Chem. Soc., 74,* 3318 (1952).
135. Doukas, H. M., and T. D. Fontaine, *J. Am. Chem. Soc., 73,* 5917 (1951).
136. Gaylord, N. G., *Experientia, 10,* 351 (1954).
137. Gaylord, N. G., and J. R. Snyder, *Chemistry and Industry, 1954,* 1234.
138. Ness, R. K., H. G. Fletcher, Jr., and C. S. Hudson, *J. Am. Chem. Soc., 73,* 3742 (1951).
139. Newman, M. S., and H. S. Whitehouse, *J. Am. Chem. Soc., 71,* 3664 (1949).
140. Badger, G. M., J. E. Campbell, J. W. Cook, R. A. Raphael, and A. I. Scott, *J. Chem. Soc., 1950,* 2326.
141. Newman, M. S., and C. W. Muth, *J. Am. Chem. Soc., 73,* 4627 (1951).
142. Wille, F., and F. Knörr, *Chem. Ber., 85,* 841 (1952).
143. Hinder, M., and M. Stoll, *Helv. Chim. Acta, 33,* 1308 (1950).
144. Voser, W., D. E. White, H. Heusser, O. Jeger, and L. Ruzicka, *Helv. Chim. Acta, 35,* 830 (1952).
145. Witkop, B., and J. B. Patrick, *J. Am. Chem. Soc., 74,* 3855 (1952).
146. Stoll, A., A. Hofmann, and T. Petrzilka, *Helv. Chim. Acta, 34,* 1544 (1951).
147. Wolfrom, M. L., and K. Anno, *J. Am. Chem. Soc., 74,* 5583 (1952).
148. Sowden, J. C., *J. Am. Chem. Soc., 74,* 4377 (1952).
149. Adams, G. A., *Can. J. Chem., 30,* 698 (1952).
150. Sarett, L. H., G. E. Arth, R. M. Lukes, R. E. Beyler, G. I. Poos, W. F. Johns, and J. M. Constantin, *J. Am. Chem. Soc., 74,* 4974 (1952).

151. Wendler, N. L., R. P. Graber, R. E. Jones, and M. Tishler, *J. Am. Chem. Soc.*, 74, 3630 (1952).
152. Ciba Ltd., Brit. Pat. 665,337 (January 23, 1952).
153. Ringold, H. J., G. Rosenkranz, and C. Djerassi, *J. Am. Chem. Soc.*, 74, 3441 (1952).
154. Hunger, A., and T. Reichstein, *Helv. Chim. Acta*, 35, 1073 (1952).
155. Hunger, A., and T. Reichstein, *Chem. Ber.*, 85, 635 (1952).
156. Sannié, C., and H. Lapin, *Bull. soc. chim. France*, [5] 19, 1080 (1952).
157. Wendler, N. L., R. P. Graber, R. E. Jones, and M. Tishler, *J. Am. Chem. Soc.*, 72, 5793 (1950).
158. Gerstein, M., R. A. Lad, and H. I. Schlesinger, *Abstracts of Papers*, 110th Meeting American Chemical Society, Chicago, Illinois, September 1946, p. 26P.
159. Claus, C. J., and J. L. Morganthau, Jr., *J. Am. Chem. Soc.*, 73, 5005 (1951).
160. Buchta, E., and H. Bayer, *Ann.*, 573, 227 (1951).
161. Dreiding, A. S., and J. A. Hartman, *J. Am. Chem. Soc.*, 75, 939 (1953).
162. Vonderwahl, R., and H. Schinz, *Helv. Chim. Acta*, 35, 2368 (1952).
163. Petuely, F., and H. F. Bauer, *Monatsh.*, 83, 758 (1952).
164. Greenhalgh, C. W., H. B. Henbest, and E. R. H. Jones, *J. Chem. Soc.*, 1952, 2375.
165. Wear, R. L., *J. Am. Chem. Soc.*, 73, 2390 (1951).
166. Spriggs, A. S., C. M. Hill, and G. W. Senter, *J. Am. Chem. Soc.*, 74, 1555 (1952).
167. Hochstein, F. A., *J. Am. Chem. Soc.*, 71, 305 (1949).
168. Siegel, S., and S. Coburn, *J. Am. Chem. Soc.*, 73, 5494 (1951).
169. Cook, J. W., A. R. Gibb, R. A. Raphael, and A. R. Somerville, *J. Chem. Soc.*, 1951, 503.
170. Cook, J. W., R. A. Raphael, and A. I. Scott, *J. Chem. Soc.*, 1952, 4416.
171. Frank, R. L., and H. K. Hall, Jr., *J. Am. Chem. Soc.*, 72, 1645 (1950).
172. Blanchard, J. P. and H. L. Goering, *J. Am. Chem. Soc.*, 73, 5863 (1951).
173. Conroy, H., *J. Am. Chem. Soc.*, 74, 3046 (1952).
174. Birch, A. J., J. A. K. Quartey, and H. Smith, *J. Chem. Soc.*, 1952, 1768.
175. Woodward, R. B., F. Sondheimer, D. Taub, K. Heusler, and W. M. McLamore, *J. Am. Chem. Soc.*, 74, 4223 (1952).
176. Woodward, R. B., F. Sondheimer, D. Taub, K. Heusler, and W. M. McLamore, *J. Am. Chem. Soc.*, 73, 2403 (1951).
177. Sarett, L. H., R. M. Lukes, G. I. Poos, J. M. Robinson, R. E. Beyler, J. M. Vandegrift, and G. E. Arth, *J. Am. Chem. Soc.*, 74, 1393 (1952).
178. Seifert, P., and H. Schinz, *Helv. Chim. Acta*, 34, 728 (1951).
179. Freudenberg, K., and G. Wilke, *Chem. Ber.*, 85, 78 (1952).
180. Reynaud, P., and J. Matti, *Compt. rend.*, 235, 1230 (1952).
181. Meystre, C., and A. Wettstein, *Helv. Chim. Acta*, 32, 1978 (1949).
182. Syntex, S. A., Brit. Pat. 646,979 (November 29, 1950).
183. Ciba Akt., Swiss Pat. 274,087 (June 1, 1951).
184. Rosenkranz, G., and S. Kaufmann, U. S. Pat. 2,588,294 (March 4, 1952).
185. Miescher, K., and C. Meystre, U. S. Pat. 2,623,885 (December 30, 1952).
186. Julian, P. L., E. W. Meyer, W. J. Karpel, and W. Cole, *J. Am. Chem. Soc.*, 73, 1982 (1951).
187. Patel, D. K., V. Petrow, R. Royer, and I. A. Stuart-Webb, *J. Chem. Soc.*, 1952, 161.
188. Meystre, C., and K. Miescher, *Helv. Chim. Acta*, 32, 1758 (1949).
189. Belleau, B., and T. F. Gallagher, *J. Am. Chem. Soc.*, 74, 2816 (1952).
190. Chatterjee, A., and P. Karrer, *Helv. Chim. Acta*, 33, 802 (1950).

191. Janot, M. M., and R. Goutarel, *Bull. soc. chim. France,* [5] *18,* 588 (1951).
192. Karrer, P., R. Schwyzer, and A. Flam, *Helv. Chim. Acta, 35,* 851 (1952).
193. Elderfield, R. C., and A. P. Gray, *J. Org. Chem., 16,* 506 (1951).
194. Tarbell, D. S. and J. C. Bill, *J. Am. Chem. Soc., 74,* 1234 (1952).
195. Sutton, D. A., *Chemistry and Industry, 1951,* 272.
196. Matic, M., and D. A. Sutton, *J. Chem. Soc., 1952,* 2679.
197. Mustafa, A., *J. Chem. Soc., 1952,* 2435.
198. Mustafa, A., *J. Chem. Soc., 1949,* 1662.
199. Boekelheide, V., W. E. Langeland, and Chu-Tsin Liu, *J. Am. Chem. Soc.,* 73, 2432 (1951).
200. Campbell, T. W., and G. M. Coppinger, *J. Am. Chem. Soc., 74,* 1469 (1952).
201. *Chem. Eng. News, 31,* 2334 (1953).
202. Karrer, P., and G. Widmark, *Helv. Chim. Acta, 34,* 34 (1951).
203. Rapoport, H., and R. M. Bonner, *J. Am. Chem. Soc., 73,* 2872 (1951).
204. Findlay, S. P., and L. F. Small, *J. Am. Chem. Soc., 73,* 4001 (1951).
205. Gates, M., and G. Tschudi, *J. Am. Chem. Soc., 74,* 1109 (1952).
206. Schmid, H., and P. Karrer, *Helv. Chim. Acta, 33,* 863 (1950).
207. Bentley, K. W., and R. Robinson, *Experientia, 6,* 353 (1950).
208. Stork, G., *J. Am. Chem. Soc., 73,* 504 (1951).
209. Stork, G., *J. Am. Chem. Soc., 74,* 768 (1952).
210. Schmid, H., and P. Karrer, *Helv. Chim. Acta, 34,* 1948 (1951).
211. Robinson, R., *Nature, 160,* 815 (1947).
212. Bentley, K. W., and R. Robinson, *J. Chem. Soc., 1952,* 947.
213. Heymann, H., and L. F. Fieser, *J. Am. Chem. Soc., 73,* 5252 (1951).
214. Robinson, R., and R. Mirza, *Nature, 166,* 929 (1950).
215. Mirza, R., and R. Robinson, *Nature, 166,* 997 (1950).
216. Karrer, P., and M. Seyhan, *Helv. Chim. Acta, 33,* 2209 (1950).
217. Elstow, W. E., and B. C. Platt, *Chemistry and Industry, 1950,* 824.
218. Karrer, P., C. H. Eugster, and P. Waser, *Helv. Chim. Acta, 32,* 2381 (1949).
219. Kenner, G. W., and M. A. Murray, *J. Chem. Soc., 1950,* 406.
220. Findlay, S. P., *J. Am. Chem. Soc., 73,* 3008 (1951).
221. Babcock, J. C., and L. F. Fieser, *J. Am. Chem. Soc., 74,* 5472 (1952).

CHAPTER 12

Reduction of

NITROGEN-CONTAINING ORGANIC COMPOUNDS

12.1 AMINES

The reaction of LAH with primary and secondary amines is postulated to proceed with the formation of organometallic compounds (1), according to the equations:

$$LiAlH_4 + 4 RNH_2 \longrightarrow LiAl(NHR)_4 + 4 H_2 \qquad (12\text{-}1)$$

$$LiAlH_4 + 4 R_2NH \longrightarrow LiAl(NR_2)_4 + 4 H_2 \qquad (12\text{-}2)$$

No reaction occurs between LAH and tertiary amines.

In contrast to LAH, the ethereal solution of the addition compound $AlH_3 \cdot AlCl_3$, obtained by treatment of aluminum hydride with ethereal aluminum chloride, does not react with primary amines (2).

Aluminum hydride reacts with trimethylamine to form adducts containing one and two moles of amine per mole of hydride (3,4). Stecher and Wiberg (3) reported that polymeric aluminum hydride reacts with trimethylamine to form the adducts which apparently result from cleavage of the polymeric chain. When an ethereal solution of monomeric aluminum hydride is treated with excess trimethylamine a clear, stable solution is formed which, after distillation of the ether and unreacted amine, yields a white solid residue of the composition $AlH_3 \cdot 2N(CH_3)_3$, formulated as

$$
\begin{array}{c}
H \qquad \quad N(CH_3)_3 \\
\diagdown \qquad \vdots \\
H \underline{\quad\quad} Al \\
\diagup \qquad \vdots \\
H \qquad \quad N(CH_3)_3 \\
\text{I}
\end{array}
$$

When the ethereal aluminum hydride solution is treated with one mole of trimethylamine, on distillation of the ether from the clear solution the residual solid has the composition $AlH_3 \cdot N(CH_3)_2$, formulated as

$$
\begin{array}{c}
H \quad\quad H \quad H \\
\diagdown \quad \diagup \quad \diagup \\
(CH_3)_3N\cdots\cdots Al \qquad Al\cdots\cdots N(CH_3)_3 \\
\diagup \quad\quad \diagup \\
H \quad\quad H \quad H \\
\text{II}
\end{array}
$$

When II is dissolved in ether the simple formula $AlH_3 \cdot N(CH_3)_3$ is indicated indicating that the ether probably weakens the hydrogen bridge in

729

II to form the adduct

$$\begin{array}{c} H \diagdown \quad N(CH_3)_3 \\ H \!-\!\!\! \diagup Al \cdots \\ H \diagup \quad O(C_2H_5)_2 \end{array}$$

III

Solution of II in an ethereal trimethylamine solution yields the diaminate (I) (4).

Sodium and lithium borohydrides are soluble in primary and secondary amines with no apparent reaction. Although lithium borohydride does not react with trimethylamine (5), the reaction between the borohydride and various amine salts yields boron derivatives (6). Thus, methylammonium chloride (IV) in ether solution is converted to N-trimethylborazole, dimethylammonium chloride (V) yields N-dimethylaminoborine and trimethylammonium chloride (VI) yields trimethylamineborine.

$$3\ CH_3NH_3Cl + 3\ LiBH_4 \xrightarrow[98\%]{} (CH_3)_3N_3B_3H_3 + 3\ LiCl + 9\ H_2 \qquad (12\text{-}3)$$
IV

$$(CH_3)_2NH_2Cl + LiBH_4 \xrightarrow[91\%]{} (CH_3)_2NBH_2 + LiCl + 2\ H_2 \qquad (12\text{-}4)$$
V

$$(CH_3)_3NHCl + LiBH_4 \xrightarrow[86\%]{} (CH_3)_3N:BH_3 + LiCl + H_2 \qquad (12\text{-}5)$$
VI

Aluminum borohydride reacts with trimethylamine to form an addition compound which decomposes at 40–60° to yield a mixture of products which are not the parent substances (7). The addition reaction apparently involves the removal of borine groups in the form of trimethylamineborine $(CH_3)_3N:BH_3$ (5,8). While sodium borohydride does not react with trimethylamine, magnesium borohydride forms an addition compound $Mg(BH_4)_2 \cdot N(CH_3)_3$ which loses trimethylamine on heating for three hours at 100° (8). Beryllium borohydride reacts with trimethylamine to form an addition compound $Be(BH_4)_2 \cdot N(CH_3)_3$ which reacts further with the amine at 100° according to the equation:

$$Be(BH_4)_2 \cdot N(CH_3)_3 + (CH_3)_3N \rightleftarrows BeBH_5 \cdot N(CH_3)_3 + (CH_3)_3N:BH_3$$
VII   (12-6)

Decomposition of VII yields trimethylamine and an oily material which reacts with diborane to form beryllium borohydride (9).

Lithium gallium hydride, analogous to LAH, reacts with primary and secondary amines to liberate hydrogen but does not react with tertiary amines (10).

12.2 NITRILES

12.2.1 Reductions with Lithium Aluminum Hydride

The reduction of nitriles with LAH can be directed to yield either a primary amine (11-13) or an aldehyde (14) by the appropriate choice of reaction conditions.

Nystrom and Brown (13) postulated that the reduction of the nitrile to yield the primary amine consumes one-half mole of LAH per mole of nitrile and set forth the equation:

$$2 \; RC \!\equiv\! N + LiAlH_4 \;\rightarrow\; (RCH_2N)_2LiAl \xrightarrow{H_2O} RCH_2NH_2 \quad (12\text{-}7)$$

Zaugg and Horrom (15) have similarly claimed the utilization of one-half mole of LAH per mole of nitrile. Amundsen and Nelson (16) have reported that the reduction of one mole of nitrile requires one mole of LAH and have suggested that only half of the hydrogen of LAH is available for the reduction when the reaction is carried out below 35°. Nace and Smith (17) have found that in the reduction of cyclohexanone cyanohydrin the best yields are obtained with a ratio of two moles of LAH per mole of cyanohydrin. Welvart (18) has found that the course of the reduction of α-piperidinonitriles can be directed by varying the LAH/nitrile ratio. Zaugg and Horrom (19) have found that in the reduction of α,α-diphenyl-β-substituted propionitriles the optimum ratio is two moles of LAH per mole of nitrile. They have concluded that the number of moles of reducing agent per mole of nitrile necessary to form the intermediate complex varies with the type of compound and for preparative purposes a large excess of LAH can be used to good advantage.

Application of the Gilman-Schulze color test to the reaction of LAH with p-tolunitrile indicates a combining ratio of approximately two moles of nitrile per mole of LAH (13). Amundsen and Nelson (16) stated that the Gilman-Schulze test is not suitable for following the course of a reduction since it shows two moles of benzonitrile per mole of LAH and a 1:1 ratio with capronitrile while the actual reduction indicates a 1:1 ratio in each case.

Nystrom and Brown (13) reported that the intermediate complexes formed from LAH and nitriles are stable in a nitrogen atmosphere, but are pyrophoric in contact with air.

12.2.1.a *Aliphatic Nitriles.* The reduction of aliphatic nitriles to amines has been carried out with the nitriles derived from fatty acids as well as those containing pyridine, quinoline, thiophene, thianaphthene, pyrazole, imidazole, and indole nuclei.

The reductions to yield the primary amines usually proceed without difficulty and compare favorably with other methods of reduction. The reduction of 1-cyclohexenylacetonitrile (VIII) with LAH yields 74% of 2-(1-cyclohexenyl)ethylamine while catalytic hydrogenation over Raney cobalt in methanol at $60°$ and 90 atmospheres pressure proceeds in 90% yield (20).

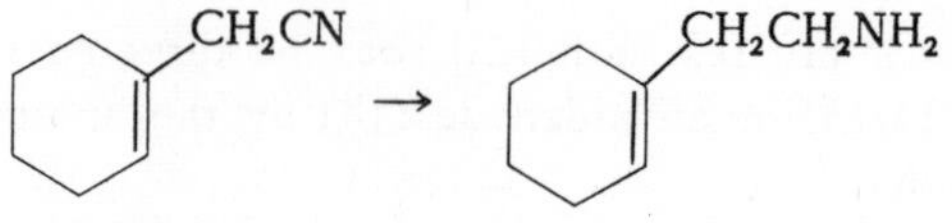

$$(12\text{-}8)$$

VIII

Jones (21) reported that while the LAH reduction of 3-cyanomethyl-pyrazole (IX) and 1-benzyl-4-cyanomethylpyrazole (X) gives the expected aminoethyl derivative, reduction of 4-cyanomethylpyrazole (XI) with LAH in ether gives none of the expected 4-(β-aminoethyl)pyrazole.

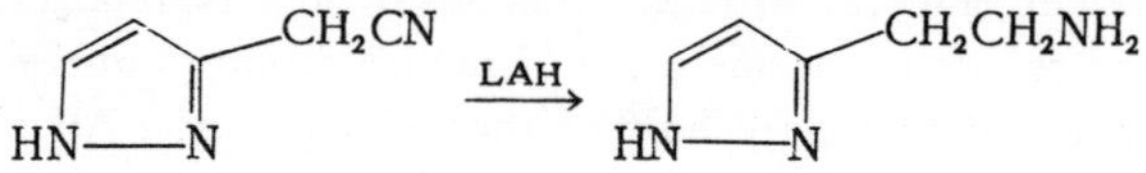

$$(12\text{-}9)$$

IX

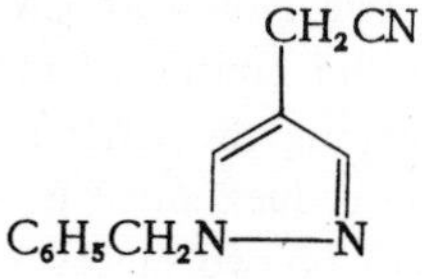

X 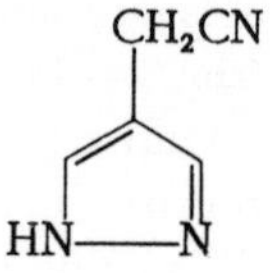   XI

While reduction of 4-quinolylacetonitrile (XII) with LAH in ether or tetrahydrofuran gives only traces of the primary amine, reduction with sodium in ethanol yields 3-aminoethyl-1,2,3,4-tetrahydroquinoline (22).

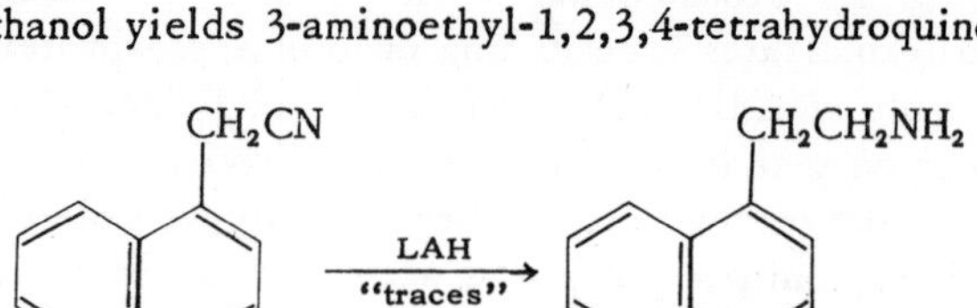

$$(12\text{-}10)$$

XII

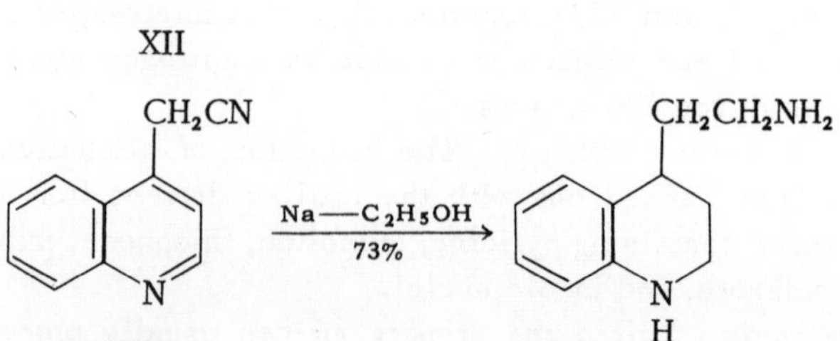

$$(12\text{-}11)$$

XII

Acetone homoquinonitrile (XIII) is reported not to be reduced with LAH "under the usual conditions" (23).

$$\underset{\text{XIII}}{\begin{array}{c} CH_3 \quad\quad CH_3 \\ \diagdown \quad \diagup \\ C \\ \diagup \quad \diagdown \\ O \quad\quad\quad O \\ \\ OH \\ \\ OH \\ CH_2CN \end{array}}$$

The reduction of alkylcyanoacetic esters (XIV) as well as other cyano-acids and esters has been utilized in the synthesis of aminoalcohols with antitubercular activity (24,25).

$$\underset{\text{XIV}}{\underset{COOR}{\overset{C_{10}H_{21}CHCN}{|}}} \xrightarrow{\text{LAH}} \underset{CH_2OH}{\overset{C_{10}H_{21}CHCH_2NH_2}{|}} \tag{12-12}$$

In some cases ring closure accompanies the formation of open-chain aminoalcohols (24).

$$\underset{\text{XV}}{\overset{CN}{\underset{COOC_2H_5}{\overset{|}{C_{10}H_{21}CCH_2CH_2CN}}}} \xrightarrow{\text{LAH}} \underset{CH_2OH}{\overset{CH_2NH_2}{\overset{|}{C_{10}H_{21}CCH_2CH_2CH_2NH_2}}} + \underset{\substack{\\ H \\ N}}{\overset{\substack{H_2 \\ C}}{H_2NCH_2\diagdown C \diagup CH_2}} \tag{12-13}$$

Brown (26) has observed that while the LAH reduction of 2,2-disubstituted-4-phenoxybutyronitriles (XVI) yields the expected 2,2-disubstituted-4-phenoxybutylamines, cyclization occurs in the case of the isopropyl derivative.

$$\underset{\text{XVI}}{C_6H_5OCH_2CH_2\underset{R}{\overset{R}{C}}CN} \xrightarrow[80-90\%]{\text{LAH}} C_6H_5OCH_2CH_2\underset{R}{\overset{R}{C}}CH_2NH_2 \tag{12-14}$$

$$R = CH_3, C_2H_5, C_6H_5, CH_3C_6H_4$$

$$
\underset{\substack{| \\ C_3H_7(i)}}{\overset{\substack{C_3H_7(i) \\ |}}{C_6H_5OCH_2CH_2\underset{|}{C}CN}} \xrightarrow{\text{LAH}} \quad \begin{array}{c} H_2C \!\!-\!\! C\!\!\diagup^{C_3H_7(i)}_{\diagdown C_3H_7(i)} \\ | \qquad\quad | \\ H_2C \diagdown \quad \diagup CH_2 \\ N \\ H \end{array} \qquad (12\text{-}15)
$$

$$
\text{XVII} \qquad\qquad\qquad\qquad \text{H}
$$

While the reduction of trimethylacetonitrile yields 86% of neopentyl-amine, triphenylacetonitrile is not reduced at 25° (13).

The LAH reduction of α- and β-aminonitriles presents some unusual aspects. Zaugg and Horrom (19) reported that the attempted reduction of α,α-diphenyl-β-dimethylaminopropionitrile (XVIII) with either one-half mole or one mole LAH per mole of nitrile gives a complex mixture from which no pure product can be isolated. When two moles of LAH are employed per mole of nitrile the expected diamine (XIX) is isolated in good yield. The α,α-diphenyl-β-pyrrolidino- and piperidinopropionitriles are also readily converted to the diamines under these conditions although the diethylaminonitrile can not be successfully reduced, yielding a product with a wide boiling range from which pure derivatives can not be isolated. The reduction of XVIII and its diethylamino analogue with sodium in ethanol results in cleavage of the nitrile group to yield the monoamine in place of the diamine. Hydrogenation of XVIII with Raney nickel in the presence of methanolic ammonia results in cleavage at a different point to yield β,β-diphenylethylamine (19).

$$
\xrightarrow[86.5\%]{\text{LAH}} \quad \underset{\substack{| \\ CH_2NH_2}}{(C_6H_5)_2CCH_2N(CH_3)_2} \qquad (12\text{-}16)
$$

$$
\text{XIX}
$$

$$
\underset{\substack{| \\ CN}}{(C_6H_5)_2CCH_2N(CH_3)_2} \quad \xrightarrow{\text{H}_2\,:\,\text{Raney Ni}} \quad \underset{\substack{| \\ CH_2NH_2}}{(C_6H_5)_2CH} \qquad (12\text{-}17)
$$

$$
\text{XVIII} \qquad \xrightarrow[65\%]{\text{Na}-\text{C}_2\text{H}_5\text{OH}} \quad (C_6H_5)_2CHCH_2N(CH_3)_2 \qquad (12\text{-}18)
$$

Amundsen and Nelson pointed out that complications can be expected when the LAH reduction of nitriles with an α-hydrogen is carried out (16). Phenylacetonitrile yields a reaction mixture which quickly turns a very dark green when exposed to the atmosphere. Nelson, Leubner and Burk (27) found that the LAH reduction of 2-anilinophenylacetonitrile (XX) gives 25% of 2-anilino-2-phenylethylamine (XXI) but that the major product is N-benzylaniline (XXII) in 41% yield.

$$C_6H_5NHCHCN \xrightarrow{LAH} C_6H_5NHCHCH_2NH_2 + C_6H_5NHCH_2C_6H_5 \quad (12\text{-}19)$$

with C_6H_5 below the first carbon and C_6H_5 below the product carbon.

| XX | XXI | XXII |

Welvart similarly reported abnormal reductions with α-aminonitriles (18). The addition of an ethereal solution of an α-piperidinonitrile (XXIII) (R_1 = H, R_2 = C_2H_5, i-C_3H_7; R_1 = CH_3, R_2 = C_2H_5; R_1R_2 = $(CH_2)_5$) to an LAH solution cooled to $-5°$ gives 45–60% of the diamine (XXIV) and 20–25% of a triamine (XXV). When the reagent is added to the solution of the nitrile at ordinary temperatures the yields of diamine and triamine are reversed.

$$\text{(piperidine)}N-\underset{R_2}{\overset{R_1}{C}}-CN \xrightarrow{LAH} \text{(piperidine)}N-\underset{R_2}{\overset{R_1}{C}}-CH_2NH_2 +$$

| XXIII | XXIV |

$$\text{(piperidine)}N-\underset{R_2}{\overset{R_1}{C}}-CH_2NHCH_2-\underset{R_2}{\overset{R_1}{C}}-N\text{(piperidine)} \quad (12\text{-}20)$$

XXV

LAH reduction yields the diamine and an unidentified condensation product when R_1 = H and R_2 = H or C_6H_5. The formation of the secondary amine in the reduction is explained by the two mechanisms (12-21) or (12-22):

$$3\ RCN \rightarrow 3\ RCH{=}NH \rightarrow \overset{RCH{=}N}{\underset{RCH{=}N}{>}}CHR \rightarrow RCH_2NH_2 + (RCH_2)_2NH$$
$$(12\text{-}21)$$

$$RCN \rightarrow RCH_2N(LiAl)_{1/2} \xrightarrow{RCN} RC\overset{N(LiAl)_{1/4}}{\underset{N(LiAl)_{1/4}}{<}} \xrightarrow{LAH} (RCH_2)_2N(LiAl)_{1/4}$$

with RCH_2NH_2 below the first, CH_2R below the center, and $(RCH_2)_2NH$ below the last.

$$(12\text{-}22)$$

By this mechanism an excess of LAH favors diamine formation while excess aminonitrile leads to the triamine. Experimentally the reduction can be directed towards the di- or triamines by change of operating conditions.

The LAH reduction of aliphatic nitriles to amines is summarized in Table LXXI.

TABLE LXXI

LAH Reduction of Aliphatic Nitriles

	Nitrile	Product	% Yield	Ref.
C_2H_3N	Acetonitrile	Ethylamine	...	1
C_4H_7N	Butyronitrile	n-Butylamine	57	2
$C_5H_5N_3$	3-Cyanomethylpyrazole	3-(β-Aminomethyl)pyrazole	53[3]	4
	4(5)-Cyanomethylimidazole	Histamine	45	5
			35[6]	5
$C_5H_7NO_2$	Methyl 3-cyanopropionate	4-Amino-1-butanol	...	7
C_5H_9N	Pivalonitrile	Neopentylamine	86	8
C_6H_5NS	2-Thienylacetonitrile	β-2-Thienylethylamine	34	9
	3-Thienylacetonitrile	β-3-Thienylethylamine	30	10
$C_6H_{13}NSi$	β-Trimethylsilylpropionitrile	3-Trimethylsilylpropylamine	19	10
$C_7H_{12}N_2$	α-Piperidinoacetonitrile	2-Piperidinoethylamine	82	11,12
		Condensation product (unidentified)[13]	...	14
$C_7H_{13}N$	n-Hexyl cyanide	n-Heptylamine	68	15
C_8H_4ClO	p-Chlorobenzoyl cyanide	2-Amino-1-p-chlorophenylethanol	89	16
C_8H_5NO	Benzoyl cyanide	2-Amino-1-phenylethanol	...[17]	18
C_8H_7N	Benzyl cyanide	2-Phenylethylamine	30	16
$C_8H_{11}N$	1-Cyclohexenylacetonitrile	2-(1-Cyclohexenyl)ethylamine	86	16
$C_8H_{13}NO$	trans-2-Cyanomethylcyclohexanol	trans-2-Aminomethylcyclohexanol	61	15
$C_8H_{15}N$	Caprylonitrile	n-Octylamine	74	19
$C_8H_{15}NO_2$	γ,γ-Diethoxybutyronitrile	4,4-Diethoxybutylamine	70–75	20,21
$C_9H_{16}N_2$	α-Piperidinobutyronitrile	2-Piperidino-n-butylamine[13]	89–92	2
		Bis-(2-piperidino-n-butyl)amine[13]	55.8	22
$C_{10}H_7NS$	3-Cyanomethylthianaphthene	3-Aminoethylthianaphthene	...	14
		3-Hydroxyethylthianaphthene	32	23

Molecular formula	Nitrile	Product	Yield (%)	Reference
$C_{10}H_8N_2$	3-Indolylacetonitrile	Tryptamine	...	24,25
$C_{10}H_{16}N_2$	Sebaconitrile	1,10-Diaminodecane	40	1,26
$C_{10}H_{18}N_2$	2-Piperidinoisovaleronitrile	2-Piperidino-isomylamine [13] Bis-(2-piperidino-isoamyl)amine	...	14
	α-Piperidino-α-methylbutyronitrile	2-Piperidino-2-methylbutylamine [13] Bis-(2-piperidino-2-methylbutyl)amine	...	14
$C_{10}H_{19}N$	Caprinitrile	n-Decylamine	92	2
$C_{11}H_8N_2$	4-Quinolylacetonitrile	4-Aminoethylquinoline	Traces	27
$C_{11}H_{11}NO_4$	3,4,5-Trimethoxybenzoyl cyanide	2-Hydroxy-2-(3,4,5-trimethoxyphenyl)-ethylamine	61	28
$C_{11}H_{13}NO_3$	3,4,5-Trimethoxyphenylacetonitrile	β-(3,4,5-Trimethoxyphenyl)ethylamine (mescaline)	40	29
			71[17]	28
	3,4,5-Trimethoxybenzyl C^{14}-cyanide	β-(3;4,5-Trimethoxyphenyl)-1-C^{14}-ethylamine	...	30
$C_{12}H_{11}N_3$	1-Benzyl-4-cyanomethylpyrazole	1-Benzyl-4-(β-aminoethyl)pyrazole	...	4
	1-Benzyl-2-cyanomethylimidazole	1-Benzyl-2-(β-aminoethyl)imidazole	88	31
$C_{12}H_{15}NO$	2,2-Dimethyl-4-phenoxybutyronitrile	2,2-Dimethyl-4-phenoxybutylamine	80—90	32
$C_{12}H_{20}N_2$	1-N-Piperidino-1-cyanocyclohexane	1-N-Piperidino-1-aminomethylcyclohexane [13] Bis-[1-(1'-N-piperidinocyclohexyl)methyl]-amine	...	14
$C_{13}H_{16}N$	α-Piperidino-α-phenylacetonitrile	2-Piperidino-2-phenylethylamine [13] Condensation product (unidentified)	...	14
$C_{13}H_{25}N$	Lauronitrile	Tridecylamine	90	26
$C_{14}H_{12}N_2$	2-Anilinophenylacetonitrile	N-Benzylaniline 2-Anilino-2-phenylethylamine	41 25	33
$C_{14}H_{19}NO$	2,2-Diethyl-4-phenoxybutyronitrile	2,2-Diethyl-4-phenoxybutyronitrile	80—90	32
$C_{15}H_{11}NO_2$	m-Benzyloxybenzoyl cyanide	2-Amino-1-(m-benzyloxyphenyl)ethanol	...	18
$C_{15}H_{27}NO_2$	Ethyl α-decylcyanoacetate	2-Aminomethyldodecanol	...	34
$C_{16}H_{13}NO$	2,2-Diisopropyl-4-phenoxybutyronitrile	3,3-Diisopropylpyrrolidine	9[35,36]	32
$C_{17}H_{14}N_2O$	5-Benzyloxyindoleacetonitrile	5-Benzyloxytryptamine	...	37

(Continued)

TABLE LXXI (Continued)

Nitrile	Product	% Yield	Ref.
$C_{17}H_{18}N_2$ α,α-Diphenyl-β-dimethylaminopropionitrile	2,2-Diphenyl-3-dimethylaminopropylamine	86	38
$C_{17}H_{31}NO_2$ Ethyl α-dodecylcyanoacetate	2-Aminomethyltetradecanol	....	34
2-β-Cyanoethyltetradecanoic acid	4-Hydroxymethylhexadecylamine	....	34
$C_{18}H_{30}N_2O_2$ Ethyl 2-cyano-2-cyanoethyldodecanoate	4-Hydroxymethyl-4-aminomethyltetradecylamine[39]	....	34
$C_{19}H_{20}N_2$ α,α-Diphenyl-β-pyrrolidinopropionitrile	2,2-Diphenyl-3-pyrrolidinopropylamine	82	38
$C_{19}H_{22}N_2$ α,α-Diphenyl-β-diethylaminopropionitrile	Product with wide boiling range	....	38
$C_{19}H_{35}NO_2$ Ethyl α-tetradecylcyanoacetate	2-Aminomethylhexadecanol	....	34
$C_{20}H_{22}N_2$ α,α-Diphenyl-β-piperidinopropionitrile	2,2-Diphenyl-3-piperidinopropylamine	71	38
$C_{22}H_{19}NO$ 2,2-Diphenyl-4-phenoxybutyronitrile	2,2-Diphenyl-4-phenoxybutylamine	80–90	32
$C_{22}H_{39}NO_4$ Ethyl 2-cyanoethyl-2-carbethoxytetradecanoate	4,4-Di-(hydroxymethyl)hexadecylamine	....	34
$C_{24}H_{23}NO$ 2,2-Ditolyl-4-phenoxybutyronitrile	2,2-Ditolyl-4-phenoxybutylamine	80–90	32

References — Table LXXI

[1]H. I. Schlesinger and A. E. Finholt, U. S. Pat. 2,576,311 (November 27, 1951).
[2]L. H. Amundsen and L. S. Nelson, *J. Am. Chem. Soc.*, *73*, 242 (1950).
[3]Isolated as dipicrate.
[4]R. G. Jones, *J. Am. Chem. Soc.*, *71*, 3994 (1949).
[5]M. Protiva and J. Pliml, *Chem. Listy,* in press; through M. Ferles and J. Rudinger, *Chem. Listy,* *47*, 135 (1953).
[6]Reduction carried out in tetrahydrofuran.
[7]R. F. Brown and N. van Gulick, *Abstracts of Papers,* 122nd Meeting American Chemical Society, Atlantic City, N. J., September 1952, p. 7M.
[8]D. Y. Curtin and S. M. Gerber, *J. Am. Chem. Soc.*, *74*, 4052 (1952).
[9]B. F. Crowe and F. F. Nord, *J. Org. Chem.*, *15*, 81 (1950).
[10]W. Herz, *J. Am. Chem. Soc.*, *73*, 351 (1951).
[11]L. H. Sommer and J. Rockett, *ibid.*, *73*, 5130 (1951).
[12]L. H. Sommer, U. S. Pat. 2,557,802 (June 19, 1951).
[13]See text.
[14]Z. Welvart, *Compt. rend.*, *233*, 1121 (1951).
[15]E. Larsson, *Trans. Chalmers Univ. Technol.*, Gothenburg, *94*, 15 (1950).
[16]A. Burger and F. D. Hornbaker, *J. Am. Chem. Soc.*, *74*, 5514 (1952).
[17]Isolated as hydrochloride.
[18]A. W. D. Avison, *J. Applied Chem. (London)*, *1*, 469 (1951).
[19]O. Schnider and J. Hellerbach, *Helv. Chim. Acta*, *33*, 1437 (1950).
[20]M. Mousseron and M. Canet, *Bull. soc. chim. France*, [5] *19*, 247 (1952).
[21]M. Mousseron, R. Jacquier, M. Mousseron-Canet, and R. Zagdoun, *ibid.*, [5] *19*, 1042 (1952).
[22]R. Lukeš and J. Trojánek, *Chem. Listy*, *46*, 383 (1952); through M. Ferles and J. Rudinger, *Chem. Listy*, *47*, 135 (1953).
[23]W. Herz, *J. Am. Chem. Soc.*, *72*, 4999 (1950).
[24]P. E. Norris and F. F. Blicke, *J. Am. Pharm. Assoc.*, *41*, 637 (1952).
[25]E. R. H. Jones, H. B. Henbest, G. F. Smith, and J. A. Bentley, *Nature*, *169*, 485 (1952).
[26]R. F. Nystrom and W. G. Brown, *J. Am. Chem. Soc.*, *70*, 3738 (1948).
[27]K. Eiter and E. Mrazak, *Monatsh.*, *83*, 915 (1952).
[28]A. Dornow and G. Petsch, *Arch. pharm.*, *285*, 323 (1952).
[29]M. U. Tsao, *J. Am. Chem. Soc.*, *73*, 5495 (1951).
[30]W. Block and K. Block, *Chem. Ber.*, *85*, 1009 (1952).
[31]R. G. Jones, *J. Am. Chem. Soc.*, *71*, 383 (1949).
[32]R. F. Brown, private communication.
[33]N. J. Leonard, G. W. Leubner, and E. H. Burk, Jr., *J. Org. Chem.*, *15*, 979 (1950).
[34]V. C. Barry, J. G. Belton, R. M. Kelly, and D. Twomey, *Nature*, *166*, 303 (1950).
[35]Isolated as hydrobromide.
[36]85% starting material recovered.
[37]M. E. Speeter, R. V. Heinzelmann, and D. I. Weisblat, *J. Am. Chem. Soc.*, *73*, 5514 (1951).
[38]H. E. Zaugg and B. W. Horrom, *ibid.*, *75*, 292 (1953).
[39]Ring closure also observed.

12.2.1.b   *Alicyclic Nitriles.* The LAH reduction of saturated alicyclic
nitriles proceeds normally to yield the corresponding amines. Thus,
1-cyano-1,2-epoxycyclohexane (XXVI) yields 1-aminomethylcyclohexanol
(28–30) while 2-cyanocyclohexanone (XXVII) and *trans*-2-cyanocyclo-
hexanol (XXVIII) yield *trans*-2-aminomethylcyclohexanol (28,29,31).

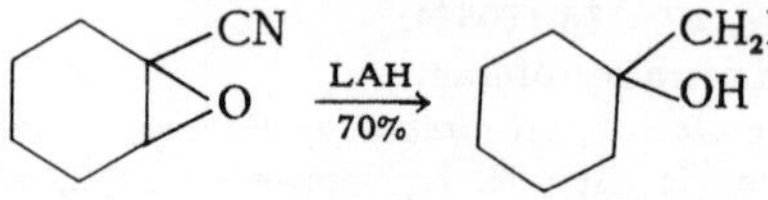

$$\text{(12-23)}$$

XXVI

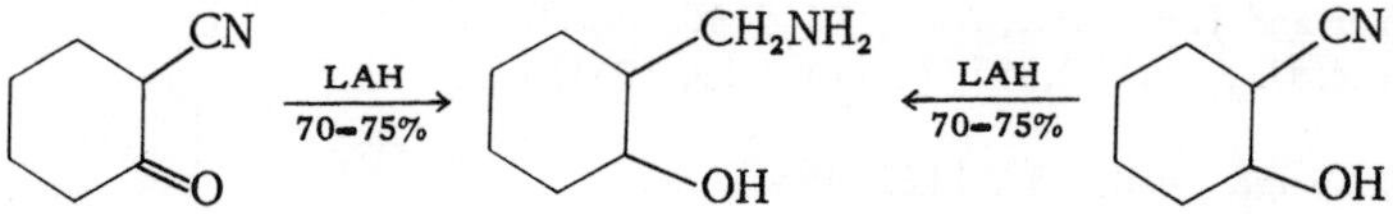

$$\text{(12-24)}$$

XXVII   XXVIII

Ajmaline, $C_{20}H_{26}N_2O_2$, is a polycyclic alkaloid of unknown structure
from the roots of *Rauwolfia serpentine.* Both ajmaline and the isomeric
isoajmaline obtained on heating the former, afford oximes. Treatment of
the oximes with hydrogen chloride and acetic anhydride in acetic acid
solution followed by methanolic potassium hydroxide yields anhydroajmaline oxime and anhydroisoajmaline oxime, respectively. The anhydro-
derivatives, $C_{20}H_{25}N_3O$, contain a cyano group, and on reduction with
LAH are converted to ajmaline and isoajmaline, respectively. These results are interpreted as indicating that ajmaline and isoajmaline contain
the partial formula XXIX. It is proposed that the reduction involves

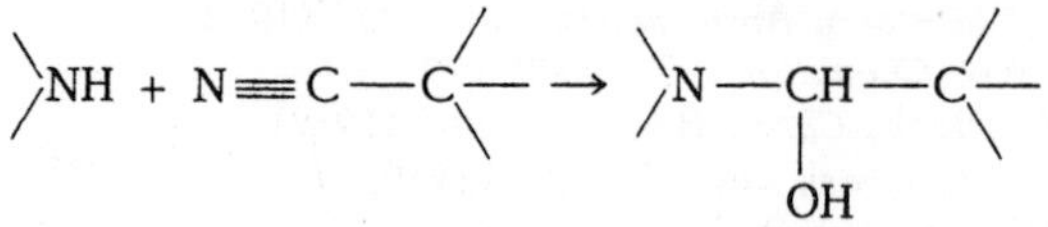

$$\text{(12-25)}$$

XXIX

wherein the nitrile is initially converted to an aldehyde which then reacts with the active amino hydrogen (32). The reduction of nitriles to
aldehydes is discussed in Section 12.2.1.g.

12.2.1.c   *Aromatic and Heterocyclic Nitriles.* The reduction of aromatic nitriles in the benzene as well as pyridine and pyrazole series is
summarized in Table LXXII. Paddock (33) has shown that the electron
donor properties of benzonitrile permits LAH reduction to take place in
the absence of ether.

TABLE LXXII

LAH Reduction of Aromatic Nitriles

	Nitrile	Product	% Yield	Ref.
C_7H_4BrN	p-Bromobenzonitrile	p-Bromobenzylamine	....	1
C_7H_4ClN	p-Chlorobenzonitrile	p-Chlorobenzylamine	81	2
C_7H_5N	Benzonitrile	Benzylamine	72	3,4
			83	2
			....	5
C_8H_7N	o-Tolunitrile	o-Xylylamine	88	3,4
$C_{10}H_{10}ClN_3O_2$	2-Methyl-3-amino-4-carbethoxy-5-cyano-6-chloropyridine	2-Methyl-3-amino-4-hydroxymethyl-5-amino-methylpyridine	....	6
$C_{10}H_{11}N_3O_2$	2-Methyl-3-amino-4-carbethoxy-5-cyanopyridine	2-Methyl-3-amino-4-hydroxymethyl-5-amino-methylpyridine	....[7]	8
$C_{11}H_9N_3$	1-Benzyl-4-cyanopyrazole	1-Benzyl-4-aminomethylpyrazole	72[7]	9
$C_{13}H_{14}N_2$	9-Cyanojulolidine	9-(Aminomethyl)julolidine	55[10]	11
$C_{14}H_{11}NO$	5-Methoxy-2-cyanobiphenyl	2-Phenyl-4-methoxybenzylamine	80	12

[1] N. S. Corby, G. W. Kenner, and A. R. Todd, J. Chem. Soc., 1952, 3669.
[2] L. H. Amundsen and L. S. Nelson, J. Am. Chem. Soc., 73, 242 (1950).
[3] H. I. Schlesinger and A. E. Finholt, U. S. Pat. 2,576,311 (November 27, 1951).
[4] R. F. Nystrom and W. G. Brown, J. Am. Chem. Soc., 70, 3738 (1948).
[5] E. Wiberg and M. Schmidt, Z. Naturforsch., 6b, 171 (1951).
[6] K. J. Verrill and A. M. Schneider, Brit. Pat. 686,012 (January 14, 1953).
[7] Isolated as hydrochloride.
[8] T. Matsukawa and K. Sirakawa, J. Pharm. Soc. Japan, 71, 1498 (1952).
[9] R. G. Jones, J. Am. Chem. Soc., 71, 3994 (1949).
[10] Isolated as acetyl derivative.
[11] P. A. S. Smith and Tung-Yin Yu, J. Org. Chem., 17, 1281 (1952).
[12] C. K. Bradsher and W. J. Jackson, Jr., J. Am. Chem. Soc., 74, 4880 (1952).

12.2.1.d *Cyanohydrins*. Nystrom and Brown reported that cyanohydrins form insoluble precipitates which remove LAH from the solution
and hence are reduced in relatively poor yield (13). These side reactions
have been overcome by the use of higher LAH/nitrile ratios (17,34,35)
and by the use of the cyanohydrin acetate (34,35). In some cases the reduction product is contaminated with the carbinol formed by reduction of
the carbonyl compound resulting from dissociation of the cyanohydrin
(35,36).

Heusser *et al.* (34) and Nace and Smith (17) found that in the usual
method of working up the reaction mixture from a cyanohydrin reduction
the filter cake retains a considerable quantity of the reduction product.
By extraction with appropriate solvents the product is obtained in good
yield. Heusser *et al.* reported that the hydroxyamine is obtained when
the filter cake from the reduction of the cyanohydrin acetate, XXX, is extracted with a mixture of methanol and chloroform, but extraction with
acetone yields the spirooxazolidine.

(12-26)

Cyanohydrins reduced with LAH are summarized in Table LXXIII.

12.2.1.e α,β-*Unsaturated Nitriles*. The LAH reduction of α,β-un-
saturated nitriles has been reported as yielding in some cases the unsaturated amine and in others the saturated amine. Elderfield, Pitt and
Wempen found that β-ethyl-γ-methoxycrotonitrile (XXXI) is reduced to the
corresponding primary amine in 50–67% yield without affecting the double
bond (37). Weisler (38,39) has patented the preparation of β-ionylidene-
ethylamine and Vitamin A amine by LAH or aluminum hydride reduction
of the corresponding nitriles (XXXII) and (XXXIII).

TABLE LXXIII

LAH Reduction of Cyanohydrins

Cyanohydrin	Product	Ref.
6-Acetoxy-6-cyanobicyclo[3.2.0]-2-heptene	6-Aminomethyl-6-hydroxybicyclo[3.2.0]-2-heptene Bicyclo[3.2.0]-2-hepten-6-ol }	1
Cyclohexanone cyanohydrin	1-Aminomethylcyclohexanol	2
	Product not indicated	3
3β,17β-Diacetoxy-17-iso-$\Delta^{5,6}$-etiocholenic acid nitrile	17α-Aminomethyl-$\Delta^{5,6}$-androstene-3β,17β-diol	4
3,4-Dibenzyloxybenzaldehyde cyanohydrin	2-Amino-1-(3,4-dibenzyloxyphenyl)ethanol] 3,4-Dibenzyloxybenzyl alcohol }	5
Mandelonitrile	2-Amino-1-phenylethanol	6
Menthone cyanohydrin	Product not indicated	3
3,4,5-Trimethoxybenzaldehyde cyanohydrin	2-Amino-1-(3,4,5-trimethoxyphenyl)ethanol	7

[1] J. D. Roberts and W. F. Gorham, *J. Am. Chem. Soc.*, 74, 2278 (1952).

[2] H. R. Nace and B. B. Smith, *ibid.*, 74, 1861 (1952).

[3] H. C. Neumann, Dissertation, through ref. 4.

[4] H. Heusser, P. T. Herzig, A. Fürst, and P. A. Plattner, *Helv. Chim. Acta*, 33, 1093 (1950).

[5] A. W. D. Avison, *J. Applied Chem. (London)*, 1, 469 (1951).

[6] R. F. Nystrom and W. G. Brown, *J. Am. Chem. Soc.*, 70, 3738 (1948).

[7] A. Dornow and G. Petsch, *Arch. pharm.*, 284, 160 (1951).

$$CH_3OCH_2C\!=\!CHCN \xrightarrow{LAH} CH_3OCH_2C\!=\!CHCH_2NH_2 \quad (12\text{-}27)$$
$$\underset{C_2H_5}{|} \qquad\qquad\qquad \underset{C_2H_5}{|}$$

XXXI

CH=CHC=CHCN

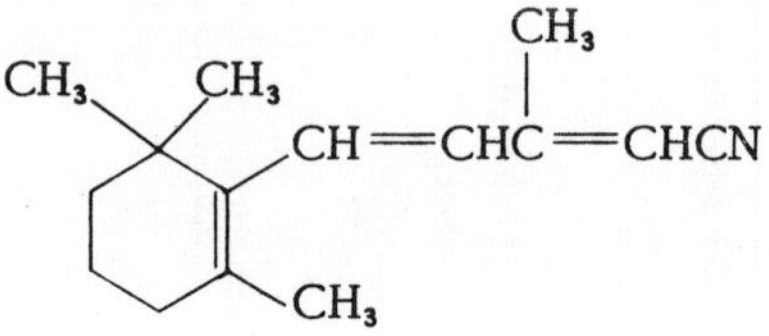

XXXII

CH=CHC=CHCH=CHC=CHCN

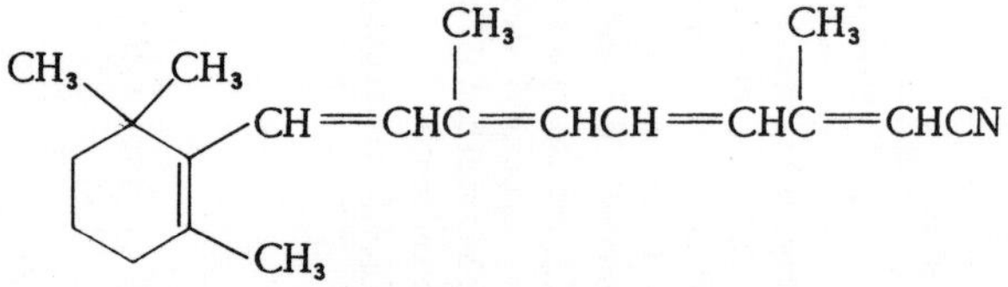

XXXIII

The reduction of XXXII to the unsaturated aldehyde is discussed in Section 12.2.1.g. The reduction of 3β-acetoxy-20-cyanopregna-5,17-diene (XXXIV) yields the unsaturated amine (40).

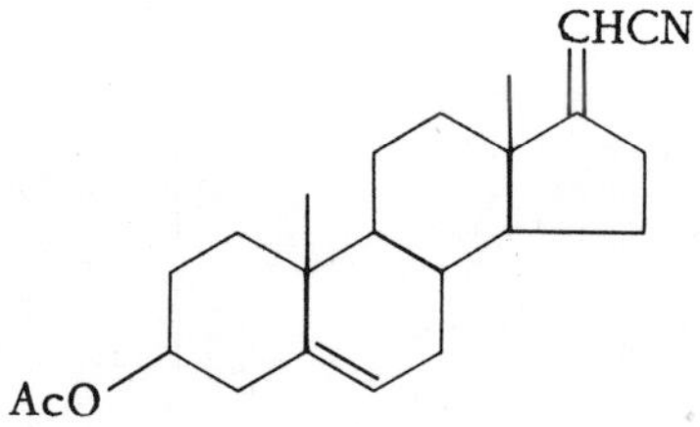

XXXIV

In contrast, Dornow, Messwarb, and Frey (41) reported that the LAH reduction of methyl α-cyanocinnamate (XXXV), its 4-methoxy or 3,4-methylenedioxy derivatives gives the saturated 3-aminoalcohol.

$$C_6H_5CH\!=\!CCOOCH_3 \xrightarrow{LAH} C_6H_5CH_2CHCH_2OH \quad (12\text{-}28)$$
$$\underset{CN}{|} \qquad\qquad\qquad \underset{CH_2NH_2}{|}$$

XXXV

The corresponding reductions of isoamylidene cyanoacetic acid (XXXVI) and citralidene cyanoacetic acid (XXXVII) to the saturated aminoalcohols indicate that the reduction of the double bond is not dependent upon the conjugation of a phenyl group and a reducible group.

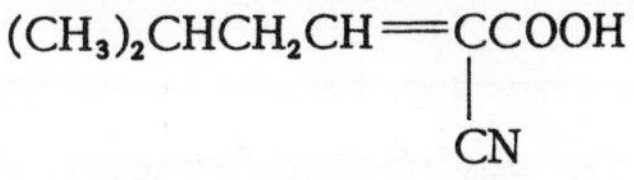

$$(CH_3)_2CHCH_2CH = \underset{\underset{CN}{|}}{C}COOH$$

XXXVI

$$(CH_3)_2C = CHCH_2CH_2\underset{\underset{CH_3}{|}}{C} = CHCH = \underset{\underset{CN}{|}}{C}COOH$$

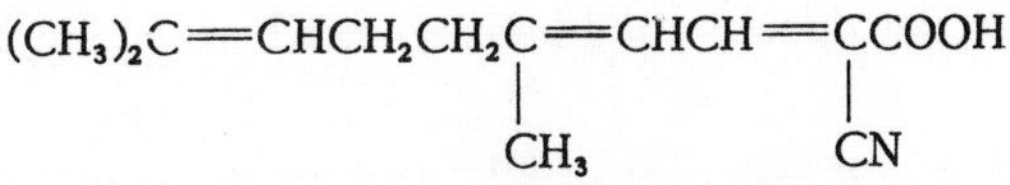

XXXVII

Mousseron and his co-workers (28,31,42) have reported that the reduction of 1-cyanocyclohexene with excess LAH at ambient temperature gives a 60% yield of aminomethylcyclohexane while reduction with inverse addition of LAH at $-15°$ gives the saturated aldehyde in 60% yield. The mechanism proposed (28) for these reactions involves the preliminary formation of the complex ion (XXXVIII) which upon hydrolysis gives the saturated aldehyde through the intermediate imine. In the presence of excess LAH, XXXVIII is converted to the metallic complex XXXIX which on hydrolysis yields the saturated amine.

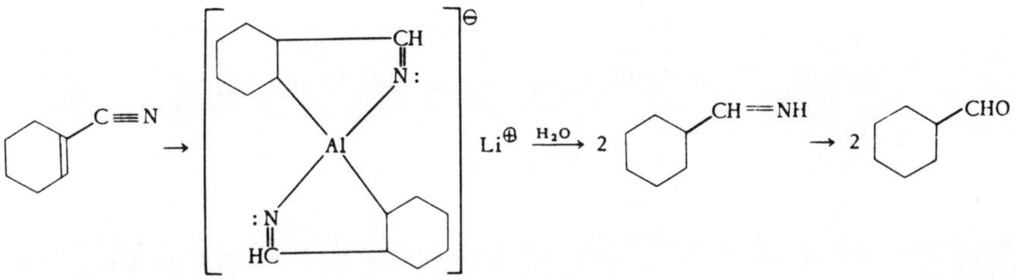

XXXVIII   (12-29)

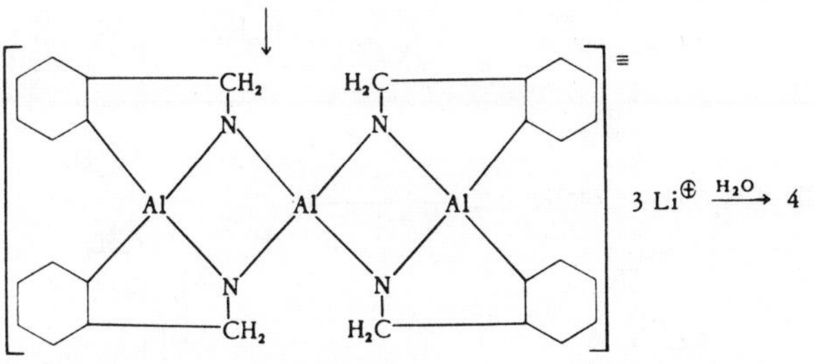

XXXIX   (12-30)

The reduction of N,N′-diphenylcyanoformamidine (XL) which contains a conjugated carbon-nitrogen double bond yields the amidine (XLI) (43).

$$C_6H_5N = C - NHC_6H_5 \xrightarrow{LAH} C_6H_5N = C - NHC_6H_5 \qquad (12\text{-}31)$$
$$\qquad\qquad |\qquad\qquad\qquad\qquad\qquad\qquad\quad |$$
$$\qquad\qquad CN \qquad\qquad\qquad\qquad\qquad\qquad CH_2NH_2$$

$$\qquad\qquad XL \qquad\qquad\qquad\qquad\qquad\qquad\quad XLI$$

The reduction of α,β-diphenyl-β-methoxyacrylonitrile, m.p. 106° (XLII), obtained by methylation of α-cyanodesoxybenzoin, with one-half mole of LAH yields α-benzylphenylacetonitrile (XLIII) in which demethylation and reduction of the double bond has occurred while the cyano group is intact (44).

$$C_6H_5C = CC_6H_5 \xrightarrow{LAH} C_6H_5CHCH_2C_6H_5 \qquad (12\text{-}32)$$
$$\qquad |\quad\ |\qquad\qquad\qquad\qquad\qquad |$$
$$\qquad CN\ \ OCH_3 \qquad\qquad\qquad\qquad CN$$

$$\qquad\quad XLII \qquad\qquad\qquad\qquad\qquad XLIII$$

12.2.1.f *Selective Reductions.* Several attempts have been made to apply the technique of selective reduction to an oxygen function without affecting the nitrogen function on a compound possessing two different reactive groups (45). Avison and Morrison (46) have successfully reduced ethyl 5-chloro-2-cyano-2-phenylvalerate (XLIV) to 5-chloro-2-cyano-2-phenyl-1-pentanol (XLV) although attempts at distillation have resulted in decomposition.

$$\qquad\quad C_6H_5 \qquad\qquad\qquad\qquad\qquad\ C_6H_5$$
$$\qquad\quad |\qquad\qquad\qquad\qquad\qquad\qquad\quad |$$
$$ClCH_2CH_2CH_2CCOOC_2H_5 \rightarrow ClCH_2CH_2CH_2CCH_2OH \qquad (12\text{-}33)$$
$$\qquad\quad |\qquad\qquad\qquad\qquad\qquad\qquad\quad |$$
$$\qquad\quad CN \qquad\qquad\qquad\qquad\qquad\qquad CN$$

$$\qquad\quad XLIV \qquad\qquad\qquad\qquad\qquad\ XLV$$

The N-methylamide (XLVI) derived from XLIV is cyclized on treatment with sodium ethoxide to the piperidone (XLVII).

$$\qquad\qquad\qquad\qquad\qquad\qquad\qquad\qquad C_6H_5\diagdown\quad\diagup CN$$
$$\qquad\qquad\qquad\qquad\qquad\qquad\qquad\qquad\qquad\diagup C$$
$$\qquad\quad C_6H_5 \qquad\qquad\qquad\qquad\qquad H_2C\qquad NCH_3$$
$$\qquad\quad |\qquad\qquad\qquad\qquad\qquad\qquad |\qquad\quad |$$
$$ClCH_2CH_2CH_2CCONHCH_3 \xrightarrow{NaOC_2H_5} \qquad\qquad\qquad\qquad (12\text{-}34)$$
$$\qquad\quad |\qquad\qquad\qquad\qquad\qquad H_2C\diagdown\quad\diagup CH_2$$
$$\qquad\quad CN \qquad\qquad\qquad\qquad\qquad\qquad C$$
$$\qquad\quad XLVI \qquad\qquad\qquad\qquad\qquad\qquad H_2$$

$$\qquad\qquad\qquad\qquad\qquad\qquad\qquad\qquad\qquad XLVII$$

Neither XLVI nor XLVII have been selectively reduced with LAH, yielding mixtures of basic products from which a pure compound has not been isolated.

The non-reduction of the nitrile group has been shown in equation (12-32), wherein the LAH reduction of α,β-diphenyl-β-methoxyacrylonitrile yields α-benzylphenylacetonitrile (44).

Reynaud and Matti (47) studied the action of aluminum isopropoxide and LAH on a mono- and disubstituted β-ketonitrile. The reduction of benzoylphenylacetonitrile (XLVIII) with the aluminum alkoxide and isopropanol gives 1,2-diphenyl-2-cyanoethanol.

$$\underset{\text{XLVIII}}{\underset{\overset{|}{C_6H_5}}{C_6H_5COCHCN}} \xrightarrow{\text{Al}(i\text{-OPr})_3} \underset{\overset{|}{OH}\quad\overset{|}{C_6H_5}}{C_6H_5CH\text{---}CHCN} \qquad (12\text{-}35)$$

The addition of one-quarter mole of LAH (sufficient to reduce the ketonic function) to one mole of XLVIII results in the evolution of hydrogen and the formation of an ether-insoluble complex which quantitatively generates the starting material on acid treatment. The complex is represented as arising by the reaction of LAH and an active hydrogen according to equation (12-36) or (12-37).

$$4\ \underset{\overset{|}{CN}}{\underset{\overset{|}{C_6H_5COCH}}{}} + \text{LiAlH}_4 \rightarrow \left[\underset{\overset{|}{CN}}{\underset{\overset{|}{C_6H_5COC\text{---}}}{\overset{\overset{|}{C_6H_5}}{}}}\right]_4 \text{LiAl} + 4\ H_2 \qquad (12\text{-}36)$$

$$4\ \underset{\overset{|}{CN}}{\underset{C_6H_5C}{\overset{OH}{}}}=\underset{}{\overset{C_6H_5}{C}} + \text{LiAlH}_4 \rightarrow \left[\underset{\overset{|}{CN}}{C_6H_5C}=\overset{\overset{|}{C_6H_5}}{\underset{}{C}}\right]_4 \text{LiAl} + 4\ H_2 \qquad (12\text{-}37)$$

The reaction of 2-benzoyl-2-phenyl-4-diethylaminobutyronitrile (XLIX) with both LAH and aluminum isopropoxide results in cleavage of the quaternary carbon-carbonyl bond to yield 2-phenyl-4-diethylaminobutyronitrile (L). The by-product from the alkoxide reaction is isopropyl benzoate and that from the LAH reaction is benzaldehyde since the reaction is carried out with the inverse addition of a calculated amount of hydride.

$$\underset{\text{XLIX}}{\underset{C_2H_5}{\overset{C_2H_5}{}}\!\!\diagup}\!\!\!\!\!\underset{}{\overset{}{NCH_2CH_2}\underset{\overset{|}{CN}}{\overset{\overset{|}{C_6H_5}}{C}}COC_6H_5} \rightarrow \underset{\text{L}}{\underset{C_2H_5}{\overset{C_2H_5}{}}\!\!\diagup}\!\!\!\!\!\underset{}{\overset{}{NCH_2CH_2}\underset{\overset{|}{CN}}{\overset{\overset{|}{C_6H_5}}{CH}}} \qquad (12\text{-}38)$$

12.2.1.g *Reduction of Nitriles to Aldehydes.* As discussed in Section 12.2.1.e, equation (12-29), nitriles can be reduced with LAH to the corresponding aldehydes by the inverse addition of the calculated amount of hydride at low temperatures (14). Friedman proposed a procedure whereby one-quarter mole of LAH in ether or tetrahydrofuran is added to one mole of nitrile at temperatures maintained below 0°. The mixture is allowed to warm to room temperature and upon cessation of the exothermic reaction the mixture is decomposed and the aldehyde isolated in the usual manner. The reduction apparently involves the formation of the imine.

$$RC \equiv N + \tfrac{1}{4} \text{ LiAlH}_4 \rightarrow RCH = N \xrightarrow[4]{\text{LiAl}} \xrightarrow{\text{H}_2\text{O}} RCH = O \qquad (12\text{-}39)$$

This technique has been applied to the following nitriles to yield the corresponding aldehydes:

Nitrile	% Aldehyde	Ref.
1-Cyanocyclohexane	60	28,31,42
1-Cyanocyclopropane	48	48,49
Trifluoroacetonitrile	46	50
4-Dimethylamino-3-methyl-2,2-diphenylbutyronitrile	24	51
4-Dimethylamino-2,2-diphenylvaleronitrile	28	51
β-Ionylideneacetonitrile	7–34	52–54

The reduction of β-ionylideneacetonitrile (LI) to β-ionylideneacetaldehyde has been of great interest due to its potential utility in the synthesis of vitamin A and its derivatives. The LAH reductions are generally carried out by adding an ethereal solution of the hydride at −50° to a solution of the nitrile in various solvents. The products include (β-ionylidene)ethylamine and unreacted nitrile as well as the aldehyde (52–54).

The relative proportions of products under varying conditions are summarized below.

Moles Nitrile/Moles LAH	Solvent	% Aldehyde	% Amine	% Nitrile
0.02/0.005	Ether	11.6		33
0.02/0.02	Ether	7	55	
0.02/0.01	Ether	34	12	7.5
0.02/0.01	Cyclohexane	12.5	20	
0.02/0.01	Triethylamine	29	21	
0.02/0.01	Petroleum ether (40–60°)	21		

Herz (55) found that the reduction of 3-cyanomethylthianaphthene gives the primary amine accompanied by a neutral compound formulated as the 3-hydroxyethylthianaphthene. The latter may have arisen by preliminary formation of the aldehyde followed by reduction with excess LAH.

Claus and Morgenthau (56) unsuccessfully attempted to prepare β-methylmercaptopropionaldehyde by the reduction of β-methylmercapto-propionitrile (LII) according to Friedman's method. However, the aldehyde has been prepared in good yield from the corresponding nitrile by LAH reduction of an ortho ester to an acetal followed by hydrolysis to the aldehyde. The reaction scheme is as follows:

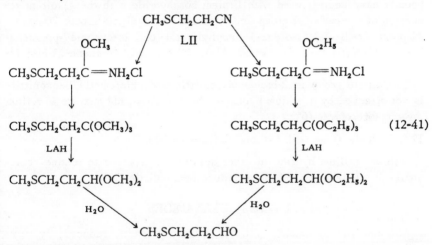

$$(12\text{-}41)$$

12.2.2 Reductions with Aluminum Hydride

As mentioned in Section 12.2.1.e, the patents on the reduction of β-ionylideneacetonitrile and vitamin A nitrile to the corresponding amines refer to the use of either LAH or aluminum hydride as the reducing agents (38,39).

Acetonitrile is reduced to ethylamine with an ethereal solution of the aluminum hydride-aluminum chloride addition compound (2). Similarly, benzonitrile is reduced to benzylamine in 79% yield (57). The proposed simplified mechanism for the reduction of nitriles involves the two-stage addition of the hydride.

$$—C\equiv N \xrightarrow{+alH} —CH=\mathrm{Nal} \xrightarrow{+alH}$$

$$—CH_2—\mathrm{Nal}_2 \xrightarrow{+2\,H_2O} —CH_2NH_2 \qquad (12\text{-}42)$$

al = 1 equivalent Al

12.2.3   Reductions with Magnesium and Zinc Aluminum Hydrides

Both magnesium (58,59) and zinc aluminum hydrides (59) reduce aceto-nitrile to ethylamine.

12.2.4   Reactions with Sodium Borohydride

The non-reduction of the nitrile group by sodium borohydride (60), per-mitting selective reduction, has been utilized in the reduction of the fol-lowing compounds to the nitrile-containing products: N-cyanotropinone, (61), 20-cyano-17-pregnene-21-ol-3,11-dione-3-dimethylketal (62).

12.2.5   Reactions with Lithium Borohydride

The non-reduction of the nitrile group by lithium borohydride has found particular utility in the reduction of corticosteroids. The following com-pounds have been treated with lithium borohydride with the resultant re-duction of the carbonyl group and retention of the nitrile group: 20-cyano-17-pregnene-21-ol-3,11-dione-3-dimethyl ketal (62), 20-cyano-17-pregnene-21-ol-3,11-dione-3-diethyl ketal (63), 20-cyano-17-pregnene-21-ol-3,11-dione-3-monosemicarbazone (62,64).

The nitrile group in 2-bromobutyronitrile and chloromethylbenzonitrile is not attacked by a lithium hydride-lithium borohydride mixture in reflux-ing tetrahydrofuran (65).

12.2.6   Reductions with Lithium Gallium Hydride

Lithium gallium hydride in ether solution is reported to reduce aceto-nitrile to ethylamine but fails to reduce benzonitrile (10).

12.3   CYANAMIDES

Although the cyanamide group is ordinarily readily reduced, by cata-lytic means, the group in N-cyanonortropinone (LIII) is resistant to so-dium borohydride (61).

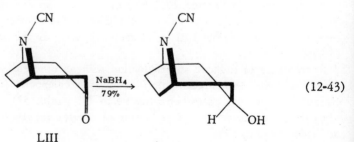

(12-43)

LIII

12.4 ISOCYANIDES

In the only reported example of the LAH reduction of an isocyanide, phenyl isocyanide (LIV) is reduced with excess LAH in ether solution to N-methylaniline (66).

$$C_6H_5N \mathrel{\raise.3ex\hbox{$\equiv$}} C \xrightarrow[79\%]{LAH} C_6H_5NHCH_3 \qquad (12\text{-}44)$$
$$\text{LIV}$$

12.5 ISOCYANATES

The reduction of phenyl isocyanate (LV) with ethereal LAH yields N-methylaniline (67,68).

$$C_6H_5N = C = O \xrightarrow{LAH} C_6H_5NHCH_3 \qquad (12\text{-}45)$$
$$\text{LV}$$

The overall reaction has been postulated as requiring three-quarters of a mole of LAH per mole of isocyanate (68). The reduction of dehydro-abietyl isocyanate (LVI) has been utilized in the synthesis of the N-methyldehydroabietylamine (69).

$$(12\text{-}46)$$

12.6 OXIMES

The reduction of oximes consumes one-half mole of LAH and yields primary amines as indicated in the following partial equation:

$$2 R_2C = NOH + LiAlH_4 \rightarrow 2 R_2CHNH_2 \qquad (12\text{-}47)$$

Smith, Maienthal, and Tipton have found that the best ratio of oxime to LAH is 1 to 1.5 moles and have reported that the Gilman-Schulze color tests can not be successfully applied to the reduction of oximes with LAH (70).

12.6.1 Aldoximes

The reduction of aliphatic and aromatic aldoximes, to primary amines, with LAH is summarized in Table LXXIV.

$$\overset{H}{RC} = NOH \xrightarrow{LAH} RCH_2NH_2 \qquad (12\text{-}48)$$

TABLE LXXIV

LAH Reduction of Aldoximes

	Oxime	Product	% Yield	Ref.
A. Aliphatic				
C_4H_7NO	Crotonaldoxime	Crotylamine	50	1
C_4H_9NO	n-Butyraldoxime	n-Butylamine	47	2
$C_7H_{15}NO$	n-Heptaldoxime	n-Heptylamine	50–75	3,4
			65–79	2
C_9H_9NO	Cinnamaldoxime	3-Phenyl-1-aminopropane	84	4
		3-Phenyl-1-amino-2-propene	53	5
$C_{14}H_{12}N_2O_3$	p-Phenoxyphenylglyoxime	p-Phenoxyphenylethylenediamine	...	6
$C_{16}H_{17}NO_3$	3-Methoxy-4-benzyloxyphenylacetaldoxime	β-(3-Methoxy-4-benzyloxy)phenylethylamine	...	7
$C_{17}H_{19}NO_3$	α-(3-Methoxy-4-benzyloxyphenyl)propionaldoxime	β-(3-Methoxy-4-benzyloxyphenyl)propylamine	31	8
B. Aromatic				
C_7H_7NO	Benzaldoxime	Benzylamine	50–75	3,4

[1] D. Y. Curtin and S. M. Gerber, J. Am. Chem. Soc., 74, 4052 (1952).
[2] D. R. Smith, M. Maienthal, and J. Tipton, J. Org. Chem., 17, 294 (1952).
[3] E. Larsson, Svensk Kem. Tid., 61, 242 (1949); Chem. Abstracts, 44, 1898 (1950).
[4] E. Larsson, Trans. Chalmers Univ. Technol., Gothenburg, 94, 21 (1950); Chem. Abstracts, 45, 1494 (1951).
[5] C. R. Walter, Jr., J. Am. Chem. Soc., 74, 5185 (1952).
[6] A. Funke and C. Favre, Bull. soc. chim. France, [5] 18, 832 (1951).
[7] J. Finkelstein, J. Am. Chem. Soc., 73, 550 (1951).
[8] A. H. Sommers and A. W. Weston, ibid., 73, 5749 (1951).

12.6.2 Ketoximes

The reduction of ketoximes with LAH usually yields primary amines as the only product. However, the amine in some cases is accompanied by an isomeric secondary amine.

12.6.2.a *Acyclic Ketoximes*. The LAH reduction of acyclic ketoximes generally proceeds without difficulty to the primary amine.

$$R - \underset{\underset{NOH}{\|}}{C} - R' \xrightarrow{LAH} R - \underset{\underset{NH_2}{|}}{CH} - R' \qquad (12\text{-}49)$$

The LAH reduction of 2-oximino-3-ketoesters presents an interesting picture. Gregory and Malkin (71) reported that an attempt to reduce methyl 3-keto-2-oximinooctadecanoate (LVII) with LAH gave a "mixture of long-chain amines" from which no pure substance could be isolated. Fisher (72) repeated this reduction and obtained a product which on benzoylation in pyridine and recrystallization from ethanol gives tribenzoyl dihydrosphingosine (LVIII).

$$CH_3(CH_2)_{14}\underset{\underset{O}{\|}}{C} - \underset{\underset{NOH}{\|}}{C}COOCH_3 \xrightarrow[2.\ C_6H_5COCl]{1.\ LAH} CH_3(CH_2)_{14}\underset{\underset{OB}{|}}{CH} - \underset{\underset{NHB}{|}}{C}HCH_2OB$$

$$\text{LVII} \hspace{4cm} \text{LVIII} \qquad (12\text{-}50)$$

$$B = COC_6H_5$$

Hayes and Gever (73) reported that the reduction of ethyl α-oximinofuroylacetate (LIX) with a large excess of LAH in ether gives approximately 2% of the expected aminodiol (LX) isolated as the oxalic acid salt. LAH reduction of the methyl ester of LIX also proceeds in "poor" yield.

$$\text{(12-51)}$$

LIX   LX

However, catalytic hydrogenation of the methyl ester in the presence of palladium in acetic anhydride, gives methyl α-acetaminofuroylacetate.

Elphimoff-Felkin, Felkin, Tchoubar, and Welvart (74) found that the reduction of ethyl α-oximinobenzoylacetate (LXI) by zinc and acetic acid, by aluminum isopropoxide, by the Bouveault-Blanc method and by LAH does not give good results. Viscontini and Adank (75) reported that only one substance could be isolated, in about 7% yield, as a crystalline product from the reduction of LXI with LAH. This product, m.p. 179-180°, based on an elemental analysis has the constitution of either the Schiff's base (LXII) or the oxazolidine derivative (LXIII).

$$C_6H_5C-C-COOC_2H_5 \xrightarrow{\text{LAH}}$$
$$\quad\; \| \quad\; \|$$
$$\quad\; O \quad NOH$$

LXI

$$\begin{array}{cc} C_6H_5CH-CHCOOH & C_6H_5CH-CHCOOH \\ \;\;\; | \qquad\quad | & \;\;\; | \qquad\quad | \\ \;\;\; OH \quad N=CHC_6H_5 & \;\;\; O \qquad NH \end{array} \quad \text{or} \qquad (12\text{-}52)$$
$$\qquad\qquad\qquad\qquad\qquad\qquad\qquad\qquad CH$$
$$\qquad\qquad\qquad\qquad\qquad\qquad\qquad\qquad |$$
$$\qquad\qquad\qquad\qquad\qquad\qquad\qquad\qquad C_6H_5$$

LXII   LXIII

The formation of benzaldehyde in the course of the reaction is indicated by the isolation of either LXII or LXIII. Additional work by Viscontini (76) has revealed that if the reduction of LXI is carried out under reflux with excess LAH the normal reaction yielding *allo*-DL-3-phenyl-2-amino-1,3-propanediol (LXIV) is observed.

$$C_6H_5C-C-COOC_2H_5 \xrightarrow{\text{LAH}} C_6H_5CH-CHCH_2OH$$
$$\quad\; \| \quad\; \| \qquad\qquad\qquad\qquad\quad | \qquad\quad | \qquad (12\text{-}53)$$
$$\quad\; O \quad NOH \qquad\qquad\qquad\qquad OH \quad NH_2$$

LXI   LXIV

The abnormal behavior of LXI has been attributed to a dissociation of the 2-amino-3-hydroxyester into an aldehyde and ethyl glycinate.

$$RCH-CHCOOC_2H_5 \qquad RCHO + CH_2-COOC_2H_5$$
$$\;\; | \qquad\quad | \qquad\qquad\rightarrow \qquad\qquad\qquad\;\; | \qquad (12\text{-}54)$$
$$\;\; OH \quad NH_2 \qquad\qquad\qquad\qquad\qquad\qquad NH_2$$

Treatment of α,β-dimorpholinobenzylacetone oxime (LXV) with LAH in ether by the Soxhlet technique fails to reduce the oxime. Similarly, catalytic hydrogenation with palladium-on-charcoal at 50 psi pressure of hydrogen fails to reduce LXV (77).

$$C_6H_5CH-CH-CCH_3$$
$$\quad\; | \qquad\quad | \qquad\; \|$$
$$\quad\; N \qquad\quad N \quad NOH$$

LXV

The reduction of acyclic ketoximes with LAH, yielding the primary amine, is summarized in Table LXXV.

TABLE LXXV

LAH Reduction of Acyclic Ketoximes

	Oxime	Product	% Yield	Ref.
C_4H_9NO	2-Butanone oxime	sec-Butylamine	60	1
$C_7H_{15}NO$	2-Heptanone oxime	2-Aminoheptane	32	2
	2,4-Dimethyl-3-pentanone oxime	3-Amino-2,4-dimethylpentane	40	2
$C_9H_{11}NO$	3-Phenyl-2-propanone oxime	2-Amino-3-phenylpropane	47	3
$C_9H_{11}NO_2$	3-Phenoxy-2-propanone oxime	2-Amino-3-phenoxypropane	50–75	1,4
$C_{10}H_{11}NO$	Benzalacetone oxime	2-Amino-4-phenyl-3-butene	40–50	5
$C_{15}H_{15}NO_2$	1,1-Diphenylpropan-2-on-1-ol oxime	1,1-Diphenyl-2-aminopropanol	55	3
	3-Phenoxy-3-phenyl-2-propanone oxime	2-Amino-3-phenoxy-3-phenylpropane	15	6
$C_{17}H_{19}NO_3$	3-(3-Benzyloxy-4-methoxyphenyl)-2-propanone oxime	3-(3-Benzyloxy-4-methoxyphenyl)-2-aminopropane	40–50	5
	3-(3-Methoxy-4-benzyloxyphenyl)-2-propanone oxime	3-(3-Methoxy-4-benzyloxyphenyl)-2-aminopropane	40	7
$C_{18}H_{21}NO_3$	3-(3-Methoxy-4-benzyloxyphenyl)-2-butanone oxime	3-(3-Methoxy-4-benzyloxyphenyl)-2-aminobutane	56	7
			17	7

[1]E. Larsson, *Trans. Chalmers Univ. Technol., Gothenburg*, 94, 21 (1950); *Chem. Abstracts*, 45, 1494 (1951).
[2]D. R. Smith, M. Maienthal, and J. Tipton, *J. Org. Chem.*, 17, 294 (1952).
[3]C. R. Walter, Jr., *J. Am. Chem. Soc.*, 74, 5185 (1952).
[4]E. Larsson, *Svensk Kem. Tid.*, 61, 242 (1949); *Chem. Abstracts*, 44, 1898 (1950).
[5]M. Kopp, *Compt. rend.*, 235, 247 (1952).
[6]H. Felkin, *ibid.*, 230, 304 (1950).
[7]A. H. Sommers and A. W. Weston, *J. Am. Chem. Soc.*, 73, 5749 (1951).

12.6.2.b   Alicyclic Ketoximes.   The reduction of alicyclic ketoximes with LAH, yielding alicyclic amines, is summarized in Table LXXVI.

The LAH reduction of anhydroajmaline oxime and anhydroisoajmaline oxime, $C_{20}H_{25}N_3O$, to ajmaline and isoajmaline, $C_{20}H_{26}N_2O_2$, respectively, has been discussed in Section 12.2.1.b. Since the structures of these polycyclic alkaloids are unknown the course of the oxime reduction cannot be ascertained.

12.6.2.c   Aromatic Ketoximes.   The reduction of aromatic ketoximes with LAH yields the corresponding primary amine accompanied, in many cases, by an isomeric secondary amine. Larsson (66,78) found that the reduction of acetophenone oxime (LXVI) gives 1-phenylethylamine as the main product and N-ethylaniline as the accompanying isomer.

$$\underset{\substack{\| \\ NOH}}{C_6H_5CCH_3} \xrightarrow{LAH} \underset{\substack{| \\ NH_2}}{C_6H_5CHCH_3} + C_6H_5NHC_2H_5 \tag{12-55}$$

LXVI

Smith, Maienthal, and Tipton (70) found that propiophenone oxime as well as acetophenone oxime is reduced to the corresponding amine and N-alkylaniline. The result appears to be due to a rearrangement of the oxime, under the reaction conditions, to an amide which is then reduced as usual to a secondary amine.

$$RR'C=NOH \rightarrow RCONHR' \text{ or } R'CONHR \tag{12-56}$$

Kopp (79) found that the temperature and time of refluxing influences considerably the course of the reaction, notably in regard to the formation of secondary amines, in the reduction of aryloxyketoximes.

Walter (80) reported that while the LAH reduction of acetophenone and p-chloro- and p-bromoacetophenone oximes gives the corresponding amine, the reduction of m-nitroacetophenone oxime does not yield the simple amine. However, the color of the reaction mixture indicates that conversion of the aryl nitro to an azo group has occurred, probably along with reduction of the oxime.

The reduction of benzophenone oxime with LAH has been successfully carried out in tetrahydrofuran (81) but not in ether (70).

The diketone, 1,6-diketojulolidine, readily forms a crystalline dioxime (LXVII) which has not been reduced by sodium and methanol, sodium amalgam, hydrogen with a palladium-on-carbon catalyst or LAH (82).

LXVII

TABLE LXXVI

LAH Reduction of Alicyclic Ketoximes

Oxime		Product	% Yield	Ref.
C_5H_9NO	Cyclopentanone oxime	Cyclopentylamine	33	1
$C_6H_{11}NO$	Cyclohexanone oxime	Cyclohexylamine	50–75	2
			86	3
			42	4
			61	1
			71[5]	1
$C_7H_{13}NO$	2-Methylcyclohexanone oxime	trans-2-Methylcyclohexylamine	53	1
	3-Methylcyclohexanone oxime	trans-3-Methylcyclohexylamine	43	1
	4-Methylcyclohexanone oxime	trans-4-Methylcyclohexylamine	81	1
$C_{10}H_{17}NO$	2,2-Tetramethylenecyclohexanone oxime	2,2-Tetramethylenecyclohexylamine	66	4
$C_{12}H_{15}NO_2$	2-Phenoxycyclohexanone oxime	2-Phenoxycyclohexylamine	40–50	6
$C_{12}H_{21}NO$	2,2-Pentamethylenecycloheptanone oxime	2,2-Pentamethylenecycloheptylamine	40	4
$C_{18}H_{19}NO$	2,2-Diphenylcyclohexanone oxime	2,2-Diphenylcyclohexylamine	80[7]	8

[1] D. R. Smith, M. Maienthal, and J. Tipton, J. Org. Chem., 17, 294 (1952).
[2] E. Larsson, Svensk Kem. Tid., 61, 242 (1949); Chem. Abstracts, 44, 1898 (1950).
[3] E. Larsson, Trans. Chalmers Univ. Technol., Gothenburg, 94, 21 (1950); Chem. Abstracts, 45, 1494 (1951).
[4] C. R. Walter, Jr., J. Am. Chem. Soc., 74, 5185 (1952).
[5] Reduction carried out in tetrahydrofuran.
[6] M. Kopp, Compt. rend., 235, 247 (1952).
[7] Reduction carried out in isopropyl ether-diethyl ether mixture.
[8] A. Burger and W. B. Bennet, J. Am. Chem. Soc., 72, 5414 (1950).

The reduction of various aromatic ketoximes is summarized in Table LXXXVII.

12.6.3   α,β-Unsaturated Oximes

While the reduction of crotonaldoxime (LXVIII) is reported (26) to yield the unsaturated amine, Larsson (66) found that reduction of cinnamaldoxime (LXIX) gives the saturated amine. Walter, however, has been able to isolate the unsaturated amine in good yield (80).

$$RCH\!\!=\!\!CHC\overset{H}{=}NOH \xrightarrow{\text{LAH}} RCH\!\!=\!\!CHCH_2NH_2 \text{ or } RCH_2CH_2CH_2NH_2$$

LXVIII: R = CH_3 (12-57)
LXIX: R = C_6H_5

The reduction of the oxime of benzalacetone (LXX) has been reported to yield the unsaturated amine (80).

$$\underset{\underset{NOH}{\overset{\|}{}}}{C_6H_5CH\!\!=\!\!CHCCH_3} \xrightarrow[55\%]{\text{LAH}} \underset{\underset{NH_2}{\overset{|}{}}}{C_6H_5CH\!\!=\!\!CHCHCH_3} \quad (12\text{-}58)$$

LXX

Tarbell and Bill (83) have reported that the LAH reduction of the oxime of 4,5-benztropolone methyl ether (LXXI) followed by acetylation yields 5-acetaminobenzsuberone-4 (LXXII). The 4,5-benztropolone nucleus has been shown to possess many of the properties of a phenol.

LXXI   LXXII   (12-59)

12.6.4   Selective Reductions

Felkin (45) found that by the addition of an ethereal LAH solution, containing the theoretical quantity of reducing agent, to a solution of a keto aldoxime at room temperature it is possible to selectively reduce the carbonyl function without affecting the oxime grouping.

$$C_6H_5COC\overset{H}{=}NOH \xrightarrow[34\%]{\text{LAH}} \underset{\underset{OH}{\overset{|}{}}}{C_6H_5CHC}\overset{H}{=}NOH \quad (12\text{-}60)$$

TABLE LXXVII

LAH Reduction of Aromatic Ketoximes

	Oxime	Product	% Yield	Ref.
C_8H_8BrNO	p-Bromoacetophenone oxime	1-(p-Bromophenyl)ethylamine	65	1
C_8H_8ClNO	p-Chloroacetophenone oxime	1-(p-Chlorophenyl)ethylamine	57	1
C_8H_9NO	Acetophenone oxime	1-Phenylethylamine	43	1
			67	2
		1-Phenylethylamine	50–75 }	3,4
		N-Ethylaniline	10–15 }	
		1-Phenylethylamine	56 }	5
		N-Ethylaniline	16 }	
$C_9H_{11}NO$	Propiophenone oxime	1-Phenylpropylamine	48 }^{6}	5
		N-Propylaniline	14 }	
$C_{13}H_{11}NO$	Benzophenone oxime	Benzhydrylamine	60^6	7
			0	5
$C_{14}H_{12}N_2O_3$	p-Phenoxyphenylglyoxime	p-Phenoxyphenylethylenediamine	....	8
$C_{14}H_{13}NO_2$	Benzoin oxime	1,2-Diphenyl-2-hydroxyethylamine	13	1
$C_{15}H_{15}NO_2$	α-Methyl-α-phenoxyacetophenone oxime	1-Phenyl-2-phenoxypropylamine	40–50	9
$C_{20}H_{17}NO_2$	α-Phenyl-α-phenoxyacetophenone oxime	1,2-Diphenyl-2-phenoxyethylamine	40–50	9

[1] C. R. Walter, Jr., J. Am. Chem. Soc., 74, 5185 (1952).
[2] H. Felkin, Compt. rend., 230, 304 (1950).
[3] E. Larsson, Svensk Kem. Tid., 61, 242 (1949); Chem. Abstracts, 44, 1898 (1950).
[4] E. Larsson, Trans. Chalmers Univ. Technol., Gothenburg, 94, 21 (1950); Chem. Abstracts, 45, 1494 (1951).
[5] D. R. Smith, M. Maienthal, and J. Tipton, J. Org. Chem., 17, 294 (1952).
[6] Reduction carried out in tetrahydrofuran.
[7] A. Hochstein, J. Am. Chem. Soc., 71, 305 (1949).
[8] A. Funke and C. Favre, Bull. soc. chim. France, [5] 18, 832 (1951).
[9] M. Kopp, Compt. rend., 235, 247 (1952).

Similarly, he selectively reduced the ester group in the oxime of 3-carbethoxy-3-ethyl-2-pentanone (LXXIII) without attacking the oximino grouping.

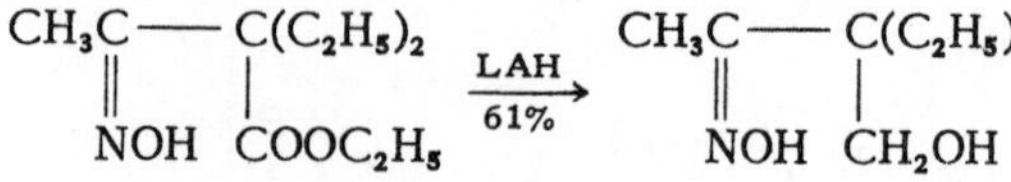

$$
\begin{array}{ccc}
\underset{\substack{\| \\ NOH}}{CH_3C}\text{---}\underset{\substack{| \\ COOC_2H_5}}{C(C_2H_5)_2} & \xrightarrow[61\%]{LAH} & \underset{\substack{\| \\ NOH}}{CH_3C}\text{---}\underset{\substack{| \\ CH_2OH}}{C(C_2H_5)_2}
\end{array} \qquad (12\text{-}61)
$$

LXXIII

12.7 UREAS

Treatment of N,N'-diphenylurea with an ethereal LAH solution for 30 hours is reported to yield a 78% recovery of starting material (68).

The two-stage reduction of hydantoins with LAH is discussed in Section 10.3.3.a. Reduction of 5-phenyl- and 3-methyl-5-phenylhydantoin (LXXIV) with ethereal LAH yields the 2(3H)-imidazolone (LXXV). The urea grouping in LXXV is reduced with difficulty, by prolonged refluxing, to the imidazole (LXXVI) (84).

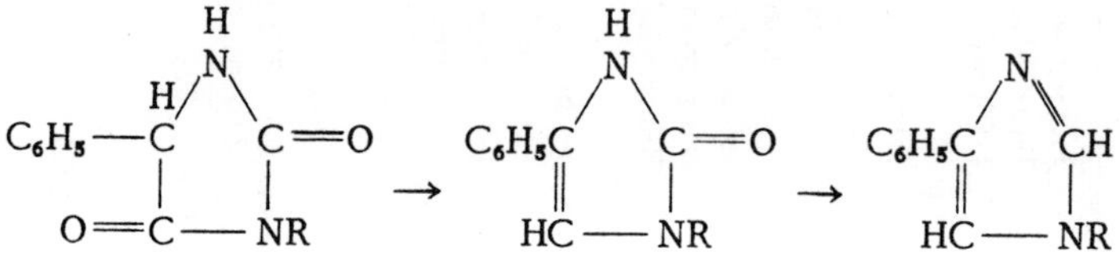

$$ \qquad (12\text{-}62) $$

LXXIV   LXXV   LXXVI

The hydantoin nucleus is resistant to attack by sodium borohydride.

The resistance of the urea grouping in semicarbazones to attack by lithium borohydride is discussed in Section 12.16.4.

12.8 NITROGEN OXIDES

The reduction of benzo[c]cinnoline N-oxide (LXXVII) with LAH yields benzo[c]cinnoline (85).

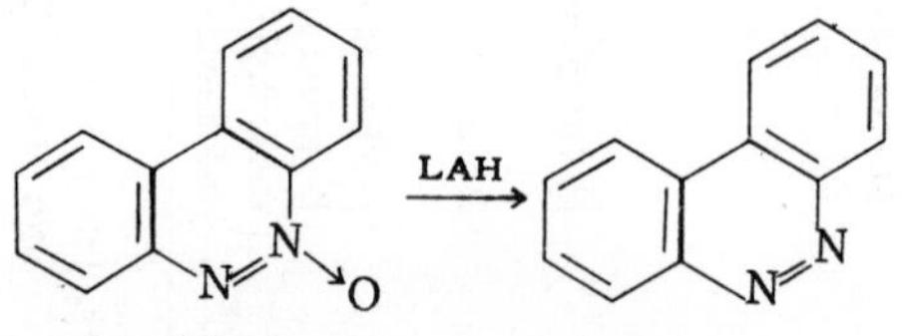

$$ \qquad (12\text{-}63) $$

LXXVII

This reaction actually involves the reduction of an azoxy group (Section 12.13.2).

The reduction of pyridine-N-oxide-2-azo-p-dimethylaniline (LXXVIII) yields pyridine-2-azo-p-dimethylaniline (86).

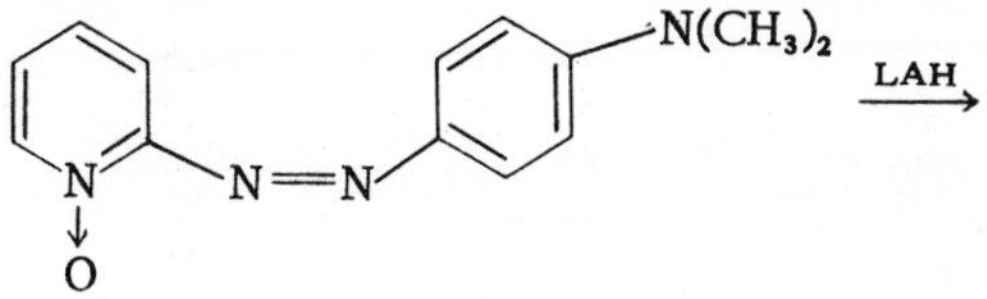

LXXVIII

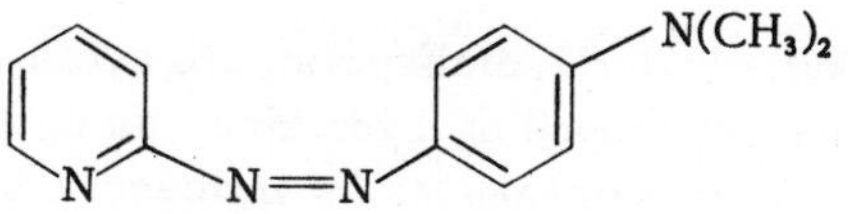

(12-64)

12.9 NITROSO COMPOUNDS

12.9.1 C-Nitroso Compounds

The reduction of aromatic nitroso compounds is reported to consume one-half mole of LAH per mole of nitroso compound to yield the corresponding azo compound (87). Gilman and Goreau have shown that the color test devised for aromatic nitro compounds is applicable to nitroso derivatives (88).

The LAH reduction of p-nitrosodimethylaniline (LXXIX) yields 80% of 4,4'-bis(dimethylamino)azobenzene (12,89).

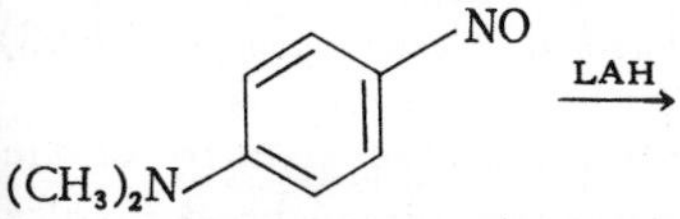

LXXIX

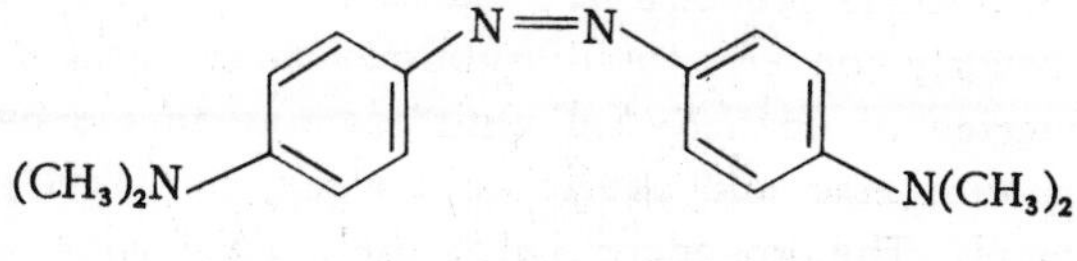

(12-65)

12.9.2 Nitrosamines

The reduction of disubstituted nitrosamines with an ethereal LAH solution yields unsymmetrical disubstituted hydrazines.

$$R_2NNO \xrightarrow{LAH} R_2NNH_2 \qquad (12\text{-}66)$$

This method has been utilized in the preparation of the following hydrazine derivatives with the indicated yields:

	% Yield	Ref.
N,N-Dimethylhydrazine	78	90
N,N-Diethylhydrazine	49	91
N,N-Di-*n*-propylhydrazine	76	91,92
N,N-Di-*n*-butylhydrazine	46	91,92
N,N-Di-*n*-amylhydrazine	65	91,92
N,N-Dicyclohexylhydrazine	48	93
N,N-Pentamethylenehydrazine	75	93
N-Methyl-N-phenylhydrazine	77	93
N,N-Diphenylhydrazine	90	94

While dialkyl, alkylaryl, dialicyclic, and cyclic nitrosamines are readily reduced to the corresponding hydrazines using LAH, the course of the reduction of diaryl nitrosamines is influenced by the quantity of LAH. The addition of N-nitrosodiphenylamine to excess LAH yields diphenylamine (90).

$$(C_6H_5)_2NNO \xrightarrow[74\%]{LAH} (C_6H_5)_2NH \tag{12-67}$$

By using equimolar quantities of reactants N,N-diphenylhydrazine is obtained in 73% yield along with approximately 20% of diphenylamine. The yield of hydrazine is increased to more than 90% by inverse addition (94). The course of the reaction is represented by:

$$2 (C_6H_5)_2NNO + 2 LiAlH_4 \rightarrow [(C_6H_5)_2NN]_2LiAl + LiAlO_2 + 2 H_2$$
$$\downarrow H_2O$$
$$2 (C_6H_5)_2NNH_2 + LiAlO_2 \tag{12-68}$$

Hanna and Schueler (93) have postulated that the greater polarity of the nitrogen-oxygen bond as compared to the nitrogen-nitrogen bond results in initial attack at the former position. The polar character of the nitrogen-nitrogen bond is presumably enhanced by aromatic rings so that excess LAH readily converts the diarylnitrosamine to the diarylamine.

The reduction of an N,N-dialkylnitrosamine to the hydrazine may be carried out with zinc and acetic acid when the alkyl group is methyl, ethyl or propyl. The procedure yields the dialkylamine as the main product when higher alkyl groups are present (92,95).

12.10 ALIPHATIC NITRO COMPOUNDS

12.10.1 Reductions with Lithium Aluminum Hydride

The LAH reduction of aliphatic nitro compounds consumes one and one-half moles of hydride per mole of nitro compound to yield the corresponding amine (11-13), according to the equation:

$$2 \, RNO_2 + 3 \, LiAlH_4 \rightarrow (RN)_2LiAl + 2 \, LiAlO_2 + 6 \, H_2$$

$$\downarrow H_2O$$

$$2 \, RNH_2 + LiOH + Al(OH)_3 \qquad (12\text{-}69)$$

12.10.1.a   *Saturated Nitro Compounds.*   Nystrom and Brown (13) reported that undiluted nitromethane reacts with LAH at room temperature with explosive violence while higher aliphatic nitro compounds are less reactive. The reduction of 2-nitrobutane gives 85% of 2-aminobutane (12,13) while phenylnitromethane yields 91% of benzylamine (96).

The addition of an ethereal solution of 2-benzylthio-2-phenylnitroethane (LXXX) to an ethereal LAH solution results in a 56% yield of the corresponding amine isolated as the hydrochloride (97).

$$\underset{\text{LXXX}}{\underset{\text{SCH}_2\text{C}_6\text{H}_5}{\overset{\text{C}_6\text{H}_5\text{CHCH}_2\text{NO}_2}{|}}} \xrightarrow{\text{LAH}} \underset{\text{SCH}_2\text{C}_6\text{H}_5}{\overset{\text{C}_6\text{H}_5\text{CHCH}_2\text{NH}_2}{|}} \qquad (12\text{-}70)$$

The reduction of LXXX with iron and hydrochloric acid yields 11% of the amine hydrochloride. The LAH reduction of 1-ethylthio-1-nitromethylcyclohexane (LXXXI) yields the substituted aminomethylcyclohexane (97).

$$(12\text{-}71)$$

LXXXI

The LAH reduction of 1-phenyl-2-nitropropane (LXXXII) followed by hydrolysis with an aqueous sodium potassium tartrate solution yields β-phenylisopropylamine (98).

$$\underset{\text{LXXXII}}{\underset{\text{CH}_3}{\overset{\text{C}_6\text{H}_5\text{CH}_2\text{CHNO}_2}{|}}} \xrightarrow{\text{LAH}} \underset{\text{CH}_3}{\overset{\text{C}_6\text{H}_5\text{CH}_2\text{CHNH}_2}{|}} \qquad (12\text{-}72)$$

The reduction of 1-anilino-1-phenyl-2-nitroethane (LXXXIII) gives the expected diamine in low yield, with N-benzylaniline being formed in larger amounts than that of the desired amine (27).

$$\underset{\text{LXXXIII}}{\underset{\text{NHC}_6\text{H}_5}{\overset{\text{C}_6\text{H}_5\text{CHCH}_2\text{NO}_2}{|}}} \xrightarrow{\text{LAH}} \underset{\text{NHC}_6\text{H}_5}{\overset{\text{C}_6\text{H}_5\text{CHCH}_2\text{NH}_2}{|}} + \text{C}_6\text{H}_5\text{CH}_2\text{NHC}_6\text{H}_5 \qquad (12\text{-}73)$$

Catalytic hydrogenation of LXXXIII over a platinum oxide catalyst also gives the diamine in low yield, with aniline and N-benzylaniline as the predominant products. It is of interest that the products represented in equation (12-73) are also obtained by the LAH reduction of 2-anilino-phenylacetonitrile (27).

Reduction of methyl 4-methyl-4-nitropentanoate (LXXXIV) yields the expected amino alcohol (99).

$$CH_3\underset{\overset{|}{NO_2}}{\overset{\overset{|}{CH_3}}{C}}CH_2CH_2COOCH_3 \xrightarrow{LAH} CH_3\underset{\overset{|}{NH_2}}{\overset{\overset{|}{CH_3}}{C}}CH_2CH_2CH_2OH \qquad (12\text{-}74)$$

LXXXIV

12.10.1.b *Nitroolefins.* The LAH reduction of α,β-unsaturated nitro derivatives, as in β-nitrostyrene (LXXXV) results in the formation of the saturated amine in good yield (11,13).

$$C_6H_5CH=CHNO_2 \xrightarrow{LAH} C_6H_5CH_2CH_2NH_2 \qquad (12\text{-}75)$$

LXXXV

This reaction has had wide application in the synthesis of substituted β-phenylethylamines. The LAH reduction of β-nitrostyrenes to β-phenylethylamines is summarized in Table LXXVIII.

As indicated in Table LXXVIII, the synthesis of alkoxy derivatives has had the major emphasis due to the relationship between these compounds and the cactus alkaloids, specifically mescaline. The latter, β-(3,4,5-trimethoxyphenyl)ethylamine (LXXXVI), has previously been synthesized in two steps with an overall yield of 25% according to the following scheme (100):

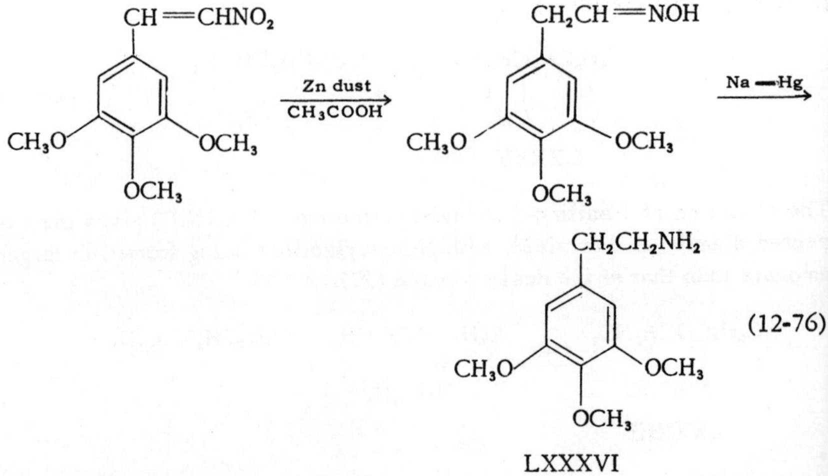

LXXXVI

TABLE LXXVIII

LAH Reduction of β-Nitrostyrenes to β-Phenylethylamines

Formula	β-Nitrostyrene	Product	% Yield	Ref.
$C_8H_7NO_2$	β-Nitrostyrene	β-Phenylethylamine	60	1
$C_9H_6BrNO_4$	3,4-Methylenedioxy-5-bromo-β-nitrostyrene	β-(3,4-Methylenedioxy-5-bromophenyl)ethylamine	40[2,3]	4
$C_9H_7NO_4$	3,4-Methylenedioxy-β-nitrostyrene	β-(3,4-Methylenedioxyphenyl)ethylamine	70[3,5]	4
	3,4-Methylenedioxy-β-nitrostyrene	β-(3,4-Methylenedioxyphenyl)ethylamine	86[3]	4
	3,4-Methylenedioxy-β-nitrostyrene	β-(3,4-Methylenedioxyphenyl)ethylamine	60[6]	7, 8
$C_9H_9NO_3$	4-Methoxy-β-nitrostyrene	β-(4-Methoxyphenyl)ethylamine	53	9
$C_9H_9NO_4$	2-Hydroxy-3-methoxy-β-nitrostyrene	β-(2-Hydroxy-3-methoxyphenyl)ethylamine	81[10]	11
	3-Hydroxy-4-methoxy-β-nitrostyrene	β-(3-Hydroxy-4-methoxyphenyl)ethylamine	68[10]	11
	4-Hydroxy-3-methoxy-β-nitrostyrene	β-(4-Hydroxy-3-methoxyphenyl)ethylamine	80[10]	11
$C_{10}H_9NO_5$	3-Methoxy-4,5-methylenedioxy-β-nitrostyrene	β-(3-Methoxy-4,5-methylenedioxyphenyl)ethylamine	49	12
$C_{10}H_{11}NO_4$	2,3-Dimethoxy-β-nitrostyrene	β-(2,3-Dimethoxyphenyl)ethylamine	....	13
	2,5-Dimethoxy-β-nitrostyrene	β-(2,5-Dimethoxyphenyl)ethylamine	87	13
$C_{11}H_{13}NO_5$	2,3,4-Trimethoxy-β-nitrostyrene	β-(2,3,4-Trimethoxyphenyl)ethylamine	86[10]	4
	3,4,5-Trimethoxy-β-nitrostyrene	β-(3,4,5-Trimethoxyphenyl)ethylamine	77[10]	4
	3,4,5-Trimethoxy-β-nitrostyrene	β-(3,4,5-Trimethoxyphenyl)ethylamine	86[10]	14
	3,4,5-Trimethoxy-β-nitrostyrene	β-(3,4,5-Trimethoxyphenyl)ethylamine	74[3]	15
$C_{16}H_{15}NO_4$	2-Benzyloxy-3-methoxy-β-nitrostyrene	β-(2-Benzyloxy-3-methoxyphenyl)ethylamine	75	16
	4-Benzyloxy-3-methoxy-β-nitrostyrene	β-(4-Benzyloxy-3-methoxyphenyl)ethylamine	74[17]	18

References — Table LXXVIII

[1]R. F. Nystrom and W. G. Brown, *J. Am. Chem. Soc.*, 70, 3738 (1948).
[2]Reflux 2 hours with calculated amount of ethereal LAH.
[3]Isolated as hydrochloride.
[4]M. Erne and F. Ramirez, *Helv. Chim. Acta*, 33, 912 (1950).
[5]Reflux 10 hours with excess ethereal LAH.
[6]Dioxane used as solvent for nitrostyrene.
[7]W. J. Gensler and C. M. Samour, *J. Am. Chem. Soc.*, 72, 3318 (1950).
[8]W. J. Gensler and C. M. Samour, *ibid.*, 73, 5555 (1951).
[9]J. Bernstein, H. L. Yale, K. Losee, M. Holsing, J. Martins, and W. A. Lott, *ibid.*, 73, 906 (1951).
[10]Isolated as picrate.
[11]F. A. Ramirez and A. Burger, *J. Am. Chem. Soc.*, 72, 2781 (1950).
[12]K. E. Hamlin and A. W. Weston, *ibid.*, 71, 2210 (1949).
[13]R. I. T. Cromartie and J. Harley-Mason, *J. Chem. Soc.*, 1952, 2525.
[14]F. Benington and R. D. Morin, *J. Am. Chem. Soc.*, 73, 1353 (1951).
[15]A. Dornow and G. Petsch, *Arch. pharm.*, 284, 160 (1951).
[16]D. Ginsburg, *Bull. soc. chim. France*, [5] 17, 510 (1950).
[17]Reduction carried out in tetrahydrofuran.
[18]J. Finkelstein, *J. Am. Chem. Soc.*, 73, 550 (1951).

The one step reduction with LAH is reported to proceed in 74–86% yield (101–103). The major disadvantage in the LAH reduction of β-nitrostyrenes is the long reaction time necessitated by the low ether solubility of many of the starting materials.

The LAH reduction of β-methyl-β-nitrostyrenes also yields the saturated amines. Thus, 1-phenyl-2-nitro-1-propene is reduced to β-phenylisopropylamine, isolated in 89% yield as the picrate (101), and 1-(3,4-dimethoxyphenyl)-2-nitro-1-propene yields β-(3,4-dimethoxyphenyl)isopropylamine (104). The reduction of α-nitrostilbene (LXXXVII) yields 1,2-diphenylethylamine (96).

$$C_6H_5CH = CC_6H_5 \quad \xrightarrow[74\%]{LAH} \quad C_6H_5CH_2CHC_6H_5 \qquad (12\text{-}77)$$
$$\underset{NO_2}{|} \qquad\qquad\qquad \underset{NH_2}{|}$$

LXXXVII

The LAH reduction of heterocyclic nitroolefins in the thiophene and thiazole series to the heterocyclic alkylamines is summarized in Table LXXIX.

In the alicyclic series, Ashley and Davis (105) reported that the LAH reduction of 3-cyclohexyl-2-nitro-2-propen-1-ol (LXXXVIII) gives the saturated amino alcohol.

$$(12\text{-}78)$$

LXXXVIII

TABLE LXXIX

LAH Reduction of Heterocyclic Nitroolefins

	Nitroolefin	Product	% Yield
	Thienyl Nitroolefins[1]		
$C_6H_4ClNO_2S$	5-Chloro-2-(ω-nitrovinyl)thiophene	β-(5-Chloro-2-thienyl)ethylamine	50
$C_6H_5NO_2S$	2-(ω-Nitrovinyl)thiophene	β-(2-Thienyl)ethylamine	63
$C_7H_7NO_2S$	5-Methyl-2-(ω-nitrovinyl)thiophene	β-(5-Methyl-2-thienyl)ethylamine	67
	1-(2-Thienyl)-2-nitro-1-propene	β-(2-Thienyl)isopropylamine	65
$C_8H_9NO_2S$	5-Ethyl-2-(ω-nitrovinyl)thiophene	β-(5-Ethyl-2-thienyl)ethylamine	70
	1-(2-Thienyl)-2-nitro-1-butene	1-(2-Thienyl)-2-aminobutane	69
$C_9H_{11}NO_2S$	5-Propyl-2-(ω-nitrovinyl)thiophene	β-(5-Propyl-2-thienyl)ethylamine	70
	Thiazolyl Nitroolefins[2]		
$C_6H_6N_2O_2S$	1-(4-Thiazolyl)-2-nitro-1-propene	β-(4-Thiazolyl)isopropylamine	30[3]
	1-(5-Thiazolyl)-2-nitro-1-propene	β-(5-Thiazolyl)isopropylamine	31[4]

[1] R. T. Gilsdorf and F. F. Nord, J. Org. Chem., 15, 807 (1950).
[2] M. Erne, F. Ramirez, and A. Burger, Helv. Chim. Acta, 34, 143 (1951).
[3] Isolated as dipicrate.
[4] Isolated as dihydrobromide.

Gilsdorf and Nord (98) have carried out a detailed study of the reverse addition of LAH to 1-phenyl-2-nitro-1-propene (LXXXIX) and have isolated a variety of products by varying the reaction temperature and the ratio of reactants. The stepwise course of the reduction has been demonstrated by the isolation of the amine, hydroxylamine, oxime and nitroparaffin. Addition of an amount of LAH, calculated as sufficient for the reduction of the nitro group, to an ethereal solution of LXXXIX maintained at -30 to $-40°$, followed by hydrolysis with an aqueous sodium potassium tartrate solution affords a 44% yield of β-phenylisopropylamine (XC) and a 23% yield of N-(β-phenylisopropyl)hydroxylamine (XCI).

$$
\underset{\text{LXXXIX}}{\underset{|}{\overset{}{C_6H_5CH}} \overset{}{=\!=} \underset{NO_2}{\overset{}{CCH_3}}} \rightarrow \underset{XC}{\underset{NH_2}{\overset{}{C_6H_5CH_2CHCH_3}}} + \underset{XCI}{\underset{NHOH}{\overset{}{C_6H_5CH_2CHCH_3}}} \qquad (12\text{-}79)
$$

The hydroxylamine is convertible to the amine by a further reduction with LAH. When the reverse addition at -30 to $-40°$ is carried out with an amount of LAH calculated as one-half of that necessary for reduction of the nitro group, in addition to an 8% yield of the amine and 34% of the hydroxylamine, phenylacetoxime (XCII) is isolated in 16% yield.

$$
\underset{\text{LXXXIX}}{\underset{NO_2}{\overset{}{C_6H_5CH}} \overset{}{=\!=} CCH_3} \rightarrow \underset{XC}{\underset{NH_2}{\overset{}{C_6H_5CH_2CHCH_3}}} +
$$

$$
\underset{XCI}{\underset{NHOH}{\overset{}{C_6H_5CH_2CHCH_3}}} + \underset{XCII}{\underset{NOH}{\overset{}{C_6H_5CH_2CCH_3}}} \qquad (12\text{-}80)
$$

The mixture of XCI and XCII was incorrectly described as benzyl methyl ketimine in a preliminary communication (106). When the reverse addition at $-40°$ to $-50°$ is carried out with a slight excess of LAH over the amount required for the reduction of the double bond, hydrolysis with sodium potassium tartrate gives the nitroparaffin, 1-phenyl-2-nitropropane (XCIII), which is further reducible to the saturated amine by a normal LAH reduction.

$$
\underset{\text{LXXXIX}}{\underset{NO_2}{\overset{}{C_6H_5CH}} \overset{}{=\!=} CCH_3} \rightarrow \underset{XCIII}{\underset{NO_2}{\overset{}{C_6H_5CH_2CHCH_3}}} \rightarrow \underset{XC}{\underset{NH_2}{\overset{}{C_6H_5CH_2CHCH_3}}} \qquad (12\text{-}81)
$$

The overall course of the reduction has been outlined as in Flow Sheet IV wherein all hydrolyses are carried out with aqueous sodium potassium tartrate.

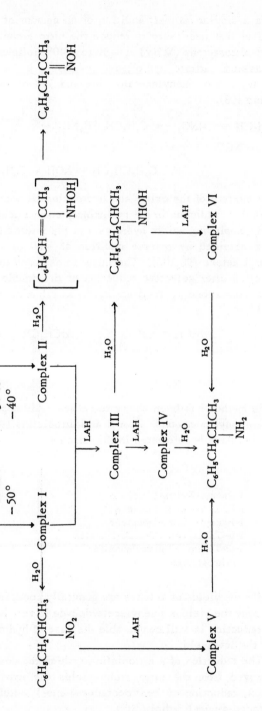

FLOW SHEET IV

In a similar manner, addition of an amount of LAH calculated as one-half of that necessary to reduce the nitro group, to an ethereal solution of β-nitrostyrene (XCIV) at -30 to $-40°$, followed by an aqueous sodium potassium tartrate hydrolysis, results in a 6% yield of β-phenylethylamine, 16% of phenylacetaldoxime and 33% of N-(β-phenylethyl)hydroxylamine (98).

$$C_6H_5CH \!=\! CHNO_2 \;\rightarrow\; C_6H_5CH_2CH_2NH_2 \;+$$

XCIV

$$C_6H_5CH_2CH \!=\! NOH \;+\; C_6H_5CH_2CH_2NHOH \qquad (12\text{-}82)$$

The mixture of the oxime and hydroxylamine was erroneously reported as phenylacetaldimine in the preliminary communication (106).

By employing acidic hydrolysis of the intermediate organometallic complex obtained by reverse addition at -40 to $-50°$, the product is an α-aryl ketone (98,106). The latter is assumed to arise by a modified Nef reaction after selective reduction of the double bond of the nitroolefin. The corresponding N-(β-aralkyl)hydroxylamine is also obtained in low yield.

$$\underset{\text{XCV}}{\overset{\displaystyle ArCH \!=\! CR}{\underset{\displaystyle NO_2}{|}}} \quad \xrightarrow[\text{2. HCl}]{\text{1. LAH}} \quad \overset{\displaystyle ArCH_2CR}{\underset{\displaystyle O}{\|}} \;+\; \underset{\displaystyle NHOH}{\overset{\displaystyle ArCH_2CHR}{|}} \qquad (12\text{-}83)$$

This method has been shown to be generally applicable for the synthesis of carbonyl compounds from β-arylnitroolefins (98). The following nitroolefins have been treated in this manner:

	% Carbonyl Compound
1-Phenyl-2-nitro-1-propene	29
1-Phenyl-2-nitro-1-butene	62
1-Phenyl-2-nitro-1-pentene	52
1-o-Chlorophenyl-2-nitro-1-pentene	62
1-(2-Thienyl)-2-nitro-1-propene	43
β-Nitrostyrene	0-5

While the yields of ketones are generally good, in the reduction of β-nitrostyrene the yield of phenylacetaldehyde is very low. While the mechanism of reduction is still comparable the ease of hydrolysis may be responsible for the low yield.

The reduction of a nitroolefin in which the double bond is considerably removed from the nitro group yields the expected unsaturated amine. Thus, reduction of 2-nitrooctadec-4-ene-1,3-diol (XCVI) yields 2-aminooctadec-4-ene-1,3-diol (107).

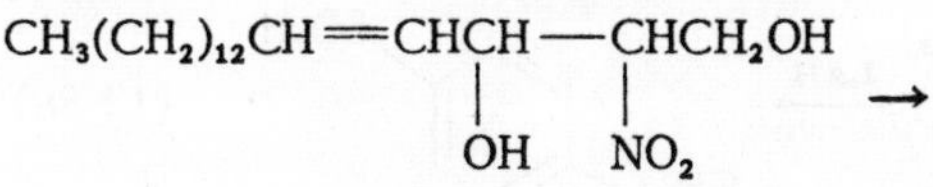

$$CH_3(CH_2)_{12}CH \!=\! CHCH \!-\! CHCH_2OH$$

with OH and NO_2 substituents on the respective carbons, →

XCVI

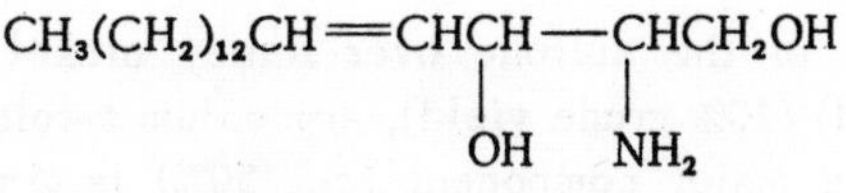

$$CH_3(CH_2)_{12}CH \!=\! CHCH \!-\! CHCH_2OH \qquad (12\text{-}84)$$

with OH and NH_2 substituents.

The reduction of the unconjugated 1-nitromethylcyclohexane (XCVII) unexpectedly yields the saturated aminomethylcyclohexane (28,42).

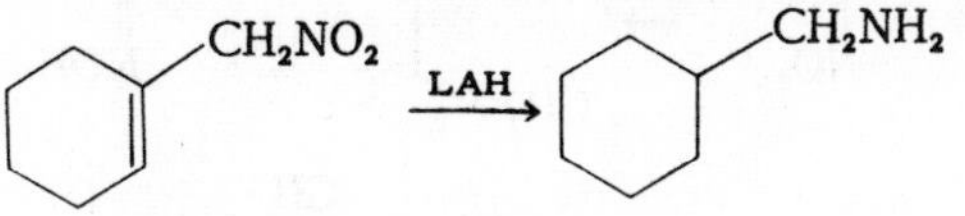

$$\qquad (12\text{-}85)$$

XCVII

The reduction of the double bond in this reaction is attributed to the conjugation existing in the tautomeric form (XCVIII) (28):

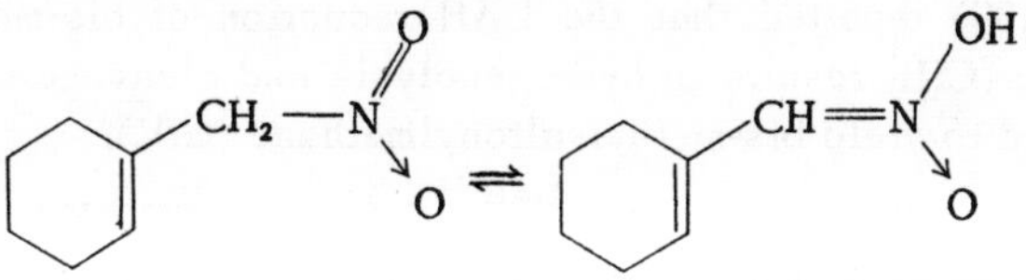

$$\qquad (12\text{-}86)$$

XCVIII

12.10.1.c Reductive Cleavage. Kharasch and Cameron (108) reported that 1-nitroethyl *p*-tolyl sulfide (XCIX) yields the oxime (C) on LAH reduction. The odor of *p*-thiocresol is detected in the reaction mixture.

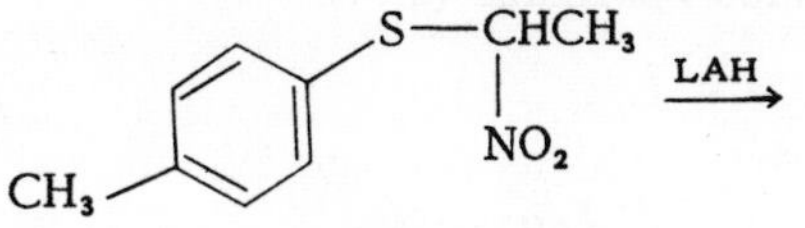

XCIX

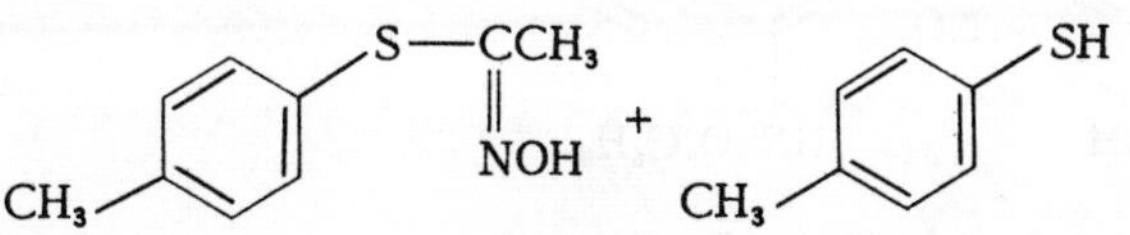

$$+ \qquad (12\text{-}87)$$

C

The reactions shown in equations (12-80), (12-82), and (12-87) are the only recorded instances of the LAH reduction of a nitro compound to an oxime. Catalytic hydrogenation of XCIX over Raney nickel or Adam's catalyst results in no uptake of hydrogen in 48 hours.

The LAH reduction of 1-nitroethyl *p*-tolyl sulfone (CI) results in cleavage of the carbon-sulfur bond to give an 80% crude yield of *p*-toluenesulfinic acid (108).

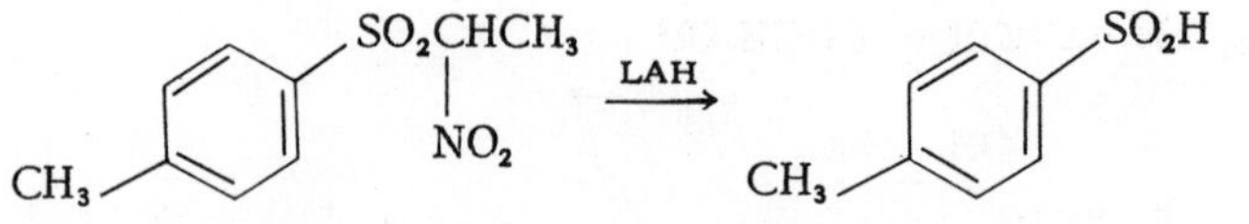

$$\text{(structure)} \xrightarrow{\text{LAH}} \text{(structure)} \qquad (12\text{-}88)$$

Reduction of the sulfone over Raney nickel yields the corresponding oxime (CII) (10% crude yield), ammonium p-toluenesulfinate (28%) and an oil, whose major component (*ca.* 50%) is p-toluenesulfinic acid, contaminated with some p-toluenesulfonic acid (108).

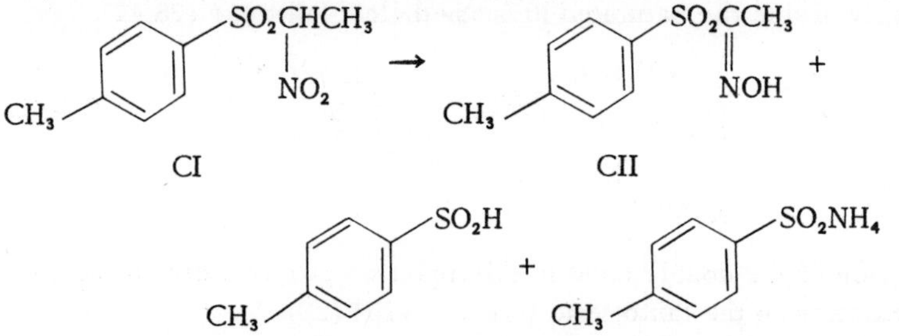

$$\text{(structure CI)} \rightarrow \text{(structure CII)} +$$

CI   CII

$$\text{(structure)} + \text{(structure)} \qquad (12\text{-}89)$$

Backer (109) reported that the LAH reduction of bis-methylsulfonyl-nitromethane (CIII) results in hydrogenolysis and cleavage of the carbon-nitrogen bond to yield bis-methylsulfonylmethane (CIV).

$$CH_3SO_2CHSO_2CH_3 \xrightarrow{\text{LAH}} CH_3SO_2CH_2SO_2CH_3$$
$$\underset{NO_2}{|} \qquad\qquad (12\text{-}90)$$

CIII   CIV

Adams and Moje (110) reported a similar cleavage in the LAH reduction of bis-(1,4-naphthalenedibenzenesulfonamido-2)nitromethane (CV) to bis-(1,4-naphthalenedibenzenesulfonamido-2)methane (CVI).

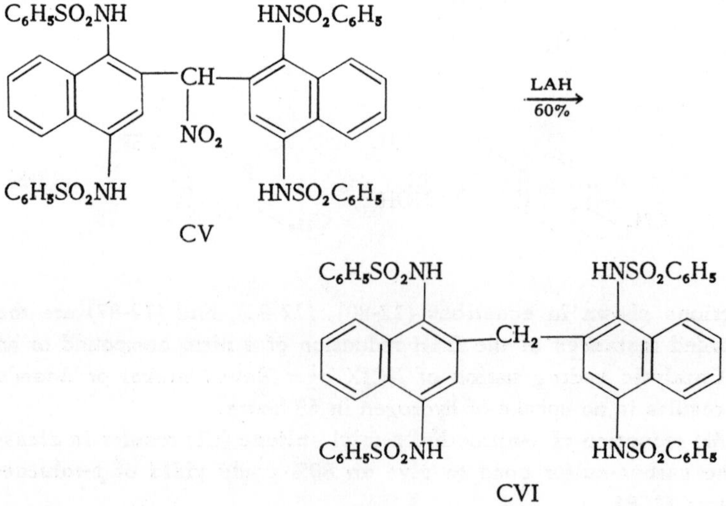

$C_6H_5SO_2NH$ $HNSO_2C_6H_5$

$\xrightarrow[60\%]{\text{LAH}}$

$C_6H_5SO_2NH$ $HNSO_2C_6H_5$

CV

$C_6H_5SO_2NH$ $HNSO_2C_6H_5$

$$(12\text{-}91)$$

$C_6H_5SO_2NH$ $HNSO_2C_6H_5$

CVI

The LAH reduction of 1-anilino-1-phenyl-2-nitroethane to N-benzyl-aniline has been shown in equation (12-73).

12.10.2 Reductions with Aluminum Hydride

The milder reducing action of the aluminum hydride-aluminum chloride addition compound, as compared with LAH, permits the reduction of nitro-methane to methylamine in 79% yield (57). The proposed reaction mech-anism involves a two-stage addition of the hydride:

$$
-\underset{\underset{O^{\ominus}}{\overset{\oplus}{N}}}{\overset{O}{\diagup}} \xrightarrow{+\,alH} -\underset{\underset{OH}{N}}{\overset{Oal}{\diagup}} \xrightarrow{-\,alH} -N{=}O \xrightarrow{+\,alH}
$$

$$
-NH-Oal \xrightarrow{+\,alH} -NH_2 \qquad (12\text{-}92)
$$

12.10.3 Reactions with Sodium Borohydride

The selective reduction of aliphatic nitroketones and nitroaldehydes to nitrocarbonyls can be carried out with sodium borohydride in aqueous methanol in neutral, basic or acidic media (111). The following nitro-carbonyl compounds have been subjected to this treatment: 4-nitro-1-butanal, 4-nitro-1-pentanal, 4-nitro-4-methyl-1-pentanal, 4,4-dinitro-1-pentanal, 5-nitro-2-pentanone, 5-nitro-2-hexanone, 5-nitro-5-methyl-2-hexanone, 5,5-dinitro-2-pentanone, 5,5-dinitro-2-hexanone.

12.11 AROMATIC NITRO COMPOUNDS

12.11.1 Reductions with Lithium Aluminum Hydride
The reduction of aromatic nitro compounds with LAH usually yields azo derivatives (11-13) according to the overall equation:

$$
2\ ArNO_2 + 2\ LiAlH_4 \longrightarrow Ar{-}N{=}N{-}Ar + 2\ LiAlO_2 + 4\ H_2
$$

$$(12\text{-}93)$$

Nystrom and Brown (13) observed that the immediate appearance of the azo color upon adding an aromatic nitro compound to an LAH solution at room temperature constitutes a simple test for the nitro group. This ob-servation has been made the basis of a qualitative test for aromatic nitro and nitroso compounds by Gilman and Goreau (88) and Nelson and Las-kowski (112), as discussed in Section 5.3.

The reduction of various aromatic nitro compounds to azo compounds is summarized in Table LXXX. Brown (113) has observed that mixtures of LAH and certain aromatic nitro compounds darken when exposed to air with subsequent reduction in the yield of azo compound.

Kvasnicka (114), in a short review on the reduction of organic com-pounds with complex borohydrides, compared LAH and sodium borohydride and indicated that m-nitrobenzaldehyde (CVII) is reduced with LAH to m-aminobenzyl alcohol. However, the source of this reference was not indicated nor can any reference to such a reduction be found. The reduc-

TABLE LXXX

LAH Reduction of Aromatic Nitro to Azo Compounds

Nitro Compound	Product	% Yield	Ref.
C6H4BrNO2 p-Nitrobromobenzene	4,4'-Dibromoazobenzene	88	1,2
C6H5NO2 Nitrobenzene	Azobenzene	84	1,2
C7H5NO3 m-Nitrobenzaldehyde	m,m'-Azobenzyl alcohol	28.5	3
C7H7NO2 p-Nitrotoluene	p-Azotoluene p-Toluidine[5]	65 } 10 }	4
C8H8N2O3 m-Nitroacetophenone oxime		:::	6
C9H11NO2 Nitromesitylene	Azomesitylene	71	1,2
C11H14N2O5 Ethyl DL-threo-β-p-nitrophenylserinate	Red azo compounds[7]	:::	8
Ethyl D- and L- threo-β-p-nitrophenylserinate	Red azo compounds[7]	:::	8
C12H8N2O4 2,2'-Dinitrodiphenyl	Benzo[c]cinnoline	92	9
		90	10
C17H21NO4 (-)-Pulegyl p-nitrobenzoate	(-)-Pulegol Solid azo alcohol[6]	35 } ::: }	11

[1] R. F. Nystrom and W. G. Brown, J. Am. Chem. Soc., 70, 3738 (1948).
[2] H. I. Schlesinger and A. E. Finholt, U. S. Pat. 2,576,311 (November 27, 1951).
[3] N. G. Gaylord and J. A. Snyder, Rec. trav. chim., 72, 1007 (1953).
[4] E. Wiberg and A. Jahn, Z. Naturforsch., 7b, 580 (1952).
[5] Product not isolated but color of reaction mixture indicated conversion of nitro to azo group.
[6] C. R. Walter, Jr., J. Am. Chem. Soc., 74, 5185 (1952).
[7] Product not further identified.
[8] G. Carrara, E. Pace, and G. Cristiani, J. Am. Chem. Soc., 74, 4949 (1952).
[9] G. M. Badger, J. H. Seidler, and B. Thomson, J. Chem. Soc., 1951, 3207.
[10] R. F. Nystrom, unpublished work, through W. G. Brown, in Organic Reactions, Vol. VI, p. 469.
[11] A. K. Macbeth and J. S. Shannon, J. Chem. Soc., 1952, 4748.

tion of CVII with an ethereal solution of LAH actually yields the expected m,m'-azobenzyl alcohol (115).

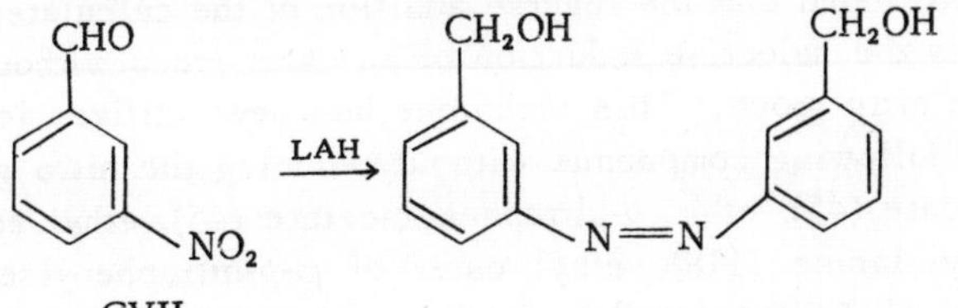

$$(12\text{-}94)$$

CVII

Barton and Rosenfelder (116) carried out the LAH reduction of the mixture of p-nitrobenzoates obtained by the reaction of isodehydrocholesteryl p-nitrobenzoate and mercuric acetate. Since the steroidal moiety was the focus of attention in this investigation the fate of the aromatic nitro group was not reported. Similarly, the reduction of (−)-pulegyl p-nitrobenzoate yields (−)-pulegol and a solid azo alcohol which was not further identified since the subject of the investigation was the pulegol (117). Based on the expected behavior of the nitro group the product in both cases should be the p,p'-azobenzyl alcohol.

Although LAH reduction of nitro compounds according to equation (12-93) involves the participation of two molecules of such compounds, in the case of 2,2′-dinitrodiphenyl (CVIII) formation of the azo group is intramolecular (13,85).

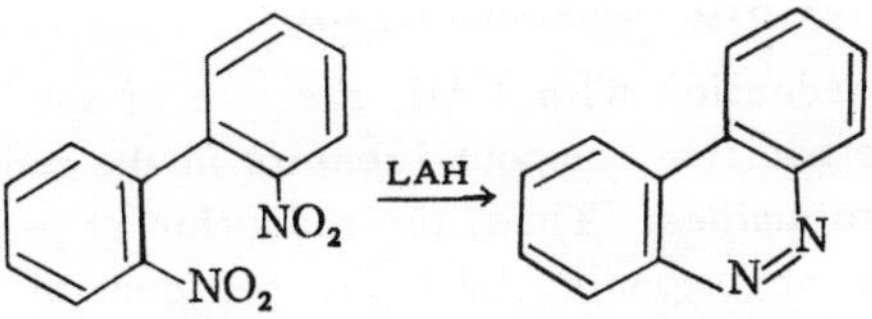

$$(12\text{-}95)$$

CVIII

Ried and Müller (68) reported that the reduction of 4,4′-dinitroazobenzene (CIX) with LAH in a tetrahydrofuran-ether mixture gives 55% of 4,4′-diaminoazobenzene with no evidence of polyazo compounds.

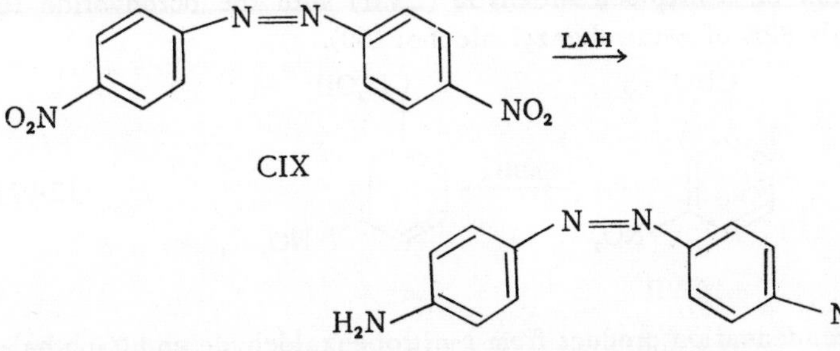

CIX

$$(12\text{-}96)$$

Wiberg and Jahn (57) have shown that the LAH reduction of p-nitrotoluene yields 65% of p-azotoluene and 10% of p-toluidine. This is the only other case of the formation of an amine in the LAH reduction of an aromatic nitro compound.

Felkin (45) found that the inverse addition of the calculated amount of LAH permits the selective reduction of an ester group without attacking an aromatic nitro group. This technique has been utilized in the reduction of the following compounds without reducing the nitro group: ethyl *p*-nitrobenzoate (45), ethyl *p*-nitrophenylacetate (45), ethyl ester of DL-*p*-nitrophenylalanine (118), ethyl ester of β-*p*-nitrophenylserine (119), ethyl ester of DL-*erythro*-β-*p*-nitrophenylserine (120), ethyl ester of D-*erythro*-β-*p*-nitrophenylserine (120), ethyl ester of L-*erythro*-β-*p*-nitrophenylserine (120), ethyl ester of N-dichloroacetyl-O-acetyl-*p*-nitrophenylserine (121), *trans*-2-methyl-4-carbethoxy-5-*p*-nitrophenyloxazoline (122), *trans*-2-dichloromethyl-4-carbethoxy-5-*p*-nitrophenyloxazoline (122), *trans*-2-phenyl-4-carbethoxy-5-*p*-nitrophenyloxazoline (122), α-acetamido-*p*-nitrocinnamaldehyde (123).

Carrara, Pace, and Cristiani (120) reported that the selective reduction of the ethyl ester of *erythro*-β-*p*-nitrophenylserine with LAH yields *erythro*-*p*-nitrophenyl-2-amino-1,3-propanediol in excellent yield. Attempts to apply the same selective reduction to the ethyl ester of *threo*-DL-β-*p*-nitrophenylserine and its optical antipodes, under a variety of conditions have failed to yield the expected diols but have given red oils whose reactions are characteristic of azo compounds.

12.11.2   Reductions with Aluminum Hydride

In contrast to reduction with LAH, the use of the aluminum hydride-aluminum chloride addition compound results in the reduction of aromatic nitro compounds to amines. Thus, the reduction of *p*-nitrotoluene yields 72% of *p*-toluidine accompanied by a few per cent of the azo compound (57). The proposed mechanism of reduction is the same as in the case of the aliphatic compounds, equation (12-92).

12.11.3   Reactions with Sodium Borohydride

The aromatic nitro group is resistant to attack by sodium borohydride. Thus, reduction of *m*-nitrobenzaldehyde (CVII) with the borohydride in methanol yields 82% of *m*-nitrobenzyl alcohol (60).

$$(12\text{-}97)$$

The aldol condensation product from *p*-nitrobenzaldehyde and α-phthalimidoacetaldehyde (CX) is reduced with sodium borohydride in methanol to the corresponding propanediol without attacking the aromatic nitro group (124).

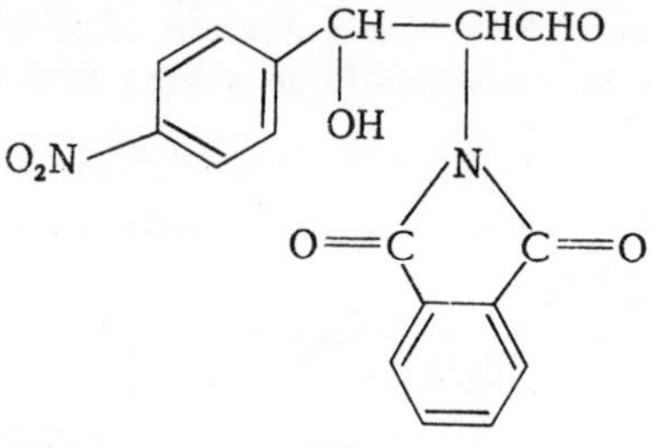

CX

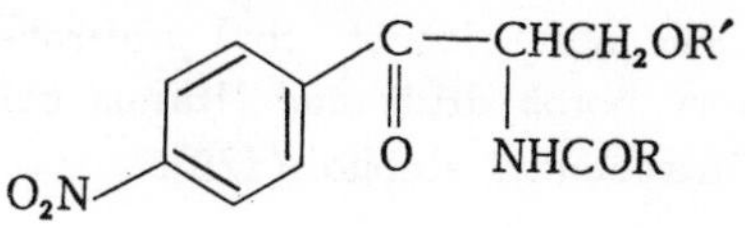

CXI

Similarly, α-acylamido-β-hydroxy- and acetoxy-p-nitropropiophenones (CXI) are reduced to 1-p-nitrophenyl-2-acylamido-1,3-propanediols (125).

12.11.4 Reactions with Potassium Borohydride

The non-reduction of the nitro group in CX (124,126) and CXI (125) is also observed with the use of potassium borohydride in aqueous methanol. The reduction of ethyl p-nitrobenzoate with a mixture of potassium borohydride and lithium chloride is discussed in Section 12.11.5.

12.11.5 Reductions with Lithium Borohydride

When nitrobenzene is refluxed for 18 hours in an ether-tetrahydrofuran mixture with excess lithium borohydride, 30% of nitrobenzene is recovered as well as 22% of aniline and 30% of an intractable dark red oil (127). The reduction of m-nitroacetophenone (CXII) with lithium borohydride in tetrahydrofuran, with ice cooling, yields 1-(m-nitrophenyl)ethanol (127).

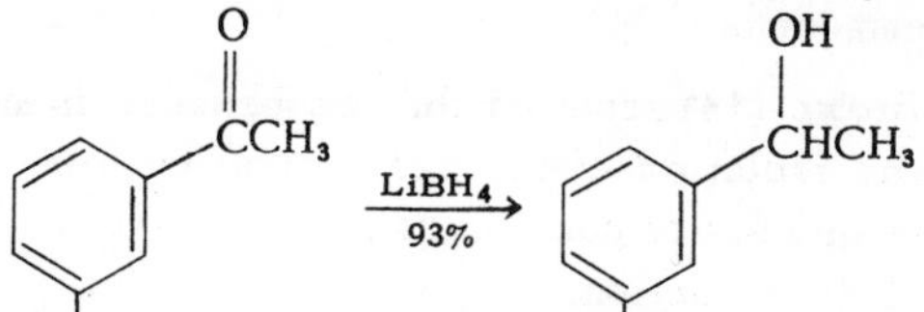

(12-98)

CXII

The reduction of p-nitrobenzyl chloride (CXIII) and 5-chloromethyl-1-nitronaphthalene (CXIV) with lithium hydride and a little lithium borohydride in tetrahydrofuran yields 72% of p-nitrotoluene and 67% of 5-methyl-1-nitronaphthalene, respectively. In both cases 8-20% of the azo compound accompanies the nitro derivative (65).

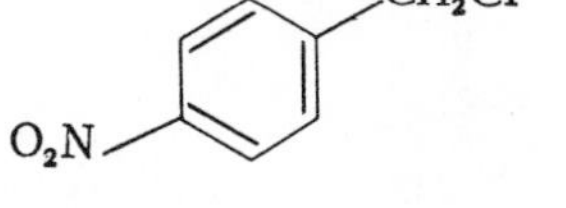

CXIII

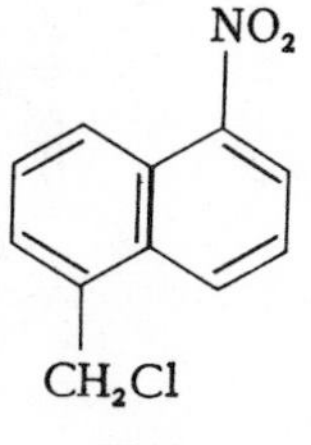

CXIV

The reduction of ethyl p-nitrobenzoate (CXV) with a mixture of potassium borohydride and lithium chloride in tetrahydrofuran yields 86% of p-nitrobenzyl alcohol (128).

CXV   (12-99)

12.12 HYDROXYLAMINE DERIVATIVES

The only reported LAH reduction of a hydroxylamine derivative is that of the conversion of N-(β-phenylisopropyl)hydroxylamine (CXVI) to β-phenylisopropylamine (98).

$$\underset{\underset{\text{CXVI}}{\text{NHOH}}}{C_6H_5CH_2CHCH_3} \xrightarrow[37\%]{\text{LAH}} \underset{\text{NH}_2}{C_6H_5CH_2CHCH_3} \qquad (12\text{-}100)$$

12.13 AZO AND AZOXY COMPOUNDS

12.13.1 Azo Compounds

Nystrom and Brown (13) reported that azobenzene is not reduced with LAH at 25°. The isolation of the azo derivative from the reduction of aryl nitro, nitroso and azoxy compounds is indicative of the resistance of the azo group to LAH reduction.

The azo group remains intact in the LAH reduction of 2-methyl-3′-carboxyazobenzene (CXVII) (129), 4,4′-dinitroazobenzene (CXVIII) (68) and pyridine-N-oxide-2-azo-p-dimethylaniline (CXIX) (86).

CXVII   CXVIII

CXIX

Bohlmann (130) has reported that azobenzene (CXX) is reduced with LAH to hydrazobenzene after three days reaction time.

$$C_6H_5N{=}NC_6H_5 \xrightarrow[90\%]{LAH} C_6H_5NHNHC_6H_5 \qquad (12\text{-}101)$$

CXX

By building the azo group into an aromatic system it becomes reducible with LAH. Thus, benzo[c]cinnoline (CXXI) is reduced with LAH, after three hours, to a dihydro derivative whose sensitivity does not permit its isolation. It is identified by its reducing action on a neutral silver salt solution.

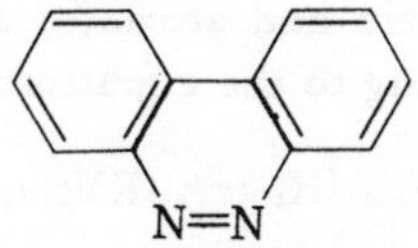

CXXI

Bohlmann has postulated that the reduction of CXX and CXXI proceeds in the polar forms.

Ried and Müller (68) have found that the reaction of C,N,N′-triphenylformazan (CXXII) in an ether-tetrahydrofuran solution with excess LAH results in a reductive cleavage of the nitrogen-nitrogen double bond to ω-phenylbenzamidrazone and aniline.

$$C_6H_5C\begin{cases} {=}N{-}NHC_6H_5 \\ {-}N{=}NC_6H_5 \end{cases} \xrightarrow{LAH} C_6H_5C\begin{cases} {=}N{-}NHC_6H_5 \\ {-}NH_2 \end{cases} + C_6H_5NH_2 \qquad (12\text{-}102)$$

CXXII

12.13.2 Azoxy Compounds

The reduction of azoxybenzene (CXXIII) with LAH yields azobenzene in almost quantitative yield (12,13).

$$C_6H_5\underset{\substack{\downarrow \\ O}}{N}{=}NC_6H_5 \xrightarrow{LAH} C_6H_5N{=}NC_6H_5 \qquad (12\text{-}103)$$

CXXIII

The reduction consumes one-half mole of LAH (13,81) according to the equation:

$$2\ Ar\underset{\substack{\downarrow \\ O}}{N}{=}NAr + LiAlH_4 \rightarrow 2\ ArN{=}NAr + LiAlO_2 + 2\ H_2 \qquad (12\text{-}104)$$

In contrast, azoxycyclohexane is reported to undergo no reduction with LAH in refluxing ether (131). Catalytic hydrogenation over platinum oxide in the presence of methanolic hydrogen chloride yields N,N'-dicyclohexylhydrazine.

The LAH reduction of benzo[c]cinnoline N-oxide (CXXIV) to benzo-[c]cinnoline (85) involves the reduction of a cyclic azoxy compound (equation (12-63).

12.14   AZIDES AND DIAZO COMPOUNDS

12.14.1   Azides

The reduction of aliphatic and aromatic azides with LAH yields primary amines (132), according to the equation:

$$4 \ RN_3 + LiAlH_4 \longrightarrow (RNH)_4AlLi + 4 N_2$$

$$\downarrow H_2O \qquad\qquad (12\text{-}105)$$

$$4 \ RNH_2$$

The reduction of α-azidoketones yields α-aminocarbinols.

$$2 \ RCCH_2N_3 + LiAlH_4 \longrightarrow \left[\begin{array}{c} RCHCH_2NH \\ | \\ O \end{array}\right]_2 AlLi + 2 N_2$$
$$\underset{O}{\|}$$

$$\downarrow H_2O$$

$$\underset{OH}{RCHCH_2NH_2} \qquad\qquad (12\text{-}106)$$

These reactions have been applied to the following azides (132):

Azide	Product	% Yield
β-Phenylethylazide	β-Phenylethylamine	89
α-Naphthylazide	α-Naphthylamine	79
Triazoacetone	1-Amino-2-propanol	48
Phenacyl azide	1-Phenyl-2-aminoethanol	49

12.14.2   Diazo Compounds

12.14.2.a *Reductions with Lithium Aluminum Hydride.* Ried and Müller (68) have reported that LAH reduction of diazoacetic ester (CXXIV) yields 72% of ethanolamine. In addition small amounts of other products are formed, which have not been identified but which are postulated as a mixture of hydrazinoethanol and hydraziethanol.

$$C_2H_5OCOCH_2N_2 \xrightarrow{\text{LAH}} HOCH_2CH_2NH_2 \qquad (12\text{-}107)$$

CXXIV

Gruber and Renner (133) have examined the reduction of various diazoketones. Diazoacetophenone (CXXV) is reduced with LAH to 93% of 1-phenyl-2-aminoethanol and 3% of acetophenone.

$$C_6H_5COCHN_2 \xrightarrow{\text{LAH}} C_6H_5CHCH_2NH_2 + C_6H_5COCH_3 \qquad (12\text{-}108)$$

CXXV |
                         OH

Catalytic hydrogenation over platinum gives 21 to 50% ketone with no aminoalcohol or other products. Reduction over platinum oxide gives 15% ketone, 3% aminoalcohol and 47% of 2,5-diphenylpyrazine resulting from self-condensation of the aminoketone.

LAH reduction of the diazoketone from stearic acid, 1-diazononadecan-2-one (CXXVI), affords 1-aminononadecan-2-ol in 99% yield.

$$CH_3(CH_2)_{16}COCHN_2 \xrightarrow{\text{LAH}} CH_3(CH_2)_{16}CHCH_2NH_2 \qquad (12\text{-}109)$$

CXXVI |
                                      OH

Reduction of the diazoketone from sebacic acid, 1,12-bis-diazododecan-2,11-dione (CXXVII), with LAH by an extraction technique, yields 24% of dodecan-2,11-dione and a resinous residue but no amino alcohol.

$$N_2CHCO(CH_2)_8COCHN_2 \xrightarrow{\text{LAH}} CH_3CO(CH_2)_8COCH_3 \qquad (12\text{-}110)$$

CXXVII

Both CXXVI and CXXVII are catalytically reduced over platinum oxide to the ketone without the isolation of aminoalcohol.

LAH reduction of the diazoketone from veratric acid, 3,4-dimethoxydiazoacetophenone, has given no definite product.

12.14.2.b *Reductions with Sodium Borohydride.* Chaiken and Brown have reported that the reduction of benzene diazonium chloride with sodium borohydride yields a mixture of benzene, aniline and phenylhydrazine (60).

$$C_6H_5N_2Cl \rightarrow C_6H_6 + C_6H_5NH_2 + C_6H_5NHNH_2 \qquad (12\text{-}111)$$

12.15   QUATERNARY AMMONIUM SALTS

12.15.1   Reductions with Lithium Aluminum Hydride

12.15.1.a *Reduction to o-Dihydro Derivatives.* Schmid and Karrer (134) reported that the reduction of quinoline methiodide (CXXVIII) with LAH in ether gives 1-methyl-1,2-dihydroquinoline.

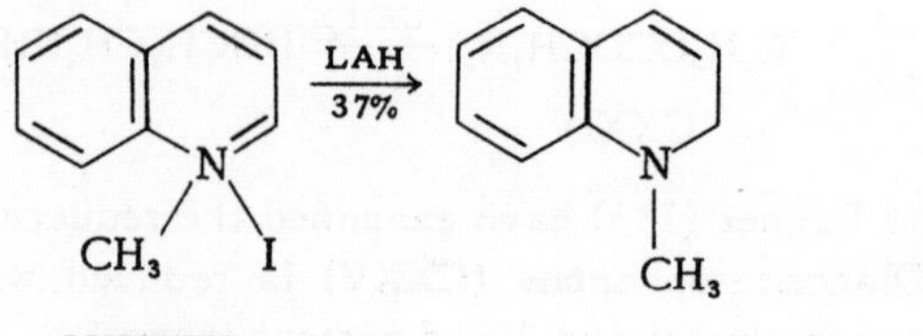

(12-112)

CXXVIII

The reduction of isoquinoline methiodide gives 2-methyl-1,2-dihydroiso-quinoline. Various quaternary salts which have been reduced with LAH to yield the corresponding N-alkyl-1,2-dihydro derivatives are tabulated in Table LXXXI.

TABLE LXXXI

LAH Reduction of Quaternary Salts (134)

Quaternary Salt	% 1,2-Dihydro Compound
Quinoline methiodide	37
Quinoline n-butiodide	43
2-Phenylquinoline methiodide	....
Isoquinoline methiodide	70
Isoquinoline n-butiodide	76
1-Phenylisoquinoline methiodide	66
Phenanthridine methiodide (135)	....
Papavarine methiodide (134,136)	29
Berberine sulfate	100

Karrer (137,138) has shown that the action of LAH is similar to that of the Grignard reagent since organomagnesium compounds react with quaternary salts of cyclic bases to give N-alkyl-o-dihydro derivatives.

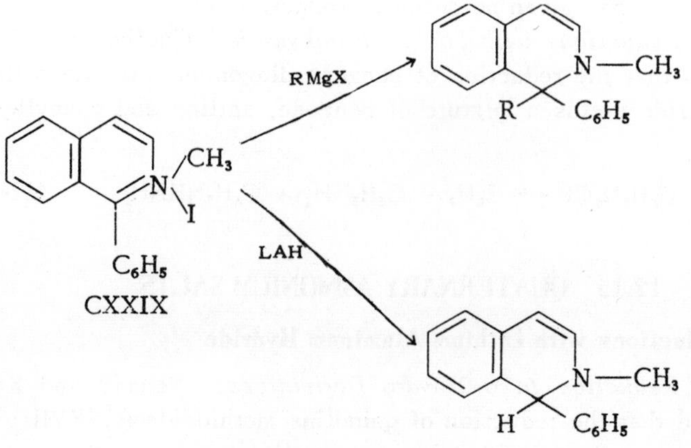

(12-113)

(12-114)

CXXIX

The reduction of berberine sulfate (CXXX) to dihydroanhydroberberine (CXXXI) indicates that the nature of the anion apparently does not affect the reduction.

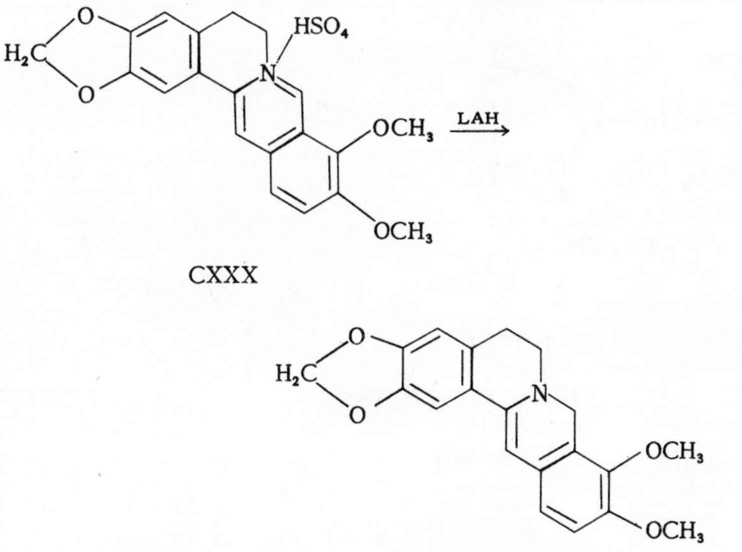

CXXX

(12-115)

CXXXI

Schmid and Karrer (134) have postulated that the reduction proceeds according to the following scheme wherein the unstable ammonium hydride (CXXXII) is stabilized through the mesomeric form (CXXXIII) to a 1,2-dihydro derivative in which the proton migrates from the nitrogen atom to the nucleophilic alpha-carbon atom.

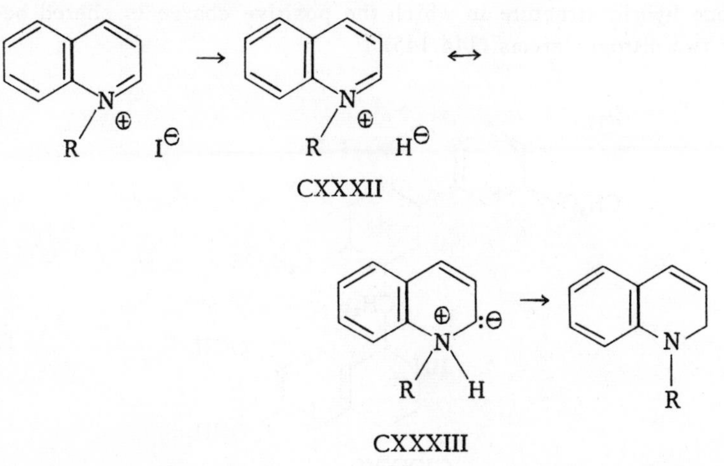

CXXXII

(12-116)

CXXXIII

Karrer and Krishna (138–140) reported that the reaction of LAH in tetrahydrofuran with thiamine (CXXXIV) yields about 14% of dihydrothiamine (CXXXV), m.p. 138° (see Section 12.15.3).

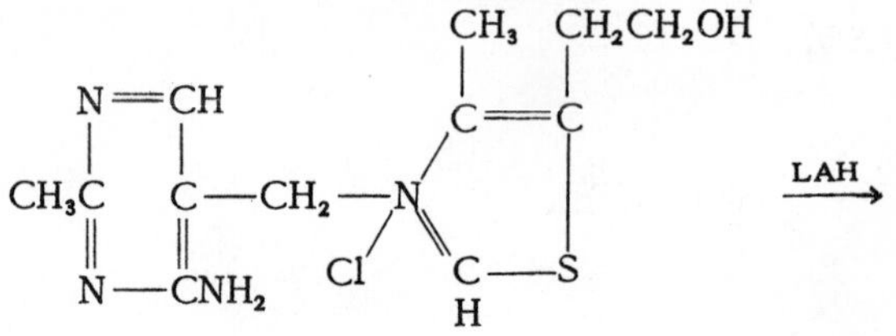

CXXXIV

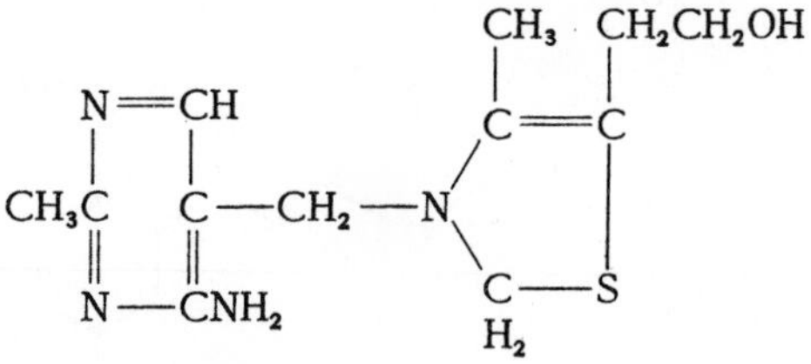

(12-117)

CXXXV

The reduction of CXXXIV with sodium hyposulfite results in cleavage to the thiazole and pyrimidine components (141).

Oxidation of the alkaloid emetine, for which structure CXXXVI has been advanced (142,143), with mild oxidizing agents such as ferric chloride, bromine, iodine or mercuric acetate, yields rubremetinium salts for which Battersby, Openshaw, and Wood have advanced structure CXXXVII, a resonance hybrid structure in which the positive charge is shared between the two nitrogen atoms (144,145).

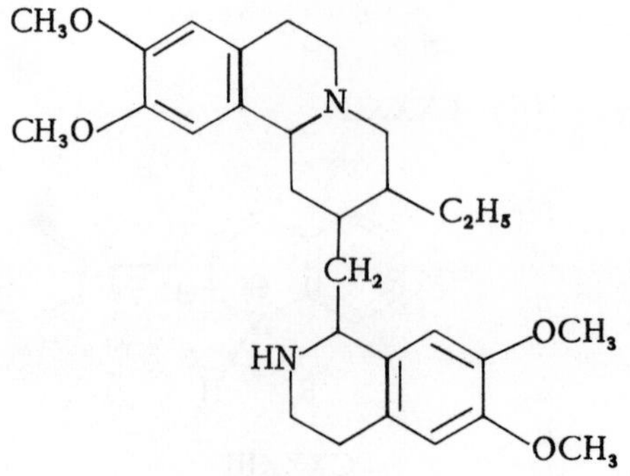

CXXXVI

CXXXVII

Karrer, Eugster, and Rüttner (146) proposed structure CXXXVIII for rubremetinium salts and criticized structure CXXXVII on the grounds that it contains two O-dihydropyridine rings (D and E) which should be highly susceptible to oxidation under the conditions of the preparation by heating emetine with excess bromine or iodine (147). Openshaw and Wood (148) have replied that ring E is part of the 3,4-dihydroisoquinoline system, the stability of which is well known.

Karrer and Rüttner (147) reported that the reduction of rubremetinium bromide (CXXXVIII) with LAH in ether gives a crystalline compound, m.p. 157–158°, which analyzes as a dihydrorubremetine, $C_{29}H_{34}O_4N_2$. By analogy with the reduction of simple isoquinolinium salts the product, o-dihydrodehydroemetine, was assigned structure CXXXIX.

On catalytic reduction the o-dihydrodehydroemetine absorbed one mole of hydrogen to give a mixture of tetrahydrorubremetines, one of which is identical with that obtained by zinc dust reduction of CXXXVIII. This product, m.p. 134°, tetrahydrodehydroemetine, was assigned structure CXL. The second product, m.p. 194°, isotetrahydrodehydroemetine, which has the same ultraviolet absorption spectra as CXL, is strongly laevorotatory, $[\alpha]_D$-380°.

Openshaw and Wood (148) carried out the hydrogenation of rubremetinium chloride in ethanol, in the presence of sodium acetate and platinum oxide. One mole of hydrogen was absorbed and the product consisted of a mixture of two stereoisomeric dihydrorubremetines, the α-isomer having $[\alpha]_D$ -395°, m.p. 198°, and the β-isomer $[\alpha]_D$ +406°, m.p. 202°. The properties of the isomers were considered consistent with structure CXLI, the formation of two isomers being due to the formation of a new asymmetric center in the reduction.

CXXXVII   CXLI   (12-120)

The interpretation of the LAH reduction of the rubremetinium salt has been questioned since reduction of CXXXVIII to CXXXIX introduces a new asymmetric center, but only one crystalline product was isolated. The further hydrogenation of this apparently homogeneous product gave rise to two isomeric tetrahydro compounds, although no new asymmetric center is formed in this reaction. These two compounds have absorption spectra identical with that of α-dihydrorubremetine and one of them, isotetrahydrodehydroemetine, resembles this substance in its melting point and exceptionally high laevorotation as well as its analysis.

In view of the confusing information, Tietz and McEwen (149) set out to repeat the reduction procedures for rubremetinium chloride. Hydrogenation of rubremetinium chloride by the method of Openshaw and Wood (148) resulted in the absorption of two moles of hydrogen, the second mole in a period greater than 100 hours. Two products were obtained from the hydrogenation. One, m.p. 196.2-197.2°, $[\alpha]_D$ -392°, corresponds to α-dihydrorubremetine and to isotetrahydrodehydroemetine, and the second, m.p. 132.0–132.8° corresponds to tetrahydrodehydroemetine. By interrupting the hydrogenation after one mole of hydrogen was absorbed, β-dihydrorubremetine, m.p. 201.5–202.5°, $[\alpha]_D$ +402°, was isolated.

Reduction of rubremetinium chloride, first by treatment with LAH, then catalytically with hydrogen, according to the method of Karrer and Rüttner (147), gave two products. One, m.p. 195.0–195.6°, corresponds to iso-tetrahydrodehydroemetine and is identical with α-dihydrorubremetine. The second product, m.p. 131.4–132.4°, corresponds to tetrahydrode-hydroemetine and is identical with the product from the direct hydrogenation of rubremetinium chloride. Whereas Karrer and Rüttner reported that the product of the LAH reduction, o-dihydrodehydroemetine, took up one mole of hydrogen on catalytic hydrogenation, Tietz and McEwen observed the uptake of two moles of hydrogen and have suggested that o-dihydro-dehydroemetine, m.p. 156.5–157.5°, is the product of an elimination reaction. While structure CXLI is suitable for tetrahydrodehydroemetine and isotetrahydrodehydroemetine, Tietz and McEwen have proposed that Woodward's structure for the rubremetinium cation (CXLII) accommodates the observed reactions.

CXLII

12.15.1.b *Displacement Reactions.* The apparent influence of steric hindrance on the reduction of quaternary salts has been reported in several instances. Kenner and Murray (150) reported that the reduction of strychnine methosulfate (CXLIII) with LAH in tetrahydrofuran gives a 62% yield of strychnine (CXLIV), in which an S_N^2 displacement of the methyl group has occurred.

CXLIII   CXLIV   (12-121)

As discussed in Section 10.2.1.b, Goutarel *et al.* (151) reported that the Hofmann degradation of gelsemine methiodide gives "des-N-methyl-gelsemine" while dihydrogelsemine methiodide gives "des-N-methyldi-hydrogelsemine." Habgood, Marion, and Schwarz (152) and Prelog, Patrick, and Witkop (153) found that the products of the Hofmann degradation are N(a)-methylgelsemine derivatives and not des-N-methyl bases. Goutarel *et al.* (151) reported that the LAH reduction of the methiodide of "des-N-methylgelsemine" in dioxane gives the same product as the LAH reduction of the des-base. Similarly, LAH reduction of "des-N-methyl-dihydrogelsemine" and its methiodide gives the same desoxo derivative. Formulating these reactions in terms of the revised structures:

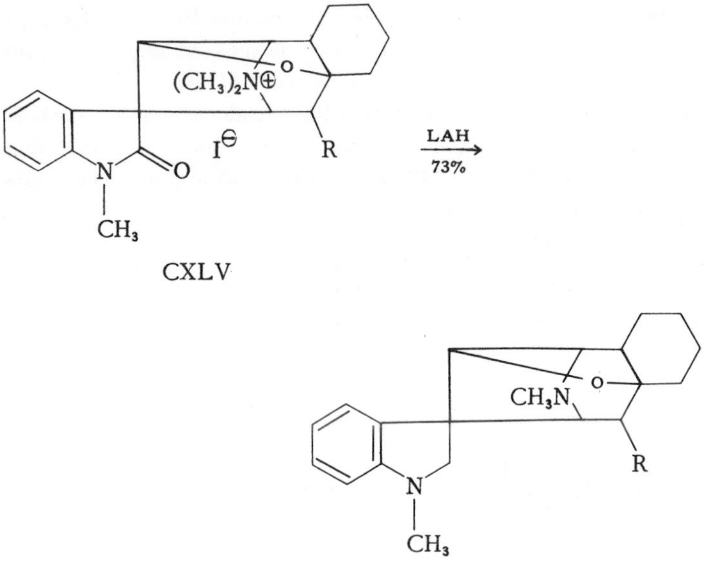

CXLV

(12-122)

R: $=CH_2$ $-CH_3$

Here, as in the reduction of CXLIII a displacement of the methyl group has occurred.

Forbes (154) has recently reported that the LAH reduction of Schiff's base methiodides yields secondary amines. No equations were given but the reaction apparently is represented as in equation (12-123).

$$R-CH=N-R' \xrightarrow{LAH} RCH_2NHR' \qquad (12\text{-}123)$$
with CH$_3$ and I on the nitrogen

Treatment of thebaine (CXLVI) with anhydrous magnesium iodide yields a product postulated as CXLVII. Reduction of CXLVII with LAH proceeds rapidly with the evolution of methane and the formation of a phenolic secondary amine postulated as CXLVIII (155).

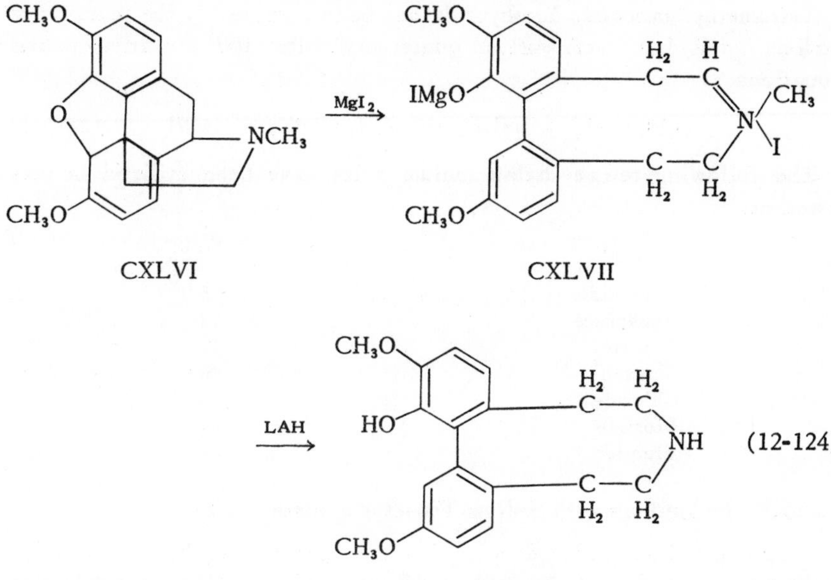

CXLVI   CXLVII

(12-124)

CXLVIII

12.15.2 Reductions with Sodium Borohydride

The reduction of thiamine (CL) with sodium borohydride in a neutral aqueous solution at $0°$ has been reported to give in good yield a product,, m.p. $140°$, which was originally postulated (156) as a dihydrothiamine. However, it was subsequently reported (157) that the reduction yields tetrahydrothiamine, accompanied by a small amount of dihydrothiamine II, m.p. $175°$. The nature of dihydrothiamine II is discussed in Section 12.15.3.

A spectrophotometric method for the assay of cozymase (Coenzyme I, diphosphopyridine nucleotide, DPN) (CXLIX) has been described, involving reduction with sodium borohydride to dihydrocozymase (158).

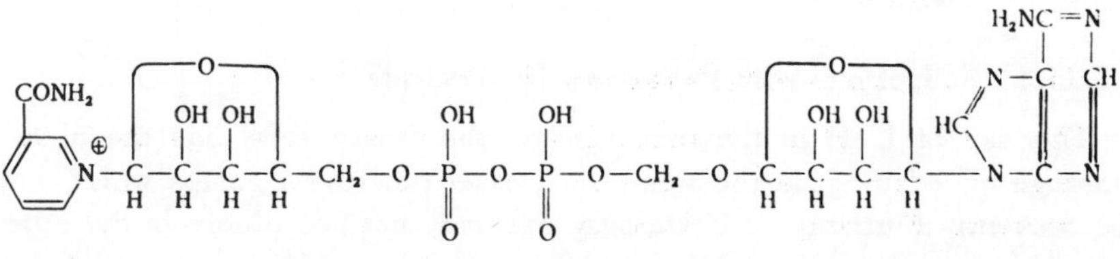

CXLIX

Coenzyme II (triphosphopyridine nucleotide) has similarly been analyzed by borohydride reduction (159).

Tetramethylammonium borohydride has been prepared by the reaction of sodium borohydride with various quaternary salts (160) according to the equations:

$$(CH_3)_4NOH + NaBH_4 \rightarrow (CH_3)_4NBH_4 + NaOH \qquad (12\text{-}125)$$

The following tetramethylammonium salts have been utilized in this reaction:

Salt	% Yield
Hydroxide	93
Phosphate	90
Oxalate	79
Acetate	86
Chloride	76
Bromide	....
Fluoride	....

12.15.3 Reductions with Sodium Trimethoxyborohydride

Thiamine (CL) is reduced by sodium trimethoxyborohydride in aqueous methanol at $-15°$ at pH 7 to dihydrothiamine I, m.p. 151°, in 40% yield. This material is identical with a purified sample of dihydrothiamine prepared by LAH reduction (equation 12-117).

$$(12\text{-}126)$$

Dihydrothiamine I is converted to dihydrothiamine II, after solution in hot water and extraction with chloroform. Infrared spectra and potentiometric titration data indicate that dihydrothiamine II is formed from I by a ring closure in which the alcohol group adds to the double bond of the thiazoline ring (157).

12.15.4 Reductions with Potassium Borohydride

The use of LAH in the reduction of quaternary salts has the disadvantage of reducing, at the same time, other functional groups which may be present. Further, the quaternary salt may not be soluble in the ethereal solvent utilized in LAH reactions. Panouse (161) has reported that the use of potassium borohydride in alkaline solution permits more selective reduction than LAH. Quaternary pyridinium salts derived from glucose are reduced in quantitative yield to o-dihydro derivatives. Thus,

N-tetraacetylglucosidylpyridinium bromide (CLI) and N-tetraacetylglucosidylnicotinamide bromide (CLII) are reduced to the o-dihydropyridine
and o-dihydronicotinamide, respectively.

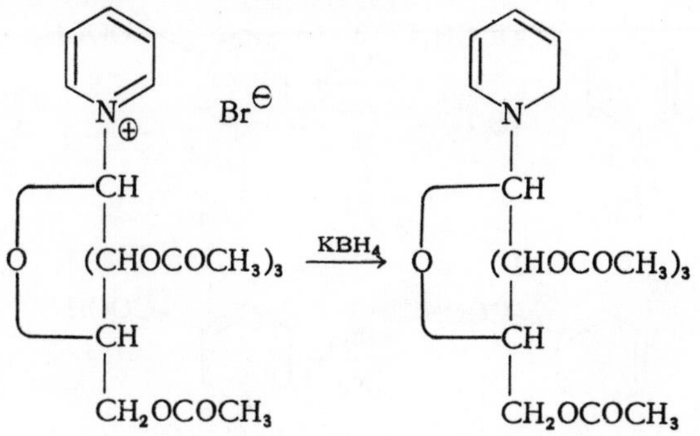

(12-127)

CLI

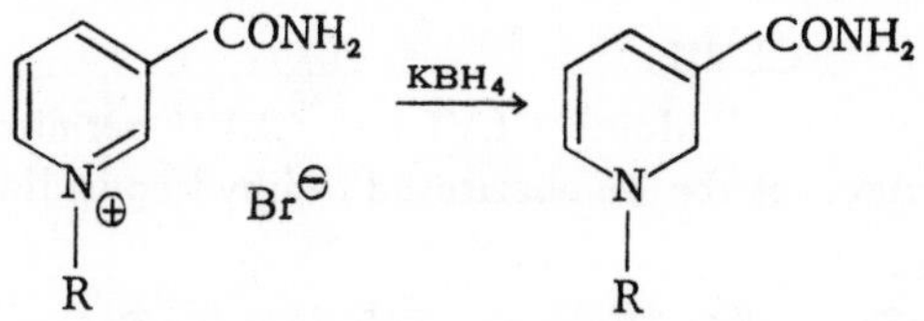

(12-128)

CLII   CLIII

The indicated structure of the 3-substituted o-dihydropyridine (CLIII)
was established in later work (162), since the alternate 1,6-dihydro structure is also possible.

Reduction of pyridine methiodide (CLIV) with potassium borohydride
yields N-methyl-1,2,5,6-tetrahydropyridine instead of the dihydro derivative (161).

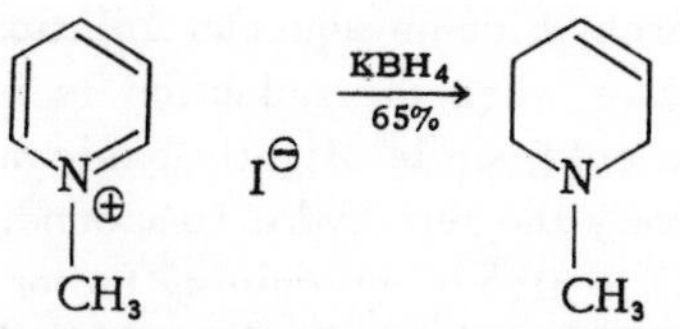

(12-129)

CLIV

The reduction of nicotinamide methiodide (CLV) is more complex and
gives a mixture of the o-dihydro and tetrahydro derivatives.

(12-130)

CLV

The reduction of methyl nicotinate methiodide (CLVI) permits the synthesis of arecoline, the principal alkaloid of the betel nut, while nicotinic acid methiodide (CLVII) is reduced to arecardine (162).

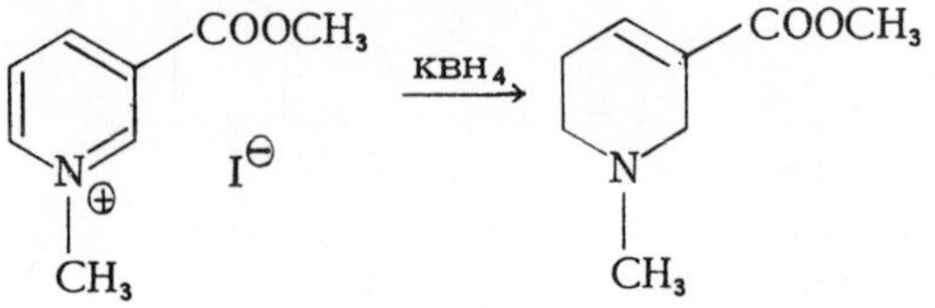

$$\text{(12-131)}$$

CLVI

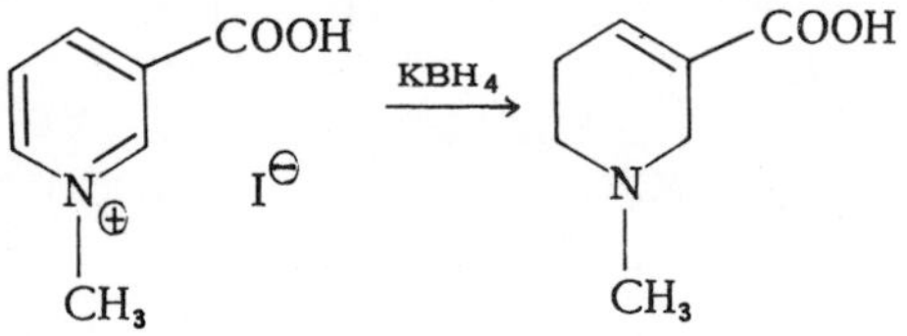

$$\text{(12-132)}$$

CLVII

The syntheses of the alkaloids CLVI and CLVII permitted the formulation of the structures of the 3-substituted o-dihydropyridines according to the scheme:

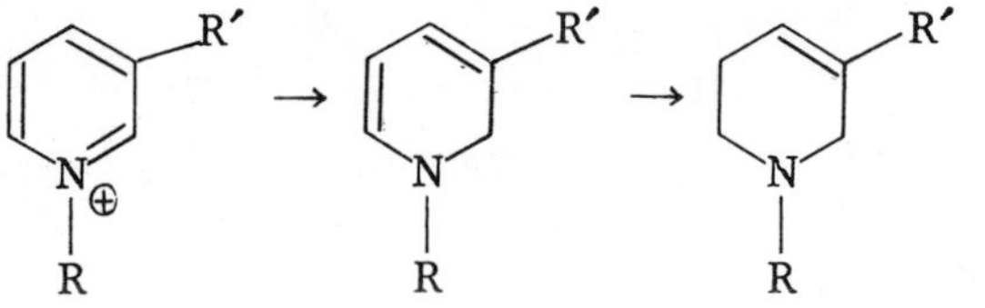

$$\text{(12-133)}$$

CLVIII

Panouse (162) established that the reduction of quaternary pyridinium salts by potassium borohydride in aqueous solution favors the formation of the dihydro derivative when the reduction is carried out in strongly alkaline medium in the cold, while slightly basic medium and heat yields principally or exclusively the tetrahydro compound. The nature of R and R' in equation (12-133) is also a determining factor.

Torossian (163) found that the reduction of N-alkylquinolinium (CLIX) and N-alkylisoquinolinium (CLX) salts with potassium borohydride in neutral aqueous solution gives N-alkyl-1,2,3,4-tetrahydro derivatives, without the isolation of o-dihydro compounds.

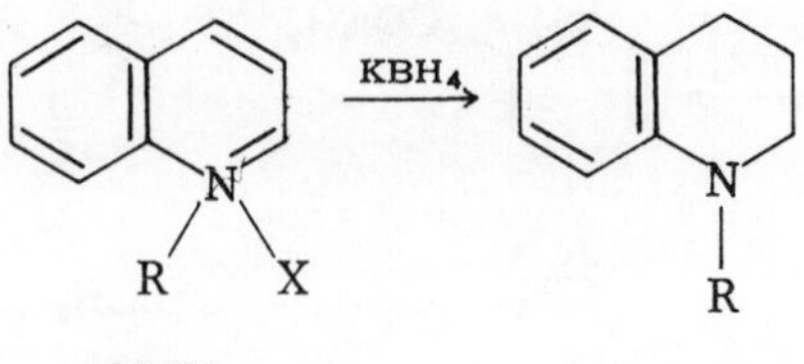

$$\text{(12-134)}$$

CLIX

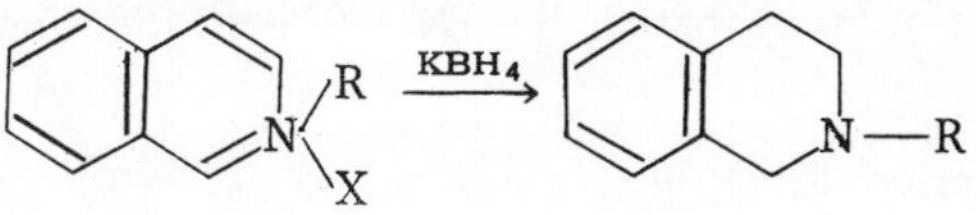

(12-135)

CLX

By this method the following salts have been reduced:

R	Quinoline Derivatives, % Yield	Isoquinoline Derivatives, % Yield
Methyl	70	85
Ethyl	72	91
n-Propyl	62	93
n-Butyl	50	73

When the reduction is carried out in alkaline medium, a mixture of the o-dihydro and tetrahydro compounds are obtained. However, the dihydro derivative is extremely unstable and oxidizes and polymerizes very rapidly. Torossian postulated that since the action of sodium hydroxide on quinoline methiodide, without benefit of reducing agent, yields N-methyl-1,2,3,4-tetrahydroquinoline, it is probable that the alkalinity of the reaction medium permits partial reduction by the borohydride to dihydro derivatives which are then converted to tetrahydro compounds.

12.15.5   Reductions with Lithium Borohydride

The synthesis of tetramethylammonium borohydride according to equation (12-125) has been carried out with lithium borohydride as well as with the sodium compound (160).

$$(CH_3)_4NF + LiBH_4 \longrightarrow (CH_3)_4NBH_4 + LiF \qquad (12-136)$$

The following tetramethylammonium salts have been utilized in this reaction:

Salt	% Yield
Fluoride	98.5
Phosphate	....
Carbonate	....
Oxalate	....

12.16   REDUCTION OF THE CARBON-NITROGEN DOUBLE BOND

12.16.1   Reductions with Lithium Aluminum Hydride

The reduction or non-reduction of the carbon-nitrogen double bond with LAH is directly related to the structure of the compound under discussion and the reaction conditions.

The reductions of isocyanates, R—N=C=O (Section 12.5), oximes,

R_2C=NOH (Section 12.6), quaternary salts, $\diagdown C=N\diagup^{R}_{X}$ (Section 12.15)

and isothiocyanates, R—N=C=S (Section 13.19) involve the reduction of the carbon-nitrogen double bond.

$$\diagup C=N— \ \rightarrow \ \diagup CH—NH \qquad (12\text{-}137)$$

12.16.1.a *Amidines, Hydrazidines, and Guanidines.* Ehrensvärd and Stjernholm (43) reported that the reduction of N,N'-diphenylcyanoformamidine (CLXI) with LAH in ether results in the formation of .the glycine-N,N'-diphenylamidine (CLXII) in which the amidine structure is intact.

$$\begin{array}{c} C_6H_5N \\ \diagdown \\ \diagup C—C^{13}N \\ C_6H_5NH \end{array} \xrightarrow{\text{LAH}} \begin{array}{c} C_6H_5N \\ \diagdown \\ \diagup C—C^{13}H_2NH_2 \\ C_6H_5NH \end{array} \qquad (12\text{-}138)$$

$$\text{CLXI} \qquad\qquad\qquad \text{CLXII}$$

Ried and Müller (68) found that the reaction of the triphenylformazone (CLXIII) with excess LAH in a refluxing ether-tetrahydrofuran mixture results in a reductive cleavage of the azo double bond to form ω-phenylbenzamidrazone and aniline while the hydrazidine grouping is not attacked.

$$\begin{array}{c} \diagup^{NNHC_6H_5} \\ C_6H_5C \\ \diagdown \\ N=NC_6H_5 \end{array} \xrightarrow{\text{LAH}} \begin{array}{c} \diagup^{NNHC_6H_5} \\ C_6H_5C \\ \diagdown \\ NH_2 \end{array} + C_6H_5NH_2 \qquad (12\text{-}139)$$

$$\text{CLXIII}$$

The presence of benzaldehyde phenylhydrazone has also been indicated.

Gilsdorf and Nord (164) reported that when N,N-diethylbenzamidine (CLXIV) is refluxed with LAH in ether, in addition to the recovery of CLXIV in 72.5% yield, 15% of benzylamine is obtained.

$$\begin{array}{c} \diagup^{NH} \\ C_6H_5C \\ \diagdown \\ N(C_2H_5)_2 \end{array} \xrightarrow{\text{LAH}} C_6H_5CH_2NH_2 \qquad (12\text{-}140)$$

$$\text{CLXIV}$$

The formation of benzylamine is analogous to the isolation of benzyl alcohol from the LAH reduction of N,N-diethylbenzamide (Section 10.1.1.d.2).

Rheim and Jutisz (165) attempted to prepare argininol by LAH reduction of esterified arginine (CLXV). However, "difficulties were encountered owing to the instability of the guanido group."

$$\underset{\text{NH}_2}{\overset{\displaystyle\overset{\text{NH}}{\|}}{\text{H}_2\text{NC}-\text{NHCH}_2\text{CH}_2\text{CH}_2\text{CHCOOR}}}$$

CLXV

When arginine was benzoylated prior to ester formation the resultant
ethyl ester of dibenzoylarginine was successfully reduced to dibenzoylargininol with LAH in tetrahydrofuran solution. Hydrolysis with sulfuric
acid gave the desired argininol. Fromageot and his co-workers (166)
have reported, without experimental details, that the ethyl ester of arginine is reduced with LAH to argininol.

   12.16.1.b *Imines.* Elphimoff-Felkin (167) reported that 1-cyano-1-
(2′-tetrahydropyranoxy)cyclohexane (CLXVI) reacts normally with the
Grignard reagent to form the ketimine (CLXVII). With excess LAH CLXVII
is reduced to the corresponding aminoether which is hydrolyzed with
hydrochloric acid to yield the hydrochloride of the amino alcohol.

CLXVI   CLXVII

(12-141)

$$R = CH_3, C_2H_5, C_6H_5$$

   The "abnormal" Hoesch reaction of 4,6-diethylresorcinol and acrylonitrile yields a stable iminochloride, m.p. 156°, formulated as CLXVIII.
Treatment of CLXVIII with excess LAH in a mixture of ether and dioxane
yields three reduction products. The main product in about 70% yield is
a primary amine, $C_{13}H_{20}NCl$, postulated as CLXIX. The second reduction
product, in about 20% yield, is a neutral product, $C_{13}H_{18}ClNO$, m.p. 169°.
A 1,2-benz-4-aza-3-oxacycloheptane structure (CLXX) is postulated for
this product which on further treatment with LAH gives the primary amine

(CLXIX). The third reduction product, m.p. 122°, is alkali soluble and may have arisen from CLXX since it can also be obtained from CLXX on heating with 10% sodium hydroxide. No formula has been advanced for this product, $C_{13}H_{17}ClO_2$ (168).

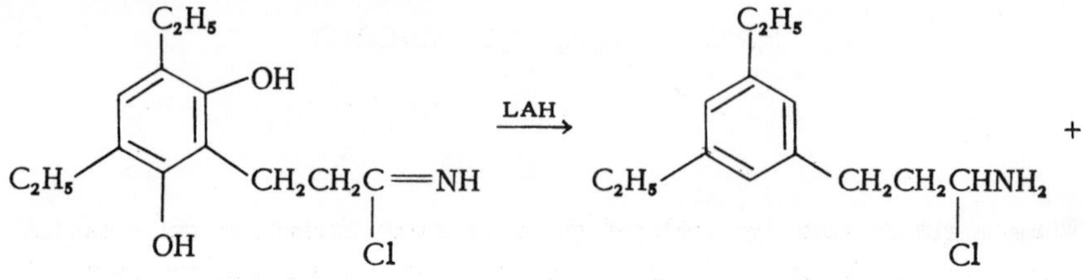

CLXVIII   CLXIX

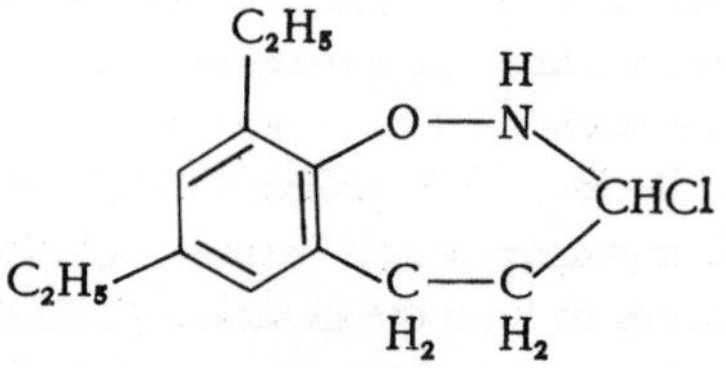

CLXX

12.16.1.c Schiff's Bases. The LAH reduction of Schiff's bases yields the corresponding secondary amine, according to the equation (13):

$$4 \, RCH{=\!=}NR' + LiAlH_4 \rightarrow (RCH_2NR')_4LiAl \xrightarrow{H_2O} RCH_2NHR'$$

$$(12\text{-}143)$$

The reduction of various Schiff's bases is summarized in Table LXXXII.

TABLE LXXXII

LAH REDUCTION OF SCHIFF'S BASES

Formula	Schiff's Bases	% Yield Amine	Ref.
$C_8H_{15}NO$	N-Cyclohexylideneaminoethanol	60	1
$C_9H_{10}NOBr$	p-Bromobenzalaminoethanol	....[2]	3
$C_{13}H_{13}NO$	α-Naphthalaminoethanol	....[2]	3
$C_{13}H_{15}N$	Benzalaniline	93	4
$C_{13}H_{17}N$	Benzalaminocyclohexane	80	1
	N-Cyclohexylidenebenzylamine	65	1
$C_{15}H_{19}N$	Cinnamalaminocyclohexane	70	1

[1] M. Mousseron, R. Jacquier, M. Mousseron-Canet, and R. Zagdoun, *Bull. soc. chim. France*, [5] 19, 1042 (1952).

[2] Reduction carried out in dioxane.

[3] E. D. Bergmann, D. Lavie, and S. Pinchas, *J. Am. Chem. Soc.*, 73, 5662 (1951).

[4] R. F. Nystrom and W. G. Brown, *ibid.*, 70, 3738 (1948).

The attempted reduction of N-cyclohexylmethyleneimine (CLXXI) with LAH in ether has been unsuccessful. The non-reduction of 1-piperidino-cyclohexene (CLXXII) and benzylidene-bis-piperidine (CLXXIII) is indicative of the specificity of azomethine reduction (28).

CLXXI   CLXXII   CLXXIII

12.16.1.d *Hydrazones.* The LAH reduction of formaldehyde N,N-dimethylhydrazone (CLXXIV) yields trimethylhydrazine (169).

$$(CH_3)_2N-N=CH_2 \xrightarrow{LAH} (CH_3)_2N-NHCH_3 \qquad (12\text{-}144)$$

CLXXIV

The reduction of the phenylhydrazone of benzoylglyoxal (CLXXV) with LAH in ether at ordinary temperatures is reported to give a crystalline red-claret compound, m.p. 138.5°, containing 16.5–16.79% nitrogen. This product was not further investigated (74).

CLXXV   CLXXVI

The LAH reduction of ethyl 2-phenylhydrazinobenzoyl acetate (CLXXVI) in refluxing ether yields 45% of the phenylhydrazone of benzaldehyde as the only isolatable product (76).

The reaction of 2,2-dimethylsuccinic anhydride with phenylhydrazine yields a phenylhydrazide which on reduction with LAH is converted to a mixture of neutral and basic products. Although the products have not been identified, the basic material which is the minor component of the mixture has been found to reduce Benedict's solution (26).

12.16.1.e *Endocyclic Carbon-Nitrogen Double Bonds.* The carbon-nitrogen multiple bond in various heterocyclic compounds is susceptible to reduction.

Jones and Kornfeld (170) reported, without details, that esters of oxazole carboxylic acid undergo extensive decomposition when treated with LAH. Mousseron and Canet (29) reported that the LAH reduction of 2-methyltetrahydrobenzoxazole (CLXXVII) gives *trans*-2-ethylaminocyclohexanol.

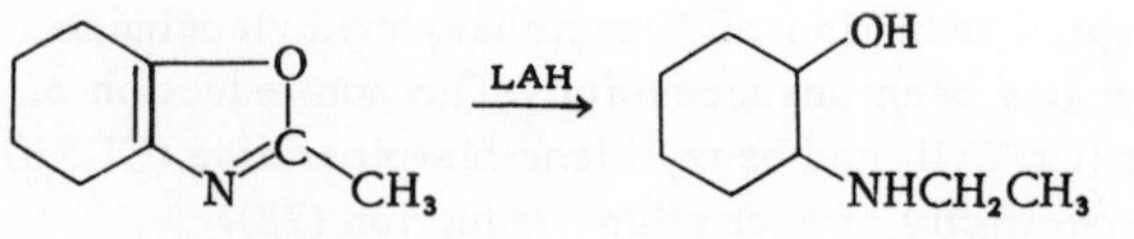

(12-145)

CLXXVII

Although the authors considered this transformation as a rearrangement a hydrogenolysis reaction is more likely. Reduction of the carbon-nitrogen double bond yields an —NH—CH—O— grouping which, as discussed in Section 12.17, undergoes cleavage at the carbon-oxygen linkage. The somewhat unexpected reduction of the carbon-carbon double bond may be attributed to the presence of the adjacent electron donor groups acting individually or in concert or vinylogously through the carbon-nitrogen double bond, as discussed in Section 16.1.

The oxazoline ring is not attacked when reduction is carried out with the theoretical quantity of LAH at 0°. The reduction product is decomposed with cold acetic acid and the oxazoline or the amino alcohol can be obtained according to the duration of the contact of the reduction product with acetic acid and the concentration of the latter. Thus, *trans*-2-aryl- or alkyl-4-carbethoxy-5-aryloxazolines (CLXXVIII) are reduced to *trans*-2,5-disubstituted-4-hydroxymethyloxazolines which can then be hydrolyzed to amino alcohols (74,122).

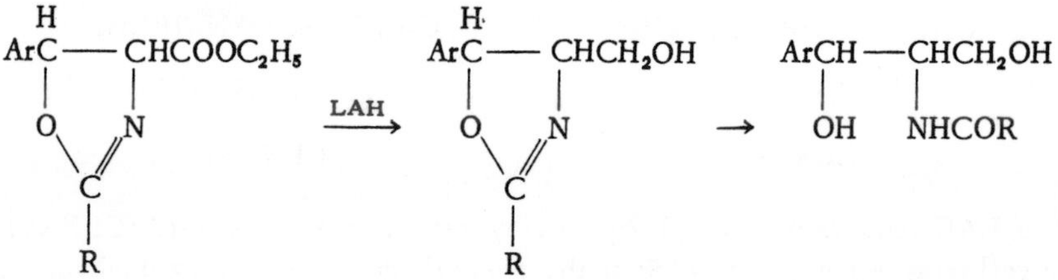

CLXXVIII   (12-146)

Ar	R	Ref.
C_6H_5	C_6H_5	74,171
	CH_3	172
	Cl_2CH	171,173
$p\text{-}O_2NC_6H_4$	C_6H_5	122
	CH_3	122
	Cl_2CH	122

The reduction of 6-keto-2-phenyl-4,5-benzo-1,3-oxazine (benzoylanthranil) (CLXXIX) with LAH is reported to yield 84% of o-benzamino-benzyl alcohol.

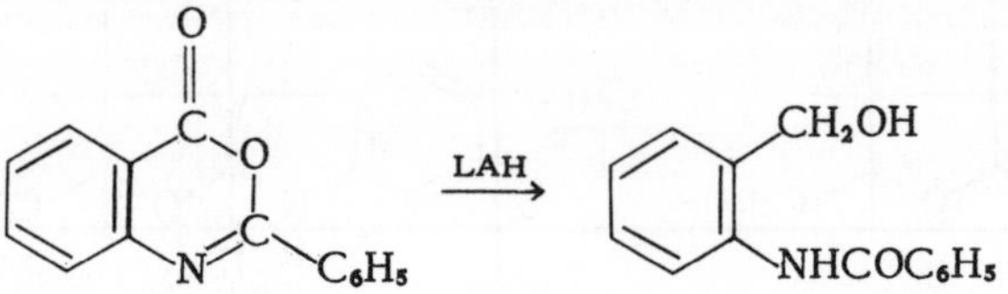

CLXXIX

(12-147)

When the reduction is carried out with one-quarter equivalent of LAH a crystalline product is obtained, m.p. 180–181°, empirical formula $C_{14}H_{11}NO_2$. The ultraviolet spectrum indicates a secondary amine group and a carbonyl group which lead to the postulation of a 6-keto-2-phenyl-4,5-benzo-2,3-dihydro-1,3-oxazine (CLXXX) (174).

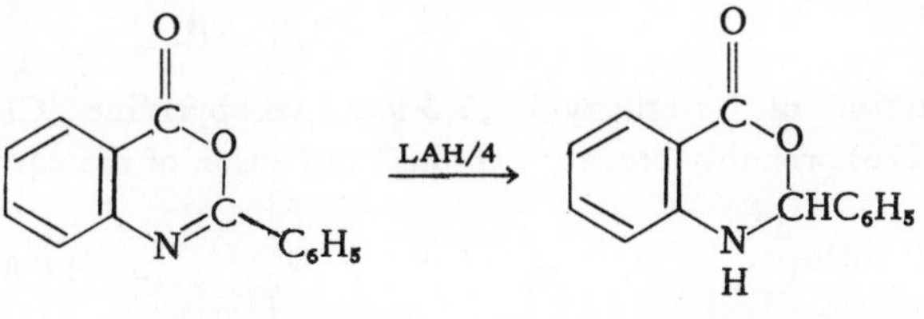

CLXXIX   CLXXX

(12-148)

As discussed in Section 10.2.1.b, bromoallogelsemine hydrobromide (CLXXXI) on treatment with LAH in dioxane yields desoxohydroxytetrahydrogelsemine (CLXXXIII). Bromohydroxydihydrogelsemine (CLXXXII), which is formed on warming CLXXXI with acid, is postulated as an intermediate in the reduction (175).

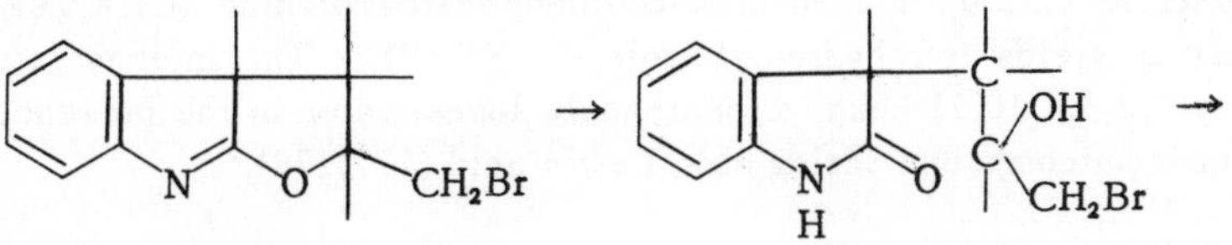

CLXXXI   CLXXXII

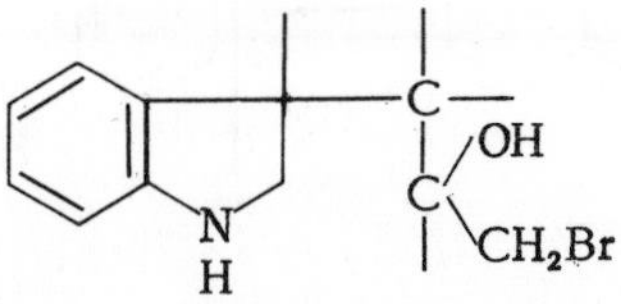

CLXXXIII

(12-149)

A more likely explanation involves reduction of the carbon-nitrogen double bond, followed by cleavage of the resultant —NCO— grouping as discussed in Section 12.17.

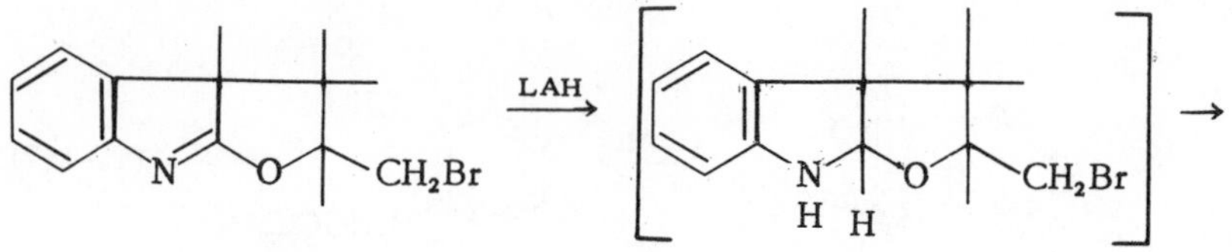

800   REDUCTION OF NITROGEN-CONTAINING COMPOUNDS   12.16

CLXXXI

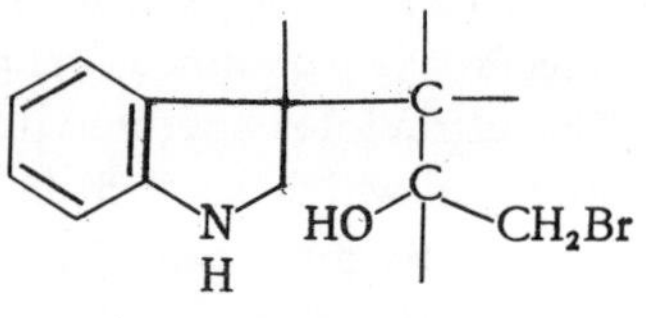

(12-150)

CLXXXIII

The reduction of 2-methoxy-3,4,5,6-tetrahydropyridine (CLXXXIV) to piperidine (176) probably proceeds through reduction of the carbon-nitrogen double bond, followed by cleavage of the —NCO— grouping.

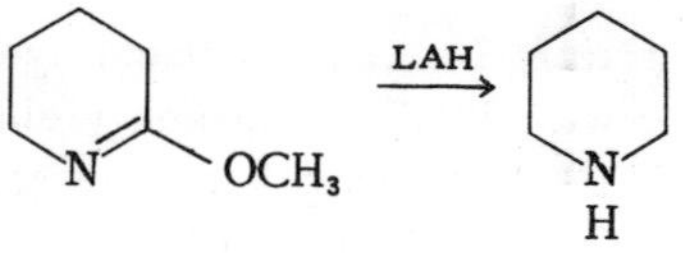

(12-151)

CLXXXIV

The LAH reduction of 11-hydroxytetrahydrocarbazolenine (CLXXXV) quantitatively yields tetrahydrocarbazole (CLXXXVI). The intermediate 11-hydroxy-1,2,3,4,10,11-hexahydrocarbazole loses water in the presence of the aluminum compound acting as a Lewis acid (177,178).

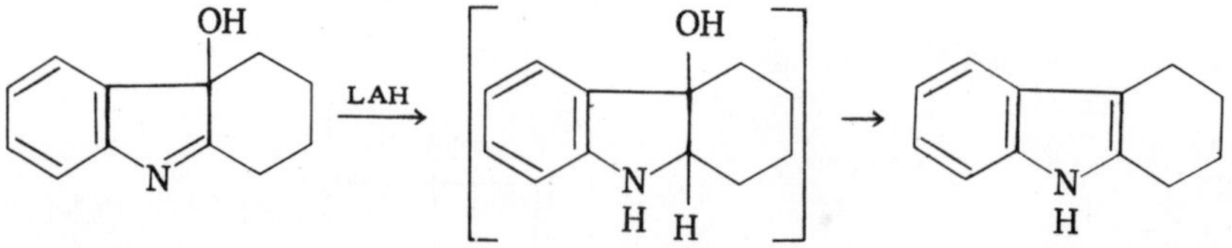

CLXXXV

CLXXXVI

(12-152)

The reduction of 2-phenyl-3-methyl-3-hydroperoxyindolenine (CLXXXVII) with ethereal LAH yields 2-phenylskatole (CLXXXVIII) (179). Since the product of the reduction of the hydroperoxide is the 3-hydroxy compound the conversion of CLXXXVII to CLXXXVIII is analogous to the reduction of CLXXXV in equation (12-152).

CLXXXVII

(12-153)

CLXXXVIII

Although pyridine derivatives can usually be reduced with LAH without attack on the heterocyclic nucleus, the latter has been reported to be re-ducible.   Hochstein (81) reported that pyridine is unsatisfactory as a solvent for LAH in the quantitative determination of active hydrogen since it is reduced by LAH.   de Mayo and Rigby (180) found that reflux-ing pyridine (CLXXXIX) with LAH in di-*n*-butyl ether gives a 10% yield of piperidine, isolated as the *p*-toluenesulfonyl derivative, and no un-changed pyridine is recovered.   Reduction of 2-hydroxypyridine under the same conditions gives a mixture of pyridine and piperidine.

(12-154)

CLXXXIX

The reduction of esters of pyridinecarboxylic acids proceeds satisfactorily at low temperatures but at high temperatures small amounts of piperidyl carbinols accompany the expected pyridyl carbinols (181).

Bohlmann (130) reported that on warming an ethereal pyridine solution with LAH an addition compound is formed which is difficultly soluble in ether and on decomposition gives a labile dihydro compound with a piperidine-like odor and strong reducing characteristics.   The non-reduc-tion of 2,4,6-triphenylpyridine with LAH is attributed to steric hindrance.

Wiberg and Henle (182) have utilized a solution of LAH in ether-pyridine, prepared by treatment of a concentrated ether solution of LAH with absolute pyridine, for the preparation of cuprous hydride from the corresponding iodide.   An ether-pyridine mixture has also been used in the LAH reduction of various pyrrole dyestuffs (183).

Bohlmann (130) reported that quinoline (CXC) forms an addition com-pound with LAH which on decomposition with water gives a crystalline dihydro compound, m.p. 40–41°. Treatment of the crude reduction product with alcoholic picric acid gives two different picrates, an orange picrate, m.p. 180–192°, in 80% yield, and a red picrate, m.p. 170° (d. 130°), in 5% yield. Both picrates analyze for the picrate of dihydroquinoline. Analogous dihydro compounds are formed by treatment of quinoline with lithium alkyl or phenyl.

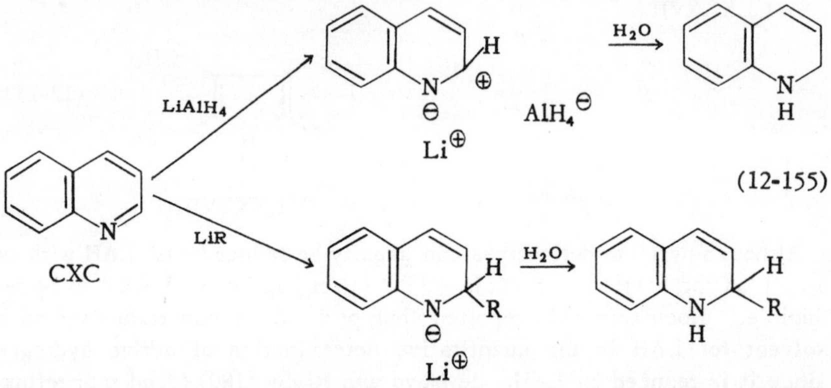

$$(12\text{-}155)$$

$$(12\text{-}156)$$

Craig and Gregg (184) found that Bohlmann's directions for the LAH reduction of quinoline give a 90% yield of a product which, if purified by extraction with cyclohexanone, has m.p. 72–74° but whose absorption spectrum and other properties correspond to those of 1,2-dihydroquinoline.

Treatment of 2-hydroxyquinoline (CXCI) with LAH in di-*n*-butyl ether has been reported to give a mixture of quinoline and tetrahydroquinoline (180).

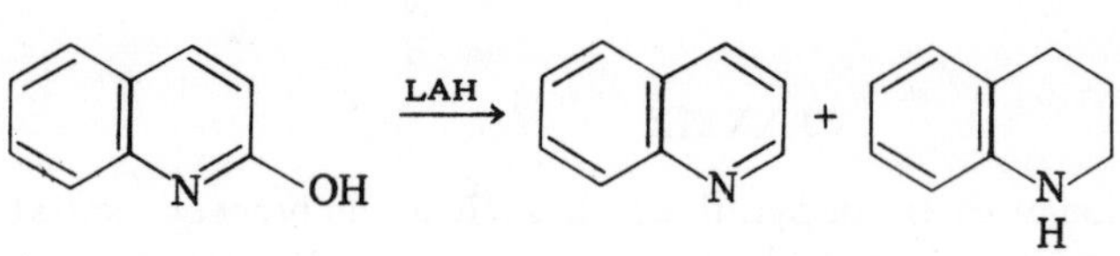

$$(12\text{-}157)$$

CXCI

Although Bohlmann (130) reported that 2-phenylquinoline is not reduced with LAH, Druey, and Hüni (185) found that tetrahydroquinoxalines are obtained from 2-oxo-1,2-dihydroquinoxalines (CXCII) on reduction with LAH.

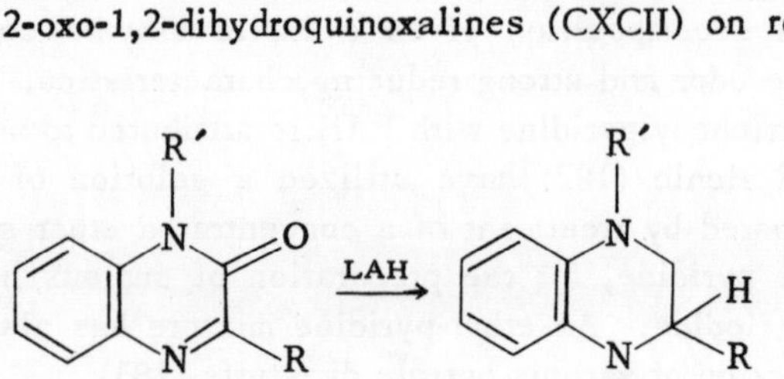

$$(12\text{-}158)$$

CXCII

The tetrahydro compound is the product even when R = phenyl. Treatment of a quinoxalinum salt (CXCIII) with alkali yields a pseudo base (CXCIV) which is converted to the tetrahydroquinoxaline on reduction with LAH or with hydrogen over platinum oxide.

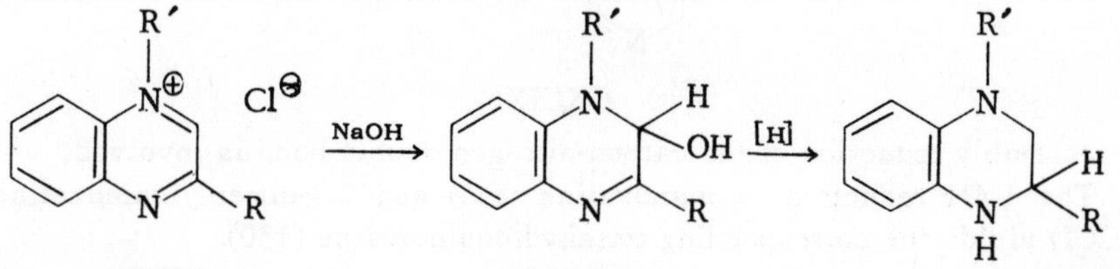

CXCIII   CXCIV   (12-159)

Bohlmann found that benzimidazole (CXCV) reacts with LAH in the cold to form a salt, while in a refluxing benzene-ether mixture the product is dihydrobenzimidazole (130).

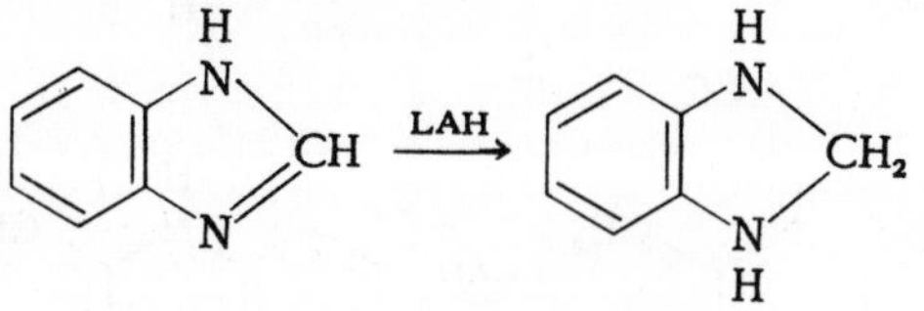

                                                    (12-160)

CXCV

The reduction of acridine (CXCVI) in refluxing ether-benzene yields 9,10-dihydroacridine. It has been postulated that the 9,10-dihydro compound is either formed directly or the 9,11-dihydro compound is first formed and then rearranges (130).

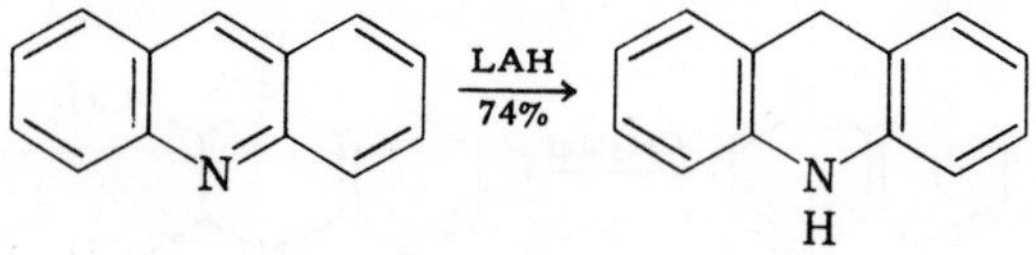

                                                    (12-161)

CXCVI

The reduction of phenanthridine (CXCVII) with LAH in ethereal solution yields 5,6-dihydrophenanthridine (CXCVIII) (186).

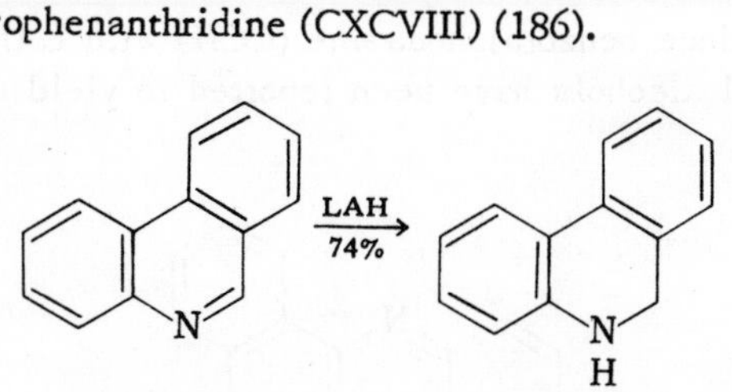

                                                    (12-162)

CXCVII   CXCVIII

The reduction of 6-chlorophenanthridine also yields CXCVIII (85).

Jones and Kornfeld reported that esters of pyrazine carboxylic acid (CXCIX) undergo extensive decomposition when treated with LAH (170).

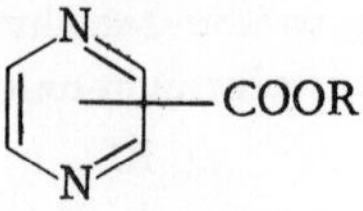

CXCIX

Presumably reduction of the carbon-nitrogen double bond is involved.

The LAH reduction of quinoxaline (CC) and 2,3-dimethylquinoxaline (CCI) yields the corresponding tetrahydroquinoxaline (130).

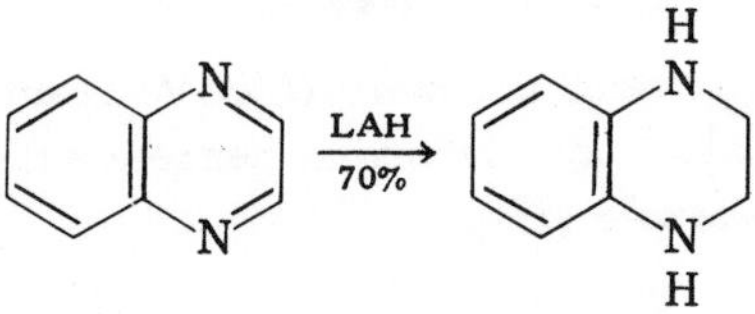

$$(12\text{-}163)$$

CC

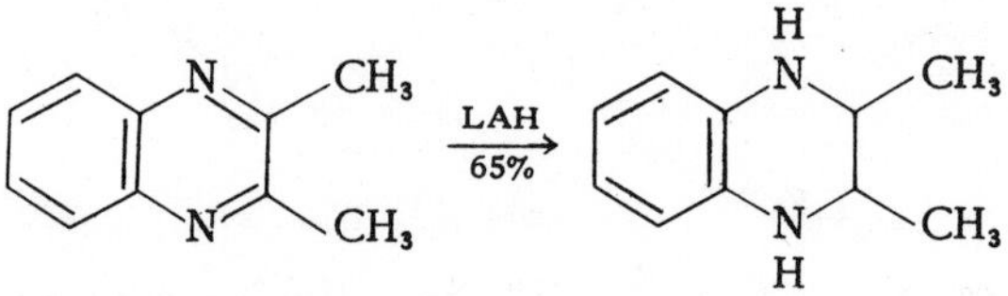

$$(12\text{-}164)$$

CCI

This reaction is analogous to the reduction of quinoxaline (CC) with methylmagnesium iodide to yield 2,3-dimethyltetrahydroquinoxaline (187).

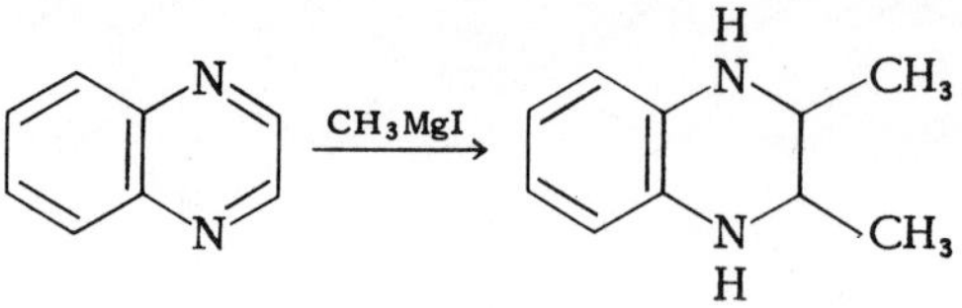

$$(12\text{-}165)$$

CC

Attempts to reduce benzo[a]phenazine (CCII) with LAH or sodium and methyl or isoamyl alcohols have been reported to yield unchanged starting material (85).

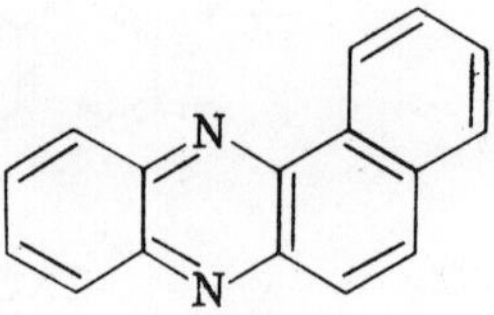

CCII

The reduction of phenazine (CCIII) with LAH in refluxing ether has been found by Birkofer and Birkofer to yield 5,10-dihydrophenazine (CCIV) (188). The reduction of phenazine esters with ethereal LAH has given the hydroxymethylphenazine. By dropping the yellow colored ester solution into the ethereal LAH solution a temporary red color appears which has been attributed to the formation of the N-monohydrophenazyl radical.

Bohlmann (130) reported that treatment of phenazine (CCIII) with LAH in a cold 1 : 1 benzene ether mixture gives a 90% yield of a blue molecular complex containing phenazine and 5,10-dihydrophenazine in equimolar amounts.

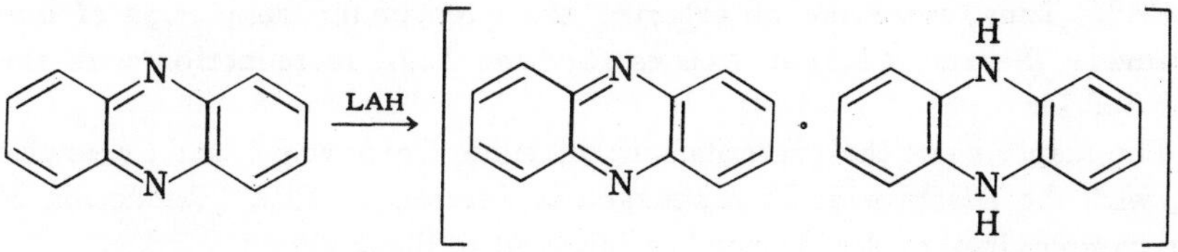

CCIII   CCIV   (12-166)

The dihydro compound (CCIV) is the sole product when the solvent mixture is refluxed. In this case, as with acridine, the unresolved question is whether the 5,10-dihydro compound is formed directly or if an intermediate which rearranges to CCIV is the initial product.

The reduction of 4-hydroxy-6,7-benzoquinazoline (CCV) is reported to yield 1,2-dihydro-4-hydroxy-6,7-benzoquinazoline (189).

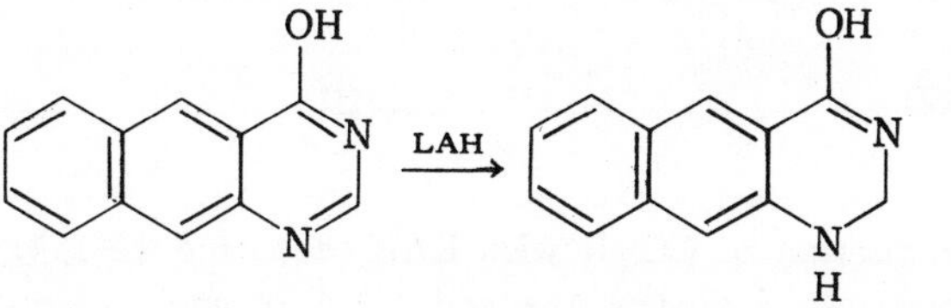

                                        (12-167)

CCV

Dehydrogenation of the alkaloid veatchine, for which the partial structure CCVI has been advanced, with selenium yields a mixture of bases, each containing a carbon-nitrogen double bond. Treatment of these bases with LAH results in the reduction of the double bonds to yield secondary amines (190,191).

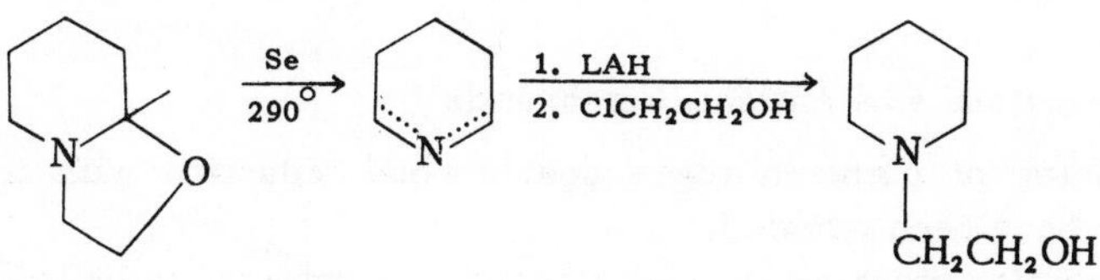

                                        (12-168)

CCVI

In a similar manner, pyrolysis of the alkaloid atisine with selenium yields a base showing an infrared spectrum similar to one of the veatchine pyrolysis products, i.e., a carbon-nitrogen double bond is indicated. Reduction of the atisine pyrolysis base with LAH followed by reaction with 2-chloroethanol yields a compound isomeric with the corresponding product from veatchine (191).

12.16.2 Reductions with Sodium Borohydride

In only a limited number of compounds has reduction of the carbon-nitrogen double bond under the influence of sodium borohydride been reported. Thus, there are no reported examples of the subjection of isocyanates (Section 12.5) or oximes (Section 12.6) to reduction with the borohydride.

The reduction of the quaternaries, thiamine, Coenzyme I, and Coenzyme II, with the borohydride is discussed in Section 12.15.2. Reduction of the carbon-nitrogen double bond is involved in these cases.

The reduction of 2-phenyl-3-methyl-3-hydroperoxyindolenine (CCVII) with sodium borohydride in ethanol yields a mixture of 2-phenyl-3-methyl-3-hydroxyindolenine (CCVIII) and 2-phenylskatole (CCIX) (179).

CCVII   CCVIII   CCIX

(12-169)

As in the reduction of CCVII with LAH (equation 12-153), the formation of CCIX probably involves the reduction of the hydroperoxide to the 3-hydroxy compound, as in CCVIII, as well as the saturation of the carbon-nitrogen double bond. Dehydration of the intermediate yields CCIX.

12.16.3 Reductions with Potassium Borohydride

The reduction of the carbon-nitrogen double bond in quaternary ammonium salts with potassium borohydride is discussed in Section 12.15.4. No other examples of such reduction have been reported.

12.16.4 Reactions with Lithium Borohydride

No examples of carbon-nitrogen double bond reduction with lithium borohydride have been reported.

The azomethine grouping in semicarbazones is reported to be resistant to attack by lithium borohydride in tetrahydrofuran. This has been utilized in the preferential reduction of carbonyl and ester groups in the presence of semicarbazone linkages to yield carbinol semicarbazones which can be hydrolyzed to carbonyl compounds. The following steroid semicarbazones have been subjected to this treatment: cortisone acetate 3-monosemicarbazone (64,192), cortisone-3,20-bis-semicarbazone (64), 11-dehydrocorticosterone-3,20-bis-semicarbazone (64), 20-cyano-17-pregnene-21-ol-3,11-dione 3-monosemicarbazone (62,64).

12.17   COMPOUNDS CONTAINING THE —NĊO— GROUPING

It has been shown in Section 11.3.1 that the —O—Ċ—O— grouping is generally resistant to attack by LAH. On the contrary, the —N̶—Ċ—O— grouping is attacked by LAH to yield products resulting from cleavage of the carbon-oxygen linkage (193).

Oxazolidines, containing the —NĊO— grouping in a heterocyclic ring (CCX), are cleaved under the influence of LAH to yield 2-amino-alkanols.

$$\text{CCX} \xrightarrow{\text{LAH}} \quad (12\text{-}170)$$

CCX

Bergmann, Lavie, and Pinchas have treated the following substituted oxazolidines with LAH in dioxane to yield the corresponding N-substituted-2-aminoalkanol (194):

Formula	Compound	% Amino Alcohol
$C_{11}H_{15}NO$	2-Ethyl-3-phenyloxazolidine	55.5
$C_{11}H_{15}NO_2$	2-p-Anisyl-3-methyloxazolidine	50
$C_{11}H_{23}NO$	2,4,5,5-Tetramethyl-2-isobutyloxazolidine	58
$C_{12}H_{23}NO$	4,5,5-Trimethyl-2-pentamethyleneoxazolidine	....
$C_{12}H_{25}NO$	2,2-Di-n-propyl-4,5,5-trimethyloxazolidine	62.5
$C_{15}H_{31}NO$	2-n-Propyl-3-(α,γ-dimethylbutyl)-4,5,5-trimethyloxazolidine	57

The reduction of the steroidal oxazolidine (CCXI) with LAH in ether is reported to yield the β-aminoalcohol (34).

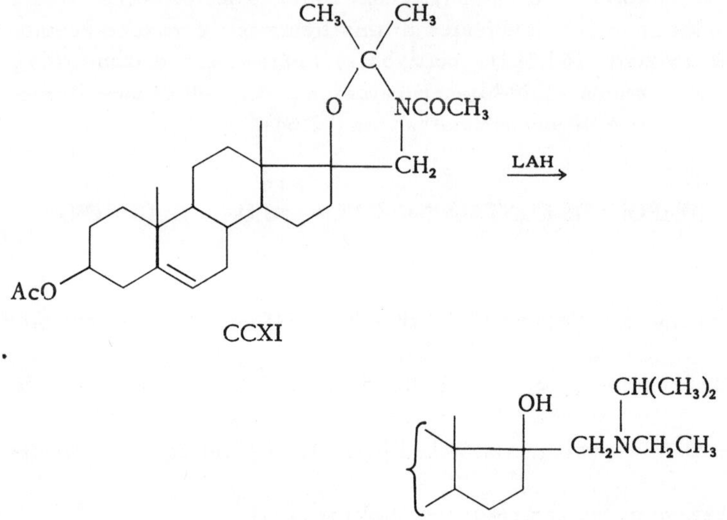

CCXI

$$\begin{array}{c}\text{OH} \quad \overset{\displaystyle CH(CH_3)_2}{\underset{}{|}} \\ \text{———} CH_2NCH_2CH_3\end{array}$$

(12-171)

The cleavage of the oxazolidine ring with LAH is analogous to the opening that occurs with the Grignard reagent (195).

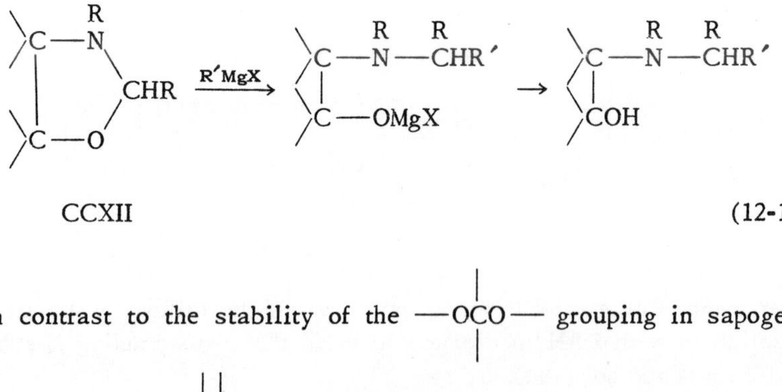

CCXII   (12-172)

In contrast to the stability of the —O$\overset{|}{C}$O— grouping in sapogenic spirostanes, the —N$\overset{||}{C}$O— grouping in solasodine (CCXIII) is cleaved with ethereal LAH (196). Solasodine hydrochloride behaves in a similar manner. While LAH cleaves the oxide ring without reducing the double bond, hydrogenolysis over palladium-on-charcoal reduces the double bond to yield solasodanol (CCXIV). Hydrogenolysis over platinum oxide reduces the double bond and cleaves the oxide ring.

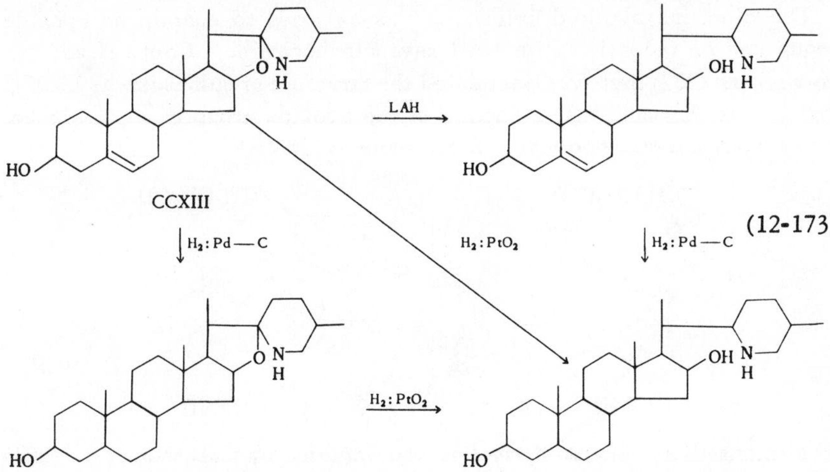

(12-173)

CCXIII

CCXIV

Tomatidine, the aglycone of tomatine, a glycosidal alkaloid isolated from the tomato plant, is reduced by LAH to dihydrotomatidine, the reaction being considered as the opening of an oxidic ring (147,198). It has been proposed that tomatidine is identical with solasodanol (CCXIV), the saturated analog of solasodine (CCXIII) (199,200).

Solanocapsin, an alkaloid isolated from *Solanum pseudocapsicum* L., is reduced with LAH to a product resulting from cleavage of an ether linkage (201). Structure CCXV has been proposed for solanocapsin, the cleavage reaction therefore being the expected —NCO— cleavage.

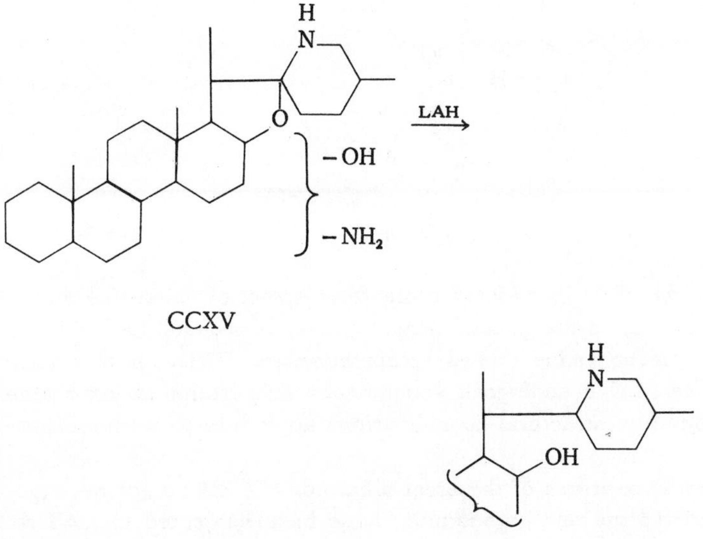

CCXV

(12-174)

The cinchona alkaloid quinamine was assumed to contain an epoxide group and on reduction with LAH gave cinchonamine. Goutarel and his co-workers (202) therefore postulated the structure of quinamine as CCXVI and it was assumed that reduction of the epoxide group gave an alcohol which split out water to give cinchonamine (CCXVII).

CCXVI   CCXVII

The intermediate dihydro derivative was isolated by Culvenor *et al.* (203) and subsequently dehydrated to cinchonamine by heat. The intermediate was not further examined and consequently the direction of ring opening to give the tertiary alcohol was not determined. Witkop has proposed structure CCXVIII for quinamine (204). Although LAH reduction in this case does not distinguish between the two postulated structures, the intermediate cleavage product probably having the same structure in both cases, opening of the tetrahydrofuran ring does not seem improbable due to the presence of the —NCO— grouping.

CCXVIII

Epiquinamine which is considered a diastereoisomer of quinamine due to epimerization at C_8 in the quinuclidene nucleus, is reduced by LAH to a isomeride of cinchonamine termed epicinchonamine (203). In this case the dihydro derivative undergoes spontaneous dehydration at room temperature. The same structural considerations apply here as with cinchonamine.

The dihydro derivatives of the ergot alkaloids (CCXIX) ergosine, ergocristine, ergocryptine and ergocornine, have been subjected to LAH reduction and three kinds of reduction products have been isolated (205). These include, as shown in equation (10-113), a polyamine, an amino-alcohol and a piperazine derivative.

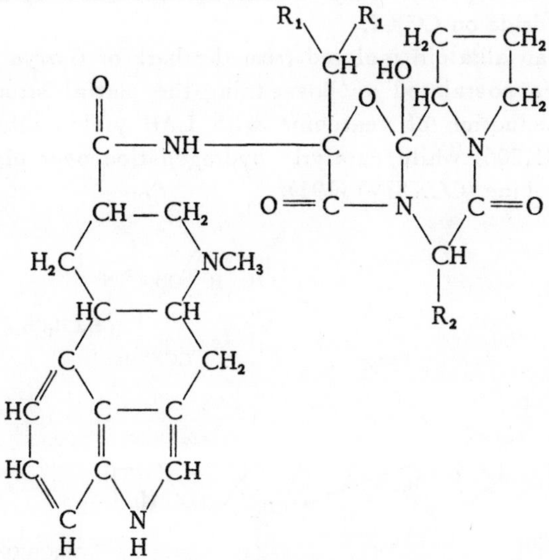

$$R_1 \diagdown \diagup R_1$$

(structure CCIX)

CCIX

Examination of the postulated ergot structure (CCXIX) reveals the presence of the following elements:

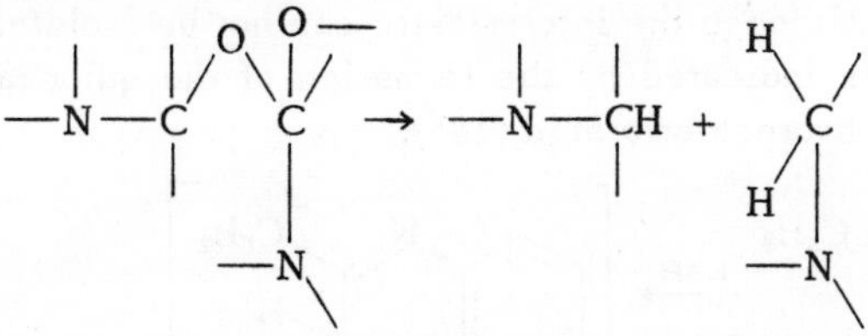

$$\begin{array}{c} \text{O} \quad \overset{\text{O}}{\underset{}{-}} \\ | \quad | \diagup \quad | \diagup \\ -N-C \quad C \quad \rightarrow \quad -N-CH \quad + \quad \diagup C \\ | \quad | \qquad\qquad | \qquad\qquad H \diagdown | \\ \quad -N \diagdown \qquad\qquad\qquad\qquad -N \diagdown \end{array} \qquad (12\text{-}175)$$

The reduction products reveal the cleavage of the carbon-oxygen linkage and provide evidence for the structure advanced for the ergot alkaloids.

The stable ozonide of 2-phenylskatole (CCXX) is reduced by LAH to o-benzylaminophenylmethylcarbinol (CCXXI) (179).

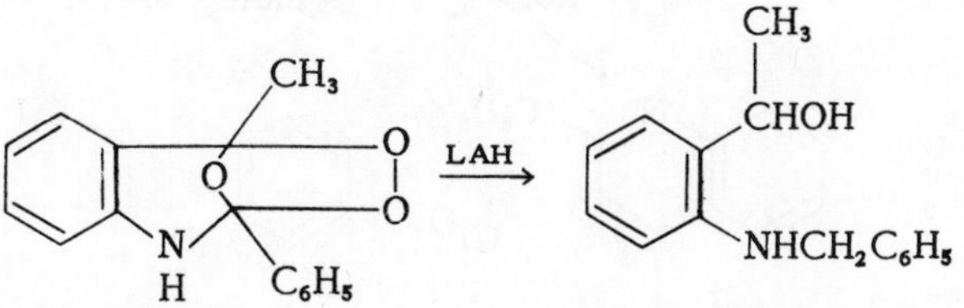

$$\xrightarrow{\text{LAH}} \qquad (12\text{-}176)$$

CCXX   CCXXI

The product is indicative of the cleavage of the —N̈C̈O— grouping although o-benzaminophenylmethylcarbinol is produced by the action of
sodium borohydride on CCXX.

Veatchine, an alkaloid isolated from the bark of *Garrya veatchii* Kellogg, has been postulated as possessing the partial structure CCXXII
(190,191). Reduction of veatchine with LAH yields dihydroveatchine
(CCXXIII) (191,206) while catalytic hydrogenation over platinum yields
tetrahydroveatchine (CCXXIV) (191).

The LAH reduction of 2-keto-1,2-dihydroquinoxalines generally yields
tetrahydroquinoxalines. In the case of the hydroxyethyl derivative
(CCXXV) the reduction proceeds through an intermediate with an intact
double bond. Although the intermediate can not be isolated and analyzed
its formation is indicated by the formation of the quinoxalinium salt on
treatment with hydrochloric acid (185).

Quinoxalinium salts such as CCXXVII are converted to the pseudobase (CCXXVI) with alkali and the latter with LAH or catalytic reduction over platinum oxide yields the corresponding tetrahydroquinoxaline (CCXXVIII).

The reduction of N-methyl-α-pyrrolidone or 3-ketooctahydropyrrocoline (CCXXIX) with one quarter mole of LAH permits the isolation of the carbinol-amine in the form of the tautomeric aldehyde (207–210).

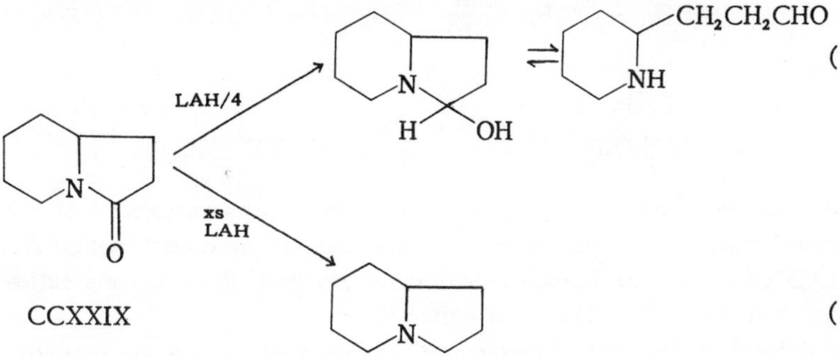

(12-180)

CCXXIX

(12-181)

The use of excess LAH prevents the stopping of the reaction at the intermediate stage (209). Here the first stage of the reduction yields the carbinol-amine which is cleaved at the carbon-oxygen bond with excess LAH.

The LAH reduction of 3-keto-4-methyl-2,2-diphenylmorpholine (CCXXX) is reported to yield a mixture of 3-hydroxy-4-methyl-2,2-diphenylmorpholine (CCXXXI) and 4-methyl-2,2-diphenylmorpholine (CCXXXII). The further action of LAH on the carbinol-amine (CCXXXI) yields CCXXXII (211).

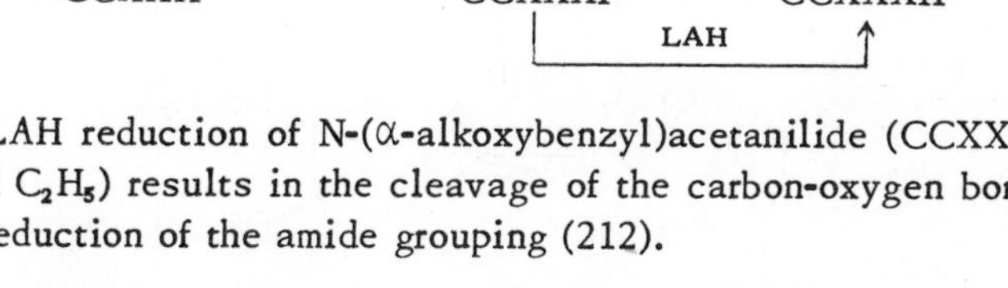

(12-182)

CCXXX   CCXXXI   CCXXXII

The LAH reduction of N-(α-alkoxybenzyl)acetanilide (CCXXXIII): R = CH_3 and C_2H_5) results in the cleavage of the carbon-oxygen bond as well as the reduction of the amide grouping (212).

(12-183)

CCXXXIII

The reduction of N-(α-acetoxybenzyl)acetanilide similarly yields N-ethyl-N-phenylbenzylamine as one of the products.

The LAH reduction of 2,3-diphenyl-2-ethoxyethylenimine (CCXXXIV) yields cis-2,3-diphenylethylenimine (CCXXXV).

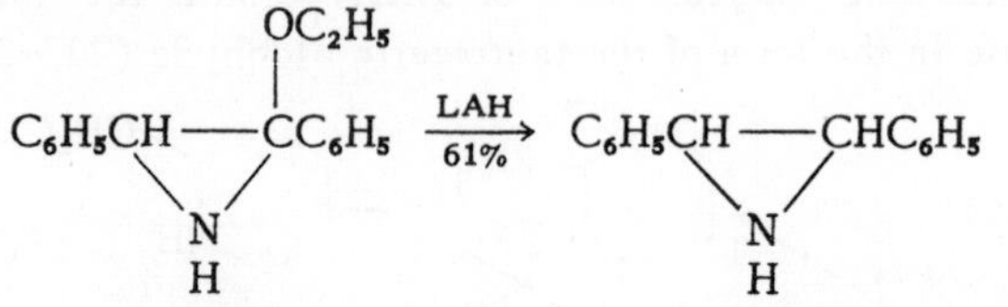

$$
\underset{\text{CCXXXIV}}{\underset{H}{\overset{OC_2H_5}{C_6H_5CH-CC_6H_5}}} \xrightarrow[61\%]{LAH} \underset{\text{CCXXXV}}{\underset{H}{C_6H_5CH-CHC_6H_5}} \qquad (12\text{-}184)
$$

CCXXXIV is formed as an intermediate in the Neber rearrangement of the p-toluenesulfonate of desoxybenzoin oxime and on treatment with LAH yields CCXXXV. An analogous reaction occurs with the p-toluenesulfonate of p,p'-dichlorodesoxybenzoin oxime (213).

In the reductive cleavage of unsymmetrical epoxides, as in the steroids, by LAH, a secondary oxide linkage is cleaved in preference to a tertiary (214). Similarly, LAH reductions of 1-methyl-1,2-epoxycyclohexane and 1-cyano-1,2-epoxycyclohexanone yield the expected 1-substituted cyclohexanols (Section 11.2.1.b).

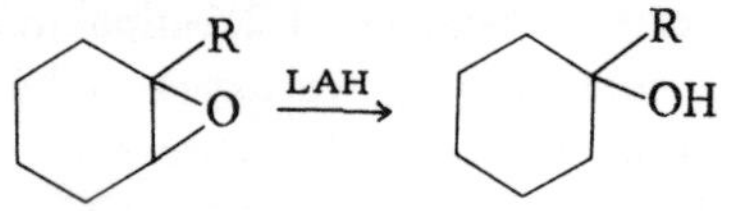

$$
\text{CCXXXVI} \xrightarrow{LAH} \qquad (12\text{-}185)
$$

CCXXXVI

In contrast, LAH reduction of 1-dimethylamino-1,2-epoxycyclohexane (CCXXXVII), which contains an —NCO— grouping, yields the secondary alcohol resulting from cleavage of the oxide ring at the tertiary carbon (28,30,31).

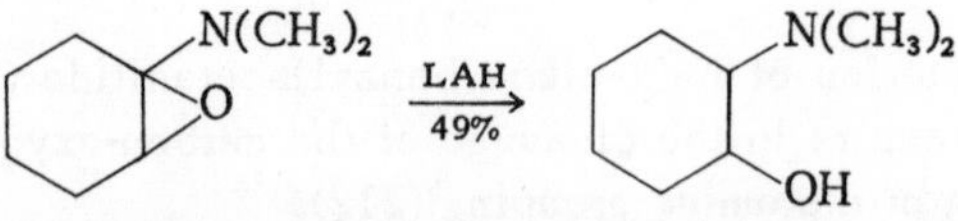

$$
\text{CCXXXVII} \xrightarrow[49\%]{LAH} \qquad (12\text{-}186)
$$

CCXXXVII

The conversion of 1-hydroxymethylbenzotriazole (CCXXXVIII) to 1-methylbenzotriazole (CCXXXIX) has been carried out through the halide (214).

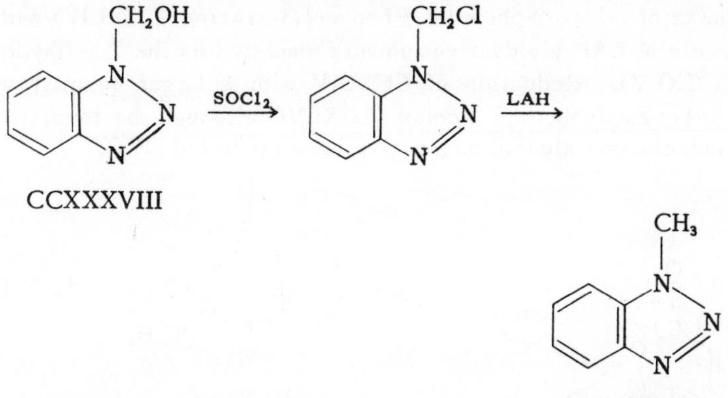

CCXXXVIII

(12-187)

CCXXXIX

An attempt to reduce CCXXXVIII directly to CCXXXIX by reduction with LAH in a benzene-ether-dioxane mixture has been unsuccessful due to the precipitation of the intermediate complex and its subsequent insolubility (215).

The reported reduction of 2-methoxy-3,4,5,6-tetrahydropyridine (CCXL) to piperidine (176) probably occurs by cleavage of the —N$\overset{|}{\underset{|}{\overset{|}{C}}}$O— grouping following reduction of the carbon-nitrogen double bond.

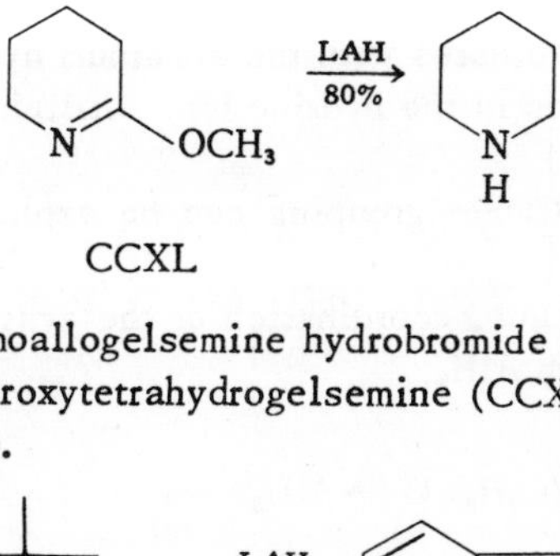

(12-188)

CCXL

The reduction of bromoallogelsemine hydrobromide (CCXLI) with LAH in dioxane to desoxohydroxytetrahydrogelsemine (CCXLII) probably follows the same course (175).

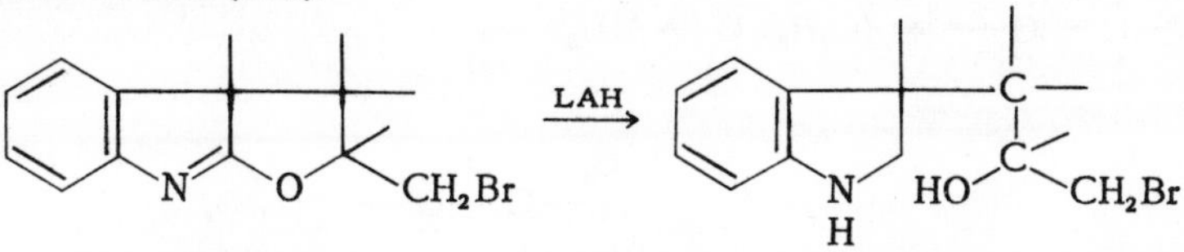

CCXLI   CCXLII   (12-189)

The cleavage of 2-methyltetrahydrobenzoxazole (CCXLIII) to 2-ethyl-aminocyclohexanol probably follows the indicated pattern (29).

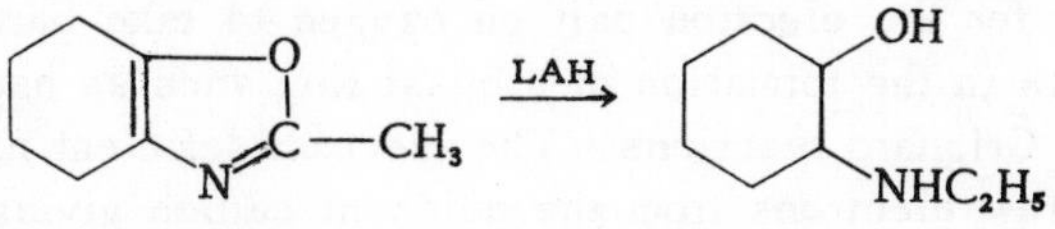

(12-190)

CCXLIII

The treatment of 6-keto-2-phenyl-4,5-benzo-1,3-oxazine (CCXLIV) with one-quarter mole of LAH yields a compound formulated as the 2,3-dihydro derivative (CCXLV). Reduction of CCXLIV with a larger quantity of LAH yields o-benzaminobenzyl alcohol (CCXLVI) although the formation of o-benzylaminobenzyl alcohol might have been predicted (174).

Paddock (33) has suggested that there is an equilibrium in an ethereal LAH solution

$$AlH_4^{\ominus} \rightleftharpoons H^{\ominus} + AlH_3 \qquad (12\text{-}193)$$

and that the ether coordinates with the aluminum hydride while the active entity in LAH reactions is the hydride ion. Utilizing this suggestion the cleavage of the $-\overset{\mid}{\underset{\mid}{N}}\overset{\mid}{C}O-$ grouping can be explained by analogy with Grignard reactions. Thus, coordination of the available electron pair on nitrogen can occur with AlH_3.

The tendency for the electron pair on oxygen to take part in hydrogen bonding results in the formation of a quasi ring such as has been postulated in many Grignard reactions. The electron deficient nitrogen would tend to withdraw electrons from the adjacent carbon giving the latter a positive character. The hydride ion present in the solution, according to Paddock's postulation, could displace the ethereal oxygen resulting in cleavage of the carbon-oxygen bond:

$$(12\text{-}195)$$

Hatch and Cram (213) have formulated the cleavage in the reduction of the ethoxyethylenimines as follows:

$$(12\text{-}196)$$

12.18   COMPOUNDS CONTAINING THE —NCS— GROUPING

Reduction of 1-nitroethyl p-tolylsulfide (CCXLVII) with LAH yields p-thiocresol among the reaction products (108).

$$(12\text{-}197)$$

CCXLVII

LAH reduction of the corresponding sulfone (CCXLVIII) gives p-toluene-sulfinic acid in good yield (108).

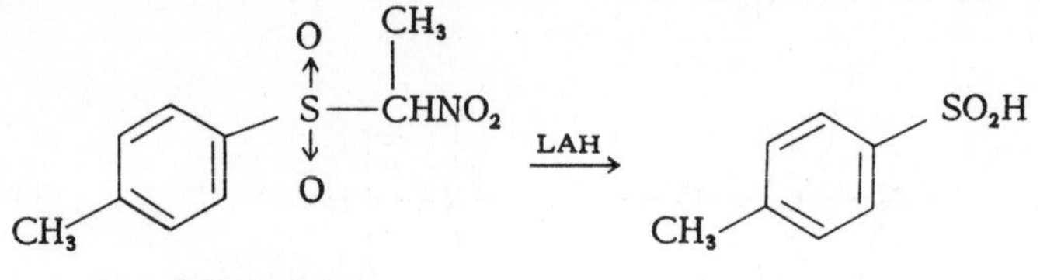

$$(12\text{-}198)$$

CCXLVIII

In these cases, scission of the carbon-sulfur bond in an $-\overset{|}{N}-\overset{|}{C}-S-$ grouping has occurred under the influence of LAH. It is of interest to note that thiocyanates, containing the grouping $-S-C\equiv N$, are reduced by LAH to thiols indicating, as above, cleavage of the carbon-sulfur bond.

Treatment of thiobenzamide (CCXLIX) with excess LAH yields benzyl-amine. The reaction with 0.5 mole of LAH at low temperatures yields benzonitrile and benzylamine (216).

$$C_6H_5C\overset{S}{\underset{NH_2}{\diagdown}} \xrightarrow{\text{LAH}} C_6H_5CN + C_6H_5CH_2NH_2 \qquad (12\text{-}199)$$

CCXLIX

Although the reaction appears to involve an elimination of hydrogen sulfide to give the nitrile followed by reduction to the amine, an analogy exists here to the stepwise reduction of amides to the carbinol-amine followed by cleavage of the $-\overset{|}{N}\overset{|}{C}O-$ grouping.

The addition of an ethereal solution of bis-methylsulfonylnitromethane (CCL) to an ethereal LAH solution liberates hydrogen and yields a little bis-methylsulfonylmethane and ammonia. The major part of the starting material is recovered (109).

$$CH_3SO_2\underset{NO_2}{\overset{|}{C}HSO_2CH_3} \xrightarrow{\text{LAH}} CH_3SO_2CH_2SO_2CH_3 \qquad (12\text{-}200)$$

CCL

The cleavage of the carbon-nitrogen bond in this case, contrary to the indications of the previous examples appears worthy of reexamination.

12.19 HETEROCYCLIC NITROGEN COMPOUNDS

The reduction of various heterocyclic nitrogen compounds has been discussed in the sections on lactams (Section 10.2), ketones (Section 7.2), and the reduction of the carbon-nitrogen double bond (Section 12.16) and will therefore be mentioned only briefly here.

12.19.1 Compounds Containing Saturated Heterocyclic Nuclei

The treatment of saturated monocyclic nitrogen heterocycles with the complex hydrides generally results in retention of the ring structure. Thus, the ethylene imine (CCLI), pyrrolidine (CCLII), piperidine (CCLIII), and piperazine (CCLIV) nuclei are not attacked by LAH and other complex hydrides.

CCLI   CCLII   CCLIII   CCLIV

While morpholine (CCLV) is resistant to attack by the hydrides, oxazolidines (CCLVI) are cleaved by LAH due to the presence of the $-\overset{|}{\underset{|}{N}}\overset{|}{\underset{|}{C}}O-$ linkage (Section 12.17).

CCLV   CCLVI

Among the saturated bicyclic systems, octahydroindole (CCLVII), quinuclidine (CCLVIII) octahydroindolizine (CCLIX) and octahydroquinolizine (CCLX) nuclei are not attacked by LAH.

CCLVII   CCLVIII   CCLIX   CCLX

Polycyclic systems in which an aromatic ring is fused to a saturated heterocyclic ring are not cleaved by LAH. Thus, tetrahydroquinoline (CCLXI), tetrahydroisoquinoline (CCLXII), indoline (CCLXIII), and hexa-hydrobenzpyridocoline (CCLXIV) nuclei are retained while substituent functional groups are reduced.

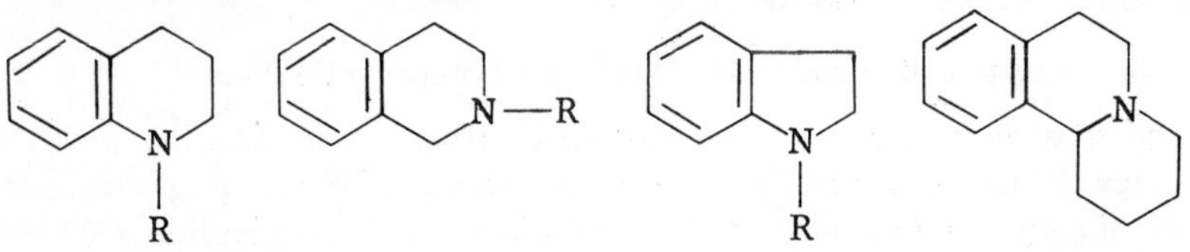

CCLXI   CCLXII   CCLXIII   CCLXIV

12.19.2 Pyrroles

Reductions with LAH in the pyrrole (CCLXV) series yield the appropriate pyrrole derivatives. The LAH reduction of pyrrole dyestuffs (CCLXVI) retains the macrocyclic structure intact (183).

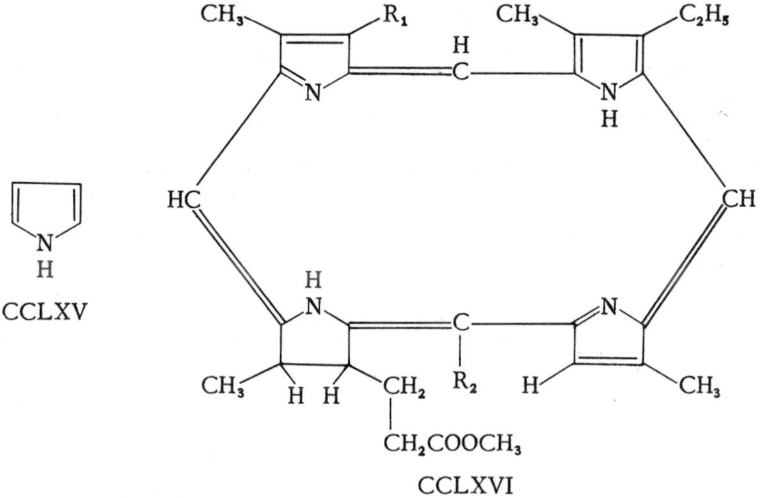

CCLXV

CCLXVI

12.19.3 Indoles and Carbazoles

As discussed in Section 10.2.1.b, the LAH reduction of oxindoles (CCLXVII) is dependent upon the substituents in the 1- and 3-positions, the products including indoles and indolines.

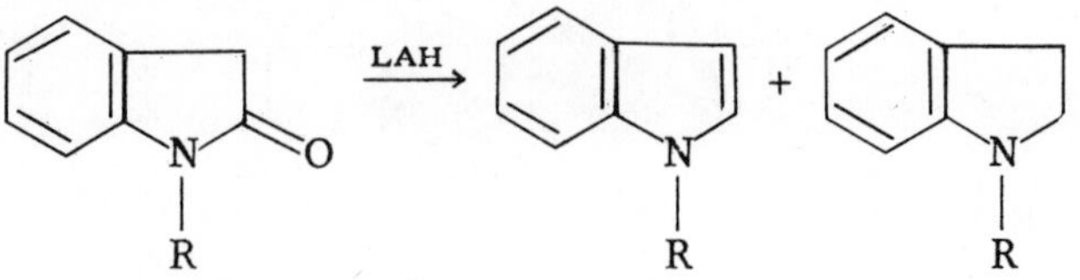

CCLXVII

The reduction of dioxindoles (CCLXVIII) yields indoles and oxindoles.

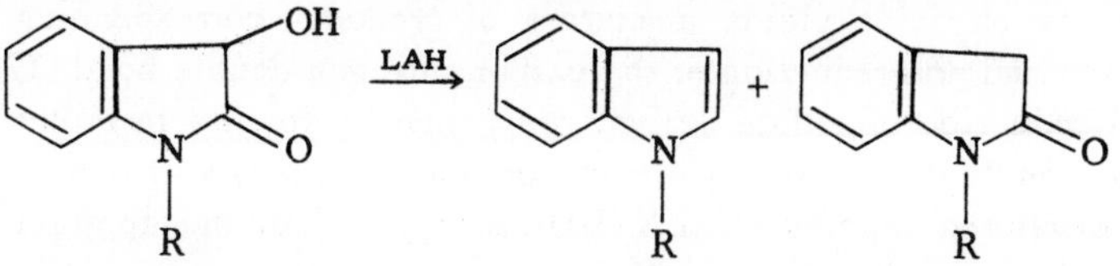

(12-202)

CCLXVIII

The reduction of naphthostyrils (CCLXIX), containing the oxindole structure, yields indolines.

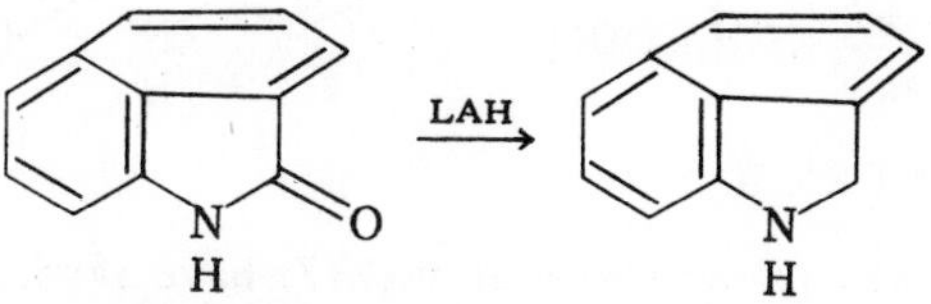

(12-203)

CCLXIX

As discussed in Section 7.2.1.i, the LAH reduction of *gem*-disubstituted *pseudo*-indoxyls (CCLXX) yields hydrogenolysis, reduction, or rearrangement products dependent upon the bulk of the substituents next to the carbonyl group.

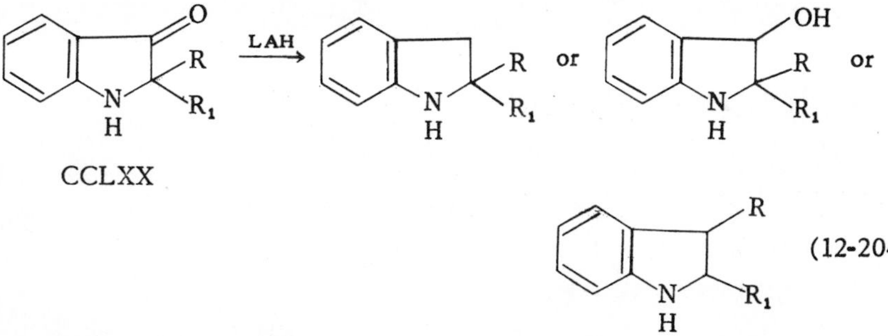

CCLXX

(12-204)

As discussed in Section 12.16.1.e, the LAH reduction of the indolenine (CCLXXI) as well as tetrahydrocarbazolenine (CCLXXII) nuclei results in reduction of the carbon-nitrogen double bond.

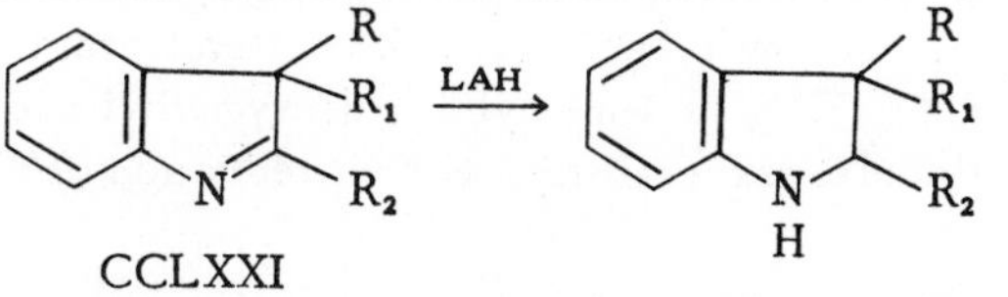

(12-205)

CCLXXI

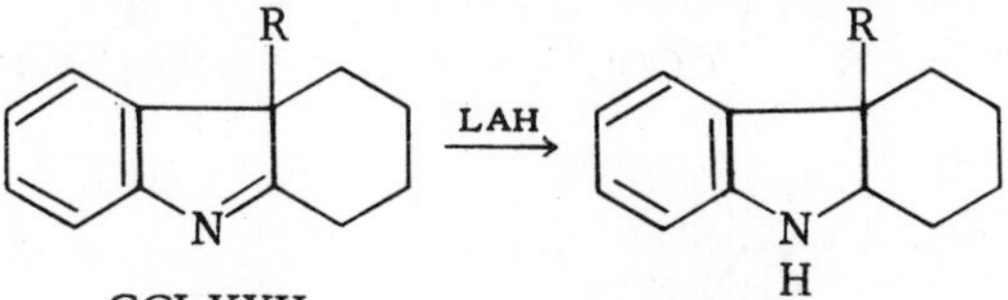

(12-206)

CCLXXII

The reduction of CCLXXI, where R = OOH, R_1 = methyl and R_2 = phenyl, with sodium borohydride yields a mixture of products corresponding to both reduction and non-reduction of the carbon-nitrogen double bond (179).

The LAH reduction of indole derivatives generally results in retention of the indole nucleus. Thus, indole is not reduced (217) with LAH and 2- and 3-substituted indoles (CCLXXIII) are reduced to the appropriate indole derivatives.

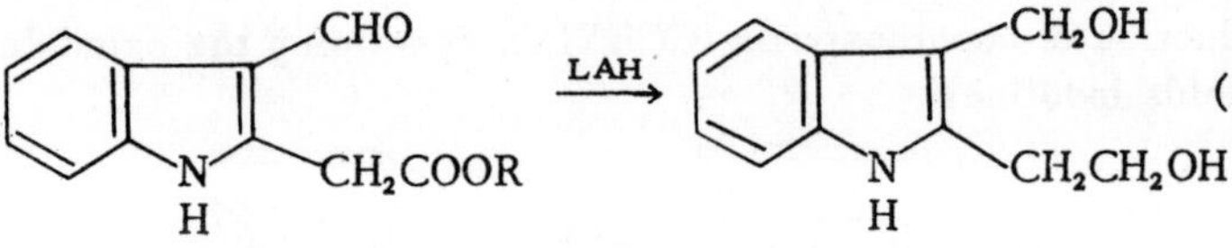

(12-207)

CCLXXIII

On the other hand, Julian and Printy (217) have reported that 1-methyl-indole (CCLXXIV) and 1,3-dimethylindole (CCLXXV) are reduced with LAH in ether to the corresponding indolines, in 25–30% yield.

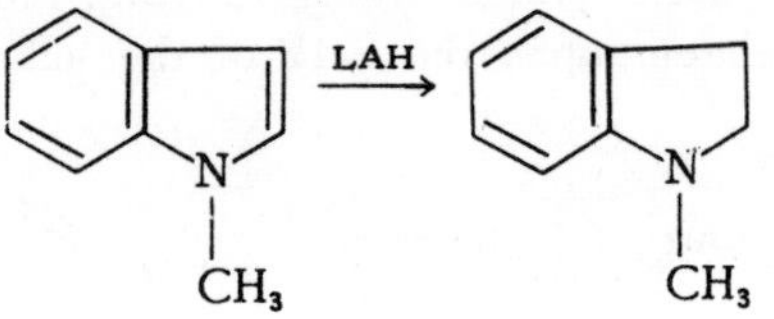

(12-208)

CCLXXIV

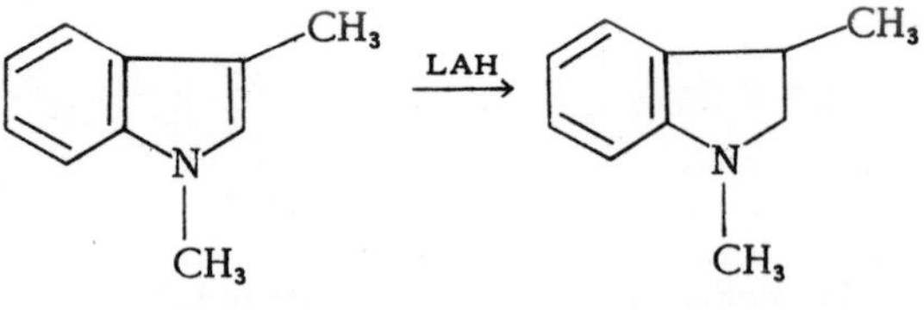

(12-209)

CCLXXV

However, Eiter and Svierak (218) reported that the LAH reductions of 1-methylindole-2-carboxylic acid (CCLXXVI) and ethyl 1-methylindolyl-3-acetate (CCLXXVII) give 1-methyl-2-hydroxymethylindole and 1-methyl-3-hydroxyethylindole, respectively, without reduction of the double bond.

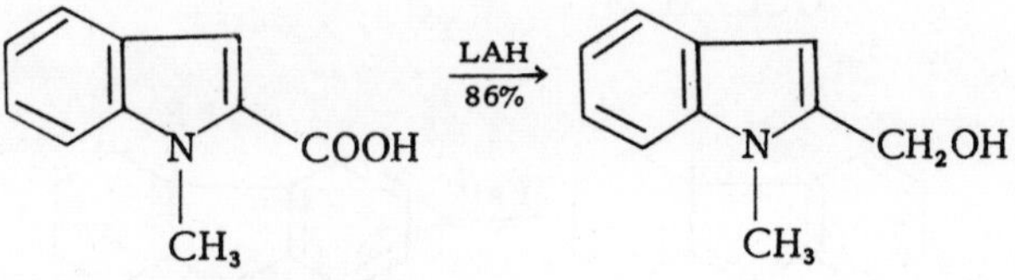

(12-210)

CCLXXVI

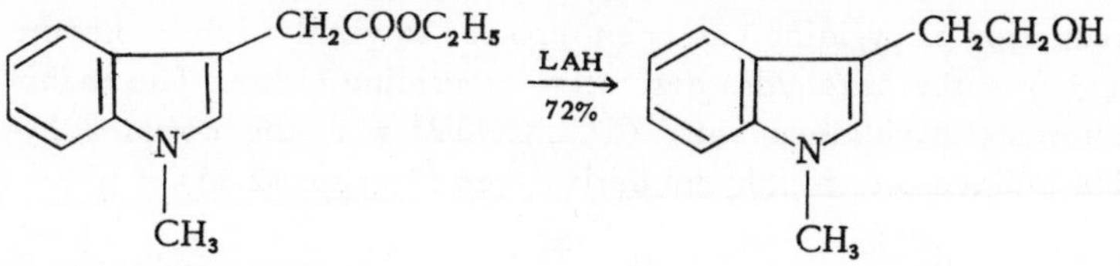

(12-211)

CCLXXVII

The LAH reduction of alkaloids containing the hexahydroindoloquino-lizine (CCLXXVIII) or the dihydrobenzindoloquinolizine (CCLXXIX) nuclei retains these heterocycles.

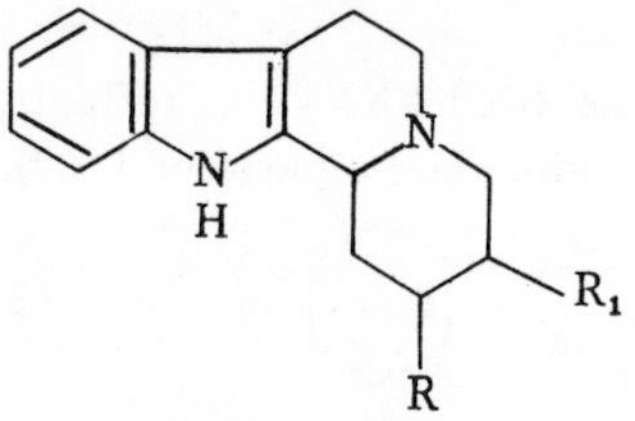

CCLXXVIII 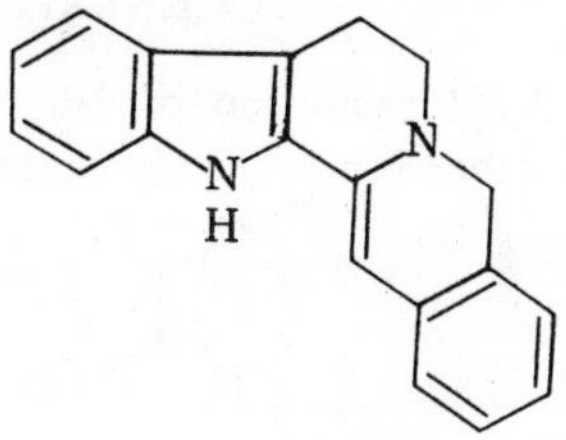   CCLXXIX

The attempted LAH reductions of 1,2-benzo-7,8-(2′,3′-indolo)-3,4-dihydro-6-quinolizone (CCLXXX) (219) and 4-quinolizone (CCLXXXI) (220) are reported to yield unchanged starting material.

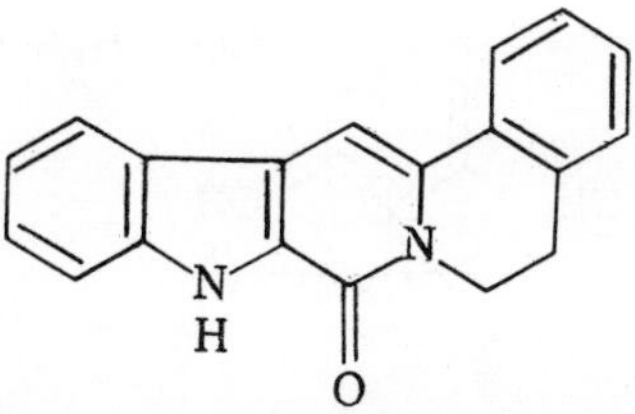

CCLXXX 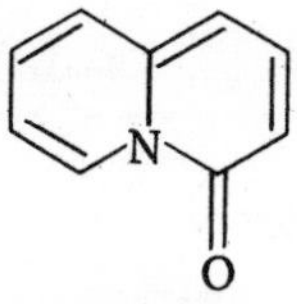   CCLXXXI 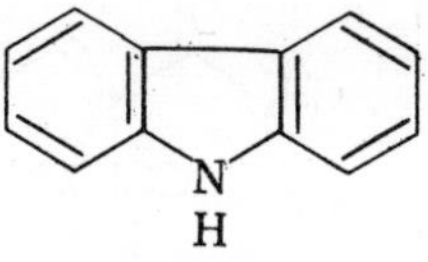   CCLXXXII

The carbazole moiety (CCLXXXII) is not attacked by LAH.

12.19.4 Pyridine Derivatives

As discussed in Section 12.16.1.e, the reduction of pyridine (CCLXXXIII) derivatives with LAH generally proceeds without attack on the heterocyclic nucleus. However, under more drastic conditions such as a higher reaction temperature and a prolonged reaction time, piperidine derivatives are formed.

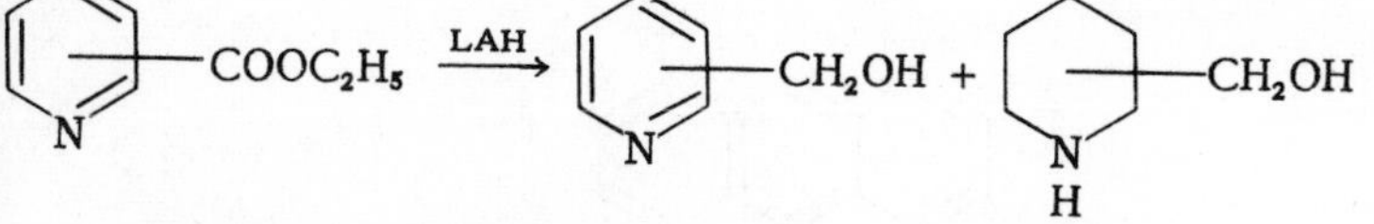

(12-212)

CCLXXXIII

The LAH reduction of pyridine has been reported to yield a labile dihydro compound (130) or the hexahydro derivative piperidine (180). The reduction of quaternary pyridinium salts (CCLXXXIV) with the complex hydrides yields o-dihydro or tetrahydro derivatives (Section 12.15).

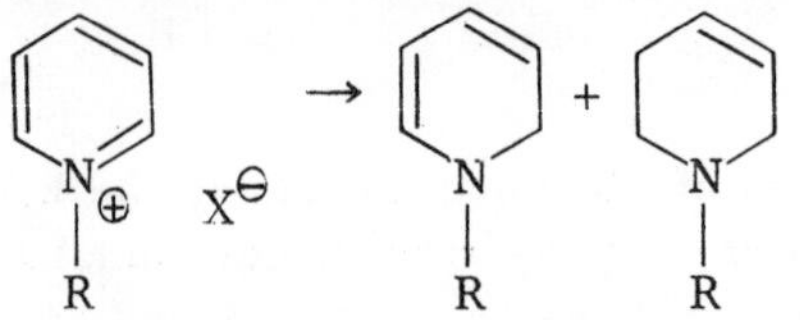

$$\text{(12-213)}$$

CCLXXXIV

The LAH reduction of 2-hydroxypyridine (CCLXXXV) in refluxing di-n-butyl ether yields small quantities of pyridine and piperidine (180).

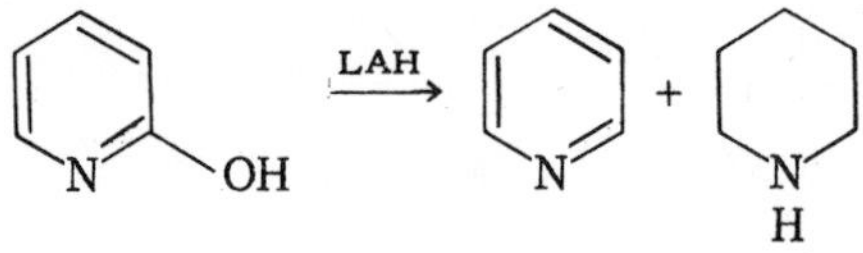

$$\text{(12-214)}$$

CCLXXXV

The α-hydroxy group is retained intact in the treatment of the 2-pyridols, CCLXXXVI (221), CCLXXXVII (222), and CCLXXXVIII (223) with LAH.

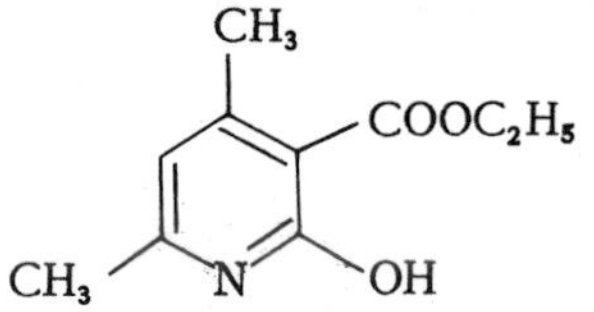

CCLXXXVI

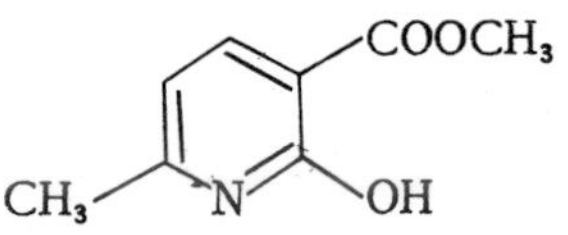

CCLXXXVII

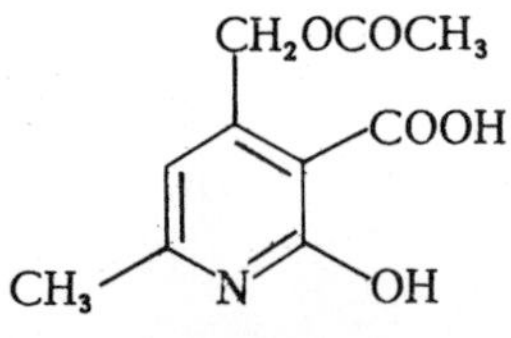

CCLXXXVIII

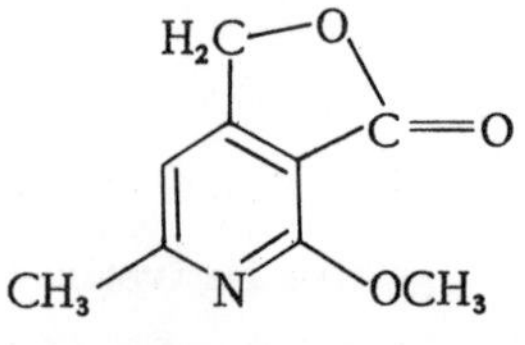

CCLXXXIX

The attempted LAH reduction of the 2-methoxypyridine, CCLXXXIX, has been reported to be unsuccessful (223). The hydroxy group is not attacked by LAH in the reduction of 4-hydroxy-6,7-benzoquinazoline (CCXC) (189).

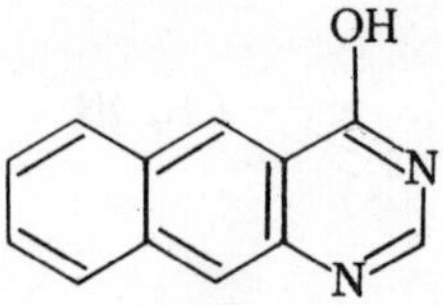

CCXC

The LAH reduction of the 2(1)-pyridone (CCXCI) in di-n-butyl ether yields the 2-pyridol (222).

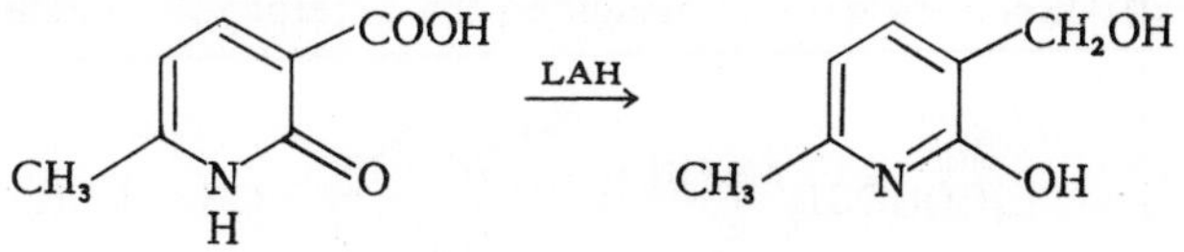

(12-215)

CCXCI

The attempted LAH reduction of the 2(1)-pyridones, CCXCII and CCXCIII, has been unsuccessful (223).

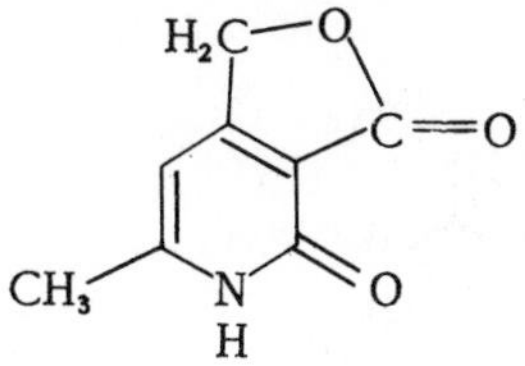

CCXCII 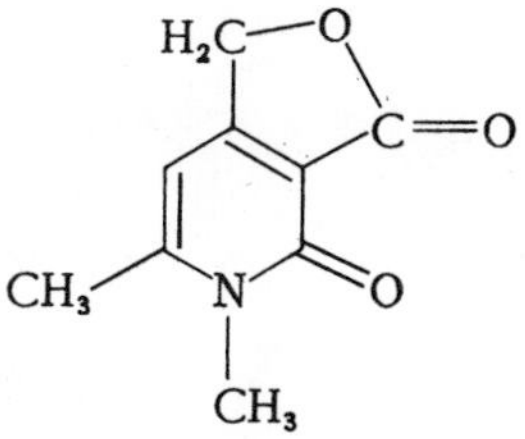   CCXCIII

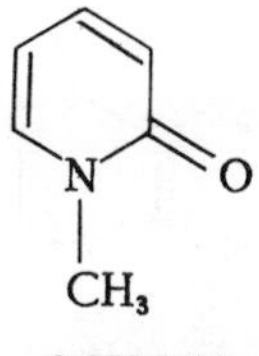

CCXCIV 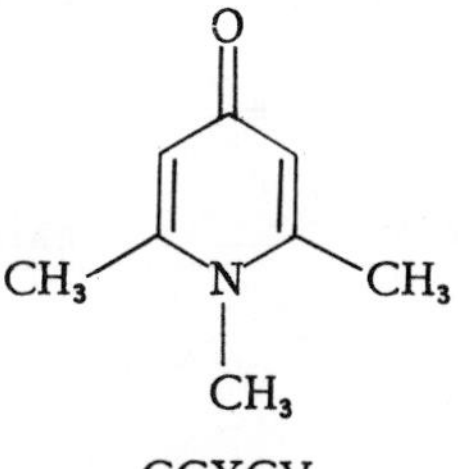   CCXCV

The LAH reduction of N-methylpyridone (CCXCIV) has been reported to yield 7% of methylamine and a trace of an N-methylpyridinium salt isolated as the picrate (180). An unsuccessful attempt to reduce 1,2,6-trimethyl-4-pyridone (CCXCV) with LAH has been attributed to the low ether solubility of the pyridone (224).

The reduction of pyridine-N-oxide-2-azo-p-dimethylaniline (CCXCVI) with excess LAH yields pyridine-2-azo-p-dimethylaniline (86).

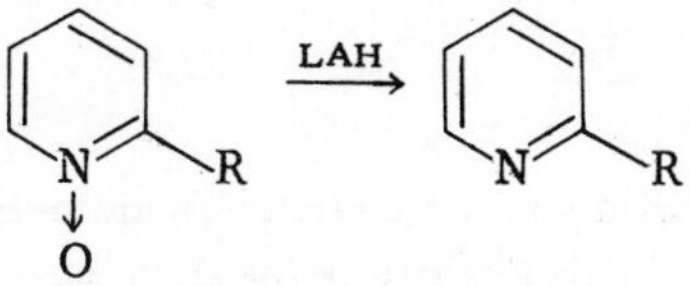

(12-216)

CCXCVI

12.19.5   Quinoline Derivatives

The LAH reduction of quinoline (CCXCVII) and isoquinoline derivatives generally proceeds without attack on the heterocyclic nucleus.

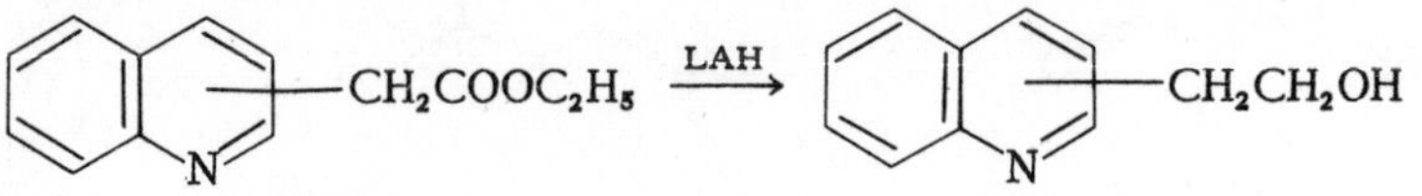

$$\text{CCXCVII} \quad \xrightarrow{\text{LAH}} \quad \text{CH}_2\text{CH}_2\text{OH} \qquad (12\text{-}217)$$

CCXCVII

The LAH reduction of quinoline (CCXCVIII) is reported to yield 1,2-dihydroquinoline (130,184).

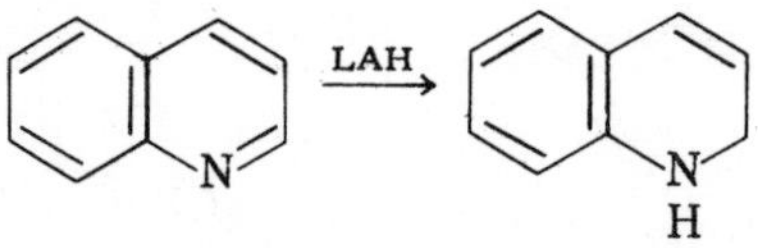

$$\xrightarrow{\text{LAH}} \qquad (12\text{-}218)$$

CCXCVIII

The reduction of 2-hydroxyquinoline (CCXCIX) with LAH in refluxing di-*n*-butyl ether is reported to yield quinoline and tetrahydroquinoline (180).

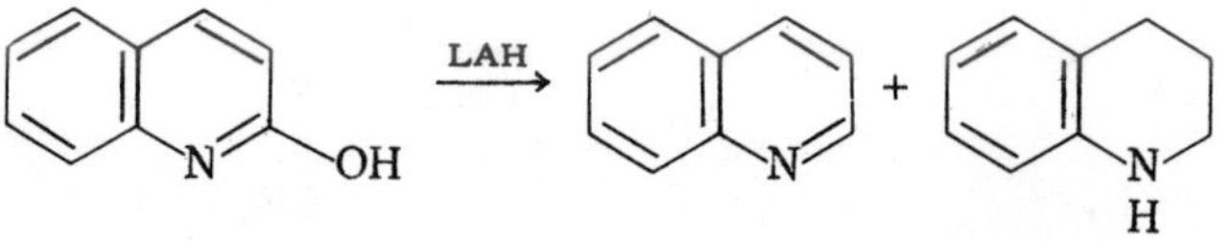

$$\xrightarrow{\text{LAH}} \qquad + \qquad (12\text{-}219)$$

CCXCIX

The reduction of N-methylquinolone (CCC) has been reported to yield 20% of an N-methylquinolinium salt identified as the platinichloride (180).

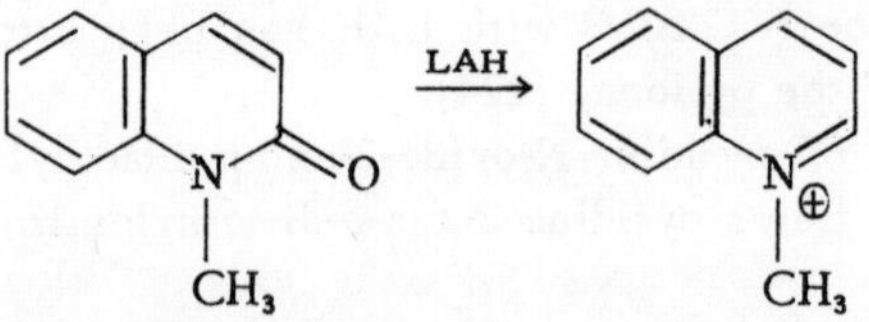

$$\xrightarrow{\text{LAH}} \qquad (12\text{-}220)$$

CCC

The reduction of quinolinium (CCCI) and isoquinolinium salts with LAH yields 1,2-dihydro derivatives while potassium borohydride yields 1,2,3,4-tetrahydro derivatives.

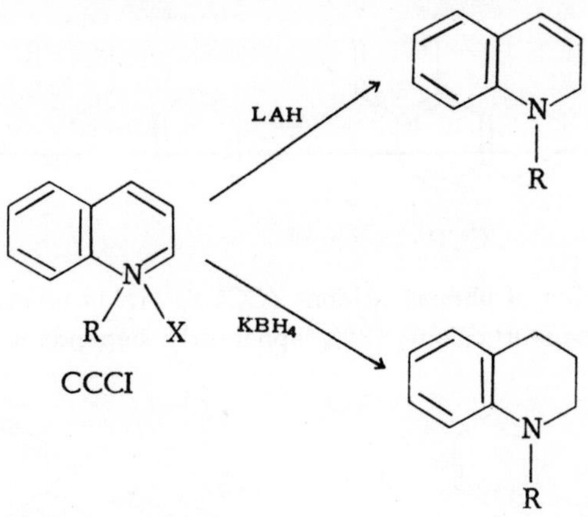

(12-221)

LAH

KBH₄

CCCI

(12-222)

12.19.6 Acridines and Related Compounds

The LAH reduction of acridine (CCCII) yields 9,10-dihydroacridine (130).

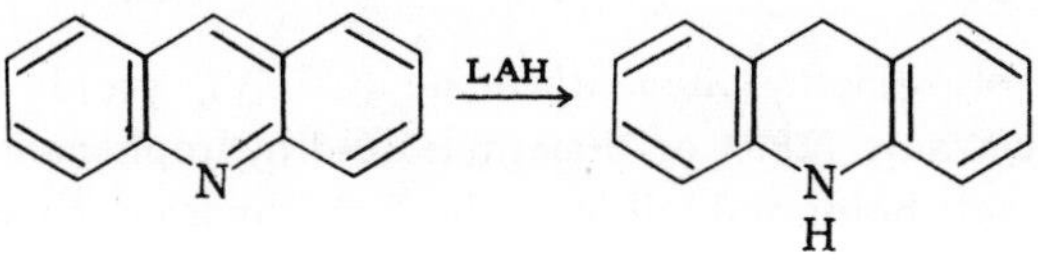

LAH

(12-223)

CCCII

The reduction of benz[a]acridin-12(7H)-one (CCCIII) yields a molecular complex of benz[a]acridine and 7,12-dihydrobenz[a]acridine (85).

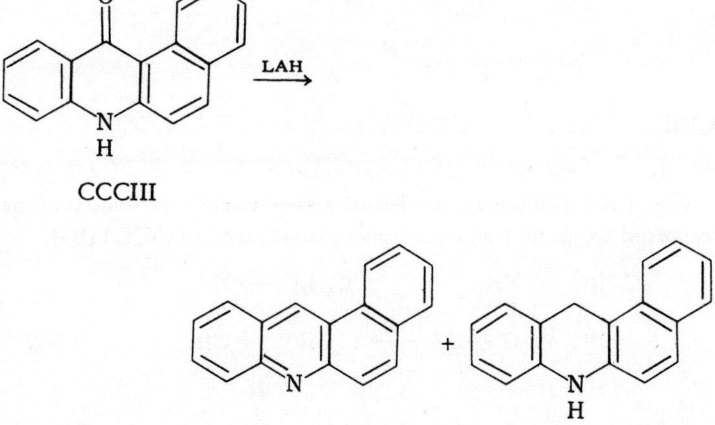

LAH

CCCIII

+ (12-224)

The LAH reduction of phenanthridine (CCCIV) (186) and 6-chloro-phenanthridine (85) yields 5,6-dihydrophenanthridine.

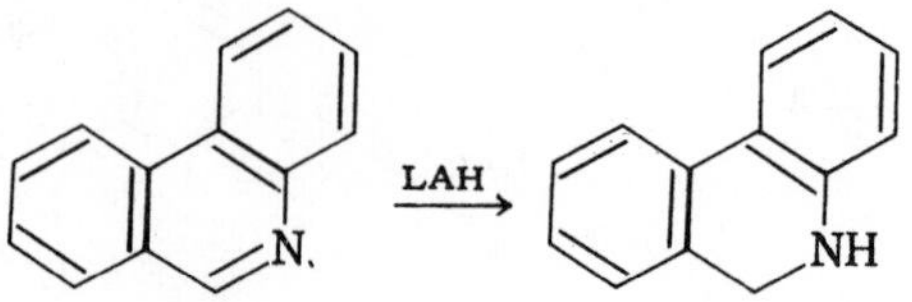

(12-225)

CCCIV

The LAH reduction of phenanthridone (CCCV) yields phenanthridine (180) or 5,6-dihydrophenanthridone (85), apparently dependent upon the LAH concentration.

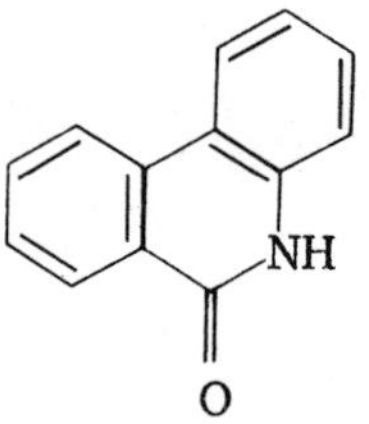

CCCV 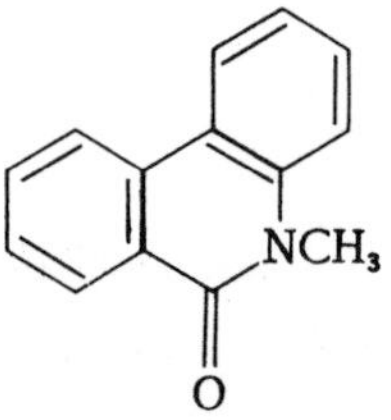   CCCVI

The reduction of N-methylphenanthridone (CCCVI) yields the N-methyl-phenanthridinium salt (180) or 5-methyl-5,6-dihydrophenanthridine (135), the quaternary salt being reducible to the 5,6-dihydro derivative (135).

12.19.7 Azoles and Related Compounds

The pyrazole (CCCVII) (21,225) and isoindazole (CCCVIII) (226) nuclei are resistant to attack by LAH.

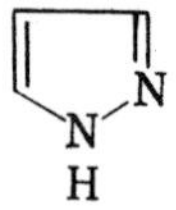

CCCVII 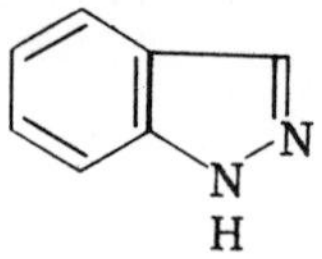   CCCVIII 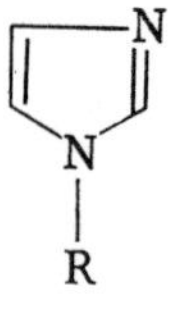   CCCIX

The imidazole nucleus (CCCIX) is resistant to attack by LAH (166, 227-231). The LAH reduction of 1-methyl-4-phenyl-2(3H)-imidazolone (CCCX) is reported to yield 1-methyl-4-phenylimidazole (CCCXI) (84).

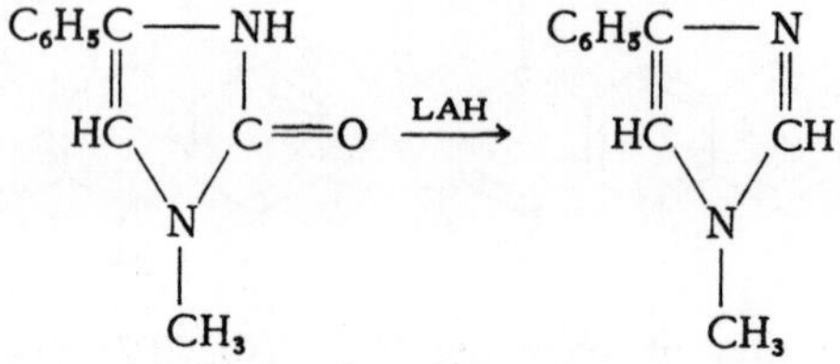

(12-226)

CCCX   CCCXI

The LAH reduction of benzimidazole (CCCXII) under forcing conditions, yields dihydrobenzimidazole (130).

$$\text{CCCXII} \xrightarrow{\text{LAH}} \qquad (12\text{-}227)$$

CCCXII

The LAH reduction of benzotriazole (CCCXIII) derivatives results in retention of the heterocyclic nucleus (214,215). Treatment of 1-benzyl-4-[(1-hydroxy)isopropyl]triazole (CCCXIV) with LAH at 0° indicates that the nucleus is not attacked (232).

CCCXIII   CCCXIV

As discussed in Section 12.16.1.e, oxazole carboxylic esters are attacked by LAH, and while 2-methyltetrahydrobenzoxazole (CCCXV) is cleaved by LAH to 2-ethylaminocyclohexanol the oxazoline (CCCXVI) nucleus is retained intact after treatment with LAH at low temperatures.

CCCXV   CCCXVI

The thiazole nucleus (CCCXVII) is resistant to attack by LAH even under conditions involving large excesses of the reducing agent and elevated temperatures (233). A benzothiazolyl derivative (CCCXVIII) has been reported to yield the corresponding LAH reduction product without reduction of the heterocyclic nucleus (234).

CCCXVII   CCCXVIII

12.19.8   Azines and Related Compounds

The pyrazine (CCCXIX) nucleus undergoes decomposition when treated with LAH (170). The LAH reduction of quinoxaline (CCCXX) (130) and 2-oxo-1,2-dihydroquinoxalines (CCCXXI) (185) yields 1,2,3,4-tetrahydroquinoxalines.

CCCXIX   CCCXX   CCCXXI

Although the phenazine nucleus can be retained intact in the LAH reduction of phenazine derivatives (188), the treatment of phenazine (CCCXXII) itself with LAH yields 5,10-dihydrophenazine (CCCXXIII) (188) or a molecular complex of phenazine and the dihydro compound (130).

(12-228)

CCCXXII   CCCXXIII

The attempted LAH reduction of benzo[a]phenazine (CCCXXIV) has been reported to be unsuccessful (85).

The reduction of benzo[c]cinnoline N-oxide (CCCXXV) yields benzo-[c]cinnoline (85) which is reducible to a dihydro derivative which has not been isolated but has been characterized by its reducing properties (130).

CCCXXIV   CCCXXV

The LAH reduction of 4-hydroxy-6,7-benzoquinazoline (CCCXXVI) yields 1,2-dihydro-4-hydroxy-6,7-benzoquinazoline (189).

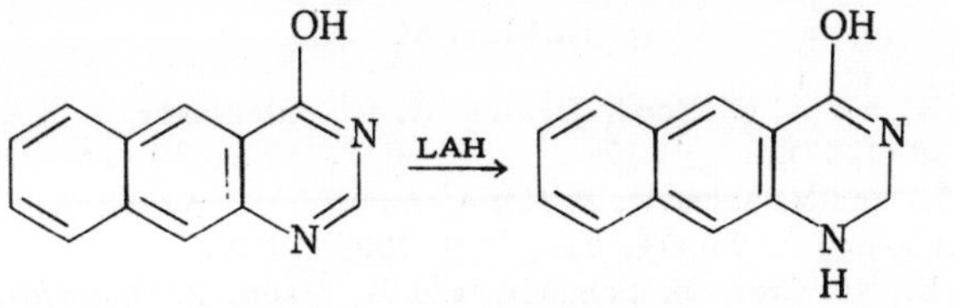

(12-229)

CCCXXVI

The pyrimidine moiety in thiamine (CCCXXVII) is not attacked by LAH (139,235), sodium borohydride or sodium trimethoxyborohydride (156,157). The attempted reduction of 2-amino-4-hydroxy-6-methyl-5-pyrimidylacetic acid (CCCXXVIII) with LAH has been reported to be unsuccessful (236). The purine system in cozymase is similarly not attacked by sodium borohydride (158).

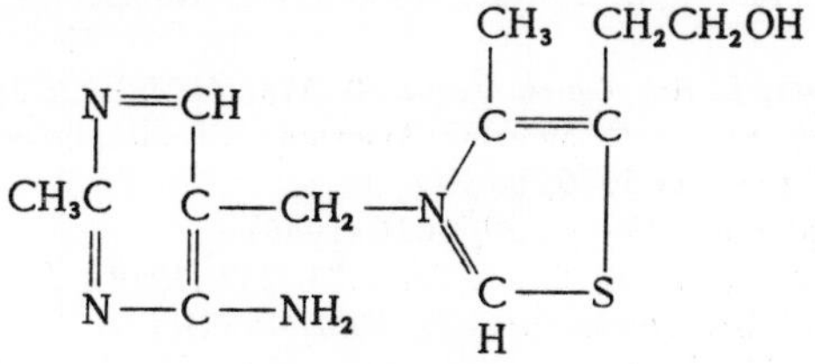

CCCXXVII 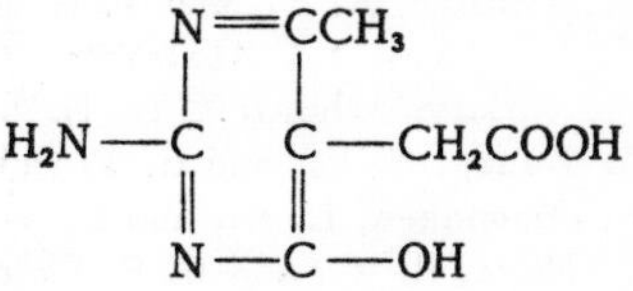   CCCXXVIII

The reduction of 6-keto-2-phenyl-4,5-benzo-1,3-oxazine (CCCXXIX) with excess LAH yields o-benzaminobenzyl alcohol while reduction with one-quarter mole of LAH yields a product postulated as 6-keto-2-phenyl-4,5-benzo-2,3-dihydro-1,3-oxazine (equations 12-147 and 12-148) (174).

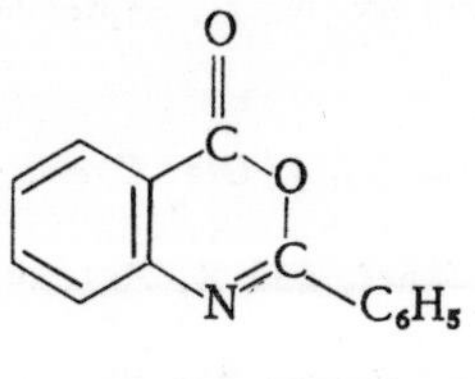

CCCXXIX 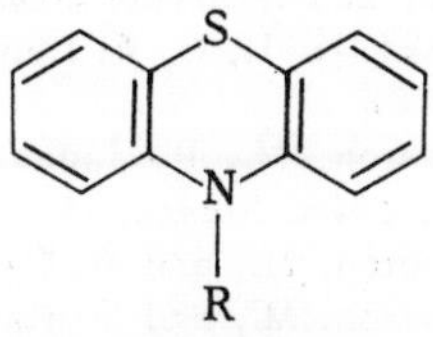   CCCXXX

The phenothiazine nucleus (CCCXXX) is not attacked by LAH (237, 238).

REFERENCES

1. Finholt, A. E., A. C. Bond, Jr., and H. I. Schlesinger, *J. Am. Chem. Soc.*, 69, 1199 (1947).
2. Wiberg, E., and M. Schmidt, *Z. Naturforsch.*, 6b, 333 (1951).
3. Stecher, O., and E. Wiberg, *Ber.*, 75B, 2003 (1942).
4. Wiberg, E., H. Graf, M. Schmidt, and R. Usón, *Z. Naturforsch.*, 7b, 578 (1952).
5. Schlesinger, H. I., and H. C. Brown, *J. Am. Chem. Soc.*, 62, 3429 (1940).
6. Schaeffer, G. W., and E. R. Anderson, *J. Am. Chem. Soc.*, 71, 2143 (1949).
7. Schlesinger, H. I., R. T. Sanderson and A. B. Burg, *J. Am. Chem. Soc.*, 62, 3421 (1940).
8. Wiberg, E., and R. Bauer, *Z. Naturforsch.*, 7b, 58 (1952).
9. Burg, A. B., and H. I. Schlesinger, *J. Am. Chem. Soc.*, 62, 3425 (1940).
10. Wiberg, E., and M. Schmidt, *Z. Naturforsch.*, 6b, 171 (1951).
11. Schlesinger, H. I., and A. E. Finholt, U. S. Pat. 2,567,972 (September 18, 1951).
12. Schlesinger, H. I., and A. E. Finholt, U. S. Pat. 2,576,311 (November 27, 1951).
13. Nystrom, R. F., and W. G. Brown, *J. Am. Chem. Soc.*, 70, 3738 (1948).
14. Friedman, L., *Abstracts of Papers*, 116th Meeting American Chemical Society, Atlantic City, N. J., September 1949, p. 5M.
15. Zaugg, H. E., and B. W. Horrom, *Anal. Chem.*, 20, 1026 (1948).
16. Amundsen, L. H., and L. S. Nelson, *J. Am. Chem. Soc.*, 73, 242 (1950).
17. Nace, H. R., and B. B. Smith, *J. Am. Chem. Soc.*, 74, 1861 (1952).
18. Welvart, Z., *Compt. rend.*, 233, 1121 (1951).
19. Zaugg, H. E., and B. W. Horrom, *J. Am. Chem. Soc.*, 75, 292 (1953).
20. Schnider, O., and J. Hellerbach, *Helv. Chim. Acta*, 33, 1437 (1950).
21. Jones, R. G., *J. Am. Chem. Soc.*, 71, 3994 (1949).
22. Eiter, K., and E. Mrazak, *Monatsh.*, 83, 915 (1952).
23. Grewe, R., and E. Nolte, *Ann.*, 575, 1 (1951).
24. Barry, V. C., J. G. Belton, R. M. Kelly, and D. Twomey, *Nature*, 166, 303 (1950).
25. Barry, V. C., and D. Twomey, *Abstracts of Papers*, XIIth International Congress of Pure and Applied Chemistry, New York, N. Y., September 1951, p. 308.
26. Brown, R. F., private communication.
27. Leonard, N. J., G. W. Leubner, and E. H. Burk, Jr., *J. Org. Chem.*, 15, 979 (1950).
28. Mousseron, M., R. Jacquier, M. Mousseron-Canet, and R. Zagdoun, *Bull. soc. chim. France*, [5] 19, 1042 (1952).
29. Mousseron, M., and M. Canet, *Bull. soc. chim. France*, [5] 19, 247 (1952).
30. Mousseron, M., and M. Canet, *Bull. soc. chim. France*, [5] 18, 792 (1951),
31. Mousseron, M., R. Jacquier, M. Mousseron-Canet, and R. Zagdoun, *Compt. rend.*, 235, 177 (1952).
32. Anet, F. A. L., D. Mukherji, R. Robinson, and E. Schlittler, *Chemistry and Industry*, 1952, 442.
33. Paddock, N. L., *Nature*, 167, 1070 (1951).
34. Heusser, H., P. T. Herzig, A. Fürst, and P. A. Plattner, *Helv. Chim. Acta*, 33, 1093 (1950).
35. Roberts, J. D., and W. F. Gorham, *J. Am. Chem. Soc.*, 74, 2278 (1952).
36. Avison, A. W. D., *J. Applied Chem. (London)*, 1, 469 (1951).

37. Elderfield, R. C., B. M. Pitt, and I. Wempen, *J. Am. Chem. Soc.*, 72, 1334 (1950).
38. Weisler, L., U. S. Pat. 2,583,194 (January 22, 1952).
39. Weisler, L., Brit. Pat. 684,757 (December 24, 1952).
40. Patel, D. K., V. Petrow, R. Royer, and I. A. Stuart-Webb, *J. Chem. Soc.*, 1952, 161.
41. Dornow, A., G. Messwarb, and H. H. Frey, *Chem. Ber.*, 83, 445 (1950).
42. Jacquier, R., and R. Zagdoun, *Bull. soc. chim. France*, [5] 19, 698 (1952).
43. Ehrensvärd, G., and R. Stjernholm, *Acta Chem. Scand.*, 3, 971 (1949).
44. Reynaud, P., and J. Matti, *Compt. rend.*, 235, 1230 (1952).
45. Felkin, H., *Compt. rend.*, 230, 304 (1950).
46. Avison, A. W. D., and A. L. Morrison, *J. Chem. Soc.*, 1950, 1474.
47. Reynaud, P., and J. Matti, *Bull. soc. chim. France*, [5] 18, 612 (1951).
48. Smith, L. I., and E. R. Rogier, *J. Am. Chem. Soc.*, 73, 4047 (1951).
49. Lowy, P. H., *J. Am. Chem. Soc.*, 74, 1355 (1952).
50. Henne, A. L., R. L. Pelley, and R. M. Alm, *J. Am. Chem. Soc.*, 72, 3370 (1950).
51. Yandik, M., and A. A. Larsen, *J. Am. Chem. Soc.*, 73, 3534 (1951).
52. Huisman, H. O., A. Smit, S. Vromen, and L. G. M. Fisscher, *Rec. trav. chem.*, 71, 899 (1952).
53. Huisman, H. O., Ger. Pat. 857, 952 (December 4, 1952).
54. N. V. Philips' Gloeilampenfabrieken, Fr. Pat. 1,022,925 (March 11, 1953).
55. Herz, W., *J. Am. Chem. Soc.*, 72, 4999 (1950).
56. Claus, C. J., and J. L. Morgenthau, Jr., *J. Am. Chem. Soc.*, 73, 5005 (1951).
57. Wiberg, E., and A. Jahn, *Z. Naturforsch.*, 7b, 580 (1952).
58. Wiberg, E., and R. Bauer, *Z. Naturforsch.*, 7b, 131 (1952).
59. Wiberg, E., through *European Scientific Notes*, No. 7-1, January 1, 1953.
60. Chaikin, S. W., and W. G. Brown, *J. Am. Chem. Soc.*, 71, 122 (1949).
61. Nickon, A., and L. F. Fieser, *J. Am. Chem. Soc.*, 74, 5566 (1952).
62. Wendler, N. L., R. P. Graber, R. E. Jones, and M. Tishler, *J. Am. Chem. Soc.*, 74, 3630 (1952).
63. Wendler, N. L., R. P. Graber, R. E. Jones and M. Tishler, *J. Am. Chem. Soc.*, 72, 5793 (1950).
64. Wendler, N. L., Huang-Minlon and M. Tishler, *J. Am. Chem. Soc.*, 73, 3818 (1951).
65. Friedman, L., *Abstracts of Papers*, 122nd Meeting American Chemical Society, Atlantic City, N. J., September 1952, p. 46M.
66. Larsson, E., *Trans. Chalmers Univ. Technol., Gothenburg*, 94, 15 (1950).
67. Wessely, R., and W. Swoboda, *Monatsh.*, 82, 621 (1951).
68. Ried, W., and F. Müller, *Chem. Ber.*, 85, 470 (1952).
69. Zeiss, H. H., and W. B. Martin, Jr., *Abstracts of Papers*, 121st Meeting American Chemical Society, Buffalo, N. Y., March 1952, p. 41K.
70. Smith, D. R., M. Maienthal, and J. Tipton, *J. Org. Chem.*, 17, 294 (1952).
71. Gregory, G. I., and T. Malkin, *J. Chem. Soc.*, 1951, 2453.
72. Fisher, N., *Chemistry and Industry*, 1952, 130.
73. Hayes, K., and G. Gever, *J. Org. Chem.*, 16, 269 (1951).
74. Elphimoff-Felkin, I., H. Felkin, B. Tchoubar, and Z. Welvart, *Bull. soc. chim. France*, [5] 19, 252 (1952).
75. Viscontini, M., and K. Adank, *Helv. Chim. Acta*, 35, 1342 (1952).
76. Viscontini, M., *Helv. Chim. Acta*, 35, 1803 (1952).
77. Cromwell, N. H., and Kwan-Chung Tsou, *J. Org. Chem.*, 15, 1219 (1950).

834   REDUCTION OF NITROGEN-CONTAINING COMPOUNDS

78. Larsson, E., *Svensk Kem. Tid.*, *61*, 242 (1949); *Chem. Abstracts*, *44*, 1898 (1950).
79. Kopp, M., *Compt. rend.*, *235*, 247 (1952).
80. Walter, C. R., Jr., *J. Am. Chem. Soc.*, *74*, 5185 (1952).
81. Hochstein, F. A., *J. Am. Chem. Soc.*, *71*, 305 (1949).
82. Braunholtz, J. T., and F. G. Mann, *J. Chem. Soc.*, *1952*, 3046.
83. Tarbell, D. S. and J. C. Bill, *J. Am. Chem. Soc.*, *74*, 1234 (1952).
84. Wilk, I. J., and W. J. Close, *J. Org. Chem.*, *15*, 1020 (1950).
85. Badger, G. M., J. H. Seidler, and B. Thomson, *J. Chem. Soc.*, *1951*, 3207.
86. Fraessinger, R. W., and E. V. Brown, *Abstracts of Papers*, 121st Meeting American Chemical Society, Buffalo, N. Y., March 1952, p. 24K.
87. Brown, W. G., in *Organic Reactions*, Vol. VI, p. 471.
88. Gilman, H., and T. N. Goreau, *J. Am. Chem. Soc.*, *73*, 2939 (1951).
89. Nystrom, R. F., unpublished work, through W. G. Brown, in *Organic Reactions*, Vol. VI, p. 506.
90. Schueler, F. W., and C. Hanna, *J. Am. Chem. Soc.*, *73*, 4996 (1951).
91. Vogel, A. I., W. T. Cresswell, G. H. Jeffery, and J. Leicester, *J. Chem. Soc.*, *1952*, 538.
92. Leicester, J., and A. I. Vogel, *Research*, *3*, 148 (1950).
93. Hanna, C., and F. W. Schueler, *J. Am. Chem. Soc.*, *74*, 3693 (1952).
94. Poirier, R. H., and F. Benington, *J. Am. Chem. Soc.*, *74*, 3192 (1952).
95. Skita, A., and H. Rolfes, *Ber.*, *53*, 1251 (1920).
96. Dornow, A., and F. Boberg, *Ann.*, *578*, 94 (1952).
97. Parham, W. E., and F. L. Ramp, *J. Am. Chem. Soc.*, *73*, 1293 (1951).
98. Gilsdorf, R. T., and F. F. Nord, *J. Am. Chem. Soc.*, *74*, 1837 (1952).
99. Brown, R. F., and N. van Gulick, *Abstracts of Papers*, 122nd Meeting American Chemical Society, Atlantic City, N. J., September 1952, p. 7M.
100. Späth, E., *Monatsh.*, *40*, 144 (1919).
101. Erne, M., and F. Ramirez, *Helv. Chim. Acta*, *33*, 912 (1950).
102. Benington, F., and R. D. Morin, *J. Am. Chem. Soc.*, *73*, 1353 (1951).
103. Dornow, A., and G. Petsch, *Arch. pharm.*, *284*, 160 (1951).
104. Bu'Lock, J. D., and J. Harley-Mason, *J. Chem. Soc.*, *1951*, 2248.
105. Ashley, J. N., and M. Davis, *J. Chem. Soc.*, *1952*, 63.
106. Gilsdorf, R. T., and F. F. Nord, *J. Am. Chem. Soc.*, *72*, 4327 (1950).
107. Egerton, M. J., G. I. Gregory, and T. Malkin, *J. Chem. Soc.*, *1952*, 2272.
108. Kharasch, N., and J. L. Cameron, *J. Am. Chem. Soc.*, *75*, 1077 (1953).
109. Backer, H. J., *Rec. trav. chim.*, *68*, 844 (1949).
110. Adams, R., and W. Moje, *J. Am. Chem. Soc.*, *74*, 5557 (1952).
111. Shechter, H., D. E. Ley, and L. Zeldin, *J. Am. Chem. Soc.*, *74*, 3664 (1952).
112. Nelson, L. S., and D. E. Laskowski, *Anal. Chem.*, *23*, 1495, 1776 (1951).
113. Brown, W. G., private communication, through ref. 88.
114. Kvasnicka, E., *Österr. Chem. Ztg.*, *52*, 26 (1951).
115. Gaylord, N. G., and J. A. Snyder, *Rec. trav. chim.*, *72*, 1007 (1953).
116. Barton, D. H. R., and W. J. Rosenfelder, *J. Chem. Soc.*, *1951*, 2381.
117. Macbeth, A. K., and J. S. Shannon, *J. Chem. Soc.*, *1952*, 4748.
118. Dornow, A., and G. Winter, *Chem. Ber.*, *84*, 307 (1951).
119. Bergmann, E. D., H. Bendas, and W. Taub, *J. Chem. Soc.*, *1951*, 2673.
120. Carrara, G., E. Pace, and G. Cristiani, *J. Am. Chem. Soc.*, *74*, 4949 (1952).
121. Huebner, C. F., and C. R. Scholz, *J. Am. Chem. Soc.*, *73*, 2089 (1951).
122. Elphimoff-Felkin, I., H. Felkin, and Z. Welvart, *Compt. rend.*, *234*, 1789 (1952).
123. Eiter, K., and E. Sackl, *Monatsh.*, *83*, 123 (1952).

124. Société des Usines Chimiques Rhone Poulenc, Australian Pat. Appln. 955/51 (February 21, 1951).
125. Parke, Davis and Co., Australian Pat. Appln. 13,395/52 (October 15, 1952).
126. Parke, Davis and Co., Australian Pat. Appln. 10,904/52 (June 24, 1952).
127. Nystrom, R. F., S. W. Chaikin, and W. G. Brown, *J. Am. Chem. Soc.*, *71*, 3245 (1949).
128. Paul, R., and N. Joseph, *Bull. soc. chim. France*, [5] *19*, 550 (1952).
129. Smith, D. H., J. R. Schwartz and G. W. Wheland, *J. Am. Chem. Soc.*, *74*, 2282 (1952).
130. Bohlmann, F., *Chem. Ber.*, *85*, 390 (1952).
131. Langley, B. W., B. Lythgoe, and L. S. Rayner, *J. Chem. Soc.*, *1952*, 4191.
132. Boyer, J. H., *J. Am. Chem. Soc.*, *73*, 5865 (1951).
133. Gruber, W., and H. Renner, *Monatsh.*, *81*, 751 (1950).
134. Schmid, H., and P. Karrer, *Helv. Chim. Acta*, *32*, 960 (1949).
135. Karrer, P., L. Szabo, H. J. V. Krishna, and R. Schwyzer, *Helv. Chim. Acta*, *33*, 294 (1950).
136. Schmid, H., and P. Karrer, *Helv. Chim. Acta*, *33*, 863 (1950).
137. Karrer, P., *Bull. soc. chim. France*, [5] *17*, 907 (1950).
138. Karrer, P., *Angew. Chem.*, *62*, 334 (1950).
139. Karrer, P., and H. Krishna, *Helv. Chim. Acta*, *33*, 555 (1950).
140. Karrer, P., *Angew. Chem.*, *63*, 37 (1951).
141. Karrer, P., W. Graf, and J. Schukri, *Helv. Chim. Acta*, *28*, 1523 (1945).
142. Battersby, A. R., and H. T. Openshaw, *Experientia*, *5*, 398 (1949).
143. Battersby, A. R., and H. T. Openshaw, *J. Chem. Soc.*, *1949*, 3207.
144. Battersby, A. R., H. T. Openshaw, and H. C. S. Wood, *Experientia*, *5*, 114 (1949).
145. Openshaw, H. T., and H. C. S. Wood, *Abstracts of Papers*, XIIth International Congress of Pure and Applied Chemistry, New York, N. Y., September 1951, p. 413.
146. Karrer, P., C. H. Eugster, and O. Rüttner, *Helv. Chim. Acta*, *31*, 1219 (1948).
147. Karrer, P., and O. Rüttner, *Helv. Chim. Acta*, *33*, 291 (1950).
148. Openshaw, H. T., and H. C. S. Wood, *J. Chem. Soc.*, *1952*, 391.
149. Tietz, R. T., and W. E. McEwen, *J. Am. Chem. Soc.*, *75*, 4945 (1953).
150. Kenner, G. W., and M. A. Murray, *J. Chem. Soc.*, *1950*, 406.
151. Goutarel, R., M. M. Janot, V. Prelog, and R. P. A. Sneeden, *Helv. Chim. Acta*, *34*, 1962 (1951).
152. Habgood, T., L. Marion, and H. Schwarz, *Helv. Chim. Acta*, *35*, 638 (1952).
153. Prelog, V., J. B. Patrick, and B. Witkop, *Helv. Chim. Acta*, *35*, 640 (1952).
154. Forbes, private communication, through ref. 155.
155. Bentley, K. W., and R. Robinson, *J. Chem. Soc.*, *1952*, 947.
157. Bonvicino, G., and D. J. Hennessy, *Abstracts of Papers*, 117th Meeting American Chemical Society, Philadelphia, Pa., April 1950, p. 48C.
157. Bonvicino, G. E., and D. J. Hennessy, *Abstracts of Papers*, 122nd Meeting American Chemical Society, Atlantic City, N. J., September 1952, p. 7C.
158. Mathews, M. B., *J. Biol. Chem.*, *176*, 229 (1948).
159. Conn, E., through ref. 158.
160. Banus, M. D., R. W. Bragdon, and T. R. P. Gibb, Jr., *J. Am. Chem. Soc.*, *74*, 2346 (1952).
161. Panouse, J. J., *Compt. rend.*, *233*, 260 (1951).
162. Panouse, J. J., *Compt. rend.*, *233*, 1200 (1951).
163. Torossian, R., *Compt. rend.*, *235*, 1312 (1952).

164. Gilsdorf, R. T., and F. F. Nord, *J. Am. Chem. Soc.*, **74**, 1855 (1952).
165. Rheim, A., and M. Jutisz, *Biochim. et Biophys. Acta*, **9**, 645 (1952).
166. Fromageot, C., M. Jutisz, D. Meyer, and L. Pénasse, *Biochim. et Biophys. Acta*, **6**, 283 (1950).
167. Elphimoff-Felkin, I., *Compt. rend.*, **236**, 387 (1953).
168. Elstow, W. E. and B. C. Platt, *Chemistry and Industry*, **1952**, 449.
169. Class, J. B., and J. G. Aston, *J. Am. Chem. Soc.*, **73**, 2359 (1951).
170. Jones, R. G., and E. C. Kornfeld, *J. Am. Chem. Soc.*, **73**, 107 (1951).
171. Moersch, G. W., and A. C. Moore, U. S. Pat. 2,562,114 (July 24, 1951).
172. Hoffmann-LaRoche and Co., Akt., Brit. Pat. 681,130 (October 15, 1952).
173. Hoffmann-LaRoche and Co., Akt., Swiss Pat. 275,968 (October 1, 1951).
174. Witkop, B., J. B. Patrick, and H. M. Kissman, *Chem. Ber.*, **85**, 949 (1952).
175. Goutarel, R., M. M. Janot, V. Prelog, R. P. A. Sneeden, and W. I. Taylor, *Helv. Chim. Acta*, **34**, 1139 (1951).
176. Lukeš, R., and O. Červinka, unpublished work, through M. Ferles and J. Rudinger, *Chem. Listy*, **47**, 104, 140 (1953).
177. Witkop, B., and J. B. Patrick, *Experientia*, **6**, 183 (1950).
178. Witkop, B., and J. B. Patrick, *J. Am. Chem. Soc.*, **73**, 2188 (1951).
179. Witkop, B., and J. B. Patrick, *J. Am. Chem. Soc.*, **74**, 3855 (1952).
180. de Mayo, P., and W. Rigby, *Nature*, **166**, 1075 (1950).
181. Mićović, V. M., and M. L. Mihailović, *Rec. trav. chim.*, **71**, 970 (1952).
182. Wiberg, E., and W. Henle, *Z. Naturforsch.*, **7b**, 250 (1952).
183. Kalojanoff, A., *Ann.*, **577**, 147 (1952).
184. Craig, D., and E. C. Gregg, Jr., *J. Am. Chem. Soc.*, **75**, 2252 (1953).
185. Druey, J., and A. Hüni, *Helv. Chim. Acta*, **35**, 2301 (1952).
186. Wooten, W. C., and R. L. McKee, *J. Am. Chem. Soc.*, **71**, 2946 (1949).
187. Bergstrom, F. W., and R. A. Ogg, Jr., *J. Am. Chem. Soc.*, **53**, 245 (1931).
188. Birkofer, L., and A. Birkofer, *Chem. Ber.*, **85**, 286 (1952).
189. Etienne, A., and M. Legrand, *Compt. rend.*, **229**, 220 (1949).
190. Bartlett, M. F., W. I. Taylor, and K. Weisner, *Chemistry and Industry*, **1953**, 173.
191. Bartlett, M. F., J. Edwards, W. I. Taylor, and K. Wiesner, *Chemistry and Industry*, **1953**, 323.
192. Huang-Minlon and R. H. Pettebone, *J. Am. Chem. Soc.*, **74**, 1562 (1952).
193. Gaylord, N. G., *Experientia*, **10**, 351 (1954).
194. Bergmann, E. D., D. Lavie, and S. Pinchas, *J. Am. Chem. Soc.*, **73**, 5662 (1951).
195. Senkus, M., *J. Am. Chem. Soc.*, **67**, 1515 (1945).
196. Briggs, L. H., and R. H. Locker, *J. Chem. Soc.*, **1950**, 3020.
197. Sato, Y., A. Katz, and E. Mosettig, *J. Am. Chem. Soc.*, **73**, 880 (1951); **74**, 538 (1952).
198. Fontaine, T. D., J. S. Ard, and R. M. Ma, *J. Am. Chem. Soc.*, **73**, 878 (1951).
199. Fontaine, T. D., through L. H. Briggs, W. E. Harvey, R. H. Locker, W. A. McGillivray, and R. N. Seelye, *J. Chem. Soc.*, **1950**, 3013.
200. Kuhn, R., and I. Löw, *Chem. Ber.*, **85**, 416 (1952).
210. Schlittler, E., and H. Uehlinger, *Helv. Chim. Acta*, **35**, 2034 (1952).
202. Goutarel, R., M. M. Janot, V. Prelog, and W. I. Taylor, *Helv. Chim. Acta*, **33**, 150 (1950).
203. Culvenor, C. C. J., L. J. Goldsworthy, K. S. Kirby, and R. Robinson, *J. Chem. Soc.*, **1950**, 1485.
204. Witkop, B., *J. Am. Chem. Soc.*, **72**, 2311 (1950).
205. Stoll, A., A. Hofman, and T. Petrzilka, *Helv. Chim. Acta*, **34**, 1544 (1951).

206. Wiesner, K., S. K. Figdor, M. F. Bartlett, and D. R. Henderson, *Can. J. Chem.*, *30*, 608 (1952).
207. Galinovsky, F., and R. Weiser, *Experientia*, *6*, 377 (1950).
208. Galinovsky, F., A. Wagner, and R. Weiser, *Monatsh.*, *82*, 551 (1951).
209. Galinovsky, F., O. Vogl, and R. Weiser, *Monatsh.*, *83*, 114 (1952).
210. King, J. A., V. Hofmann, and F. H. McMillan, *J. Org. Chem.*, *16*, 1100 (1951).
211. Morrison, A. L., R. F. Long, and M. Königstein, *J. Chem. Soc.*, *1951*, 952.
212. Burgstahler, A. W., *J. Am. Chem. Soc.*, *73*, 3021 (1951).
213. Hatch, M. J., and D. J. Cram, *J. Am. Chem. Soc.*, *75*, 38 (1953).
214. Burckhalter, J. H., V. C. Stephens, and L. A. R. Hall, *J. Am. Chem. Soc.*, *74*, 3868 (1952).
215. Gaylord, N. G., *J. Am. Chem. Soc.*, *76*, 285 (1954).
216. Cronyn, M. W., and J. E. Goodrich, *J. Am. Chem. Soc.*, *74*, 3936 (1952).
217. Julian, P. L., and H. C. Printy, *J. Am. Chem. Soc.*, *71*, 3206 (1949).
218. Eiter, K., and O. Svierak, *Monatsh.*, *83*, 1453 (1952).
219. Boekelheide, V., and C. Ainsworth, *J. Am. Chem. Soc.*, *72*, 2134 (1950).
220. Boekelheide, V., and J. P. Lodge, Jr., *J. Am. Chem. Soc.*, *73*, 3681 (1951).
221. Mariella, R. P., and E. P. Belcher, *J. Am. Chem. Soc.*, *73*, 2616 (1951).
222. Mariella, R. P., and A. J. Havlik, *J. Am. Chem. Soc.*, *74*, 1915 (1952).
223. Mariella, R. P., and E. P. Belcher, *J. Am. Chem. Soc.*, *74*, 4049 (1952).
224. Campbell, K. N., J. F. Ackerman, and B. K. Campbell, *J. Org. Chem.*, *15*, 337 (1950).
225. Dvoretzky, I., and G. H. Richter, *J. Org. Chem.*, *15*, 1285 (1950).
226. Snyder, H. R., C. B. Thompson, and R. L. Hinman, *J. Am. Chem. Soc.*, *74*, 2009 (1952).
227. Jones, R. G., *J. Am. Chem. Soc.*, *71*, 383 (1949).
228. Jones, R. G., and K. C. McLaughlin, *J. Am. Chem. Soc.*, *71*, 2444 (1949).
229. Karrer, P., M. Suter, and P. Waser, *Helv. Chim. Acta*, *32*, 1936 (1949).
230. Jílek, J. O., and M. Protiva, *Collection Czech. Chem. Commun.*, *15*, 659 (1950).
231. Protiva, M., and J. Pliml, *Chem. Listy*, in press, through M. Ferles and J. Rudinger, *Chem. Listy*, *47*, 135 (1953).
232. Moulin, F., *Helv. Chim. Acta*, *35*, 167 (1952).
233. Conover, L. H., and D. J. Tarbell, *J. Am. Chem. Soc.*, *72*, 5221 (1950).
234. Wishingsky, H., and M. Rubin, *Abstracts of Papers*, XIIth International Congress of Pure and Applied Chemistry, New York, N. Y., September 1951, p. 307.
235. Karrer, P., and H. Krishna, *Helv. Chim. Acta*, *35*, 459 (1952).
236. Schrage, A., and G. H. Hitchings, *J. Org. Chem.*, *16*, 1153 (1951).
237. Dahlbom, R., and T. Ekstrand, *Acta Chem. Scand.*, *5*, 102 (1951).
238. Dahlbom, R., *Acta Chem. Scand.*, *6*, 310 (1952).

CHAPTER 13

Reduction of
SULFUR-CONTAINING ORGANIC COMPOUNDS

13.1 THIOETHERS, THIOLS AND COMPOUNDS CONTAINING

THE —S$\overset{|}{\underset{|}{C}}$O— GROUPING

13.1.1 Thioethers or Sulfides

Analogous to the behavior of ethers, thioethers or sulfides, R—S—R′, are resistant to attack by the complex metal hydrides (1,2).

Although cleavage occurs in the LAH reduction of cyclohexyloxyacetic acid, no cleavage products have been isolated in the reduction of the corresponding thio analogue (3).

$$C_6H_{11}OCH_2COOH \xrightarrow{\text{LAH}} C_6H_{11}OCH_2CH_2OH + C_6H_{11}OH \quad (13\text{-}1)$$

$$C_6H_{11}SCH_2COOH \xrightarrow{\text{LAH}} C_6H_{11}SCH_2CH_2OH \quad (13\text{-}2)$$

2,2-Disubstituted-1,3-propanediols are prepared by LAH reduction of the corresponding malonic ester. However, although the LAH reduction of ethyl ethylmercaptomalonate (I) appears to proceed normally, none of the desired diol is obtained, apparently due to degradation to volatile products (4).

$$\underset{\text{I}}{\begin{array}{c}C_2H_5 \quad COOC_2H_5 \\ \diagdown \;\; / \\ C \\ \diagup \;\; \diagdown \\ C_2H_5S \quad COOC_2H_5\end{array}} \qquad \underset{\text{II}}{\begin{array}{c} S-CHNO_2 \\ | \\ CH_3 \end{array}}$$

The cleavage of the carbon-sulfur linkage in 1-nitroethyl-p-tolylsulfide (II) to yield p-cresol (equation (12-197) under the influence of LAH (5) is

related to the presence of the —N$\overset{||}{\underset{|}{C}}$S— grouping (Section 12.18).

The reaction of a Δ^4-3-ketosteroid with benzyl mercaptan in the presence of zinc chloride yields the 3-benzylthioenol ether. This reaction has been utilized in the treatment of Δ^4-3,17-dione steroids wherein the isolated 17-keto group is untouched. LAH reduction then reduces the 17-keto group while the 3-keto group is protected in the form of the 3-thioenol ether which is resistant to attack by LAH. Hydrolysis of the thioenol ethers with dilute mineral acids yields the Δ^4-3-ketosteroid. This

838

sequence of reactions has been utilized in the synthesis of testosterone from 4-androstenedione (III) (6-8).

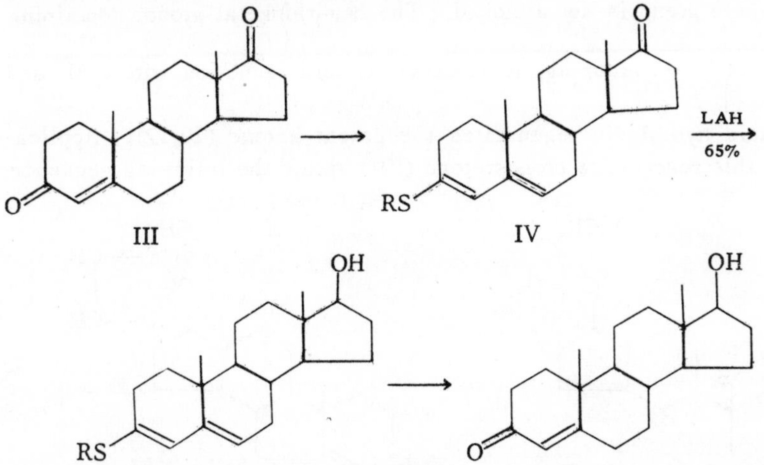

III   IV

$$\text{LAH} \atop 65\%$$

(13-3)

The 3-(β-hydroxyethyl)thioenol ether (IV : R = $HOCH_2CH_2$) has also been utilized in the synthesis of testosterone (6-8). The 3-benzylthioenol ethers of progesterone and 17α-hydroxyprogesterone have been subjected to treatment with LAH to yield the corresponding 20β-hydroxy-3-benzyl-thioenol ethers in 60 and 62% yield, respectively (9). The action of Raney nickel (fully active or partially deactivated) on 3-thioenol ethers (V) results in desulfurization (8,10).

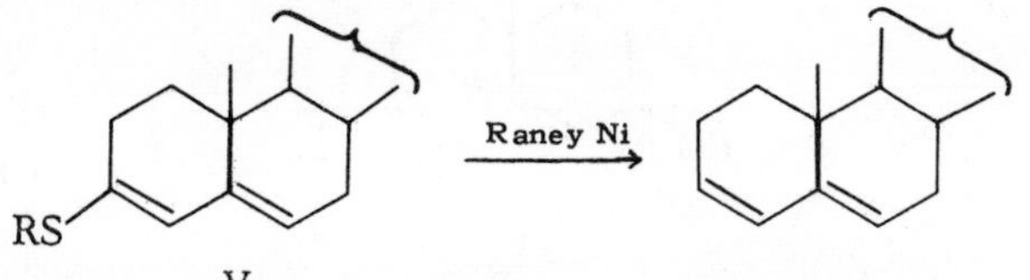

Raney Ni

(13-4)

V

13.1.2 Compounds Containing the —SCO— Grouping

Analogous to the non-reduction of 1,3-dioxolanes, 2,2-pentamethylene-1,3-thioxolane (VI) is not attacked by LAH in refluxing dioxane (11).

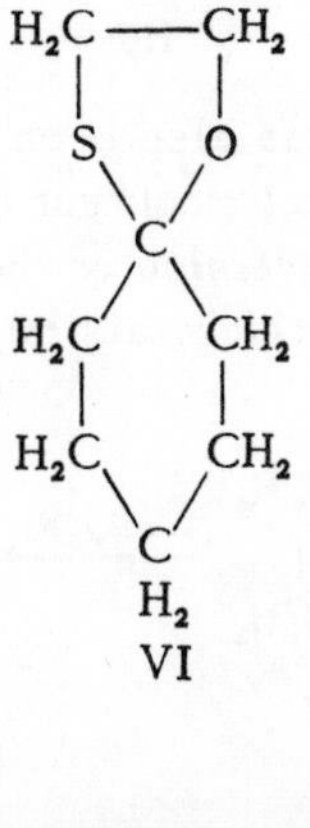

$$H_2C\text{——}CH_2$$

S   O

C

H_2C CH_2

H_2C CH_2

C

H_2

VI

Using β-mercaptoethanol in the presence of zinc chloride an unconjugated carbonyl group is converted to a cyclic ethylenehemithioketal while a Δ^4-3-keto group is not attacked. The hemithioketal group, containing

the —SCO— grouping, is resistant toward reduction with LAH and

upon acid hydrolysis regenerates the parent ketone (10,12). Application of this reaction to progesterone (VII) yields the following sequence (12):

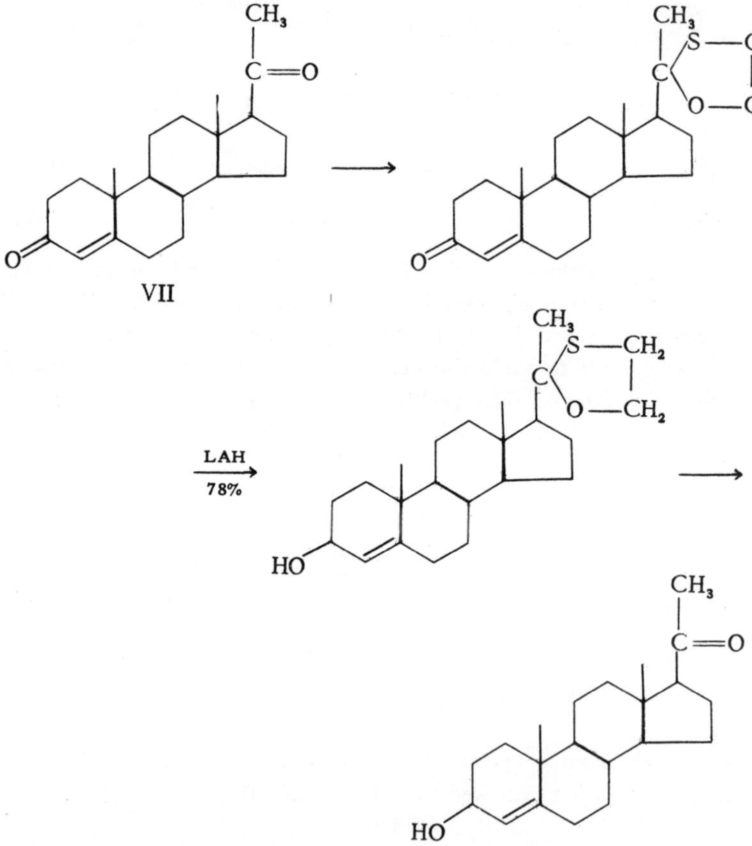

VII

LAH
⟶
78%

(13-5)

This sequence of reactions has also been applied to 4-androstene-3,17-dione (10). While Raney nickel treatment of 3-thioenol ethers results in desulfurization and hence conversion of the original carbonyl group into methylene, reaction with hemithioketals regenerates the parent ketone in good yield (10,12).

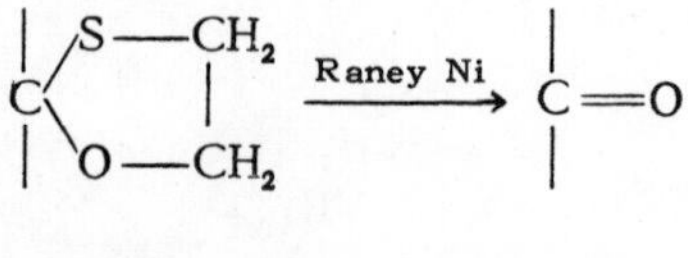

(13-6)

Both LAH reduction and treatment with Raney nickel have been utilized with allopregnane-3β-acetoxy-11,20-dione (VIII) (13).

(13-7)

13.1.3   Thiols or Mercaptans

The reaction of thiols with LAH involves the active hydrogen, the starting material being recovered on hydrolysis. The reaction of dithiols results in the generation of hydrogen sulfide and the formation of thiols (14).

$$R_2C\begin{matrix} \diagup SH \\ \diagdown SH \end{matrix} \xrightarrow{\text{LAH}} R_2CHSH + H_2S \qquad (13\text{-}8)$$

This reaction has been applied to the following dithiols, with the mercaptans being isolated in the indicated yields in the form of the 2,4-dinitrophenylsulfides.

	% Mercaptan
1,1-Propanedithiol	52
2,2-Propanedithiol	47
3,3-Pentanedithiol	48
1,1-Cyclohexanedithiol	55

13.2   DISULFIDES

The reduction of disulfides with LAH cleaves the sulfur-sulfur linkage to form a complex which on hydrolysis yields mercaptans. Hydrogen is

TABLE LXXXIII
LAH Reduction of Disulfides

	Disulfide	Product	% Yield	Ref.
$C_8H_{18}S_2$	Di-n-butyl disulfide	n-Butyl mercaptan	96	1
	n-Butyl-tert-butyl disulfide	n-Butyl mercaptan ⎫	96	1
		tert-Butyl mercaptan ⎭	···[2]	
	Di-tert-butyl disulfide	tert-Butyl mercaptan	···	1
$C_{10}H_{22}S_2$	Diisoamyl disulfide	Isoamyl mercaptan	95	1
$C_{12}H_{10}S_2$	Diphenyl disulfide	Phenyl mercaptan	80	1
$C_{12}H_{22}S_2$	Bis-(2-hydroxycyclohexyl)disulfide	trans-1-Cyclohexanol-2-thiol	95	3,4
$C_{14}H_{14}S_2$	Dibenzyl disulfide	Benzyl mercaptan	75	1
	Di-p-tolyl disulfide	p-Thiocresol	86[6]	1
$C_{16}H_{34}S_2$	Di-n-octyl disulfide	n-Octyl mercaptan	98	7
$C_{24}H_{50}S_2$	Di-tert-dodecyl disulfide	Product not isolated[8]	···[2]	1
$C_{54}H_{86}S_2$	Bis-3-(7-dehydrocholesteryl)disulfide	Cholesta-5,7-diene-3-thiol	30	9–13
$C_{54}H_{90}S_2$	Dicholesteryl disulfide	Thiocholesterol	88	5,10–13

[1] R. C. Arnold, A. P. Lien, and R. M. Alm, J. Am. Chem. Soc., 72, 731 (1950).
[2] Reduction carried out in tetrahydrofuran at 65°.
[3] M. Mousseron and M. Canet, Bull. soc. chim. France, [5] 18, 792 (1951).
[4] M. Mousseron, R. Jacquier, M. Mousseron-Canet, and R. Zagdoun, ibid., [5] 19, 1042 (1952).
[5] J. Strating and H. J. Backer, Rec. trav. chim., 69, 638 (1950).
[6] Inverse addition.
[7] L. Field and F. A. Grunwald, J. Org. Chem., 16, 946 (1951).
[8] Reaction not completed, 67% of theoretical hydrogen evolved.
[9] J. Strating and H. J. Backer, Rec. trav. chim., 69, 909 (1950).
[10] J. Strating, U. S. Pat. 2,549,991 (April 24, 1951).
[11] J. Strating, Ger. Pat. 820,435 (November 12, 1951).
[12] N. V. Philips' Gloeilampenfabrieken, Brit. Pat. 681,217 (October 22, 1952).
[13] N. V. Philips' Gloeilampenfabrieken, Fr. Pat. 1,019,922 (January 29, 1953).

liberated as a product of the reaction according to the equation:

$$2 \ RSSR + LiAlH_4 \longrightarrow (RS)_4LiAl + 2 \ H_2 \qquad (13\text{-}9)$$

The reduction is influenced considerably by steric factors (1,15). While the reaction of unbranched disulfides proceeds rapidly in ether, the incorporation of branched structures around the disulfide linkage increases the difficulty of the reduction. Di-*n*-butyl disulfide is reduced rapidly in ether while *n*-butyl-*tert*-butyl disulfide is reduced at a moderate rate. Di-*tert*-butyl disulfide is not reduced in ether solution (1,15) but reacts rapidly in tetrahydrofuran at 65° (15). The reduction of di-*tert*-dodecyl disulfide proceeds very slowly even under the latter conditions (15).

The reduction of various disulfides with LAH is summarized in Table LXXXIII.

Arnold, Lien, and Alm (15) have pointed out that the reduction of disulfides, proceeding by a scission of a sulfur-sulfur bond, must involve a different mechanism than the nucleophilic displacement on carbon proposed for compounds having electronegative elements such as oxygen, nitrogen or halogen attached to carbon, since the latter mechanism would yield hydrocarbons rather than the observed mercaptans from disulfides. Bordwell and McKellin (16) and Mousseron and his co-workers (3) have proposed a displacement of sulfur by attack of aluminohydride or hydride ion on sulfur.

13.3 TRISULFIDES

The reduction of trisulfides yields mercaptans according to the equation:

$$2 \ RSSSR + 2 \ LiAlH_4 \longrightarrow (RS)_4LiAl + LiAlS_2 + 4 \ H_2 \qquad (13\text{-}10)$$

On acidification hydrogen sulfide is liberated as well as mercaptans.

This reaction has been applied to a limited number of compounds, as indicated below.

	% Mercaptan	Ref.
Di-*n*-propyl trisulfide	66	15
Di-isopropyl trisulfide	65	15
Di-*tert*-dodecyl trisulfide	....	14

The reduction of the simple trisulfides is carried out in ether while that of the tertiary compound is carried out in tetrahydrofuran at 65°. The blocking effect of the tertiary alkyl groups around the trisulfide linkage is apparently weaker than around the disulfide linkage since the reaction proceeds more rapidly with di-*tert*-dodecyl trisulfide than with the disulfide and yields the quantitative amount of hydrogen according to equation (13-10).

13.4 TETRASULFIDES

Isopropyl tetrasulfide (IX), the only example of this type of compound whose reduction with LAH has been reported, has yielded 12% isopropyl mercaptan, isolated as the 2,4-dinitrophenyl sulfide (14).

$$(CH_3)_2CH—S—\overset{\overset{\displaystyle S}{\uparrow}}{S}—S—CH(CH_3)_2 \xrightarrow{\text{LAH}} (CH_3)_2CHSH \quad (13\text{-}11)$$
$$\underset{IX}{}$$

13.5 EPISULFIDES

The LAH reduction of 1,2-epithiocyclohexane (X) is analogous to that of 1,2-epoxycyclohexane and yields cyclohexanethiol (3,17).

$$(13\text{-}12)$$

13.6 SULFOXIDES

13.6.1 Reductions with Lithium Aluminum Hydride

Although it was originally reported by Strating and Backer (1) that sulfoxides are not attacked by LAH, it has since been reported by independent workers that sulfoxides may be reduced to thioethers by LAH in the usual solvents (18,19).

It has been reported that diphenyl sulfoxide is reduced to diphenyl sulfide (20) while 4-androstene-3,17-dione 3-benzylsulfoxidoenol ether (XI) is reduced with LAH in tetrahydrofuran to testosterone 3-benzyl-thioenol ether (9).

$$(13\text{-}13)$$

Bordwell and McKellin have proposed that the reduction proceeds by attack of $AlH_4^{\ominus}$ ions on sulfur to displace oxygen or by attack on oxygen (16). Brown has indicated that the reduction consumes one-half mole of LAH per mole of sulfoxide (21).

13.6.2 Reductions with Sodium Borohydride

Protogen-B, a sulfur-containing compound isolated from liver and pre-sumed to be a sulfoxide, on reduction with sodium borohydride yields a dithiol, while treatment with Raney nickel gives octanoic acid (22). Mild oxidation of the dithiol gives a disulfide for which structure XII has been postulated and the name 5-thioctic acid has been proposed.

$$CH_2(CH_2)_2CH(CH_2)_3COOH$$
$$S \underline{\hspace{2cm}} S$$

XII

Synthesis of XII gives 6-thioctic acid (6,8-dithiooctanoic acid) as a by-product. Oxidation to the sulfoxide followed by reduction with sodium borohydride gives the dithiol which is reoxidized with iodine to the intra-molecular disulfide (23).

13.7 SULFONES

The reduction or non-reduction of sulfones is a function of sulfone structure and reaction conditions. Strating and Backer (1) reported that sulfones are not reduced by LAH. Bordwell and McKellin (16), in an ex-cellent study on the reduction of sulfones, reported that increasing the reaction temperature to 92° results in the reduction of compounds which are not attacked in refluxing diethyl ether at 35°.

13.7.1 Open-chain Sulfones

13.7.1.a *Aliphatic Sulfones.* The following open-chain aliphatic sul-fones have been treated with LAH in diethyl ether with resultant reten-tion of the sulfone grouping:

		Ref.
$C_2H_6O_2S$	Dimethylsulfone	16
$C_3H_7NO_6S$	Bis-methylsulfonylnitromethane	24
$C_4H_{10}O_2S$	Diethylsulfone	16
$C_8H_{18}O_2S$	Di-*n*-butylsulfone	16

While treatment of di-*n*-butylsulfone with three moles of LAH in diethyl ether at 35° for 24 hours results in an 83% recovery of sulfone and no yield of reduced product, when the reduction is carried out in ethyl butyl ether at 92°, after 2.5 hours a 26% yield of di-*n*-butylsulfide is obtained, and after 18 hours the yield of sulfide is 73% (16). The treatment of di-*tert*-butylsulfone with LAH at 92° for 18 hours gives no sulfide (16). This inertness is rationalized by assuming a steric effect analogous to the non-reduction of di-*tert*-butylsulfide.

Cronyn (25) reported that sulfones of the type $RCH(SO_2C_2H_5)_2$ are not reduced with LAH. This is attributed to the formation of a salt which resists further reaction. Reduction of sulfones of the type $R_2C(SO_2C_2H_5)_2$ does not proceed as expected. Treatment of 5,5-bis-(ethylsulfonyl)-2,8-dimethylnonane (XII) with three moles of LAH in diethyl ether gives a 61% yield of 3-isoamyl-6-methyl-2-heptene.

$$[(CH_3)_2CHCH_2CH_2]_2C\begin{matrix} SO_2C_2H_5 \\ \\ SO_2C_2H_5 \end{matrix} \xrightarrow{\text{LAH}} [(CH_3)_2CHCH_2CH_2]_2C{=}CHCH_3$$

XII   (13-14)

The proposed mechanism involves attack on the α-hydrogen of the disulfone to initiate an intramolecular 1,3-nucleophilic displacement of sulfinate to give an intermediate three-membered sulfone which loses sulfur dioxide to give the alkene.

$$R_2C\begin{matrix}SO_2CH_2CH_3 \\ \\ SO_2CH_2CH_3\end{matrix} \rightarrow R_2C \rightarrow R_2C{-}CHCH_3 + SO_2CH_2CH_3$$

XIII   (13-15)

$$R_2C{=}CHCH_3 + SO_2$$

Reduction of 5,5-bis-(ethylsulfonyl)nonane (XIV) with four moles of LAH in ether gives 50% 3-butyl-2-heptene (XV) and 13% 5-ethylthiononane (XVI).

$$(CH_3CH_2CH_2CH_2)_2C\begin{matrix}SO_2C_2H_5 \\ \\ SO_2C_2H_5\end{matrix} \xrightarrow{\text{LAH}}$$

XIV

$$(CH_3CH_2CH_2CH_2)_2C{=}CHCH_3 \quad (XV)$$
$$+ \qquad (13\text{-}16)$$
$$(CH_3CH_2CH_2CH_2)_2CH{-}S{-}CH_2CH_3 \quad (XVI)$$

Reduction of XIV with three moles of LAH in tetrahydrofuran gives 63% of XV. Reduction of 1,1-bis-(ethylsulfonyl)cyclobutane with LAH gives at least one sulfur-containing product which has not been further identified.

   13.7.1.b *Aromatic Sulfones.* Nystrom (20) and Marvel and Caesar (26) reported that diarylsulfones are not reduced with LAH in ether but the latter suggested that the use of tetrahydrofuran might improve the reaction. Reduction of di-p-tolylsulfone (XVII), presumably under the latter conditions, gives p-toluenesulfinic acid (27).

$$\xrightarrow[31\%]{\text{LAH}}$$

(13-17)

XVII

Knüsli (28) reported that reduction of a series of substituted diphenyl-sulfones (XVIII) with LAH in a mixture of ether and benzene results in retention of the sulfone grouping.

$$R_2N-C_6H_4-SO_2-C_6H_4-NHCOCH_2NR'_2 \quad \xrightarrow{\text{LAH}}$$

XVIII

$$R_2N-C_6H_4-SO_2-C_6H_4-NHCH_2CH_2NR'_2 \tag{13-18}$$

R	R'
CH_3	CH_3, C_2H_5, $n\text{-}C_3H_7$, $n\text{-}C_4H_9$
C_2H_5	C_2H_5

Bordwell and McKellin (16) have shown that diphenylsulfone (XIX) is reduced to diphenylsulfide in 71% yield after two hours at 92° while 12 hours at 35° results in non-reduction.

$$C_6H_5SO_2C_6H_5 \xrightarrow{\text{LAH}} C_6H_5SC_6H_5 \tag{13-19}$$
$$\text{XIX}$$

13.7.1.c Aralkyl Sulfones. The product of the LAH reduction of aralkyl sulfones is apparently dependent upon the structure of the sulfone. The reduction of p-tolylacetonylsulfone (XX) in ethereal solution results in retention of the sulfone group (29).

$$CH_3\text{-}C_6H_4\text{-}SO_2CH_2COCH_3 \xrightarrow[\text{75\%}]{\text{LAH}} CH_3\text{-}C_6H_4\text{-}SO_2CH_2CH_2CH_3 \tag{13-20}$$
$$\text{XX}$$

Reduction of 1-nitroethyl p-tolylsulfone (XXI) results in cleavage to yield p-toluenesulfinic acid (XXII) (5).

$$CH_3\text{-}C_6H_4\text{-}SO_2CHCH_3(NO_2) \xrightarrow[\text{80\%}]{\text{LAH}} CH_3\text{-}C_6H_4\text{-}SO_2H \tag{13-21}$$
$$\text{XXI} \qquad\qquad\qquad \text{XXII}$$

Benzyl p-tolylsulfone (XXIII) also gives XXII as the reduction product (27).

$$CH_3\text{-}C_6H_4\text{-}SO_2CH_2\text{-}C_6H_5 \xrightarrow{\text{LAH}} CH_3\text{-}C_6H_4\text{-}SO_2H \tag{13-22}$$
$$\text{XXIII} \qquad\qquad\qquad \text{XXII}$$

Field and Settlage (30) reported that the reaction of p-tolylsulfonyl-carbinol (XXIV) with p-toluenesulfonyl chloride in the presence of pyridine gives a product which has been presumed to be p-tolylsulfonyl-carbinyl p-toluenesulfonate (XXV). The LAH reduction of XXV gives a mixture of di-p-tolyidisulfide and p-thiocresol.

$$(13\text{-}23)$$

The reduction of phenyl ethyl sulfone (XXVI) with a $9:1$ mole ratio of LAH to sulfone in ether for one-half hour gives no sulfide, while with a $3:1$ ratio reduction at $92°$ for two hours gives 14%, and after 8 hours 60% of phenyl ethyl sulfide (XXVII). The reduction of phenyl vinyl sulfide (XXVIII) at $92°$ after 2.5 hours and 18 hours gives 12% and 14%, respectively, of XXVII (16).

$$(13\text{-}24)$$

13.7.2 Disulfones

Strating and Backing (1) reported that the LAH reduction of di-p-tolyl disulfone (XXIX) in ethereal solution gives 60% of di-p-tolyl disulfide and 13% of p-thiocresol.

$$(13\text{-}25)$$

TABLE LXXXIV

LAH Reduction of Cyclic Sulfones[1]

	Sulfone	LAH/Sulfone Ratio	T, °C.	Time, Hrs.	Product	% Yield
$C_3H_6O_2S$	Thiacyclobutane 1-dioxide (I)	10/1	35	0.5	Thiacyclobutane	61
$C_4H_6O_2S$	Thiacyclopent-3-ene 1-dioxide (II)	3/1	35	2	[2]	....
$C_4H_8O_2S$	Thiacyclopentane 1-dioxide (III)	9/1	35	0.5	Thiacyclopentane	75
$C_5H_{10}O_2S$	2-Methylthiacyclopentane 1-dioxide (IV)	3/1	35	1	2-Methylthiacyclopentane	79
	Thiacyclohexane 1-dioxide (V)	10/1	35	1	[3]	....
		3/1	35	12	Thiacyclohexane	trace
		3/1	92	4	Thiacyclohexane	41
$C_8H_6O_2S$	Benzothiophene 1-dioxide (VI)	9/1	35	0.5	2,3-Dihydrobenzothiophene	33
		9/1	35	18	2,3-Dihydrobenzothiophene	79
$C_8H_8O_2S$	2,3-Dihydrobenzothiophene 1-dioxide (VII)	9/1	35	0.5	2,3-Dihydrobenzothiophene	92
		2/1	35	1	2,3-Dihydrobenzothiophene	86
		1.1/1	35	1	2,3-Dihydrobenzothiophene	83
$C_9H_{10}O_2S$	2,3-Dihydro-1,4-benzothiapyran 1-dioxide (VIII)	10/1	35	2	2,3-Dihydro-1,4-benzothiapyran	trace
		3/1	35	5	2,3-Dihydro-1,4-benzothiapyran[3]	9
		3/1	92	24	2,3-Dihydro-1,4-benzothiapyran	67
$C_{12}H_8O_2S$	Dibenzothiophene 5-dioxide (IX)	1.1/1	35	1	Dibenzothiophene	74
$C_{16}H_{10}O_2S$	Benzo[d]naphtho[2,1-b]thiophene 7-dioxide (X)[4]	xs LAH	35	....	Benzo[d]naphtho[2,1-b]thiophene	65

[1] F. G. Bordwell and W. H. McKellin, J. Am. Chem. Soc., 73, 2251 (1951).
[2] No sulfide recovered from dark-colored polymeric product.
[3] Ninety per cent recovery of starting sulfone.
[4] R. G. Bordwell, W. H. McKellin, and D. Babcock, J. Am. Chem. Soc., 73, 5566 (1951).

CHART TO TABLE LXXXIV

13.7.3 Cyclic Sulfones

Bordwell and McKellin (16) reported that the LAH reduction of 5-membered ring sulfones is roughly 100 times as rapid as that of 6-membered ring and open-chain sulfones.

The reaction of benzothiophene 1-dioxide (XXX) with excess LAH in diethyl ether yields 33% of 2,3-dihydrobenzothiophene in 30 minutes and 79% in 18 hours. Benzothiophene is not reduced in measurable quantity in 18 hours while 2,3-dihydrobenzothiophene 1-dioxide (XXXI) gives 92% of dihydrobenzothiophene in 30 minutes.

$$\underset{\underset{O_2}{\underset{XXX}{}}}{\text{(structure)}} \xrightarrow{\text{LAH}} \text{(structure)} \xleftarrow{\text{LAH}} \underset{\underset{O_2}{\underset{XXXI}{}}}{\text{(structure)}} \qquad (13\text{-}26)$$

The first stage of the reduction is postulated as a slow reduction of XXX to XXXI since benzothiophene is apparently not an intermediate in the reduction.

Although the reduction of 6-membered ring sulfones, as in XXXII and XXXIII, proceeds with difficulty in diethyl ether at 35°, the yield is considerably increased in ethyl butyl ether at 92°.

$$\underset{\underset{O_2}{\underset{XXXII}{}}}{\text{(structure)}} \qquad\qquad \underset{\underset{O_2}{\underset{XXXIII}{}}}{\text{(structure)}}$$

The LAH reduction of various cyclic sulfones is summarized in Table LXXXIV.

13.7.4 Mechanism of Reduction

The reduction of sulfones is postulated (16) as resulting from a displacement of oxygen by attack of $AlH_4^{\ominus}$ ions on sulfur. An alternate mechanism is the attack of aluminohydride ions on oxygen.

13.8 SULFONIC ACIDS AND ANHYDRIDES

No examples of the LAH reduction of sulfonic acids have been reported.

Field and Grunwald (31) have reported that the LAH reduction of benzenesulfonic anhydride (XXXIV) yields either benzenesulfinic acid (XXXV) or thiophenol (XXXVI) depending upon the reaction conditions. Addition of 0.62 mole of LAH per mole of XXXIV in ether at $-70°$ gives 63% of the acid (XXXV) and a trace of XXXVI.

$$(C_6H_5SO_2)_2O \xrightarrow[-70°]{\text{LAH}} C_6H_5SO_2H + C_6H_5SH \qquad (13\text{-}27)$$
$$\quad\text{XXXIV} \qquad\qquad\quad \text{XXXV} \qquad \text{XXXVI}$$

The addition of 1.98 moles of LAH per mole of XXXIV in refluxing ether gives a quantitative yield of XXXVI.

$$(C_6H_5SO_2)_2O \xrightarrow[35°]{LAH} C_6H_5SH \qquad (13\text{-}28)$$

XXXIV   XXXVI

The sulfinic acid is apparently an intermediate in the reduction, as in the reduction of sulfonyl halides (Section 13.9).

13.9 SULFONYL HALIDES

Strating and Backer (1) reported that the LAH reduction of sulfonyl chlorides gives thiols without the intermediate formation of disulfides. Sulfinic acids, sulfinyl chlorides and sulfenyl chlorides were also eliminated as intermediates since they are reduced with LAH to disulfides.

The reduction of p-toluenesulfonyl chloride (XXXVII) with 1.5 moles of ethereal LAH gives 90% of thiocresol while p-tert-butylbenzenesulfonyl chloride (XXXVIII) gives 76% of p-tert-butylthiophenol and 8% of di-p-tert-butylphenyldisulfide (1).

$$(13\text{-}29)$$

XXXVII

$$(13\text{-}30)$$

XXXVIII

The formation of the disulfide appears contrary to the postulation of Strating and Backer unless it is formed in a reaction which is not related to the formation of the thiol. The thiol is postulated as arising through a replacement of the chlorine atom in the sulfonyl chloride with hydrogen and the reduction of the "primary sulfone," without being transformed to the sulfinic acid, to the thiol (1).

$$\underset{Cl}{\overset{O_2}{RS}} \rightarrow \underset{H}{\overset{O_2}{RS}} \rightarrow RSH \qquad (13\text{-}31)$$

Marvel and Caesar (26) reported that the reduction of XXXVII with 3.8 moles of LAH in ether at 35° gives 50% of p-thiocresol while the reduction of 1-butanesulfonyl chloride (XXXIX) with 3.2 moles of LAH in ether gives 45% of n-butylmercaptan isolated as the mercury mercaptide.

$$CH_3CH_2CH_2CH_2SO_2Cl \xrightarrow{LAH} CH_3CH_2CH_2CH_2SH \qquad (13\text{-}32)$$
$$\text{XXXIX}$$

The following stoichiometric equation was proposed:

$$2\ RSO_2Cl + 3\ LiAlH_4 \rightarrow (RS)_2LiAlCl_2 + 6\ H_2 + 2\ LiAlO_2 \quad (13\text{-}33)$$

Caesar (27) reported that the reduction of phenoxybenzene-4,4'-disulfonyl chloride (XL) with LAH in tetrahydrofuran gives phenoxybenzene-4,4'-dithiol.

$$(13\text{-}34)$$

A sulfinic acid was tentatively identified after reduction of the disulfonyl chloride (32).

Schlesinger and Finholt (33) and Nystrom (20) reported the formation of a mixture of 60% of thiophenol and 32% of diphenyl disulfide by the LAH reduction of benzenesulfonyl chloride (XLI).

$$C_6H_5SO_2Cl \xrightarrow{LAH} C_6H_5SH + C_6H_5S\!-\!SC_6H_5 \qquad (13\text{-}35)$$
$$\text{XLI}$$

Field and Grunwald (31) attempted to duplicate the report of Strating and Backer (1) that treatment of p-toluenesulfonyl chloride (XXXVII) with 1.5 moles (0% excess) of LAH gives 90% thiocresol, according to equation (13-29). A 90% yield of an impure product, m.p. 38–81°, was obtained from which pure p-thiocresol could not be obtained by the recommended recrystallization procedure from aqueous alcohol. Reduction of XXXVII with a 23% excess of LAH gives 71% of p-thiocresol while a 42% excess gives 83% of p-thiocresol. The inverse addition of a 62% excess of LAH to a refluxing sulfonyl chloride solution in ether gives 89% of p-thiocresol and 7% of p-toluenesulfinic acid (XLII).

$$(13\text{-}36)$$

The inverse addition of 0.57 mole of LAH to an ethereal solution of XXXVII while maintaining the temperature at $-20°$ gives a 93% yield of p-toluenesulfinic acid (XLII). Normal addition followed by refluxing reduces the yield of XLII to 63–77%. The stoichiometry of the reduction was proposed as follows:

$$2\ RSO_2Cl + LiAlH_4 \rightarrow (RSO_2)_2LiAlCl_2 + 2\ H_2 \qquad (13\text{-}27)$$

Strating and Backer (1) reported that disulfides are not intermediates in the reduction of sulfonyl chlorides to thiols. Sulfinic acids were also excluded as intermediates since they are reduced to disulfides. Field and Grunwald (31) obtained di-*p*-tolydisulfide in 25% yield by the addition of the sulfonyl chloride to an amount of LAH insufficient to reduce it completely to the thiocresol but more than sufficient to reduce it to the sulfinic acid salt. A similar reduction of benzenesulfonyl chloride (XLI) gave 37% of diphenyldisulfide and 48% of benzenesulfinic acid.

$$C_6H_5SO_2Cl \xrightarrow{\text{LAH}} C_6H_5SO_2H + C_6H_5S\text{---}SC_6H_5 \qquad (13\text{-}38)$$
$$\text{XLI}$$

The inverse addition of 0.63 mole of LAH to an ethereal solution of XLI at $-65°$ gives 89% of benzenesulfinic acid. The mechanism of the reduction has been postulated (16,31) as a nucleophilic attack of aluminohydride ion on sulfur displacing the chloride ion, followed by attack of the complex ion on the hydrogen of the resulting sulfinic acid with the formation of a sulfinate salt and hydrogen.

$$RSO_2Cl \xrightarrow{\text{AlH}_4^{\ominus}} RSO_2H + Cl^{\ominus}$$
$$\xrightarrow{\text{AlH}_4^{\ominus}} RSO_2^{\ominus} + H_2 \qquad (13\text{-}39)$$

Alternatively the reaction may occur via an unstable intermediate formed from the sulfonyl chloride and $AlH_4^{\ominus}$ to give the products in one step.

The rapid reduction of the *p*-toluenesulfinic acid salt, preformed at $-20°$, to *p*-thiocresol in 85% yield upon heating with excess LAH shows that the sulfinic acid salt is not stable once formed and may be an intermediate in the reduction to the thiol.

Field and Grunwald (31) postulated two competing paths in the reduction of sulfonyl halides to thiols:

a) The formation of a sulfinate salt and its direct reduction by excess LAH;

b) Reaction of the sulfonyl chloride with the sulfinate salt giving a disulfone, or with a metal mercaptide giving a thiosulfonate, either of which is reducible to a disulfide, followed by reduction of the disulfide to the thiol.

These steps can be schematically summarized as follows:

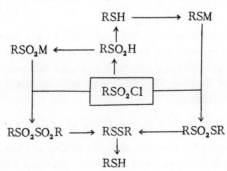

The inverse addition of LAH to an ethereal solution of β-styrene-sulfonyl chloride (XLIII) at $-70°$ has been reported to give 78% of β-styrenesulfinic acid isolated as the sodium salt.

$$C_6H_5CH{=}CHSO_2Cl \xrightarrow{\text{LAH}} C_6H_5CH{=}CHSO_2H \qquad (13\text{-}40)$$
$$\text{XLIII}$$

Reduction of methanesulfonyl chloride at $-70°$ liberates 85–90% of the quantity of hydrogen corresponding to reduction to the methanesulfinate salt. However, attempted isolation of the acid has been unsuccessful (31).

13.10 SULFONIC ESTERS

13.10.1 Reductions with Lithium Aluminum Hydride

The LAH reduction of sulfonic esters usually proceeds by one of two reaction paths to yield either hydrocarbons or phenols (34–36).

$$ROSO_2R' \xrightarrow{\text{LAH}} RH + HOSO_2R' \qquad (13\text{-}41)$$

$$ROSO_2R' \xrightarrow{\text{LAH}} ROH + HOSOR' \qquad (13\text{-}42)$$

13.10.1.a *Aliphatic and Alicyclic Sulfonic Esters.* The LAH reduction of alkyl tosylates generally proceeds according to equation (13-41). Gilman (37,38) found that the alkyl esters of aromatic sulfonic acids react with both aromatic and aliphatic Grignard reagents, giving the hydrocarbon and the alkyl halide. Kenner and Murray (39) reported that the catalytic hydrogenation of alkyl tosylates over Raney nickel gives alcohols according to equation (13-42).

Schmid and Karrer (34) reported that the LAH reductions can be carried out in refluxing benzene-ether mixtures, frequently only after prolonged periods. On the other hand, Strating and Backer (1) point out that the reduction of sulfonic esters of primary alcohols occurs almost completely instantaneously while several hours refluxing in ether suffices for the esters of secondary alcohols. The LAH reduction of codeine tosylate cannot be carried out in ether (40) but is accomplished in high yields in tetrahydrofuran (40,41).

The LAH reduction of various aliphatic and alicyclic sulfonic esters, including mesylates and tosylates, to hydrocarbons is summarized in Table LXXXV.

The LAH reduction of alicyclic sulfonic esters to hydrocarbons has been utilized in the synthesis of labeled compounds. Thus, Alexander has converted *l*-menthyl tosylate to *trans-p*-menthane (XLV) with LAH while on reduction with lithium aluminum deuteride the product is 3-deutero-*trans-p*-methane (XLVI) (42).

TABLE LXXXV

LAH Reduction of Sulfonic Esters to Hydrocarbons

Sulfonic Ester	Product	% Yield	Ref.
	Aliphatic		
C$_8$H$_{14}$O$_4$S 2-Methylcyclopentan-1-one-2-methyl mesylate (I)	2,2-Dimethylcyclopentanol	89	1
C$_{10}$H$_{14}$O$_3$S n-Propyl tosylate	Propane	...	2
	p-Toluenesulfonic acid	...	
C$_{11}$H$_{10}$O$_3$S Methyl naphthalene β-sulfonate (II)	Methane	...	2
	Naphthalene β-sulfonic acid	72[3]	
C$_{14}$H$_{20}$O$_4$S (+)cis-3-Hydroxycyclohexylmethyl tosylate	(−)cis-3-Methylcyclohexanol	36[4,5]	6
cis-3-Hydroxycyclohexylmethyl tosylate	Endomethyleneoxycyclohexane	...	7
trans-3-Hydroxycyclohexylmethyl tosylate	trans-3-Methylcyclohexanol	54[4,5]	6
C$_{17}$H$_{20}$O$_4$S (−)-β-Ethoxyphenylethyl tosylate	(−)-Ethyl α-methylbenzyl ether	49	8
C$_{17}$H$_{36}$O$_3$S n-Cetyl mesylate	n-Hexadecane	92	2
C$_{19}$H$_{18}$O$_4$S 3-Methoxy-2-naphthylmethyl tosylate	3-Methoxy-2-methylnaphthalene	90[9]	10
C$_{19}$H$_{23}$O$_5$NS$_2$ N-Tosyl-L-prolinyl tosylate (III)	N-Tosyl-L-2-methylpyrrolidine	26[9]	11
C$_{19}$H$_{26}$O$_8$S 6-Tosyldiacetone-D-galactose<1,5>	Diacetone-D-fucose<1,5>	59[12]	13
C$_{19}$H$_{28}$O$_5$S Tetrapyranyl ether of cis-cyclohexyl-3-methyl tosylate	cis-3-Methylcyclohexyl tetrapyranyl ether	...	7
Tetrapyranyl ether of trans-cyclohexyl-3-methyl tosylate	trans-3-Methylcyclohexyl tetrapyranyl ether	...	7
C$_{21}$H$_{24}$O$_9$ S$_2$ 4,6-Ditosyl-2,3-anhydro-α-methyl-D-alloside	4-Tosyl-α-methyl-D-digitoxoside	52[14]	15
	α-Methyl-D-digitoxoside	70[16]	15
C$_{23}$H$_{25}$O$_5$NS$_2$ N-Tosyl-D-phenylalaninol tosylate (IV)	β-Tosylamino-D-phenylpropane	47[12]	11
N-Tosyl-DL-phenylalaninol tosylate (IV)	β-Tosylamino-DL-phenylpropane	65[9]	11
C$_{23}$H$_{40}$O$_3$S n-Cetyl tosylate	n-Hexadecane	96	2
C$_{27}$H$_{24}$O$_3$S 2,2,2-Triphenylethyl tosylate	1,1,2-Triphenylethane	35	17
C$_{27}$H$_{32}$O$_4$N$_2$S Yohimbyl alcohol monotosylate (V)	16-Methylyohimbol (VI)	75[9]	18
C$_{29}$H$_{34}$O$_{12}$S$_3$ 2,4,6-Tritosyl-β-methyl-D-idoside-3-methyl ether	2,4-Ditosyl-β-methyl-D-idomethyloside-3-methyl ether	...[9]	19

Formula	Tosylate	Product	Yield	Ref.
$C_{30}H_{31}O_8NS_3$	N-Tosyl-L-tyrosinol ditosylate (VII)	β-Tosylamino-L-p-hydroxyphenylpropane	77[9]	11
$C_{37}H_{56}O_3S$	Trametenol tosylate	Trametene	"good"[12]	20
$C_{37}H_{56}O_4S$	Trametenediol monotosylate	sec-Trametene alcohol	47	20
$C_{41}H_{44}O_8N_2S_3$	Yohimbyl alcohol tritosylate	16-Methylyohimban	50[9]	18
Alicyclic				
$C_{17}H_{26}O_3S$	l-Menthyl tosylate	p-Menthane	trace[12]	13
		p-Menthene	55	21
		trans-p-Menthane	46[22]	21
		3-Deutero-trans-p-menthane	67[9]	23
$C_{25}H_{27}O_5NS$	Codeine tosylate (VIII)	Δ7-Desoxycodeine	90[9]	24
	Neopine tosylate (IX)	Δ8-Desoxycodeine	48[25]	24
$C_{28}H_{40}O_4S$	3-Tosyloxy-5-pregnen-20-one	5-Pregnen-20-ol (mixture of isomers)	...[12]	26
$C_{34}H_{54}O_3S$	Cholestan-3-ol tosylate	Cholestane	83	2
	Cholestan-7β-ol tosylate	Cholestan-3-ol	...	
		p-Thiocresol		
		Cholestane	92	26
$C_{41}H_{44}O_8N_2S_3$	Yohimbyl alcohol tritosylate	16-Methylyohimban	50[9]	18

CHART TO TABLE LXXXV

$C_7H_7 = p$-tolyl

I	II

III	IV

V	VI

CHART TO TABLE LXXXV (*continued*)

VII

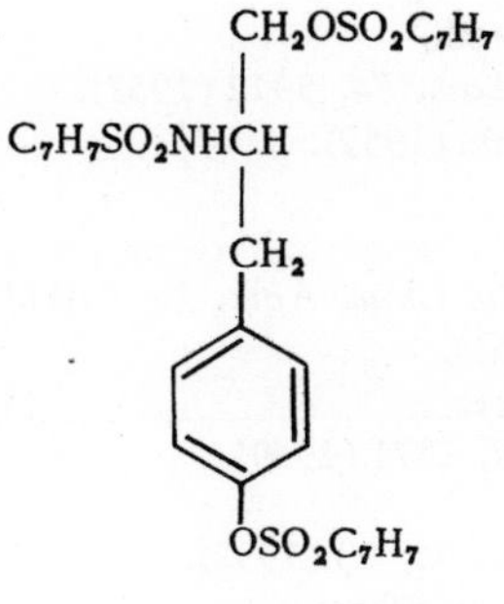

CH₂OSO₂C₇H₇

C₇H₇SO₂NHCH

CH₂

OSO₂C₇H₇

VIII

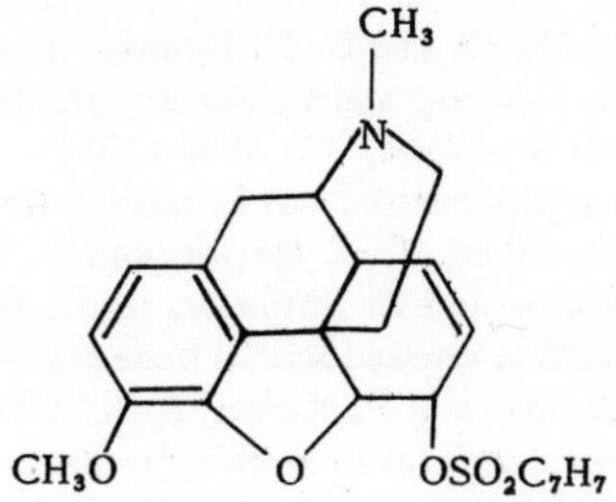

CH₃

N

CH₃O   O   OSO₂C₇H₇

IX

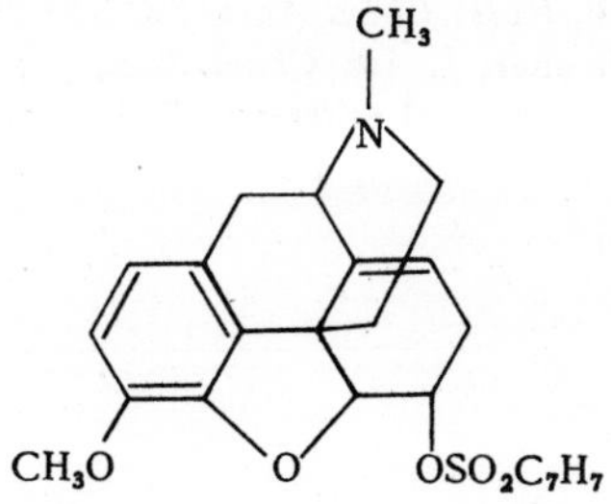

CH₃

N

CH₃O   O   OSO₂C₇H₇

References — Table LXXXV

[1]A. Eschenmoser and A. Frey, *Helv. Chim. Acta*, 35, 1660 (1952).
[2]J. Strating and H. J. Backer, *Rec. trav. chim.*, 69, 638 (1950).
[3]Isolated as barium salt.
[4]Reduction carried out in di-*n*-propyl ether.
[5]Yield based on diol from which tosylate prepared.
[6]D. S. Noyce and D. B. Denney, *J. Am. Chem. Soc.*, 74, 5912 (1952).
[7]H. L. Goering and C. Serres, Jr., *ibid.*, 74, 5908 (1952).
[8]K. Mislow, *ibid.*, 73, 3954 (1951).
[9]Reduction carried out in tetrahydrofuran.
[10]A. Ebnöther, T. M. Meijer, and H. Schmid, *Helv. Chim. Acta*, 35, 910 (1952).
[11]P. Karrer and K. Ehrhardt, *ibid.*, 34, 2202 (1951).
[12]Reduction carried out in benezene-ether mixture.
[13]H. Schmid and P. Karrer, *Helv. Chim. Acta*, 32, 1371 (1949).
[14]Reflux one hour in tetrahydrofuran.
[15]H. R. Bolliger and P. Ulrich, *Helv. Chim. Acta*, 35, 93 (1952).
[16]Reflux six hours in tetrahydrofuran or 15 hours in ether.
[17]F. G. Bordwell, B. M. Pitt, and M. Knell, *J. Am. Chem. Soc.*, 73, 5004 (1951).
[18]P. Karrer and R. Saemann, *Helv. Chim. Acta*, 35, 1932 (1952).
[19]R. Fischer and H. R. Bolliger, unpublished work, through ref. 15.
[20]W. Gruber and G. Proske, *Monatsh.*, 81, 1024 (1950).
[21]E. R. Alexander, *J. Am. Chem. Soc.*, 72, 3796 (1950).
[22]Reduction carried out with lithium aluminum deuteride.
[23]P. Karrer and G. Widmark, *Helv. Chim. Acta*, 34, 34 (1951).
[24]H. Rapoport and R. M. Bonner, *J. Am. Chem. Soc.*, 73, 2872 (1951).
[25]Reduction carried out in di-*n*-butyl ether-tetrahydrofuran mixture.
[26]P. Karrer, H. Asmis, K. N. Sareen, and R. Schwyzer, *Helv. Chim. Acta*, 34, 1022 (1951).

(13-43)

(13-44)

The unsaturated hydrocarbon, *p*-menthene, has been reported as a trace product in the reduction of *l*-menthyl tosylate to *p*-menthane (34).

The LAH reduction of 2,2,2-triphenylethyl tosylate (XLVII) proceeds as expected to yield the hydrocarbon. However, the neopentyl system rearranges readily under basic conditions so that the product is 1,1,2-triphenylethane (XLVIII). Rearrangement also occurs in the reaction of XLVII with methylmagnesium iodide to yield 1,2,2-triphenylpropane (XLIX) (43).

$$
\begin{array}{c}
C_6H_5 \\
| \\
C_6H_5CCH_2OSO_2-\!\!\!\!\underset{XLVII}{\underset{C_6H_5}{\big|}}\!\!\!\!-\!\!\!\!\text{(}\!\!\!\!\text{)}\!\!\!\!-CH_3
\end{array}
\xrightarrow[\substack{\text{LAH}\\35\%}]{}
\begin{array}{c}
C_6H_5 \\
| \\
C_6H_5CHCH_2C_6H_5 \quad (13\text{-}45)\\
XLVIII
\end{array}
$$

$$
\xrightarrow[\substack{CH_3MgI\\35\%}]{}
\begin{array}{c}
C_6H_5 \\
| \\
C_6H_5CH_2CCH_3 \quad (13\text{-}46)\\
| \\
C_6H_5 \\
XLIX
\end{array}
$$

Goering and Serres (44) reported that the monotosylate of cis-3-hydroxycyclohexylmethanol (L) can not be reduced directly to the 3-methylcyclohexanol with LAH, presumably in diethyl ether, but instead is converted to the endomethyleneoxy compound (LI). It has been postulated that this conversion involves formation of the alkoxide ion which undergoes internal displacement.

$$
\underset{L}{\text{OH} \quad CH_2OSO_2-\!\!\text{(}\!\!\text{)}\!\!-CH_3}
\xrightarrow{\text{LAH}}
O^{\ominus} \rightarrow CH_2 \!\!-\!\! OSO_2-\!\!\text{(}\!\!\text{)}\!\!-CH_3
$$

$$
\longrightarrow \underset{LI}{\text{(O}\!\!-\!\!CH_2)} \quad (13\text{-}47)
$$

In order to prevent oxide formation the monotosylate is converted to the tetrahydropyranyl ether (LII) which is not isolated but immediately reduced with LAH. The ether (LIII) obtained in this way is converted to cis-3-methylcyclohexanol by acid hydrolysis.

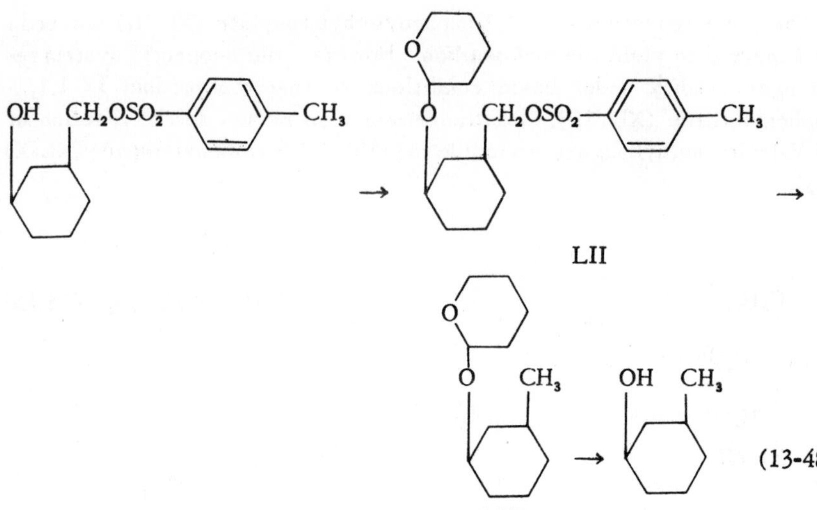

(13-48)

Noyce and Denney (45) reported that the reduction of *trans*- and (+)-*cis*-L is "unsatisfactory in di-*n*-butyl ether, and experimentally more satisfactory in di-*n*-propyl ether as solvent rather than tetrahydrofuran" to yield 3-methylcyclohexanol. The (−)-*cis*-3-methylcyclohexanol from (+)-*cis*-L is contaminated with a small amount of highly dextrorotatory olefin whose presence is also indicated in the infrared spectrum. It is possible that the supposed alkene is actually LI.

Attempts to reduce the mesyloxy group in LIV to the methyl group by means of LAH in an ether-benzene solution are reported to have given an uncrystallizable gum (46).

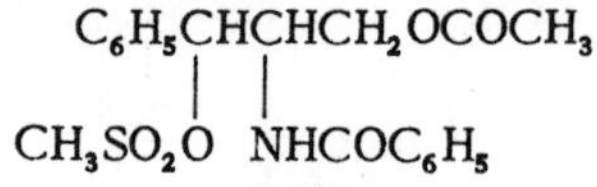

$$C_6H_5CHCHCH_2OCOCH_3$$
$$CH_3SO_2O \quad NHCOC_6H_5$$
LIV

The attempted reduction of *p*-tolylsulfonylcarbinyl tosylate (LV) has been reported to yield di-*p*-tolyl disulfide and *p*-thiocresol rather than the expected methyl-*p*-tolyl sulfone (30).

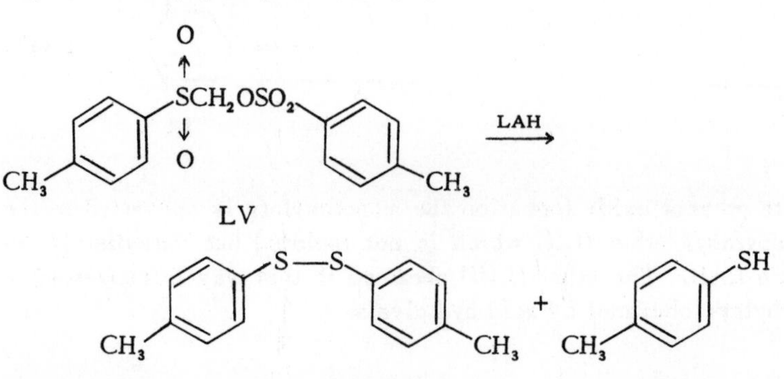

(13-49)

Cram (47) has carried out an extensive stereochemical study of the LAH reduction of various tosylates to hydrocarbons and olefins. Treatment of the p-toluenesulfonate of L-(+)-threo-3-phenyl-2-butanol (LVI) with a saturated ethereal LAH solution gives trans-2-phenyl-2-butene and (+)-2-phenylbutane while the p-toluenesulfonate of L-(+)-erythro-3-phenyl-2-butanol (LVII) gives cis-2-phenyl-2-butene and (+)-2-phenylbutane.

$$\text{LVI} \xrightarrow{\text{LAH}} \qquad (13\text{-}50)$$

$$\text{LVII} \xrightarrow{\text{LAH}} \qquad (13\text{-}51)$$

The elimination reaction giving the olefin is predominantly trans in its steric course and follows a bimolecular mechanism.

$$\text{LVI} \xrightarrow{\text{LAH}} \qquad (13\text{-}52)$$

Transition states

$$\text{LVII} \xrightarrow{\text{LAH}} \qquad (13\text{-}53)$$

In the reduction that accompanies the elimination reaction the major reaction is that of simple nucleophilic displacement of the tosylate group by the aluminohydride ion. Some migration of the phenyl group occurs during the reaction producing partially racemized 2-phenylbutane. Probable paths for the formation of racemic hydrocarbon are indicated in Flow Sheet V and involve the phenonium sulfonate ion-pair as intermediate.

Treatment of the p-toluenesulfonates of the isomers of 2-phenyl-3-pentanol (LVIII) and 3-phenyl-2-pentanol (LIX) with solutions of LAH produces four sets of products. All of the isomers undergo a simple reduction reaction and a reduction with rearrangement to give mixtures of 2- and 3-phenylpentane, as well as a simple elimination and an elimination with rearrangement to give 2- and 3-phenylpentenes (48).

FLOW SHEET V

$$\overset{1}{C}H_3\overset{2}{C}H —\overset{3}{C}H\overset{4}{C}H_2\overset{5}{C}H_3$$

$$C_6H_5 \quad OTs$$

LVIII

| LAH

CH$_3$CHC$_3$H$_7$ + C$_2$H$_5$CHC$_2$H$_5$ + 2-phenyl- + 3-phenyl-   (13-54)

     pentenes   pentenes

$\quad$ C$_6$H$_5$ $\qquad\qquad$ C$_6$H$_5$

simple $\qquad$ reduction- $\qquad$ simple $\qquad$ elimina-

reduction $\quad$ rearrange- $\quad$ elimina- $\quad$ tion-

$\qquad\qquad$ ment $\qquad\qquad$ tion $\qquad\quad$ rearrange-

$\qquad\qquad\qquad\qquad\qquad\qquad\qquad\qquad\qquad$ ment

C$_2$H$_5$CHC$_2$H$_5$ + CH$_3$CHC$_3$H$_7$ + 3-phenyl- + 2-phenyl-   (13-55)

     pentenes   pentenes

$\quad$ C$_6$H$_5$ $\qquad\qquad$ C$_6$H$_5$

| LAH

$$\overset{5}{C}H_3\overset{4}{C}H_2\overset{3}{C}H —\overset{2}{C}H\overset{1}{C}H_3$$

$$C_6H_5 \quad OTs$$

LIX

The simple reduction reaction occurs without alteration of the stereo-chemistry at carbon atom 2 while the reduction rearrangement reaction is stereospecific and carbon atom 2 is inverted during the rearrangement. The extent to which the latter reaction takes place as compared to the simple reduction varies with the configuration and structure of the starting material and is affected by steric influences, *erythro* compounds giving a higher percentage of rearranged to unrearranged alkylbenzene than starting materials of the *threo* configuration. The higher the concentration of LAH in the reducing solution, the greater is the amount of rearranged alkylbenzene and the larger the amount of rearranged olefin. A catalytic effect of LAH on the isomerization of the tosylates is considered probable although it has been suggested (49) that aluminum hydride, a weak acid, is the actual catalyst and not the relatively basic LAH. The greater part of rearranged olefin and alkylbenzene comes from rearranged sulfonate ester. Polarimetric and infrared analyses indicate that small amounts of unconjugated and optically active 4-phenyl-2-pentene are produced in the elimination-rearrangement reaction.

13.10.1.b *Sugar Tosylates.* The LAH reduction of sugar tosylates frequently yields alcohols. While 6-tosyldiacetone-D-galactose <1,5> (LX) is reduced after 30 hours refluxing in a benzene-ether mixture to diacetone-D-fucose <1,5>, the primary tosylate group in 1-tosyl-β-diacetone-D-fructose <2,6> (LXI) is reduced to the alcohol, i.e., β-diacetone-D-fructose <2,6>, after 48 hours refluxing (34).

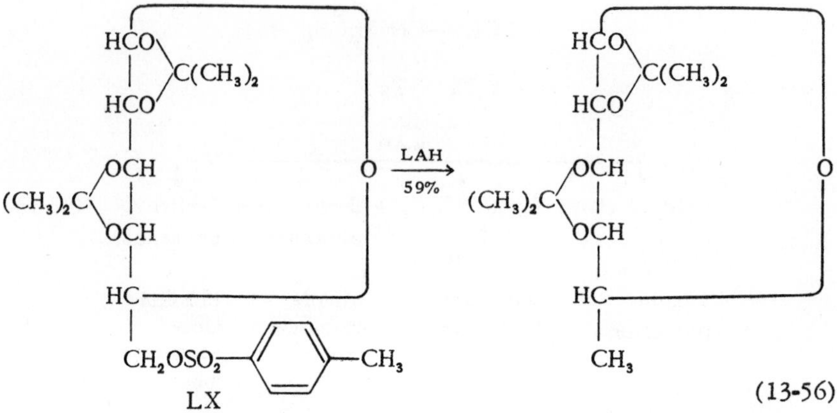

LX

(13-56)

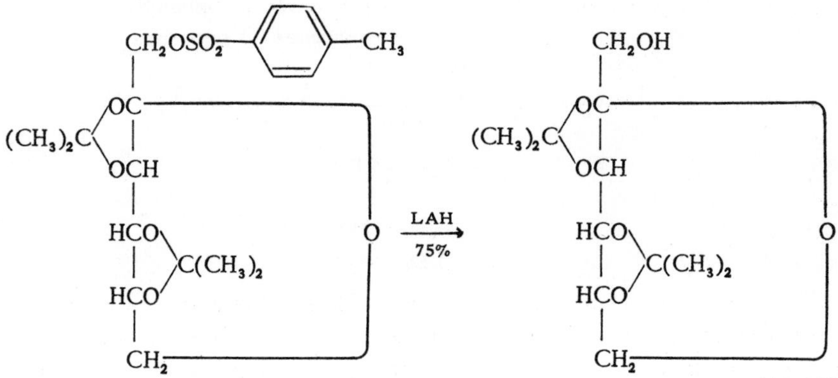

LXI

(13-57)

The tosylate group in LXI is converted into *p*-toluenesulfinic acid and *p*,*p*′-ditolyldisulfide.

The LAH reduction of 3-tosyldiacetone-D-glucose<1,4> (LXII) in a benzene-ether mixture after 28 hours yields diacetone-D-glucose<1,4> and *p*-toluenesulfinic acid (34).

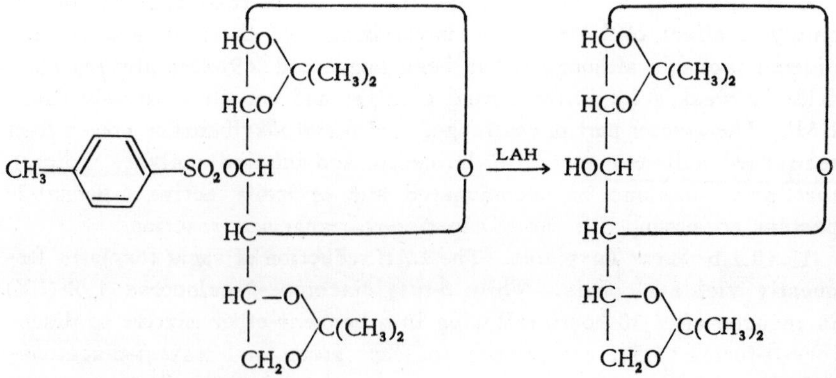

LXII

(13-58)

2-Tosyl-4,6-benzylidene-α-methyl-D-altroside-3-methyl ether (LXIII) is recovered unchanged after one hour treatment with LAH in tetrahydrofuran. After 30 hours an almost quantitative yield of 4,6-benzylidene-α-methyl-D-altroside-3-methyl ether is obtained (50).

$$\text{LXIII} \qquad \xrightarrow{\text{LAH}} \qquad (13\text{-}59)$$

The greater resistance of the secondary tosylate group as compared to the primary group to LAH reduction is shown in the isolation of the 2,4-ditosyl compound after one-half hour of refluxing of 2,4,6-tritosyl-β-methyl-D-idoside-3-methyl ether (LXIV) with LAH in tetrahydrofuran (52).

$$\text{LXIV} \qquad \xrightarrow{\text{LAH}} \qquad (13\text{-}60)$$

By varying the reaction conditions Bolliger and his co-workers have selectively reduced the three functional groups in 4,6-ditosyl-2,3-anhydro-α-methyl-D-alloside (LXV) and have observed the following relative reactivities: epoxide > primary tosylate > secondary tosylate. Treatment of LXV with LAH in an ether-tetrahydrofuran mixture at 18° for 6 hours gives 47% of the 4,6-ditosyl-2-desoxy compound (LXVI) and 43% of unchanged LXV (53). Refluxing LXV for one hour in tetrahydrofuran reduces the terminal primary methylenetosyloxy group to methyl and opens the epoxide ring to yield 4-tosyl-α-methyl-D-digitoxoside (LXVII) (51). Refluxing LXV for 6 hours in tetrahydrofuran or 15 hours in ether reduces the secondary tosyloxy group as well as regenerates the original hydroxyl group to yield α-methyl-D-digitoxoside (LXVIII) (51).

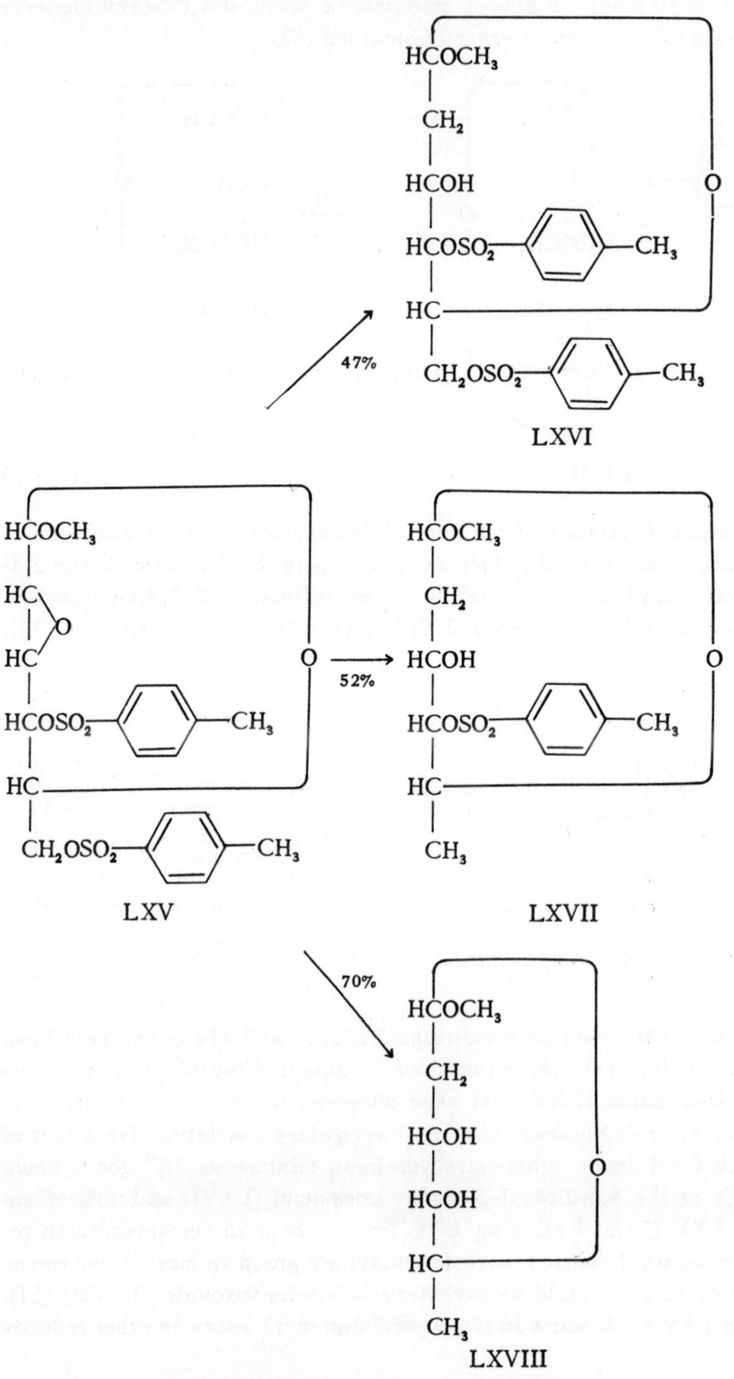

(13-61)

LXVI

52%

(13-62)

LXV   LXVII

70%

(13-63)

LXVIII

13.10.1.c *Triterpene Tosylates.* Although LAH reduction of the tosylates of the triterpene derivatives, trametenol (LXIX) and trametenediol
(LXX) yields hydrocarbons (54),

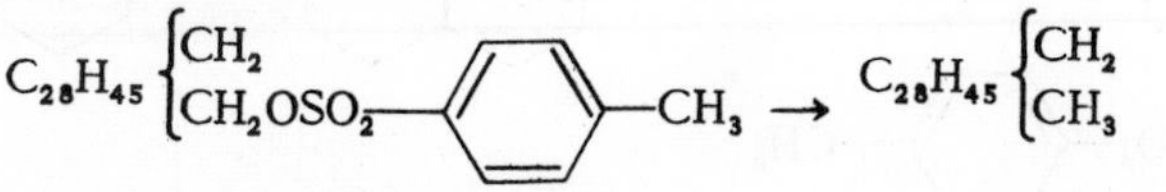

$$C_{28}H_{45} \begin{cases} CH_2 \\ CH_2OSO_2 \end{cases} \!\!\!\!\!\!\!\! \longrightarrow\!\!\!\! CH_3 \rightarrow C_{28}H_{45} \begin{cases} CH_2 \\ CH_3 \end{cases} \qquad (13\text{-}64)$$

LXIX

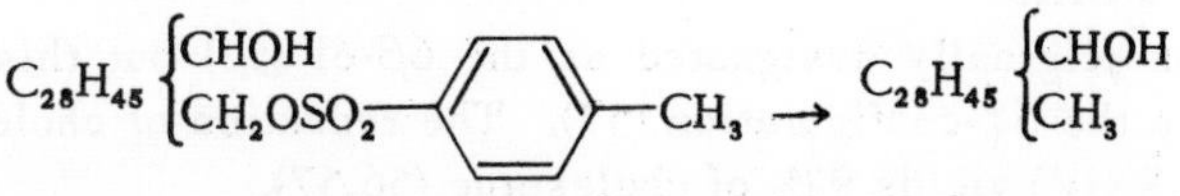

$$C_{28}H_{45} \begin{cases} CHOH \\ CH_2OSO_2 \end{cases} \!\!\!\!\!\!\!\! \longrightarrow\!\!\!\! CH_3 \rightarrow C_{28}H_{45} \begin{cases} CHOH \\ CH_3 \end{cases} \qquad (13\text{-}65)$$

LXX

the reduction of the monoacetate tosylate of moradiol (LXXI) yields
moradiol (55).

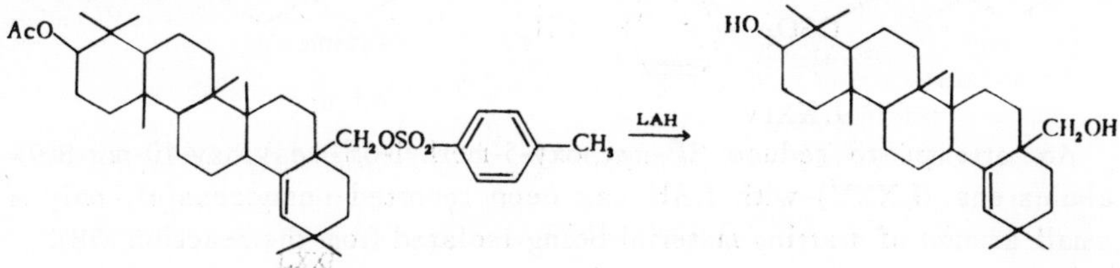

LXXI   (13-66)

13.10.1.d *Steroid Tosylates.* The course of the LAH reduction of
sterol tosylates is determined by the position of the sulfonic ester groups
as well as the unsaturation present. The reduction of cholestan-3-ol
tosylate (LXXII) is reported to yield 83% of cholestane accompanied by
cholestan-3-ol (1).

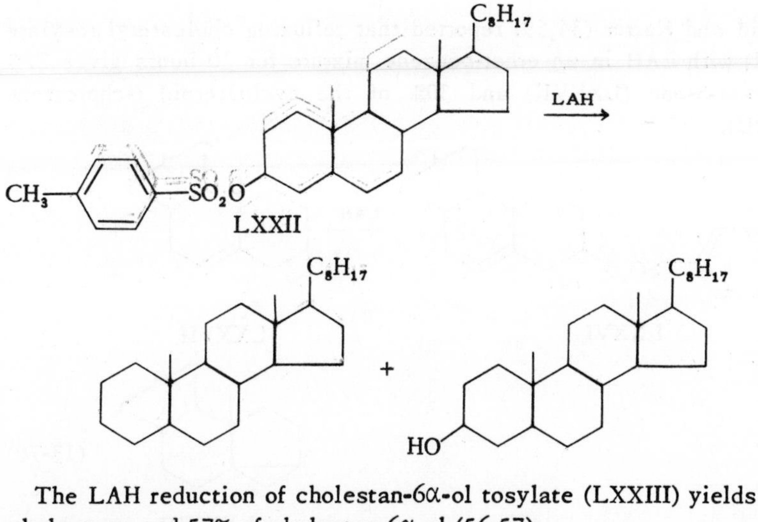

LXXII

(13-67)

The LAH reduction of cholestan-6α-ol tosylate (LXXIII) yields 38% of
cholestane and 57% of cholestan-6α-ol (56,57).

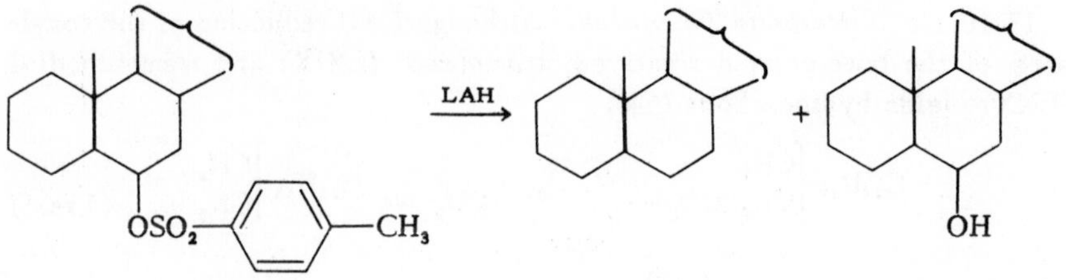

LXXIII (13-68)

LXXIII was originally designated as the 6β-ol (56) but this was later corrected to the 6α-configuration (57). The reduction of cholestan-7β-ol tosylate (LXXIV) yields 92% of cholestane (56,57).

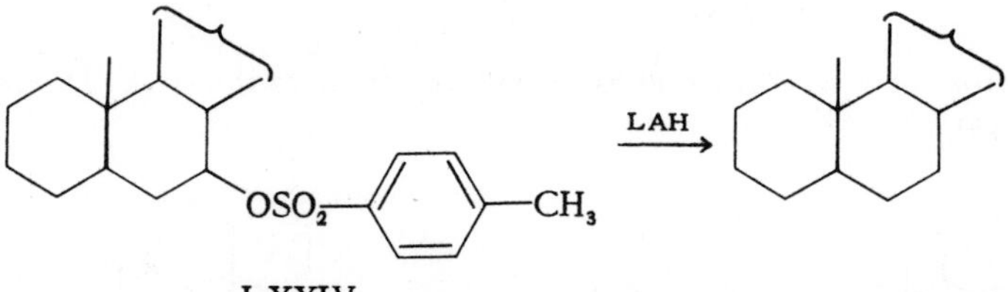

(13-69)

LXXIV

An attempt to reduce 3β-methoxy-5-methyl-6β-mesyloxy-10-nor-8(9)-cholestene (LXXV) with LAH has been reported unsuccessful, only a small amount of starting material being isolated from the reaction (58).

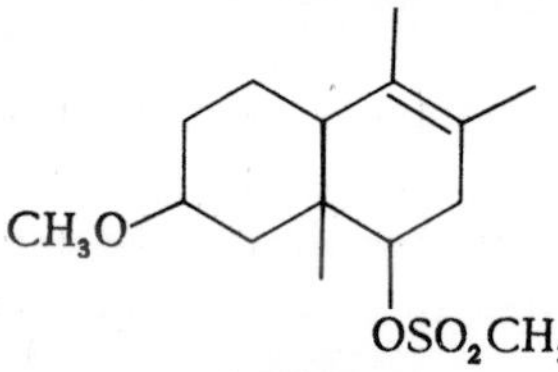

LXXV

Schmid and Karrer (34,59) reported that refluxing cholesteryl tosylate (LXXVI) with LAH in an ether-benzene mixture for 20 hours gives 22% of cholest-5-ene (LXXVII) and 30% of the cyclosteroid *i*-cholestene (LXXVIII).

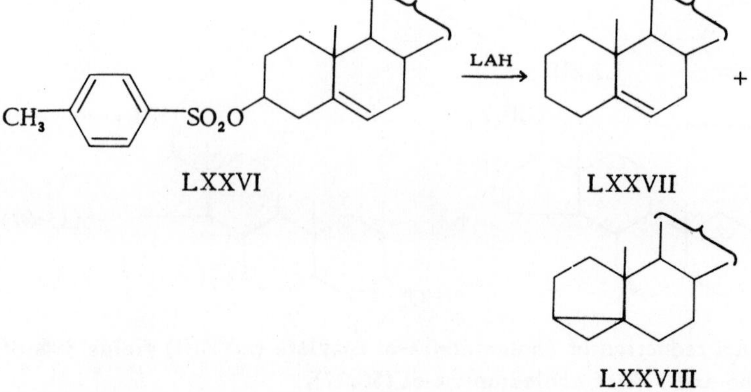

LXXVI   **LXXVII**

(13-70)

LXXVIII

Strating and Backer (1) reported that LAH reduction of LXXVI in ether gives 22% of cholest-5-ene (LXXVII) after one-half hour while a 4-hour reflux is sufficient to give 94% of a mixture of LXXVII and LXXVIII. After 3 hours refluxing, cholesteryl mesylate is converted in 86% yield to a mixture of LXXVII and LXXVIII in which the hydrocarbons are present in a different proportion than when derived from the tosylate.

The reduction of the epimeric *epi*-cholesteryl tosylate (LXXIX) has been reported to yield 19% of cholest-5-ene (LXXVII) and 74% of cholesta-3,5-diene (LXXX) while no cyclosteroid is isolated (60).

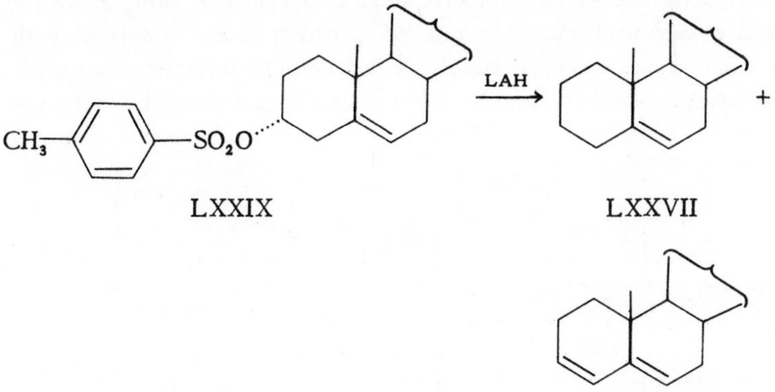

LXXIX   LXXVII

LXXX   (13-71)

The LAH reduction of 3-tosyloxy-5-pregnen-20-one (LXXXI) is reported to yield a product with a wide melting point whose analysis corresponds to a pregnenol. Oxidation of the product with chromic acid yields 5-pregnen-20-one. The reduction product has therefore been considered to be a mixture of isomeric 5-pregnen-20-ols (56).

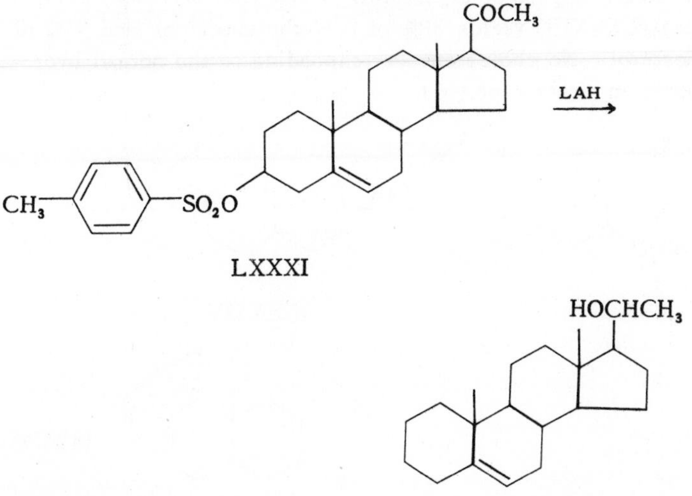

LXXXI

(13-72)

In view of the products obtained in the LAH reduction of the Δ^5-steroids LXXVI, LXXIX, LXXXII, and LXXXIII it is probable that the wide melting point of the product is indicative of the presence of analogous compounds.

The LAH reduction of 3-tosyloxycholest-5-en-4-ol (LXXXII) yields an inhomogeneous product which has been separated chromatographically into three fractions: 29% of cholest-5-en-4-ol, 3% of cholest-4-ene, and 5.8% of an unidentified product, $C_{27}H_{46}O$, m.p. 98°. The latter compound yields a p-nitrobenzoyl ester, m.p. 169-170°, and on catalytic hydrogenation over platinum oxide in acetic acid takes up one mole of hydrogen to yield a saturated alcohol, m.p. 84°, which is not identical with any known cholestanol or coprostanol. It has been postulated that an unstable iso-cholesten-4-ol is formed which is stabilized through rearrangement (56).

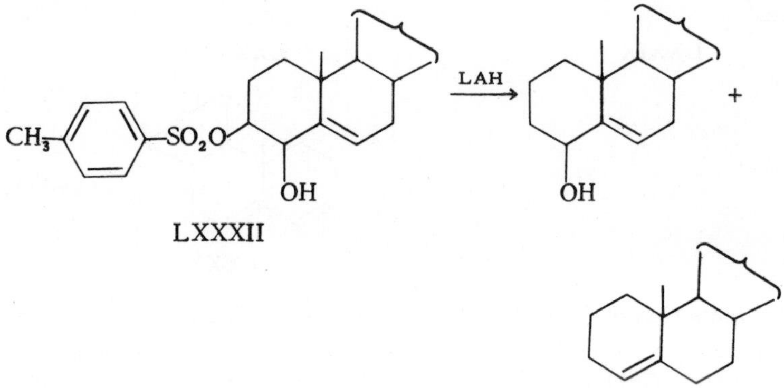

LXXXII

(13-73)

Reduction of ergosteryl tosylate (LXXXIII) yields 56% of $\Delta^{7,22}$-i-ergostatriene and a small amount of ergosterol. Reduction of 7-dehydrocholesteryl tosylate (LXXXIII) yields 38% of Δ^7-i-cholestadiene and 55% of 7-dehydrocholesterol. No cholestene corresponding to the normal hydrocarbon is isolated in either case (61).

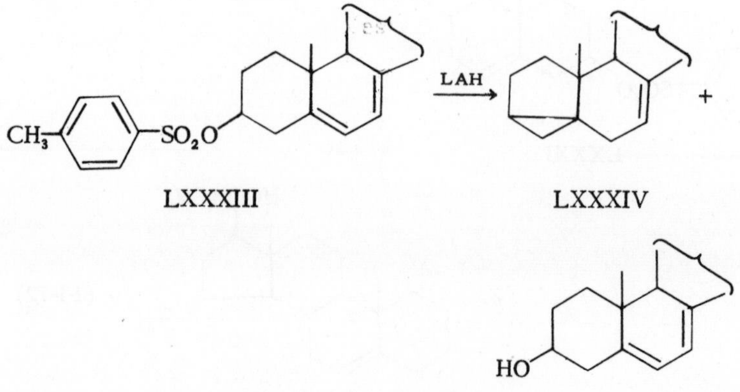

LXXXIII   LXXXIV

(13-74)

The i-steroid has been postulated as arising through a resonance stabilization:

$$\text{LXXXIII} \xrightarrow{-OTs} \left[\quad \rightleftharpoons \quad \right] \xrightarrow{+H^{\ominus}} \text{LXXXIV}$$

(13-75)

13.10.1.e *Alkaloid Tosylates*. As indicated in Table LXXXV, the LAH reduction of alkaloid tosylates in which the sulfonic ester grouping is attached to a non-aromatic ring or to a side chain yields the corresponding hydrocarbon. Thus, codeine (40,41) and neopine (40) tosylates are reduced to the desoxy compounds. The LAH reduction of yohimbyl alcohol tritosylate (LXXXV) yields 16-methylyohimban (62).

$$\xrightarrow[50\%]{\text{LAH}}$$

LXXXV   (13-76)

13.10.1.f *Aromatic Sulfonic Esters*. The LAH reduction of aryl sulfonic esters yields phenols instead of the hydrocarbons obtained from alkyl tosylates (1,34). This is the case with both tosylates and mesylates. Aryl esters of aromatic sulfonic acids do not react with alkyl Grignard reagents, while arylmagnesium halides yield diarylsulfones and phenols (37). Catalytic hydrogenation over Raney nickel converts aryl tosylates into aromatic hydrocarbons (39).

$$\text{ArOSO}_2\text{R} \begin{cases} \xrightarrow{\text{H}_2:\text{Raney Ni}} \text{ArH} + \text{HOSO}_2\text{R} & (13\text{-}77) \\ \xrightarrow{\text{H}^{\ominus}:\text{LAH}} \text{ArOH} + \text{HO}_2\text{SR} & (13\text{-}78) \end{cases}$$

The LAH reduction of various aryl esters of sulfonic acids to phenols is summarized in Table LXXXVI.

13.10.2 Reductions with Lithium Borohydride

Friedman (63) has reported, without experimental details, that tosylates are readily "hydrogenolyzed" with a mixture of lithium hydride and lithium borohydride in tetrahydrofuran.

TABLE LXXXVI

LAH Reduction of Aryl Sulfonic Esters to Phenols

Compound		Product	% Yield	Ref.
$C_7H_8O_3S$	Phenyl mesylate	Phenol	100 }	1
		Methyl mercaptan	...[2] }	
$C_{13}H_{12}O_3S$	Phenyl tosylate	Phenol	...	3
		p-Toluenesulfinic acid	...	
		p,p′-Ditolylsulfoxide	...	
$C_{17}H_{14}O_3S$	β-Naphthyl tosylate	β-Naphthol	21 } [4]	1
		p-Thiocresol	12 }	
$C_{20}H_{28}O_4S$	d-Camphor-10-sulfonate of L-(+)-2-sec-butylphenol (I)	L-(+)-2-sec-Butylphenol	44	5
$C_{24}H_{25}O_5NS$	Morphine monotosylate (II)	Morphine	...	6
$C_{24}H_{25}O_7NS_2$	N-Tosyl-L-tyrosine methyl ester tosylate (III)	N-Tosyl-L-tyrosinol	81.5[7]	8
$C_{30}H_{31}O_8NS_3$	N-Tosyl-L-tyrosinol ditosylate (IV)	L-p-Hydroxyphenyl-β-(tosylamino)propane	77[7]	8

[1] J. Strating and H. J. Backer, Rec. trav. chim., 69, 638 (1950).

[2] Isolated as lead mercaptide.

[3] H. Schmid and P. Karrer, Helv. Chim. Acta, 32, 1371 (1949).

[4] 50% unchanged tosylate recovered.

[5] F. Hawthorne and D. J. Cram, J. Am. Chem. Soc., 74, 5859 (1952).

[6] P. Karrer and G. Widmark, Helv. Chim. Acta, 34, 34 (1951).

[7] Reduction carried out in tetrahydrofuran.

[8] P. Karrer and K. Ehrhardt, Helv. Chim. Acta, 34, 2202 (1951).

CHART TO TABLE LXXXVI

13.11 SULTONES

The LAH reduction of sultones is related to that of sulfonic esters as the reduction of lactones is related to that of carboxylic esters. Thus, the reduction of 1,8-naphthosultone (LXXXVI:R = H) yields 1-mercapto-8-hydroxynaphthalene and 8,8'-dihydroxy-1,1'-dinaphthyldisulfide (64,65).

LXXXVI   (13-79)

Similarly 5-methyl-1,8-naphthosultone (LXXXVI: R = CH$_3$) is reduced to the corresponding methyl derivative.

The reaction of 1,8-naphthosultone with the Grignard reagent results in opening of the sultone ring to yield a perihydroxy diarylsulfone (65).

LXXXVI   (13-80)

13.12 SULFONAMIDES

Strating and Backer (1) reported that sulfonamides are not attacked by LAH. Marvel and Caesar (26,27,32) reported that the reduction of unsubstituted arylsulfonamides is unsuccessful in ether or in tetrahydrofuran. Field and Grunwald (31) attributed the refractory behavior of the unsubstituted compounds to the resistance of the rapidly formed anion RSO$_2$NH$^\ominus$ to further attack by a negatively charged ion. Treatment of N,N-diethylbenzenesulfonamide (LXXXVII), which cannot form such an anion, with one mole of LAH in tetrahydrofuran, after 18 hours of refluxing gives 43% of benzenesulfinic acid (LXXXVIII) and a 33% recovery of the sulfonamide. When the reduction of LXXXVII is carried out with two moles of LAH in tetrahydrofuran, after 7 days of refluxing the products are 57% of the sulfinic acid (LXXXVIII) and 10% of thiophenol as well as diethylamine.

$$C_6H_5SO_2N(C_2H_5)_2 \xrightarrow{LAH} C_6H_5SO_2H + C_6H_5SH + (C_2H_5)_2NH \quad (13-81)$$

LXXXVII   LXXXVIII

The LAH reduction of 1-methyl-2-(ω-N-methyl-p-toluenesulfonamido-pentyl)piperidine (LXXXIX) in ether has been reported to yield 1-methyl-2-ω-methylaminopentylpiperidine (66).

$$\text{LXXXIX} \xrightarrow[90\%]{\text{LAH}} \qquad (13\text{-}82)$$

The non-reduction of the sulfonamide grouping has been reported in the following compounds:

		Ref.
$C_7H_9NO_5S$	2-methyl-3-sulfonamido-5-carbomethoxyfuran	67
$C_{13}H_{11}NO_4S$	o-benzenesulfonamidobenzoic acid	68
$C_{14}H_{13}NO_4S$	o-(p-toluenesulfonamido)benzoic acid	68
$C_{17}H_{13}NO_4S$	o-(2-naphthalenesulfonamido)benzoic acid	68
$C_{23}H_{25}NO_5S_2$	N-(p-toluenesulfonyl)-D- or DL-phenylalaninol-p- toluenesulfonate	69
$C_{24}H_{25}NO_7S_2$	methyl ester of N-(p-toluenesulfonyl)-L-tyrosine-p- toluenesulfonate	69
$C_{30}H_{31}NO_8S_3$	N-(p-toluenesulfonyl)-L-tyrosinol-di-(p-toluenesulfonate)	69
$C_{45}H_{35}N_5O_{10}S_4$	bis-(1,4-naphthalenedibenzenesulfonamido-3)- nitromethane	70

The LAH reduction of sulfonamides in which the amido nitrogen is part of a heterocyclic nucleus presents a varied picture. Reduction of N-(p-toluenesulfonyl)-L-prolinol-p-toluenesulfonate (XC), where the nitrogen is part of a pyrrolidine ring, results in retention of the sulfonamide grouping (69).

$$\text{XC} \longrightarrow \qquad (13\text{-}83)$$

Reductive cleavage occurs when the nitrogen atom is part of a heterocyclic nucleus with aromatic character. Thus, reduction of 9-p-toluenesulfonylcarbazole (XCI) in tetrahydrofuran yields 90% carbazole and 90% p-thiocresol (71).

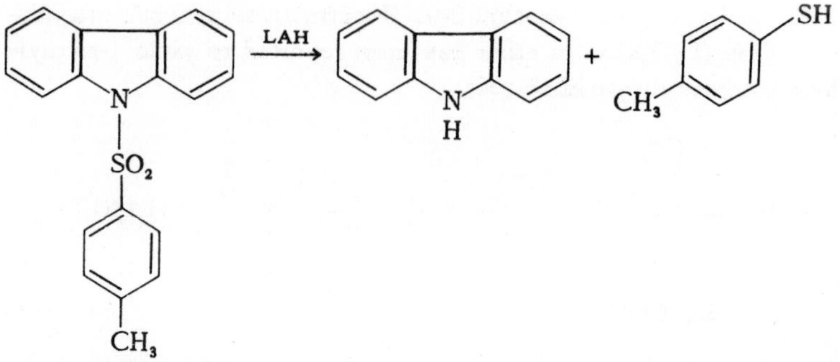

(13-84)

XCI

A similar reductive cleavage is reported in the LAH reduction of yohimbyl alcohol tritosylate in tetrahydrofuran (equation 13-76) (62). This behavior parallels the behavior of the corresponding carboxylic acid amides (Section 10.1.1.d.2).

Although the sulfonamide grouping remains intact, a cleavage of the nitrogen-carbon bond occurs in the LAH reduction of N,N'-diaryl-α-sulfonyldianthranilides (XCII: R = C_6H_5, p-$CH_3C_6H_4$, 2-$C_{10}H_7$) (68).

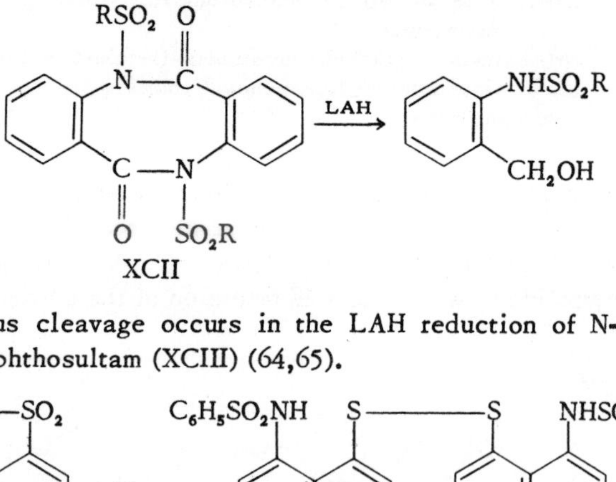

(13-85)

XCII

An analogous cleavage occurs in the LAH reduction of N-benzenesulfonyl-1,8-naphthosultam (XCIII) (64,65).

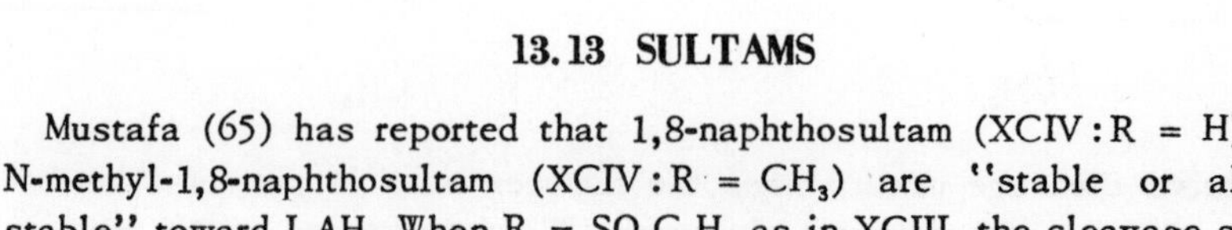

XCIII

(13-86)

13.13 SULTAMS

Mustafa (65) has reported that 1,8-naphthosultam (XCIV: R = H) and N-methyl-1,8-naphthosultam (XCIV: R = CH_3) are "stable or almost stable" toward LAH. When R = $SO_2C_6H_5$ as in XCIII, the cleavage shown in equation (13-86) occurs to yield dibenzenesulfonyl-8,8'-diamino-1,1'-dinaphthyldisulfide (64,65). The behavior of the sultams towards the

Grignard reagent is analogous to the behavior towards the complex metal hydride.   Thus,   1,8-naphthosultam   and   the   N-methyl   analogue (XCIV : R = H and CH$_3$) are stable toward phenylmagnesium bromide. However,   N-benzenesulfonyl-1,8-naphthosultam   (XCIV : R = SO$_2$C$_6$H$_5$)   is cleaved   to   yield   8-benzenesulfonyl-1-benzenesulfonylnaphthylamine (XCV : R = SO$_2$C$_6$H$_5$) (65).

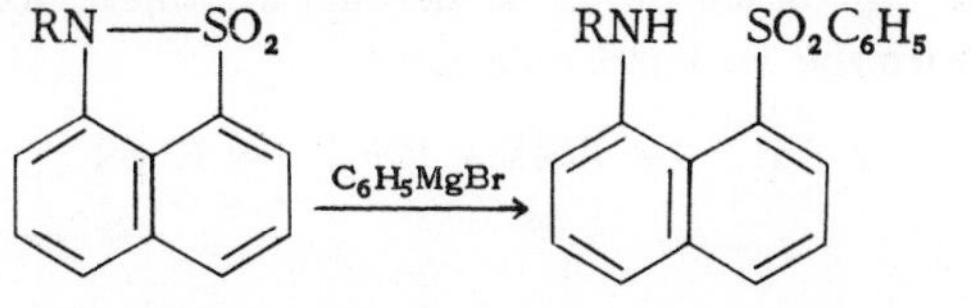

$$RN{-\!\!-}SO_2 \qquad RNH \quad SO_2C_6H_5$$

(13-87)

XCIV   XCV

13.14 SULFINIC ACID DERIVATIVES

The reduction of p-toluenesulfinic acid (XCVI) with LAH has been reported to give 44% of di-p-tolyldisulfide accompanied by the odor of p-thiocresol. The reduction of p-toluenesulfinyl chloride (XCVII) gives 66% of the disulfide and 22% of the thiocresol (1).

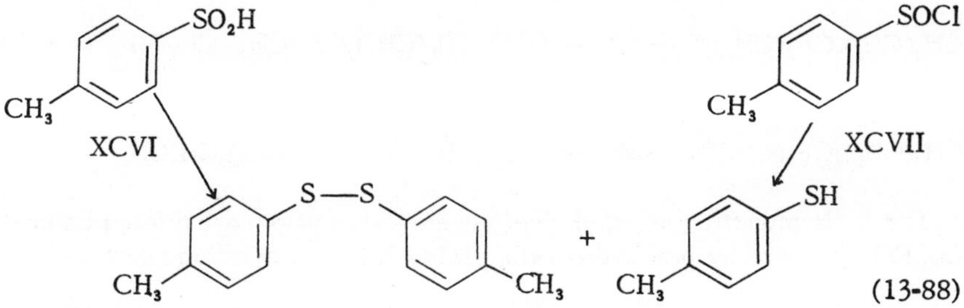

(13-88)

The products are explained by the intermediate formation of a mercaptan. The first products of the reduction, the sulfenic acid and chloride, react with the mercaptan, as soon as it is formed, to yield the disulfide.

$$RSO_2H \rightarrow RSOH \rightarrow RSH$$
$$\underset{}{\overset{RSH}{\longrightarrow}} RSSR \qquad (13\text{-}89)$$

$$RSOCl \rightarrow RSCl \rightarrow RSH$$
$$\underset{}{\overset{RSH}{\longrightarrow}} RSSR \qquad (13\text{-}90)$$

13.15 SULFENIC ACID DERIVATIVES

No example of the LAH reduction of a sulfenic acid has been reported. The LAH reduction of p-toluenesulfenyl chloride (XCVIII) gives 88% of di-p-tolyldisulfide (1).

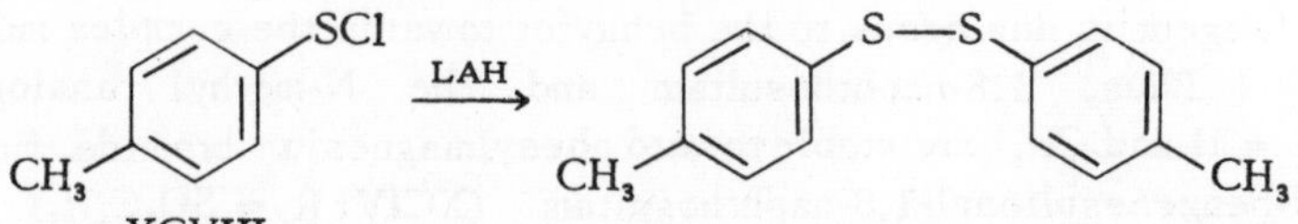

XCVIII (13-91)

As in the case of the sulfinic acid derivatives the disulfide formation is attributed to the formation of a mercaptan which, as soon as it is formed, reacts with the sulfenyl chloride.

$$2\ RSCl \longrightarrow RSH + RSCl \longrightarrow RSSR \qquad (13\text{-}92)$$

13.16 THIO ACID DERIVATIVES

13.16.1 Reductions with Lithium Aluminum Hydride

The reduction of a mixture of ethyl and *n*-butyl thioldifluorodecanoate with LAH has been reported to yield difluorodecanol. The esters utilized have been a mixture of 5,5- and 6,6-difluoro isomers and hence the product is a mixture of 5,5- and 6,6-difluorodecanols (72).

$$\left.\begin{array}{c} CH_3(CH_2)_3CF_2(CH_2)_4C(=O){-}SR \\ + \\ CH_3(CH_2)_4CF_2(CH_2)_3C(=O){-}SR \end{array}\right] \xrightarrow{LAH} \begin{array}{c} CH_3(CH_2)_3CF_2(CH_2)_4CH_2OH \\ + \\ CH_3(CH_2)_4CF_2(CH_2)_3CH_2OH \end{array} \qquad (13\text{-}93)$$

The LAH reduction of ethyl S-*o*-(α-methylallenyl)phenyl thiolcarbonate (XCIX), followed by acid hydrolysis, yields 2,3-dimethylthianaphthene (C).

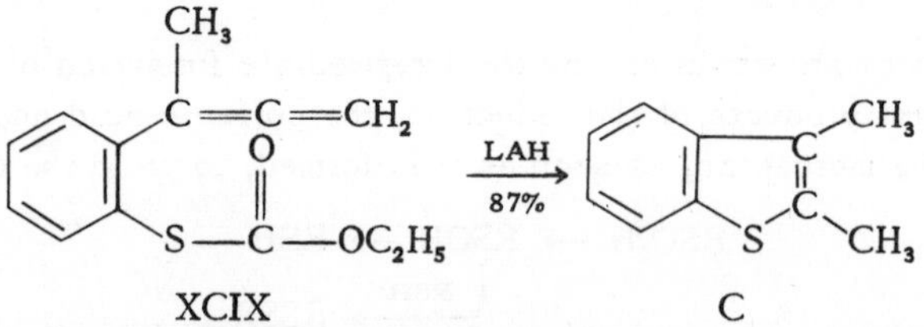

XCIX C (13-94)

When the ester is refluxed with ethanolic potassium hydroxide an 82% yield of C is obtained (73).

The reaction of trichloromethylsulfenyl chloride with sodium-*m*-thiocresolate yields hexa-*m*-tolylthio-dimethyltrisulfide. Oxidation of the trisulfide yields, besides a disulfide and other products, a compound formulated as the ester of trithiopercarbonic acid. Reduction of *m*-tolyl trithiopercarbonate with LAH yields *m*-thiocresol, methanol, methyl mercaptan, and hydrogen sulfide (74).

$$ArSNa + Cl_3CSCl \rightarrow (ArS)_3CSSSC(SAr)_3$$

$$ArS-\underset{\underset{O}{\|}}{C}-SSAr$$

$\downarrow$ LAH

$$Ar = \text{(3-methylphenyl, with } CH_3 \text{ substituent)}$$

$$ArSH + CH_3OH + CH_3SH + H_2S \quad (13\text{-}95)$$

The LAH reduction of a trithio analog of carbonic acid proceeds in the expected manner. The reduction of 1,3-dithia-4-cyclopentene-2-thione (CI) yields ethylene dithiol (CII). Reduction with sodium and alcohol also yields CII (75).

$$\underset{CI}{\overset{HC=CH}{\underset{S \quad S}{\underset{\underset{\underset{S}{\|}}{C}}{\diagdown\diagup}}}} \xrightarrow{\text{LAH}} HS-CH=CH-SH \quad (13\text{-}96)$$

CII

Cronyn and Goodrich (76) have reported that the products isolated from the action of LAH on thiobenzamide (CIII) point to an elimination of hydrogen sulfide to give a nitrile followed by normal reduction to the amine. The normal addition of 1.26 moles of LAH at low temperatures gives 64% of benzylamine, isolated as the benzenesulfonamide. The inverse addition of 0.54 mole of LAH gives 8% of benzylamine, 30% of benzonitrile and 33% of unreacted amide.

$$\underset{CIII}{C_6H_5\overset{\overset{S}{\|}}{C}-NH_2} \xrightarrow{\text{LAH}} C_6H_5CH_2NH_2 + C_6H_5CN \quad (13\text{-}97)$$

It has been reported that heating thioacetamide with sodium ethoxide results in the elimination of hydrogen sulfide to give acetonitrile (77). In its reaction with CIII LAH apparently acts as a base.

13.16.2 Reactions with Sodium Borohydride

Ethyl 6-ketooct-7-enoate has been treated with thioacetic acid and the resultant thiol ester, presumably CIV, reduced with sodium borohydride in methanol and hydrolyzed to give DL-8-thioloctan-6-ol-1-oic acid (CV) (23).

$$CH_3\overset{O}{\overset{\|}{C}}-SCH_2CH_2\overset{O}{\overset{\|}{C}}(CH_2)_4COOC_2H_5 \rightarrow HSCH_2CH_2\overset{OH}{\overset{|}{C}}H(CH_2)_4COOH$$

CIV   CV   (13-98)

No indication is given of the fate of the thiol ester in the course of the reduction. The mercaptan may have resulted from either the reduction or the subsequent hydrolysis.

13.17 THIOLSULFONIC ESTERS

Strating and Backer reported that the major product in the LAH reduction of thiolsulfonic esters, which are also called disulfoxides, is the disulfide (1).

Reduction of methyl methanethiolsulfonate ("dimethyl disulfoxide") (CVI) in ether gives 80% of dimethyl disulfide and 17% of methyl mercaptan isolated as mercuric methyl mercaptide.

$$CH_3S\overset{\overset{O}{\uparrow}}{\underset{\underset{O}{\downarrow}}{-}}SCH_3 \xrightarrow{\text{LAH}} CH_3S-SCH_3 + CH_3SH \qquad (13\text{-}99)$$

CVI

The mercaptan probably arises from reduction of the disulfide. The reduction of p-tolyl p-toluenethiolsulfonate (CVII) yields 75% of di-p-tolyl disulfide.

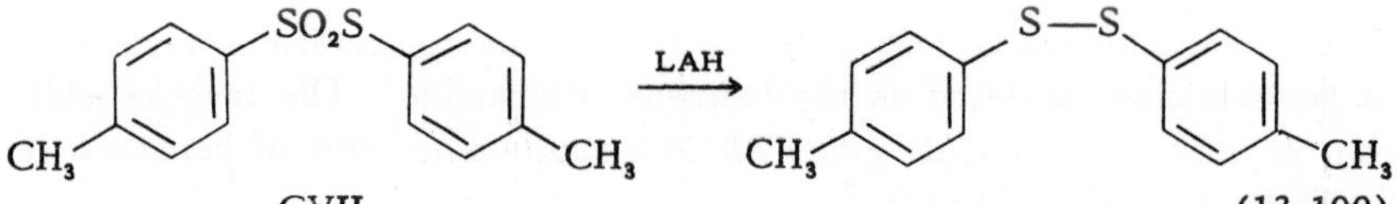

CVII   (13-100)

The actual complexity of the reaction is indicated by the isolation of a considerable quantity of p-tolyl p-toluenethiolsulfonate (CVII), in addition to 28% of di-p-tolyl disulfide, from the LAH reduction of methyl p-toluenethiolsulfonate (CVIII). A strong odor of p-thiocresol is also detected.

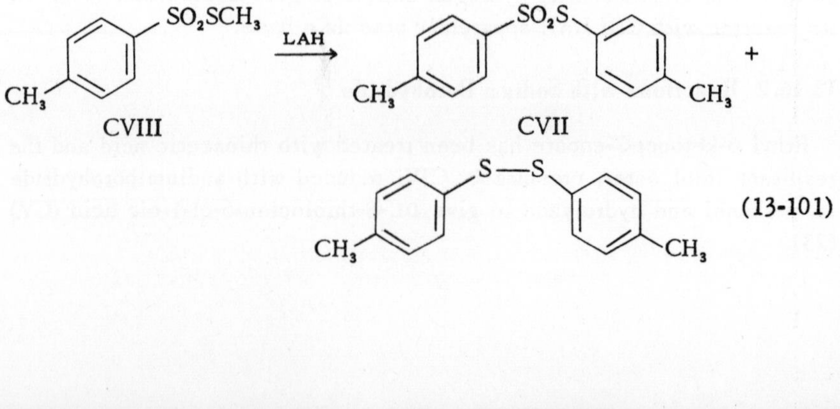

CVIII   CVII   +

(13-101)

13.18 THIOCYANATES

Strating and Backer reported that the LAH reduction of thiocyanates yields thiols (1,78).

$$RSCN \xrightarrow{LAH} RSH \qquad (13\text{-}102)$$

This reaction has been applied to the reduction of the following compounds to the corresponding thiol:

	% Yield	Ref.
p-Tolyl rhodanide	94	1
Cholesteryl 3-rhodanide	81	1,78–82
7-Dehydrocholesteryl 3-rhodanide	67	78–82
Ergosteryl 3-rhodanide	....	83

Mousseron *et al.* (3,17) reported that the reduction of 1,2-dithiocyano-cyclohexane (CIX) with ethereal LAH gives only about 10% of the normal reduction product, *trans*-cyclohexane-1,2-dithiol (CX), and 70% of 1,2-epithiocyclohexane (CXI).

$$(13\text{-}103)$$

CIX   CX   CXI

The formation of CXI is accounted for by the following mechanism (3):

$$(13\text{-}104)$$

CIX   CXI

13.19 ISOTHIOCYANATES

Ried and Müller (84) have reported that the LAH reduction of phenyl isothiocyanate (mustard oil) yields 78% of N-methylaniline accompanied by the evolution of hydrogen sulfide.

$$C_6H_5N=C=S \xrightarrow{LAH} C_6H_5NHCH_3 + H_2S \qquad (13\text{-}105)$$

The stoichiometric relationship is set forth as follows:

$$4\,C_6H_5NCS + 3\,LiAlH_4 \xrightarrow{H_2O} 4\,C_6H_5NHCH_3 + 4\,H_2S + 3\,LiOH +$$
$$3/2\,Al_2O_3 \cdot H_2O \qquad (13\text{-}106)$$

The reduction is analogous to the reduction of phenyl isocyanate to N-methylaniline (84,85).

13.20 THIOKETONES

Mustafa and Hilmy have reported the LAH reduction of various xanthiones to the corresponding xanthenes (86). Thus, xanthione (CXII) is reduced to xanthene, thioxanthione (CXIII) yields 83% of thioxanthene and 3,4-benzoxanth-9-thione (CXIV) yields 3,4-benzoxanthene.

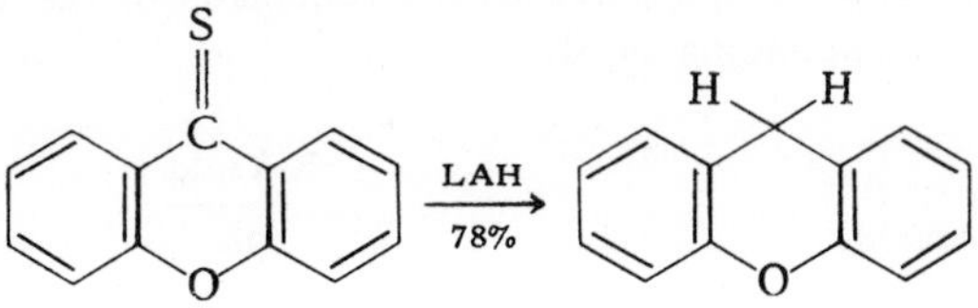

(13-107)

CXII

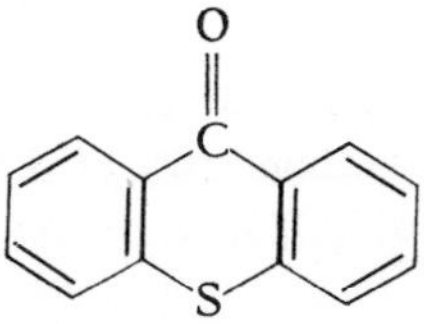

CXIII 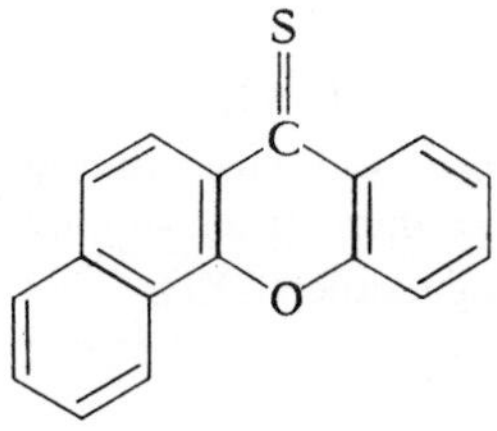   CXIV

These reactions are not characteristic of the usual reduction of a ketone to a carbinol but are rather representative of the hydrogenolysis reaction induced by the presence of the vinylogous electron donor, as discussed in Section 16.1. The corresponding oxygen compounds, xanthone, thioxanthone, and 3,4-benzoxanthone, also yield the hydrogenolysis products instead of the carbinols. Michler's thioketone (CXV) also undergoes the hydrogenolysis reaction.

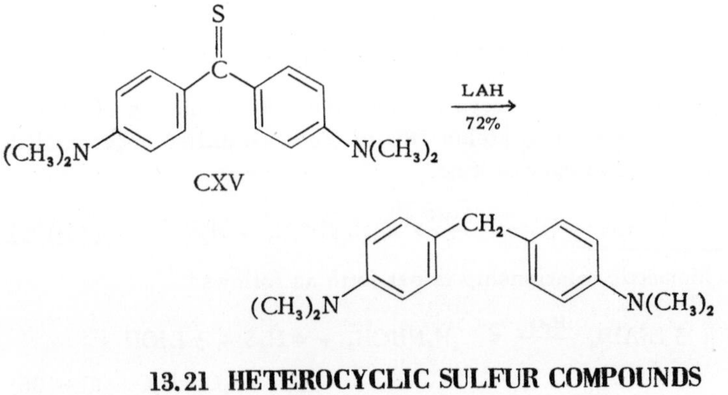

CXV

(13-108)

13.21 HETEROCYCLIC SULFUR COMPOUNDS

Heterocyclic sulfur compounds are generally resistant to attack by the complex hydrides.

The thioether linkage in thiacyclobutane-, thiacyclopentane-, and thia-cyclohexane-1-dioxide is not cleaved by LAH (16).

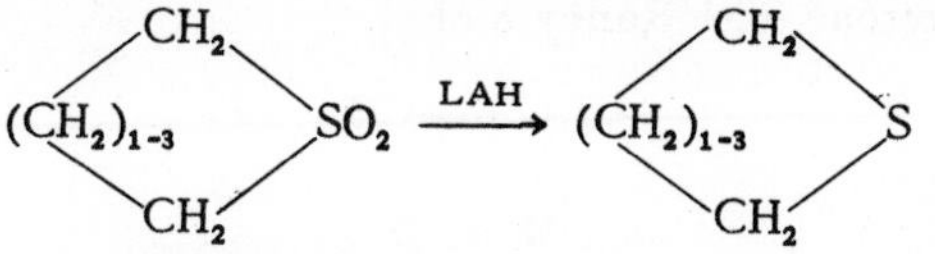

$$
\begin{array}{c}
\text{CXVI}
\end{array}
\qquad (13\text{-}109)
$$

Further, LAH reduction of 2,3-dihydrobenzothiophene- (CXVII) and 2,3-dihydro-1,4-benzothiapyran-1-dioxide (CXVIII) results in retention of the heterocyclic nucleus.

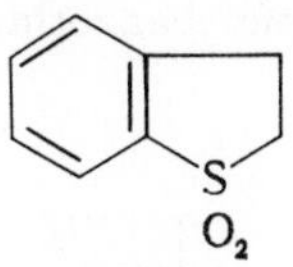

CXVII 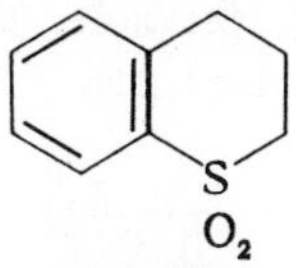   CXVIII 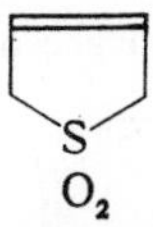   CXIX

The attempted LAH reduction of thiacyclopent-3-ene-1-dioxide (CXIX) has resulted in the formation of dark-colored polymeric material without recovery of the expected sulfide (16).

Numerous reductions with both LAH and sodium borohydride have been carried out with compounds containing the thiophene (CXX) and thia-naphthene (CXXI) nucleus without any reported reduction of the hetero-cyclic moiety.

CXX 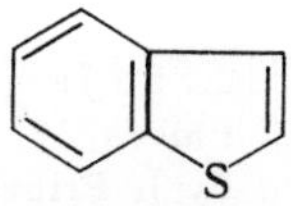   CXXI

Similarly, the dibenzothiophene (CXXII) (16), benzo[d]naphtho[2,1-b]-thiophene (CXXIII) (87) and thioxanthene (CXXIV) (86) nuclei remain in-tact after treatment with LAH.

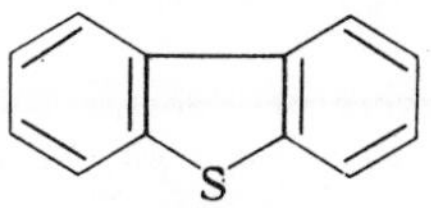

CXXII 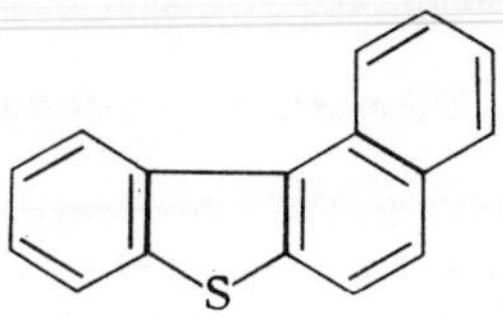   CXXIII 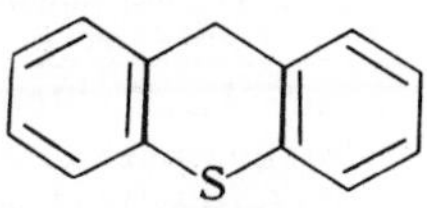   CXXIV

The reduction of β-hydroxythiophthen (CXXV) with LAH yields a hydro-genolysis product in which the heterocyclic nucleus is retained (88).

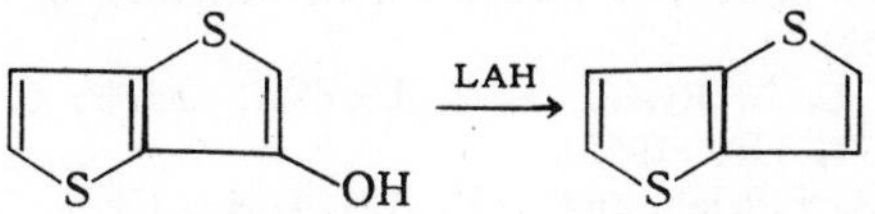

CXXV   (13-110)

As mentioned earlier, the hemithioketal and thioxolane (CXXVI) groupings are resistant to attack by LAH. In contrast, the hemithioketal is
reduced to the ketone with Raney nickel.

$$H_2C\text{----}CH_2$$

CXXVI

The phenothiazine (CXXVII), thiazole (CXXVIII), and benzothiazole
(CXXIX) nuclei are not attacked by LAH.

CXXVII   CXXVIII   CXXIX

REFERENCES

1. Strating, J., and H. J. Backer, *Rec. trav. chim.*, 69, 638 (1950).
2. Knüsli, E., *Experientia*, 8, 262 (1952).
3. Mousseron, M., R. Jacquier, M. Mousseron-Canet, and R. Zagdoun, *Bull. soc. chim. France*, [5] 19, 1042 (1952).
4. Yale, H. L., E. J. Pribyl, W. Braker, J. Bernstein, and W. A. Lott, *J. Am. Chem. Soc.*, 72, 3716 (1950).
5. Kharasch, N., and J. L. Cameron, *J. Am. Chem. Soc.*, 75, 1077 (1953).
6. Rosenkranz, G., S. Kaufmann, and J. Romo, *J. Am. Chem. Soc.*, 71, 3689 (1949).
7. Syntex, S. A., Brit. Pat. 662,400 (December 5, 1951).
8. Rosenkranz, G., S. Kaufmann, and J. Romo, U. S. Pat. 2,609,378 (September 2, 1952).
9. Romo, J., M. Romero, C. Djerassi, and G. Rosenkranz, *J. Am. Chem. Soc.*, 73, 1528 (1951).
10. Romo, J., G. Rosenkranz, and C. Djerassi, *Abstracts of Papers*, XIIth International Congress of Pure and Applied Chemistry, New York, N. Y., September 1951, p. 406.
11. Bergmann, E. D., D. Lavie, and S. Pinchas, *J. Am. Chem. Soc.*, 73, 5662 (1951).
12. Romo, J., G. Rosenkranz, and C. Djerassi, *J. Am. Chem. Soc.*, 73, 4961 (1951).
13. Djerassi, C., E. Batres, J. Romo, and G. Rosenkranz, *J. Am. Chem. Soc.*, 74, 3634 (1952).
14. Cairns, T. L., G. L. Evans, A. W. Larchar, and B. C. McKusick, *J. Am. Chem. Soc.*, 74, 3982 (1952).
15. Arnold, R. C., A. P. Lien, and R. M. Alm, *J. Am. Chem. Soc.*, 72, 731 (1950).

16. Bordwell, F. G., and W. H. McKellin, *J. Am. Chem. Soc.,* 73, 2251 (1951).
17. Mousseron, M., and M. Canet, *Bull. soc. chim. France,* [5] 18, 792 (1951).
18. Brown, W. G., 1950 Spring Lecture Series, North Jersey Section, American Chemical Society, New Brunswick, N. J., through ref. 9, footnote 17.
19. Pitt, B. M., through ref. 16.
20. Nystrom, R. F., unpublished work, through W. G. Brown, in *Organic Reactions,* Vol. VI, p. 508.
21. Brown, W. G., in *Organic Reactions,* Vol. VI, p. 471.
22. Brockman, J. A., Jr., E. L. R. Stokstad, E. L. Patterson, J. V. Pierce, M. Macchi, and F. P. Day, *J. Am. Chem. Soc.,* 74, 1868 (1952).
23. Bullock, M. W., J. A. Brockman, Jr., E. L. Patterson, J. V. Pierce, and E. L. R. Stokstad, *J. Am. Chem. Soc.,* 74, 3455 (1952).
24. Backer, H. J., *Rec. trav. chim.,* 68, 844 (1949).
25. Cronyn, M. W., *J. Am. Chem. Soc.,* 74, 1225 (1952).
26. Marvel, C. S., and P. D. Caesar, *J. Am. Chem. Soc.,* 72, 1033 (1950).
27. Caesar, P. D., Ph.D. thesis, University of Illinois, 1950; through C. S. Marvel, private communication.
28. Knüsli, E., *Gazz. chim. ital.,* 80, 522 (1950).
29. Backer, H. J., J. Strating, and J. Drenth, *Rec. trav. chim.,* 70, 365 (1951).
30. Field, L., and P. H. Settlage, *J. Am. Chem. Soc.,* 73, 5870 (1951).
31. Field, L., and F. A. Grunwald, *J. Org. Chem.,* 16, 946 (1951).
32. Marvel, C. S., private communication, through ref. 31.
33. Schlesinger, H. I., and A. E. Finholt, U. S. Pat. 2,576,311 (November 27, 1951).
34. Schmid, H., and P. Karrer, *Helv. Chim. Acta,* 32, 1371 (1949).
35. Karrer, P., *Bull. soc. chim. France,* [5] 17, 907 (1950).
36. Karrer, P., *Angew. chem.,* 62, 334 (1950).
37. Gilman, H., and N. J. Beaber, *J. Am. Chem. Soc.,* 47, 518 (1925).
38. Gilman, H., and L. L. Heck, *J. Am. Chem. Soc.,* 50, 2223 (1928).
39. Kenner, G. W., and M. A. Murray, *J. Chem. Soc.,* 1950, 406.
40. Rapoport, H., and R. M. Bonner, *J. Am. Chem. Soc.,* 73, 2872 (1951).
41. Karrer, P., and G. Widmark, *Helv. Chim. Acta,* 34, 34 (1951).
42. Alexander, E. R., *J. Am. Chem. Soc.,* 72, 3796 (1950).
43. Bordwell, F. G., B. M. Pitt, and M. Knell, *J. Am. Chem. Soc.,* 73, 5004 (1951).
44. Goering, H. L., and C. Serres, Jr., *J. Am. Chem. Soc.,* 74, 5908 (1952).
45. Noyce, D. S., and D. B. Denney, *J. Am. Chem. Soc.,* 74, 5912 (1952).
46. Fodor, G., J. Kiss, and I. Sallay, *J. Chem. Soc.,* 1951, 1858.
47. Cram, D. J., *J. Am. Chem. Soc.,* 74, 2149 (1952).
48. Cram, D. J., *J. Am. Chem. Soc.,* 74, 2152 (1952).
49. Brown, H. C., private communication, through ref. 48.
50. Bolliger, H. R., and P. Ulrich, unpublished work, through ref. 51.
51. Bolliger, H. R., and P. Ulrich, *Helv. Chim. Acta,* 35, 93 (1952).
52. Fischer, R., and H. R. Bolliger, unpublished work, through ref. 51.
53. Bolliger, H. R., and M. Thürkauf, *Helv. Chim. Acta,* 35, 1426 (1952).
54. Gruber, W., and G. Proske, *Monatsh.,* 81, 1024 (1950).
55. Barton, D. H. R., and C. J. W. Brooks, *J. Chem. Soc.,* 1951, 257.
56. Karrer, P., and H. Asmis, K. N. Sareen, R. Schwyzer, *Helv. Chim. Acta,* 34, 1022 (1951).
57. Karrer, P., H. Asmis, K. N. Sareen, and R. Schwyzer, *Helv. Chim. Acta,* 35, 427 (1952).
58. Shealy, Y. F., and R. M. Dodson, *J. Org. Chem.,* 16, 1427 (1951).

59. Schmid, H., and K. Kägi, *Helv. Chim. Acta*, 33, 1582 (1950).
60. Schmid, H., and K. Kägi, *Helv. Chim. Acta*, 35, 2194 (1952).
61. Karrer, P., and H. Asmis, *Helv. Chim. Acta*, 35, 1926 (1952).
62. Karrer, P., and R. Saemann, *Helv. Chim. Acta*, 35, 1932 (1952).
63. Friedman, L., *Abstracts of Papers*, 122nd Meeting American Chemical Society, Atlantic City, N. J., September 1952, p. 46 M.
64. Mustafa, A., and M. Kamel, *Science*, 118, 411 (1953).
65. Mustafa, A., unpublished work, through A. Mustafa, *Chem. Revs.*, 54, 195 (1954).
66. Lukeš, R., and J. Kovář, unpublished work, through M. Ferles and J. Rudinger, *Chem. Listy*, 47, 143 (1953).
67. Scully, J. F., and E. V. Brown, *Abstracts of Papers*, 121st Meeting American Chemical Society, Buffalo, N. Y., March 1952, p. 44K.
68. Mustafa, A., *J. Chem. Soc.*, 1952, 2435.
69. Karrer, P., and K. Ehrhardt, *Helv. Chim. Acta*, 34, 2202 (1951).
70. Adams, R., and W. Moje, *J. Am. Chem. Soc.*, 74, 5557 (1952).
71. Kulka, M., and R. H. F. Manske, *J. Org. Chem.*, 17, 1501 (1952).
72. Newman, M. S., M. W. Renoll, and I. Auerbach, *J. Am. Chem. Soc.*, 70, 1023 (1948).
73. Gaertner, R., *J. Am. Chem. Soc.*, 74, 2991 (1952).
74. Backer, H. J., and E. Westerhuis, *Rec. trav. chim.*, 71, 1071 (1952).
75. Challenger, F., E. A. Mason, E. C. Holdsworth, and R. Emmott, *Chemistry and Industry*, 1952, 714.
76. Cronyn, M. W., and J. E. Goodrich, *J. Am. Chem. Soc.*, 74, 3936 (1952).
77. Jorgensen, C. V., *J. prakt. Chem.*, [2] 66, 33 (1902).
78. Strating, J., and H. J. Backer, *Rec. trav. chim.*, 69, 909 (1950).
79. Strating, J., U. S. Pat. 2,549,991 (April 24, 1951).
80. Strating, J., Ger. Pat. 820,435 (November 12, 1951))
81. N. V. Philips' Gloeilampenfabrieken, Brit. Pat. 681,217 (October 22, 1952).
82. N. V. Philips' Gloeilampenfabrieken, Fr. Pat. 1,019,922 (January 29, 1953).
83. Buisman, J. A. K., and P. Westerhof, *Rec. trav. chim.*, 71, 925 (1952).
84. Ried, W., and F. Müller, *Chem. Ber.*, 85, 470 (1952).
85. Wessely, F., and W. Swoboda, *Monatsh.*, 82, 621 (1951).
86. Mustafa, A., and M. K. Hilmy, *J. Chem. Soc.*, 1952, 1343.
87. Bordwell, F. G., W. H. McKellin, and D. Babcock, *J. Am. Chem. Soc.*, 73, 5566 (1951).
88. Challenger, F., B. Fishwick, and J. L. Holmes, *Chemistry and Industry*, 1952, 519.

CHAPTER 14

Reduction of

HALOGEN-CONTAINING ORGANIC COMPOUNDS

14.1 ALKYL, ARYLMETHYL, AND ALICYCLIC HALIDES

14.1.1 Reductions with Lithium Aluminum Hydride

The reduction of alkyl halides to hydrocarbons by the action of LAH follows a mechanism based on a bimolecular reaction of a nucleophilic hydride complex with a carbon atom. Primary halides react more readily than secondary which are more reactive than tertiary halides. Primary halides give better yields than secondary ones while tertiary halides give mostly olefins. The order of reactivity of the halogens is iodides > bromides > chlorides. No examples of the LAH reduction of fluorides have been reported.

Nystrom and Brown (1) postulated the overall reaction:

$$4 \, RX + LiAlH_4 \rightarrow 4 \, RH + LiAlX_4 \qquad (14\text{-}1)$$

Johnson, Blizzard, and Carhart (2) stated that not all four of the hydrogen atoms in LAH show the same reactivity toward alkyl halides, the reaction probably proceeding in at least two steps:

$$RX + LiAlH_4 \rightarrow RH + LiX + AlH_3 \qquad (14\text{-}2)$$

$$3 \, RX + AlH_3 \rightarrow 3 \, RH + AlX_3 \qquad (14\text{-}3)$$

The first step is presumed to be much more rapid than the second.

Dibeler (3) carried out a study of the reduction of halomethanes with LAH in di-n-butyl ether and reported that no hydrocarbons other than methane are detected. This has been considered indicative that the reduction is a stepwise process, since simultaneous stripping off of several halogen atoms would greatly increase the probability of coupling to form unsaturated and saturated molecules.

The reduction of halides with LAH is postulated as proceeding by a nucleophilic displacement (S_N^2) reaction. The Walden inversion which is a criterion for a bimolecular attack at a saturated carbon atom should therefore yield optically active products from active halides. This has been demonstrated in the reduction of α-chloroethylbenzene and 2-chloro-2-phenylpropionic acid, as discussed in Sections 14.1.1.i and 14.1.1.g, respectively, and in the reduction of 1-chloro-1,2-epoxycyclohexane, as discussed in Section 14.1.1.b.

14.1.1.a *Unconjugated Alkyl Halides*. The reaction of LAH with alkyl halides is often slow and does not occur in reasonable time in refluxing diethyl ether. The use of higher boiling solvents such as tetra-hydrofuran and di-*n*-butyl ether permits the application of higher tempera-tures and accelerates the reaction (2-4).

Dibeler reported that while the reduction of various mono-, di-, and trihalomethanes with LAH yields methane (3) the use of lithium aluminum deuteride yields the corresponding deuterated methane (5).

While attempts to reduce 4-chloro-1,6-heptadiene with LAH in tetra-hydrofuran have been unsuccessful, the corresponding bromo derivative (I) gives 1,6-heptadiene, although in poor yield (6).

$$CH_2 = CHCH_2CHCH_2CH = CH_2 \xrightarrow{\text{LAH}} CH_2 = CHCH_2CH_2CH_2CH = CH_2$$
$$\underset{\displaystyle Br}{|}$$

$$\text{I} \hspace{6cm} (14\text{-}4)$$

The LAH reduction of various unconjugated alkyl halides is summarized in Table LXXXVII.

14.1.1.b *Unconjugated Alicyclic Halides.* The LAH reduction of chloro- (7) or bromoundecafluorocyclohexane (8) yields undecafluorocyclo-hexane, the chlorine and bromine being removed more readily than the fluorine. The replacement of the chlorine atoms is surprising in view of the fact that chlorocyclohexane has been reported as failing to undergo reduction with LAH (2) and in view of the general stability of chlorofluoro compounds.

The reduction of bromocyclohexane with LAH in tetrahydrofuran is re-ported to yield 10% of cyclohexane and a trace of olefin (2). Less than 5% of the halogen is removed when *trans*-2-chloro- (II) or 2-iodocyclo-hexanol are refluxed with LAH in ether solution. In the case of the chloro-hydrin (II), if the ether is evaporated after the reflux period is completed, an extremely violent reaction occurs and a small amount of cyclopentyl-formaldehyde and tars are isolated (9).

$$\text{II} \hspace{6cm} (14\text{-}5)$$

The reduction of 1-chloro-2,3-epoxycyclohexane (III) yields 70% of *cis*-2-chlorocyclohexanol and 20-25% of cyclohexanol (9-11).

$$\text{III} \hspace{6cm} (14\text{-}6)$$

Reduction of 1-chloro-1,2-epoxycyclohexane (IV) yields 10-30% of *cis*-2-chlorocyclohexanol and 70% of cyclohexanol (9-11).

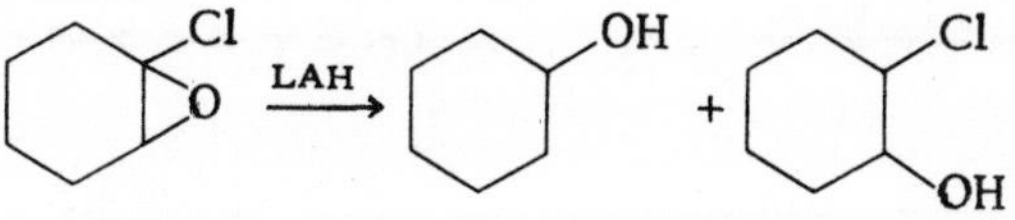

$$(14\text{-}7)$$

IV

In this case, the attack of the hydride ion on the tertiary carbon atom in IV proceeds with Walden inversion to yield the *cis*-chlorocyclohexanol. The predominant reaction, the attack on the secondary carbon, yields a *gem*-halohydrin which is either directly reduced to the carbinol or loses the elements of hydrogen chloride to yield a ketone which is reduced to the carbinol.

Ness, Fletcher, and Hudson (12) reported that the LAH reduction of acetylated glycopyranosyl bromides, prepared by treatment of the fully acetylated glycopyranose with 30% hydrogen bromide in glacial acetic acid, gives the corresponding 1,5-anhydroglycitols. Thus, ,β-D-glucopyranose pentaacetate (V) is converted to 1,5-anhydro-D-glucitol (VI):

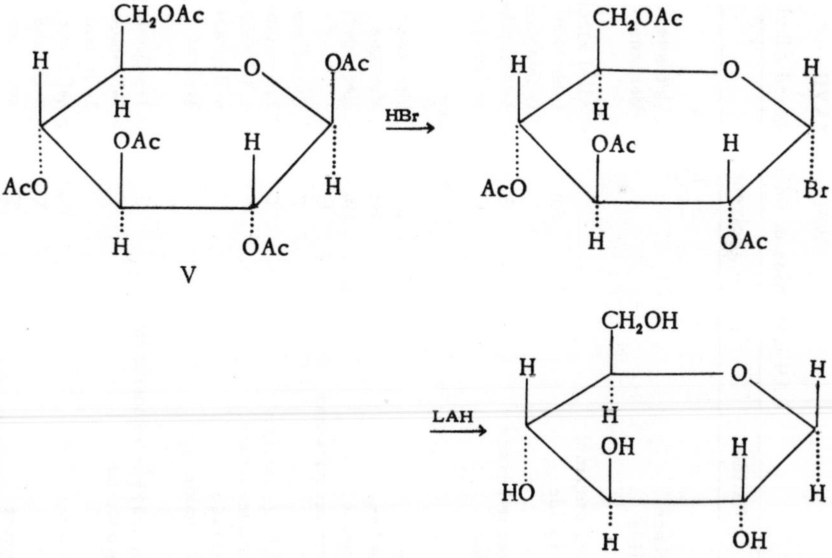

V

VI $(14\text{-}8)$

Tetraacetyl-D-galactofuranosyl chloride has been converted to 1,4-anhydro-D-galactitol by this method (13). Analogous compounds are tabulated in Table LXXXVIII. The ease of reduction of the glycopyranosyl and furanosyl halides is probably related to the existence of the α-haloether grouping. The latter is known to react very readily with the Grignard reagent. The LAH reduction of α-haloethers is discussed in Section 14.1.1.e.

The catalytic hydrogenation of the bromide of 1-*p*-methoxyphenyl-2-methyl-3-ethyl-6-methoxyindene (VII) over platinum oxide in glacial acetic acid has been reported to yield a reduction product (VIII) which is saturated

TABLE LXXXVII

LAH Reduction of Unconjugated Alkyl Halides

Halide	Solvent[1]	Product	% Yield	Ref.
A. Iodides				
Diiodomethane CH_2I_2	Bu	Methane	85	2
Methyl iodide CH_3I	E	Methane	100	3
2,3-Diiodo-1-propanol $C_3H_6I_2$		Allyl alcohol	...	4
tert-Butyl iodide C_4H_9I	Bu	Isobutane	...	5
		Isobutylene	...	5
1-Iodo-4-methylhexane $C_7H_{15}I$	E	3-Methylhexane	95	6
Cetyl iodide $C_{16}H_{33}I$	E	n-Hexadecane	...	3,4
B. Bromides				
Bromoform $CHBr_3$	Bu	Methane	60	2
Dibromomethane CH_2Br_2	Bu	Methane	93	2
Methyl bromide CH_3Br	Bu	Methane	98	2
1,2,3,4-Tetrabromobutane $C_4H_6Br_4$	E	?	...	5
	T	Butadiene	"very poor"	8
4-Bromo-1,6-heptadiene $C_7H_{11}Br$	T	1,6-Heptadiene	5	5
Diethyl bromomalonate $C_7H_{11}BrO_4$	T	1,3-Propanediol	76	9
2-Bromoheptane $C_7H_{15}Br$	T	n-Heptane	71	5
Styrene dibromide $C_8H_8Br_2$	T	Styrene	0	3
1-p-Bromophenyl-2-bromoethanol $C_8H_8Br_2O$	E	1-p-Bromophenylethanol	90	10
1,2-Dibromooctane $C_8H_{16}Br_2$	T	2-Bromooctane	26 [11]	5
		1-Octene	17 [11]	5
	Bu	1-Octene	64	9
n-Octyl bromide $C_8H_{17}Br$	Bu	n-Octane	96	9
2-Bromooctane	T	n-Octane	30 [12]	5

Formula	Compound				
$C_9H_{19}Br$	2-Bromo-2-methyloctane	Bc	2-Methyloctenes	76	5
$C_{10}H_{13}BrO$	β-Ethoxyphenylethyl bromide	E	Ethyl α-phenylethyl ether Styrene	25⎱ ...⎰	13
$C_{10}H_{21}Br$	1-Bromodecane	T	n-Decane	72	5
	(−)-3-Methyl-5-bromononane	T	(+)-3-Methylnonane	62	14
$C_{20}H_{32}Br_2N_2O_2$	Bromoallogelsemine hydrobromide	D	Desoxohydroxytetrahydrogelsemine	...	15
$C_{27}H_{44}Br_2O$	Zymosterol dibromide	B-E	Zymosterol	91	16

C. Chlorides

Formula	Compound				
CCl_4	Carbon tetrachloride	Bu	Methane	36	2
$CHCl_3$	Chloroform	Bu	Methane	52	2
CH_2Cl_2	Dichloromethane	Bu	Methane	81	2
C_3H_5ClO	Epichlorohydrin	Ec	2-Propanol	88	5
$C_4H_8Cl_2O$	Ethyl α,β-dichloroethyl ether	T	Ethyl β-chloroethyl ether	53	5
C_4H_9ClO	L-(+)-erythro-3-Chloro-2-butanol	E or T	2-Butanol	"low"	17
$C_{12}H_{25}Cl$	Dodecyl chloride	T	n-Dodecane	98	9
$C_{24}H_{41}Cl$	24-Chlorocholane	T	Cholane	83	18

References—Table LXXXVII

[1]Bu = di-*n*-butyl ether; E = diethyl ether; T = tetrahydrofuran; Bc = dibutyl carbitol; D = dioxane; B = benzene; Ec = diethyl carbitol.

[2]V. H. Dibeler, *J. Research Natl. Bur. Standards,* 44, 363 (1950).

[3]R. F. Nystrom and W. G. Brown, *J. Am. Chem. Soc.,* 70, 3738 (1948).

[4]H. I. Schlesinger and A. E. Finholt, U. S. Pat. 2,576,311 (November 27, 1951).

[5]L. W. Trevoy and W. G. Brown, *J. Am. Chem. Soc.,* 71, 1675 (1949).

[6]H. E. Heller, *ibid.,* 74, 4858 (1952).

[7]Unidentified unsaturated liquid containing bromine.

[8]J. L. Everett and G. A. R. Kon, *J. Chem. Soc., 1950,* 3131.

[9]J. E. Johnson, R. H. Blizzard, and H. W. Carhart, *J. Am. Chem. Soc.,* 70, 3664 (1948).

[10]R. E. Lutz, R. L. Wayland, Jr., and H. G. France, *ibid.,* 72, 5511 (1950).

[11]22% starting material recovered.

[12]29% starting material recovered.

[13]K. Mislow, *J. Am. Chem. Soc.,* 73, 3954 (1951).

[14]R. L. Letsinger and J. G. Traynham, *ibid.,* 72, 849 (1950).

[15]R. Goutarel, M. M. Janot, V. Prelog, R. P. A. Sneeden, and W. I. Taylor, *Helv. Chim. Acta,* 34, 1139 (1951).

[16]W. J. Adams, V. Petrow, and R. Royer, *J. Chem. Soc., 1951,* 678.

[17]P. J. Leroux and H. J. Lucas, *J. Am. Chem. Soc.,* 73, 41 (1951).

[18]F. Wessely and W. Swoboda, *Monatsh.,* 82, 437 (1951).

to bromine in chloroform but still contains 12.15% bromine. Treatment with LAH lowers the bromine content to 8.3% while a subsequent reduction with zinc powder and acetic acid lowers the content to 5% bromine (14).

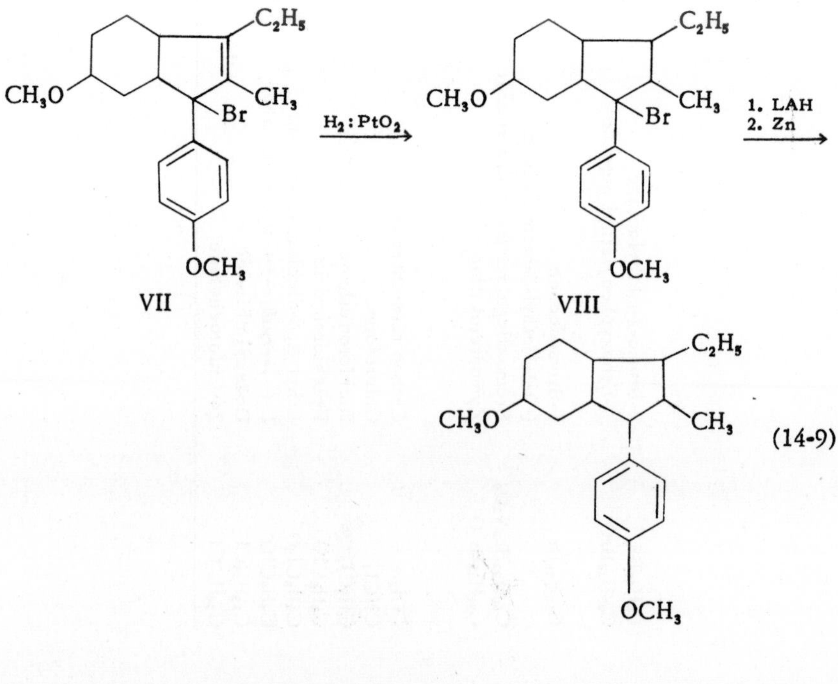

VII   VIII   (14-9)

The reduction of various unconjugated alicyclic halides is summarized in Table LXXXVIII.

14.1.1.c *Conjugated Halides.* The LAH reduction of conjugated halides such as allylic and benzyl halides proceeds quite readily although the order of reactivity of the halogens is still a factor.

1. *Allylic halides.* Hatch and his co-workers have carried out a series of syntheses of chloropropenes and butenes by the selective reduction of an allylic chloride while retaining vinylic halides:

$$\underset{\substack{\\ \text{IX}}}{\underset{R_1}{\overset{R}{>}}C=\overset{\overset{R_2}{|}}{C}-CH_2Cl} \xrightarrow{\text{LAH}} \underset{R_1}{\overset{R}{>}}C=\overset{\overset{R_2}{|}}{C}-CH_3 \qquad (14\text{-}10)$$

	R	R_1	R_2	Ref.
cis	H	Cl	H	15
trans	H	Cl	H	15
α	H	Cl	F	16
β	H	Cl	F	16
cis	H	Cl	Cl	17
trans	H	Cl	Cl	17
	Cl	Cl	F	18
	Cl	Cl	Cl	18
	COOC$_2$H$_5$	Cl	Cl	19
cis	CH$_3$	Cl	Cl	19
trans	CH$_3$	Cl	Cl	19

The reduction of 2,3,3-trichloro-1-butene (X) with LAH yields *trans*-2,3-dichloro-2-butene (XI) as the only product of an apparent allylic rearrangement (19).

$$\underset{\substack{\\ \overset{|}{Cl} \\ \\ X}}{\overset{\overset{Cl}{|}}{CH_3C}}-\underset{\substack{\\ \\ \\ }}{\overset{\overset{Cl}{|}}{C}}=CH_2 \xrightarrow[58\%]{\text{LAH}} \underset{\substack{\\ \overset{|}{Cl} \\ \\ XI}}{CH_3C}=\overset{\overset{Cl}{|}}{C}CH_3 \qquad (14\text{-}11)$$

The isolation of only the *trans* product instead of both geometric isomers is indicative of the occurrence of steric hindrance. Sodium carbonate hydrolysis of X yields both *cis-* and *trans-*XI by allylic rearrangement.

The reaction of 1,5-cyclooctadiene (XII) with N-bromosuccinimide yields two isomeric monobromocyclooctadienes. One of the isomers yields XII on treatment with LAH and is accordingly 3-bromo-1,5-cyclo-octadiene (XIII), unless allylic rearrangement occurs during the reaction. The second isomer, on treatment with LAH, gives a mixture of cyclo-octadienes which has not been identified but is catalytically reduced to

TABLE LXXXVIII

LAH Reduction of Unconjugated Alicyclic Halides

Halide	Product	% Yield	Ref.
A. Bromides			
C_6BrF_{11} Bromoundecafluorocyclohexane	Undecafluorocyclohexane	15	1
$C_6H_{11}Br$ Bromocyclohexane	Cyclohexane	10 $\bigg\}^2$	3
	Olefin	trace	
$C_8H_8Br_2$ Cyclooctatetraene dibromide	Cyclooctatetraene	$\cdots\bigg\}^2$	4
	Bicyclo[4.2.0]octa-2,4-diene	$\cdots$	
$C_{12}H_{17}BrO_7$ Triacetyl-α-L-rhamnopyranosyl bromide	1,5-Anhydro-L-rhamnitol	87^5	6
$C_{14}H_{19}BrO_9$ Tetraacetyl-α-D-glucopyranosyl bromide	1,5-Anhydro-D-glucitol	67^5	6
	1,5-Anhydro-D-mannitol	74^5	6
$C_{26}H_{21}BrO_7$ Tetraacetyl-α-D-mannopyranosyl bromide	1,4-Anhydro-D-ribitol	$\cdots$	7
1-Bromo-2,3,5-tribenzoyl-D-ribose			
B. Chlorides			
C_6ClF_{11} Chloroundecafluorocyclohexane	Undecafluorocyclohexane	59	8
C_6H_9ClO 1-Chloro-1,2-epoxycyclohexane	Cyclohexanol	70–75 $\bigg\}$	9–11
	cis-2-Chlorocyclohexanol	10–30	
1-Chloro-2,3-epoxycyclohexane	Cyclohexanol	20–25 $\bigg\}$	9–11
	cis-2-Chlorocyclohexanol	70	
$C_{14}H_{19}ClO_9$ Tetraacetyl-D-galactofuranosyl chloride	1,4-Anhydro-D-galactitol	41	12

References—Table LXXXVIII

[1]G. B. Barlow and J. C. Tatlow, *J. Chem. Soc.*, 1952, 4695.
[2]Reduction carried out in tetrahydrofuran.
[3]J. E. Johnson, R. H. Blizzard, and H. W. Carhart, *J. Am. Chem. Soc.*, 70, 3664 (1948).
[4]A. C. Cope, A. C. Haven, Jr., F. L. Ramp, and E. R. Trumbull, *ibid.*, 74, 4867 (1952).
[5]Based on pentaacetate.
[6]R. K. Ness, H. G. Fletcher, Jr., and C. S. Hudson, *J. Am. Chem. Soc.*, 72, 4547 (1950).
[7]F. Weygand and F. Wirth, *Chem. Ber.*, 85, 1000 (1952).
[8]J. C. Tatlow and R. E. Worthington, *J. Chem. Soc.*, 1952, 1251.
[9]M. Mousseron-Canet and R. Jacquier, *Bull. soc. chim. France*, [5] 19, 698 (1952).
[10]M. Mousseron, R. Jacquier, M. Mousseron-Canet, and R. Zagdoun, *ibid.*, [5] 19, 1042 (1952).
[11]M. Mousseron, R. Jacquier, M. Mousseron-Canet, and R. Zagdoun, *Compt. rend.*, 235, 177 (1952).
[12]R. K. Ness, H. G. Fletcher, Jr., and C. S. Hudson, *J. Am. Chem. Soc.*, 73, 3742 (1951).

cyclooctane. The second isomer has been formulated as 6-bromo-1,4-cyclooctadiene (XIV) (20).

$$\text{(14-12)}$$

Treatment of XII with two equivalents of N-bromosuccinimide gives 5,8-dibromo-1,3-cyclooctadiene which gives an unidentified mixture of cyclooctadienes on treatment with LAH (20).

The reduction of these and other conjugated halides is summarized in Table LXXXIX.

Attempts to reduce 7-bromocholesterol benzoate, which contains an allylic bromine, with lithium aluminum deuteride have met with partial success. Although its presence has been indicated by the Liebermann-Burchard determination, no cholesterol has been isolated from the reaction mixture (21).

2. *Propargylic halides.* The reduction of the propargylic halide, 1-bromo-2-heptyne (XV) yields a mixture of 2-heptyne and 1,2-heptadiene. A 0.4:0.125 ratio of halide: LAH gives a 15:1 ratio of products.

TABLE LXXXIX

LAH Reduction of Conjugated Halides

	Halide	Product	% Yield	Ref.
A. Allylic Halides				
C₃H₂Cl₃F	1,1,1-Trichloro-2-fluoro-1-propene	1,1-Dichloro-2-fluoro-1-propene	51	1
C₃H₂Cl₄	1,1,2,3-Tetrachloro-1-propene	1,1,2-Trichloro-1-propene	56[2]	1
C₃H₃Cl₂F	α-1,3-Dichloro-2-fluoro-1-propene, b.p. 41.7°	1-Chloro-2-fluoro-1-propene, b.p. 28–31° (100 mm.)	56[3]	4
	β-1,3-Dichloro-2-fluoro-1-propene, b.p. 46° (44 mm.)	1-Chloro-2-fluoro-1-propene, b.p. 58.5°	66	4
C₃H₃Cl₃	cis-1,2,3-Trichloro-1-propene	cis-1,2-Dichloro-1-propene	63[5]	6
	trans-1,2,3-Trichloro-1-propene	trans-1,2-Dichloro-1-propene	71[5]	6
C₃H₄Cl₂	cis-1,3-Dichloro-1-propene	cis-1-Chloro-1-propene	46[5]	7
	trans-1,3-Dichloro-1-propene	trans-1-Chloro-1-propene	50[5]	7
C₃H₅Br	Allyl bromide	Propene	85	8
C₄H₅Cl₃	cis-1,2,3-Trichloro-2-butene	cis-2,3-Dichloro-2-butene	...	9
	trans-1,2,3-Trichloro-2-butene	trans-2,3-Dichloro-2-butene	72	10
	2,3,3-Trichloro-1-butene	trans-2,3-Dichloro-2-butene	71	10
C₄H₆Br₂	trans-1,4-Dibromo-2-butene	trans-2-Butene	58	10
C₆H₇Cl₃O₂	Ethyl α,β,γ-trichlorocrotonate (mixture of isomers)	cis-2,3-Dichloro-2-buten-1-ol	72[11]	12
		trans-2,3-Dichloro-2-buten-1-ol	59 ⎱ 10	10
C₈H₁₀Br₂	5,8-Dibromo-1,3-cyclooctadiene	Mixture of cyclooctadiene	56	13
C₈H₁₁Br	3-Bromo-1,5-cyclooctadiene	1,5-Cyclooctadiene	39	13
	6-Bromo-1,4-cyclooctadiene	Mixture of cyclooctadienes	...	13

B. Benzylic Halides

1. Benzenoid

C_7H_7Br	Benzyl bromide	Toluene	78^2	12
C_7H_7Cl	Benzyl chloride	Toluene	72^2	12
			....^{2}	9
C_7H_7I	Benzyl iodide	Toluene	86	12
$C_8H_8Br_2$	Styrene dibromide	Styrene	71^2	12
			0	8
$C_{11}H_9Br$	2-Bromomethyl-C^{14}-naphthalene	2-Methyl-C^{14}-naphthalene	71^{14}	15
$C_{11}H_{12}Br_2O_2$	Ethyl 2,3-dibromo-3-phenylpropionate	Hydrocinnamyl alcohol	59^2	12
$C_{12}H_{15}ClO_3$	2-Chloromethyl-C^{14}-3,5,6-trimethyl-4-acetoxy-phenol	Durohydroquinone-α-C^{14}	89	16
$C_{13}H_9Br$	9-Bromofluorene	Fluorene	$30]^2$ $34]^2$	12
$C_{13}H_{11}Br$	Diphenylbromomethane	Dibiphenyleneethane Diphenylmethane	$38]^2$ $25]^2$	12
$C_{14}H_{12}Br_2$	meso-1,2-Diphenyl-1,2-dibromoethane	Tetraphenylethane	98^2	12
$C_{16}H_{12}Br_2$	4,5-Bis-(bromomethyl)phenanthrene	trans-Stilbene Cyclic ether of 4,5-bis-(hydroxymethyl)-phenanthrene	....^{17}	18
$C_{19}H_{15}Cl$	Triphenylchloromethane	Triphenylmethane	98	12

2. Heterocyclic

$C_7H_6ClN_3$	1-Chloromethylbenzotriazole	1-Methylbenzotriazole	50^2	19
			86^2	20
$C_{10}H_{13}Cl_2N$	3,5-Bis-(chloromethyl)-2,4,6-trimethylpyridine	Pentamethylpyridine	^{2,21}	22

References—Table LXXXIX

[1]L. F. Hatch and D. W. McDonald, *J. Am. Chem. Soc.*, 74, 3328 (1952).
[2]Reduction carried out in tetrahydrofuran.
[3]Reduction carried out in diethyl cellosolve.
[4]L. F. Hatch and D. W. McDonald, *J. Am. Chem. Soc.*, 74, 2911 (1952).
[5]Reduction carried out in diisopropyl ether.
[6]L. F. Hatch, J. J. D'Amico, and E. V. Ruhnke, *J. Am. Chem. Soc.*, 74, 123 (1952).
[7]L. F. Hatch and R. H. Perry, Jr., *ibid.*, 71, 3262 (1949).
[8]R. F. Nystrom and W. G. Brown, *ibid.*, 70, 3738 (1948).
[9]H. I. Schlesinger and A. E. Finholt, U. S. Pat. 2,576,311 (November 27, 1951).
[10]L. F. Hatch and J. J. D'Amico, *J. Am. Chem. Soc.*, 73, 4393 (1951).
[11]Reduction carried out in diethyl carbitol.
[12]L. W. Trevoy and W. G. Brown, *J. Am. Chem. Soc.*, 71, 1675 (1949).
[13]A. C. Cope, C. L. Stevens, and F. A. Hochstein, *ibid.*, 72, 2510 (1950).
[14]Based on starting carbinol.
[15]R. V. Phillips, L. W. Trevoy, L. B. Jaques, and J. W. T. Spinks, *Can. J. Chem.*, 30, 844 (1952).
[16]A. A. Bothner-By, *J. Am. Chem. Soc.*, 73, 4228 (1951).
[17]Reduction carried out in benzene-ether mixture.
[18]G. M. Badger, J. E. Campbell, J. W. Cook, R. A. Raphael, and A. I. Scott, *J. Chem. Soc.*, 1950, 2326.
[19]J. A. Burckhalter, V. C. Stephens, and L. A. R. Hall, *J. Am. Chem. Soc.*, 74, 3868 (1952).
[20]N. G. Gaylord, *ibid.*, 76, 285 (1954).
[21]"Not very good yield."
[22]P. Karrer and S. Mainoni, *Helv. Chim. Acta*, 34, 2151 (1951).

$$CH_3(CH_2)_3C \equiv CCH_2Br \xrightarrow[94\%]{LAH} CH_3(CH_2)_3C \equiv CCH_3 \ +$$

XV

$$CH_3(CH_2)_3CH = C = CH_2 \quad (14\text{-}13)$$

On the other hand, the reduction of 3-bromo-1-heptyne (XVI) with a 0.15 : 0.2 ratio of halide: LAH gives 1-heptyne and 1,2-heptadiene in a 1 : 9 ratio.

$$CH_3(CH_2)_3CHC \equiv CH \xrightarrow[48\%]{LAH} CH_3(CH_2)_3CH_2C \equiv CH \ +$$
$$\underset{\displaystyle Br}{|}$$

XVI

$$CH_3(CH_2)_3CH = C = CH_2 \quad (14\text{-}14)$$

Conversion of the halides with magnesium to organomagnesium bromides, followed by hydrolysis, gives mixtures of the same products (22).

Two mechanisms have been proposed to account for the reaction products. The first assumes a dynamic equilibrium in the starting halide between acetylenic and allenic compounds:

$$R\!-\!C\!\equiv\!C\!-\!CH_2Br \rightleftharpoons \left[\begin{array}{c} R\!-\!C\!\equiv\!C\!-\!\overset{\oplus}{C}H_2 \\ \updownarrow \\ R\!-\!\overset{\oplus}{C}\!=\!C\!=\!CH_2 \end{array} \right] \quad \overset{\ominus}{Br} \rightleftharpoons R\!-\!\overset{\underset{\displaystyle Br}{|}}{C}\!=\!C\!=\!CH_2$$

$$\downarrow \overset{\ominus}{H} \text{ (LAH)}$$

$$RC\!\equiv\!CCH_3 \ + \ RCH\!=\!C\!=\!CH_2 \qquad\qquad (14\text{-}15)$$

The second mechanism postulates an $S_N^{2'}$ reaction as well as an S_N^2:

$$R\!-\!C\!\equiv\!C\!-\!CH_2 \!\!\curvearrowleft\!\! Br \xrightarrow{\text{LAH}} R\!-\!C\!\equiv\!C\!-\!CH_3 \ + \ Br^{\ominus} \ (S_N^2)$$

$$\overset{\ominus}{H}$$

$$(14\text{-}16)$$

$$R\!-\!C\!\overset{\curvearrowright}{\equiv}\!C\!-\!CH_2 \!\!\curvearrowleft\!\! Br \xrightarrow{\text{LAH}} R\!-\!CH\!=\!C\!=\!CH_2 \ + \ Br^{\ominus} \ (S_N^{2'})$$

$$\overset{\ominus}{H}$$

$$(14\text{-}17)$$

3. *Benzylic halides.* The reduction of benzylic halides follows the expected pattern, the halides having the order of reactivity iodide > bromide > chloride. Benzyl chloride is not reduced in refluxing ether (23) but is reduced to toluene in 72% yield after one-half hour in tetrahydrofuran at 65° (4).

Trevoy and Brown (4) reported that the reduction of diphenylbromomethane yields tetraphenylethane as well as the expected diphenylmethane. Similarly, the reduction of 9-bromofluorene yields dibiphenyleneethane as well as fluorene. The coupling products arise from the reaction of the halide and the organometallic compound arising from the reaction of the halide and LAH. An organometallic derivative has been indicated as an intermediate in the reduction of triphenylchloromethane, as well (24).

The non-reduction of fluorides is exhibited even with the reactive benzylic halides. Thus, ethyl *p*-trifluoromethylbenzoate (XVII) is reduced to *p*-trifluoromethylbenzyl alcohol (25). Jones (26) reported that the treatment of methyl 5-amino-6-methyl-2-trifluoromethyl-3-pyridinecarboxylate (XVIII) with LAH in ether gives an unstable product which decomposes during all attempts to purify it.

XVII

XVIII

The reduction of 4,5-bis-(bromomethyl)phenanthrene (XIX) with LAH or catalytic hydrogenation over palladium-on-strontium carbonate is reported to yield the cyclic ether of 4,5-bis-(hydroxymethyl)phenanthrene as the only isolable product (27).

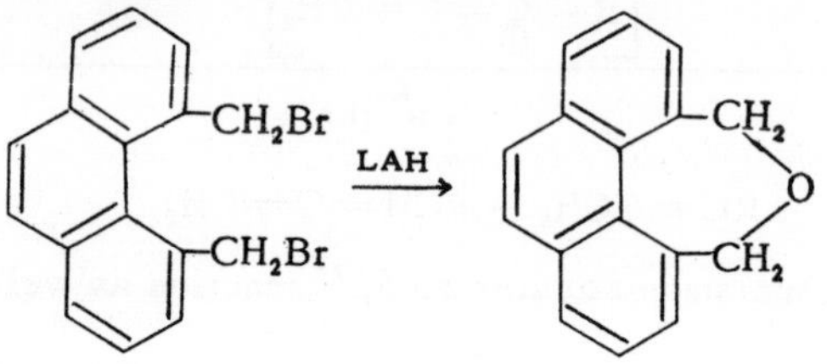

(14-18)

XIX

The normally reactive benzylic bromide can be retained by selective reduction. Thus, the inverse addition of a calculated amount of LAH results in the reduction of methyl p-bromomethylbenzoate to p-bromomethyl-benzyl alcohol (28).

The LAH reduction of the benzylic halide, 2-chloro-2-phenylpropionic acid, is discussed in Section 14.1.1.g.

The LAH reduction of benzylic halides is summarized in Table LXXXIX.

4. *Vinyl halides.* As shown in equation (14-10), vinylic halides such as XX are generally not attacked by LAH. Thus, Hatch and his coworkers have selectively reduced the allylic chloride in XX when R and/or R_1 and/or R_2 are halogen atoms (15-19).

XX

$$CH_3(CH_2)_7C = C(CH_2)_7COOH$$ with Br, Br

XXI

Dibromooleic acid (XXI) is reduced to the corresponding alcohol without attacking the olefinic bromine (29).

The reaction of trichloroethylene and sodium phenolate yields a dichlorovinylphenyl ether whose structure is postulated as XXII or XXIII, the latter being the preferred structure. Treatment with LAH leaves the compound unchanged (30).

$$C_6H_5ONa + ClCH = CCl_2 \rightarrow C_6H_5OCH = CCl_2 \text{ or } C_6H_5OC = CH \text{ (Cl, Cl)}$$

XXII   XXIII

(14-19)

The reaction of ω-bromostyrene (XXIV), containing a vinylic bromine atom, is reported to yield styrene after 19 hours treatment with LAH in tetrahydrofuran at 65° (4).

$$C_6H_5CH =\!\!= CHBr \xrightarrow[49\%]{LAH} C_6H_5CH =\!\!= CH_2 \qquad (14\text{-}20)$$
$$\text{XXIV}$$

The vinylic halide in methyl 20-bromo-3β-hydroxy-Δ^{17}-pregnen-21-oate (XXV) is not attacked by LAH in refluxing ether (31–33).

$$\text{XXV} \qquad\qquad\qquad \text{XXVI}$$

The attempted LAH reduction of 3-chloro-5,5-dimethyl-2-cyclohexenone (XXVI) results in the recovery of starting material (34).

14.1.1.d   Vicinal Dihalides.   The reduction of 1,2-dihaloalkanes generally yields olefins instead of the expected saturated hydrocarbons. Thus, the following vicinal dihalides have been reduced to olefins:

		Ref.
$C_3H_6I_2$	2,3-diiodo-1-propanol	4
$C_4H_6Br_4$	1,2,3,4-tetrabromobutane	4
$C_8H_8Br_2$	styrene dibromide	4
$C_8H_{16}Br_2$	1,2-dibromooctane	4
$C_{14}H_{12}Br_2$	meso-1,2-dibromo-1,2-diphenylethane	4
$C_{27}H_{44}Br_2O$	Δ^8-cholestene-24,25-dibromo-3β-ol (zymosterol dibromide)	35

Styrene dibromide does not react with LAH at 25° (1) but at 65°, in tetrahydrofuran, styrene is formed (4).

The reduction of ethyl 2,3-dibromo-3-phenylpropionate (XXVII) yields hydrocinnamyl alcohol instead of an olefin (4).

$$C_6H_5\overset{\overset{\displaystyle Br}{|}}{C}H —\overset{\overset{\displaystyle Br}{|}}{C}H\overset{\overset{\displaystyle O}{\|}}{C} —OC_2H_5 \xrightarrow{LAH} C_6H_5CH_2CH_2CH_2OH \qquad (14\text{-}21)$$
$$\text{XXVII}$$

Although it is possible that this is an example of the direct replacement of bromine by hydrogen, it is more likely that here, as in the analogous styrene dibromide, the dihalide is converted to the olefin. However, the resultant olefin is conjugated, as in cinnamic acid, and is reduced to the saturated alcohol.

The reduction of cyclooctatetraene dibromide (XXVIII) with LAH in tetrahydrofuran yields a mixture of 1,3,5-cyclooctatriene (XXX) and bicyclo[4.2.0]octa-2,4-diene (XXIX).

$$\text{XXVIII} \qquad\qquad \text{XXIX} \qquad \text{XXX} \tag{14-22}$$

XXX is in mobile equilibrium with XXIX, the open structure being formed through bridge opening (36).

14.1.1.e *Haloethers.* The ready reduction of the halogen in the α-haloether grouping in glycopyranosyl and furanosyl halides has been mentioned in Section 14.1.1.b. The LAH reduction of ethyl α,β-dichloroethyl ether (XXXI) in tetrahydrofuran at 65° yields 53% of ethyl β-chloroethyl ether after a one-half hour reaction period (4).

$$\underset{\underset{\text{XXXI}}{}}{CH_3CH_2O\overset{\overset{\displaystyle Cl}{|}}{C}HCH_2Cl} \xrightarrow{\;LAH\;} CH_3CH_2OCH_2CH_2Cl \tag{14-23}$$

Here the ease of reduction of the α-haloether determines the course of the reduction rather than the olefin formation from the vicinal dihalide.

The reduction of β-ethoxyphenethyl bromide (XXXII) yields the expected ethyl α-methylbenzyl ether and styrene (37).

$$\underset{\underset{\text{XXXII}}{}}{C_6H_5\overset{\overset{\displaystyle }{|}}{\underset{\underset{OC_2H_5}{|}}{C}}HCH_2Br} \xrightarrow{\;LAH\;} C_6H_5\underset{\underset{OC_2H_5}{|}}{C}HCH_3 + C_6H_5CH\!=\!CH_2 \tag{14-24}$$

14.1.1.f *Haloketones.* Trevoy and Brown (4) reported that the reduction of *p*-bromophenacyl bromide (XXXIII) with excess LAH in ether gives 1-(*p*-bromophenyl)ethanol.

$$\text{XXXIII} \tag{14-25}$$

Analogously, ω-bromoacetophenone is reduced to 1-phenylethanol (38).

Lutz, Wayland, and France (39) carried out a study of the LAH reduction of α-haloketones and found that the reduction of XXXIII with a slightly more than equimolar amount of LAH in ether at 0° or 35° gives XXXIV in a "yield similar to Trevoy and Brown" accompanied by very small amounts of *p*-bromophenylbromohydrin (XXXV). By using an amount of LAH only slightly in excess of that needed for the reduction of the carbonyl group the bromohydrin (XXXV) is obtained in 69% yield at 25°.

$$\text{XXXIII} \xrightarrow[69\%]{\text{LAH/4}} \text{XXXV} \xrightarrow[90\%]{\text{LAH}} \text{XXXIV} \quad (14\text{-}26)$$

XXXV is reduced with an equimolar amount of LAH to XXXIV. Desyl chloride (XXXVI) and p-chlorophenacyl bromide with close to one-quarter mole of LAH are reduced to 76% erythro-stilbene chlorohydrin and 77% p-chlorophenylbromohydrin, respectively.

$$C_6H_5C\underset{\overset{\|}{O}}{—}\underset{\overset{|}{Cl}}{CHC_6H_5} \xrightarrow[50-76\%]{\text{LAH}} C_6H_5CH\underset{\overset{|}{OH}}{—}\underset{\overset{|}{Cl}}{CHC_6H_5} \quad (14\text{-}27)$$

XXXVI

Varying the temperature from 0° to 35° in the reduction of XXXVI does not appreciably affect results but inverse addition of LAH to the α-chloroketone reduces the yield to 30% due to the condensation of XXXVI and the chlorohydrin. Desyl bromide is similarly reduced to erythro-stilbene bromohydrin.

The reduction of XXXIII to XXXIV in 90% yield by LAH in which one equivalent of hydrogen has been destroyed by the addition of a calculated amount of allyl or ethyl iodide, is considered evidence for the relatively easy reducibility of the halogen of the halohydrin or haloketone as compared with the more difficult reducibility of an ordinary alkyl halide.

Felkin has carried out the selective reduction of a number of α-haloketones by the inverse addition of the theoretical amount of LAH to an ether solution of the haloketone at room temperature (40). Thus, 1-chloro-1-benzoylcyclohexane gives 50% of 1-chloro-1-(α-hydroxybenzyl)cyclohexane, 2-chlorocyclohexanone gives 65% of α-chlorocyclohexanol and α-chlorodesoxybenzoin gives 95% of 1-chloro-1,2-diphenylethanol. While the action of LAH on α-chloroketones can theoretically lead to two isomeric chlorohydrins, they are actually formed in equal quantities. Thus, the α-chlorocyclohexanol is a mixture of equal parts of the cis and trans isomers while the 1-chloro-1,2-diphenylethanol is a mixture of equal parts of the erythro and threo isomers. In contrast to this the reaction of α-chlorocyclohexanone with the Grignard reagent yields a mixture of chlorohydrins in which the *cis* isomer predominates. This difference is attributed to the relatively large dimensions of the anion from the organomagnesium compound which approaches the ketone function on the side opposite to the chlorine atom to form the *cis* product. On the contrary the hydride ion from the LAH is smaller so that its approach is not sterically hindered by the chlorine to yield an equimolecular mixture of *cis* and *trans*-chlorohydrins.

The LAH reduction of 3-bromo-1,1,1-trifluoropropanone (XXXVII) with ethereal LAH yields 75% of 3-bromo-1,1,1-trifluoro-2-propanol (XXXVIII) accompanied by 3,3,3-trifluoro-2-propanol (41).

$$BrCH_2CCF_3 \xrightarrow{\text{LAH}} BrCH_2CHCF_3 + CH_3CHCF_3 \quad (14\text{-}28)$$

$$\underset{\text{O}}{\|} \qquad\qquad \underset{\text{OH}}{|} \qquad \underset{\text{OH}}{|}$$

XXXVII   XXXVIII

The reduction of XXXVII with sodium borohydride in aqueous solution gives XXXVIII in a 48% crude yield. The lower yield is explained by the formation of a stable hydrate when the ketone is placed in water, thus reducing the available free carbonyl groups and making the reduction more difficult. Reduction with aluminum isopropoxide yields XXXVIII in 49% crude yield but requires a one week reaction period.

The reduction of 1,3-dichloroacetone (XXXIX) with LAH at $-2°$ yields 77% of 1,3-dichloro-2-propanol while reduction with aluminum isopropoxide proceeds in only 20–25% yield (42,43). The reduction of pentachloroacetone (XL) with LAH at $-15°$ to $+20°$ or with sodium borohydride in alcohol solution yields pentachloroisopropanol (44). Treatment of hexachloroacetone (XLI) with aluminum isopropoxide yields only traces of hexachloroisopropanol while LAH reduction at $-5°$ proceeds in 97% yield (45). Octachloromethylethyl ketone (XLII) which can not be reduced with aluminum isopropoxide, is reduced with LAH in ether at $-5°$ to octachloro-*sec*-butanol in 65% yield (45). On the other hand, decachloropentanone-3 (XLIII) is resistant to attack by LAH but under vigorous reaction conditions a product of undetermined structure is formed, mostly by removal of chlorine (45).

$$ClCH_2CCH_2Cl \qquad\qquad Cl_3CCCHCl_2 \qquad\qquad Cl_3CCCl_3$$

$$\underset{\text{O}}{\|} \qquad\qquad\qquad \underset{\text{O}}{\|} \qquad\qquad\qquad \underset{\text{O}}{\|}$$

XXXIX   XL   XLI

$$\underset{\qquad\ \ \text{Cl}}{\overset{\text{Cl}}{|}} \qquad\qquad \overset{\text{Cl}\quad\ \ \text{Cl}}{|\qquad\ |}$$

$$Cl_3C-C-CCl_3 \qquad Cl_3CC-C-CCl_3 \qquad CF_3CCH_3$$

$$\underset{\text{O}\ \ \text{Cl}}{\|\quad|} \qquad\qquad \underset{\text{Cl}\ \ \text{O}\ \ \text{Cl}}{|\quad\ \|\quad|} \qquad\quad \underset{\text{O}}{\|}$$

XLII   XLIII   XLIV

Treatment of 1,1,1-trifluoroacetone (XLIV) with LAH, even in refluxing ether, yields 82-85% of 3,3,3-trifluoro-2-propanol (46,47).

The LAH reduction of α-chloro-3,4-dihydroxyacetophenone yields 1-(3,4-dihydroxyphenyl)ethanol.   Reduction with sodium borohydride or aluminum isopropoxide leaves the chlorine atom to yield 1-(3,4-dihydroxyphenyl)-2-chloroethanol (48).

Shoppee and Summers have successfully prepared 3-halocholestan-6β-ol by the LAH reduction of 3-halocholestan-6-one (XLV) at low temperatures. Thus, 3α-chloro- and bromocholestan-6-one (49) and 3β-iodo-, chloro- and bromocholestan-6-one (50) have been reduced to the corresponding 3α- and β-halocholestan-6β-ol in high yields.

$$(14\text{-}29)$$

XLV

14.1.1.g   *Haloacids.*   Eliel and Freeman (51) have carried out an investigation of the steric course of the reduction of 2-chloro-2-phenylpropionic acid (XLVI) with LAH.   Racemic XLVI is reduced to 2-phenyl-1-propanol (XLVII) in 25% yield by LAH in tetrahydrofuran.   A 26% yield of 2-phenyl-1,2-propanediol (XLVIII) is also obtained in the reduction, as well as small amounts of 2-phenylpropanal and acetophenone.

$$(14\text{-}30)$$

XLVI   XLVII   XLVIII

The carbonyl compounds apparently originate during the isolation process. The reduction of optically active XLVI gives 29-38% of XLVII which is 61-67% racemized while 15-20% of XLVIII is formed with nearly complete inversion.   Reduction of XLVI in ether solution gives racemized XLVII but very little glycol (XLVIII).   The methyl ester of XLVI is reduced with LAH in ether to 62% of XLVII which is 37% racemized.

The authors have postulated the following mechanism as best accounting for the experimental facts:

$$C_6H_5CCl(CH_3)COO^{\ominus} \xrightarrow{\text{LAH}} \underset{B}{CH_3C(C_6H_5)C=O} \xrightarrow{\text{LAH}} \underset{XLVIII}{CH_3C(OH)(C_6H_5)CH_2OH}$$

$$C_6H_5CCl(CH_3)COOCH_3 \xrightarrow{\text{LAH}} \underset{C}{C_6H_5CCl(CH_3)CH_2O^{\ominus}}$$

$$-Cl^{\ominus} \downarrow + H^{\ominus}$$

$$\underset{D}{CH_3CH(C_6H_5)CHO} \xrightarrow{\text{LAH}} \underset{XLVII}{CH_3CH(C_6H_5)CH_2OH}$$

The salt formed from the chloroacid (A) and LAH may undergo an internal displacement with inversion to the α-lactone (B) which is then further reduced in the normal manner without inversion. An alternative path for the chloroacid (A) and the only path available for the methyl ester leads to the chlorohydrin anion (B) which undergoes a hydride shift with loss of chloride ion to yield the aldehyde (D) which is further reduced to XLVII. Partial racemization appears to take place in the transformation of C to D.

Evidence for the postulated hydride shift has been obtained by the addition of one-half mole of LAH in ether to the methyl ester. Decomposition of the reaction mixture with acid gives a very unstable chlorine compound which loses hydrogen chloride. On distillation 11% of 2-phenylpropanal (D) is obtained. Basic decomposition gives 18% of α-methylstyrene oxide. Both the epoxide and the aldehyde (D) probably are formed from the primary reaction product 2-chloro-2-phenyl-1-propanol (C) during the isolation process.

Further work by Eliel and his co-workers (52) has shown that chlorohydrins are isolated readily in the LAH reduction of α-chloro acids such as XLIX when R is hydrogen, methyl or ethyl.

$$\underset{Cl}{RCHCOOH} \xrightarrow{\text{LAH}} \underset{Cl}{RCHCH_2OH} \qquad (14\text{-}31)$$

XLIX

$$R = H, CH_3, C_2H_5$$

α-Chloroisobutyric acid (L) and substituted α-chlorophenylacetic acids (LI) give the alcohols directly under ordinary conditions. The chlorohydrins are intermediates in the reduction to the alcohols since the use of a limited amount of LAH with inverse addition permits the isolation of the chlorohydrins. The latter can be further reduced to the corresponding alcohols.

$$(CH_3)_2\underset{\underset{\textstyle L}{|}}{\underset{\textstyle Cl}{C}}COOH \xrightarrow{\text{LAH}} (CH_3)_2CHCH_2OH \qquad (14\text{-}32)$$

$$C_6H_5\underset{\underset{\textstyle LI}{|}}{\underset{\textstyle Cl}{\overset{\overset{\textstyle R}{|}}{C}}}COOH \xrightarrow{\text{LAH}} C_6H_5\overset{\overset{\textstyle R}{|}}{C}HCH_2OH + C_6H_5\underset{\underset{\textstyle OH}{|}}{\overset{\overset{\textstyle R}{|}}{C}}CH_2OH \qquad (14\text{-}33)$$

$$R = H, CH_3, C_6H_5$$

Glycols are formed only from the acids (LI) and their proportion increases with increasing bulk of R.

14.1.1.h *The* $-N\!=\!\overset{|}{C}\!-\!Cl$ *grouping.* The "abnormal" Hoesch reaction of 4,6-diethylresorcinol and acrylonitrile yields a stable iminochloride formulated as LII. Treatment of LII with excess LAH in an ether-dioxane mixture yields a neutral product (20%) formulated as LIII, a primary amine (70%) (LIV), and an alkali soluble product, $C_{13}H_{17}ClO_2$ which may have arisen from LIII during the workup. Further treatment of LIII with LAH yields the primary amine (LIV) (53).

$$(14\text{-}34)$$

The chlorine is retained in all three of the reduction products. The extremely unusual nature of the transformations postulated in the LAH reduction of LII as well as the conversion of LIII to LIV suggests the need for additional information regarding these reactions.

In contrast to the postulated stability of the chlorine in the $-N = \overset{|}{C} - Cl$ grouping in LII, the reduction of 6-chlorophenanthridine (LV) yields 5,6-dihydrophenanthridine (54).

$$\text{(14-35)}$$

LV

14.1.1.i *Lithium Hydride-LAH as Reducing Agent.* Johnson, Blizzard, and Carhart (2) have found that the use of lithium hydride greatly decreases the amount of LAH necessary to reduce halides. The LAH actually acts as a catalyst since only a small amount of LAH is necessary to bring about the hydrogenolysis of halides by lithium hydride. The LAH is a hydrogen carrier since no reduction occurs with lithium hydride alone. The reaction was originally postulated as

$$RX + LiH \xrightarrow{LAH} RH + LiX \qquad (14\text{-}36)$$

although Brown (55) has proposed that the initial reaction involves the alkyl halide and LAH to form aluminum hydride which reforms LAH by reaction with lithium hydride.

$$LiAlH_4 + RX \rightarrow LiX + AlH_3 \qquad (14\text{-}37)$$

$$AlH_3 + LiH \rightarrow LiAlH_4 \qquad (14\text{-}38)$$

Halides which have been reduced to hydrocarbons by this technique are summarized in Table XC.

As mentioned earlier, the bromine and chlorine atoms in chloro- and bromoundecafluorocyclohexane are reduced by LAH (7,8). Similarly, 1-chloro-1,2-epoxy-, and 1-chloro-2,3-epoxycyclohexane yield cyclohexanol as one of the reduction products (9–11). On the other hand, Johnson, Blizzard, and Carhart (2) have reported that chlorocyclohexane is not reduced with 0.13 mole of LAH and 1.5 moles of lithium hydride in tetrahydrofuran. The tertiary halide, 5-chloro-5-n-butylnonane, is not reduced with 0.4 mole of LAH and 3.0 moles of lithium hydride. The effect of reaction temperature is seen in the non-reduction of 3-chloromethylheptane in ether solution and the 96% yield of hydrocarbon obtained in tetrahydrofuran solution.

14.1.1.j *Non-reduced Halides.* Numerous halogen compounds have been subjected to treatment with LAH under a variety of reaction conditions. In addition to those cases already cited, such as the non-reduction of vinylic halides, other non-aromatic halides have been treated with LAH without hydrogenolysis of the halogen atom, under the conditions utilized. A summary of previously unmentioned non-reduced halides is shown in Table XCI.

14.1.2   Reactions with Aluminum Hydride

Aliphatic halides are not attacked by the aluminum hydride-aluminum chloride addition compound. Neither *n*-octyl bromide nor *n*-octyl iodide are reduced to *n*-octane (56).

14.1.3   Reactions with Sodium Borohydride

Only a limited number of halides have been subjected to treatment with sodium borohydride. In no case has reduction of the halogen atom been reported. The following compounds have been treated with the borohydride with retention of the halogen atom: chloral hydrate (57), 3-bromo-1,1,1-trifluoropropanone (41), pentachloroacetone (44), α-chloro-3,4-dihydroxyacetophenone (48), ω-bromoacetophenone (57), *dl*-N-[2-hydroxy-1-(2-thenoyl)ethyl]dichloroacetamide (58), α-dichloroacetamido-β-hydroxy-*p*-nitropropiophenone (59), α-dichloroacetamido-β-acetoxy-*p*-nitropropiophenone (59), α-dichloroacetamido-β-dichloroacetoxy-*p*-nitropropiophenone (59).

14.1.4   Reactions with Potassium Borohydride

In the only reported halide reaction, α-dichloroacetamido-β-hydroxy-*p*-nitropropiophenone is reduced with potassium borohydride in aqueous methanol to the halogen-containing reduction product (59).

14.1.5   Reductions with Lithium Borohydride

Friedman (60) has recently reported that, in contrast to the reduction of halides with LAH-lithium hydride, the use of a little lithium borohydride with lithium hydride in refluxing tetrahydrofuran is effective as a hydrogenolyzing agent without reducing other reactive groups. The reduction of 1-bromooctane and benzyl chloride by this technique gives the hydrocarbons in better than 90% yield, although the rate of reaction is slower than the corresponding LAH system. Polymethylbenzenes, 2,2,3,3-tetramethylbutane, and neopentane have been prepared by utilizing high boiling ethers and distilling the hydrocarbons from the reaction mixture as soon as formed. Bromides and iodides are readily reduced in tetrahydrofuran while chlorides with the exception of activated chlorides require higher temperatures.

The selective reducing action of lithium borohydride has permitted the reduction of halides without attacking nitriles and N,N-dialkylamides

TABLE XC

Reduction of Halides with Lithium Hydride–LAH

	Halide	Solvent	% Hydrocarbon	Ref.
	Aliphatic			
$C_4H_6Cl_2$	cis-1,4-Dichloro-2-butene	THF	40–60[1]	2
	trans-1,4-Dichloro-2-butene	THF	40–60[1]	2
$C_5H_8Br_2O$	3,3-Bis-(bromomethyl)propionaldehyde	Et$_2$O	44	3
$C_7H_{15}Br$	2-Bromoheptane	THF	92	4
$C_8H_{16}Br$	1,2-Dibromooctane	THF	80[5]	4
$C_8H_{17}Br$	1-Bromooctane	Et$_2$O	72	4
		Bu$_2$O	64	4
		THF	95	4
	3-Bromomethylheptane	THF	98	4
$C_8H_{17}Cl$	3-Chloromethylheptane	Et$_2$O	96	4
$C_{13}H_{27}Cl$	5-Chloro-5-n-butylnonane	THF	0	4
	Alicyclic			
$C_6H_{11}Cl$	1-Chlorocyclohexane	THF	0	4
	Benzylic			
C_7H_7Cl	Benzyl chloride	THF	98	4
C_8H_9Cl	Chloromethyltoluene	THF	97	6
	dl-α-Chloroethylbenzene	THF	....[7]	8
	(−)-α-Chloroethylbenzene[9]	THF	79[10]	8
	(+)-α-Chloroethylbenzene	THF	57	8
$C_8H_{10}Cl_2S$	3,4-Bis-(chloromethyl)-2,5-dimethylthiophene	THF	67	11
C_9H_7ClS	3-Chloromethylthianaphthene	THF	92	12

Formula	Name	Solvent	Yield	
C₉H₁₁ClS	Chloromethyl-o-xylene	THF	97	6
	Chloromethyl-m-xylene	THF	98	6
	Chloromethyl-p-xylene	THF	97	6
C₁₀H₁₃Cl	Chloromethylpseudocumene	THF	96	6
	Chloromethylhemimellitene	THF	97	6
	Chloromethylmesitylene	THF	97	6
C₁₀H₁₂Cl₂	Bis-(chloromethyl)-o-xylene	THF	94	6
	Bis-(chloromethyl)-m-xylene	THF	94	6
	Bis-(chloromethyl)-p-xylene	THF	94	6
C₁₁H₁₄Cl₂	Bis-(chloromethyl)pseudocumene	THF	93	6
	Bis-(chloromethyl)hemimellitene	THF	92	6
	Bis-(chloromethyl)mesitylene	THF	92	6

¹Isolated as dibromide.
²K. Mislow and H. M. Hellman, *J. Am. Chem. Soc.*, 73, 244 (1951).
³M. S. Kharasch and G. Büchi, *J. Org. Chem.*, 14, 84 (1949).
⁴J. E. Johnson, R. H. Blizzard, and H. W. Carhart, *J. Am. Chem. Soc.*, 70, 3664 (1948).
⁵By-product olefin 14% (calculated as octene).
⁶C. D. Shacklett and H. A. Smith, *J. Am. Chem. Soc.*, 73, 766 (1951).
⁷By-product meso-2,3-diphenylbutane.
⁸E. L. Eliel, *J. Am. Chem. Soc.*, 71, 3970 (1949).
⁹Reduction with lithium deuteride-lithium aluminum deuteride.
¹⁰By-product mixture of meso- and (+)-2,3-diphenylbutane.
¹¹R. Gaertner and R. G. Tonkyn, *J. Am. Chem. Soc.*, 73, 5872 (1951).
¹²R. Gaertner, *ibid.*, 74, 2991 (1952).

TABLE XCI

Non-aromatic Halides Treated with LAH without Reduction of Halogen

	Halide	Solvent	Conditions	Ref.
	A. Fluorides			
CF_3AsI_2	Trifluoromethyldiiodoarsine			1
C_2F_3ClO	Trifluoroacetyl chloride	E	Reflux	2,3
C_2F_3N	Trifluoroacetonitrile	E	Added at Dry Ice temp., warmed to room temp.	3
C_2HF_2ClO	Difluoroacetyl chloride	E	Reflux	4
$C_2HF_3O_2$	Trifluoroacetic acid	E	Reflux, stir at room temp.	5–7
$C_2H_2F_3NO$	Trifluoroacetamide	E	16 hours at 20°	8
$C_3HF_5O_2$	Pentafluoropropionic acid	E	Reflux, stir at room temp.	5–7,9
$C_4HF_7O_2$	Heptafluorobutyric acid	E	Reflux, stir at room temp.	5–7,10
$C_4H_7F_7NO$	Heptafluorobutyramide	E	Reflux, stir at room temp.	5
$C_4H_5F_3O$	4,4,4-Trifluorobutyraldehyde	E		11
$C_5H_8F_2O_3$	Ethyl 2,2-difluoro-3-hydroxypropionate	E		12
$C_6H_9F_3O_2$	n-Butyl trifluoroacetate	E	Reflux	13
$C_8H_{10}F_4O_4$	Diethyl 2,2,3,3-tetrafluorosuccinate	E		12,14
$C_9H_{10}F_6O_4$	Diethyl 2,2,3,3,4,4-hexafluoroglutarate	E		12,14
$C_{10}H_{10}F_8O_4$	Diethyl 2,2,3,3,4,4,5,5-octafluoroadipate	E		12
$C_{12}H_{22}F_2OS$	Ethyl thiol-5,5- and 6,6-difluorodecanoate $\}^{15}$	E		16
$C_{14}H_{26}F_2OS$	n-Butyl thiol-5,5- and 6,6-difluorodecanoate			
	B. Bromides			
$C_5H_8Br_4$	Pentaerythrityl bromide	T	65°	17
	C. Chlorides			
C_2Cl_4O	Trichloroacetyl chloride	E		18
C_2HCl_3O	Dichloroacetyl chloride	E		18
$C_2HCl_3O_2$	Trichloroacetic acid	E		18

Formula	Compound	Solvent	Temp.	Ref.
$C_2H_2Cl_2O$	Chloroacetyl chloride	E		18
	Chloroacetyl-2-C^{14} chloride	E		19
$C_2H_2Cl_2O_2$	Dichloroacetic acid	E		18
$C_2H_3ClO_2$	Chloroacetic acid	E		18,20
$C_3H_4Cl_2O$	L-(+)-α-Chloropropionyl chloride	E	0°	21
$C_3H_5ClO_2$	β-Chloropropionic-1-C^{14} acid	E	0°	22
$C_4H_5Cl_3O_2$	Ethyl trichloroacetate	E		18
$C_4H_6Cl_2O_2$	Ethyl dichloroacetate	E		18
$C_4H_7ClO_2$	Ethyl chloroacetate	E		18
	Methyl β-chloropropionate-1-C^{14}	E	0°	23
	α-Chloro-n-butyric acid	E		24
C_4H_9Cl	n-Butyl chloride	E	25°	25
$C_6H_9Cl_3O_2$	Methyl tris-(chloromethyl)acetate	E		26
$C_7H_{10}Cl_2O_4$	Diethyl 2,2-dichloromalonate	E	Ice cooling	27
$C_{13}H_{12}Cl_2N_2O_5$	trans-2-Dichloromethyl-4-carbethoxy-5-p-nitrophenyloxazoline	E	0°	28
$C_{13}H_{13}Cl_2NO_3$	l-ψ-2-Dichloromethyl-4-carbethoxy-5-phenyloxazoline	E		29
	l-threo-2-Dichloromethyl-4-carbethoxy-5-phenyloxazoline	E	0°	30
$C_{13}H_{15}ClN_2O$	5-Chloro-2-cyano-2-phenyl-N-methylvaleramide	E		31
$C_{13}H_{23}Cl_3O_2$	Methyl 12,12,12-trichlorododecanoate	E		32
$C_{14}H_{16}ClNO_2$	Ethyl 5-chloro-2-cyano-2-phenylvalerate	E	Reflux	31
$C_{15}H_{16}Cl_2N_2O_7$	Ethyl ester N-dichloroacetyl-O-acetyl-p-nitrophenylserine	E		33

References—Table XCI

[1]E. G. Waleschewski, through *European Scientific Notes*, 6, 142 (1952).
[2]A. L. Henne, R. M. Alm, and M. Smook, *J. Am. Chem. Soc.*, 70, 1968 (1948).
[3]A. L. Henne, R. L. Pelley, and R. M. Alm, *ibid.*, 72, 3370 (1950).
[4]A. L. Henne and R. L. Pelley, *ibid.*, 74, 1426 (1952).
[5]D. R. Husted and A. H. Ahlbrecht, *ibid.*, 74, 5422 (1952).
[6]D. R. Husted and A. H. Ahlbrecht, U. S. Pat. 2,568,500 (September 18, 1951).
[7]Minnesota Mining and Manufacturing Co., Brit. Pat. 676,273 (July 23, 1952).
[8]E. J. Bourne, S. H. Henry, C. E. M. Tatlow, and J. C. Tatlow, *J. Chem. Soc.*, 1952, 4014.
[9]E. T. McBee, J. F. Higgins, and O. R. Pierce, *J. Am. Chem. Soc.*, 74, 1387 (1952).
[10]A. F. Benning, U. S. Pat. 2,559,749 (July 10, 1951).
[11]E. T. McBee, A. E. Kelley, and E. Rapkin, *J. Am. Chem. Soc.*, 72, 5071 (1950).
[12]E. T. McBee, W. F. Marzluff, and O. R. Pierce, *ibid.*, 74, 444 (1952).
[13]K. N. Campbell, J. O. Knobloch, and B. K. Campbell, *ibid.*, 72, 4380 (1950).
[14]A. L. Henne and S. B. Richter, *ibid.*, 74, 5420 (1952).
[15]Mixture.
[16]M. S. Newman, M. W. Renoll, and I. Auerbach, *J. Am. Chem. Soc.*, 70, 1023 (1948).
[17]L. W. Trevoy and W. G. Brown, *ibid.*, 71, 1675 (1949).
[18]C. E. Sroog, Chen Ming Chih, F. A. Short, and H. M. Woodburn, *ibid.*, 71, 1710 (1949).
[19]H. R. V. Arnstein, *Biochem. J.*, 48, 27 (1951).
[20]L. S. Nelson, D. E. Laskowski, and H. A. Porte, *J. Chem. Ed.*, 28, 648 (1951).
[21]W. Fickett, H. K. Garner, and H. J. Lucas, *J. Am. Chem. Soc.*, 73, 5063 (1951).
[22]J. P. Ryan and P. R. O'Connor, *ibid.*, 74, 5866 (1952).
[23]H. Schmid and K. Schmid, *Helv. Chim. Acta*, 35, 1879 (1952).
[24]B. I. Halperin, H. B. Donahoe, J. Kleinberg, and C. A. Vander Werf, *J. Org. Chem.*, 17, 623 (1952).
[25]R. F. Nystrom and W. G. Brown, *J. Am. Chem. Soc.*, 70, 3738 (1948).
[26]W. H. Urry and J. R. Eiszner, *ibid.*, 74, 5822 (1952).
[27]B. Berkoz and B. F. Daubert, *ibid.*, 73, 2968 (1951).
[28]I. Elphimoff-Felkin, H. Felkin, and Z. Welvart, *Compt. rend.*, 234, 1789 (1952).
[29]G. W. Moersch and A. C. Moore, U. S. Pat. 2,562,114 (July 24, 1951).
[30]F. Hoffmann-LaRoche and Co., Akt., Swiss Pat. 275,968 (October 1, 1951).
[31]A. W. D. Avison and A. L. Morrison, *J. Chem. Soc.*, 1950, 1474.
[32]G. Dupont, R. Dulou, and P. Quentin, *Bull. soc. chim. France*, [5] 18, 59 (1951).
[33]C. F. Huebner and C. R. Scholz, *J. Am. Chem. Soc.*, 73, 2089 (1951).

while the nitro group is slowly attacked. The following halides have been treated with lithium borohydride-lithium hydride in tetrahydrofuran:

Halide	Product	% Yield
2-Bromobutyronitrile	Butyronitrile	88
Chloromethylbenzonitrile	Tolunitrile	91
5-Chloromethyl-1-nitronaphthalene	5-Methyl-1-nitronaphthalene	67
	Azo compound	8-20
p-Nitrobenzyl chloride	p-Nitrotoluene	72
	Azo compound	8-20

14.1.6 Reactions with Aluminum Borohydride

The reactions of aluminum borohydride and alkyl halides differ markedly from those of the other complex metal hydrides. Carbon tetrachloride is not attacked by aluminum borohydride while chloroform is converted to methylene dichloride. The latter, in a separate reaction, is not attacked by the borohydride. Iodoform and methylene iodide do not react with aluminum borohydride while methyl iodide is attacked to yield methane, methyldiboranes, diborane and hydrogen. Ethylene bromide yields methane, ethane, ethyl diboranes, diborane, and hydrogen, in a violent reaction. While carbon tetrafluoride is not attacked, methylene difluoride yields methane, diborane, methyldiboranes, and hydrogen (61).

14.2 AROMATIC HALIDES

14.2.1 Reductions with Lithium Aluminum Hydride

Aromatic halides are extremely resistant to hydrogenolysis with LAH. Only a limited number of aryl halides have been successfully reduced.

Trevoy and Brown have found that the LAH reduction of 1-chloro-2-iodobenzene (LVI) in tetrahydrofuran at 65° for one half hour gives 40% of chlorobenzene and 38% of the dihalide is recovered (4).

$$\qquad\qquad (14\text{-}39)$$

LVI

p-Fluorotoluene does not react after 24 hours at 65°.

Johnson, Blizzard, and Carhart reported that after a 3-hour reflux period in tetrahydrofuran p-bromotoluene is reduced with 0.25 mole of LAH and 2.0 moles of lithium hydride to yield 14% of toluene (2).

When 3,4-methylenedioxy-5-bromo-β-nitrostyrene (LVII) is refluxed for 2 hours with the theoretical amount of LAH the product is 3,4-methylenedioxy-5-bromo-β-phenylethylamine (LVIII). When LVII is refluxed with excess LAH for 10 hours the aromatic bromine is eliminated to

yield LIX. By employing conditions between the two extremes of LAH
concentration and reaction time, a mixture of LVIII and LIX is obtained
(62).

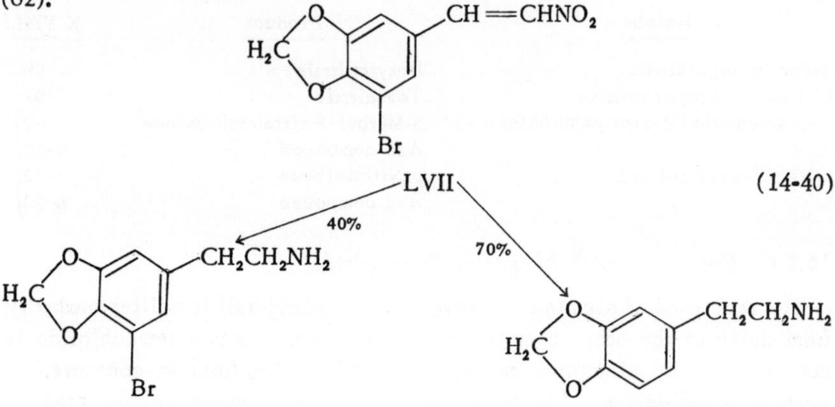

$$(14\text{-}40)$$

LVIII   LIX

Stork and Conroy reported that the LAH reduction of the ethylene ketal
of 5-bromo-7,8-dimethoxy-2-tetralone-1-N-methylacetamide (LX) is extremely slow and leads to considerable removal of aromatic bromine although no definite product has been isolated (63).

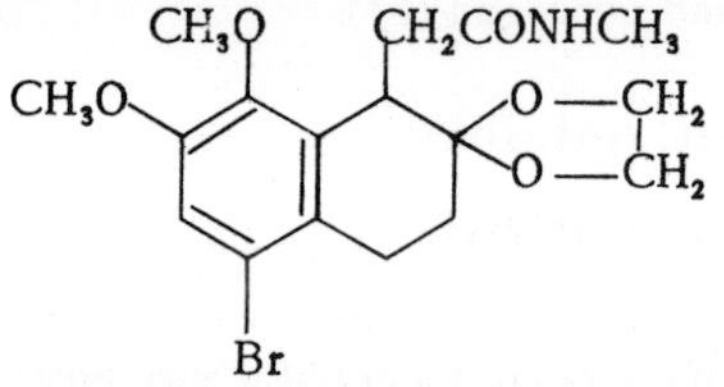

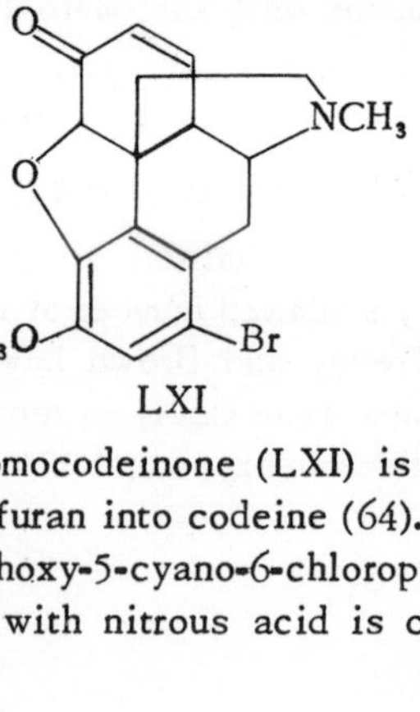

LX   LXI

Gates and Tschudi have reported that 1-bromocodeinone (LXI) is directly converted by LAH in refluxing tetrahydrofuran into codeine (64).

The reduction of 2-methyl-3-amino-4-carbethoxy-5-cyano-6-chloropyri-
dine (LXII) yields LXIII, which on treatment with nitrous acid is converted to pyridoxine hydrochloride (LXIV) (65).

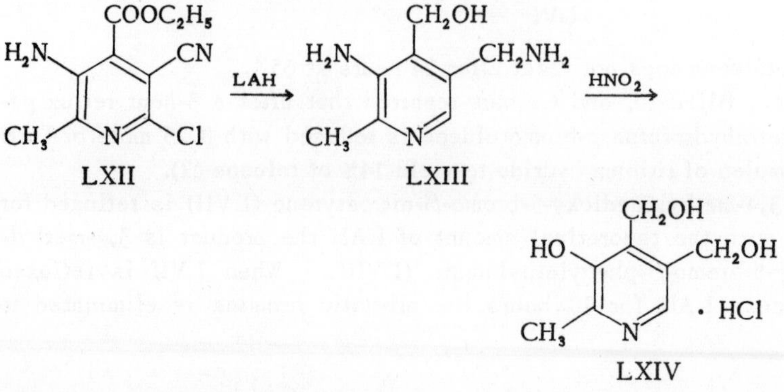

LXII   LXIII

$$(14\text{-}41)$$

LXIV

The LAH reduction of 6-chlorophenanthridine (LXV) yields 5,6-dihydro-phenanthridine (54).

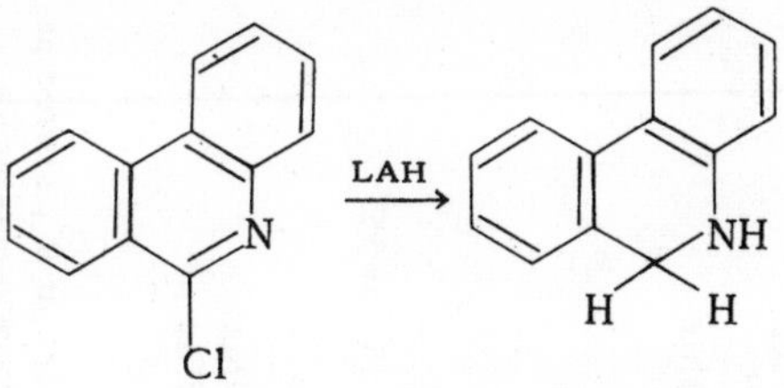

(14-42)

LXV

Diphenyliodonium bromide (LXVI) undergoes an exothermic reaction with LAH to yield 41% of benzene, 81% of iodobenzene and 2.6% of bromobenzene (66).

$$[(C_6H_5)_2]^{\oplus}Br^{\ominus} \xrightarrow{\text{LAH}} C_6H_6 + C_6H_5I + C_6H_5Br \qquad (14\text{-}43)$$

LXVI

The reaction of LXVI with ethylmagnesium bromide yields ethyl benzene, iodobenzene, and biphenyl (67).

Aromatic halides which have been treated with LAH without hydro-genolysis of the halogen under the conditions utilized are summarized in Table XCII.

14.2.2 Reductions with Aluminum Hydride

While aliphatic halides are not attacked, benzylic halides are reduced with the aluminum hydride-aluminum chloride addition compound. Benzyl bromide is reduced to toluene in 26% yield while benzyl iodide is reduced to the hydrocarbon in 41% yield (56).

14.2.3 Reactions with Sodium Borohydride

In the only reported relevant case, the halogen atom in α-p'-bromo-benzamido-β-hydroxy-p-nitropropiophenone is not attacked by sodium borohydride in ethanol solution (59).

TABLE XCII

Aromatic Halides Treated with LAH without Reduction of Halogen

Halide	Solvent	Conditions	Ref.
A. Fluorides			
Pentafluorobenzoic acid ($C_7HF_5O_2$)	E	Reflux	1
o-Fluorobenzoic acid ($C_7H_5FO_2$)	E	Reflux	2
p-Fluorotoluene (C_7H_7F)	T	65°	3
2-Fluoro-4-methoxybenzoyl chloride ($C_8H_6ClFO_2$)	E	Reflux	4
B. Bromides			
p-Nitrobromobenzene ($C_6H_4BrNO_2$)	E		5,6
p-Bromobenzonitrile (C_7H_4BrN)	E		7
m-Bromobenzoic acid ($C_7H_5BrO_2$)	E		8
p-Bromobenzoic acid	E		8
p-Bromophenacyl bromide ($C_8H_6Br_2O$)	E	0°,25° or 35°	3,9
p-Bromoacetophenone (C_8H_7BrO)	E		10
1-(p-Bromophenyl)-2-bromoethanol ($C_8H_8Br_2O$)	E	35°	9
p-Bromoacetophenone oxime (C_8H_8BrNO)	E	Reflux	11
N-p-Bromobenzylideneethanolamine ($C_9H_{10}NOBr$)	E	Reflux	12
Ethyl ester of l-3,5-dibromotyrosine ($C_{11}H_{13}Br_2NO_3$)	T-E		13
Ethyl ester of dl-p-bromophenylalanine ($C_{11}H_{14}BrNO_2$)	E		13
Methyl 2-ethylene ketal of 5-bromo-7,8-dimethoxy-2-tetralone-1-acetate ($C_{17}H_{21}BrO_6$)	E	Added at 0°, stirred at room temperature	14
2-Ethylene ketal-5-bromo-7,8-dimethoxy-2-tetralone-1-(N-dimethylacetamide) ($C_{18}H_{24}BrNO_5$)	E	25°	14
p-Bromobenzylidenefluorene ($C_{20}H_{13}Br$)	....		15
3,4-Dimethyl-4-phenyl-3-hexyl-p-bromobenzoate ($C_{21}H_{25}BrO_2$)	E	Reflux	16
C. Chlorides			
5-Chloro-2-(ω-nitrovinyl)thiophene ($C_6H_4ClNO_2S$)	E	Reflux	17
p-Chlorobenzonitrile (C_7H_4ClN)	E	Reflux	18

Formula	Compound	Method	Condition	Ref.
$C_7H_5ClO_2$	o-Chlorobenzoic acid	E		5,6
	m-Chlorobenzoic acid	E		19
	p-Chlorobenzoic acid	⋮		19
$C_7H_7ClO_3$	Ethyl 5-chloro-2-furoate	E	Reflux	20
C_8H_4ClNO	p-Chlorobenzoyl cyanide	E	Reflux	21
$C_8H_5ClO_2$	7-Chlorophthalide	E	Reflux	22
$C_8H_5ClO_4$	3-Chlorophthalic acid	E	Reflux	22
C_8H_6BrClO	p-Chlorophenacyl bromide	E	25°	9
C_8H_7ClO	p-Chloroacetophenone	E		10
C_8H_8ClNO	p-Chloroacetophenone oxime	E	Reflux	11
$C_9H_7ClO_4$	1-Methyl-2-hydrogen-3-chlorophthalate	E	Reflux	22
	2-Methyl-1-hydrogen-3-chlorophthalate	E	Reflux	22
$C_9H_6ClNO_2$	1-o-Chlorophenyl-2-nitro-1-propene	E	−40° to −50°	23
$C_{10}H_7ClN_2OS$	2-(p-Chlorobenzamido)thiazole	E	Reflux	24
$C_{10}H_9ClO_4$	Methyl 3-chlorophthalate	E	Reflux	22
	Methyl 4-chlorophthalate	E	Reflux	22
$C_{11}H_{13}ClO_2$	4-Chloro-3,5-dimethylphenoxyacetone	⋮		25
$C_{12}H_9ClO$	6-Chloro-2-acetonaphthone	⋮		26
	7-Chloro-1-acetonaphthone	⋮		27
$C_{12}H_9ClO_2$	7-Chloro-1-naphthylacetic acid	E	Reflux	27
$C_{13}H_8Cl_2O$	p,p-Dichlorobenzophenone	E	Reflux	28
$C_{14}H_{10}Cl_2O_2$	Di-p-chlorophenylacetic acid	T-E	Reflux	29
$C_{15}H_{11}ClO$	p-Chlorobenzalacetophenone	E	Reflux	30
	Benzal-p-chloroacetophenone	E	Reflux	30
$C_{15}H_{12}Cl_2O$	1,1-Di-p-chlorophenyl-2-propanone	E	Reflux	29
$C_{18}H_{14}Cl_2Si$	Diphenyl-p-chlorophenylchlorosilane	E	Reflux	31
$C_{20}H_{13}Cl$	p-Chlorobenzylidenefluorene	E	Reflux	32
$C_{21}H_{27}ClNO$	4-Phenyl-4-p-chlorophenyl-6-dimethylamino-3-heptanone	D	Reflux	33
$C_{22}H_{15}Cl$	p-Chlorobenzylidene-2,3,6,7-dibenzoheptafulvene	⋮		34

References—Table XCII

[1]E. T. McBee and E. Rapkin, *J. Am. Chem. Soc.*, 73, 1366 (1951).

[2]A. Sveinbjornsson and C. A. Vander Werf, *ibid.*, 73, 1378 (1951).

[3]L. W. Trevoy and W. G. Brown, *ibid.*, 71, 1675 (1949).

[4]E. L. Bennett and C. Niemann, *ibid.*, 72, 1806 (1950).

[5]R. F. Nystrom and W. G. Brown, *ibid.*, 70, 3738 (1948).

[6]H. I. Schlesinger and A. E. Finholt, U. S. Pat. 2,576,311 (November 27, 1951).

[7]N. S. Corby, G. W. Kenner, and A. R. Todd, *J. Chem. Soc.*, 1952, 3669.

[8]C. G. Swain and W. P. Langsdorf, Jr., *J. Am. Chem. Soc.*, 73, 2813 (1951).

[9]R. E. Lutz, R. L. Wayland, Jr., and H. G. France, *ibid.*, 72, 5511 (1950).

[10]K. B. Everard, L. Kumar, and L. E. Sutton, *J. Chem. Soc.*, 1951, 2807.

[11]C. R. Walter, Jr., *J. Am. Chem. Soc.*, 74, 5185 (1952).

[12]E. D. Bergmann, D. Lavie, and S. Pinchas, *ibid.*, 73, 5662 (1951).

[13]A. Dornow and G. Winter, *Chem. Ber.*, 84, 307 (1951).

[14]G. Stork and H. Conroy, *J. Am. Chem. Soc.*, 73, 4743 (1951).

[15]D. Lavie, *Bull. Research Council Israel*, 1, 135 (1951).

[16]D. J. Cram and J. D. Knight, *J. Am. Chem. Soc.*, 74, 5835 (1952).

[17]R. T. Gilsdorf and F. F. Nord, *J. Org. Chem.*, 15, 807 (1950).

[18]L. H. Amundsen and L. S. Nelson, *J. Am. Chem. Soc.*, 73, 242 (1950).

[19]Neville, unpublished work; through W. G. Brown in *Organic Reactions*, Vol. VI, p. 504.

[20]K. Hayes, G. Gever, and J. Orcutt, *J. Am. Chem. Soc.*, 72, 1205 (1950).

[21]A. Burger and E. D. Hornbaker, *ibid.*, 74, 5514 (1952).

[22]R. F. Bird and E. E. Turner, *J. Chem. Soc.*, 1952, 5050.

[23]R. T. Gilsdorf and F. F. Nord, *J. Am. Chem. Soc.*, 74, 1837 (1952).

[24]I. A. Kaye and C. L. Parris, *J. Org. Chem.*, 16, 1761 (1951).

[25]B. J. Ludwig, W. A. West, and W. E. Currie, *J. Am. Chem. Soc.*, 74, 1935 (1952).

[26]C. C. Price and G. H. Schilling, *ibid.*, 70, 4265 (1948).

[27]C. C. Price and Sing Tuh Voong, *J. Org. Chem.*, 14, 111 (1949).

[28]M. S. Newman and N. C. Deno, *J. Am. Chem. Soc.*, 73, 3644 (1951).

[29]E. J. Skerrett and D. Woodcock, *J. Chem. Soc.*, 1952, 3308.

[30]C. S. Rondestvedt, Jr., *J. Am. Chem. Soc.*, 73, 4509 (1951).

[31]H. Gilman and G. E. Dunn, *ibid.*, 73, 3404 (1951).

[32]E. D. Bergmann, G. Berthier, D. Ginsburg, Y. Hirshberg, D. Lavie, S. Pinchas, B. Pullman, and A. Pullman, *Bull. soc. chim. France*, [5] 18, 661 (1951).

[33]M. E. Speeter, L. C. Cheney, and S. B. Binkley, *J. Am. Chem. Soc.*, 72, 1659 (1950).

[34]A. Pullman, B. Pullman, E. D. Bergmann, D. Ginsburg, and D. Lavie, *Bull. Research Council Israel*, 1, No. 4, 85 (1952).

REFERENCES

1. Nystrom, R. F., and W. G. Brown, *J. Am. Chem. Soc.*, 70, 3738 (1948).
2. Johnson, J. E., R. H. Blizzard, and H. W. Carhart, *J. Am. Chem. Soc.*, 70, 3664 (1948).
3. Dibeler, V. H., *J. Research Natl. Bur. Standards*, 44, 363 (1950).
4. Trevoy, L. W., and W. G. Brown, *J. Am. Chem. Soc.*, 71, 1675 (1949).
5. Dibeler, V. H., and F. L. Mohler, *J. Research Natl. Bur. Standards*, 45, 441 (1950).
6. Everett, J. L., and G. A. R. Kon, *J. Chem. Soc.*, 1950, 3131.
7. Tatlow, J. C., and R. E. Worthington, *J. Chem. Soc.*, 1952, 1251.
8. Barlow, G. B., and J. C. Tatlow, *J. Chem. Soc.*, 1952, 4695.
9. Mousseron, M., R. Jacquier, M. Mousseron-Canet, and R. Zagdoun, *Bull. soc. chim. France*, [5] 19, 1042 (1952).
10. Mousseron-Canet, M., and R. Jacquier, *Bull. soc. chim. France* [5] 19, 698 (1952).
11. Mousseron, M., R. Jacquier, M. Mousseron-Canet, and R. Zagdoun, *Compt. rend.*, 235, 177 (1952).
12. Ness, R. K., H. G. Fletcher, Jr., and C. S. Hudson, *J. Am. Chem. Soc.*, 72, 4547 (1950).
13. Ness, R. K., H. G. Fletcher, Jr., and C. S. Hudson, *J. Am. Chem. Soc.*, 73, 3742 (1951).
14. van der Zanden, J. M., and G. de Vries, *Rec. trav. chim.*, 71, 733 (1952).
15. Hatch, L. F., and R. H. Perry, Jr., *J. Am. Chem. Soc.*, 71, 3262 (1949).
16. Hatch, L. F., and D. W. McDonald, *J. Am. Chem. Soc.*, 74, 2911 (1952).
17. Hatch, L. F., J. J. D'Amico, and E. V. Ruhnke, *J. Am. Chem. Soc.*, 74, 123 (1952).
18. Hatch, L. F., and D. W. McDonald, *J. Am. Chem. Soc.*, 74, 3328 (1952).
19. Hatch, L. F., and J. J. D'Amico, *J. Am. Chem. Soc.*, 73, 4393 (1951).
20. Cope, A. C., C. L. Stevens, and F. A. Hochstein, *J. Am. Chem. Soc.*, 72, 2510 (1950).
21. Fukushima, D. K., S. Lieberman, and B. Praetz, *J. Am. Chem. Soc.*, 72, 5205 (1950).
22. Wotiz, J. H., *J. Am. Chem. Soc.*, 73, 693 (1951).
23. Schlesinger, H. I., and A. E. Finholt, U. S. Pat. 2,576,311 (November 27, 1951).
24. Nystrom, R. F., unpublished work, through W. G. Brown, in *Organic Reactions*, Vol. VI, p. 481.
25. Hass, H. B., and M. L. Bender, *J. Am. Chem. Soc.*, 71, 1767 (1949).
26. Jones, R. G., *J. Am. Chem. Soc.*, 74, 1489 (1952).
27. Badger, G. M., J. E. Campbell, J. W. Cook, R. A. Raphael, and A. I. Scott, *J. Chem. Soc.*, 1950, 2326.
28. Charpentier-Morize, M., and B. Tchoubar, *Compt. rend.*, 233, 1621 (1951).
29. Khan, N. A., F. E. Deatherage, and J. B. Brown, *J. Am. Oil Chemists' Soc.*, 28, 27 (1951).
30. Ziegler, E., and W. Klementschitz, *Monatsh.*, 81, 113 (1950).
31. Wagner, R. B., and J. A. Moore, *J. Am. Chem. Soc.*, 71, 4160 (1949).
32. Wagner, R. B., and J. A. Moore, *J. Am. Chem. Soc.*, 72, 5301 (1950).
33. Wagner, R. B., and J. A. Moore, U. S. Pat. 2,606,198 (August 5, 1952).
34. Frank, R. L., and H. K. Hall, Jr., *J. Am. Chem. Soc.*, 72, 1645 (1950).
35. Adams, W. J., V. Petrow, and R. Royer, *J. Chem. Soc.*, 1951, 678.
36. Cope, A. C., A. C. Haven, Jr., F. L. Ramp, and E. R. Trumbull, *J. Am. Chem. Soc.*, 74, 4867 (1952).

37. Mislow, K., J. Am. Chem. Soc., 73, 3954 (1951).
38. Trevoy, L. W., unpublished work, through ref. 57.
39. Lutz, R. E., R. L. Wayland, Jr., and H. G. France, J. Am. Chem. Soc., 72, 5511 (1950).
40. Felkin, H., Compt. rend., 231, 1316 (1950).
41. McBee, E. T., and T. M. Burton, J. Am. Chem. Soc., 74, 3022 (1952).
42. Schlenk, H., and B. Lamp, J. Am. Chem. Soc., 73, 5493 (1951).
43. Schlenk, H., and B. W. De Haas, Nuclear Sci. Abstracts, 5, 543 (1951).
44. Ciba Ltd., Australian Pat. Appln. 9261/52.
45. Geiger, M., E. Usteri, and C. Gränacher, Helv. Chim. Acta, 34, 1335 (1951).
46. Henne, A. L., M. A. Smook, and R. L. Pelley, J. Am. Chem. Soc., 72, 4756 (1950).
47. Henne, A. L., and R. L. Pelley, J. Am. Chem. Soc., 74, 1426 (1952).
48. Coll, A. L. P., Afinidad, 25, 549 (1950); Chem. Abstracts, 45, 7981 (1951).
49. Shoppee, C. W., and G. H. R. Summers, J. Chem. Soc., 1952, 1790.
50. Shoppee, C. W., and G. H. R. Summers, J. Chem. Soc., 1952, 1786.
51. Eliel, E. L., and J. P. Freeman, J. Am. Chem. Soc., 74, 923 (1952).
52. Eliel, E. L., and M. C. Herrmann, Abstracts of Papers, 122nd Meeting American Chemical Society, Atlantic City, N. J., September 1952, p. 46M.
53. Elstow, W. E., and B. C. Platt, Chemistry and Industry, 1952, 449.
54. Badger, G. M., J. H. Seidler, and B. Thomson, J. Chem. Soc., 1951, 3207.
55. Brown, W. G., In Organic Reactions, Vol. VI, p. 481.
56. Wiberg, E., and A. Jahn, Z. Naturforsch., 7b, 580 (1952).
57. Chaikin, S. W., and W. G. Brown, J. Am. Chem. Soc., 71, 122 (1949).
58. Hermann, E. C., and A. Kreuchunas, J. Am. Chem. Soc., 74, 5168 (1952).
59. Parke, Davis and Co., Australian Pat. Appln. 13,395/52 (October 15, 1952).
60. Friedman, L., Abstracts of Papers, 122nd Meeting American Chemical Society, Atlantic City, N. J., September 1952, p. 46M.
61. Gerstein, M., R. A. Lad, and H. I. Schlesinger, Abstracts of Papers, 110th Meeting American Chemical Society, Chicago, Ill., September 1946, p. 26P.
62. Erne, M., and F. Ramirez, Helv. Chim. Acta, 33, 912 (1950).
63. Stork, G., and H. Conroy, J. Am. Chem. Soc., 73, 4743 (1951).
64. Gates, M., and G. Tschudi, J. Am. Chem. Soc., 74, 1109 (1952).
65. Verrill, K. J., and A. M. Schneider, Brit. Pat. 686,012 (January 14, 1953).
66. Beringer, F. M., and E. M. Gindler, unpublished work, private communication.
67. Beringer, F. M., A. L. Brierly, M. Drexler, E. J. Geering, and E. M. Gindler, Abstracts of Papers, 121st Meeting American Chemical Society, Buffalo, N. Y., March 1952, p. 3K.

CHAPTER 15

Reduction of
CARBON-CARBON MULTIPLE BONDS

15.1 CARBON-CARBON DOUBLE BONDS

15.1.1 Reductions with Lithium Aluminum Hydride

15.1.1.a *Non-aromatic Systems.* Under the usual conditions olefins and other compounds containing isolated double bonds are resistant to attack by LAH.

1. *Alkenyl compounds.* The reduction of polar groups can be selectively carried out without attacking conjugated or unconjugated double bonds. Thus, crotonaldehyde (I) is reduced to crotyl alcohol (1), vinylacrylic acid (II) is reduced to penta-2,4-dien-1-ol (2), and methyl 2,4,6-heptatrienoate (III) is reduced to 2,4,6-heptatrien-1-ol (2).

$$CH_3CH{=}CHCHO \xrightarrow{LAH} CH_3CH{=}CHCH_2OH \quad (15\text{-}1)$$
$$I$$

$$CH_2{=}CHCH{=}CHCOOH \xrightarrow{LAH} CH_2{=}CHCH{=}CHCH_2OH \quad (15\text{-}2)$$
$$II$$

$$CH_2{=}CHCH{=}CHCH{=}CHCOOCH_3 \xrightarrow{LAH}$$
$$III$$

$$CH_2{=}CHCH{=}CHCH{=}CHCH_2OH \quad (15\text{-}3)$$

However, Ziegler (3) has reported that certain α-olefins can be treated with LAH or aluminum hydride to form addition products which are capable of being added to ethylene or α-olefins to yield a "stepwise organometallic synthesis" of paraffins. This is discussed in Section 16.3.2.

Isolated examples of the reduction of the double bond in aliphatic compounds have been reported. Treatment of allyl alcohol with LAH in ether at room temperature results only in the replacement of the hydroxyl group active hydrogen. Under forcing conditions, in di-n-butyl ether at 100° for 3 hours, a 24% yield of n-propanol is obtained (4). Freedman and Becker (5) have reported the partial reduction of the α,β-unsaturation in 2-hexenoic acid (IV) upon treatment with LAH in ether. A 58% yield of a mixture of alcohols has been obtained which showed, by quantitative bromination, a 25.0–28.5% reduction of the double bond. Reduction of α-ethylcrotonamide (V) is reported to yield the saturated β-ethylbutylamine after a 20-hour reflux period with LAH in ether (6–8). Although the published literature indicates the product as α-ethylbutylamine (6) the patent literature (7,8) correctly designates the product as the β-ethyl-butylamine. The reaction of β-angelica lactone (VI) with LAH in tetra-hydrofuran at $65°$ for 4 hours yields 1,4-pentanediol, isolated as the diacetate in 10% yield (9).

$$CH_3CH_2CH_2CH = CHCOOH \qquad CH_3\overset{H}{C} = CCONH_2 \qquad$$

$$\underset{C_2H_5}{|}$$

IV   V 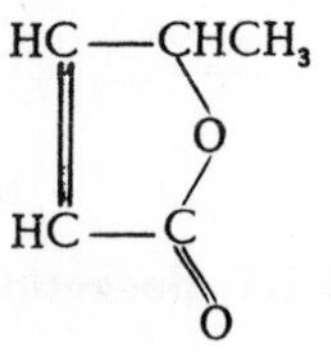   VI

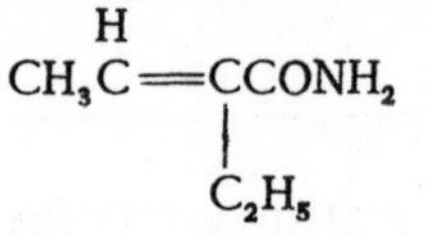

Attempts to reduce the double bond in mesityl oxide and 3-*tert*-butyl-3-penten-2-one with LAH have been unsuccessful (10), the former giving 2-methyl-2-penten-4-ol in 90% yield (11).

The presence of cyano and ester groups in α,β-unsaturated cyano-acetic acids (VII) activates the double bond sufficiently to result in its reduction with LAH in ether at room temperature (12).

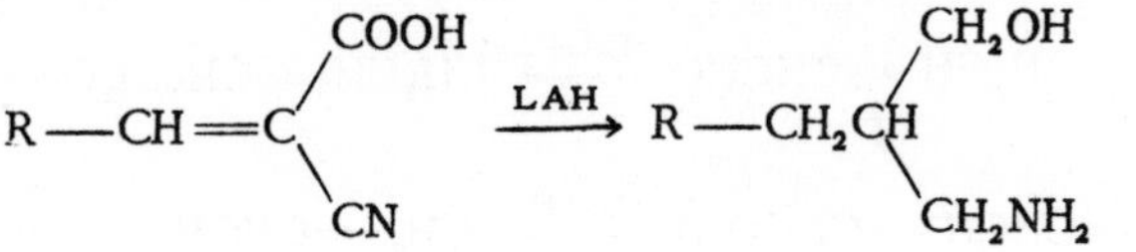

$$R - CH = C \overset{COOH}{\underset{CN}{<}} \xrightarrow{LAH} R - CH_2C\overset{CH_2OH}{\underset{CH_2NH_2}{<}} \qquad (15\text{-}4)$$

VII

$$R = (CH_3)_2CHCH_2 -, (CH_3)_2C = CHCH_2CH_2C = CH -$$
$$\underset{CH_3}{|}$$

The LAH reduction of 3-cyclohexyl-2-nitro-2-propen-1-ol in refluxing ether is reported to yield the saturated α-amino alcohol (13).

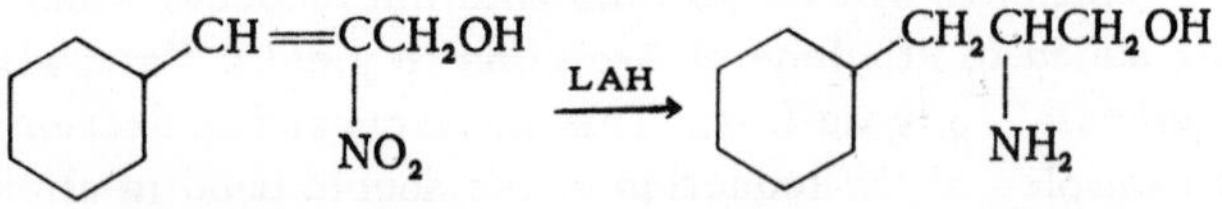

$$\xrightarrow{LAH} \qquad (15\text{-}5)$$

VIII

Ziegler (3) has reported the selective reduction of the external double bond in 4-vinyl-1-cyclohexene (IX).

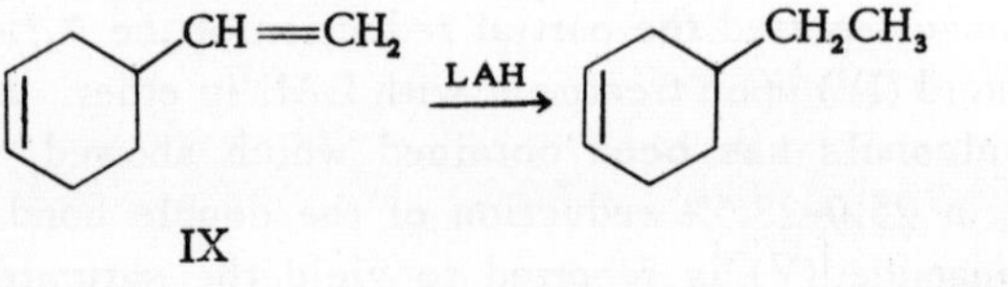

$$\xrightarrow{LAH} \qquad (15\text{-}6)$$

IX

Dreiding and Hartman (14) have shown, however, that the methylene group in 2-methylenecyclohexanone is not reduced with LAH.

2. *Cycloalkenyl compounds*. Although the LAH reduction of 1-cyclo-hexenecarboxylic acid (X) (14-16), 1-carbethoxycyclohexene (15,16), 1-cyclohexenecarboxamide (XI) (16), N,N-dimethyl-1-cyclohexenecarbox-amide (15,16), N,N-pentamethylene-1-cyclohexenecarboxamide (15,16), 1-cyclohexenecarboxaldehyde (XII) (15,16), 1-cyclohexen-3-one (XIII) (15-17), 1-methyl-1-cyclohexen-3-one (15-19), 4-isopropyl-2-cyclohexen-1-one (20), and 1-methyl-4-isopropyl-1-cyclohexen-3-one (20) yields the

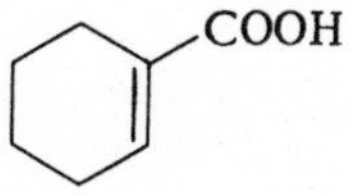

X 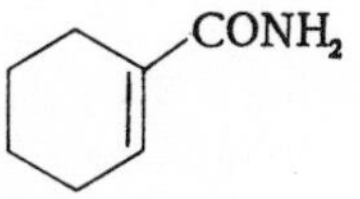   XI 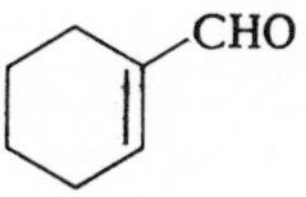   XII 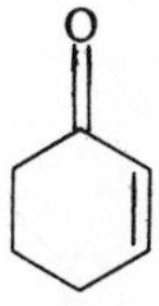   XIII

corresponding 1-cyclohexene derivative, the reduction of 1-cyanocyclo-hexene (XIV) (15-17) and 1-nitromethylcyclohexene (XV) (15,16) with excess LAH under ambient temperatures yields the saturated 1-aminomethylcyclohexane.

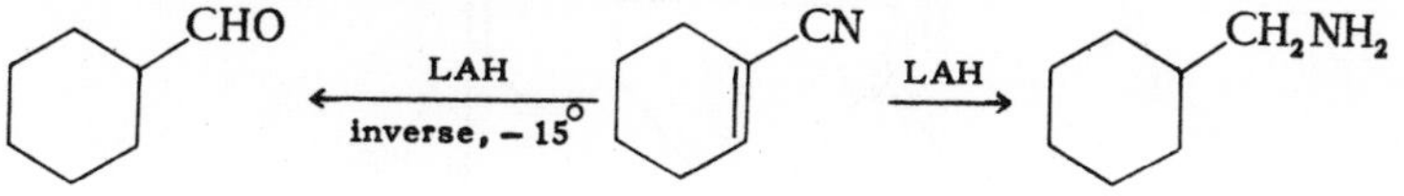

XIV   (15-7)

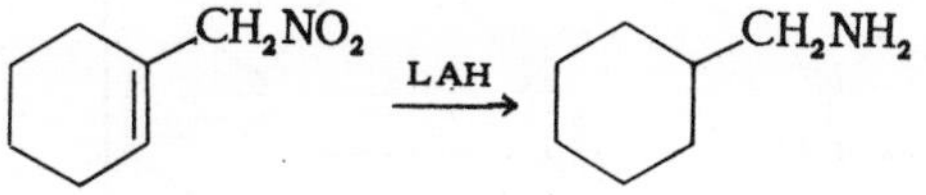

XV   (15-8)

Even though the reduction of XIV is carried out by the inverse addition of a reduced quantity of LAH at $-15°$ to yield the aldehyde, the double bond is still saturated. The reduction of the double bond in XV is postu-lated as proceeding through a tautomeric conjugation (16).

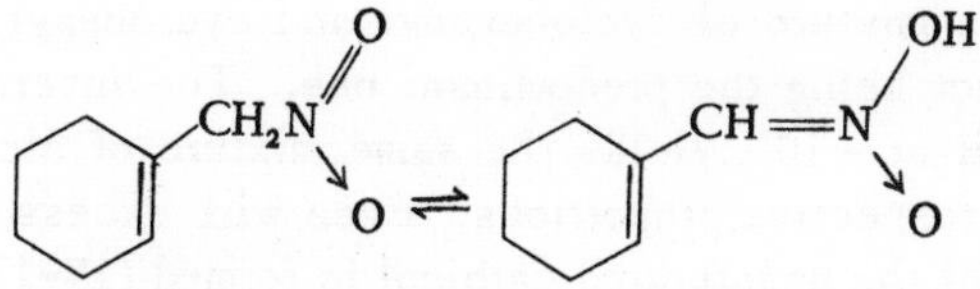

XV   (15-9)

The reduction of the double bond in XIV is postulated (16) as proceeding through complexes analogous to that postulated in the reduction of cin-namyl derivatives (Section 15.1.1.b.1).

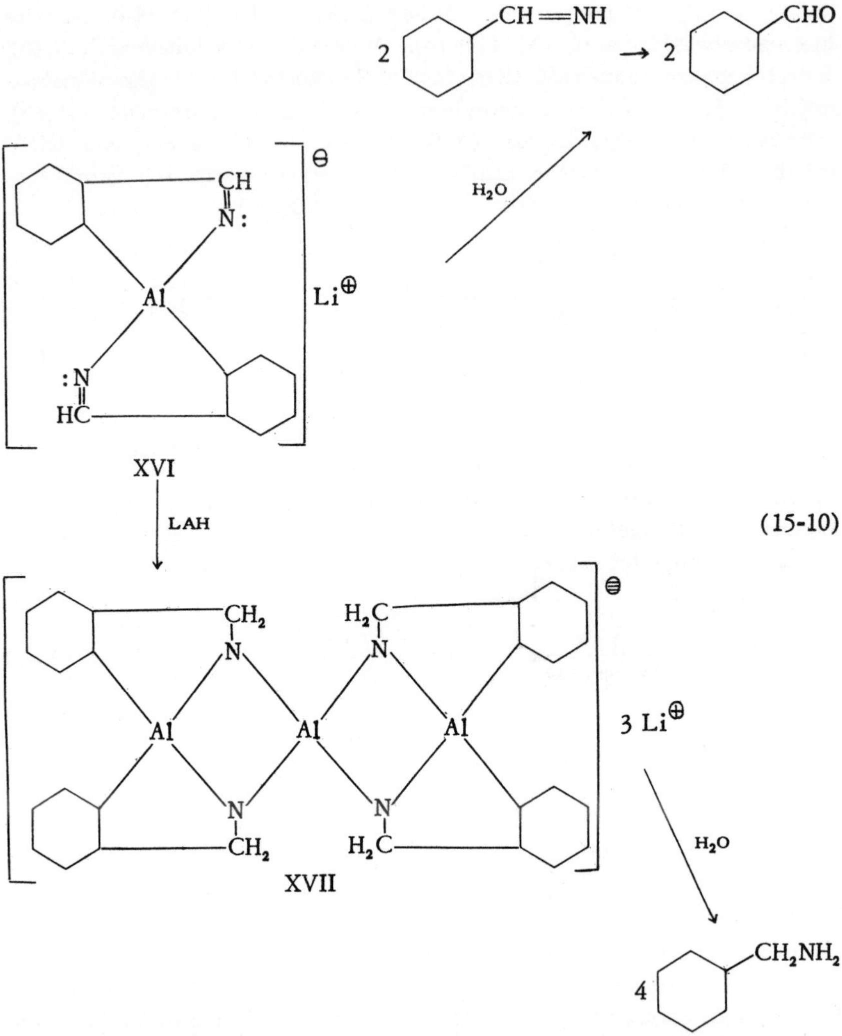

$$2 \text{ [cyclohexyl]CH}=\text{NH} \xrightarrow{H_2O} 2 \text{ [cyclohexyl]CHO}$$

XVI

↓ LAH   (15-10)

XVII

$3 \text{ Li}^{\oplus}$

$\xrightarrow{H_2O}$

$4 \text{ [cyclohexyl]CH}_2\text{NH}_2$

The direct reduction of 1-cyclohexenyl methyl ketone (XVIII) with LAH at 20° yields a mixture of cyclohexenyl and cyclohexyl carbinols, the saturated product being the predominant one. The inverse reduction of XVIII with LAH at −10° yields the same mixture of alcohols but with reversal of the respective proportions. Even with excess LAH in refluxing ether some of the unsaturated carbinol is formed (15-17).

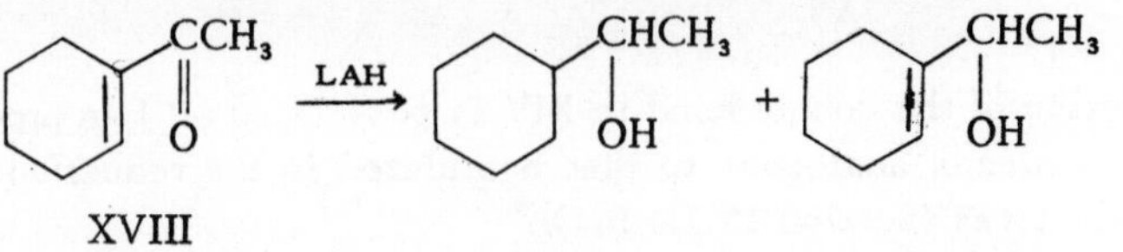

XVIII   (15-11)

Reduction of XVIII with aluminum isopropoxide similarly yields a mixture of saturated and unsaturated alcohols. The LAH reduction of the double bond in XVIII is postulated as proceeding through a complex analogous to XVI (16).

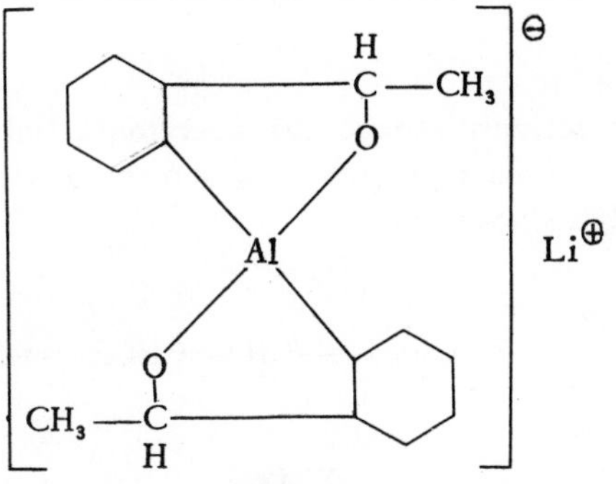

XIX

Contrary to the reduction of XVIII, the reduction of 2-acetyl-1,3,3-tri-methylcyclohexene (XX) with LAH in ether is reported to give an 80% yield of the cyclohexenyl carbinol (21) while the reduction of 1-acetyl-4,4-dimethylcyclohexene (XXI) gives 84% of the unsaturated carbinol (22).

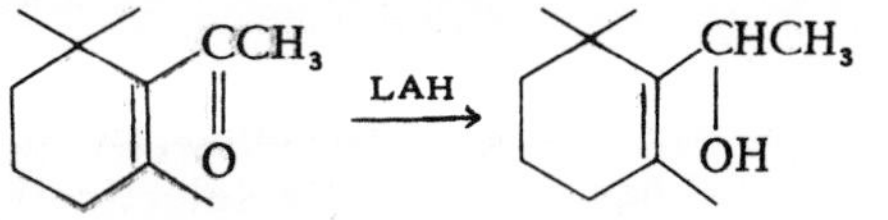

XX

$$(15\text{-}12)$$

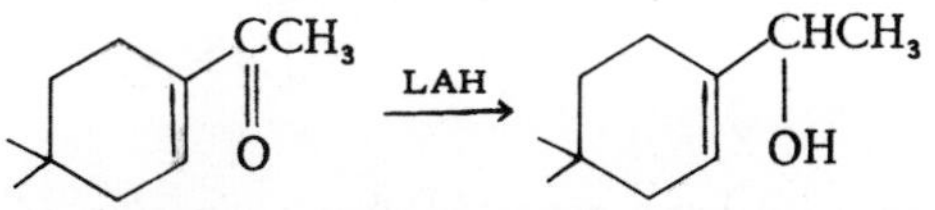

XXI

$$(15\text{-}13)$$

The LAH reduction of compounds in which the cyclohexenyl group is conjugated with a number of double bonds followed by a reducible group results in the retention of the unsaturation. This has found wide application in the synthesis of vitamin A derivatives and precursors.

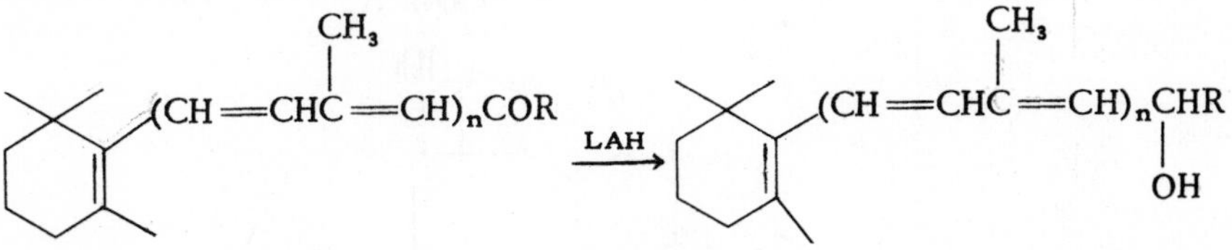

XXII

$$(15\text{-}14)$$

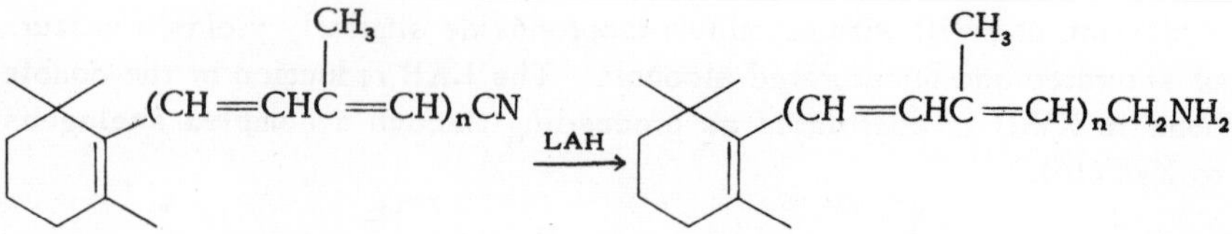

XXIII   (15-15)

Attempts to selectively reduce the acetylenic linkage in XXIV with LAH in ether have given a product in which the allylic double bond has been preferentially reduced (23).

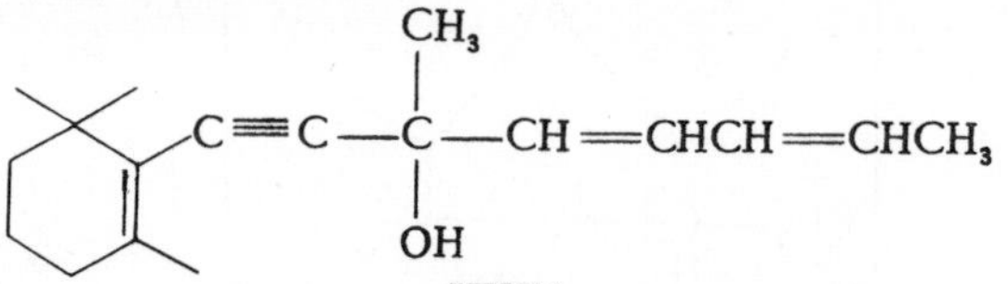

XXIV

Among other unsaturated alicyclic compounds which have been treated with LAH, the cyclopropene ring in sterculic acid (XXV) (24) as well as cyclooctatetraene (XXVI) (25) are not readily reduced.

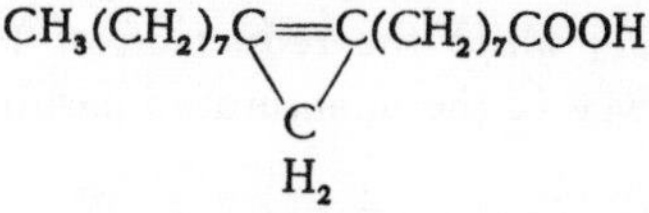

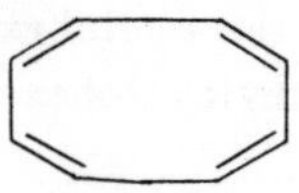

$CH_3(CH_2)_7C=C(CH_2)_7COOH$

XXV   XXVI

While the double bond in 1-cyclopentenecarboxylic acid is not attacked by LAH (14), Ziegler (3) has successfully selectively reduced a double bond in the bridged diene XXVII.

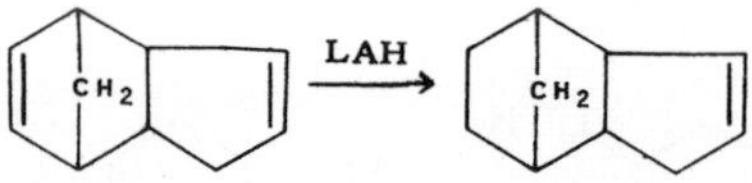

XXVII   (15-16)

Woodward et al. (26) have reported that reduction of 3-keto-$\Delta^{4,9(11),16}$-etiocholatrienate (XXVIII) with sodium borohydride in ethanol gives a mixture of 3α- and 3β-hydroxy esters. The infrared spectrum of the product shows a slight inflection indicating some reduction of the 16,17-double bond. When LAH is used for the reduction the product has a pronounced band showing reduction of the 16,17-double bond without reduction of the ester group.

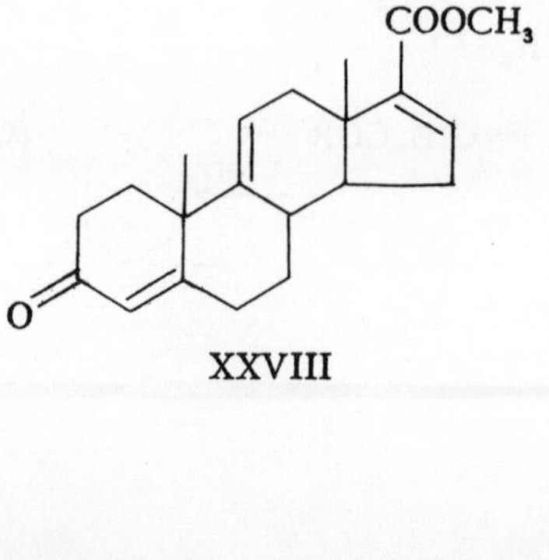

XXVIII

15.1.1.b *Aromatically Conjugated Systems.* While the reduction of double bonds in purely aliphatic or alicyclic compounds occurs only in isolated cases, as indicated above, the presence of the double bond in a structural grouping containing an aromatic ring at one end and a polar functional group at the other, i.e., $Ar\overset{|}{C}=\overset{|}{C}CO$ or $Ar\overset{|}{C}=\overset{|}{C}CN\diagdown$, generally results in the saturation of the carbon-carbon double bond under normal reaction conditions.

1. *The $Ar\overset{|}{C}=\overset{|}{C}CO$ grouping.* Hochstein and Brown (4) carried out an investigation of the addition of LAH to double bonds and found that whereas the normal procedure, i.e., direct addition of the unsaturated compound to an ethereal LAH solution at room temperature or under reflux conditions, converts cinnamaldehyde (XXIX) to hydrocinnamyl alcohol, the reverse addition with the calculated amount of LAH added to the aldehyde below 10° gives cinnamyl alcohol.

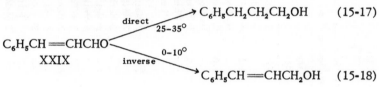

$$C_6H_5CH=CHCHO \xrightarrow[\text{inverse}]{\text{direct}} \begin{cases} \xrightarrow{25-35°} C_6H_5CH_2CH_2CH_2OH \quad (15\text{-}17) \\ \xrightarrow{0-10°} C_6H_5CH=CHCH_2OH \quad (15\text{-}18) \end{cases}$$

XXIX

The reaction of cinnamyl alcohol at room temperature with LAH to replace the active hydrogen in a rapid reaction followed by a slower reaction to yield, after hydrolysis, hydrocinnamyl alcohol has prompted the postulation that the reduction occurs in two successive stages:

$$C_6H_5CH=CHCHO \qquad C_6H_5CH=CHCH_2OH$$

$$\downarrow \text{LAH} \qquad \nearrow \text{LAH}$$

$$(C_6H_5CH=CHCH_2O)_4AlLi \xrightarrow{H_2O} C_6H_5CH=CHCH_2OH \quad (15\text{-}19)$$

$$\downarrow \text{LAH}$$

$$(C_6H_5\overset{|}{C}HCH_2CH_2O\text{---})_2AlLi \xrightarrow{H_2O} C_6H_5CH_2CH_2CH_2OH \quad (15\text{-}20)$$

Since the reduction of the double bond occurs at a moderate rate under normal conditions, it is possible to direct the reduction to yield either the unsaturated or the saturated product by the use of the appropriate reaction conditions.

The reduction of various cinnamyl type compounds in which reduction of the double bond accompanies functional group reduction is summarized in Table XCIII. Where different investigators have obtained dissimilar results these are included in Table XCIII for comparison purposes.

TABLE XCIII

LAH Reduction of Compounds Containing the $ArC{=}C{-}C{=}O$ Grouping with Reduction of the Carbon-Carbon Double Bond

Compound	Temp., °C.	Time, Hrs.	Product	% Yield	Ref.
$C_9H_6O_2$ Coumarin	35	24	3-(o-Hydroxyphenyl)propanol	50 ⎱	1 ⎱
			o-Hydroxycinnamyl alcohol[2]	10 ⎰	
	25	1.3	cis-o-Hydroxycinnamyl alcohol[2]	75	3
C_9H_8O Cinnamaldehyde	35	...	Hydrocinnamyl alcohol	87	4
	−10 to +10	0.67	Cinnamyl alcohol[2]	90	5
$C_9H_8O_2$ Cinnamic acid	35	...	Hydrocinnamyl alcohol	85	6,7
$C_{10}H_{10}O$ Benzalacetone	35	1.5	1-Phenyl-3-butanol	87	8
			1-Phenyl-3-butanol	80	9
	35	...	1-Phenyl-1-buten-3-ol[2]	99	10
$C_{10}H_{10}O_2$ p-Methylcinnamaldehyde	...	...	3-p-Tolylpropanol	80	11
2-Methylcinnamic acid	0–5	24	2-Methylcinnamyl alcohol[2]	83	12
	...	...	2-Methylcinnamyl alcohol[2]	⎱ ...	12
			2-Methyl-3-phenylpropanol	⎰ ...	
p-Methylcinnamic acid	...	...	p-Methylcinnamyl alcohol[2]	90	13
	...	...	p-Methylcinnamyl alcohol[2]	⎱ ...	14
			3-p-Tolylpropanol	⎰ ...	
$C_{11}H_9NO_2$ Methyl α-cyanocinnamate	0	0.5	2-Benzyl-3-amino-1-propanol	30	15
$C_{11}H_{12}O_3$ Ethyl o-hydroxycinnamate	25	...	3-o-Hydroxyphenyl-1-propanol	100	3
$C_{12}H_9NO_4$ Methyl β-(3,4-methylenedioxyphenyl)-α-cyanoacrylate	0	...	2-(3,4-Methylenedioxybenzyl)-3-amino-1-propanol	33	15
$C_{11}H_{11}NO_3$ Methyl β-(4-methoxyphenyl)-α-cyanoacrylate	0	...	2-(4-Methoxybenzyl)-3-amino-1-propanol	33	15
$C_{15}H_{11}ClO$ p-Chlorobenzalacetophenone	35	...	1-Phenyl-3-p-chlorophenyl-1-propanol	88	16
Benzal-p-chloroacetophenone	35	...	1-p-Chlorophenyl-3-phenyl-1-propanol	95	16

Formula	Compound / Product			Yield %	Ref
$C_{15}H_{12}O$	Benzalacetophenone	35	0.25		
	1,3-Diphenyl-2-propen-1-ol[2]			65	1
	1,3-Diphenyl-1-propanol			...	14
$C_{16}H_{14}O$	Benzal-p-methylacetophenone	35	...		
	1-p-Tolyl-3-phenyl-1-propanol			97	16
$C_{16}H_{14}O_2$	Anisalacetophenone	35	...		
	1-Phenyl-3-p-anisyl-1-propanol			88 }	16
	β-Anisylpropiophenone			...	16
$C_{17}H_{14}O$	Benzal-p-methoxyacetophenone	35	...		
	1-p-Anisyl-3-phenyl-1-propanol			90	16
	1,5-Diphenyl-3-pentanol	35	...	94	8
	Dibenzalacetone	...	...		
	1,5-Diphenyl-1,4-pentadien-3-ol[17]			73	18

[1] F. A. Hochstein, J. Am. Chem. Soc., 71, 305 (1949).
[2] Double bond not reduced.
[3] P. Karrer and P. Banerjea, Helv. Chim. Acta, 32, 1692 (1949).
[4] R. F. Nystrom and W. G. Brown, J. Am. Chem. Soc., 70, 3738 (1948).
[5] F. A. Hochstein and W. G. Brown, ibid., 70, 3484 (1948).
[6] R. F. Nystrom and W. G. Brown, ibid., 69, 2548 (1947).
[7] H. I. Schlesinger and A. E. Finholt, U. S. Pat. 2,576,311 (November 27, 1951).
[8] E. Larsson, Trans. Chalmers Univ. Technol., Gothenburg, 94, 15 (1950).
[9] P. P. T. Sah, Z. Vitamin-, Hormon- u. Fermentforsch., 3, 324 (1949); through M. Ferles and J. Rudinger, Chem. Listy, 47, 113 (1953).
[10] J. S. Meek, F. J. Lorenzi, and S. J. Cristol, J. Am. Chem. Soc., 71, 1830 (1949).
[11] P. P. T. Sah, loc. cit., through M. Ferles and J. Rudinger, Chem. Listy, 47, 112 (1953).
[12] Liang Li and W. H. Elliott, J. Am. Chem. Soc., 74, 4089 (1952).
[13] C. J. Collins, unpublished work, through W. G. Brown, in Organic Reactions, Vol. VI, p. 504.
[14] W. G. Brown, in Organic Reactions, Vol. VI, p. 482.
[15] A. Dornow, G. Messwarb, and H. H. Frey, Chem. Ber., 83, 445 (1950).
[16] C. S. Rondestvedt, Jr., J. Am. Chem. Soc., 73, 4509 (1951).
[17] Reduction carried out in 1:1 ether-benzene mixture.
[18] F. Bohlmann, Chem. Ber., 85, 1144 (1952).

Hochstein (9) reported that the reduction of coumarin (XXX) gives mainly the saturated 3-(o-hydroxyphenyl)propanol, accompanied by the cinnamyl alcohol (XXXI).

XXX   XXXI   (15-21)

Karrer and Banerjea (27) obtained only the unsaturated alcohol (XXXI) in 75% yield. In contrast, ethyl coumarate (XXXII) gives the saturated alcohol under all conditions, reduction in the quantity of LAH resulting only in the recovery of unreacted ester.

XXXII   (15-22)

Reduction of p-methylcinnamic acid yields the cinnamyl alcohol in high yield and some unsaturated alcohol accompanies the saturated alcohol even after prolonged refluxing with an excess of an ethereal LAH solution (28). Although reduction of 2-methylcinnamic acid at 0–5° yields 2-methylcinnamyl alcohol, at higher temperatures a mixture of the saturated and unsaturated alcohols is obtained (29).

Meek, Lorenzi, and Cristol (30) reported that the reduction of benzalacetone with one-third mole of LAH "as per the directions of Nystrom and Brown" gives an oil which on distillation gives a 50% yield of 1-phenyl-1,3-butadiene. Apparently, the reduction carried out at room temperature or in refluxing ether gives the unsaturated alcohol. Larsson (11) reported that the reduction with slightly more than an equimolar amount of LAH gives an 87% yield of the saturated alcohol.

The reduction of benzalacetophenone (XXXIII: Ar = C_6H_5, R = CH_3) and dibenzalacetone (XXXIII: Ar = C_6H_5, R = C_6H_5CH=CH—) has been carried out under conditions so as to yield either the saturated or unsaturated alcohol. Rondestvedt (31) reported that the reduction of various chalcones (XXXIII: Ar = R = C_6H_5, $CH_3OC_6H_4$-(p), ClC_6H_4-(p), $CH_3C_6H_4$-(p)) with 0.6 mole of LAH per mole of XXXIII in refluxing ether gives the hydrochalcols in good yield.

$$ArCCH=CHR \xrightarrow{LAH} ArCHCH_2CH_2R \qquad (15\text{-}23)$$

$$\underset{O}{\parallel} \qquad\qquad \underset{OH}{\mid}$$

XXXIII

The initial addition is postulated as being 1,4 to the conjugated system, as discussed in Section 15.1.1.f, since a small quantity of β-anisylpropiophenone has been isolated in the reduction of anisalacetophenone. The formation of unsaturated alcohols in the reduction of benzalacetophenone and dibenzalacetone must, on the contrary, be the result of 1,2-addition to the carbonyl groups. The reduction of chalcones derived from phenols yields the unsaturated carbinols (32,33).

The activating effect of the cyanoacetic grouping is seen in the reduction of various cyanoacrylates (XXXIV) with excess LAH at 0° to the saturated amino alcohols (12).

$$\underset{\underset{\underset{XXXIV}{CN}}{|}}{ArCH=CCOOCH_3} \xrightarrow[0^\circ]{LAH} \underset{\underset{CH_2NH_2}{|}}{ArCH_2CHCH_2OH} \qquad (15\text{-}24)$$

Allen and Byers (34-36) reported that in the LAH reduction of nuclear substituted cinnamic esters (XXXV) the carbonyl group is preferentially reduced to yield the cinnamyl alcohol. The reaction of LAH and XXXV yields a complex lithium aluminum alcoholate called lithium salt A. Treatment of lithium salt A with an aqueous solution of boric acid, disodium phosphate, ammonium chloride, ammonium sulfate, or ammonium carbonate yields the nuclear substituted cinnamyl alcohol (XXXVI). Where XXXV is ethyl acetoferulate the product is coniferyl alcohol. Alternatively the substituted cinnamyl alcohol is isolated by treating lithium salt A with water to give a lithium alcoholate called lithium salt B. Treatment of the latter with carbon dioxide yields the alcohol. When the dried lithium salt B is heated with a carboxylic acid anhydride, an ester of the nuclear-substituted cinnamyl alcohol (XXXVII) is formed.

$$\xrightarrow{LAH} \text{Li Salt A} \xrightarrow{H_2O} \text{Li Salt B} \qquad (15\text{-}25)$$

XXXV → XXXVI

R	R₁	R₂	R₃	R₄	R′
C_2H_5	OCH_3	$OCOCH_3$	OCH_3	OH	
CH_3	OCH_3	OCH_3	OCH_3	OCH_3	
CH_3	$OCOCH_3$	$OCOCH_3$	OH	OH	
C_2H_5	O–CH_2–O (methylenedioxy across R_1,R_2)		O–CH_2–O (methylenedioxy across R_3,R_4)		
C_2H_5	$OCOCH_3$	OCH_3	OH	OCH_3	
C_2H_5	OC_2H_5	$OCOCH_3$	OC_2H_5	OH	

XXXV → XXXVII

R	R₁	R₂	R₃	R₄	R′
C_2H_5	OCH_3	$OCOCH_3$	OCH_3	OH	C_6H_5
C_2H_5	OCH_3	$OCOCH_3$	OCH_3	OH	CH_3
C_2H_5	OCH_3	$OCOCH_3$	OCH_3	OH	$CH_2C_6H_5$
CH_3	$OCOCH_3$	$OCOCH_3$	OH	OH	C_6H_5
C_2H_5	O–CH_2–O (methylenedioxy across R_1,R_2)		O–CH_2–O (methylenedioxy across R_3,R_4)		CH_3

The presence of hydroxy, alkoxy, methylenedioxy, or acetoxy groups on the benzene ring apparently influences the reducibility of the double bond in the substituted cinnamic acids since these reductions are carried out with an equimolar or greater quantity of LAH by direct addition at room temperature or below. Freudenberg and his co-workers have successfully reduced a number of similar compounds (37-41).

$$R_1\text{-}(C_6H_3)(R_2)(R_3)\text{-}CH{=}CHCOOR \xrightarrow{\text{LAH}} R_4\text{-}(C_6H_3)(R_5)(R_6)\text{-}CH{=}CHCH_2OH$$

XXXVIII   (15-26)

R	R₁	R₂	R₃	R₄	R₅	R₆
C_2H_5	OCH_3	$OCOCH_3$	OCH_3	OCH_3	OH	OCH_3
C_2H_5	OCH_3	OH	H	OCH_3	OH	H
H	OCH_3	OH	OCH_3	OCH_3	OH	OCH_3
H	H	OH	H	H	OH	H
CH_3	H	$OCOCH_3$	H	H	OH	H
C_2H_5	H	$OCOCH_3$	H	H	OH	H
CH_3	OCH_3	OCH_3	H	OCH_3	OCH_3	H^*

*β-(2-Methoxy-4-propylphenoxy) derivative.

It is of interest to note that whereas Freudenberg reported that the reduction of p-hydroxycinnamic acid (40) and the esters of p-acetoxycinnamate (41) gives p-hydroxycinnamyl alcohol, Karrer and Banerjea (27) reported that the reduction of ethyl o-hydroxycinnamate gives the saturated alcohol under all conditions examined.

As shown in equation (15-23), the LAH reduction of chalcones results in saturation of the double bond. However, the double bond is retained in the reduction of chalcones derived from phenols (32,33).

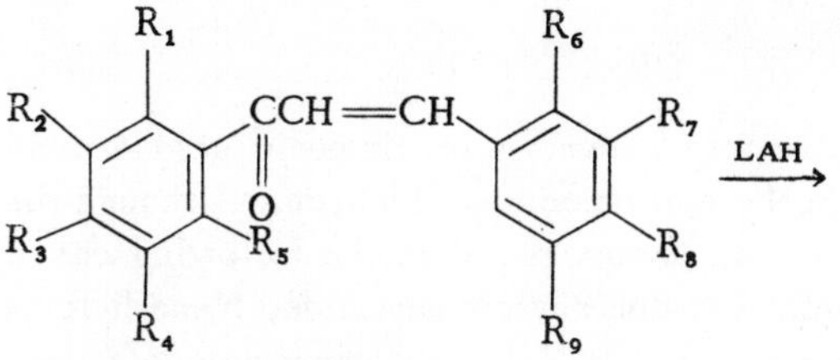

XXXIX

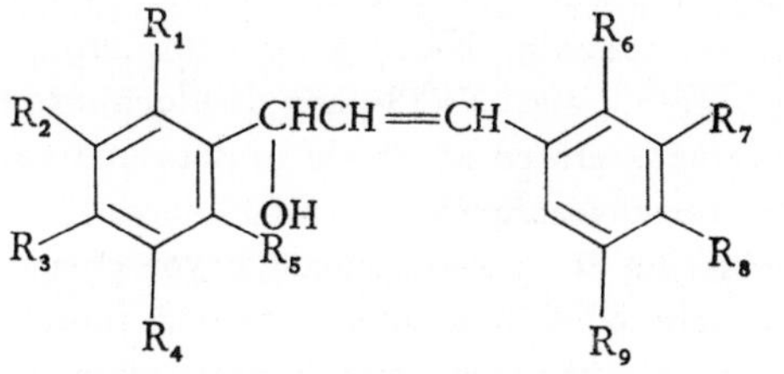

(15-27)

R_1	R_2	R_3	R_4	R_5	R_6	R_7	R_8	R_9
OH	H	OH	H	H	H	OCH_3	$OCH(CH_3)_2$	H
OH	H	OH	H	H	OH	OCH_3	H	H
OH	H	OH	H	H	H	OCH_3	OH	$CH\!=\!CHCH_3$
OH	H	OH	H	H	H	OCH_3	OH	H
OH	H	OH	H	H	H	OCH_3	OH	OCH_3
OCH_3	OH	OCH_3	H	C_3H_7	H	OCH_3	OH	OCH_3
H	OH	OCH_3	H	CH_3	H	OCH_3	OH	OCH_3
OH	OCH_3	H	C_3H_7	H	H	OCH_3	OH	OCH_3

Bohlmann (42) has prepared a series of carbinols containing up to four conjugated double bonds by the LAH reduction of the corresponding ketones $C_6H_5(CH\!=\!CH)_xCO(CH\!=\!CH)_yR$ (Table XCIII). The reaction mixture is decomposed with ammonium chloride since the conjugated carbinols undergo allylic rearrangement in the presence of acid.

$$C_6H_5(CH\!=\!CH)_2\overset{\displaystyle OH}{\overset{|}{C}H}(CH\!=\!CH)_2C_6H_5 \xrightarrow{H_2SO_4}$$

XL

$$C_6H_5(CH\!=\!CH)_2(CH\!=\!CH)_2\overset{\displaystyle OH}{\overset{|}{C}}HC_6H_5 \quad (15\text{-}28)$$

In a similar manner, the LAH reduction of polyene-1,2-diketones yields the corresponding glycols (43).

$$C_6H_5(CH=\!\!=\!\!CH)_x\underset{\substack{\|\\O}}{C}\!-\!\underset{\substack{\|\\O}}{C}(CH=\!\!=\!\!CH)_xC_6H_5 \rightarrow$$

XLI

$$C_6H_5(CH=\!\!=\!\!CH)_x\underset{\substack{|\\OH}}{CH}\!-\!\underset{\substack{|\\OH}}{CH}(CH=\!\!=\!\!CH)_xC_6H_5 \quad (15\text{-}29)$$

Wittig and Hornberger (44) treated a number of cinnamic acid amides with LAH in an effort to obtain the corresponding aldehyde. Although the attempt to obtain the aldehyde was unsuccessful in the following cases the unsaturation was retained: N,N-dimethylcinnamamide, N-methylcin-namanilide, N,N-diphenylcinnamamide, N,N-dimethylcinnamalacetamide, N,N-diphenylcinnamalacetamide. In the case of the carbazole analogs, N-cinnamoylcarbazole, N-cinnamalacetylcarbazole, N-(9-phenylnonatetra-enoyl)carbazole, and N-(13-phenyltridecahexaenoyl)carbazole, the corresponding unsaturated aldehyde is obtained using one-quarter mole LAH in ether or tetrahydrofuran.

The reduction of various cinnamyl type compounds in which the carbon-carbon double bond has been retained intact is summarized in Table XCIV. Those compounds which have given both saturated and unsaturated alcohols are in Table XCIII and are therefore not included in Table XCIV.

Hochstein and Brown (4) have concluded that in the reduction of cinnamyl alcohol with LAH one of the two hydrogen atoms required for the conversion to hydrocinnamyl alcohol is supplied by the hydrolyzing agent acting upon a carbon-aluminum bond in the intermediate complex. Failure of the complex to react with carbon dioxide has been considered evidence against a carbon-lithium bond. On the other hand, Bergmann and Lavie have postulated a carbon-lithium bond in the LAH reduction of fulvenic ketones and dibenzofulvenes, as discussed in Section 15.1.1.d.1.

Based on deuterium tracer studies and the fact that it is colorless, ether-soluble and forms 1-phenyl-1,3-propanediol on oxidation, the intermediate organometallic complex is postulated as XLII.

XLII

The complex actually represents the second stage of the reduction in some cases since the starting material would first be reduced to the cinnamyl alcohol stage.

Although in possession of the appropriate cinnamyl structure, the O-methyl derivative of dibenzoylmethane, $C_6H_5COCH=C(OCH_3)C_6H_5$, is reportedly not reduced by LAH (45).

2. *The* $Ar\overset{|}{C}=\overset{|}{C}N\diagdown$ *grouping.* The LAH reduction of compounds containing the structural grouping $Ar\overset{|}{C}=\overset{|}{C}N\diagdown$ generally results in the saturation of the carbon-carbon double bond. Thus, ω-nitrostyrene (XLIII) and substituted styrenes are reduced to β-phenylethylamine derivatives.

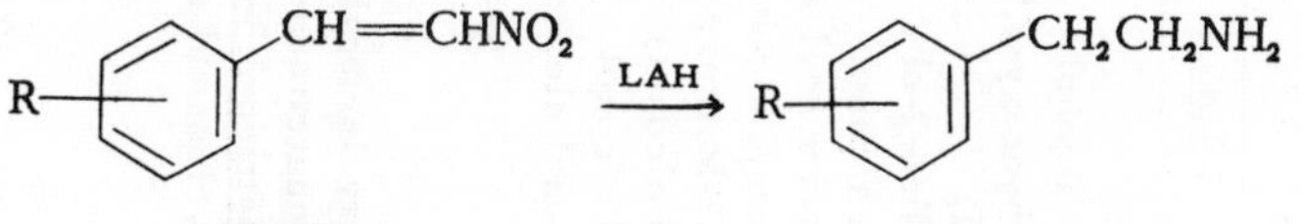

$$ (15\text{-}30) $$

XLIII

Owing to the usual low ether solubility of the substituted nitrostyrenes reductions are generally carried out by the Soxhlet technique in order to bring the material into solution. This entails the use of reaction times probably greater than necessary for the actual reduction. Thus, Erne and Ramirez have carried out the reduction of XLIV by the Soxhlet technique with ether over a period of 8 hours (46). Gensler and Samour have used dioxane as a solvent, dispensed with the Soxhlet procedure and have reduced the reaction time to 65 minutes (47).

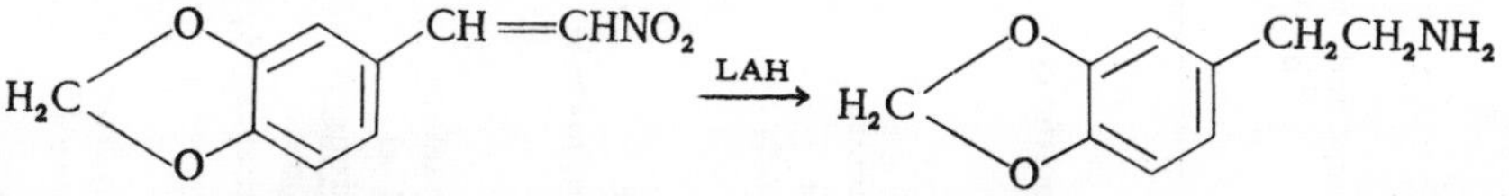

XLIV

$$ (15\text{-}31) $$

Gilsdorf and Nord (48) reported an intensive study of the reverse addition of LAH to nitroolefins to yield amine, hydroxylamine, oxime or nitroparaffin in various mixtures. In addition a ketone, e.g. phenylacetone from the reduction of 1-phenyl-2-nitro-1-propene (XLV), is formed by a modified Nef reaction on the acidic hydrolysis of intermediates.

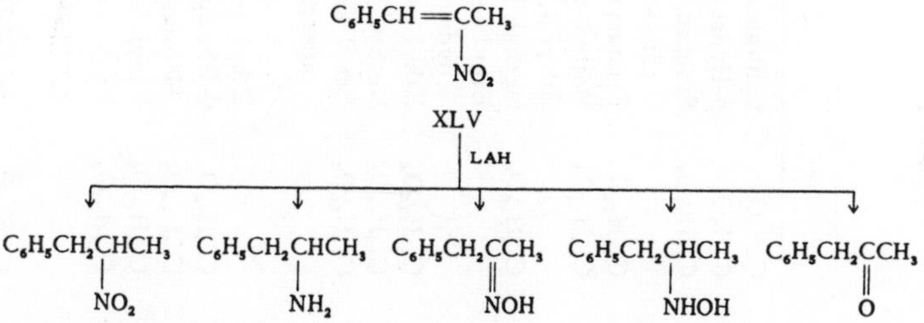

$$ (15\text{-}32) $$

TABLE XCIV

LAH Reduction of Compounds Containing the ArC=C—C=O Grouping with Retention of the Carbon-Carbon Double Bond

Compound	Product	% Yield	Ref.
C_9H_8O			
Cinnamaldehyde	Cinnamyl alcohol	90	1
$C_9H_8O_3$			
p-Hydroxycinnamic acid	p-Hydroxycinnamyl alcohol	…	2
$C_{11}H_{12}O_5$			
Sinapic acid (4-hydroxy-3,5-dimethoxycinnamic acid)	Sinapyl alcohol (4-hydroxy-3,5-dimethoxycinnamyl alcohol)	…	2
$C_{12}H_{12}O$			
Cinnamalacetone	6-Phenyl-3,5-hexadien-2-ol	80[3]	4
$C_{12}H_{12}O_4$			
Methyl p-acetoxycinnamate	p-Hydroxycinnamyl alcohol	84	5
Ethyl 3,4-methylenedioxycinnamate	3,4-Methylenedioxycinnamyl alcohol	…	6
$C_{12}H_{14}O_4$			
Methyl 3,4-dimethoxycinnamate	3,4-Dimethoxycinnamyl alcohol	…	6
Ethyl ferulate (ethyl 3-methoxy-4-hydroxycinnamate)	Coniferyl alcohol (3-Methoxy-4-hydroxycinnamyl alcohol)	80–83	7
$C_{13}H_{14}O_4$			
Ethyl p-acetoxycinnamate	p-Hydroxycinnamyl alcohol	84	5
$C_{14}H_{14}O_6$			
Methyl 3,4-diacetoxycinnamate	3,4-Dihydroxycinnamyl alcohol	…	6
$C_{14}H_{16}O_5$			
Ethyl acetoferulate (ethyl 3-methoxy-4-acetoxycinnamate)	Coniferyl alcohol	74	6
	Coniferyl alcohol	43	8
	3-Hydroxy-4-methoxycinnamyl alcohol	…	9
		…	6
$C_{15}H_{14}O$			
Ethyl 3-acetoxy-4-methoxycinnamate	3-Hydroxy-4-methoxycinnamyl alcohol	…	6
9-Phenyl-2,4,6,8-nonatetraen-1-al	9-Phenyl-2,4,6,8-nonatetraen-1-ol	50[3]	4
$C_{15}H_{14}O_2$			
9-Phenyl-4,6,8-nonatrien-2,3-dione	9-Phenyl-4,6,8-nonatrien-2,3-diol	75[3]	4
$C_{15}H_{18}O_5$			
Ethyl 3-ethoxy-4-acetoxycinnamate	3-Ethoxy-4-hydroxycinnamyl alcohol	…	6
$C_{15}H_{18}O_6$			
Ethyl acetylsinapate(ethyl 4-acetoxy-3,5-dimethoxycinnamate)	Sinapyl alcohol	40–47	10
		55–58	11
$C_{16}H_{14}O_5$			
1-(2,4-Dihydroxyphenyl)-3-(2-hydroxy-3-methoxyphenyl)-2-propen-1-one	1-(2,4-Dihydroxyphenyl)-3-(2-hydroxy-3-methoxyphenyl)-2-propen-1-ol	…	7
		…	12

Molecular formula	Reactant	Product	Yield %	Ref.
C₁₇H₁₄O	1-(2,4-Dihydroxyphenyl)-3-(3-methoxy-4-hydroxyphenyl)-2-propen-1-one	1-(2,4-Dihydroxyphenyl)-3-(3-methoxy-4-hydroxyphenyl)-2-propen-1-ol	...	12
C₁₇H₁₆O₃	Cinnamalacetophenone	1,5-Diphenyl-2,4-pentadien-1-ol	80[3]	4
	Ethyl β-phenoxycinnamate	β-Phenoxycinnamyl alcohol	90	13
C₁₇H₁₆O₆	1-(2,4-Dihydroxyphenyl)-3-(4-hydroxy-3,5-dimethoxyphenyl)-2-propen-1-one	1-(2,4-Dihydroxyphenyl)-3-(4-hydroxy-3,5-dimethoxyphenyl)-2-propen-1-ol	...	14
C₁₉H₁₆O	Benzalcinnamalacetone	1,7-Diphenyl-1,4,6-heptatrien-3-ol	50[3]	4
C₁₉H₁₈O₅	1-(2,4-Dihydroxyphenyl)-3-(3-methoxy-4-hydroxy-5-propenylphenyl)-2-propen-1-one	1-(2,4-Dihydroxyphenyl)-3-(3-methoxy-4-hydroxy-5-propenylphenyl)-2-propen-1-ol	...	12,14
C₁₉H₂₀O₅	1-(2,4-Dihydroxyphenyl)-3-(3-methoxy-4-isopropoxyphenyl)-2-propen-1-one	1-(2,4-Dihydroxyphenyl)-3-(3-methoxy-4-isopropoxyphenyl)-2-propen-1-ol	...	12
C₁₉H₂₀O₆	1-(2-Methyl-4-methoxy-5-hydroxyphenyl)-3-(4-hydroxy-3,5-dimethoxyphenyl)-2-propen-1-one	1-(2-Methyl-4-methoxy-5-hydroxyphenyl)-3-(4-hydroxy-3,5-dimethoxyphenyl)-2-propen-1-ol	...	14
C₁₉H₂₂O	Nondeca-2,4,6,8,11,13,15,17-octaen-10-one	Nondeca-2,4,6,8,11,13,15,17-octaen-10-ol	...[3]	4
C₂₁H₁₅NO	N-Cinnamoylcarbazole	Cinnamaldehyde	49	15
		Carbazole	84	
C₂₁H₁₇NO	Cinnamic acid diphenylamide	Cinnamyl alcohol	37	15
C₂₁H₁₈O	Dicinnamalacetone	1,9-Diphenyl-1,3,6,8-tetraen-5-ol	70[3]	4
C₂₁H₂₄O₆	1-(2-Hydroxy-3-methoxy-5-propylphenyl)-3-(4-hydroxy-3,5-dimethoxyphenyl)-2-propen-1-one	1-(2-Hydroxy-3-methoxy-5-propylphenyl)-3-(4-hydroxy-3,5-dimethoxyphenyl)-2-propen-1-ol	...	14
C₂₂H₁₈O₂	Bis-(ω-phenylbutadienyl)diketone	1,2-Bis-(ω-phenylbutadienyl)glycol	...[3]	16
C₂₂H₂₆O₆	Methyl β-(2-methoxy-4-propylphenoxy)-3,4-dimethoxycinnamate	β-(2-Methoxy-4-propylphenoxy)-3,4-dimethoxycinnamyl alcohol	81	13
		3,4-Dimethoxycinnamyl alcohol	8	
		Dihydroeugenol	10	
C₂₂H₂₆O₇	1-(2,4-Dimethoxy-3-hydroxy-6-propylphenyl)-3-(4-hydroxy-3,5-dimethoxyphenyl)-2-propen-1-one	1-(2,4-Dimethoxy-3-hydroxy-6-propylphenyl)-3-(4-hydroxy-3,5-dimethoxyphenyl)-2-propen-1-ol	...	14
C₂₃H₁₇NO	N-Cinnamalacetylcarbazole	Cinnamalacetaldehyde	73	15
		Carbazole	...[3]	

(continued)

TABLE XCIV (continued)

Compound		Product	% Yield	Ref.
$C_{25}H_{20}O$	1,3-Diphenyl-1,3,5,8,10,12-hexaen-7-one	1,3-Diphenyl-1,3,5,8,10,12-hexaen-7-ol	75[3]	4
$C_{26}H_{22}O_2$	Bis-(ω-phenylhexatrienyl)diketone	1,2-Bis-(ω-phenylhexatrienyl)glycol	25[3]	16
$C_{27}H_{21}NO$	N-(9-Phenylnonatetraenoyl)carbazole	9-Phenylnonatetraenal Carbazole	81 / 85 }[17]	15
$C_{31}H_{25}NO$	N-(13-Phenyltridecahexaenoyl)carbazole	13-Phenyltridecahexaenal Carbazole	60 / 91 }[17]	15

[1] F. A. Hochstein and W. G. Brown, *J. Am. Chem. Soc.*, 70, 3484 (1948).

[2] K. Freudenberg and F. Bittner, *Chem. Ber.*, 83, 600 (1950).

[3] Reduction carried out in benzene–ether mixture.

[4] F. Bohlmann, *Chem. Ber.*, 85, 1144 (1952).

[5] K. Freudenberg and G. Gehrke, *ibid.*, 84, 443 (1951).

[6] C. F. H. Allen and J. R. Byers, Jr., U. S. Pat. 2,545,439 (March 20, 1951).

[7] K. Freudenberg and H. H. Hübner, *Chem. Ber.*, 85, 1181 (1952).

[8] C. F. H. Allen and J. R. Byers, Jr., *J. Am. Chem. Soc.*, 71, 2683 (1949).

[9] C. F. H. Allen and J. R. Byers, Jr., *Science*, 107, 269 (1948).

[10] K. Freudenberg and R. Dillenburg, *Chem. Ber.*, 84, 67 (1951).

[11] K. Freudenberg, R. Kraft, and W. Heimberger, *ibid.*, 84, 472 (1951).

[12] J. C. Pew, *J. Am. Chem. Soc.*, 73, 1678 (1951).

[13] K. Freudenberg and G. Wilke, *Chem. Ber.*, 85, 78 (1952).

[14] J. C. Pew, *J. Am. Chem. Soc.*, 74, 2850 (1952).

[15] G. Wittig and P. Hornberger, *Ann.*, 577, 11 (1952).

[16] F. Bohlmann, *Chem. Ber.*, 85, 386 (1952).

[17] Reduction carried out in tetrahydrofuran–ether mixture.

Analogous compounds, as summarized in Table XCV, are obtained by the reduction of 1-phenyl-2-nitro-1-butene, 1-phenyl-2-nitro-1-pentene, 1-o-chlorophenyl-2-nitro-1-propene, 1-(2-thienyl)-2-nitro-1-propene, and β-nitrostyrene.

By treating the nitroolefin with a slight excess over the amount of LAH necessary for reduction of the double bond via inverse addition at $-40°$ to $-50°$ and hydrolyzing with sodium potassium tartrate, the nitroparaffin is formed. It is postulated that although this reaction may involve the selective reduction of the double bond, it is also possible that reduction may occur by a 1,4-addition especially in view of the polarity of the nitro group and the fact that the reduction takes place at -40 to $-50°$.

In an early communication (49) the authors reported that the inverse addition of LAH at $-30°$ to $-40°$ followed by hydrolysis with sodium potassium tartrate gives phenylacetaldimine and benzyl methyl ketimine from β-nitrostyrene and 1-phenyl-2-nitro-1-propene, respectively. This was indicative of a selective reduction of the nitro group with retention of the double bond. In their later paper (48) it was reported that the fraction originally identified as the imine is actually a mixture of the oxime and hydroxylamine.

The LAH reduction of various ω-nitrostyrene derivatives substituted on the phenyl ring as well as the side chain are summarized in Table XCV. The reduction of various heterocyclic analogs involving the thiophene and thiazole nuclei are also included in Table XCV.

3. *α,β-Unsaturated oximes.* Larsson reported that the LAH reduction of cinnamaldoxime (LXVI) in ether gives an 84% yield of 3-phenylpropylamine (50).

$$C_6H_5CH=CHCH=NOH \xrightarrow{\text{LAH}} C_6H_5CH_2CH_2CH_2NH_2 \quad (15\text{-}33)$$
$$\text{XLVI}$$

On the other hand, Walter reported that the reduction of XLVI gives the unsaturated amine in good yield.

$$C_6H_5CH=CHCH=NOH \xrightarrow[53.3\%]{\text{LAH}} C_6H_5CH=CHCH_2NH_2 \quad (15\text{-}34)$$
$$\text{XLVI}$$

The reduction of benzalacetone oxime (XLVII), in refluxing ether, also gives the unsaturated amine (51).

$$C_6H_5CH=CHCCH_3 \xrightarrow[55\%]{\text{LAH}} C_6H_5CH=CHCHCH_3 \quad (15\text{-}35)$$
$$\underset{\text{NOH}}{\|} \qquad\qquad\qquad \underset{\text{NH}_2}{|}$$
$$\text{XLVII}$$

In the reduction of the oxime of 4,5-benztropolone methyl ether (XLVIII) to 5-aminobenzsuberone-4, isolated as the acetyl derivative, reduction of

TABLE XCV

LAH Reduction of Compounds Containing the ArC=C—NO2 Grouping

Compound	Product	% Yield	Ref.
A. Benzenoid			
C8H7NO2 β-Nitrostyrene	β-Phenylethylamine	60	1
	β-Phenylethylamine	⋯	2
	β-Phenylethylamine	6 ⎤	
	Phenylacetaldoxime	16 ⎬[3]	4
	N-(β-Phenylethyl)hydroxylamine	33 ⎦	
	Phenylacetaldehyde	0–5[5]	4
C9H8BrNO4 3,4-Methylenedioxy-5-bromo-β-nitrostyrene	β-(5-Bromo-3,4-methylenedioxyphenyl)-ethylamine	40	6
	β-(3,4-Methylenedioxyphenyl)-ethylamine	70	6
C9H7NO4 3,4-Methylenedioxy-β-nitrostyrene (piperonylidenenitromethane)	β-(3,4-Methylenedioxyphenyl)-ethylamine	86[7]	6
	β-(3,4-Methylenedioxyphenyl)-ethylamine	60[8]	9
C9H8ClNO2 1-o-Chlorophenyl-2-nitro-1-propene	o-Chlorophenylacetone	62[9] ⎤[5]	4
	N-(β-o-Chlorophenylisopropyl)-hydroxylamine	⋯ ⎦	
C9H9NO2 1-Phenyl-2-nitro-1-propene	β-Phenylisopropylamine	89[10]	6
	β-Phenylisopropylamine	8 ⎤	
	N-(β-Phenylisopropyl)hydroxylamine	34 ⎬[3]	4
	Phenylacetoxime	15 ⎦	
	β-Phenylisopropylamine	44[11] ⎤	4
	N-(β-Phenylisopropyl)hydroxylamine	23 ⎦	
	Phenylacetone	29[12]	4
	1-Phenyl-2-nitropropane	56 ⎤[5]	4
	Phenylacetone	15 ⎦	

Formula	Unsaturated compound	Product	Yield (%)	Ref.
		1-Phenyl-2-nitropropane	38^{13}	4
$C_9H_9NO_3$	4-Methoxy-β-nitrostyrene	β-(4-Methoxyphenyl)ethylamine	53	14
$C_9H_9NO_4$	2-Hydroxy-3-methoxy-β-nitrostyrene	2-Hydroxy-3-methoxy-β-phenyl-ethylamine	81^{10}	15
	3-Hydroxy-4-methoxy-β-nitrostyrene	3-Hydroxy-4-methoxy-β-phenyl-ethylamine	68^{10}	15
	4-Hydroxy-3-methoxy-β-nitrostyrene	4-Hydroxy-3-methoxy-β-phenyl-ethylamine	80^{10}	15
$C_{10}H_9NO_5$	3-Methoxy-4,5-methylenedioxy-β-nitrostyrene	3-Methoxy-4,5-methylenedioxy-β-phenylethylamine	49	16
$C_{10}H_{11}NO_2$	1-Phenyl-2-nitro-1-butene	1-Phenyl-2-butanone	62 } 5	4
		N-(1-Phenyl-2-butyl)hydroxylamine	....	
$C_{10}H_{11}NO_4$	2,3-Dimethoxy-β-nitrostyrene	β-(2,3-Dimethoxyphenyl)ethylamine	87	17
	2,5-Dimethoxy-β-nitrostyrene	β-(2,5-Dimethoxyphenyl)ethylamine		17
$C_{11}H_{13}NO_2$	1-Phenyl-2-nitro-1-pentene	1-Phenyl-2-pentanone	52 } 5	4
		N-(1-Phenyl-2-amyl)hydroxylamine	....	
$C_{11}H_{13}NO_4$	1-(3,4-Dimethoxyphenyl)-2-nitro-1-propene	β-(3,4-Dimethoxyphenyl)isopropylamine		18
$C_{11}H_{13}NO_5$	2,3,4-Trimethoxy-β-nitrostyrene	β-(2,3,4-Trimethoxyphenyl)ethylamine	86^{10}	6
	3,4,5-Trimethoxy-β-nitrostyrene	β-(3,4,5-Trimethoxyphenyl)ethylamine	77^{10}	6
$C_{14}H_{11}NO_2$	α-Nitrostilbene	1,2-Diphenylethylamine	86^{10}	19
			74^7	20
			74	21
$C_{16}H_{15}NO_4$	3-Methoxy-4-benzyloxy-β-nitrostyrene	β-(3-Methoxy-4-benzyloxyphenyl)-ethylamine	$73,6^{22}$	23
	2-Benzyloxy-3-methoxy-β-nitrostyrene	β-(2-Benzyloxy-3-methoxyphenyl)-ethylamine	75	24
B. Heterocyclic				
$C_6H_4ClNO_2S$	5-Chloro-2-(ω-nitrovinyl)thiophene	β-(5-Chloro-2-thienyl)ethylamine	50	25
$C_6H_5NO_2S$	2-(ω-Nitrovinyl)thiophene	β-(2-Thienyl)ethylamine	63	25

(continued)

TABLE XCV (continued)

Compound	Product	% Yield	Ref.
$C_6H_6N_2O_2S$			
1-(4'-Thiazolyl)-2-nitro-1-propene	β-(4-Thiazolyl)isopropylamine	30[26]	27
1-(5'-Thiazolyl)-2-nitro-1-propene	β-(5-Thiazolyl)isopropylamine	31[28]	27
$C_7H_7NO_2S$			
1-(2-Thienyl)-2-nitro-1-propene	β-(2-Thienyl)isopropylamine	65	25
	2-Thienylacetone	43[5]	4
5-Methyl-2-(ω-nitrovinyl)thiophene	β-(5-Methyl-2-thienyl)ethylamine	65	25
$C_8H_9NO_2S$			
1-(2-Thienyl)-2-nitro-1-butene	1-(2-Thienyl)-2-aminobutane	69	25
5-Ethyl-2-(ω-nitrovinyl)thiophene	β-(5-Ethyl-2-thienyl)ethylamine	70	25
$C_9H_{11}NO_2S$			
5-Propyl-2-(ω-nitrovinyl)thiophene	β-(5-Propyl-2-thienyl)ethylamine	70	25

References—Table XCV

[1]R. F. Nystrom and W. G. Brown, *J. Am. Chem. Soc.*, 70, 3738 (1948).
[2]H. I. Schlesinger and A. E. Finholt, U. S. Pat. 2,567,972 (September 18, 1951).
[3]Inverse addition of one-half quantity of LAH calculated for nitro group reduction at −30° to −40°, hydrolysis with sodium potassium tartrate.
[4]R. T. Gilsdorf and F. F. Nord, *J. Am. Chem. Soc.*, 74, 1837 (1952).
[5]Inverse addition of quantity LAH calculated for double bond reduction at −40° to −50°, hydrolysis with hydrochloric acid.
[6]M. Erne and F. Ramirez, *Helv. Chim. Acta*, 33, 912 (1950).
[7]Isolated as hydrochloride.
[8]Reduction carried out in dioxane.
[9]W. J. Gensler and C. M. Samour, *J. Am. Chem. Soc.*, 72, 3318 (1950); 73, 5555 (1951).
[10]Isolated as picrate.
[11]Inverse addition quantity LAH calculated nitro group reduction at −30° to −40°, hydrolysis with sodium potassium tartrate.
[12]As in footnote 3 except hydrolysis with hydrochloric acid.
[13]As in footnote 5 except hydrolysis with sodium potassium tartrate.
[14]J. Bernstein, H. L. Yale, K. Losee, M. Holsing, J. Martins, and W. A. Lott, *J. Am. Chem. Soc.*, 73, 906 (1951).
[15]F. A. Ramirez and A. Burger, *ibid.*, 72, 2781 (1950).
[16]K. E. Hamlin and A. W. Weston, *ibid.*, 71, 2210 (1949).
[17]R. I. T. Cromartie and J. Harley-Mason, *J. Chem. Soc.*, 1952, 2525.
[18]J. D. Bu'Lock and J. Harley-Mason, *ibid.*, 1951, 2248.
[19]F. Benington and R. D. Morin, *J. Am. Chem. Soc.*, 73, 1353 (1951).
[20]A. Dornow and G. Petsch, *Arch. pharm.*, 284, 160 (1951).
[21]A. Dornow and F. Boberg, *Ann.*, 578, 94 (1952).
[22]Reduction carried out in tetrahydrofuran.
[23]J. Finkelstein, *J. Am. Chem. Soc.*, 73, 550 (1951).
[24]D. Ginsburg, *Bull. soc. chim. France*, [5] 17, 510 (1950).
[25]R. T. Gilsdorf and F. F. Nord, *J. Org. Chem.*, 15, 807 (1950).
[26]Isolated as dipicrate.
[27]M. Erne, F. Ramirez, and A. Burger, *Helv. Chim. Acta*, 34, 143 (1951).
[28]Isolated as dihydrobromide.

the double bond α,β to the oxime group accompanies the other transformations (52).

XLVIII

4. *ω-Halostyrene.* The presence of the adjacent reducible group in ω-bromostyrene is insufficient to cause reduction of the double bond since after 19 hours in tetrahydrofuran at 65° with excess LAH, a 49% yield of styrene is obtained (53).

15.1.1.c *Sulfur and Nitrogen Compounds.* Bordwell and McKellin carried out the LAH reduction of various sulfones to sulfides and reported that the reduction of benzothiophene 1-dioxide (XLIX) with a 9 : 1-sulfone : LAH ratio gives 33% of 2,3-dihydrobenzothiophene after one-half hour at 35° and 79% yield after 18 hours (54).

$$\text{XLIX} \quad \xrightarrow{\text{LAH}} \quad \text{(15-37)}$$

In contrast, benzothiophene is not reduced after 18 hours in refluxing ether. Reduction of the double bond accompanies the reduction of the α,β-unsaturated sulfone, phenyl vinyl sulfone (L), with a 3 : 1 ratio of sulfone : LAH at 92° in refluxing ethyl butyl ether after 2.5 hours (12% yield) and 18 hours (14% yield) (54).

$$C_6H_5SO_2CH=CH_2 \xrightarrow{\text{LAH}} C_6H_5SC_2H_5 \qquad (15\text{-}38)$$
$$L$$

The reduction of β-styrenesulfonyl chloride (LI) by the inverse addition of an ethereal LAH solution at −70° gives β-styrenesulfinic acid as the sodium salt with preservation of the double bond (55).

$$C_6H_5CH=CHSO_2Cl \xrightarrow[78\%]{\text{LAH}} C_6H_5CH=CHSO_2H \qquad (15\text{-}39)$$
$$LI$$

Julian and Printy reported that the reduction of 1-methyl- and 1,3-dimethylindole (LII) gives the corresponding indolines (56).

$$\xrightarrow[25\text{--}30\%]{\text{LAH}} \qquad (15\text{-}40)$$

$$LII$$

Here the $Ar\overset{|}{C}=\overset{|}{C}-N\diagup$ grouping is present as in the β-nitrostyrenes. Indole itself is not reduced by LAH in ether.

Baker, Schaub and Williams (57) reported that the reduction of various pyrrolenones (LIII) in a benzene-ether mixture results in reduction at three sites, the lactam, ester and double bond.

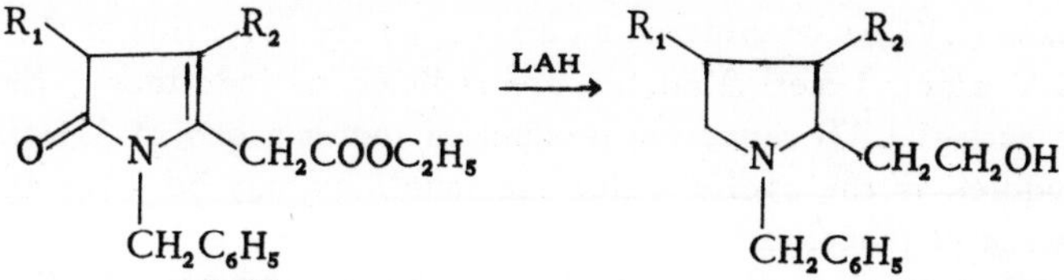

(15-41)

LIII

R_1	R_2	% Yield
H	H	47
H	CH_3	59
H	CH_3OCH_2-	41
CH_3OCH_2-	H	73

Julian and Printy (56) reported that the reduction of 1-methyloxindoles (LIV) gives the corresponding indoles and indolines. Cook, Loudon and McCloskey reported the same mixture of products from the reduction of 3-mono- or unsubstituted 1-methyloxindoles (58).

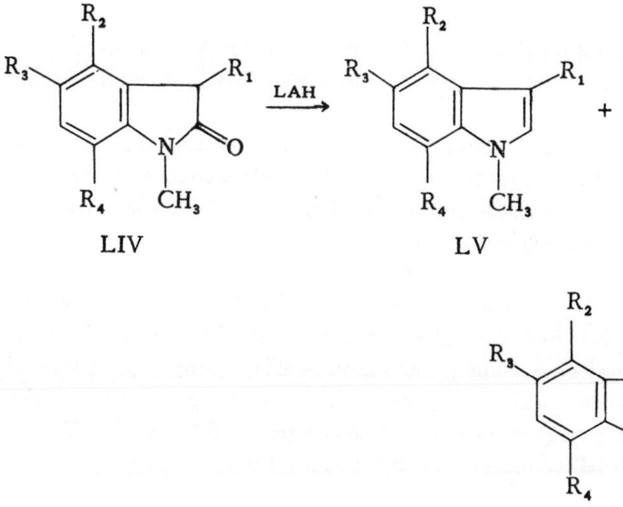

LIV   LV

(15-42)

LVI

R_1	R_2	R_3	R_4	% Yield LV	% Yield LVI	Ref.
H	H	H	H	61.8	12	56
CH_3	H	H	H	85.8	13	56
H	H	OC_2H_5	H	60	6	56
H	H	OCH_3	H	40	"Small quantity"	58
H	OCH_3	H	H	66	16	59
H	H	H	OCH_3	—	—	59

The indoline (LVI) is considered as arising by the reduction of the double bond in LV since 1-methylindoles are reduced to indolines.   However, since the normal LAH reduction product of lactams and of 3,3-disubstituted oxindoles is the cyclic amine the indolines may be a result of the normal course of reaction.

The LAH reduction of 2-methyltetrahydrobenzoxazole (LVII) yields 2-ethylaminocyclohexanol (60).

$$(15\text{-}43)$$

LVII

As discussed in Sections 12.16.1 and 12.17 the cleavage of the benzoxazole ring results from the reduction of the carbon-nitrogen double bond and cleavage of the

$$-\overset{|}{\underset{|}{N}}\overset{|}{C}O-$$

grouping.   However, the reduction of the carbon-carbon double bond is a further example of the saturation of the

$$-\overset{|}{C}=\overset{|}{C}-\overset{|}{N}-$$

grouping.

The LAH reduction of pyridine and 2-hydroxypyridine in di-n-butyl ether yields, in part, piperidine, involving carbon-carbon double bond reduction (61).   Treatment of carbethoxypyridines with LAH at elevated temperatures and with a prolonged reaction time yields small amounts of piperidyl carbinols and methylpyridines (62).   Analogously, 2-hydroxyquinoline yields, in part, tetrahydroquinoline (61).

15.1.1.d *Polar Semicyclic Double Bonds.*

1. *Fulvene derivatives.* The fulvenes are polar substances in which the semicyclic central double bond possesses a dipole moment directed toward the pentagonal ring. The polar carbon-carbon double bond should therefore respond to the action of LAH since the latter generally attacks polar systems such as the carbonyl carbon-oxygen double bond. Ziegler (3) reported the LAH reduction of 6,6-dimethylfulvene (LVIII) to the isopropylcyclopentadiene.

$$(15\text{-}44)$$

LVIII

Lavie and Bergmann carried out a series of LAH reductions with dibenzofulvenes in order to clarify the mechanism of the reaction and to provide evidence for the polar character of the central double bonds. The reduction of dibiphenyleneethylene or 9,9'-difluorenylidene (LIX) in ether gives a 93% yield of dibiphenyleneethane (63,64).

$$(15\text{-}45)$$

LIX

Goodman obtained a 77.5% yield of dibiphenyleneethane in the reduction of LIX and noted that the same product is obtained in refluxing ethanol with Raney nickel (65).

The LAH reduction of benzhydrylidenefluorene (LX) in refluxing ether or dioxane gives 9-benzyhydrylfluorene (LXII) in 100 and 42% yields, respectively, after hydrolysis of the colored intermediate product. The color of the intermediate indicates the formation of an organometallic compound. Although Hochstein and Brown have postulated the attachment of the aluminum atom to the negative carbon atom in the polar system attacked, Lavie and Bergmann favor a carbon-lithium bond. Among the arguments advanced by the latter are the fact that organoalkaline compounds containing the grouping $Ar-C-Li$ are vividly colored whereas compounds such as dibenzylmagnesium and bis-triphenylmethylmagnesium, analogous to $Ar-C-Al$, are colorless. They have concluded that, especially in the case of the fulvenes, the reducing agent is, in effect, lithium hydride $Li^{\oplus}H^{\ominus}$ which reacts with the central double bond to give the lithium addition product LXI. Further, the addition of p-chlorobenzyl chloride to the product of the reaction of LAH and LX yields 9-benzhydryl-9-p-chlorobenzylfluorene (LXIII).

$$(15\text{-}46)$$

It should be pointed out that although Hochstein and Brown (4) found that the complex from cinnamyl alcohol and LAH fails to react with carbon dioxide and hence the carbon-lithium bond was discounted, Trevoy and Brown (53) later reported that the reaction of fluorene and LAH in tetrahydrofuran gives a complex which on carbonation is converted to fluorene-9-carboxylic acid.

The LAH reduction of benzylidenefluorene (LXIV) yields a complex (LXV) which, upon hydrolysis, yields 9-benzylfluorene and a bimolecular product formulated as 9,9′-dibenzyldibiphenyleneethane (LXVI) (63,64).

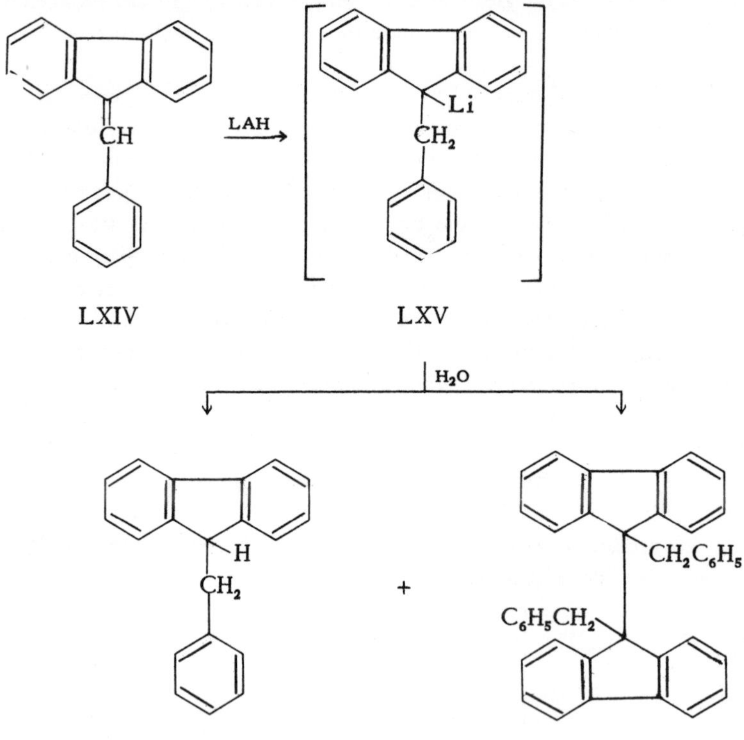

LXIV   LXV

H₂O

+   (15-47)

LXVI

The bimolecular product is probably formed by oxidation of the organometallic compound by traces of oxygen since it can be obtained in quantitative yields by bubbling a stream of dry air through a suspension of the addition product (LXV). The addition of benzyl chloride to LXV yields 84% of 9,9-dibenzylfluorene while p-chlorobenzyl chloride yields 82% of 9-benzyl-9-p-chlorobenzylfluorene.

The LAH reduction of p-bromobenzylidenefluorene (LXVII: R = Br) yields 9-p-bromobenzylfluorene while p-methoxybenzylidenefluorene

(LXVII: R = OCH$_3$) yields p-methoxybenzylfluorene and the bimolecular product 9,9′-di-(p-methoxybenzyl)dibiphenyleneethane (63,64).

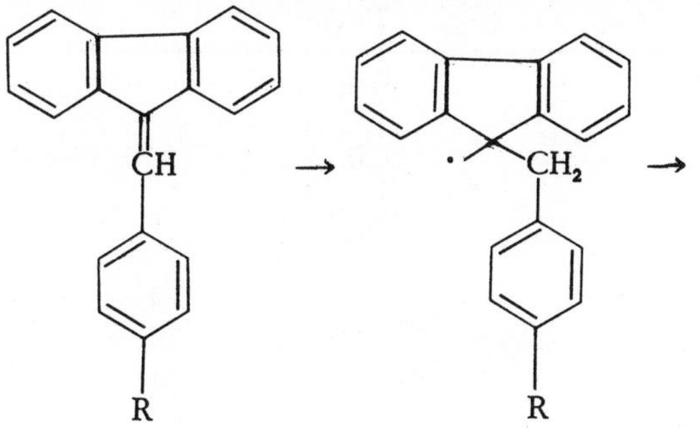

LXVII

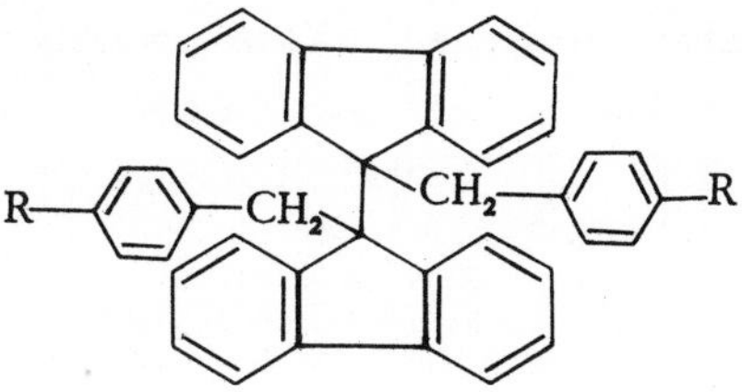

(15-48)

The dimeric product is postulated as proceeding via the attack of the negative hydride ion on the positive end of the dipole to form a radical which dimerizes (63). The LAH reduction of p-chlorobenzylidenefluorene (LXVII: R = Cl), followed by bubbling dry air through the reaction mixture, yields the dimeric 9,9′-di-(p-chlorobenzyl)dibiphenyleneethane (66). Trevoy and Brown (53) reported that the LAH reduction of 9-bromofluorene gives fluorene and dibiphenyleneethane while diphenylbromomethane gives diphenylmethane and tetraphenylethane.

These experiments indicate that these fulvenes have a polar central double bond whose moment is directed towards the five-membered ring. The negative hydride ion adds to the positive pole of the double bond, i.e., the benzylidene carbon atom, while the Li$^{\oplus}$ or the (LiAlH$_3$)$^{\oplus}$ is attached to the central carbon atom of the fluorenic system, the negative end of the dipole (63,64,67).

The reduction of ethylenefluorene to 9-ethylfluorene and 9,9′-diethyl-dibiphenyleneethane indicates that the course of the reaction is not dependent upon the presence of an aromatic group in the side chain (64). The reduction of cinnamylidenefluorene (LXVIII) yields 9-cinnamyl-fluorene indicating that the most positive carbon in the system is adjacent to the fluorene ring and not the phenyl ring.

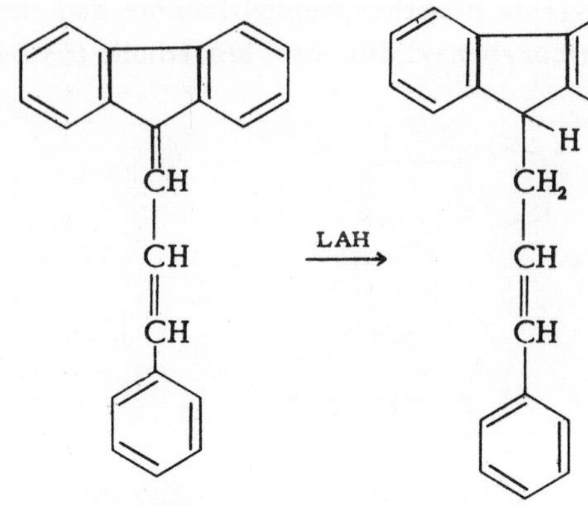

$$(15\text{-}49)$$

LXVIII

Although the methoxy group induces a polarization of the ethylene bond, 1,1-di-(p-methoxyphenyl)ethylene (LXIX) is not attacked by LAH (64). Triphenylethylene (LXX) is similarly not attacked (68).

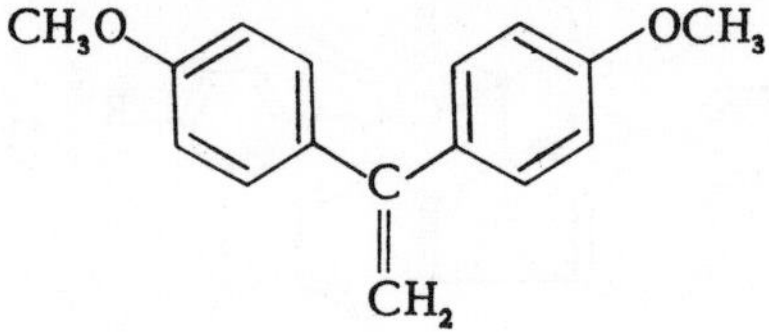

LXIX 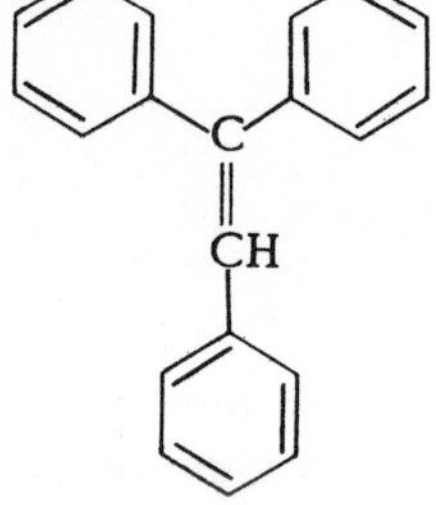   LXX

Ultraviolet absorption spectra and dipole moment measurements have indicated that the heptagonal ring in the aryl derivatives of 2,3,6,7-dibenzoheptafulvene is non-planar and therefore conjugation is destroyed. This is borne out by the fact that 1-benzylidene- and 1-p-chlorobenzylidene-2,3,6,7-dibenzo-2,4,6-cycloheptatriene (LXXI) are not attacked by LAH due to the non-polar character of the semi-cyclic double bonds (68,69).

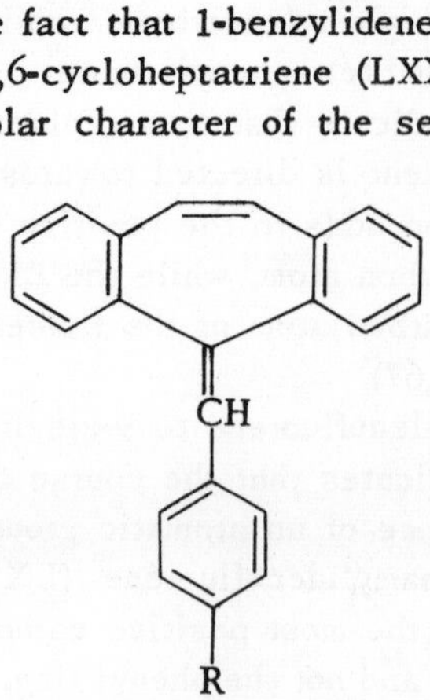

LXXI

2. *Xanthene derivatives*. In benzylidenexanthene (LXXII) the divalent oxygen participates in the resonance of the system. The heterocyclic nucleus is planar and the semicyclic double bond is polar. However, the positive extremity of the dipole is on the central carbon atom of the xanthenic system rather than on the benzylidene carbon atom as in the fulvenes. Treatment of LXXII with LAH in dioxane yields a bimolecular product postulated as sym. dixanthyldiphenylethane (LXXIII) rather than 9,9'-dibenzyldixanthyl. The formation of LXXIII is explained by the attack of the negative hydride ion on the positive end of the dipole and the dimerization of the resultant radical by traces of oxygen present in the system. In addition to LXXIII, a second reaction product is xanthone (LXXIV) rather than benzylxanthene (70).

LXXII   LXXIII   LXXIV   (15-50)

3. *Anthrone derivatives*. The LAH reduction of benzylideneanthrone (LXXV) yields anthraquinone, analogous to the formation of LXXIV (71).

LXXV

Treatment of LXXV with organomagnesium compounds similarly yields anthraquinone.

The LAH reduction of benzhydrylideneanthrone (LXXVI) yields the dimeric sym-tetraphenyl-bis-(9,10-dihydro-9-anthryl)ethane. The initial reaction is postulated as a 1,6-addition attacking the oxygen atom and liberating a valence of the central carbon in the benzhydrylidene group which is stabilized by dimerization. Hydrogenolysis and reduction yields the symmetrical dimeric product (71).

$$(15\text{-}52)$$

The 1,6-addition to LXXVI has also been reported with the Grignard reagent.

15.1.1.e *Heterocyclically Conjugated Systems*. The double bonds in 1,2-di-α-furylethylene (LXXVII) are not attacked after a 24 hour reaction period with LAH (72).

Contrary to the behavior of cinnamaldehyde, the LAH reduction of 3-α-furylacrolein (LXXVIII) yields 3-α-furylallyl alcohol (73).

15.1.1.f *1,2-Diketoethylenes*. Lutz and Gillespie (74) observed that the LAH reduction of *cis* and *trans*-dibenzoylethylene (LXXIX) gives 10% of *trans*-1,4-diphenyl-2-buten-1,4-diol (LXXX) and 88% of 1,4-diphenyl-butan-4-ol-1-one (LXXXI).

The same products are obtained from both isomers doubtless due to isomerization before reduction. The unsaturated glycol (LXXX) is the expected result of reduction of the two carbonyl groups. The hydroxy ketone (LXXXI) results from 1,4-addition of LAH to the α,β-unsaturated ketone with prior or subsequent 1,2-reduction of the carbonyl group independently of the other carbonyl group.

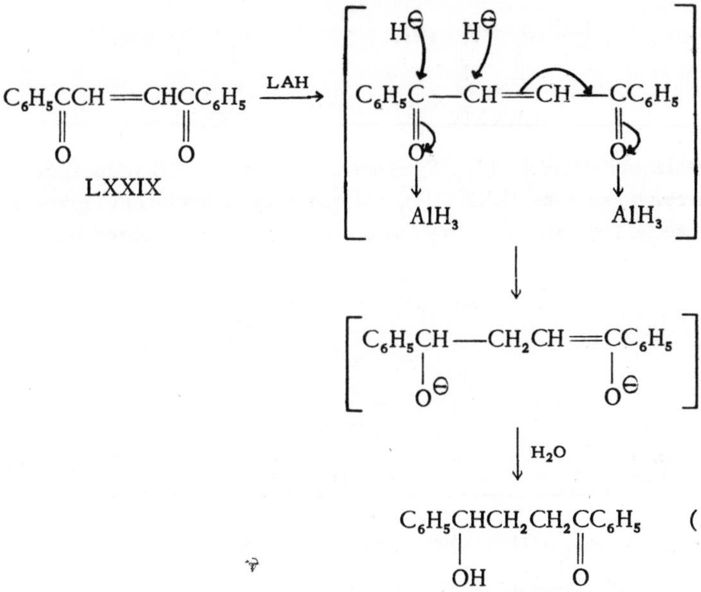

$$C_6H_5CCH = CHCC_6H_5 \xrightarrow{\text{LAH}}$$

(with structures, below the first structure:)

LXXIX

$$\begin{bmatrix} C_6H_5C-CH=CH-CC_6H_5 \\ O \qquad\qquad O \\ \downarrow \qquad\qquad \downarrow \\ AlH_3 \qquad\quad AlH_3 \end{bmatrix}$$

$$\begin{bmatrix} C_6H_5CH-CH_2CH=CC_6H_5 \\ O^{\ominus} \qquad\qquad O^{\ominus} \end{bmatrix}$$

$$\downarrow H_2O$$

$$C_6H_5CHCH_2CH_2CC_6H_5 \qquad (15\text{-}54)$$
$$\qquad OH \qquad\quad O$$

LXXXI

An intermediate cyclic transition state analogous to those proposed in Grignard reactions and in aluminum alkoxide reductions has been postulated as applicable to the LAH reductions (74).

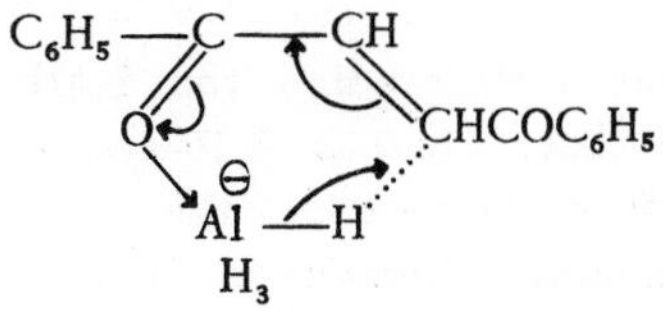

$$\begin{matrix} C_6H_5-C-CH \\ O \qquad\qquad CHCOC_6H_5 \\ \ominus \\ Al-H \\ H_3 \end{matrix}$$

LXXXII

The LAH reduction of *trans*-dimesitoylethylene (LXXXIII) gives the hydroxy ketone by 1,4-addition (74).

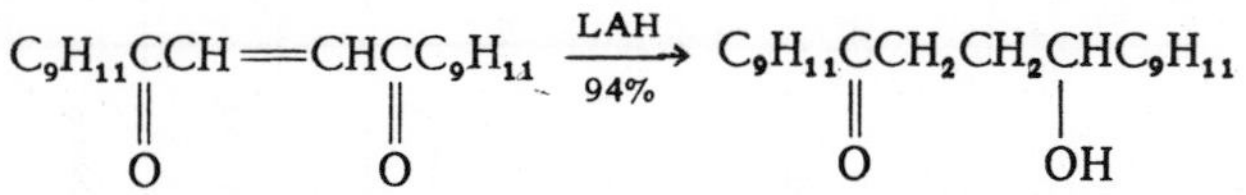

$$C_9H_{11}CCH=CHCC_9H_{11} \xrightarrow[94\%]{\text{LAH}} C_9H_{11}CCH_2CH_2CHC_9H_{11} \qquad (15\text{-}55)$$
$$\quad O \qquad\qquad O \qquad\qquad\qquad O \qquad OH$$

LXXXIII

The reduction of *trans*-dibenzoyldimethylethylene is reported to yield equal amounts of racemic and *meso* unsaturated glycols, without occurrence of 1,4-addition (75).

The LAH reduction of 1,2-dimesitylpropenone (LXXXIV) yields 1,2-dimesityl-1-propen-1-ol (LXXXV), an enol which is evidently stabilized and protected in the form of the lithium salt, and liberated upon hydrolysis (76).

$$C_9H_{11}C\underset{\underset{\displaystyle CH_2}{\|}}{-}C\underset{\underset{\displaystyle O}{\|}}{C_9H_{11}} \xrightarrow[90\%]{\text{LAH}} C_9H_{11}C\underset{\underset{\displaystyle CH_3}{\|}}{=}C\underset{\underset{\displaystyle OH}{\|}}{C_9H_{11}} \qquad (15\text{-}56)$$

$$\text{LXXXIV} \qquad\qquad\qquad \text{LXXXV}$$

Cavalla and McGhie (77,78) reported that the LAH reduction of dike-tolanostenyl acetate (LXXXVI), followed by acetylation, gives a keto-diacetate, a saturated hydroxydiacetate, and an unsaturated triacetate.

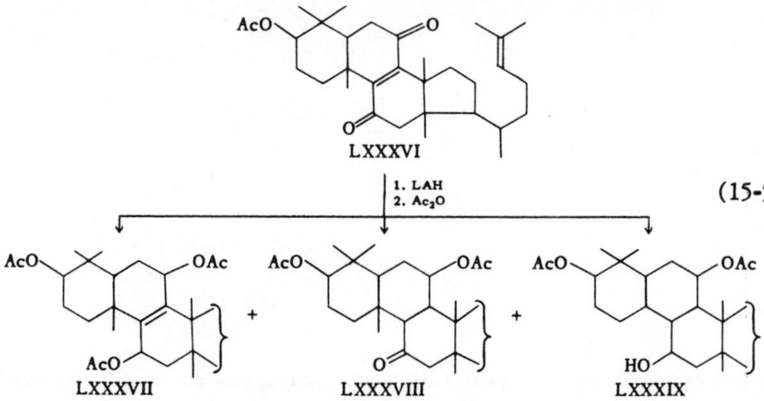

LXXXVI

(15-57)

1. LAH
2. Ac₂O

LXXXVII   +   LXXXVIII   +   LXXXIX

The formation of LXXXVIII is indicative of 1,4-addition of LAH to the conjugated system.

Boyland and Manson (79) studied the LAH reduction of various p-quinones and found that, whereas 9,10-anthraquinone is reduced to 9,10-dihydro-9,10-dihydroxyanthracene, the reduction of 1,4-naphtha-quinone (XC) gives a mixture of products, including two neutral products in which the 2,3-double bond has been reduced.

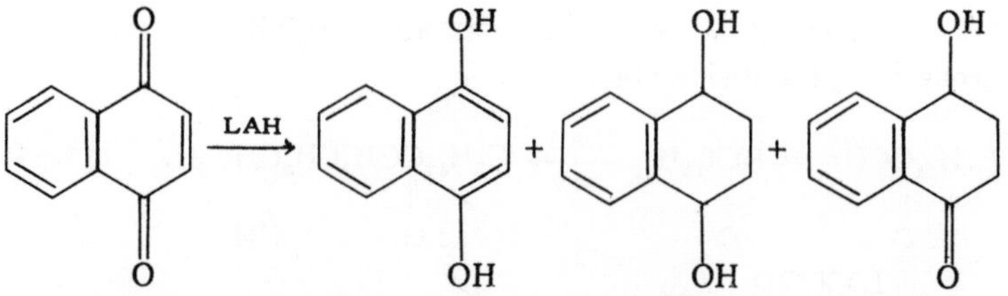

XC   XCI   XCII   (15-58)

The reduction of 2-methyl-1,4-naphthaquinone gives an analogous mix-ture of products, the relative quantities dependent upon the reaction con-ditions. The saturation of the double bond to yield XCI and XCII ap-parently results from 1,4-addition.

As mentioned in Section 15.1.1.b.1, in the reduction of chalcones (1,3-diaryl-α,β-unsaturated ketones) to saturated alcohols the initial step is apparently a 1,4-addition since some saturated ketone has been isolated from the reduction mixture (31).

15.1.1.g   *Substituted Cyclopentadienones.* Bergmann *et al.* reported that the addition of 2,3,4,5-tetraphenylcyclopentadienone (XCIII) to LAH in refluxing dioxane gives the saturated 2,3,4,5-tetraphenylcyclopenta-none whose structure was advanced based on the infrared and ultraviolet spectra (66). In a later publication, the structure was corrected to that of tetraphenylcyclopentenone (XCIV) (80).

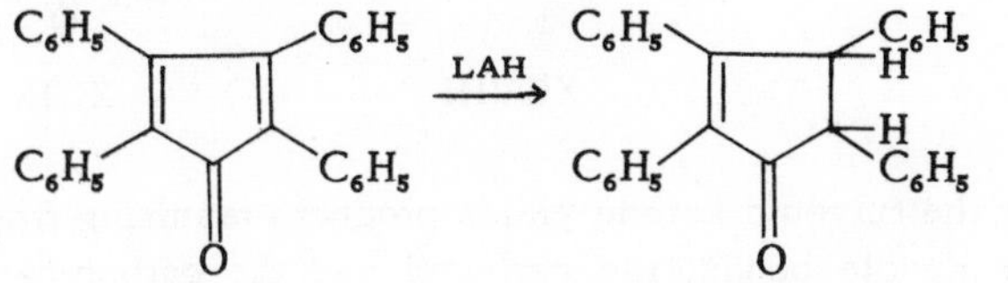

$$\text{(15-59)}$$

XCIII   XCIV

Organolithium compounds react with XCIII to yield ketones corresponding to 1,4-addition. It is proposed that in the fulvenic ketone the carbonyl group contains a true double bond rather than an ionic bond, causing a polarization of the conjugated carbon-carbon double bond.

An examination of the reduction of XCIII has been carried out by Sonntag *et al.* (81). Repetition of Bergmann's experiment has given 60% of XCIV and a trace of tetraphenylcyclopentadiene (XCV). The reduction in refluxing ether gives 73% of XCIV and 12–17% of XCV. The inverse addition at 0–10° gives 81% of 2,3,4,5-tetraphenylcyclopenta-2,4-dien-1-ol (XCVI).

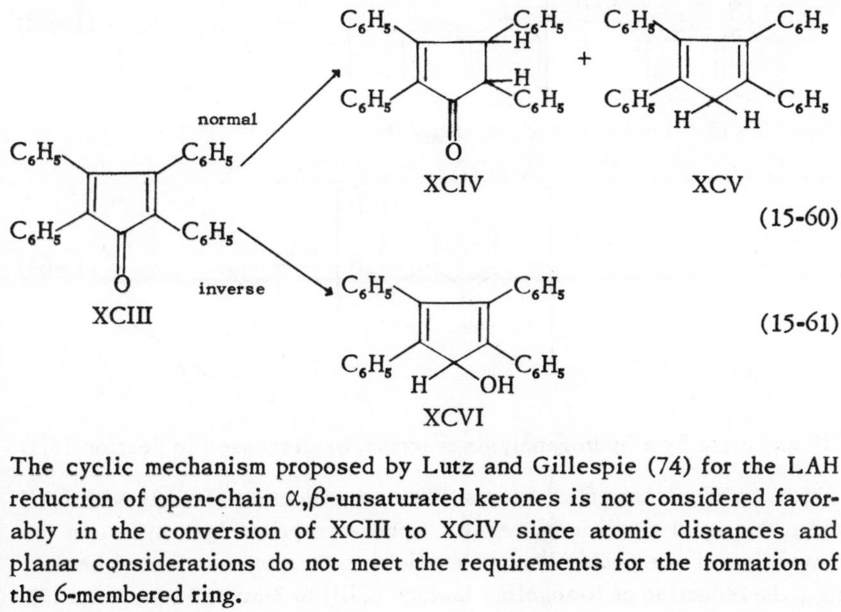

normal

XCIV   XCV

$$\text{(15-60)}$$

XCIII   inverse

$$\text{(15-61)}$$

XCVI

The cyclic mechanism proposed by Lutz and Gillespie (74) for the LAH reduction of open-chain α,β-unsaturated ketones is not considered favorably in the conversion of XCIII to XCIV since atomic distances and planar considerations do not meet the requirements for the formation of the 6-membered ring.

Bergmann *et al.* (66) reported that the LAH reduction of 2,3-diphenyl-indone (XCVII) gives 2,3-diphenylindene (XCVIII) and 2,3-diphenylhy-drindone (XCIX).

XCVII   XCVIII   XCIX   (15-62)

In this case the fulvenic ketone yields products resulting from reduction of both true double bonds, the carbonyl and the carbon-carbon bonds. Organolithium compounds add 1,4 to XCVII while the Grignard reagent adds 1,2.

15.1.1.h *Perinaphthenone.* The reduction of perinaphthenone (C) with an excess of ethereal LAH is reported to yield a mixture of perinaphthene (CI) and perinaphthanone-7 (CII) as well as phenolic material. Boekel-heide and Larrabee (82) postulated that the initial reaction intermediate undergoes further reaction:

C   CI   (15-63)

CII   (15-64)

CII may arise by a hydrogenolysis reaction, as discussed in Section 16.1.

15.1.1.i *Enols and Enol Ethers.* The non-reduction of enols with LAH under the usual conditions, results, upon appropriate hydrolysis, in the conversion of the double-bonded enolic structure to a saturated ketone, e.g., the reduction of α-angelica lactone (CIII) to 3-acetyl-1-propanol (9),

$$(15\text{-}65)$$

and the reduction of ketene dimers to hydroxy ketones (83,84).

$$(15\text{-}66)$$

However, in the reduction of 3-phenylisocoumarin (CV) the double bond in the enolic grouping is reduced (85).

$$(15\text{-}67)$$

The LAH reduction of the geometric isomer of α,β-diphenyl-β-methoxy-acrylonitrile (CVI) with m.p. $106°$ is reported to yield α-benzylphenyl-acetonitrile involving apparent demethylation and reduction of the double bond (86).

$$\underset{\substack{|\quad\;\;\;| \\ \text{CN}\;\;\text{OCH}_3 \\ \text{CVI}}}{C_6H_5C=\!\!=CC_6H_5} \xrightarrow{\text{LAH}} \underset{\substack{| \\ \text{CN}}}{C_6H_5CHCH_2C_6H_5} \qquad (15\text{-}68)$$

While the LAH reduction of various 2-hydroxymethylenic ethers of cyclohexanone (CVII), followed by acid hydrolysis, yields the corres-

$$(15\text{-}69)$$

R_1	R_2	R
H	H	$i\text{-}C_4H_9$
CH_3	H	$i\text{-}C_4H_9$
CH_3	CH_3	$i\text{-}C_4H_9$
CH_3	CH_3	CH_3

ponding unsaturated aldehyde (87), the reduction of derivatives containing substituents beta to the carbonyl group yields a mixture of saturated
and unsaturated aldehydes (88).

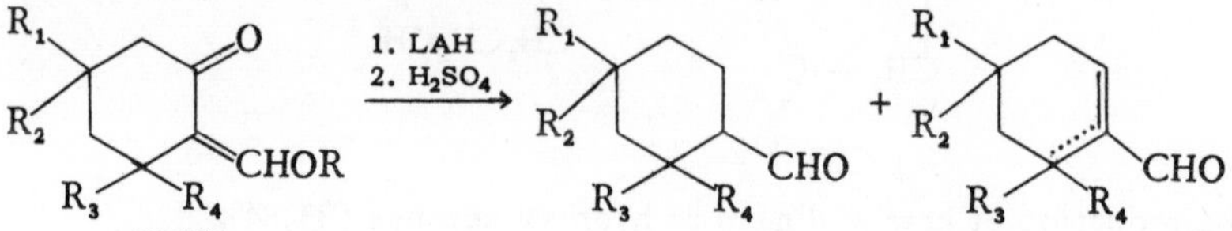

CVIII (15-70)

R	R_1	R_2	R_3	R_4
H	CH_3	CH_3	CH_3	CH_3
i-C_4H_9	CH_3	CH_3	CH_3	H
i-C_4H_9	CH_3	CH_3	CH_3	CH_3

In the reduction of 1,1,5,5-tetramethyl-4-hydroxymethylene-cyclohexan-
3-one (CIX), in addition to the mixture of saturated and unsaturated aldehydes, the glycol 5,5-dimethyl-3-hydroxycyclolavandulol (CX) is isolated
(88).

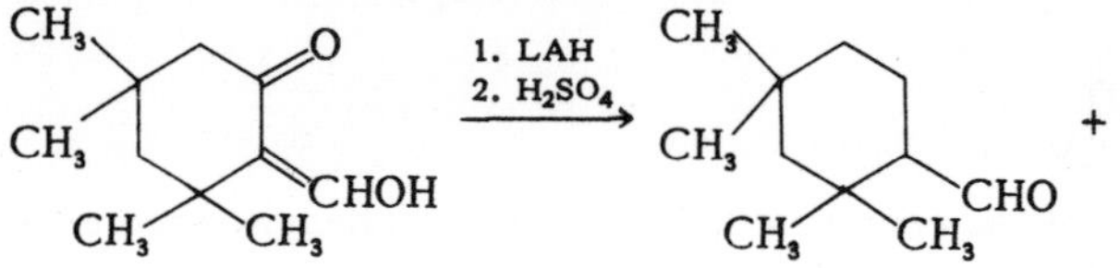

CIX 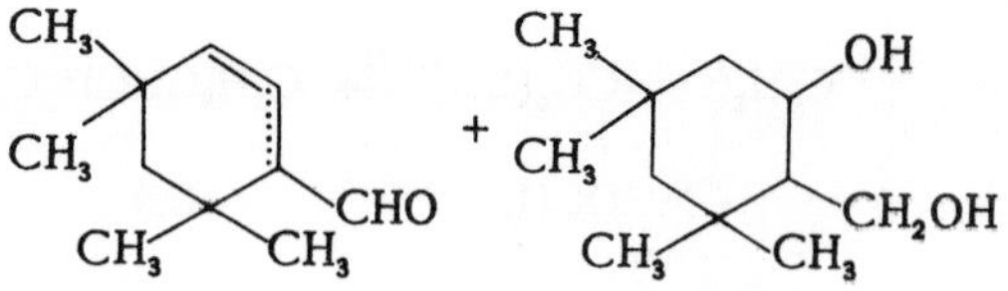 (15-71)

CX

Dreiding and Hartman (14) reported that the LAH reduction of 2-hydroxy-
methylenecyclohexanone (CXI) yields a mixture of 2-methylenecyclo-
hexanol, 1-cyclohexenemethanol and 2-hydroxymethylcyclohexanol.

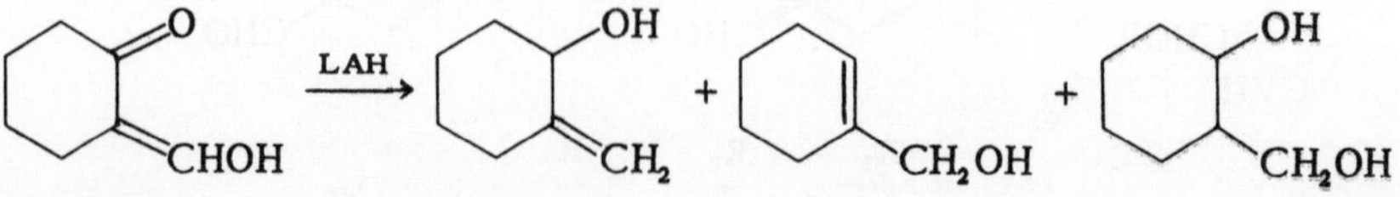

CXI (15-72)

The reduction of 2-hydroxymethylenecyclopentanone yields an analogous
mixture of products.

The reaction of enols and enol ethers with LAH is discussed in Section 11.5.

15.1.1.j   *Enol Esters.*   In the steroid series, the reduction of α,β-unsaturated ketones with the complex metal hydrides yields the corresponding unsaturated carbinol. Analogously, the reduction of the enol ether derived from the unsaturated ketone leaves the conjugated diene ether grouping intact and, on appropriate hydrolysis, the α,β-unsaturated ketone is recovered. In contrast, the reduction of the enol acetates derived from α,β-unsaturated as well as saturated steroidal ketones yields products in which carbon-carbon double bond reduction has occurred.

Dauben and Eastham investigated the LAH reduction of cholestenone enol acetate (CXII) and obtained a complex mixture consisting of cholest-4-en-3-one, cholesterol, epicholesterol and cholest-4-en-3α- and β-ols (89,90).

AcO   CXII $\rightarrow$ O   CXIII   +

HO   CXIV   +   HO   (15-73)

Cholest-4-en-3-one (CXIII) and cholesterol (CXIV) are obtained in 30–34% yield while epicholesterol is obtained in approximately 15% yield. The Δ^4-stenols are formed in only small quantities and, in fact, have never been isolated directly but have been identified by the isolation of cholestadiene after a mild acid treatment. Using the enol acetate of cholest-4-en-3-one-4-C^{14}, cholesterol-4-C^{14} has been prepared in 50% yield (based upon recovered cholestenone).

Brown (91) has confirmed the results of the LAH reduction of CXII and has further reported that aluminum hydride brings about the same results. However, the action of aluminum hydride in the presence of excess aluminum chloride gives 16% of cholest-4-ene, 20% of cholest-4-en-3-one and 49% of a molecular compound which after acetylation and fractional crystallization gives two acetates which are hydrolyzed to two diols postulated as *trans*-cholest-5-ene-3,4-diols.

The reduction of the enol acetate of cholestanone (CXV) with LAH by normal or inverse addition yields 17–20% of epicholestanol, 58% of cholestanol, and 10–21% of 3-cholestanone.

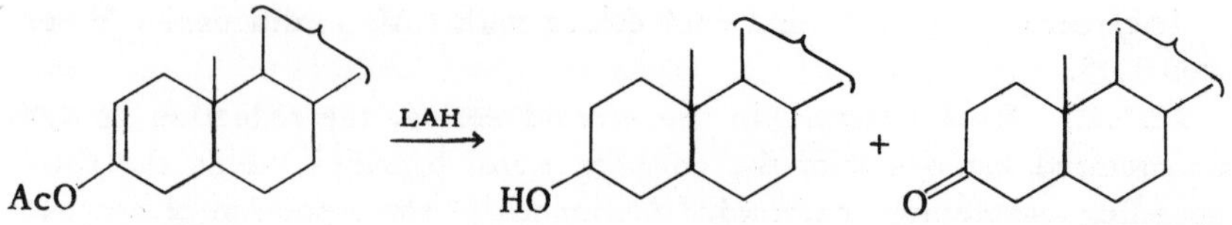

(15-74)

Reduction of the enol acetate of coprostanone (CXVI) with LAH yields 63-70% of epicoprostanol, 13-20% of coprostanol and 8-10% of coprostanone (92).

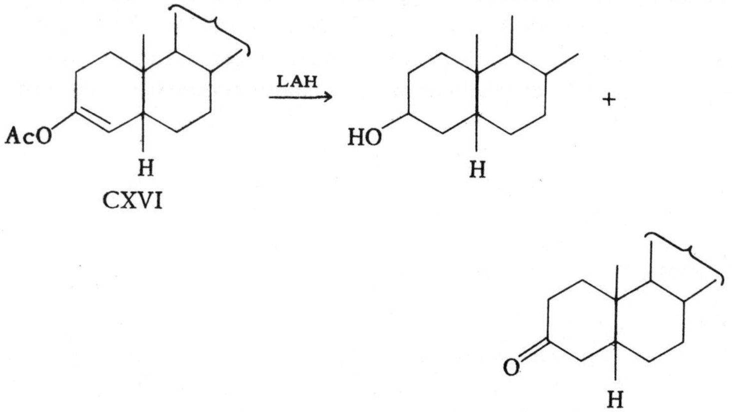

(15-75)

The reduction of enol esters is discussed in Section 9.3.

15.1.2 Reductions with Magnesium Aluminum Hydride

Although an insufficient number of examples have been reported to draw conclusions, the carbon-carbon double bond is probably unattacked by the magnesium aluminum hydride since the reactive cinnamic acid is reduced to cinnamyl alcohol (93).

15.1.3 Reductions with Sodium Borohydride

Chaikin and Brown (94) reported that normally sodium borohydride in aqueous or methanol solution does not attack double bonds. Thus, crotonaldehyde and mesityl oxide yield the corresponding unsaturated alcohols. While cinnamyl alcohol is not reduced and cinnamaldehyde yields 97% cinnamyl alcohol, the reduction of cinnamoyl chloride in dioxane solution gives 12% of hydrocinnamyl alcohol and an unhydrolyzable organo-boron product. Reduction of the carbon-carbon double bond also occurs in the reduction of crotonyl chloride although a boron-free product has not been isolated.

As mentioned in Section 15.1.1.a.2, the reduction of 3-ketoetiochola-4,9(11),16-trienate (XXVIII) with sodium borohydride in ethanol results in some reduction of the 16,17-double bond (26).

The reduction of cholestenone enol acetate (CXII) with sodium boro-hydride in a methanol-ether mixture or in aqueous ethanol yields the same mixture of products as in the reduction with LAH (equation 15-73), with the exception of cholestenone (CXIII) (95,96). The major product in 58–75% yield is cholesterol (CXIV), while epicholesterol is obtained in approximately 10% yield. Treatment of the enol acetate of cholest-4-en-3-one-3-C^{14} with sodium borohydride in ethanol has been utilized for the preparation of cholesterol-3-C^{14} in 60% yield (97). Since sodium boro-hydride does not ordinarily attack esters the initial step in the reduction of CXII is postulated as the solvolysis of the enol acetate to yield cholest-5-en-3-one which is then reduced to the epimeric cholesterols. A slow rearrangement of the Δ^5-stenone to the conjugated Δ^4-stenone is followed by reduction of the latter to the Δ^4-stenols.

The reduction of 3-acetoxycholesta-3,5,7-triene, the enol acetate of cholesta-4,7-dien-3-one (CXVII), with sodium borohydride in a methanol-ether mixture yields a mixture of epimeric cholesta-5,7-dien-3-ols con-taining 70% of 7-dehydrocholesterol (98).

$$\text{AcO} \qquad \xrightarrow{\text{NaBH}_4} \qquad \text{HO} \qquad\qquad (15\text{-}76)$$

CXVII

Reduction of the enol acetate of cholestanone (CXV) with sodium boro-hydride yields 13% of epicholestanol and 84% of cholestanol, with no ketone isolated among the reduction products (92).

15.1.4 Reductions with Potassium Borohydride

Panouse reported that reduction of pyridine methiodide (CXVIII: R = H) with a solution of potassium borohydride in aqueous sodium hydroxide yields N-methyl-1,2,5,6-tetrahydropyridine (99).

$$\xrightarrow{\text{KBH}_4} \qquad\qquad (15\text{-}77)$$

CXVIII

Reduction of nicotinamide methiodide (CXVIII: R = $CONH_2$) yields a mixture of the o-dihydro and tetrahydro derivatives (98), while nicotinic acid methiodide (CXVIII: R = COOH) and methyl nicotinate methiodide (CXVIII: R = $COOCH_3$) yield the tetrahydro derivatives (100). Torossian reported that the reduction of N-alkylquinolinium (CXIX) and isoquinolinium salts (CXX) with potassium borohydride gives tetrahydro derivatives (101).

(15-78)

CXIX

(15-79)

CXX

$$R = CH_3, C_2H_5, C_3H_7, C_4H_9$$

If the reduction is carried out in alkaline medium, a mixture of the o-dihydro and tetrahydro compounds are obtained. Torossian postulated that after partial reduction by the borohydride to the dihydro derivative, the alkalinity of the reaction mixture results in the conversion to the tetrahydro derivative.

15.1.5 Reductions with Lithium Borohydride

Lithium borohydride in tetrahydrofuran reduces crotonaldehyde to crotyl alcohol but crotonic acid, after a 2-hour reflux period, yields 10% butyric acid, 4% butanol, and 45% of starting material (102). Wittig and Hornberger (44) treated a series of cinnamamide derivatives with lithium borohydride in an attempt to obtain the unsaturated aldehyde. The following amides were treated with the borohydride with the resultant absence of reduction or the formation of the unsaturated aldehyde, in either case with retention of the carbon-carbon double bond: N,N-dimethylcinnamamide, N-methylcinnamanilide, N,N-diphenylcinnamamide, N,N-dimethylcinnamalacetamide, N,N-diphenylcinnamalacetamide, N-cinnamoylcarbazole, N-cinnamalacetylcarbazole, N-(9-phenylnonatetraenoyl)-carbazole.

Replacement of lithium borohydride with an equimolecular mixture of potassium borohydride and lithium chloride results in the reduction of ethyl cinnamate to 66% of hydrocinnamyl alcohol and 10% of cinnamyl alcohol (103).

15.2 AROMATIC HYDROCARBONS

As would be expected, aromatic hydrocarbons are generally not attacked by LAH. Sampey and Cox (104) reported that attempts to reduce naphthalene and anthracene with LAH in ether or dioxane have been unsuccessful. However, when 0.2 mole of solid LAH is shaken with 0.05 mole of molten anthracene (CXXI) at 220-230° for 6 hours, reduction occurs to yield 45-60% of a product identified as 1,2,3,4-tetrahydroanthracene by mixed melting point with a sample prepared by reduction of anthracene with Raney nickel. Increasing the reaction temperature to 240-270° or lengthening the time of heating as well as reducing the LAH concentration reduces the yield of product. Goodman (105) has repeated the work of Sampey and Cox, using identical conditions, and has found that the product consists of 44% anthracene (CXXI) and 56% of 9,10-dihydroanthracene (CXXII) which can be oxidized to anthraquinone.

$$\text{(15-80)}$$

CXXI   CXXII

Sampey and Cox (104) reported that a 22% yield of 9,10-dihydrophenanthrene is obtained by treatment of phenanthrene (CXXIV) with LAH under the conditions used in the reduction of CXXI. The product was identified as the picrate. Goodman (105) found that an 83% recovery of unchanged phenanthrene is obtained, while no reduction product is isolated.

Goodman (65) reported that when LAH is warmed with Carbitol, a slow evolution of hydrogen commences at 70° and at 90-95° a violent reaction occurs which yields a clear colorless solution possessing the property of reducing acenaphthylene (CXXIII) to acenaphthene. The reagent solution permits the use of the reducing agent at temperatures up to 200° and avoids the vigorous reaction obtained in the hydrolysis of excess LAH. Although the Carbitol solution presumably contains an alkoxide, it is noteworthy that a solution of LAH in n-butanol or ether does not reduce acenaphthylene.

$$\text{(15-81)}$$

CXXIII

Anthracene (CXXI) is recovered unchanged after being heated for three hours at the boiling point of the Carbitol-LAH reagent. Pyrene (CXXV) is not reduced by LAH in ether or with the Carbitol-LAH reagent. Naphthacene (CXXVI), pentacene (CXXVII) and perylene (CXXVIII) are equally not reduced by the Carbitol-LAH reagent or by solid LAH in boiling naphthalene solution (65).

CXXIV   CXXV   CXXVI

CXXVII   CXXVIII

Goodman (65) has stated that it is probable that aromatic rings are resistant to attack by LAH and the reduction of anthracene with LAH at a temperature above the decomposition point of the hydride is a heterogeneous reaction brought about by liberated hydrogen on a catalytic surface made available during the decomposition of the reagent.

15.3 CARBON-CARBON TRIPLE BONDS

15.3.1 Reductions with Lithium Aluminum Hydride

Isolated triple bonds are not reduced with LAH. This permits the reduction of other functional groups with retention of the acetylenic grouping. Various acetylenic compounds which have been treated with LAH with retention of isolated triple bonds are summarized in Table XCVI.

15.3.1.a *Acetylenic Carbinols.* Acetylenic carbinols containing an allylic hydroxyl group are reduced with LAH to α,β-unsaturated alcohols.

$$RC \equiv \overset{|}{C}COH \xrightarrow{\text{LAH}} RCH = CH\overset{|}{C}OH \qquad (15\text{-}82)$$

The reduction product generally has the *trans* configuration. Thus, 2-butyn-1-ol (CXXIX) is reduced to *trans*-crotyl alcohol (106).

$$CH_3C \equiv CCH_2OH \xrightarrow{\text{LAH}} CH_3CH = CHCH_2OH \qquad (15\text{-}83)$$
$$\text{CXXIX}$$

The presence of conjugated unsaturated groups permits the preparation of conjugated olefinic alcohols.

TABLE XCVI

Acetylenic Compounds Which Have Been Treated with LAH with Retention of Isolated Triple Bonds

	Compound	Product	Ref.
C_7H_8O	2-Methylhexa-3,5-diyn-2-ol	2-Methylhex-3-en-5-yn-2-ol	1
$C_7H_{11}Br$	1-Bromo-2-heptyne	2-Heptyne 1,2-Heptadiene }	2
	3-Bromo-1-heptyne	1-Heptyne 1,2-Heptadiene }	2
$C_{12}H_{14}O_2$	2,9-Dimethyldeca-3,5,7-triyn-2,9-diol	2,9-Dimethyldeca-5-yn-3,7-dien-2,9-diol	1
$C_{14}H_{14}O_2$	2,11-Dimethyldodeca-3,5,7,9-tetrayn-2,11-diol	2,11-Dimethyldodeca-5,7-diyn-3,9-dien-2,11-diol	1
$C_{18}H_{22}O_2$	Methyl 3,7-dimethyl-9-(cyclohex-1-enyl)nona-8-yn-2,4,6-trien-1-oate (from acid m.p. 179–180°)	3,7-Dimethyl-9-(cyclohex-1-enyl)nona-8-yn-2,4,6-trien-1-ol, m.p. 75–76°	3
	Methyl ester above from acid m.p. 151–152°	Oil	3
$C_{18}H_{26}O$	6-Methyl-8-(2,6-trimethylcyclohex-1-enyl)octa-7-yn-3,5-dien-2-ol	No reduction	4
$C_{18}H_{30}O_2$	Heptadeca-8-yn-10-en-1-carboxylic acid (ximenynic acid)	Octadeca-9-yn-11-en-1-ol (ximenynyl alcohol)	5,6
$C_{18}H_{32}O$	Octadeca-9-yn-11-en-1-ol (ximenynyl alcohol)	No reduction	5,6
$C_{18}H_{32}O_2$	Heptadeca-8-yn-1-carboxylic acid (stearolic acid)	Octadeca-9-yn-1-ol (stearolyl alcohol)	7
$C_{19}H_{24}O_2$	Ethyl 3,7-dimethyl-9-(cyclohex-1-enyl)nona-8-yn-2,4,6-trien-1-oate	3,7-Dimethyl-9-(cyclohex-1-enyl)nona-8-yn-2,4,6-trien-1-ol	3
$C_{22}H_{30}O_2$	Ethyl 3,7-dimethyl-9-(2,6,6-trimethylcyclohex-1-enyl)nona-8-yn-2,4,6-trien-1-oate	3,7-Dimethyl-9-(2,6,6-trimethylcyclohex-1-enyl)nona-8-yn-2,4,6-trien-1-ol (8,9-Dehydrovitamin A)	4

[1] E. R. H. Jones, M. C. Whiting, and E. B. Bates, unpublished results, private communication.

[2] J. H. Wotiz, J. Am. Chem. Soc., 73, 693 (1951).

[3] H. Bader, B. C. L. Weedon, and R. J. Woods, J. Chem. Soc., 1951, 3099.

[4] J. Attenburow, A. F. B. Cameron, J. H. Chapman, R. M. Evans, B. A. Hems, A. B. A. Jansen, and T. Walker, ibid., 1952, 1094.

[5] P. Ligthelm, E. von Rudloff, and D. A. Sutton, ibid., 1950, 3187.

[6] S. P. Ligthelm, H. M. Schwartz, and M. M. von Holdt, ibid., 1952, 1088.

[7] N. A. Khan, F. E. Deatherage, and J. B. Brown, J. Am. Oil Chemists' Soc., 28, 27 (1951).

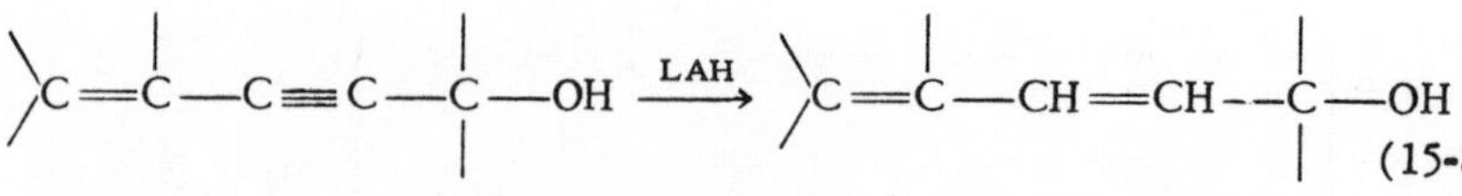

$$\text{>C=\overset{|}{C}-C\equiv C-\overset{|}{\underset{|}{C}}-OH} \xrightarrow{\text{LAH}} \text{>C=\overset{|}{C}-CH=CH-\overset{|}{\underset{|}{C}}-OH} \qquad (15\text{-}84)$$

Chanley and Sobotka (107) reported the reduction of an enynol to a dienol, wherein the olefinic unsaturation is part of a cyclohexenyl group.

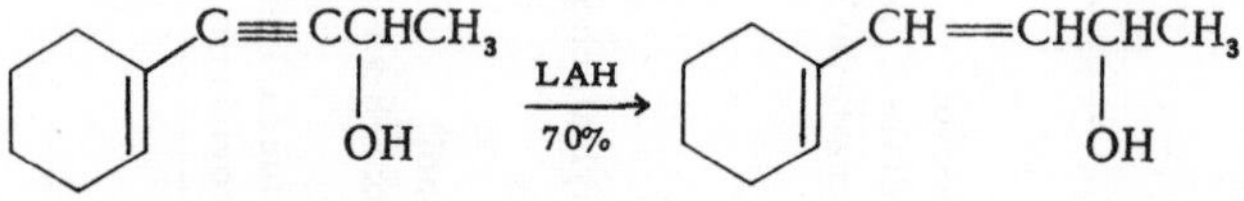

$$\text{CXXX} \xrightarrow[70\%]{\text{LAH}} \qquad (15\text{-}85)$$

CXXX

Catalytic reduction of CXXX with hydrogen over 0.3% palladium-on-calcium carbonate in ethyl acetate fails to yield more than traces of dienol. Interruption of the catalytic hydrogenation after the absorption of one mole of hydrogen gives a mixture of saturated or monounsaturated products together with unchanged enynol. Similar results are obtained with Raney nickel while no reduction is observed with copper-zinc in alcohol.

Raphael and Sondheimer (108) reported that the LAH reduction of CXXXI gives an 82% yield of the *trans*-allylic alcohol (CXXXII) while catalytic hydrogenation over palladium-on-calcium carbonate gives an 87% yield of the *cis*-CXXXII.

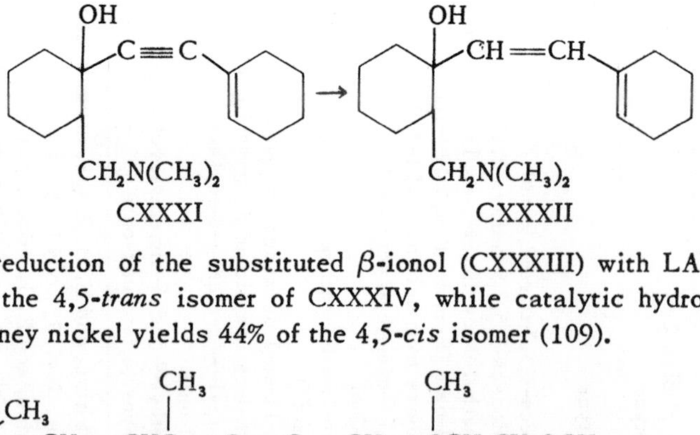

$$\text{CXXXI} \rightarrow \text{CXXXII} \qquad (15\text{-}86)$$

CXXXI   CXXXII

The reduction of the substituted β-ionol (CXXXIII) with LAH yields 88% of the 4,5-*trans* isomer of CXXXIV, while catalytic hydrogenation over Raney nickel yields 44% of the 4,5-*cis* isomer (109).

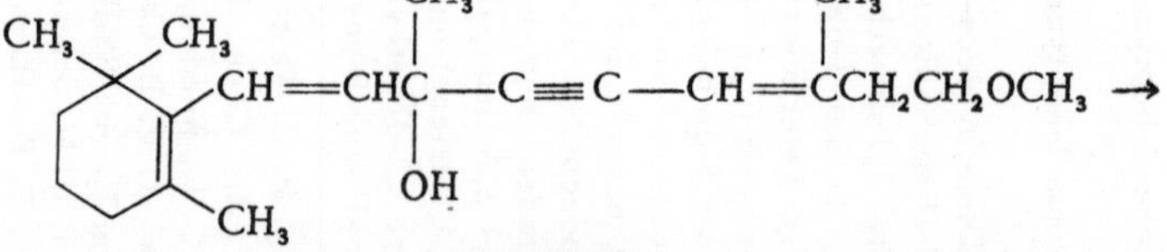

CXXXIII

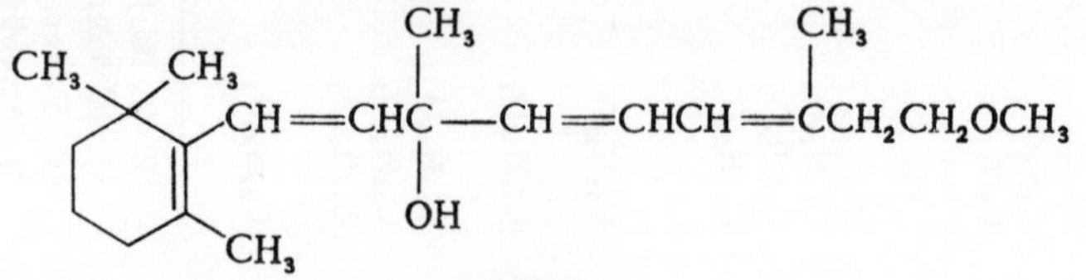

$$ (15\text{-}87) $$

CXXXIV

Jones, Whiting, and Bates have carried out an extensive study of the LAH reduction of acetylenic compounds (110). The non-reduction of isolated triple bonds and the reduction of acetylenic carbinols has resulted in the preparation of polyacetylenic alcohols:

$$(CH_3)_2C(C\equiv C)_nC(CH_3)_2 \xrightarrow{\text{LAH}}$$
$$\underset{OH}{|} \qquad \underset{OH}{|}$$

CXXXV

$$(CH_3)_2C—CH=CH(C\equiv C)_{n-2}CH=CH—C(CH_3)_2 \quad (15\text{-}88)$$
$$\underset{OH}{|} \qquad\qquad\qquad\qquad\qquad \underset{OH}{|}$$

$$n = 2,3,4$$

In all reported cases, with two exceptions, the reduction of compounds containing a hydroxyl group allylic to the triple bond results in the formation of olefinic alcohols.

The LAH reduction of 1,4-diphenyl-2-butyn-1,4-diol (CXXXVI) in ether is reported to yield *trans-trans*-1,4-diphenylbutadiene (110).

$$C_6H_5CHC\equiv CCHC_6H_5 \xrightarrow[45\%]{\text{LAH}} C_6H_5CH=CH—CH=CHC_6H_5 \quad (15\text{-}89)$$
$$\underset{OH}{|} \quad\;\; \underset{OH}{|}$$

CXXXVI

The intermediate 1,4-diphenyl-2-buten-1,4-diol apparently undergoes dehydration and rearrangement to yield the diphenylbutadiene.

Attenburrow *et al.* (23) have reported that although compounds containing the grouping CXXXVII are readily reduced to the corresponding con-

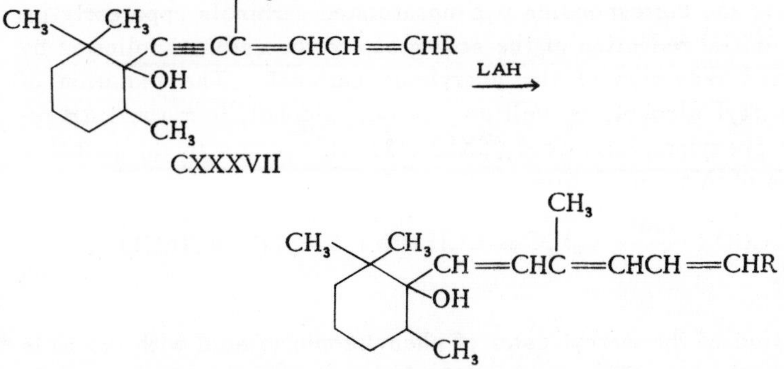

CXXXVII

$$(15\text{-}90)$$

jugated olefinic carbinols total hydrogenation and ultraviolet spectroscopy indicates that in the alcohol CXXXVIII, containing the grouping —C≡C—C(CH_3)CH=CH—, the double bond is preferentially re-
$$\underset{OH}{|}$$
duced with LAH.

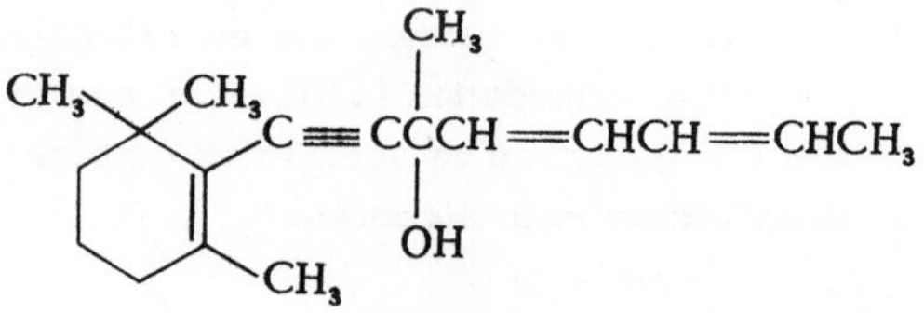

$$
\begin{array}{c}
CH_3 \\
|
\end{array}
$$

CXXXVIII

This is surprising in view of the ease of reduction of CXXXIII and other compounds in Table XCVII with analogous structures.

Since a hydroxyl group allylic to the acetylenic linkage appears to be necessary for the reduction, a mechanism similar to that proposed by Hochstein and Brown (4) for the reduction of cinnamyl alcohol to hydrocinnamyl alcohol, involving a cyclic intermediate (CXXXIX) has been proposed (23).

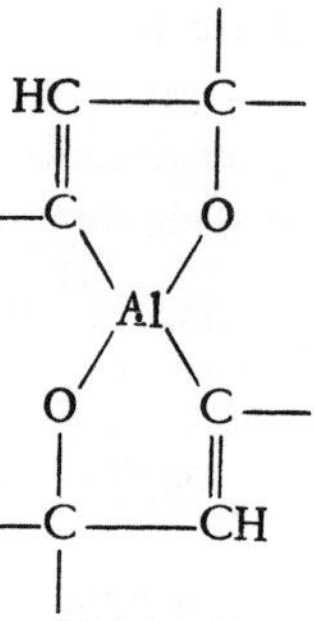

CXXXIX

The LAH reduction of various α,β-acetylenic carbinols to allylic alcohols is summarized in Table XCVII.

15.3.1.b Acetylenic Acids. The reduction of various acetylenic acids with LAH to the corresponding α,β-unsaturated carbinols apparently involves an initial reduction of the acid group to the carbinol followed by the expected reduction of the acetylenic carbinol. The isolation of phenylpropargyl alcohol, as well as cinnamyl alcohol, from the LAH reduction of phenylpropiolic acid (CXL) (111–113) points to the probable correctness of this postulation.

$$C_6H_5C \equiv CCOOH \xrightarrow{\text{LAH}} C_6H_5C \equiv CCH_2OH + C_6H_5CH = CHCH_2OH$$
CXL

(15-91)

The reduction of the methyl ester of phenylpropiolic acid with 0.5 mole of LAH in ether at $-70°$ yields 90% of phenylpropargyl alcohol, while with 1.0 mole of LAH in ether at $20°$ a 75% yield of cinnamyl alcohol is obtained (110).

The LAH reduction of propiolic acid (CXLI) (112–114) cyclohexylpropiolic acid (CXLII) (112,113) and acetylenedicarboxylic acid (CXLIII)

TABLE XCVII

LAH Reduction of α,β-Acetylenic Carbinols to α,β-Olefinic Carbinols

Compound	Product	% Yield	Ref.
C_4H_6O			
2-Butyn-1-ol	*trans*-Crotyl alcohol	....	1
C_7H_8O			
2-Methylhexa-3,5-diyn-2-ol	2-Methylhex-3-en-5-yn-2-ol	70	2
$C_8H_{10}O_2$			
Octa-3,5-diyn-2,7-diol	*trans-trans*-Octa-3,5-dien-2,7-diol	41–74	3
		45	4
$C_8H_{12}O_2$			
Oct-3-en-5-yn-2,7-diol	Octa-3,5-dien-2,7-diol	84	3
C_9H_8O			
1-Phenylprop-2-yn-1-ol	1-Phenylallyl alcohol	90	2
$C_{10}H_{14}O$			
1-(1-Hydroxycyclohexyl)but-3-en-1-yne	1-(1-Hydroxycyclohexyl)buta-1,3-diene	70	2
1-(Cyclohex-1-enyl)but-1-yn-3-ol	1-(Cyclohex-1-enyl)but-1-en-3-ol	70	5
$C_{10}H_{14}O_2$			
2,7-Dimethylocta-3,5-diyn-2,7-diol	*trans-trans*-2,7-Dimethylocta-3,5-dien-2,7-diol	50	2
$C_{12}H_{14}O_2$			
2,9-Dimethyldeca-3,5,7-triyn-2,9-diol	2,9-Dimethyldeca-5-yn-3,7-dien-2,9-diol	40	2
$C_{13}H_{20}O_3$			
7-(2-Tetrahydropyranyloxy)oct-3-yn-5-en-2-ol	7-(2-Tetrahydropyranyloxy)oct-3,5-dien-2-ol	73	3
$C_{14}H_{14}O_2$			
2,11-Dimethyldodeca-3,5,7,9-tetrayn-2,11-diol	2,11-Dimethyldodeca-5,7-diyn-3,9-dien-2,11-diol	....	2
$C_{17}H_{27}NO$			
1-(2-Dimethylaminomethyl-1-hydroxycyclohexyl)-2-(cyclohex-1-enyl)acetylene	*trans*-1-(2-Dimethylaminomethyl-1-hydroxycyclohexyl)-2-(cyclohex-1-enyl)ethylene	82	7
$C_{18}H_{28}O_2$			
8-(1-Hydroxy-2,2,6-trimethylcyclohexyl)-6-methylocta-7-yn-3,5-dien-2-ol	8-(1-Hydroxy-2,2,6-trimethylcyclohexyl)-6-methylocta-3,5,7-trien-2-ol	52	8
$C_{20}H_{30}O_2$			
9-(1-Hydroxy-2,2,6-trimethylcyclohexyl)-3,7-dimethylnona-8-yn-2,4,6-trien-1-ol	9-(1-Hydroxy-2,2,6-trimethylcyclohexyl)-3,7-dimethylnona-2,4,6,8-tetraen-1-ol	93	8
$C_{21}H_{32}O_2$			
1-(2,2,6-Trimethylcyclohex-1-enyl)-3,7-dimethyl-9-methoxynona-4-yn-1,6-dien-3-ol	4,5-*trans*-1-(2,2,6-Trimethylcyclohex-1-enyl)-3,7-dimethyl-9-methoxynona-1,4,6-trien-7-ol	88	9

References—Table XCVII

[1]Bharucha and B. C. L. Weedon, unpublished work, through ref. 3.
[2]E. R. H. Jones, M. C. Whiting, and E. B. Bates, unpublished results, private communication.
[3]R. Ahmad, F. Sondheimer, B. C. L. Weedon, and R. J. Woods, *J. Chem. Soc.*, *1952*, 4089.
[4]E. B. Bates, E. R. H. Jones, and M. C. Whiting, unpublished work, through ref. 3.
[5]J. D. Chanley and H. Sobotka, *J. Am. Chem. Soc.*, 71, 4140 (1949).
[6]E. R. H. Jones and M. C. Whiting, private communication, through ref. 3.
[7]R. A. Raphael and F. Sondheimer, *J. Chem. Soc.*, *1950*, 3185.
[8]J. Attenburrow, A. F. B. Cameron, J. H. Chapman, R. M. Evans, B. A. Hems, A. B. A. Jansen, and T. Walker, *ibid.*, *1952*, 1094.
[9]W. Oroshnik, G. Karmas, and A. D. Mebane, *J. Am. Chem. Soc.*, 74, 3807 (1952).

(114) is reported to yield the corresponding allylic alcohol without isolation of any acetylenic carbinol.

$$HC \equiv CCOOH \qquad \qquad \qquad C \equiv CCOOH \qquad \qquad \begin{array}{c} C-COOH \\ \| \\ C-COOH \end{array}$$

$$\text{CXLI} \qquad\qquad\qquad \text{CXLII} \qquad\qquad\qquad \text{CXLIII}$$

15.3.1.c Acetylenic Carbonyl Derivatives. The reduction of phenyl-propargyl aldehyde (CXLIV) and its trimer (CXLV) yields cinnamyl alcohol (115).

(15-92)

$$C_6H_5C \equiv CCHO$$
$$\text{CXLIV}$$

$$\xrightarrow[\text{57\%}]{\text{LAH}} \qquad \xleftarrow{\text{LAH}}$$

$$C_6H_5CH = CHCH_2OH$$

Attempts to reduce dibenzoylacetylene with ethereal LAH have been reported to yield dark red resinous products which have not been identified (74).

15.3.1.d Reduction of Acetylenes to Allenes. The reduction of hex-3-en-5-yn-2-ol (CXLVI) with 0.6 mole of ethereal LAH at 35° yields hexa-4,5-dien-2-ol (CXLVII) (110).

$$CH_3CHCH = CH - C \equiv CH \xrightarrow[60\%]{LAH} CH_3CHCH_2CH = C = CH_2 \quad (15\text{-}93)$$

OH	OH
CXLVI	CXLVII

An allene has also been reported in the LAH reduction of 1-bromo-2-heptyne (CXLVIII) and 3-bromo-1-heptyne (CXLIX) (116).

$$CH_3(CH_2)_3C \equiv CCH_2Br \xrightarrow{LAH} CH_3(CH_2)_3C \equiv CCH_3 +$$

CXLVIII

$$CH_3(CH_2)_3CH = C = CH_2 \quad (15\text{-}94)$$

$$CH_3(CH_2)_3CHC \equiv CH \xrightarrow{LAH} CH_3(CH_2)_3CH_2C \equiv CH +$$

Br

CXLIX

$$CH_3(CH_2)_3CH = C = CH_2 \quad (15\text{-}95)$$

15.3.1.e *Reduction of Acetylenes to Higher* α-*Olefins.* Ziegler has reported that the reaction of acetylene with LAH yields an addition product which can be treated with ethylene to form a trialkenyl lithium aluminum hydride. Hydrolysis of the latter yields an α-olefin while heating results in the formation of an α,ω-diolefin. This is discussed in Section 16.3.3.

15.3.2 Reductions with Magnesium Aluminum Hydride

Magnesium aluminum hydride apparently does not attack the non-polar triple bond since propargylaldehyde (CL) is reduced to propargyl alcohol (93,117).

$$HC \equiv CCHO \xrightarrow{Mg(AlH_4)_2} HC \equiv CCH_2OH \quad (15\text{-}96)$$

CL

REFERENCES

1. Nystrom, R. F., and W. G. Brown, *J. Am. Chem. Soc.*, **69**, 1197 (1947).
2. Mebane, A. D., *J. Am. Chem. Soc.*, **74**, 5227 (1952).
3. Ziegler, K., *Angew. Chem.*, **64**, 323 (1952).
4. Hochstein, F. A., and W. G. Brown, *J. Am. Chem. Soc.*, **70**, 3484 (1948).
5. Freedman, R. W., and E. I. Becker, *J. Am. Chem. Soc.*, **73**, 2366 (1951).
6. Uffer, A., and E. Schlittler, *Helv. Chim. Acta*, **31**, 1397 (1948).
7. Ciba S. A., Fr. Pat. 987,158 (August 9, 1951).
8. Schlittler, E., and A. Uffer, Ger. Pat. 824,491 (December 13, 1951).
9. Hochstein, F. A., *J. Am. Chem. Soc.*, **71**, 305 (1949).
10. Mosher, W. A., and J. C. Cox, Jr., *J. Am. Chem. Soc.*, **72**, 3701 (1950).
11. Larsson, E., *Trans. Chalmers Univ. Technol., Gothenburg*, **94**, 15 (1950).
12. Dornow, A., G. Messwarb, and H. H. Frey, *Chem. Ber.*, **83**, 445 (1950).

13. Ashley, J. N., and M. Davis, *J. Chem. Soc.*, *1952*, 63.
14. Dreiding, A. S., and J. A. Hartman, *J. Am. Chem. Soc.*, *75*, 939 (1953).
15. Jacquier, R., and R. Zagdoun, *Bull. soc. chim. France*, [5] *19*, 698 (1952).
16. Mousseron, M., R. Jacquier, M. Mousseron-Canet, and R. Zagdoun, *Bull. soc. chim. France*, [5] *19*, 1042 (1952).
17. Mousseron, M., R. Jacquier, M. Mousseron-Canet, and R. Zagdoun, *Compt. rend.*, *235*, 177 (1952).
18. Jacquier, R., and R. Zagdoun, *Bull. soc. chim. France*, [5] *18*, 792 (1951).
19. Bowman, M. I., C. C. Ketterer, and G. Dinga, *J. Org. Chem.*, *17*, 563 (1952).
20. Macbeth, A. K., and J. S. Shannon, *J. Chem. Soc.*, *1952*, 2852.
21. Henbest, H. B., and G. Woods, *J. Chem. Soc.*, *1952*, 1150.
22. Henbest, H. B., B. L. Shaw, and G. Woods, *J. Chem. Soc.*, *1952*, 1154.
23. Attenburrow, J., A. F. B. Cameron, J. H. Chapman, R. M. Evans, B. A. Hems, A. B. A. Jansen, and T. Walker, *J. Chem. Soc.*, *1952*, 1094.
24. Nunn, J. R., *J. Chem. Soc.*, *1952*, 313.
25. Hochstein, F. A., unpublished work; through A. C. Cope, A. C. Haven, Jr., F. L. Ramp, and E. R. Trumbull, *J. Am. Chem. Soc.*, *74*, 4867 (1952).
26. Woodward, R. B., F. Sondheimer, D. Taub, K. Heusler, and W. M. McLamore, *J. Am. Chem. Soc.*, *74*, 4223 (1952).
27. Karrer, P., and P. Banerjea, *Helv. Chim. Acta*, *32*, 1692 (1949).
28. Collins, C. J., unpublished work, through W. G. Brown, in *Organic Reactions*, Vol. VI, p. 482, 504.
29. Liang Li and W. H. Elliott, *J. Am. Chem. Soc.*, *74*, 4089 (1952).
30. Meek, J. S., F. J. Lorenzi, and S. J. Cristol, *J. Am. Chem. Soc.*, *71*, 1830 (1949).
31. Rondestvedt, C. S., Jr., *J. Am. Chem. Soc.*, *73*, 4509 (1951).
32. Pew, J. C., *J. Am. Chem. Soc.*, *73*, 1678 (1951).
33. Pew, J. C., *J. Am. Chem. Soc.*, *74*, 2850 (1952).
34. Allen, C. F. H., and J. R. Byers, Jr., *Science*, *107*, 269 (1948).
35. Allen, C. F. H., and J. R. Byers, Jr., *J. Am. Chem. Soc.*, *71*, 2683 (1949).
36. Allen, C. F. H., and J. R. Byers, Jr., U. S. Pat. 2,545,439 (March 20, 1951).
37. Freudenberg, K., and R. Dillenburg, *Chem. Ber.*, *84*, 67 (1951).
38. Freudenberg, K., R. Kraft, and W. Heimberger, *Chem. Ber.*, *84*, 472 (1951).
39. Freudenberg, K., and H. H. Hübner, *Chem. Ber.*, *85*, 1181 (1952).
40. Freudenberg, K., and F. Bittner, *Chem. Ber.*, *83*, 600 (1950).
41. Freudenberg, K., and G. Gehrke, *Chem. Ber.*, *84*, 443 (1951).
42. Bohlmann, F., *Chem. Ber.*, *85*, 1144 (1952).
43. Bohlmann, F., *Chem. Ber.*, *85*, 386 (1952).
44. Wittig, G., and P. Hornberger, *Ann.*, *577*, 11 (1952).
45. Frank, R. L., and H. K. Hall, Jr., *J. Am. Chem. Soc.*, *72*, 1645 (1950).
46. Erne, M., and F. Ramirez, *Helv. Chim. Acta*, *33*, 912 (1950).
47. Gensler, W. J., and C. M. Samour, *J. Am. Chem. Soc.*, *73*, 5555 (1951).
48. Gilsdorf, R. T., and F. F. Nord, *J. Am. Chem. Soc.*, *74*, 1837 (1952).
49. Gilsdorf, R. T., and F. F. Nord, *J. Am. Chem. Soc.*, *72*, 4327 (1950).
50. Larsson, E., *Trans. Chalmers Univ. Technol.*, *Gothenburg*, *94*, 21 (1950).
51. Walter, C. R., Jr., *J. Am. Chem. Soc.*, *74*, 5185 (1952).
52. Tarbell, D. S., and J. C. Bill, *J. Am. Chem. Soc.*, *74*, 1234 (1952).
53. Trevoy, L. W., and W. G. Brown, *J. Am. Chem. Soc.*, *71*, 1675 (1949).
54. Bordwell, F. G., and W. H. McKellin, *J. Am. Chem. Soc.*, *73*, 2251 (1951).
55. Field, L., and F. A. Grunwald, *J. Org. Chem.*, *16*, 946 (1951).
56. Julian, P. L., and H. C. Printy, *J. Am. Chem. Soc.*, *71*, 3206 (1949).
57. Baker, B. R., R. E. Schaub, and J. H. Williams, *J. Org. Chem.*, *17*, 116 (1952).

58. Cook, J. W., J. D. Loudon, and P. McCloskey, *J. Chem. Soc.*, *1951*, 1203.
59. Cook, J. W., J. D. Loudon, and P. McCloskey, *J. Chem. Soc.*, *1952*, 3904.
60. Mousseron, M., and M. Canet, *Bull. soc. chim. France*, [5] *19*, 247 (1952).
61. de Mayo, P., and W. Rigby, *Nature*, *166*, 1075 (1950).
62. Mićović, V. M., and M. L. Mihailović, *Rec. trav. chim.*, 71, 970 (1952).
63. Lavie, D., *Bull. Res. Council Israel*, *1*, 135 (1951).
64. Lavie, D., and E. D. Bergmann, *Bull. soc. chim. France*, [5] *18*, 250 (1951).
65. Goodman, I., *J. Chem. Soc.*, *1951*, 2209.
66. Bergmann, E. D., G. Berthier, D. Ginsburg, Y. Hirshberg, D. Lavie, S. Pinchas, B. Pullman, and A. Pullman, *Bull. soc. chim. France*, [5] *18*, 661 (1951).
67. Bergmann, E. D., and D. Lavie, *J. Am. Chem. Soc.*, 74, 3173 (1952).
68. Bergmann, E. D., E. Fischer, D. Ginsburg, Y. Hirshberg, D. Lavie, M. Mayot, A. Pullman, and B. Pullman, *Bull. soc. chim. France*, [5] *18*, 684 (1951).
69. Pullman, A., B. Pullman, E. D. Bergmann, D. Ginsburg, and D. Lavie, *Bull. Res. Council Israel*, *1*, No. 4, 85 (1952).
70. Bergmann, E. D., G. Berthier, E. Fischer, Y. Hirshberg, D. Lavie, A. Pullman, and B. Pullman, *Bull. soc. chim. France*, [5] *18*, 693 (1951).
71. Bergmann, E. D., Y. Hirshberg, and D. Lavie, *Bull. soc. chim. France*, [5] *19*, 268 (1952).
72. Bohlmann, F., *Chem. Ber.*, *85*, 390 (1952).
73. Lukeš, R., and J. Jarý, unpublished work; through M. Ferles and J. Rudinger, *Chem. Listy*, 47, 112 (1953).
74. Lutz, R. E., and J. S. Gillespie, Jr., *J. Am. Chem. Soc.*, 72, 2002 (1950).
75. Lutz, R. E., and J. S. Gillespie, Jr., *Abstracts of Papers*, 116th Meeting American Chemical Society, Atlantic City, N. J., September 1949, p. 8M.
76. Lutz, R. E., and D. F. Hinkley, *J. Am. Chem. Soc.*, 72, 4091 (1950).
77. McGhie, J. F., and J. F. Cavalla, *Chemistry and Industry*, *1950*, 744.
78. Cavalla, J. F., and J. F. McGhie, *J. Chem. Soc.*, *1951*, 834.
79. Boyland, E., and D. Manson, *J. Chem. Soc.*, *1951*, 1837.
80. Bergmann, E. D., *Bull. soc. chim. France*, [5] *19*, 703 (1952).
81. Sonntag, N. O. V., S. Linder, E. I. Becker and P. E. Spoerri, *J. Am. Chem. Soc.*, *75*, 2283 (1953).
82. Boekelheide, V., and C. E. Larrabee, *J. Am. Chem. Soc.*, 72, 1245 (1950).
83. Wear, R. L., *J. Am. Chem. Soc.*, 73, 2390 (1951).
84. Spriggs, A. S., C. M. Hill and G. W. Senter, *J. Am. Chem. Soc.*, 74, 1555 (1952).
85. Siegel, S., and S. Coburn, *J. Am. Chem. Soc.*, 73, 5494 (1951).
86. Reynaud, P., and J. Matti, *Compt. rend.*, 235, 1230 (1952).
87. Seifert, P., and H. Schinz, *Helv. Chim. Acta.*, 34, 728 (1951).
88. Vonderwahl, R., and H. Schinz, *Helv. Chim. Acta.*, 35, 2368 (1952).
89. Dauben, W. G., and J. F. Eastham, *J. Am. Chem. Soc.*, 72, 2305 (1950).
90. Dauben, W. G., and J. F. Eastham, *J. Am. Chem. Soc.*, 73, 3260 (1951).
91. Brown, B. R., *J. Chem. Soc.*, *1952*, 2756.
92. Dauben, W. G., R. A. Micheli, and J. F. Eastham, *J. Am. Chem. Soc.*, 74, 3852 (1952).
93. Wiberg, E., and R. Bauer, *Z. Naturforsch.*, *7b*, 131 (1952).
94. Chaikin, S. W., and W. G. Brown, *J. Am. Chem. Soc.*, 71, 122 (1949).
95. Dauben, W. G., and J. F. Eastham, *J. Am. Chem. Soc.*, 73, 4463 (1951).
96. Belleau, B., and T. F. Gallagher, *J. Am. Chem. Soc.*, 73, 4458 (1951).
97. Schwenk, E., M. Gut, and J. Belisle, *Arch. Biochem. Biophys.*, *31*, 456 (1951).

98. Dauben, W. G., J. F. Eastham, and R. A. Micheli, *J. Am. Chem. Soc.*, *73*, 4496 (1951).
99. Panouse, J. J., *Compt. rend.*, *233*, 260 (1951).
100. Panouse, J. J., *Compt. rend.*, *233*, 1200 (1951).
101. Torossian, R., *Compt. rend.*, *235*, 1312 (1952).
102. Nystrom, R. F., S. W. Chaikin, and W. G. Brown, *J. Am. Chem. Soc.*, *71*, 3245 (1949).
103. Paul, R., and N. Joseph, *Bull. soc. chim. France*, [5] *19*, 550 (1952).
104. Sampey, J. R., and J. M. Cox, *J. Am. Chem. Soc.*, *71*, 1507 (1949).
105. Goodman, I., *J. Chem. Soc.*, *1951*, 846.
106. Bharucha and B. C. L. Weedon, unpublished work; through R. Ahmad, F. Sondheimer, B. C. L. Weedon, and R. J. Woods, *J. Chem. Soc.*, *1952*, 4089.
107. Chanley, J. D., and H. Sobotka, *J. Am. Chem. Soc.*, *71*, 4140 (1949).
108. Raphael, R. A., and F. Sondheimer, *J. Chem. Soc.*, *1950*, 3185. '
109. Oroshnik, W., G. Karmas, and A. D. Mebane, *J. Am. Chem. Soc.*, *74*, 3807 (1952).
110. Jones, E. R. H., M. C. Whiting, and E. B. Bates, unpublished results, private communication.
111. Schlesinger, H. I., and A. E. Finholt, U. S. Pat. 2,576,311 (November 27, 1951).
112. Mićović, V. M., and M. L. Mihailović, *Compt. rend.*, *231*, 1238 (1950).
113. Mićović, V. M., and M. L. Mihailović, *Glasnik Khem. Drushtva Beograd*, *16*, 19 (1951), through *Chem. Abstracts*, *46*, 8609 (1952).
114. Benedict, G. E., and R. R. Russell, *J. Am. Chem. Soc.*, *73*, 5444 (1951).
115. Wille, F., and F. Knörr, *Chem. Ber.*, *85*, 841 (1952).
116. Wotiz, J. H., *J. Am. Chem. Soc.*, *73*, 693 (1951).
117. Wiberg, E., and R. Bauer, *Z. Naturforsch.*, *5b*, 397 (1950).

CHAPTER 16

MISCELLANEOUS REACTIONS WITH LAH

In addition to the reactions of LAH involving the reduction of functional groups various miscellaneous reactions have been reported.

16.1 HYDROGENOLYSIS

An increasing number of reactions resulting in hydrogenolysis under the influence of LAH have appeared in the literature. Examination of the reported examples reveals the presence of common structural features.

Conover and Tarbell (1) showed that an aromatic acid or carbonyl compound containing an amino group ortho or para to the carbon-oxygen grouping (I-VI) undergoes hydrogenolysis to a methyl or methylene group, when treated with excess LAH, usually at elevated temperatures over extended reaction periods.

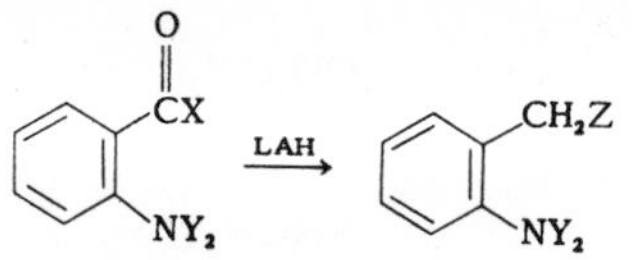

$$
\begin{array}{ll}
\text{I} & X = OH, Y = H, Z = H \\
\text{II} & X = OCH_3, Y = H, Z = H
\end{array}
\qquad (16\text{-}1)
$$

$$
\begin{array}{ll}
\text{III} & X = OH, Y = H, Z = H \\
\text{IV} & X = Z = C_6H_5, Y = H \\
\text{V} & X = Z = C_6H_4NH_2(p), Y = H \\
\text{VI} & X = Z = H, Y = CH_3
\end{array}
\qquad (16\text{-}2)
$$

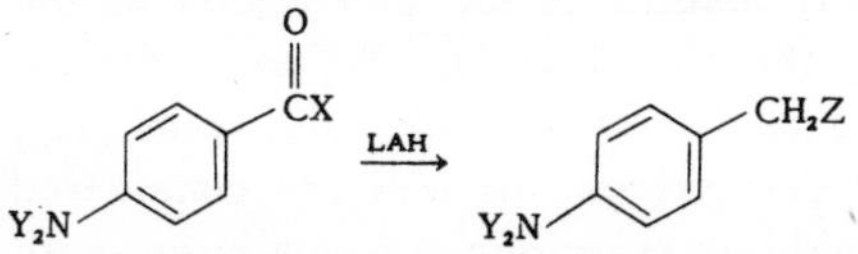

Under conditions which reduce o- and p-aminobenzoic acids to the corresponding toluidines, m-aminobenzoic acid is reduced only to m-aminobenzyl alcohol.

Support for the suggestion that the reaction proceeds with rapid formation of the benzyl alcohol, which then undergoes hydrogenolysis, is found in the fact that o-aminobenzyl alcohol (VII), after 6 days at 90° with excess LAH, is converted to o-toluidine.

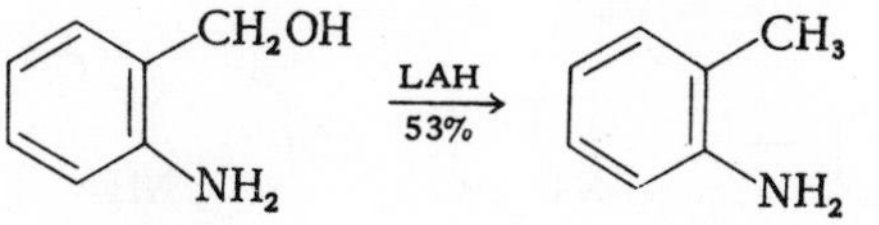

$$
\qquad (16\text{-}3)
$$

VII

The mechanism advanced to account for the observed hydrogenolyses involves attack on the oxygen of the benzyl alcohol, obtained by the initial reduction of the carbonyl function, by a positive $AlH_2^{\oplus}$ ion, followed by scission of the carbon-oxygen bond. The resonance stabilized carbonium ion thus formed can pick up a hydride ion from the LAH.

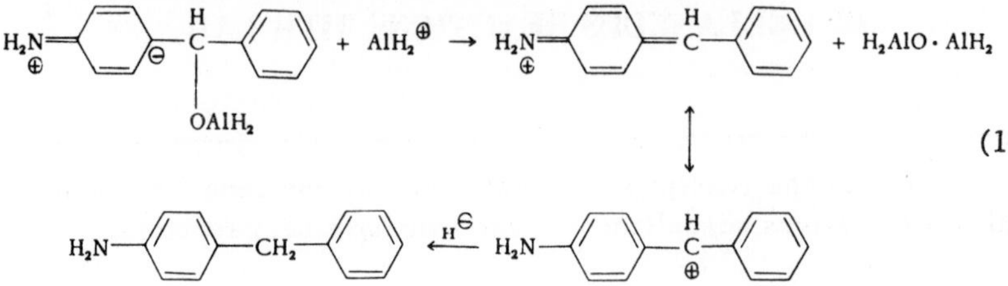

(16-4)

The LAH reduction of o-acetylbenzanilide (VIII) is reported to yield some o-ethylbenzylaniline as well as the expected o-(1-hydroxyethyl)-N-benzylaniline (2).

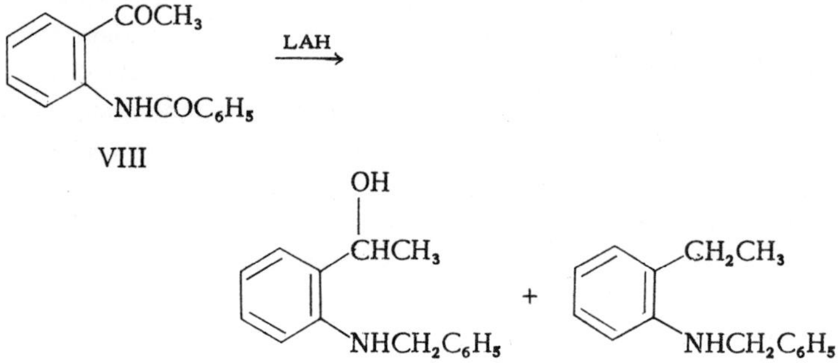

(16-5)

The reduction of amides with LAH results in the conversion of the amide carbonyl to a methylene group (Section 10.1.1). N-Formyl derivatives are converted to the corresponding N-methyl compounds. Similarly, carbamates are reduced to N-methyl derivatives. If I-VI are considered as vinylogs of an amide the hydrogenolysis reactions are consistent with amide behavior on reduction with LAH. It has been shown that β-amino α,β-unsaturated ketones behave chemically more like amides, of which they are vinylogs, than like ketones or vinyl amines (3,4) and the infrared spectra of such compounds indicate a lowering of the carbonyl band (3).

The reduction of N-methyl-α-pyrrolidone or 3-ketooctahydropyrrocoline (IX) with one-quarter mole of LAH permits the isolation, as the tautomeric aldehyde, of the carbinol amine produced in the first stage of the reduction (5-8).

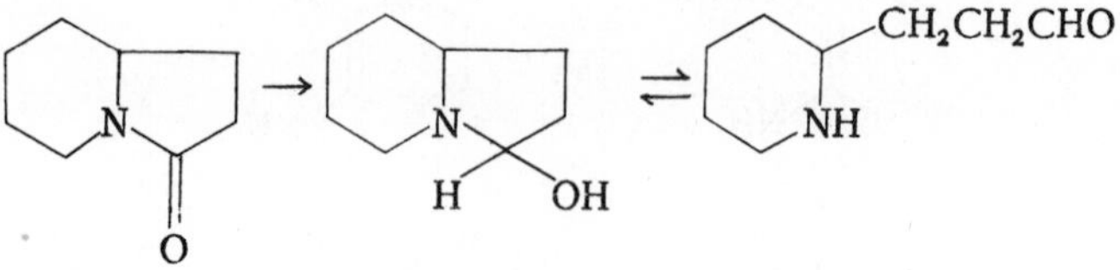

(16-6)

Thus, amide reduction appears to proceed via a carbinol stage. The reaction of a compound containing an $-\overset{\overset{\displaystyle ||}{}}{N}CO-$ grouping with LAH results in a cleavage of the carbon-oxygen bond (Section 12.17) (9). The structures undergoing hydrogenolysis are vinylogs of this grouping.

Trevoy and Brown (10) have postulated that the effective reducing agent in LAH reductions is the aluminohydride anion $AlH_4^{\ominus}$ while Paddock (11) has proposed AlH_3 and $H^{\ominus}$. Lavie and Bergmann have proposed that the reducing agent is $Li^{\oplus} H^{\ominus}$ and that a carbon-lithium bond is formed (12). The reduction of amides with LAH would then possibly proceed as follows (Section 10.1.1.a):

$$
\underset{\text{(16-6)}}{
\begin{array}{c}
\overset{\oplus \quad \ominus}{O - AlH_3} \\
R - \overset{||}{C} - \overset{..}{N} \diagdown
\end{array}
\ \leftrightarrow \
\begin{array}{c}
\overset{\ominus}{O - AlH_3} \\
R - C - \overset{..}{N} \diagdown \\
\overset{\oplus}{}
\end{array}
\ \xrightarrow{H^{\ominus}} \
\begin{array}{c}
\overset{\ominus}{O - AlH_3} \\
R - \underset{H}{\overset{|}{C}} - \overset{..}{N} \diagdown
\end{array}
}
$$

$$
\begin{array}{c}
\overset{O}{\overset{||}{}} \\
R - C - \overset{..}{N} \diagdown
\end{array}
\ \xrightarrow{Li^{\oplus} H^{\ominus}} \
\begin{array}{c}
\overset{OH}{\overset{|}{}} \\
R - \underset{Li}{\overset{|}{C}} - \overset{..}{N} \diagdown
\end{array}
\qquad (16\text{-}7)
$$

$$
\underset{Y}{\overset{OX}{R - C - N}} \diagdown \to \underset{Y}{\overset{H^{\ominus}}{R - C = N}} \diagdown \to \underset{Y}{R - \overset{H}{\overset{|}{C}} - \overset{..}{N}} \diagdown \xrightarrow{H_2O} \underset{H}{R - \overset{H}{\overset{|}{C}} - \overset{..}{N}} \diagdown
$$

$$(16\text{-}8)$$

$$X = AlH_3 \text{ or } H$$
$$Y = H \text{ or } Li$$

Extending this scheme to the hydrogenolysis reactions occurring in amide vinylogs (13).

$$
R - \underset{Y}{\overset{OX}{\overset{|}{C}}} - \overset{|}{C} = \overset{|}{C} - N \diagdown \to R - \underset{Y}{\overset{|}{C}} = \overset{|}{C} - \overset{|}{C} = N \diagdown \to
$$

$$
R' - \underset{Y}{\overset{H}{\overset{|}{C}}} - \overset{|}{C} = \overset{|}{C} - \overset{..}{N} \diagdown \qquad (16\text{-}9)
$$

The forcing reaction conditions as well as the sometimes isolation of carbinol in the reported hydrogenolysis reactions indicates the effect of vinylogy on reaction (16-8).

These considerations can be applied to reported hydrogenolysis reactions in other than the benzene series. Thus, benz[a]acridin-12(7H)-one (X) (14) and 4-keto-1,2,3,4-tetrahydroquinoline (XI) (15) are reduced to the corresponding oxygen-free compounds with LAH.

X   XI

In the indole series, spiro-[cyclopentane-1,2′-ψ-indoxyl] (XII) yields a mixture of the carbinol and methylene compounds (16,17)

XII   (16-10)

while 2-methyl-2,3′-[2′-methylindyl]-ψ-indoxyl (XIII) yields the methylene compound and a rearranged product (18).

XIII

Dioxindole and 1-methyldioxindole (XIV) are reduced to the corresponding oxindole and indole (19).

XIV   R = H or CH₃

XIV   R = H or CH$_3$

2,4-Dimethyl-3-acetylpyrrole (XV) is reduced to 2,4-dimethyl-3-ethylpyrrole and a condensation product, α,β-dipyrrylmethane, postulated as arising by condensation of the intermediate carbinol and the oxygen-free compound.

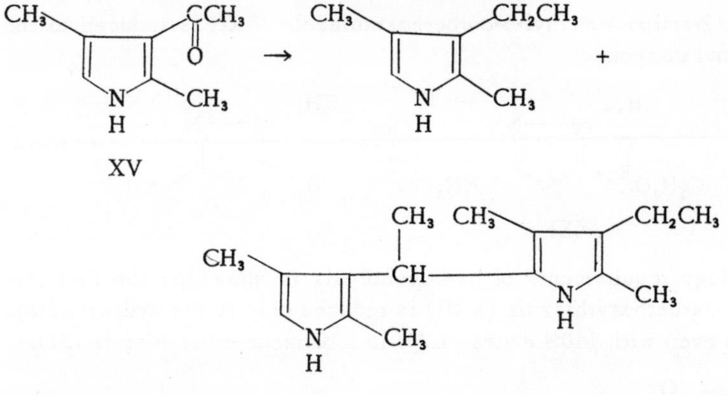

(16-12)

Similar condensation products are postulated as arising by LAH reduction of 2-methyl-3-carbethoxypyrrole (XVI) and 2,4-dimethyl-3,5-dicarbethoxypyrrole (XVII) (20).

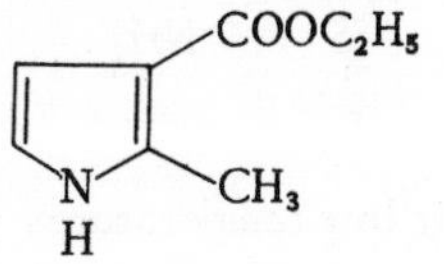

XVI 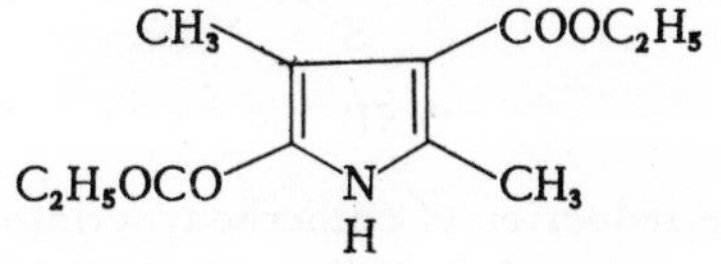   XVII

In the thiazole series, reduction of 2-amino-4,5-dicarbethoxythiazole (XVIII) with 25% excess LAH yields 2-amino-4-hydroxymethyl-5-carbethoxythiazole (XIX). Treatment of XVIII with 400% excess LAH or of XIX with 120% excess LAH yields 2-amino-4-hydroxymethyl-5-methylthiazole (XX) (21).

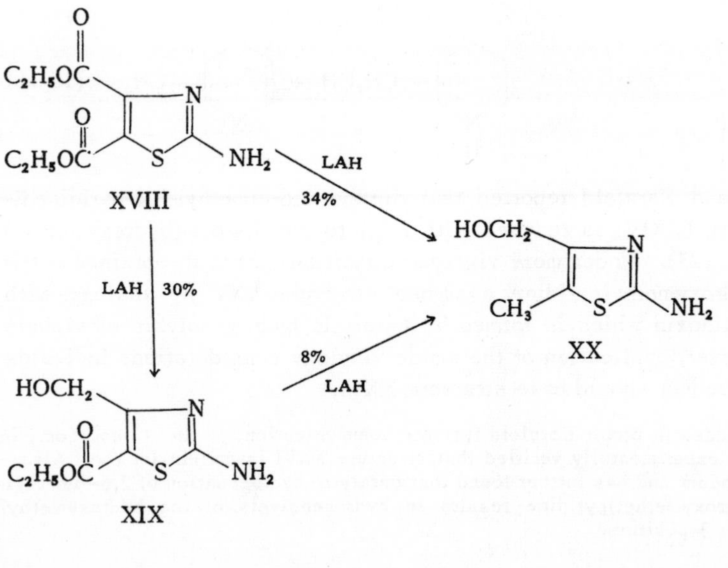

(16-13)

Similarly, 2-amino-4-methyl-5-carbethoxythiazole (XXI) is reduced to the 4,5-dimethyl compound.

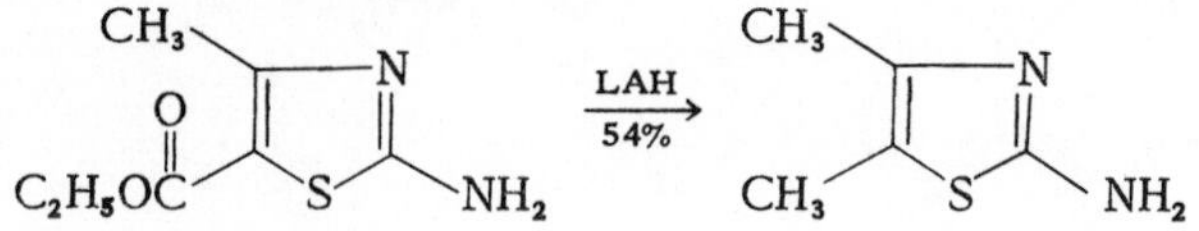

(16-14)

XXI

The vinylogy requirements of hydrogenolysis is shown by the fact that 2-amino-4-carbethoxythiazole (XXII) is reduced only to the hydroxymethyl compound even with 540% excess LAH in a benzene-ether mixture (21).

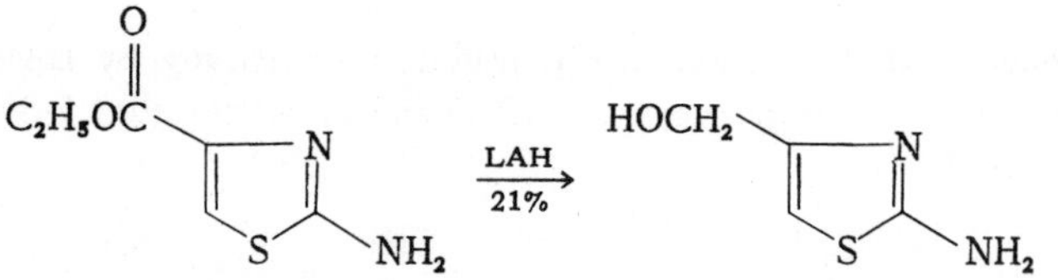

(16-15)

XXII

The reduction of carbethoxypyridines (XXIII) at low temperatures yields the corresponding hydroxymethylpyridines. However, the use of higher temperatures and extended reaction times is reported to yield small amounts of piperidyl carbinols and methylpyridines (22).

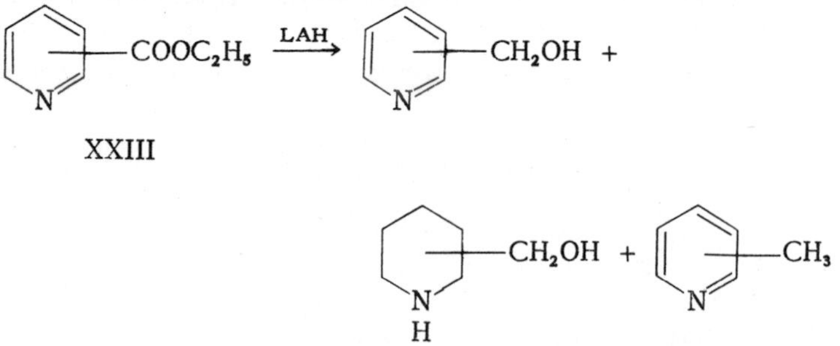

XXIII

(16-16)

Jones and Kornfeld reported that diethyl 2,6-dimethyl-3,4-pyridinedicarboxylate (XXIV) is reduced with LAH to the 3,4-bis-(hydroxymethyl) derivative (23). Under more vigorous conditions there is obtained a trimethylhydroxymethylpyridine assigned structure XXV by analogy with desoxypyridoxin which is formed by catalytic hydrogenolysis of vitamin B₆. However, application of the amide vinylogy considerations indicates that the product should have structure XXVI.*

*Note added in proof: Kornfeld (private communication, *J. Am. Chem. Soc.*, in press) has experimentally verified that structure XXVI is correct for the LAH reduction product and has further found that catalytic hydrogenation of 2,6-dimethyl-3,4-di-(hydroxymethyl)pyridine results in hydrogenolysis of the hydroxymethyl group in the 3-position.

XXIV   XXV   XXVI

de Mayo and Rigby have reported that 2-hydroxypyridine and 2-hydroxy-quinoline are reduced with LAH, in part, to pyridine and quinoline, respectively (24). These products can arise by hydrogenolysis or the reaction can proceed via the pyridone to the carbinol followed by dehydration, since normal reduction of the pyridone would yield the 1,2-dihydro derivative.

Thiobenzamide is reduced with LAH to benzylamine (25). Michler's thioketone (XXVII) is reduced to the methane derivative (26).

$$(16\text{-}17)$$

The postulated mechanisms have indicated that the hydrogenolysis reaction requires the presence of a strongly electron-donating group in the ortho or para position. Since in the reduction of carboxylic acids and esters the carbonyl group is converted to methylene, application of the vinylogy principle should permit hydrogenolysis in the presence of an oxygen atom as well as nitrogen. Thus, p,p'-dimethoxybenzophenone (XXVIII) is converted to p,p'-dimethoxydiphenylmethane with excess LAH at 90° for 11 days (1).

$$(16\text{-}18)$$

Attempts to apply hydrogenolysis conditions to the reduction of p-hydroxy-benzoic acid, ethyl p-hydroxybenzoate, methyl salicylate and 2,4-di-

hydroxybenzaldehyde have been unsuccessful due to the immediate precipitation of the complex formed by the reaction between the active
hydrogen and LAH (1).

Xanthone (XXIX), 3,4-benzoxanthone, 1,2-benzoxanthone, xanthione
(XXX), and 3,4-benzoxanth-9-thione are reduced to the corresponding
xanthenes (26).

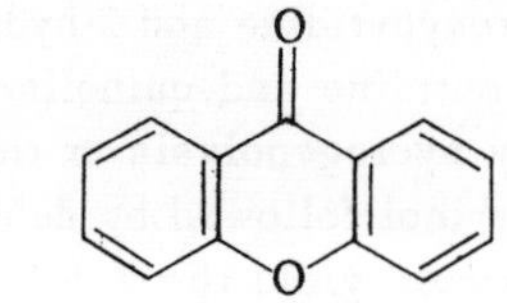

XXIX 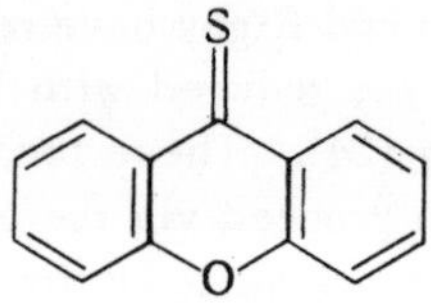   XXX

Reduction of methyl β-(2-methoxy-4-propylphenoxy)-3,4-dimethoxycinna-
mate (XXXI) yields dimethoxycinnamyl alcohol and dihydroeugenol as
well as the expected carbinol (27).

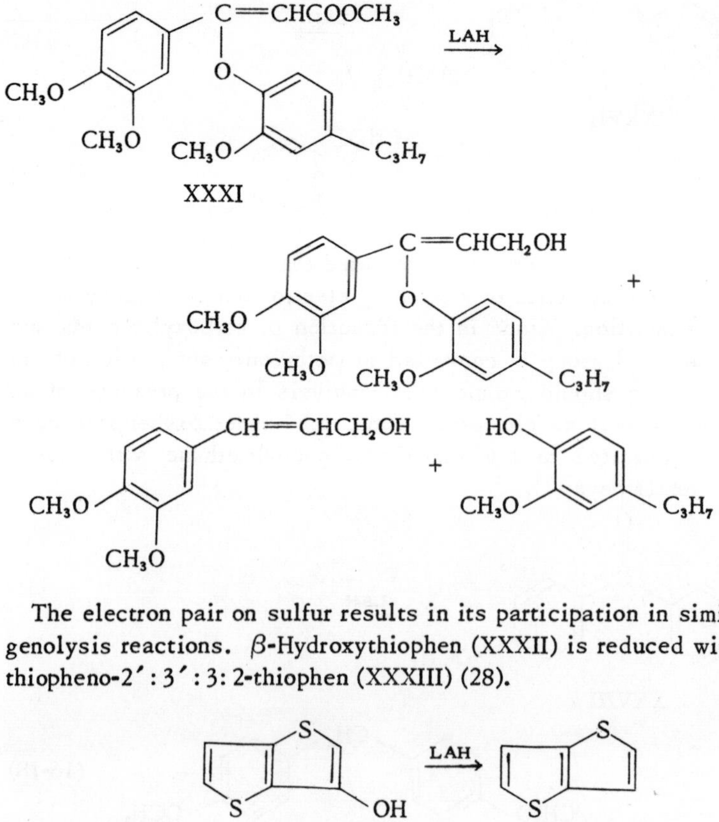

XXXI

(16-19)

The electron pair on sulfur results in its participation in similar hydrogenolysis reactions. β-Hydroxythiophen (XXXII) is reduced with LAH to
thiopheno-2′:3′:3:2-thiophen (XXXIII) (28).

(16-20)

XXXII   XXXIII

Thioxanthone (XXXIV) and thioxanthione (XXXV) undergo similar reductions (26).

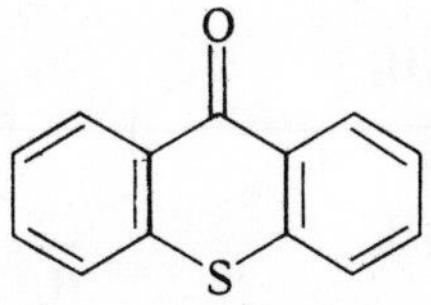

XXXIV 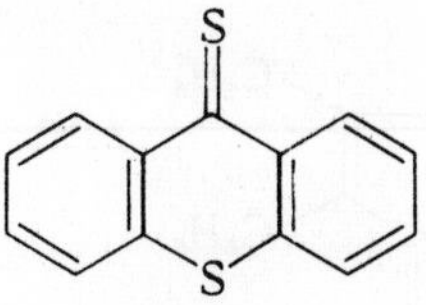   XXXV

Attempts to prepare the 2,5-dimethyl compound by the LAH reduction of the carbomethoxy group in XXXVI are reported to yield the furfuryl alcohol (XXXVII) (29).

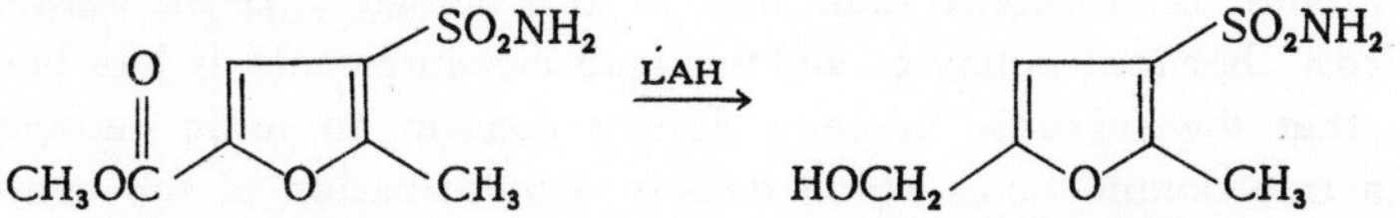

$$ \qquad\qquad (16\text{-}21) $$

XXXVI   XXXVII

Bergmann and his co-workers have shown 'that LAH will reduce the polar double bonds in the fulvenes (30–32). If the negative end of the dipole in such polar bonds is considered as a potential source of electrons, various reported hydrogenolysis reactions fall within the scope of the present discussion.

Bergmann *et al.* reported that LAH reduction of 2,3,4,5-tetraphenyl-cyclopentadienone (XXXVIII) gives the saturated ketone whose identity was based on the infrared absorption spectrum of the compound (33). A reconsideration of the spectrum has resulted in identification of the compound as the unsaturated ketone (XXXIX) (34). Sonntag, Linder, Becker, and Spoerri have reported that normal addition of LAH yields the unsaturated ketone (XXXIX) and the oxygen-free hydrogenolysis product (XL) while reverse addition yields the carbinol (XLI) (35).

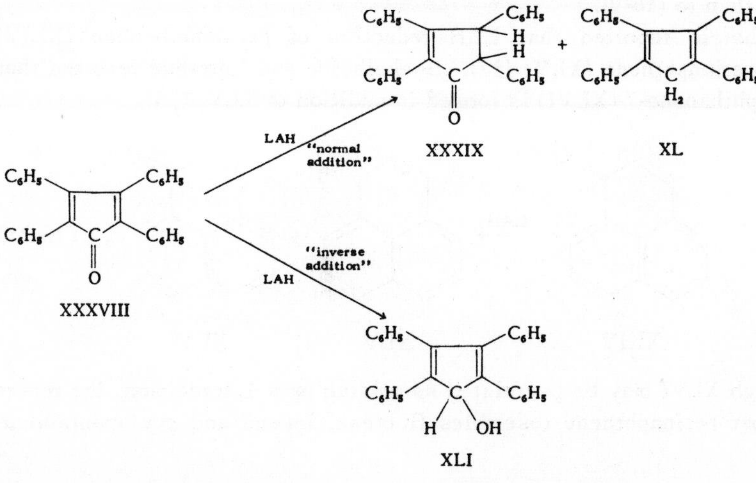

$$ \qquad\qquad (16\text{-}22) $$

XXXIX   XL

XXXVIII

$$ \qquad\qquad (16\text{-}23) $$

XLI

The reduction of 2,3-diphenylindone (XLII) similarly yields the unsaturated ketone (XLIII) and the hydrogenolysis product (33).

XLII   XLIII   (16-24)

Bergmann *et al.* (33) have shown that the chemical behavior of the fulvenic ketones is different than that of the normal α,β-unsaturated ketone. From chemical behavior and infrared measurements it has been postulated that the fulvenic ketones do not contain an ionic carbonyl group but a true double bond which causes a polarization of the conjugated double bond. Sonntag, Linder, Becker, and Spoerri (35) have indicated that the cyclic mechanism proposed for the 1,4-addition of LAH to open-chain α,β-unsaturated ketones (36) is untenable in the reaction of tetracyclone (XXXVIII). It would therefore appear that a direct attack on the double bond resulting from its polarization may be responsible for the formation of XXXIX and XLIII.

In the reaction of the fulvenic ketones with organolithium compounds the product arises by a 1,4-addition indicating that the carbon adjacent to the carbonyl group is the negative end of the dipole (33). The formation of hydrogenolysis products in the LAH reduction of XXXVIII and XLII would therefore proceed according to reaction (16-8) with the polarized double bond acting as the electron donor. The isolation of XLI under "mild" conditions, i.e., inverse addition, is in accordance with this postulation. The formation of hydrogenolysis products without forcing conditions is indicative of the operation of a reaction analogous to (16-8) rather than to (16-9).

Hochstein reported that LAH reduction of perinaphthenone (XLIV) gives perinaphthene (XLV) (37). Boekelheide and Larrabee reported that perinaphthanone-7 (XLVI) is formed in addition to XLV (38).

XLIV   XLV   XLVI   (16-25)

Although XLVI may be postulated as arising by a 1,4-addition, the report (38) that perinaphthene resembles fluorene, indene and cyclopentadiene in many respects may be indicative of the operation of the mechanism proposed here. In this regard, it is of interest that a hydrogenolysis product is reported among those resulting from the LAH reduction of fluorenone (XLVII) (33).

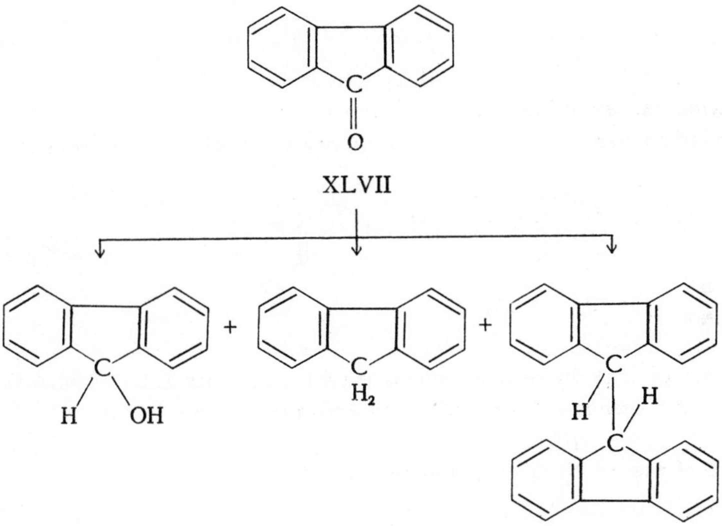

XLVII

(16-26)

Hydrogenolysis also occurs in the LAH reduction of benzhydrylidene anthrone (XLVIII) (39).

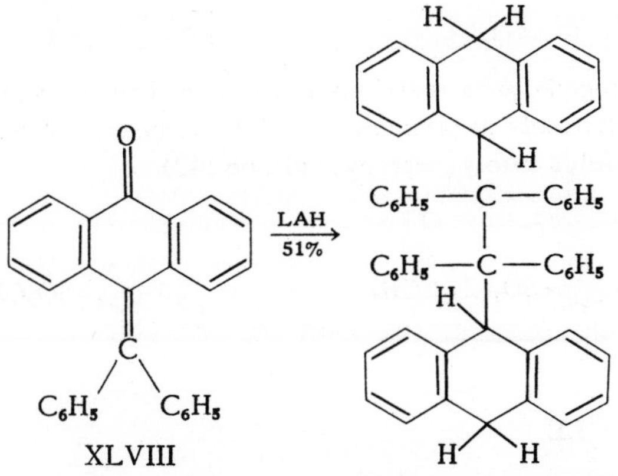

XLVIII

(16-27)

Various other reactions have been reported that involve electron-donating groups and which might be classified as hydrogenolysis reactions except that the reduction of double bonds is involved. Thus, the LAH reduction of 1-methylindole (XLIX) and 1,3-dimethylindole yields 25–30% of the corresponding indoline, although indole itself is not reduced with LAH (19).

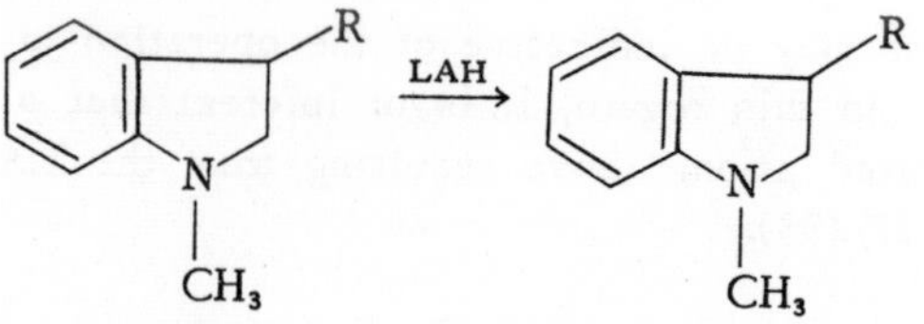

XLIX

R = H or CH₃

The reduction of benzothiophene-1-dioxide (L) yields up to 79% of 2,3-dihydrobenzothiophene although benzothiophene itself is not reduced (40).

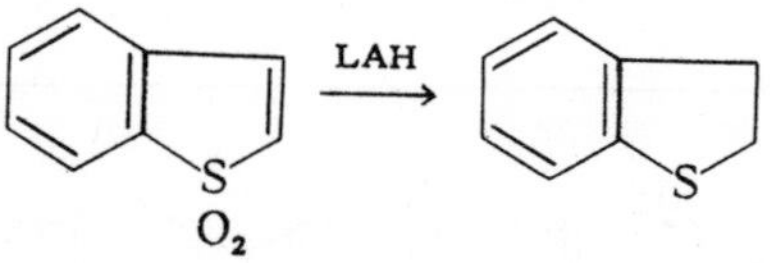

L

The treatment of 2-methyltetrahydrobenzoxazole (LI) with LAH results in reduction of the carbon-carbon and carbon-nitrogen double bonds as well

as cleavage of the $-\overset{|}{N}\overset{|}{C}O-$ grouping (41).

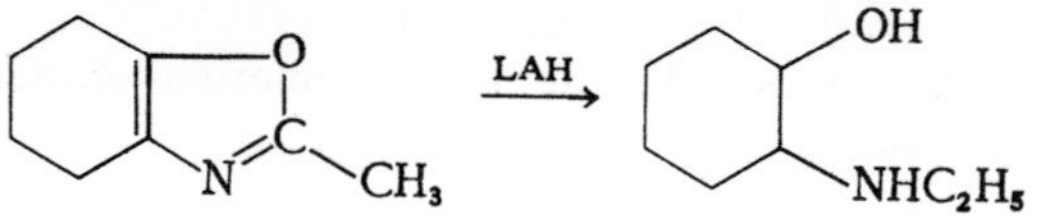

LI

Several hydrogenolyses reactions have been reported which do not appear to be classifiable at present. The LAH reduction of p-tolyl acetonyl sulfone (LII) yields p-tolyl n-propyl sulfone (42).

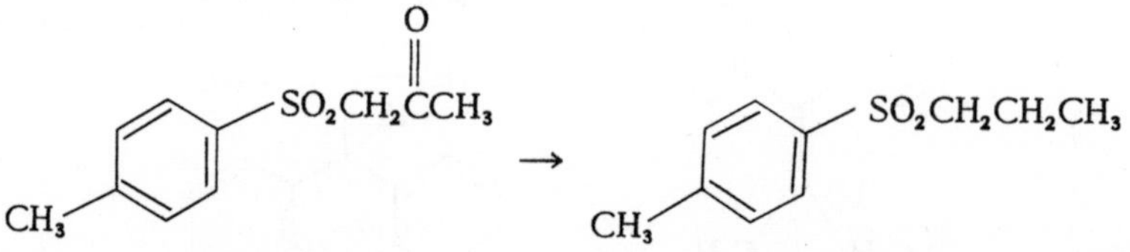

LII

(16-31)

The reduction of the nitrodisulfone (LIII) yields a little disulfone (LIV) and ammonia (43).

$$CH_3SO_2\underset{\underset{NO_2}{|}}{C}HSO_2CH_3 \xrightarrow{\text{LAH}} CH_3SO_2CH_2SO_2CH_3 \qquad (16\text{-}32)$$

LIII   LIV

A deamination is also observed in the treatment of bis-(1,4-naphthalene-dibenzenesulfonamido-2)nitromethane (LV) with LAH (44).

$$(16\text{-}33)$$

Treatment of the stable iminochloride (LVI), formed from the Hoesch reaction of acrylonitrile and 4,6-diethylresorcinol, with excess LAH yields 70% of an oxygen-free primary amine, formulated as LVII, 20% of a neutral substance formulated as LVIII and an alkali soluble, nitrogen-free compound for which no structure has been devised (45).

$$(16\text{-}34)$$

On further treatment with LAH, LVIII is converted to LVII.

16.2 OXIDATION

The Oppenauer method employing aluminum alkoxides for the oxidation of alcohols to ketones, with aldehydes and ketones as hydrogen acceptors, has been widely used since its initial appearance (46). Ott and Murray have recently patented an analogous procedure utilizing lithium aluminum complexes such as the alcoholates (47).

The lithium aluminum complex is formed by the reaction of LAH with an aldehyde, ketone, thioketone, alcohol, thioalcohol, thiophenol, phenol, ester, acid chloride, acid anhydride, primary amine, or secondary amine to yield LiAlY where Y = $(OR)_4$, $(SR)_4$, $(NR_2)_4$, and $(=NR)_2$. The hydrogen acceptor may be an aldehyde or ketone from the aliphatic, alicyclic or aromatic series and is used in twice the theoretical amount, e.g., two moles of carbonyl compound for each hydroxyl group.

The oxidation is carried out in an inert diluent or solvent such as an excess of the aldehyde or ketone used to prepare the LAH alcoholate or a hydrocarbon such as benzene, toluene, xylene or cyclohexane. The reaction is conducted at the reflux temperature of the mixture, 40–150°C., for a period of 10 to 80 hours. The LAH complex may be isolated by removal of the ether utilized in its preparation and then suspended in the hydrocarbon or the latter may be added to the ethereal solution of the complex and the ether distilled. After completion of the oxidation reaction, the mixture is acidified and steam distilled to remove the excess hydrogen acceptor, and the desired ketone reaction product is isolated by extraction.

Ott and Murray have applied this oxidation procedure to the conversion of steroid alcohols to the corresponding ketones (Table XCVIII).

It is of interest to note that oxidation of a β,γ-unsaturated steroid alcohol, as in a Δ^5-3-hydroxy compound, results in a shift of the double bond to a conjugated system such as the Δ^4-3-keto derivative. Thus, oxidation of 5-pregnene-3β-ol-20-one (LIX) yields the Δ^4-3-one, progesterone (LX).

(16-35)

LIX   LX

16.3 OLEFIN POLYMERIZATION

Although the carbon-carbon double bond is generally not attacked by LAH (Section 15.1.1), Ziegler has recently reported that α-olefins, in-

TABLE XCVIII

Oxidation Reactions with Lithium Aluminum Complexes (47)

Steroid Alcohol	LAH Complexing Agent	Hydrogen Acceptor	Oxidation Reaction Medium	Reflux Time, Hrs.	Product
5-Androstene-3β,17β-diol-17-cyclopentylpropionate	Acetone	Cyclohexanone	Toluene	18	Testosterone cyclopentyl propionate
Cholestanol	t-Butyl alcohol	Cyclohexanone	Toluene	18	Cholestanone
Cholesterol	Acetone	Cyclohexanone	Toluene	18	4-Cholesten-3-one
Dehydroepiandrosterone	Cyclopentanone	Acetone	Toluene	24	4-Androstene-3,17-dione
Methyl 3β-hydroxybisnor-5-cholenate	2-Butanone	2-Butanone	Benzene	75	3-Keto-bisnor-4-cholenic acid[a]
5-Pregnene-3β-ol-20-one	3-Pentanone	Cyclopentanone	Toluene	40	4-Pregnene-3,20-dione
Testosterone	Cyclohexanone	Cyclohexanone	Xylene	24	4-Androstene-3,17-dione

[a] Isolated after hydrolysis of the oxidation product.

cluding ethylene, can be reduced to the corresponding paraffin hydrocarbons by LAH, aluminum hydride and aluminum trialkyls. At high temperatures the aluminum trialkyls catalytically convert ethylene and other olefins into higher paraffins and olefins by polymerization (48–50).

16.3.1 Synthesis of Aluminum Alkyls and Hydrides

LAH and ethylene undergo an addition reaction at a little above 100° (48) or at 50° under 5–10 atmospheres pressure (50) to give stepwise ethylated lithium aluminum hydrides.

$$\text{Li}\begin{bmatrix} H & & H \\ & Al & \\ H & & H \end{bmatrix} \rightarrow \text{Li}\begin{bmatrix} C_2H_5 & & H \\ & Al & \\ H & & H \end{bmatrix} \rightarrow \ldots \rightarrow \text{LiAl}(C_2H_5)_4 \qquad (16\text{-}36)$$

All α-olefins behave in a similar manner. Thus, propylene and 1-hexene yield lithium aluminum tetrapropyl and lithium aluminum tetrahexyl, respectively. However, the reaction with isobutylene and cyclopentene stops after the addition of three molecules of olefin.

These additions take place even more readily with aluminum hydride than with LAH. Since the former cannot be completely freed of ether the products of such additions are mixtures of both ether-free aluminum alkyls and their etherates. Ether-free products can be obtained by treating the lithium tetraalkyls with aluminum chloride to yield the corresponding aluminum trialkyls.

$$3\ \text{LiAlR}_4 + \text{AlCl}_3 \rightarrow 3\ \text{LiCl} + 4\ \text{AlR}_3 \qquad (16\text{-}37)$$

The addition of aluminum hydride to a terminal olefinic double bond proceeds according to Markownikoff's law.

$$\text{CH}_3\text{CH}\!=\!\text{CH}_2 + \overset{+}{\text{al}}\!-\!\overset{-}{\text{H}} \rightarrow \text{CH}_3\text{CH}_2\text{CH}_2\!-\!\text{al} \qquad (16\text{-}38)$$
$$\text{al} = \tfrac{1}{3}\ \text{AlH}_3$$

The addition to a non-terminal double bond proceeds so slowly that all the aluminum hydride decomposes more rapidly into aluminum and hydrogen than it adds to the double bond. The rate of addition to propylene to produce aluminum n-propyl proceeds one hundred times more rapidly than the addition to yield aluminum sec-propyl, i.e., there are one hundred primary propyl groups formed for each secondary propyl group (48).

An interesting application of the addition of the hydride to a terminal double bond involves isobutylene. While the addition of hydrogen bromide to isobutylene gives $tert$-butyl bromide, exclusively in the absence of peroxides and to a considerable extent even in the presence of peroxides, iso-butyl bromide can be obtained by the route:

$$(CH_3)_2C{=}CH_2 \ + \ al{-}H \ \rightarrow \ (CH_3)_2CHCH_2{-}al \ \xrightarrow{Br_2}$$

$$(CH_3)_2CHCH_2Br \ + \ alBr \qquad (16\text{-}39)$$

The stepwise addition of ethylene to aluminum hydride yields first ethyl aluminum dihydride, $C_2H_5AlH_2$, and diethyl aluminum hydride, $(C_2H_5)_2AlH$. However, these can also be produced by reaction of the chloro compounds with lithium or sodium hydride:

$$C_2H_5AlCl_2 \ + \ 2 \, LiH \ \rightarrow \ C_2H_5AlH_2 \ + \ 2 \, LiCl \qquad (16\text{-}40)$$

$$(C_2H_5)_2AlCl \ + \ LiH \ \rightarrow \ (C_2H_5)_2AlH \ + \ LiCl \qquad (16\text{-}41)$$

The aluminum alkyl chlorides can be prepared from aluminum and ethyl chloride

$$2 \, Al \ + \ 3 \, C_2H_5Cl \ \rightarrow \ C_2H_5AlCl_2 \ + \ (C_2H_5)_2AlCl \qquad (16\text{-}42)$$

or from aluminum triethyl and aluminum chloride

$$(C_2H_5)_3Al \ + \ 2 \, AlCl_3 \ \rightarrow \ 3 \, C_2H_5AlCl_2 \qquad (16\text{-}43)$$

$$2 \, (C_2H_5)_3Al \ + \ AlCl_3 \ \rightarrow \ 3 \, (C_2H_5)_2AlCl \qquad (16\text{-}44)$$

The aluminum triethyl can be prepared by a number of methods:

1. the reaction of the aluminum-magnesium alloy with ethyl chloride,

$$Al_2Mg_3 \ + \ 6 \, C_2H_5Cl \ \rightarrow \ 2 \, (C_2H_5)_3Al \ + \ 3 \, MgCl_2 \qquad (16\text{-}45)$$

2. an indirect route involving the conversion of two moles of aluminum triethyl to three moles,

$$2 \, (C_2H_5)_3Al \ + \ AlCl_3 \ \rightarrow \ 3 \, (C_2H_5)_2AlCl \qquad (16\text{-}46)$$

$$3 \, (C_2H_5)_2AlCl \ + \ 3 \, NaH \ \rightarrow \ 3 \, (C_2H_5)_2AlH \ + \ 3 \, NaCl \qquad (16\text{-}47)$$

$$3 \, (C_2H_5)_2AlH \ + \ 3 \, CH_2{=}CH_2 \ \rightarrow \ 3 \, (C_2H_5)_3Al \qquad (16\text{-}48)$$

$$AlCl_3 \ + \ 3 \, NaH \ + \ 3 \, C_2H_4 \ \rightarrow \ (C_2H_5)_3Al \ + \ 3 \, NaCl \qquad (16\text{-}49)$$

3. an indirect route starting with "ethyl aluminum sesquichloride" involving the conversion of one mole of aluminum triethyl to three moles,

$$3 \, C_2H_5Cl \ + \ 2 \, Al \ \rightarrow \ (C_2H_5)_2AlCl \ + \ C_2H_5AlCl_2 \qquad (16\text{-}50)$$

$$(C_2H_5)_3Al \ + \ (C_2H_5)_2AlCl \ + \ C_2H_5AlCl_2 \ \rightarrow \ 3 \, (C_2H_5)_2AlCl \qquad (16\text{-}51)$$

$$3 \, (C_2H_5)_2AlCl \ + \ 3 \, NaH \ + \ 3 \, CH_2{=}CH_2 \ \rightarrow \ 3 \, (C_2H_5)_3Al \ + \ 3 \, NaCl$$
$$(16\text{-}52)$$

$$3 \, C_2H_5Cl \ + \ 2 \, Al \ + \ 3 \, NaH \ + \ 3 \, C_2H_4 \ \rightarrow \ 2 \, (C_2H_5)_3Al \ + \ 3 \, NaCl \qquad (16\text{-}53)$$

4. the reaction of ethylene with aluminum hydride at 60–80°,

$$AlH_3 \; + \; 3 \, CH_2 \!=\! CH_2 \; \rightarrow \; (C_2H_5)_3Al \qquad (16\text{-}54)$$

5. directly from aluminum powder, ethylene and hydrogen (50a,50b).

$$Al \; + \; 3 \, CH_2 \!=\! CH_2 \; + \; 1.5 \, H_2 \; \rightarrow \; (C_2H_5)_3Al \qquad (16\text{-}54a)$$

The reaction indicated in equation (16-54a), wherein aluminum hydride is probably an intermediate, can be utilized for the preparation of other aluminum alkyls by the substitution of the appropriate olefin. The olefins can be arranged in decreasing ease of reactivity with aluminum and hydrogen: isobutylene, propylene, ethylene, 3-methyl-1-butene, 1-butene, higher olefins. Aluminum triisobutyl, derived from the most reactive olefin, is prepared at 120° and at a pressure of 200 atmospheres, using very finely divided aluminum, preferably in a ball mill in the absence of oxygen and water (50a).

Aluminum triisobutyl can be used for the preparation of other aluminum alkyls. Disproportionation occurs in the presence of hydrogen (50a):

$$[(CH_3)_2CHCH_2]_3Al \; + \; 3 \, H_2 \; + \; 6 \, CH_2 \!=\! CH_2 \; \rightarrow$$

$$2 \, (C_2H_5)_3Al \; + \; 3 \, (CH_3)_2C \!=\! CH_2 \qquad (16\text{-}54b)$$

Displacement of the isobutyl group occurs at 120° even in the absence of hydrogen (equation 16-62).

Diethyl aluminum hydride, produced according to equation (16-41), is a colorless, distillable liquid very similar in appearance to aluminum triethyl and much more stable than aluminum hydride. By mixing diethyl aluminum hydride with an olefin in a so-called "contractometer" the addition velocity of the reaction can be kinetically followed (51). For terminal olefins the half-life period in the presence of excess olefin at 64° is 10 minutes. For non-terminal olefins it is 100 times greater. By means of diethyl aluminum hydride the following mixed aluminum trialkyls have been prepared (48):

$$(C_2H_5)_2Al \!-\! CH_2\overset{\displaystyle CH_3}{\underset{|}{C}}HC_3H_7 \qquad\qquad (C_2H_5)_2Al \!-\! \overset{\displaystyle CH_3}{\underset{|}{C}}HC_3H_7$$

$$(C_2H_5)_2Al \!-\!\!\!<\!\!\square \qquad\qquad (C_2H_5)_2Al \!-\! CH_2CH_2 \!-\!\!\!<\!\!\bigcirc$$

Aluminum triethyl forms a complex with sodium fluoride, $NaF \cdot 2Al(C_2H_5)_3$, which is capable of conducting the electric current and permits the preparation of tetraethyl lead according to the equation:

$$2 \, NaF \cdot 2Al(C_2H_5)_3 \; + \; 3 \, Pb \; \rightarrow \; 2 \, NaF \; + \; 3 \, Pb(C_2H_5)_4 \; + \; 4 \, Al \qquad (16\text{-}54c)$$

Using a cathode of any metal and an anode of lead, aluminum separates out at the cathode while quantitative formation of tetraethyl lead occurs at the anode. The tetraethyl lead does not mix with the electrolyte and separates out as a heavy lower layer underneath the electrolyte. Aluminum at the cathode is retransformed by ethylene and hydrogen into aluminum triethyl (equation 16-54a) and this adds again to the electrolyte:

$$1\ 1/3\ Al(C_2H_5)_3\ +\ Pb\ \longrightarrow\ Pb(C_2H_5)_4\ +\ 1/3\ Al \qquad (16\text{-}54d)$$

$$1\ 1/3\ Al\ +\ 4\ CH_2\!=\!CH_2\ +\ 2\ H_2\ \rightarrow\ 1\ 1/3\ Al(C_2H_5)_3 \quad (16\text{-}54e)$$

$$4\ CH_2\!=\!CH_2\ +\ 2\ H_2\ +\ Pb\ \longrightarrow\ Pb(C_2H_5)_4 \qquad (16\text{-}54f)$$

Starting with ordinary aluminum, one can obtain extremely pure aluminum by this process (50a,50b). Pure aluminum can also be obtained by decomposing aluminum triisobutyl at 250°, into aluminum, hydrogen and isobutylene (50a).

16.3.2 Synthesis of Paraffins

The addition products from aluminum hydride or LAH and olefins, on hydrolysis, give the corresponding paraffins. Thus, the α-olefins can be reduced to the saturated hydrocarbons, and the selective reduction of α-olefins in mixtures with other olefins can be carried out. Selective partial reductions, according to Markownikoff's rule, have been carried out as follows (48):

LXI   (16-55)

LXII   (16-56)

LXIII   (16-57)

As discussed in Section 16.3.1, aluminum triethyl can be prepared in a number of ways including the reaction of ethylene with aluminum hydride

at 60–80° (equation 16-54). At temperatures of about 100–120° the al — C
bond reacts with further ethylene.

$$
\underset{C_2H_5}{\overset{C_2H_5}{Al{-}C_2H_5}} \xrightarrow{C_2H_4} \underset{C_2H_5}{\overset{CH_2CH_2C_2H_5}{Al{-}C_2H_5}} \xrightarrow{C_2H_4} \underset{C_2H_5}{\overset{CH_2CH_2C_2H_5}{Al{-}CH_2CH_2C_2H_5}} \xrightarrow{C_2H_4}
$$

$$
\underset{CH_2CH_2C_2H_5}{\overset{CH_2CH_2C_2H_5}{Al{-}CH_2CH_2C_2H_5}} \quad etc. \quad (16\text{-}58)
$$

Actually the reaction does not proceed as smoothly as formulated in
equation (16-58). The structure of the reaction products is governed by
statistical laws. The conversion of the butyl groups to hexyl groups begins to take place even before all the ethyl groups have been converted
to butyl groups, and octyl groups are formed before all the hexyl groups
are formed, etc. Therefore, the end groups are mixtures of aluminum trialkyls of the general formula LXIV:

$$
\underset{(C_2H_4)_o{-}C_2H_5}{\overset{(C_2H_4)_m{-}C_2H_5}{Al{-}(C_2H_4)_n{-}C_2H_5}}
$$

LXIV

where $m + n + o$ equals the number of moles of ethylene consumed per
mole of aluminum triethyl and m, n, and o vary statistically about the
mean value $(m + n + o)/3$.

The decomposition of LXIV with water gives saturated hydrocarbons.

$$
LXIV \xrightarrow{H_2O} H(C_2H_4)_m{-}C_2H_5 + H(C_2H_4)_n{-}C_2H_5 +
$$
$$
H(C_2H_4)_o{-}C_2H_5 \quad (16\text{-}59)
$$

This represents a convenient synthesis of paraffins of even-numbered
carbon chains which can be separated by distillation. Odd-numbered
carbon chain paraffins can be produced starting from aluminum trimethyl
or aluminum tripropyl. The use of large quantities of ethylene in controlled amounts yields a whole series of aliphatic hydrocarbons ranging
from soft to hard paraffins all the way up to products with molecular
weights of approximately 5,000, representative of low molecular weight
"polyethylene."

LAH has also been utilized in the synthesis of paraffins from ethylene
(50). The triethyl lithium aluminum hydride can be prepared at 50° at
5–10 atmospheres pressure.

$$
LiAlH_4 + 3\,CH_2{=}CH_2 \rightarrow HLiAl(CH_2CH_3)_3 \quad (16\text{-}60)
$$

At 80–100° and 15 atmospheres pressure further reaction occurs

$$HLiAl(CH_2CH_3)_3 + n \ CH_2\!=\!\!CH_2 \rightarrow HLiAl[CH_2CH_2(CH_2)_nCH_3]_3 \quad (16\text{-}61)$$
$$n = 15 \text{ to } 20$$

Hydrolysis of the trialkyl lithium aluminum hydride yields the corresponding paraffin $CH_3CH_2(CH_2)_nCH_3$.

In contrast to the addition of ethylene to aluminum triethyl (equation 16-58), aluminum triisobutyl does not add ethylene (48). Instead, at 120° isobutylene is displaced by ethylene

$$(CH_3)_2CHCH_2\!-\!al + CH_2\!=\!\!CH_2 \rightarrow (CH_3)_2C\!=\!\!CH_2 + CH_3CH_2\!-\!al$$
$$(16\text{-}62)$$

indicating that ethylene has a greater affinity for al —H than isobutylene.

The reaction of aluminum tripropyl with an equivalent amount of 1-dodecene gives a reaction product, after hydrolysis, containing a fairly large amount of 2-propyldodecane

$$CH_3(CH_2)_9CH\!=\!\!CH_2 + C_3H_7\!-\!al \rightarrow CH_3(CH_2)_9\overset{\underset{\textstyle |}{C_3H_7}}{C}HCH_2\!-\!al \xrightarrow{H_2O}$$

LXV

$$CH_3(CH_2)_9\overset{\underset{\textstyle |}{C_3H_7}}{C}HCH_3 \quad (16\text{-}63)$$

However, the formation of LXV in the presence of 1-dodecene results in secondary reactions:

$$CH_3(CH_2)_9\overset{\underset{\textstyle |}{C_3H_7}}{C}HCH_2\!-\!al \qquad CH_3(CH_2)_9\overset{\underset{\textstyle |}{C_3H_7}}{C}\!=\!\!CH_2$$

$$+ \qquad\qquad \rightarrow \qquad\qquad + \qquad\qquad (16\text{-}64)$$

$$CH_3(CH_2)_9CH\!=\!\!CH_2 \qquad\qquad CH_3(CH_2)_{10}CH_2\!-\!al$$

$$CH_3(CH_2)_{10}CH_2\!-\!al \qquad\qquad CH_3(CH_2)_{10}\overset{\underset{\textstyle |}{}}{C}H_2$$

$$+ \qquad\qquad \rightarrow \qquad CH_3(CH_2)_9\overset{\underset{\textstyle |}{}}{C}HCH_2\!-\!al \quad (16\text{-}65)$$

$$CH_3(CH_2)_9CH\!=\!\!CH_2$$

Further, dimeric dodecene is formed by loss of al —H, as discussed in Section 16.3.3. Hydrolysis of the reaction mixture therefore yields a mixture of 2-propyldodecane, 2-propyldodecene, 2-dodecyldodecane, and

2-dodecyldodecene. Hydrogenation of the hydrocarbon mixture yields 2-propyldodecane and 2-dodecyldodecane which can be separated by distillation.

Polyethylene having a molecular weight between 200,000 and 500,000, a melting point between $130°$ and $140°$, and a density between 0.94 and 0.95 has been prepared by the low pressure polymerization of ethylene using various types of metal halides complexed with metal alkyls in the temperature range from $30°$ to $150°$ with pressures up to 50 atmospheres (51a).

Using a suspension of a complex prepared from aluminum triethyl and titanium tetrachloride in heptane or cyclohexane results in the rapid formation of polymer which is deposited as a white cheesy suspension. Vigorous stirring separates the polymer from the suspended catalyst particles. The ease of separation of the polymer from the catalyst depends upon how finely the catalyst is suspended, the nature of the complex, the rapidity and temperature of polymer formation and the nature of the stirring (51b).

The product of the low pressure polymerization process is a mixture of strictly linear polymer and more or less branched polymer. Natta (51c) has utilized the aluminum alkyl-metal halide complex in the preparation of polymers from propylene, 1-butene, 5-methyl-1-hexene and styrene. These polymers show an exceptional tendency to crystallize, and have low solubilities, outstanding tensile strengths and unusually high melting points, i.e., $160°$, $135°$, $125°$, and $230°$, respectively. Natta has proposed the name "isotactic" polymers and has postulated that in these materials the asymmetric carbon atoms and their substituents are arranged with a particularly high degree of regularity, i.e., block-meso-polymers.

The yield of "isotactic" polymer is only between 40–50% of the total polymer and separation is accomplished by fractionation based on the differing solubilities of "isotactic" and normal polymer. The polymerization apparently involves the formation of the long chain molecules on a solid surface, on which monomer is adsorbed. The resulting macromolecules are freed by a chain transfer step and then desorbed.

16.3.3 Synthesis of Olefins

Although the reaction of aluminum alkyls with large amounts of ethylene at 100–120° yields higher paraffins and ethylene waxes (equation 16-58), when this reaction is carried out at temperatures of about 200° a catalytic reaction occurs to yield higher α-olefins (48).

At 200° aluminum alkyls decompose into olefins and alkyl aluminum hydrides and with ethylene the latter immediately gives further aluminum trialkyl which starts a new cycle. Thus, aluminum triethyl acts as a catalyst in the conversion of ethylene into higher α-olefins.

$$\rightarrow C_2H_5 - al + n\ CH_2 = CH_2 \rightarrow C_2H_5 - (C_2H_4)_n - al \qquad (16\text{-}66)$$

$$C_2H_5 - (C_2H_4)_n - al \rightarrow C_2H_5 - (C_2H_4)_{n-1}CH = CH_2 + al - H$$
$$(16\text{-}67)$$

$$al - H + CH_2 = CH_2 \rightarrow C_2H_5 - al \qquad (16\text{-}68)$$

It is possible that, as in equation (16-62), the reaction involves the displacement of the α-olefins from the aluminum alkyls by excess ethylene.

The average molecular weight of the resultant olefins is dependent upon the catalyst: ethylene ratio, ethylene pressure, and reaction time. The reaction conditions also influence the nature of the reaction products. In addition to linear α-olefins other products are formed. The double bond in the α-olefin is not completely fixed under the reaction conditions and migration occurs from the terminal position to the interior of the molecule. The final reaction products from ethylene and aluminum alkyls at 200° and at sufficiently long contact times are branched olefins such as

$$\begin{array}{c} H(C_2H_4)_n \\ \diagdown \\ \diagup \\ H(C_2H_4)_m \end{array} C = CH_2$$

LXVI

along with linear olefins with non-terminal double bonds. Under appropriate reaction conditions primarily linear α-olefins are formed. Since the time of reaction is important for this type of ethylene polymerization a continuous process works better than batchwise polymerization in an autoclave. The use of the less reactive etherates of the aluminum alkyls favors α-olefin formation.

In order to convert ethylene to its dimer, 1-butene, with very little 1-hexene and 1-octene, the ethylene is passed through aluminum triethyl at 180°–200° at normal or slightly elevated pressures.

Analogous to the aluminum alkyl reaction, the trialkyl lithium aluminum hydride (equation 16-61) is decomposed at 180°–200° to yield LAH and the α-monoolefin, accompanied by some non-terminal olefin (50).

$$HLiAl[CH_2CH_2(CH_2)_nCH_3]_3 \rightarrow LiAlH_4 + 3\ CH_2 = CH(CH_2)_nCH_3$$
$$(16\text{-}69)$$

In contrast to the conversion of ethylene to higher olefins, propylene, 1-butene, and other α-olefins are converted to dimers. Treatment of propylene with 1% of its weight of any aluminum alkyl in an autoclave at 200° results in a pressure rise to 100 atmospheres and the formation of the dimer 2-methyl-1-pentene.

$$2\ CH_3CH = CH_2 \rightarrow \begin{array}{c} CH_3CH_2CH_2 \\ | \\ CH_3C = CH_2 \end{array} \qquad (16\text{-}70)$$

Regardless of the nature of the original aluminum alkyl it ends up as aluminum tripropyl and small quantities of the hydrocarbon $CH_3C\!=\!CH_2$

$$\underset{\overset{|}{R}}{}$$

are mixed in with the dimeric propene. The reaction mechanism is postulated as proceeding through the following steps:

$$CH_3CH\!=\!CH_2 + R\!-\!al \rightarrow CH_3\underset{\overset{|}{R}}{C}HCH_2\!-\!al \qquad (16\text{-}71)$$

This aluminum isobutyl type compound undergoes a displacement reaction:

$$CH_3CH\!=\!CH_2 + CH_3\underset{\overset{|}{R}}{C}HCH_2\!-\!al \rightarrow CH_3CH_2CH_2\!-\!al + CH_3\underset{\overset{|}{R}}{C}\!=\!CH_2$$

$$(16\text{-}72)$$

The cycle is then renewed with the aluminum tripropyl:

$$CH_3CH\!=\!CH_2 + CH_3CH_2CH_2\!-\!al \rightarrow \underset{CH_3CHCH_2\!-\!al}{\overset{CH_3CH_2CH_2}{|}} \qquad (16\text{-}73)$$

$$CH_3CH\!=\!CH_2 + \underset{CH_3CHCH_2\!-\!al}{\overset{CH_3CH_2CH_2}{|}} \rightarrow CH_3CH_2CH_2\!-\!al +$$

$$\underset{CH_3C\!=\!CH_2}{\overset{CH_3CH_2CH_2}{|}} \qquad (16\text{-}74)$$

In all the higher α-olefins, from 1-butene and 1-pentene on up, the reaction is fundamentally the same:

$$2\ RCH\!=\!CH_2 \rightarrow \underset{RC\!=\!CH_2}{\overset{RCH_2CH_2}{|}} \qquad (16\text{-}75)$$

Distillation of the dimers or of their hydrogenation products reveals that straight chain hydrocarbons corresponding to the reactions

$$CH_3CH\!=\!CH_2 + CH_3CH_2CH_2\!-\!al \rightarrow CH_3\underset{\overset{|}{al}}{C}HCH_2CH_2CH_2CH_3$$

$$(16\text{-}76)$$

$$RCH\!=\!CH_2 + CH_3CH_2CH_2CH_2\!-\!al \rightarrow R\underset{\overset{|}{al}}{C}HCH_2CH_2CH_2CH_2CH_3$$

$$(16\text{-}77)$$

are formed in only 1–5% of the total products. Further, migration of the double bond in the branched chain principal products takes place to a very minor extent (52).

The reaction of LAH with propylene and 1-butene also yields the dimers (50).

The formation of α-olefin dimers also occurs with olefins containing non-terminal double bonds such as 2-butene, 2-pentene, and 3-heptene. These reactions go considerably slower than in the case of the α-olefins since they result from systems in which, in equilibrium, the α-olefin concentration is low (48). The dimers from 1-pentene and 2-pentene have been shown to be identical (52), indicating that dimer formation in the latter case arises from 1-pentene formed by migration of the double bond in 2-pentene.

$$CH_3CH_2CH{=}CHCH_3 \rightleftarrows CH_3CH_2CH_2\underset{\underset{al}{|}}{C}HCH_3 \rightleftarrows CH_3CH_2CH_2CH{=}CH_3 \qquad (16\text{-}78)$$

If the chain length in the non-terminal olefin exceeds twelve carbons the α-olefin content in the equilibrium, due to the number of possible isomers, becomes so small that dimerization is no longer possible to any extent. This limit does not hold for α-olefins since α-dodecene and its homologues are capable of dimerization (48). By means of an apparatus suitable for continuous dimerization, the mixed dimerization of different olefins can be carried out to yield a whole series of hydrocarbons of definite structure. Thus, propylene and 1-butene yield two mixed dimers (48).

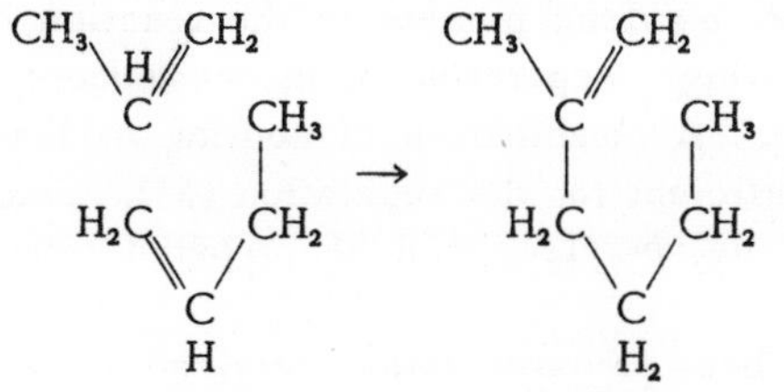

$$(16\text{-}79)$$

LXVII

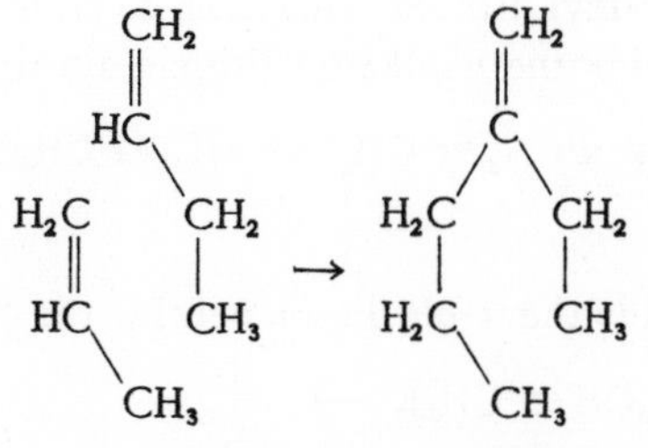

$$(16\text{-}80)$$

LXVIII

The dimers and mixed dimers prepared by these techniques can be converted into aromatic hydrocarbons by passage over chromium oxide catalysts at 400–500° (48,50,53). The mixed dimers from propylene and 1-butene, LXVII and LXVIII, both give toluene. The 1-butene dimer, 2-ethyl-1-hexene, gives 55% p-xylene, 26% o-xylene, and 19% ethylbenzene.

(16-81)

Since there is no m-xylene present in the reaction mixture and the p-xylene content is high, separation of the components of the mixture is relatively simple. A combination of cooling to low temperatures and distillation is sufficient for the separation (53). Since 1-butene is prepared from ethylene, p-xylene can be prepared from ethylene in three steps.

α-Olefins have been prepared using acetylene in the first step (50):

$$\text{LiAlH}_4 + 3\,\text{HC} \equiv \text{CH} \rightarrow \text{HLiAl(CH} = \text{CH}_2)_3 \qquad (16\text{-}82)$$

Treatment of the trivinyl lithium aluminum hydride with ethylene, as in equation (16-61), yields the trialkenyl lithium aluminum hydride:

$$\text{HLiAl(CH} = \text{CH}_2)_3 + x\,\text{CH}_2 = \text{CH}_2 \rightarrow \text{HLiAl[CH}_2\text{CH}_2(\text{CH}_2)_n\text{CH} = \text{CH}_2]_3 \qquad (16\text{-}83)$$

While hydrolysis yields the α-olefin, on heating the α,ω-diolefin is formed:

$$\text{HLiAl[CH}_2\text{CH}_2(\text{CH}_2)_n\text{CH} = \text{CH}_2]_3 \rightarrow$$

$$\text{LiAlH}_4 + 3\,\text{CH}_2 = \text{CH}(\text{CH}_2)_n\text{CH} = \text{CH}_2 \qquad (16\text{-}84)$$

16.3.4 Synthesis of Alcohols

The reaction of aluminum alkyls with oxygen results in the formation of aluminum alkoxides which can be hydrolyzed to primary alcohols (50a).

$$AlR_3 + 1.5\ O_2 \rightarrow Al(OR)_3 \xrightarrow{H_2O} 3\ ROH \qquad (16\text{-}85)$$

This reaction has been applied to the alkyls derived from isobutylene, α-methylstyrene, camphene, limonene and β-pinene.

Long chain primary fatty alcohols are prepared by the addition of oxygen to the aluminum alkyls obtained by the reaction of aluminum triethyl and ethylene (equation 16-58). Hydrolysis of the intermediate alkoxide yields the primary fatty alcohol.

$$CH_3CH_2\text{---}al + n\text{-}1\ CH_2 \!=\! CH_2 \rightarrow H\text{---}(CH_2CH_2)_n\text{---}al$$

$$(16\text{-}86)$$

$$H\text{---}(CH_2CH_2)_n\text{---}OH \leftarrow H\text{---}(CH_2CH_2)_n\text{---}O\text{---}al$$

Small quantities of nickel(II) chloride control the polymerization so that C_{10}, C_{12} and C_{14} chains predominate (50a). The cracking of paraffins such as those obtained by the Fischer-Tropsch process results in the formation of α-olefins which can be converted to aluminum alkyls, treated with oxygen and hydrolyzed to yield long chain primary fatty alcohols (50a).

REFERENCES

1. Conover, L. H., and D. S. Tarbell, *J. Am. Chem. Soc.*, 72, 3586 (1950).
2. Witkop, B., and J. B. Patrick, *J. Am. Chem. Soc.*, 74, 3855 (1952).
3. Cromwell, N. H., F. A. Miller, A. R. Johnson, R. L. Frank, and D. J. Wallace, *J. Am. Chem. Soc.*, 71, 3337 (1949).
4. Albertson, N. F., *J. Am. Chem. Soc.*, 74, 249 (1952).
5. Galinovsky, F., and R. Wieser, *Experientia*, 6, 377 (1950).
6. King, J. A., V. Hofmann, and F. H. McMillan, *J. Org. Chem.*, 16, 1100 (1951).
7. Galinovsky, F., A. Wagner, and R. Wieser, *Monatsh.*, 82, 551 (1951).
8. Galinovsky, F., O. Vogl, and R. Wieser, *Monatsh.*, 83, 114 (1952).
9. Gaylord, N. G., *Experientia*, 10, 351 (1954).
10. Trevoy, L. W., and W. G. Brown, *J. Am. Chem. Soc.*, 71, 1675 (1949).
11. Paddock, N. L., *Nature*, 167, 1070 (1951).
12. Lavie, D., and E. D. Bergmann, *Bull. soc. chim. France*, [5] 18, 250 (1951).
13. Gaylord, N. G. *Experientia*, 10, 166 (1954).
14. Badger, G. M., J. H. Seidler, and B. Thomson, *J. Chem. Soc.*, 1951, 3207.
15. Johnson, W. S., and B. G. Buell, *J. Am. Chem. Soc.*, 74, 4517 (1952).
16. Witkop, B., and J. B. Patrick, *Experientia*, 6, 183 (1950).
17. Witkop, B., *J. Am. Chem. Soc.*, 72, 614 (1950).
18. Witkop, B., and J. B. Patrick, *J. Am. Chem. Soc.*, 73, 713 (1951).
19. Julian, P. L., and H. C. Printy, *J. Am. Chem. Soc.*, 71, 3206 (1949).
20. Treibs, A., and H. Scherer, *Ann.*, 577, 139 (1952).
21. Conover, L. H., and D. S. Tarbell, *J. Am. Chem. Soc.*, 72, 5221 (1950).
22. Mićović, V. M., and M. L. Michailović, *Rec. trav. chim.*, 71, 970 (1952).

23. Jones, R. G., and E. C. Kornfeld, *J. Am. Chem. Soc.*, 73, 107 (1951).
24. de Mayo, P., and W. Rigby, *Nature*, 166, 1075 (1950).
25. Cronyn, M. W., and J. E. Goodrich, *J. Am. Chem. Soc.*, 74, 3936 (1952).
26. Mustafa, A., and M. K. Hilmy, *J. Chem. Soc.*, 1952, 1343.
27. Freudenberg, K., and G. Wilke, *Chem. Ber.*, 85, 78 (1952).
28. Challenger, F., B. Fishwick, and J. L. Holmes, *Chemistry and Industry*, 1952, 519.
29. Scully, J. F., and E. V. Brown, *Abstracts of Papers*, 121st American Chemical Society, Buffalo, New York, March 1952, p. 44K.
30. Lavie, D., and E. D. Bergmann, *Bull. soc. chim. France*, [5] 18, 250 (1951).
31. Bergmann, E. D., E. Fischer, D. Ginsburg, Y. Hirshberg, D. Lavie, M. Mayot, A. Pullman, and B. Pullman, *Bull. soc. chim. France*, [5] 18, 684 (1951).
32. Bergmann, E. D., and D. Lavie, *J. Am. Chem. Soc.*, 74, 3173 (1952).
33. Bergmann, E. D., G. Berthier, D. Ginsburg, Y. Hirshberg, D. Lavie, S. Pinchas, B. Pullman, and A. Pullman, *Bull. soc. chim. France*, [5] 18, 661 (1951).
34. Bergmann, E. D., *Bull. soc. chim. France*, [5] 19, 703 (1952).
35. Sonntag, N. O. V., S. Linder, E. I. Becker, and P. E. Spoerri, *J. Am. Chem. Soc.*, 75, 2283 (1953).
36. Lutz, R. E., and J. S. Gillespie, Jr., *J. Am. Chem. Soc.*, 72, 2002 (1950).
37. Hochstein, F. A., *J. Am. Chem. Soc.*, 71, 305 (1949).
38. Boekelheide, V., and C. E. Larrabee, *J. Am. Chem. Soc.*, 72, 1245 (1950).
39. Bergmann, E. D., Y. Hirshberg, and D. Lavie, *Bull. soc. chim. France*, [5] 19, 268 (1952).
40. Bordwell, F. G., and W. H. McKellin, *J. Am. Chem. Soc.*, 73, 2251 (1951).
41. Mousseron, M., and M. Canet, *Bull. soc. chim. France*, [5] 19, 247 (1952).
42. Backer, H. J., J. Strating, and J. Drenth, *Rec. trav. chim.*, 70, 365 (1951).
43. Backer, H. J., *Rec. trav. chim.*, 68, 844 (1949).
44. Adams, R., and W. Moje, *J. Am. Chem. Soc.*, 74, 5557 (1952).
45. Elstrow, W. E., and B. C. Platt, *Chemistry and Industry*, 1952, 449.
46. Oppenauer, in *Newer Methods of Preparative Chemistry*, Interscience Publishers, New York, N. Y., 1948, p. 143.
47. Ott, A. C., and M. F. Murray, U. S. Pat. 2,625,556 (January 13, 1953).
48. Ziegler, K., *Angew. Chem.*, 64, 323 (1952).
49. Ziegler, K., *Brennstoff Chem.*, 33, 193 (1952).
50. Ziegler, K., *European Scientific Notes*, 6, 178 (1952).
50a. Ziegler, K., lecture before XIVth International Congress of Pure and Applied Chemistry, Zurich, Switzerland, July 1955.
50b. *Chem. Eng. News*, 33, 3486 (1955).
51. Martin, H., *Angew. Chem.*, 64, 330 (1952).
51a. Mark, H., private communication, report on visit to Max Planck Institute for Coal Research, Mulheim-Ruhr, Germany.
51b. Mark, H., private communication, report on visit to Farbwerke Hoechst, Frankfurt-on-Main, Germany.
51c. Natta, G., lecture at Macromolecular Symposium, XVIIIth Conference of the International Union of Pure and Applied Chemistry, Zurich, Switzerland, July 1955.
52. Zosel, K., *Angew. Chem.*, 64, 330 (1952).
53. Sauer, H., *Angew. Chem.*, 64, 330 (1952).

CHAPTER 17

EXPERIMENTAL CONDITIONS FOR COMPLEX
METAL HYDRIDE REACTIONS

The experimental conditions for effecting complex metal hydride reactions are determined by the desired reaction temperature, the solubilities of the hydride, the compound to be reduced and the intermediate
complexes, as well as by the moisture-sensitivity of the hydride. The
latter factor is more important in the reactions of LAH, aluminum hydride, magnesium aluminum hydride and lithium borohydride than in reactions involving sodium and potassium borohydrides and sodium
trimethoxyborohydride.

17.1 REDUCTIONS WITH LITHIUM ALUMINUM HYDRIDE,
ALUMINUM HYDRIDE AND MAGNESIUM
ALUMINUM HYDRIDE

17.1.1 General

Reductions with LAH and aluminum hydride are effected by techniques
similar to those involved in Grignard reactions. The reactions are generally carried out in a flask equipped with a stirrer driven by an explosion-
proof or air-driven motor, and a reflux condenser protected against the
entrance of moisture and carbon dioxide by means of a drying tube filled
with the appropriate agent. The material to be reduced is added in solution, if readily soluble, from a similarly protected dropping funnel. When
the substance to be reduced is of limited solubility, it is placed in the
thimble of an extractor and carried into the reaction flask by the refluxing
solvent. A Soxhlet extractor or one providing continuous solvent return
is satisfactory for this purpose.

The majority of LAH reductions are carried out by the "direct" addition method, i.e., by the addition of the substance to be reduced to a
solution or slurry of LAH. The "inverse" addition method, i.e., the
addition of a calculated amount of LAH in solution to a solution of the
material to be reduced, is often used for selective reductions. The reaction results in the precipitation of an intermediate complex which is decomposed by acid or base and the product is isolated from the ether or
other solvent extract.

In a very small number of cases reductions have been carried out in
the absence of a solvent (1-3).

Several cases have been reported in which a lithium aluminum alcoholate rather than the hydride itself has been utilized as the reducing
agent (4,5).

Only a limited number of reductions have been carried out with either the aluminum hydride-aluminum chloride addition compound or magnesium aluminum hydride. In both cases reactions have been carried out in ether solution and the techniques used in LAH reductions are generally applicable to these reagents.

17.1.2 Introduction of Reactants

Reductions using "direct" or "normal" addition techniques involve addition to a solution of LAH. Such reductions can be carried out in a multitude of solvents. The choice of solvent is dependent upon the solubilities of the hydride, the compound to be reduced and the intermediate complexes. The most commonly used solvents for LAH are diethyl ether and tetrahydrofuran although dioxane, di-*n*-butyl ether, di-*n*- and isopropyl ethers, *n*-butyl ethyl ether, diethylene glycol diethyl ether, tetrahydrofurfuryloxytetrahydropyran, N-ethylmorpholine, pyridine, and various other miscellaneous solvents indicated in the tables in the previous sections have been used. The solvents or mixture of solvents of choice are also determined by the desired reaction temperature.

The preparation of solutions of LAH demands precautions necessitated by the moisture-sensitivity and reactivity of the complex metal hydride. All solvents must be carefully dried to prevent loss of LAH efficiency by reaction with water as well as to preclude the premature and potentially hazardous evolution of hydrogen. In addition, all solvents must be peroxide-free since the rapid exothermic reaction of LAH with peroxide-containing solvents has been reported to result in fires and explosions, as discussed in Section 17.1.5. Freedom from other reactive groups, such as alcohols, amines, and carbonyl derivatives, is desirable to maintain reduction efficiency.

Crushing of lumps of LAH to a coarse powder prior to solution is recommended to increase the rate of solution. This can be carried out in an inert atmosphere in a dry box or a well-ventilated hood, using aluminum foil wrapping and a rubber hammer, as illustrated in Figure 2. Grinding lumps of LAH in a mortar and pestle is an extremely dangerous practice and is not recommended since considerable heat may be generated.

Stirring the powdered LAH with the solvent yields a slurry which may be used directly for the reduction. Where reductions are carried out frequently a clarified stock solution may be desirable. This may be prepared by refluxing the slurry for several hours, followed by filtration under nitrogen pressure into a storage container or into the reaction vessel. The preparation of stock solutions of LAH in ether and tetrahydrofuran (6,7), as well as an apparatus for the storage of LAH-ether solutions from which exact aliquots may be conveniently drawn (8), is described in the literature.

Where a slurry of LAH is used, sufficient solution may be obtained by refluxing for a short period before introduction of the compound to be re-

Figure 2. Crushing of lithium aluminum hydride.

duced. However, where refluxing is utilized in the reaction period, pre-solution of the LAH is not necessary.

If the substance to be reduced, liquid or solid, is soluble in an LAH solvent, such solution is added slowly to the LAH solution or slurry, with cooling if a low temperature is desired or while maintaining gentle reflux. If the compound is not soluble in an LAH solvent then a non-reducible solvent which is miscible with the LAH solvent may be used. Toward this end benzene, petroleum ether, and mixtures of various solvents have been utilized.

For solids of limited solubility the material is placed in the thimble of a Soxhlet or continuous-return type of extractor and carried into the reaction flask by the refluxing solvent. Solid reactants have been introduced manually through the opening in a wide-bore reflux condenser or from an

Erlenmayer flask connected to a neck of the reaction vessel by means of a collapsible rubber tubing having a wide inside diameter.

Reductions involving the "inverse" addition method require the addition of LAH to a solution of the compound to be reduced. A solution of LAH, prepared as discussed previously, is added slowly while maintaining the desired temperature. This particular technique is advantageous where a calculated amount of LAH is used. A slurry of LAH in a solvent, added through a wide-bore dropping funnel, may also be employed in the "inverse" addition method.

17.1.3 The Reaction Proper

The desired reaction temperature is obtained by the proper choice of solvents. Refluxing, without stirring, is generally satisfactory for the maintenance of high temperatures. Low temperatures are obtained by external cooling and usually require stirring for adequate heat transfer.

The reaction time is determined by the ease of reduction of the compound under investigation and the solubility of the intermediate complexes. Extended reflux periods are desirable where these complexes have a low solubility in the reaction media. In the case of readily reduced compounds it is often sufficient to decompose the reaction mixture immediately after the addition of reactants is completed.

17.1.4 Isolation of Products

Reactions involving excess LAH require the destruction of this excess prior to the isolation of the reduction products. Adequate stirring and the use of an air-driven or explosion-proof motor are necessary for the safe performance of this operation. The cautious addition of water, wet ether or an ethanol-ether mixture results in the evolution of hydrogen which must be anticipated when setting up the equipment. Ethyl acetate, which does not generate hydrogen gas on reduction with LAH, is satisfactory for the decomposition of large excesses of LAH.

In order to isolate the reduction product it is necessary to decompose the intermediate complex. A dilute acid solution or a mixture of ice and acid can be used where the product is stable to acid and soluble in ether. The isolation of basic products can be accomplished by adding excess sodium hydroxide solution to dissolve the precipitated aluminum hydroxide and separating the organic phase. Frequently this procedure results in incomplete solution of the inorganic precipitate or on extraction with ether an emulsified middle layer results. If the basic product is alkali-sensitive an aqueous solution of sodium potassium tartrate may be used to form a soluble aluminum complex.

In many cases solution of the alumina is not necessary since filtration of the precipitate permits the isolation of the product from the filtrate. Frequently the alumina is formed as a voluminous precipitate which is filtered with difficulty and traps some of the reduction product. This is especially true where the product is an amine or an amino alcohol. Various procedures have been suggested in order to produce a granular precipitate which absorbs very little product and is easy to filter and wash. One proposal (9) involves the addition of an amount of water limited to a slight excess over that required for the hydrolysis of both the excess hydride and the complex. A second procedure (10) consists in decomposing the reduction complex and excess LAH with a calculated amount of water and 20% sodium hydroxide (n g. of LAH requires the successive addition of n ml. of water, $0.75n$ ml. of 20% sodium hydroxide, and $3.5n$ ml. of water). A modification of the procedure (11) involves n ml. of water, n ml. of 15% sodium hydroxide, and $3n$ ml. of water for n g. of LAH. Crystalline precipitates have recently been obtained by decomposition with isopropanol followed by the addition of a saturated sodium chloride solution (12).

The use of continuous extraction procedures may be necessary in the recovery of water-soluble products from hydrolyzed reduction mixtures in which precipitated alumina has been solubilized with excess sodium hydroxide or sodium potassium tartrate. Similarly, extraction may be necessary to recover product absorbed on granular lithium aluminate precipitates.

Treatment of the hydrolyzed reduction mixture or an extract thereof with an excess of an acid chloride or anhydride converts the product to an acyl derivative which is more readily crystallizable or extractable.

The preparation of labeled methanol and ethanol by the reduction of labeled carbon dioxide and acetic acid has involved alcoholysis of the complex with non-volatile solvents such as tetrahydrofurfuryl alcohol, diethylene glycol monobutyl ether, ethylene glycol monophenyl ether and benzyl alcohol. The more volatile reduction products are readily recovered by distillation.

17.1.5 Hazards

The evolution of hydrogen gas during the course of LAH reductions or during the hydrolysis of reduction mixtures presents a potential fire hazard. Consequently open flames and non-explosion-proof electrical equipment should be excluded from the area where operations involving LAH are carried out. The flammability of the solvents such as ether and tetrahydrofuran commonly used with LAH increases the fire hazard.

The presence of impurities in the ethereal solvents may result in fires or even explosions. Incompletely dried solvents may evolve hydrogen and ignite on the addition of LAH. Carbon dioxide has been blamed for explosions occasionally observed during the evaporation of ethereal solutions of LAH and aluminum hydride (13). Thus, explosions have occurred toward the end of distillations undertaken to remove the solvent from dimethyl ether solutions of LAH and have been traced to the presence of carbon dioxide as an impurity. The removal of carbon dioxide by fractionation of the solvent in vacuo prior to the preparation of the LAH solution renders the ether harmless. Reintroduction of carbon dioxide into the purified sample results in explosions on evaporation of the LAH solution. Treatment of diethyl ether solutions of LAH with considerable quantities of carbon dioxide results in explosions on evaporation. Heating the residue from the evaporation of impure dimethyl ether and dimethylcellosolve solutions of aluminum hydride results in detonation if a large excess of aluminum chloride is present.

It has been reported that methyl ethers contain approximately double the concentration of peroxides found in ethyl ethers. An explosion during the distillation of a solution of LAH in diethylene glycol dimethyl ether has been attributed to the presence of these peroxides and it has been recommended that LAH never be used to dry methyl ethers (14). Peroxides or their reaction products with LAH have been held responsible for the vigorous reaction and consequent fire that occurred on the addition of LAH to tetrahydrofuran which had been stored for two years over calcium hydride (15). Tetrahydrofuran should be purified immediately before use or tested with moistened potassium iodide-starch paper to assure the absence of peroxides.

The complexes from the reactions of LAH with various perfluoro compounds have been reported to detonate. The reaction of LAH with perfluorosuccinamide yields an unstable complex which detonates at room temperature. The complexes from LAH and trifluoroacetic acid, perfluorobutyramide as well as perfluoroadipamide require heating on a hot plate before the deep-seated decomposition occurs. It is recommended that LAH reductions of fluorochemicals should be carried out with relatively large volumes of ether to avoid the accumulation of solids on the sides of the flask and in the hydrolysis step, and the addition of ethanol followed by water is preferable to the addition of pure water (16).

Fires occurring during LAH or aluminum hydride reactions can be extinguished with sand. Carbon dioxide-filled fire extinguishers are not recommended. Dry chemical fire equipment containing specially treated sodium bicarbonate has been found to be effective in controlling these fires (17).

17.2 REDUCTIONS WITH LITHIUM BOROHYDRIDE

Lithium borohydride reductions are generally carried out by procedures similar to those used in LAH reductions. Either diethyl ether, tetrahydrofuran or mixtures thereof are used as solvents and reaction media although in one case a mixture of dimethylformamide and tetrahydrofuran has been used (18). Reaction temperatures vary from $0°$, maintained by external cooling, to reflux temperatures, while reaction times are determined by the nature of the reducible group. The intermediate complexes are decomposed by acid or basic hydrolysis and the product is isolated from the organic layer or extracted from the aqueous phase. In some cases the intermediate borate complex may be difficult to hydrolyze as in the reduction of polyhydroxy compounds and α-hydroxy acids.

Solid lithium borohydride is highly hygroscopic and may flash on exposure to humid air. The solid should therefore be handled in a dry, preferably inert, atmosphere. On the other hand, solutions of the borohydride are relatively insensitive to moisture and no special precautions are necessary while carrying out reactions.

Since it is difficult to store and prevent the hydrolytic decomposition of solid lithium borohydride, a readily prepared equimolar mixture of potassium borohydride and lithium chloride in tetrahydrofuran has been found to be a satisfactory replacement for lithium borohydride in the reduction of esters to alcohols (19).

17.3 REDUCTIONS WITH SODIUM BOROHYDRIDE

17.3.1 General

The experimental techniques utilized in sodium borohydride reductions are quite different from those in reductions with LAH since the borohydride need not be protected from moisture and reactions can be carried out in hydroxylic solvents. Although hydrogen is not evolved in the course of the reduction, due to the non-reaction of active hydrogens, provision must be made for the evolution of hydrogen gas as a result of the decomposition of excess borohydride at the termination of a reduction. Hydrogen gas may be evolved during a reduction if the reaction is carried out under acidic conditions.

As in the case of LAH reductions, "direct" and "inverse" addition methods are utilized in sodium borohydride reactions. The water or alkali sensitivity of the compound to be reduced dictates the choice of reaction medium and the method of addition. The desired reaction temperature may also be a determining factor in the choice of solvent. The reaction results in the formation of complexes which are hydrolyzed by acid or base and the product is isolated in the usual manner. In some cases the complexes are relatively resistant to hydrolysis and boron-free reduction products are not readily isolated. This difficulty has been overcome by more drastic hydrolysis conditions as well as by the use of ion exchange techniques or conversion of reduction products to acylated derivatives.

17.3.2 Introduction of Reactants and the Reaction Proper

Reductions with sodium borohydride are generally carried out in aqueous or alcoholic solution under neutral, basic or acidic conditions. Reductions may be carried out in neutral aqueous solutions by dissolving the required quantity of borohydride immediately before use. Since the borohydride decomposes rapidly in aqueous solution, the latter can be stabilized by the addition of a small quantity of dilute sodium hydroxide, and may be stored for a reasonable period if a sufficiently high pH is maintained. In order to obtain a suitable rate of reaction, in some cases the pH is reduced to a value of 9-10 during the actual reduction by the addition of boric acid (20). In acidic reactions the pH may be maintained at 3-4 by the addition of dilute sulfuric acid as needed (21-23). In order to avoid the acid-catalyzed decomposition of borohydride which would be caused by free acidic groups, carboxylic acids are neutralized with sodium hydroxide prior to reduction.

The majority of borohydride reductions are carried out in methanol, ethanol or aqueous alcoholic solutions. The use of aqueous dioxane and methanol-ether and dioxane-water-methanol mixtures has also been reported. A suspension of sodium borohydride in dioxane or diethylene glycol diethyl ether provides the non-aqueous medium necessary for the reduction of acid chlorides. In one case (24) a low yield obtained in the reduction of a polyhalogenated ketone with sodium borohydride in water or methanol has been attributed to the formation of a stable hydrate or hemiacetal, decreasing the quantity of available free carbonyl compound.

Normally, in the "direct" addition method, a solution of the compound to be reduced is added to a solution of sodium borohydride. In the case of alkali-sensitive compounds, a solution of such a compound is added to a solution of the hydride in order to avoid prolonged contact of unreduced compound with alkali. Compounds of low solubility are conveniently reduced by adding a solution of the hydride to a suspension of the compound; in such cases the reaction mixture becomes homogeneous as the reaction proceeds. This "inverse" addition method is used in the reduction of acid chlorides as well as in the directed reduction of various sugar lactones and steroidal enol acetates.

Reaction conditions may vary from various periods of time at 0° to prolonged refluxing, dependent upon the desired degree of reduction selectivity or the difficult reducibility of particular functional groups.

17.3.3 Isolation of Products

The reduction products from sodium borohydride reactions are generally isolated by decomposing the intermediate borates under acidic conditions. Excess borohydride is decomposed at the same time. Dilute acetic, hydrochloric, and sulfuric acids have been used for this purpose. Hydrolysis may also be accomplished, particularly when dioxane is the reaction medium, by adding water or an aqueous sodium carbonate or bicarbonate solution and raising the temperature.

The stability of the intermediate borates presents the greatest difficulty in the isolation of reduction products. In the reduction of some aromatic aldehydes and ketones heating with alkali is necessary in order to liberate the alcohols. Stable complexes are formed by α-hydroxy acids and various polyhydroxy compounds such as the sugar alcohols so that boron-free reduction products are not readily isolated. This difficulty has been overcome by treatment of the crude reduction products with methanolic hydrogen chloride or potassium hydroxide as well as by the use of ion exchange resins (21,23,25). Conversion of polyhydroxy compounds to fully acylated derivatives which are readily crystallized and hydrolyzed to the parent alcohols also overcomes product isolation difficulties.

17.4 REDUCTIONS WITH POTASSIUM BOROHYDRIDE

The techniques utilized in potassium borohydride reductions are similar to those used with the sodium compound. Reductions are carried out in aqueous or alcoholic media under neutral or alkaline conditions. Reductions of acid chlorides are carried out in inert solvents. The intermediate complex is generally decomposed with acid and the product is extracted with solvents.

The course of the reduction of quaternary pyridinium and quinolinium salts with potassium borohydride is determined by the reaction conditions. Thus, reduction carried out in strongly alkaline medium and in the cold favors the formation of dihydro derivatives while slightly basic medium and heat yields tetrahydro compounds (26). In the reduction of methyl nicotinate methiodide in a weakly alkaline solution it is reported that an aqueous borohydride solution is added rapidly to the quaternary salt and the mixture is extracted with ether as rapidly as possible, otherwise complexes are formed which are not extractable with solvents and are not the same as with the acidic decomposition of excess borohydride (27). In some cases the reaction product cannot be extracted from the aqueous phase by solvents and is isolated in the form of a derivative such as the reineckate.

The non-hygroscopic nature of potassium borohydride permits reactions to be carried out in a relatively simple manner. The hydride may be handled in air with complete safety and aqueous solutions are readily prepared. Provision must be made for the evolution of hydrogen gas resulting from the decomposition of excess borohydride at the conclusion of a given reaction.

REFERENCES

1. Sampey, J. R., and J. M. Cox, *J. Am. Chem. Soc.*, *71*, 1507 (1949).
2. Coates, G. E., *J. Chem. Soc.*, *1950*, 3481.
3. Paddock, N. L., *Nature*, *167*, 1070 (1951).
4. Goodman, I., *J. Chem. Soc.*, *1951*, 2209.
5. Bothner-By, A. A., *J. Am. Chem. Soc.*, *73*, 846 (1951).
6. Brown, W. G., in *Organic Reactions*, Vol. VI, p. 484.
7. Rapoport, H., and G. B. Payne, *J. Org. Chem.*, *15*, 1093 (1950).
8. Dillard, C. R., *J. Chem. Education*, *29*, 129 (1952).
9. Brown, W. G., in *Organic Reactions*, Vol. VI, p. 488.
10. Amundsen, L. H., and L. S. Nelson, *J. Am. Chem. Soc.*, *73*, 242 (1950).
11. Mićović, V. M., and M. L. Mihailović, *J. Org. Chem.*, *18*, 1190 (1953).
12. Brown, R. F., private communication.
13. Barbaras, G., G. D. Barbaras, A. E. Finholt, and H. I. Schlesinger, *J. Am. Chem. Soc.*, *70*, 877 (1948).
14. *Chem. Eng. News*, *31*, 2334 (1953).
15. Moffett, R. B., and B. D. Aspergren, through *Chem. Eng. News*, *32*, 4328 (1954).
16. Reid, T. S., and G. H. Smith, through *Chem. Eng. News*, *29*, 3042 (1951).
17. *Chem. Eng. News*, *32*, 1616 (1954).
18. Wendler, N. L., Huang-Minlon, and M. Tishler, *J. Am. Chem. Soc.*, *73*, 3818 (1951).
19. Paul, R., and N. Joseph, *Bull. soc. chim. France*, [5] *19*, 550 (1952).
20. Lindberg, B., and A. Misiorny, *Svensk Papperstidn.*, *55*, 13 (1952); *Chem. Abstracts*, *46*, 7942 (1952).
21. Wolfrom, M. L., and H. B. Wood, *J. Am. Chem. Soc.*, *73*, 2933 (1951).
22. Shechter, H., D. E. Ley, and L. Zeldin, *J. Am. Chem. Soc.*, *74*, 3664 (1952).
23. Wolfrom, M. L., and K. Anno, *J. Am. Chem. Soc.*, *74*, 5583 (1952).
24. McBee, E. T., and T. M. Burton, *J. Am. Chem. Soc.*, *74*, 3022 (1952).
25. Abdel-Akher, M., J. K. Hamilton, and F. Smith, *J. Am. Chem. Soc.*, *73*, 4691 (1951).
26. Panouse, J. J., *Compt. rend.*, *233*, 260 (1951).
27. Panouse, J. J., *Compt. rend.*, *233*, 1200 (1951).

CHAPTER 18

HANDLING COMPLEX METAL HYDRIDES ON
A COMMERCIAL SCALE

18.1 INTRODUCTION

Complex hydrides are being used in countless laboratories to perform specific reductions of organic compounds with ease, rapidity, and in high yields. From these many research applications eventually come a number of industrial processes. Even on a small, pilot-plant scale, engineers and development personnel, when confronted with the use of complex hydrides, have to consider the problems and hazards inherent in their application. It is the object of this chapter to discuss, as fully as practical, the various hazards and problems involved, and to outline methods and materials to be used which permit the safe and economic employment of these hydrides on a commercial scale. This knowledge is collected from the observation of actual industrial installations using these hydrides, from experience in large-scale preparation of the hydrides, and from numerous laboratory tests.

At the present time, four complex hydrides are available on a commercial basis (Metal Hydrides Incorporated, Beverly, Massachusetts): lithium aluminum hydride, sodium borohydride, potassium borohydride, and sodium trimethoxyborohydride; and as far as handling safety is concerned, they may be divided into two groups. The first group contains those hydrides which are so moisture-sensitive that contact of the hydride with moisture in any form causes spontaneous ignition, frequently violently. LAH is the chief member of this group; also included are lithium borohydride (available on pilot-plant scale only), and sodium hydride (a primary, rather than a complex hydride). The second group of complex hydrides includes the three borohydrides just mentioned, and to them, water is not a safety hazard, but rather, a purity hazard. Indeed, two of the three borohydrides, sodium and potassium, can be dissolved in water and recovered from aqueous solution in a high state of purity; while the third, sodium trimethoxyborohydride, is hydrolyzed rapidly and completely by water, however, without the evolution of sufficient heat or hydrogen to cause ignition.

All the complex hydrides, with the exception of potassium borohydride, are extremely hygroscopic and are subject to varying rates of decomposition in the presence of moisture, the rates increasing with temperature. Thus, LAH dissolved in ether may heat up sufficiently when exposed to moist air to ignite, sodium trimethoxyborohydride will absorb atmospheric moisture and promptly hydrolyze, while sodium borohydride absorbs moisture and forms the dihydrate, from which it can be recovered unchanged by vacuum treatment at low temperature. Potassium borohydride is the only hydride of the group which is not hygroscopic.

A second general problem accompanying the large-scale handling of all complex hydrides is their brittleness, which causes even large lumps, when handled in bulk, to crumble sufficiently to form fine dust, presenting the well-recognized hazard of a typical dust explosion. The dust hazard is also complicated by the fact that these dusts are highly hygroscopic. The combustion of any of the complex hydrides, or their hydrolysis, points out their outstanding chemical property, namely, that they are tremendous reservoirs of hydrogen. When a lump of LAH, for instance, burns, the first stage is the decomposition of the hydride to give hydrogen, which burns with a soft, luminous flame, followed by an intense, white-heat combustion of the metals. In dry air, LAH starts to give off hydrogen between $120-150°$, and ignites in the same range. Sodium borohydride and potassium borohydride, however, do not start to decompose until the temperature is around $500°$, to liberate hydrogen, while sodium trimethoxyborohydride melts and disproportionates to sodium borohydride, sodium methoxide and methyl borate at $240-250°$. The evolution of hydrogen by heating or moisture presents the general problem of adequate ventilation, use of explosion-proof electrical equipment, and careful choice of storage and handling areas. Since the evolution of hydrogen on the absorption of moisture is a continuing, rather than an instantaneous, process in some cases, especially once a surface coat of hydrolysis product is built up on the particle, storage containers which have been exposed to moist atmospheres should be sealed cautiously, to prevent internal pressure build-ups which would cause bursting, followed by dust explosion, and perhaps general fire. The dust hazard also dictates that spark-proof implements be utilized, with containers and operators' clothing sufficiently grounded or static-proofed.

18.2 HANDLING TECHNIQUES PECULIAR TO LITHIUM ALUMINUM HYDRIDE

The principal hazards to consider when handling LAH on an industrial scale is water in any form, and this hazard is greatly increased when LAH is dissolved in a highly inflammable solvent such as diethyl ether (the solvent most generally used with this hydride). Points from which water must be eliminated when considering commercial installations with LAH include: solvents for the LAH and for the compound to be reduced; sprinkler systems and open steam lines in areas where LAH is stored, crushed, weighed and dissolved; atmospheric moisture collecting in cold traps; and water left from the clean-out of valves, gauges, traps, etc., in processing equipment. The precautions necessary to keep LAH away from water in its handling and storage are complicated by the common industrial practice of using aqueous acids to destroy the lithium aluminum alcoholate complexes which form as the result of LAH reductions. That this can successfully be accomplished is pointed out by several large-scale commercial users who have employed the material over a period of years without accident.

The handling of LAH on an industrial scale starts with the storage of sealed cans of the hydride as received from the manufacturer. This should be carried out in an area that is free from water, steam or other high-temperature lines, the heating effect of sun, or local high-temperature processes, and be well ventilated. The cans themselves should be handled with sufficient care to prevent their rupture by dropping or banging. The hydride is generally shipped in lump form, but travel will cause a small percentage of fines to be worn off the chunks. The material as it comes from the can can be added directly to solution tanks, although its rate of solution is greatly increased by a gentle pre-crushing. In normally humid atmospheres this pre-crushing is best carried out in a dry, inert-atmosphere box, the entire contents of the can being used at a single time. In less humid atmospheres, material can be carefully crushed by wrapping the lumps in aluminum foil, and tapping gently with a rubber hammer, if the operation is carried out in a well ventilated hood which will remove dusts and the small amount of hydrogen which may be evolved. Restoring of the crushed material should be done cautiously.

It is not recommended that the solid be added directly to the compound to be reduced, since it is difficult to meter solids accurately. If a liquid which is a solvent for LAH cannot be tolerated, it can be caused to react as a slurry in a non-solvent, non-reactive media such as a hydrocarbon. *Halogenated hydrocarbons must not be used.*

The solution or slurrying of the hydride should be done in an area where the minimum amount of solvent is exposed, and if the solvent is inflammable, utmost care must be taken that sparks, flames or hot areas are not present. The equipment itself may be made of mild steel and the reductions carried out at atmospheric pressure. If the nature of the solvent demands higher pressures, naturally, pressure vessels should be used. Hydride and solutions of it are not corrosive to metals in general. Glass equipment may be used, except that traces of moisture may cause sufficient hydrolysis to form highly alkaline lithium aluminates, which will etch the glass. The containers for the hydrides should be set outdoors after emptying, to weather briefly, prior to disposal.

A standard practice in solution is to add the lump or lightly crushed hydride to a loading hopper which has been baked dry and flushed with nitrogen until there is less than one percent oxygen present. The sealed hopper is then connected to the dissolving tank containing the desired solvent (also flushed with nitrogen), and the hydride added at a rate depending upon the extent of stirring and cooling of the solution. All solvents or slurrying media must be especially dried to prevent vigorous evolution of hydrogen and the destruction of some of the reducing power. In some cases, commercial anhydrous solvents are not sufficiently dried, and should be further dried by distilling or decanting from calcium hydride, sodium hydride, or, in extreme cases, from LAH. Actual moisture determinations are advisable, with water contents of greater than 0.5% unsatisfactory. To promote solution, refluxing for several hours may be helpful. After this time, the rather voluminous but extremely light residue which remains need not be separated, since it also contains reducing power. However, for solutions of exact concentration or for crystal clarity, filtration or centrifuging will separate the undissolved residue.

Solutions of LAH can be added directly into the reduction vessel, in which case the compound to be reduced is added to it at a controlled rate, or the LAH syrup can be added at a controlled rate to the compound to be reduced. In certain reactions, cooling of the reaction vessel may be advisable to prevent loss of the solvent or reduction of double bonds. For volatile solvents, a reflux condenser is a necessity, and its capacity will dictate the rate of addition for a particular reaction.

When the reaction is complete, the excess LAH can be destroyed by the cautious addition of ethyl acetate, alcohols, moist solvent, or nitrogen gas saturated with moisture, or the careful addition of the finished mix solutions to ice water. In the case of the latter four methods, considerable volumes of hydrogen will be given off, which must be vented through a condenser or hood. It is generally preferable to run the reaction mixture into a separate vessel prior to the destruction of excess LAH by water or alcohol, to prevent contamination of the main reaction vessel by these materials. When hydrogen ceases to be evolved, indicating the complete destruction of the LAH excess, treatment with aqueous acid will destroy the lithium aluminum alcoholates, to permit recovery of the alcohols or other organic compounds. When quantities of syrup are to be destroyed, it can be added to an excess of cold ethyl acetate in ethyl ether and then washed out with water.

A typical system for carrying out LAH reductions is shown in Fig. 3.

To decompose solids in movable equipment, the equipment should be transported to an area away from inflammables and dry dioxane added to cover the solids, followed by the slow and cautious addition of either water, wet dioxane or a mixture of methanol and dioxane while venting. When it is certain that all activity has been destroyed, the apparatus may be opened with care and flushed with water to clean it thoroughly. Hydrogen gas is liberated during the decomposition; no flames or sparks or other igniting sources should be present.

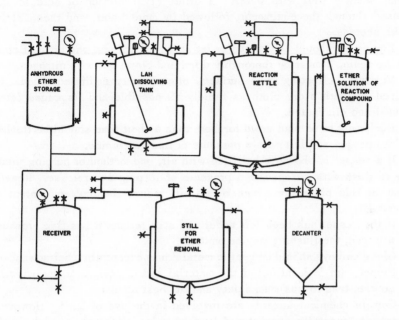

(Courtesy of Metal Hydrides Inc.)

Figure 3. In this typical system for carrying out lithium aluminum hydride reductions, anhydrous ether is added from the storage tank to make the desired solution in the dissolving tank. LAH is then pushed by nitrogen pressure into the reaction kettle, where the compound to be reduced may or may not be present, depending on which is to be used in excess. Kettle can be heated or cooled by the jacket. After reaction is complete, ethyl acetate is added to the reaction kettle to destroy excess LAH. The entire solution goes to the decanter, where water and acid are added to destroy the lithium aluminum hydride alcoholate complex. Ethereal solution of the product is then run to the ether still where condensate is collected in the receiver, dried, and returned to storage.

Solids in stationary equipment are decomposed in the same manner, being careful to allow for the build-up of pressures of hydrogen. The decomposed solution is then drawn off at the bottom and the equipment flushed with quantities of water followed by a flush with acetone and ether and drying with heat. The tank must be absolutely dry before addition of the reactants.

Light, movable equipment contaminated with the hydrides should be washed at the earliest possible moment, and this should include such equipment as flasks, glass carboys, and siphoning tubes.

The wash area should be remote from the production area. The equipment is placed on a dry metal basin, then water from a nearby hose is sprayed on gradually until there is no danger of a fire. The equipment is then washed well with water. A dilute (1%) solution of acid is then rinsed through the equipment, followed by more water, and then, lastly, with acetone.

Equipment should be drained or let stand for at least one hour. Before using again, it must be thoroughly dried and blown out with nitrogen.

Moisture collecting upon surfaces of stationary equipment should be wiped off with a dry cloth as rapidly as possible and its cause determined and eliminated.

Equipment to be shut down for more than a short time should be flushed with nitrogen and left with a pressure of that gas inside.

If a vessel is shown to be filled with air, one method of purging would be to flush with nitrogen to a pressure of 10 psig and release. Repetition of this procedure seven times will reduce the oxygen content to about 1%.

If the vessel has been left under and still retains a positive pressure of nitrogen, the flushing may be omitted.

Glass carboys should be kept in metal drums except when being washed.

Proper care in handling of the material and in equipment design will, of course, lead to maximum safety and the best results.

Certain chemical hazards are involved in the use of LAH. However, these are generally encountered first on a laboratory scale, and should not develop in a carefully-studied process in the plant. One of these is the formation of explosive intermediates when LAH reacts with fluorinated organic acids. The use of dimethyl ether as a solvent is not recommended, since it apparently picks up carbon dioxide from air very readily, and forms compounds with LAH, which, when evaporated to dryness, frequently explode violently. It is possible that other such chemical combinations exist, and careful study of any novel system is recommended, prior to scale-up.

18.3 HANDLING THE BOROHYDRIDES ON A LARGE SCALE

The problems of handling the borohydride group on an industrial scale are considerably less than those of LAH, the hazards here being principally from dust, hydrogen evolved on hydrolysis, and the normal inflammability of solvents such as isopropyl amine, tetrahydrofuran, and the lower alcohols. Sodium borohydride and trimethoxyborohydride dissolve readily in the lower primary amines and liquid ammonia, and no problem is involved in this procedure. Sodium borohydride can also be used in aqueous, alcohol, and aqueous-alcohol solutions. However, care must be taken to keep the solvent cold and the solution cold while it is being prepared, to prevent decomposition of the borohydride. If the solution is made basic (pH 12 to 13) prior to the addition of the sodium borohydride, the decomposition tendencies can be lowered. Sodium borohydride has a large heat of solution in these solvents, emphasizing the need for cooling. As long as the solutions are kept basic, they decompose at a rate of less than one per cent of the total reducing power per day at room temperature. Care must be taken not to add acidic material, or allow pH to drop below 9, nor to add certain inorganic ions such as cobalt, nickel, etc., which catalyze the rapid and complete hydrolysis of the sodium borohydride. This hydrolysis results in the evolution of 40 cubic feet of hydrogen per pound of sodium borohydride, and, if hydrolyzed quickly, can cause tremendous foaming and frothing, as well as considerable heat. While such heat is insufficient to ignite the hydrogen, such large volumes of hydrogen would cause a considerable immediate hazard. On the other hand, excess sodium borohydride, after a reaction, can be readily destroyed with inorganic acids, such organic acids as glycine or by the catalysts just mentioned, as long as adequate venting for the hydrogen is available.

Bulk sodium borohydride can be handled, crushed, loaded into hoppers, without hazard from atmospheric moisture. However, as a hygroscopic solid, this moisture will be absorbed, increasing the weight of solid and decreasing the purity proportionately. No loss in reducing power will be encountered unless attempts are made to remove the moisture by heating, even in a vacuum. Sodium borohydride must not be mixed with such acid compounds as boron halides and aluminum halides, without extreme caution, because volatile and explosive boron hydrides and aluminum borohydride, respectively, are formed. The above compounds are also highly toxic, and have an exceptionally unpleasant odor.

Sodium trimethoxyborohydride can be handled only in non-aqueous and non-alcoholic solvents, since it is readily and completely hydrolyzed by these materials. To the same extent, it must not be handled in moist or humid atmospheres, since absorption of moisture causes prompt decomposition. The amount of hydrogen evolved per pound of sodium trimethoxyborohydride is only one-thirteenth as much as for sodium borohydride, so that this hazard is considerably reduced.

Potassium borohydride is the safest, most readily handled of all of the borohydrides known, and being non-hygroscopic in normal atmospheres, it can be handled without special precautions, except for the elimination of acid materials or hydrolysis catalysts. In addition, its method of manufacture results in a free-flowing, crystalline powder which forms very little dust and has excellent flow properties. Its greater stability in aqueous and non-alcoholic solution permits forcing conditions which are not recommended with sodium borohydride.

18.4 PERSONAL SAFETY AND TOXICITY

Personnel handling complex hydrides and their solutions should wear flameproof clothing or coveralls, and goggles at all times. Face shields are recommended where handling LAH. Moleskin-type or rubber gloves are also highly recommended, since all complex hydrides are caustic in contact with the skin, the borohydrides being somewhat more irritating than LAH. If the skin is contacted with any of these, the area should be immediately flushed with copious quantities of water. Small quantities of water may increase the burn, due to the high heat of hydrolysis. The area should then be treated as for caustic burn. In cases of contact with such sensitive portions of the body as the eye, a physician should be called as soon as first aid has been given.

Additional problems are encountered with dermatitis caused by sodium borohydride and its solutions in isopropyl amine, tetrahydrofuran, liquid ammonia and ethylene diamine. Frequently solvents for the borohydrides also have toxicological hazards, and the manufacturers of the solvents should be consulted. All boron compounds are considered highly toxic when taken internally, and care must be taken not to swallow any of these materials. Dusts from the handling can be extremely irritating to the respiratory tract, and a dust-mask for operators of crushing, hopper-loading, or similar procedures should be standard equipment. However, dust must be kept to a minimum. As the procedures and recommendations described are, in general, those which would be the result of any carefully-designed operation, modified by good housekeeping practices and standard safety precautions, they are not difficult to follow. These recommendations, when considered early in the design of an operation, and when carefully followed, will prevent hazard to personnel and equipment and the loss of valuable material due to accidents.

GENERAL REFERENCE

Banus, M. D., "Safe Handling of Metal Hydrides," in *Chem. Eng. News*, 32, 2424 (1954).

INDEX

The page numbers in italics are for tables that are not included within a specific series of pages.

1025